Coincraft's Standard Catalogue
of English and UK Coins
1066 to Date

Richard Lobel
Publisher

Mark Davidson
Author of Hammered Section

Allan Hailstone
Author of Milled Section

Eleni Calligas
Editor

COINCRAFT

opposite the British Museum

45 Great Russell Street London WC1B 3LU
Telephone: 0171-636 1188 0171-637 8785
Fax: 0171-323 2860 0171-637 7635

London 1995

World-wide distribution (exc. UK) Krause Publications Inc.

**krause
publications**

Published by Standard Catalogue Publishers Ltd for Coincraft

COINCRAFT

opposite the British Museum

45 Great Russell Street London WC1B 3LU
Telephone: 0171-636 1188 0171-637 8785
Fax: 0171-323 2860 0171-637 7635

**Database typeset by BPC Whitefriars Ltd;
printed and bound by BPC Wheatons Ltd.
Both members of the British Printing Company Ltd.**

©Richard Lobel 1995
ISBN 0 9526228 07
British Library Cataloguing in Publication Data. A catalogue record for this book is available from the British Library

This book is dedicated to
Claire F. Lobel

No one has ever loved me more, or made me happier.
Without her backing and support this book would never have come to fruition.

Claire is the one person that I would like to have on my dessert island.
R.L.

Contents

17

About the Contributors

Richard Lobel, FRNS

Richard was born in Cambridge Massachusetts in 1944 and moved to London in 1968. He is a Fellow of the Royal Numismatic Society, a member of the Professional Numismatic Guild since 1974 and a member of numerous numismatic societies world-wide. He holds a degree in International Business and Macro Economics from Boston University and was accepted to the Harvard Business School to study Finance but moved to England instead, mistakenly believing that he spoke the language.

His first mentor in the coin business was the late Maurice Gould, author of many numismatic research works. Over the years he has had the privilege of knowing many famous numismatists and learning from them. His serious interest in coins dates from his first paid subscription to a coin publication in June of 1955.

He founded Coincraft, which has become the second largest firm of coin dealers in the United Kingdom. Perhaps his proudest boast is that Coincraft sells more numismatic books retail than anyone else in the UK. They deal only with collectors and publish a monthly newspaper/catalogue called *The Phoenix* and a semi-annual magazine *The Coin Collector.*

He has been listed in the *Guinness Book of Records* many times, for the legendary Edward VIII Collection, the unique 1954 Penny and for heading the consortium that bought the largest, heaviest and most expensive lot of banknotes ever sold at auction.

This book was his brainchild, his way to repay something to the hobby which has supported him for so many years. Richard stated recently that if he knew how much effort and how much money this book was going to take, he would never have started it.

Mark Davidson

Born and raised in Surrey, Mark began collecting bun pennies by date at the age of six. Encouraged in his hobby by his parents and his uncle, he soon became a keen collector and purchased his first hammered coin from the then recently discovered Colchester hoard of Henry III and Edward I pennies. At sixteen he started working for Richard Lobel and received his 'apprenticeship in the coin trade'. He started his own business at the age of twenty, dealing in all types of coins, publishing catalogues and trading from the old Saturday Charing Cross market. When that market closed in 1987, Mark started a monthly London Coin fair with Linda Monk which still flourishes today and, on the death of John Hooper, he became a partner in Croydon Coin Auctions. Mark is very well known in the trade and attends most auctions and fairs, where he enjoys meeting collectors.

Allan Hailstone

Allan was born in Coventry in 1938, and lived in various parts of England before moving to London in 1957 to read Chemical Engineering at Imperial College. Graduating in 1960, he entered industry but rapidly found that nobody appeared to know what a Chemical Engineer was. In 1962, he noticed a wants list of coins in a shop window in Canterbury, and decided on the spot to become a coin dealer.

With an amiable eccentric nature masking a deeply flawed personality, Allan met Richard Lobel many years ago, and recognised a kindred spirit; something akin to a friendship developed.

Allan can usually be found viewing at London auctions or hiding behind a newspaper at any one of several nearby coffee shops. Caring more for accuracy, language and spelling than for his fellow man, he was a natural choice for producing the milled section of this book.

Dr Eleni Calligas

Born in Athens, Eleni is a historian. After receiving her BA degree in History from the American College of Greece in 1985 and her MA in International History from the LSE in 1987, she returned to Athens where she was commissioned to write a historical study of child welfare in the 19th century. This work was published by the 'Foundation for Research into Childhood' in 1990. Moving back to London, Eleni pursued her studies at the LSE, researching the political history of the Ionian Islands during the British Protectorate (1815–1864); she was awarded her doctorate in 1994. Among the founding editors of the Greek historical journal *Istor*, she has also contributed articles to other scholarly journals, in both Greek and English.

In terms of this catalogue, her responsibilities were 'to throw it all up in the air so that it falls down a book' (Richard Lobel, interview, July 1994).

Preface

How did this book happen?

Seven years' work, incredible dedication and £250,000!

I would like to be able say that this book was created because of some great desire on my part to correct and combine a vast number of numismatic works in order to facilitate the study of the subject. *But that would be a lie!*

This book was first conceived in anger, because I was jilted! I would be willing to have a wager that not many cataloguers are so honest. But if nothing else, this book is honest, we tell it like it is, for better or worse. These are the real reasons that this book has been written. You, the reader, have the right to know and I feel you will enjoy knowing some of the trouble and effort that has gone into its creation.

For those who like statistics: an estimated 20 people years have been dedicated to the researching, writing, checking and development of this book. There are some 600 plus pages, approximately 5,000 photographs and 50,000 prices. Last but not least, its final cost is estimated to be in excess of £250,000!

All those figures are just numbers. Think of the people who have dedicated themselves to working on this book, which at times seemed an impossible task. Mark Davidson, our expert in the hammered field, has spent years checking and cross-checking details, which in most books appear only as a footnote, if they are listed at all. Allan Hailstone, our milled expert, has constantly found new and unlisted varieties, carefully checking collections and auction lots. Both have asked questions again and again, until the answers they received truly answered their query. Without these two there would not be a book. I thank you both very, very much, you have made my dream come true.

The third main stay of this book is Dr Eleni Calligas, who as Senior Editor of Standard Catalogue Publishers Ltd, a division of Coincraft, has taken all this wonderful research and actually made it into a useable book. She claims that I hired her to take all the bits and pieces, throw them up in the air and make them come down as a finished book. Personally I can not remember saying that, but it is probably true.

There are many dealers, collectors, coin firms and auction houses who have also helped us and I have tried to mention them and thank them elsewhere. To all of you, thank you for your help and your faith in this project, even occasionally when we had lost heart ourselves.

It is only now that I can sit down to thank these people, *seven years ago it was a different matter...*

I had been playing around with the idea of a new catalogue of British coins, as the existing catalogues did not fill the needs of either dealers or collectors. At that time, the Seaby catalogue was about the best around. It had first been published in 1929 and there was no longer a Seaby in charge. In all innocence, I offered to buy all or even part of the company. It would be easier to change and update an existing catalogue than to start one from scratch. A good business decision I thought, wrong!

When the subject was broached with the new owner I was, to be kind to her, rebuffed. There was no question of how much I would offer, more a feeling of being beneath consideration. As a businessman myself, if someone comes into my offices and wants to buy my company, I would at least ask them how much they wanted to pay. If they were that much in love with it and wanted to pay well over the odds, who knows, I might even sell it. My late Father always said 'you always have to ask the price before you turn something down, it might surprise you!'. I was never asked the price and that hurt me.

Some six months later half of Seaby was sold to someone else, so someone else had what might well have been mine. I had wanted to buy Seaby since 1968 and now I was not going to get it!

Before this event, the book had already been started. Peter Gerald 'Maundy' Allen had been working on it for almost a year and I steadfastly refused to believe that he could not do it all himself. Little did I realise at the time just how much work it was going to be! After numerous discussions, some of them rather heated, it was decided that the book would require two authors, experts in their own fields. Every fact had to be checked in two or three references so not only would it be correct, but there could never be any inference of plagiarism.

I had known Mark Davidson and Allan Hailstone for quite some time and had grown to respect their knowledge and integrity. In fact Mark had once worked for us, then he went out on his own and today is one of the most successful dealers in the country. I put it all down to good training! When the subject of the catalogue was brought up, after some deliberations and consideration, both agreed to take on the challenge. In retrospect if they had to do it all over again, perhaps they would have thought a little bit longer before saying yes. These two are my heroes, they took the challenge and they won the game!

The aim of this catalogue is to be the best one-volume work on English coins from 1066 to date that you will find. We expect that there will be errors and omissions no matter how much we check and recheck. With your help, we hope to correct these errors in future editions. Please let us know if we have made a mistake or left something out; your feedback is most important. By the way, Seaby are no longer coin dealers but have their books published by Batsford. This may sound a subtle difference, but it is an important one where pricing is concerned. You have to be dealing with coins everyday to know what is hot and what is not. The coin market is a constantly changing area and you have to be down amongst the players to know what is happening. You need experts who are aware and active in the market place to keep you, the collector, up to date. Book publishers publish books, coin dealers deal in coins.

This book started off in anger and has grown to be an obsession, for me and for the dedicated people who have worked long and hard on it. It will become your most important and most used reference book on the coins of England & the UK from 1066 to date. For all of us who have worked on it, it is our little bit of numismatic immortality. We hope that you will use and enjoy this book and, when you find some fact that you did not know, we hope you will appreciate all the time and effort that has gone into it.

Stay well, be happy and keep on collecting...

Conceived in anger, worked on and finished with love.

Richard Lobel, FRNS

Prices

It is my belief that if you took every coin that every coin dealer in the United Kingdom was selling on any given day and put them all together, you would still have for sale fewer than 1% of the coins listed in this book! Think of all the mintmarks, mints, grades and dates that exist and would be possible to collect. I do not mean this disrespectfully, but there are a heck of a lot of coins.

We have had to take an educated guess on many of the prices that we have listed. We worked on the assumption that a collector buys from an established coin dealer with the normal overheads. You can sometimes make great buys off a stall in the market, but other times you will regret it. If something is wrong a dealer will try and make it right, a stall holder may not want to know you. Yes, you might well be able to buy slightly cheaper, but you may well have to do without service, knowledge, reliability and the offer to return something which is not exactly to your liking.

An exceptional coin will usually bring an exceptional price! If you have a hammered coin which always turns up in Fine with the design slightly off centre and you are offered one which is extremely well struck and in Very Fine condition, then you would expect to pay a lot more money for such an exceptional coin. If a milled coin 'only' turns up in Extremely Fine and you are offered a Choice Uncirculated example, then the price will be much higher. If a coin turns up in Extremely Fine and Uncirculated condition on a regular basis, then the difference in price will not be all that great. An example is the 1887 Queen Victoria Jubilee Head Shilling.

Any time a catalogue is printed the prices are out of date. The preparation of the catalogue may well have taken years and while updates are done, the markets are constantly changing. The collecting interest of the public changes all the time and that change effects prices. At times a hoard is found and prices drop. It is my sage advice that when a hoard comes out and the prices drop, this is the time to buy. The coin market is like a pendulum, it swings too far to both sides, both high and low. When a hoard comes out, the market drops and prices drop too far. They will rebound and within a reasonable period of time even go to a higher level than when the hoard was found. This is because more collectors will want a coin when it is at a lower price. At £100 there may be little interest in a coin, but at £50 the coin becomes very interesting to collectors. If a hoard comes out and the prices drop that is the time to add one or more examples to your collection.

On some of the lower priced coins we have set a minimum selling price to try and cover some of the dealers' overheads. Please do not believe that if you have a £5 bag of 1,200 Brilliant Uncirculated 1967 Pennies it is worth 1,200 times the catalogue price. The price on a 1967 Penny allows the dealer to cover the cost of stocking the coin, taking it off the shelf when you want it, putting it in a envelope and sending it to you. Although this is time consuming and expensive, the catalogue price reflects only part of these costs.

The actual price that dealers charge will depend on how they grade the coin, their cost and what they feel the coin is worth. If I buy an auction lot for £20 and the coins are worth £50, should I sell them for £25? Certainly not! You will find that dealers work on a tighter margin on the more expensive coins; on a £500 coin the dealer may be willing to 'turn it' for a quick profit of say £40-£50 whereas on a coin costing £5 they might want £8 or even £10.

All prices in this catalogue are in British pounds sterling and at the time of going to press, June 19th 1995, one pound was worth:

Argentina Peso 1.6077
Australia $2.2089
Austria Sch. 15.8373
Bahamas $1.6080
Bahrain Dinar 0.6062
Belgium Bfr. 46.2173
Bermuda $1.6080
Brazil Real 1.4608
Brunei $2.2444
Canada $2.2220
Danish Dkr. 8.7948
East Caribbean Currency $4.3416
Egypt £5.4648
Finland Markka 6.9174
France FF. 7.9084
Germany DM 2.2522
Hong Kong HK $12.4380
Iceland Ikr. 102.028
India Rps. 50.4816
Indonesia Rup. 3585.73
Ireland Punt £0.9830
Italy Lire 2650.30
Japan Yen 135.928
Korea (South) Won 1223.73
Kuwait Dinar 0.4809

Luxembourg Lux Fr. 46.2173
Macao Pataca 12.8474
Malaysia Ringgit 3.9267
Malta Maltese Lira 0.5604
Mexico Peso 9.9452
Netherlands Flr. 2.5204
New Zealand NZ $2.4005
Norway Nkr. 10.0320
Oman Rial 0.6191
Pakistan Rpe. 49.7484
Peru New Sol 3.6082
Philippines Peso 41.2842
Poland Zloty 3.7618
Portugal Escudo 237.06
Qatar Riyal 5.8527
St. Helena £1
Saudi Arabia Riyal 6.0307
Singapore S$2.2444
South Africa Rand 5.8976
Spain Peseta 195.607
Sweden Skr. 11.6627
Switzerland Sfr. 1.8651
Thailand Baht 39.6521
Turkey Lira 69543.9
United States $1.6080

Grading

Grading is the biggest area of contention in coins. Because the price of a coin is in a great part dependent on its condition, this can be open to many interpretations, even leaving aside those dealers who deliberately overgrade their coins and then advertise them 'cheaply', to appear that they are giving you a bargain. The best advice I can give you is, if it appears too cheap, there is a reason for it.

To learn to grade properly takes years of experience and actually handling thousands of coins. You must also know how a coin was made; a hammered coin is vastly different from a milled coin. You have to know about the dies, how they were engraved, how long they lasted and what they looked like as they started to wear. You have to know what an Uncirculated example looks like before you can determine if a particular coin is worn, or if it was just struck that way. You have to learn to distinguish original lustre from something which may have been done in order to try and artificially replace that lustre. Grading correctly is even harder than it sounds.

In the old days a coin was either new or it was used, a used coin could be Fine or it could be Extremely Fine, it just was not new. Today, because of the difference in price between an almost new coin and a new coin, you have to be that much more careful. In the United States they have a crazy grading system in which there are no less than 10 different grades of Uncirculated. They grade an Uncirculated coin on a numerical basis, anywhere from 60 out of 70 to the ultimate which is 70 out of 70. The price difference between a 64/70 and a 65/70 can be anything up to ten times the price. I believe that there are three grades of Uncirculated: Uncirculated, meaning that there is no wear, Choice Uncirculated, a superior coin which might have a few light bag marks but is in the upper 10% in quality of all Uncirculated coins, and Gem Uncirculated which is in the upper 2% of coins.

Because grading is a subjective area it is best to be careful, especially if you do not know the person you are buying from. Again I suggest that you form a relationship with a coin dealer you feel comfortable with and trust. They will be happy to explain why they graded the coin as they have. Grading of coins can not be learnt overnight, but it is something that a collector has to learn.

Going from the lowest grade to the highest they are as follows. *Poor:* extremely worn and most of the detail will be missing but you will still be able to identify the coin as to type. *Fair:* there is much wear but more of the detail is visible and you will easily be able to identify the coin. *Good:* almost all of the lettering will still be there and the date will be easy to read in most cases. *Very Good:* all of the coin will be readable and some of the finer details will start to be discernible. *Fine:* the details are starting to take shape and the coin is becoming more collectable. *Very Fine:* the details are clear, there is wear on the high points but most of the fine detail shows clearly. *Extremely Fine:* there is wear on only the highest points and on copper and bronze there may even be lustre on the coin. *Uncirculated:* there is no wear on the high points but the design may not be fully struck up due to the engraving of the die or its wear. Copper and bronze may or may not have lustre, depending on where and how they were stored.

Be careful about grading and until you learn to grade yourself, deal with someone you can trust.

Below we list the grading system used in some other countries.

Britain	Proof	Unc	Extremely Fine	Very Fine	Fine	Very Good
Brazil	-	FDC	S	MBC	BC	BC/R
Denmark	M	0	01	1+	1	1(
Finland	00	0	01	1+	1	1?
France	FB	FDC	SUP	TTB	TB	B
Germany	PP	STG	VZ	SS	S	S.G.E
Italy	FS	FDC	SPL	BB	MB	B
Netherlands	-	FDC	Pr.	Z.f.	Fr.	Z.g.
Norway	M	0	01	1+	1	1(
Portugal	-	Soberba Bela	MBC	BC+	BC	
Spain	Prueba	SC	EBC	MBC	BC+	BC
Sweden	Polerad	0	01	1+	1	1?

Rarity

Rarity is a way of trying to describe how many examples of a coin still exist. A coin may be common in circulated condition but in mint state it might be very scarce, even rare. On more modern coins where an accurate mintage figure is known, assigning a rarity value is relatively easy. Of course, you still have to take into account the amount struck, how many were minted and how many still exist.

The assignment of rarity is again a subjective process. One of my first mentors, Bill Ross, used to say 'it is hard to shut that press off after just one coin was struck'. He also said 'when you go to value a coin it is what you have not seen rather than what you have seen that matters'. By that he meant that, when you see a coin that you have never seen before, forget what it catalogues, it is rare! My colleague Alan Ward once spent seven years looking for a coin which catalogues only $1.50; when he saw it he bought it. Since then, he has seen only two other examples and he bought both of them. In this case the catalogue is wrong, this coin is rare and should catalogue much more.

All dealers have their own ideas about levels of rarity and how to list them. In the old days there was a listing from C2 (Very Common) to R7 (Unique), other areas were graded on a scale going up to R22. These are confusing and I do not feel that you can be that precise, especially on early coins. I use the following nomenclature, a coin which is *scarce* I will list as 'scarce', 'Scarce' or 'SCARCE' depending on just how scarce it is. A *rare* coin will be listed as 'rare', 'Rare', 'RARE', 'Extremely Rare' or 'Unique'. This method gives the flavour of the rarity without trying to put an exact definition excluding only Unique. In this catalogue, we have used four levels of rarity, denoted by the relevant number of 'R's. The four levels range from 'R' for rare, to 'RR' very rare, 'RRR' extremely rare and 'RRRR' unique.

Errors & Omissions

Errors and omissions are going to happen, as Forrest Gump would say. This is especially true in the first edition of a new work of this size and scope. I apologise in advance to you and ask your help in correcting these errors and omissions. Bound in this catalogue is a card which you can fill in and send to us with any errors or omissions that you spot. I promise that every card will be read and appropriate action taken.

It is up to you to help us make the next edition that much better. If you find an error please let us know. If you have some additional information or photographs which we can use please let us know. We have taken the first steps, now it is in your hands to make the next edition have fewer errors and more information.

Future Editions

Future editions are planned and we shall be trying to correct the errors in this edition, add more material and keep the prices as up to date as we can. Our friends at Krause Publications Inc. have done us the singular honour of distributing our book world wide, excluding only the British Isles, Republic of Ireland, the Channel Islands and the Isle of Man. It is, to my knowledge, the first time that they have distributed a book which they did not publish.

Eventually we hope to get this catalogue out on an annual basis to reflect the changing coin market. We will, we hope, sell out of the first printing of the first edition fairly quickly and go on to a second printing. We need your help on any varieties we may have left out. Other books on British numismatics are progressing at this time and we will keep you informed.

Introduction

For the best part of a thousand years the inhabitants of England made their presence felt and influenced events taking place in the world. The prosperity this prominence built up is reflected in the nation's coinage and its study gives an insight into English heritage.

Collectors of the series can confine themselves to a simple method of collecting, such as acquiring one coin of each monarch — or can delve more deeply into the types of coin, reasons for issue, the engravers and the multitude of factors involved in the process of putting a penny in your pocket. The importance of such study was first emphasised by the nineteenth century numismatist Alexander del Mar, who wrote that 'the history of civilisation is the history of money'.

The collector certainly plays an important part in the study of coins in that he at least preserves coins for future students to examine. Remember, the collector does not really own his treasures, he is a custodian for future generations.

Just how important coins are to the study of our past can be gauged by the fact that the entire chronology of ancient art is based on a dating system by coins. Many of the long-lost masterpieces of bygone schools of art would be unknown but for coins. From early coins we can tell many things about a nation — its religions, its importance, who rules its wealth and so on. There exist coins of an ancient British ruler about whom nothing is known except for the coin inscription.

The problems of dating coins are not confined to ancient times and the British series has an area where experts are still not always in agreement! It all stems from the fact that we cannot necessarily believe what we see on a coin. In mediaeval times the majority of people could not read or write and the importance of the inscriptions was confined to the educated classes. Communications were sometimes poor, cost was a considerable factor, and all this combined to sometimes have the coinage retain the same inscription long after the death of the monarch it was intended for.

So we read the inscription HENRICUS on coins for Henry I that were also issued by Henry II, Richard I, John I and Henry III. Similarly, it is impossible to identify from the inscription the coins of Edward I, II and III. Many years of study have led numismatists to attribute these Edward pennies on a basis of stylistic differences. It gets worse! Some coins of Edward VI were issued with the name and portrait of Henry VIII. The shilling of Edward VI has the distinction of being the first English coin to be dated. Although it does not apply to the English series, it is interesting to note that some coins actually give a wrong year date deliberately! The best example of this is the Maria Theresa dollar which is dated 1780. The inhabitants of the areas bordering the Red Sea came to trust this coin and, when trading, insisted on exchanging only for Maria Theresa dollars. The result is that such coins dated 1780 are minted even today.

One of the principal methods of dating English coins is the 'privy' or mintmarks found on them. Die numbers found on many milled coins also provide useful information. The English series can absorb the attention of a collector for a lifetime. Some collectors specialise in certain areas, such as hammered coins, milled coins or even the coins of just one mint or monarch. The coinage of Charles I, for example, is full of varieties. Certainly, forming such collections is an interesting and exciting hobby which can give years of pleasure. It is often overlooked that collectors enjoy the advantage of meeting people of similar interests in coin clubs up and down the country. Club meetings are often as much social get-togethers as occasions to swap and study. The major museums of the nation are there to assist the student and are well worth visiting to examine the numismatic collections. The British Museum has the finest collection of coins in the world.

The new collector will soon come across the investment potential of coins. Investment is best left to experienced collectors as, without knowledge, it is a pure gamble. The best investment a collector can make is in enjoying the hobby itself which will keep his mind active, interested and healthy and may well lead to a long and happy life. Of course collecting coins can be a sound financial investment — but usually this is because of the passage of time. Few collectors who have spent more than 20 years at the hobby have ever lost out when they have decided to sell. Just look at a priced catalogue of 20 years ago and compare it with a current one!

The collector who puts together a selection of coins to illustrate an area of numismatics and who studies them and comes to understand them, is likely to unintentionally make a good investment. Of course the collector has to pay attention to the value of a coin. He wants to know that if he does decide to sell it later on, he will get at least some of his money back! There is no substitute quite as good as experience but beginners can at least follow the basic guidelines of all collecting areas: know your dealer! Has he been in business for a long time, has he got a shop where you can go back to? If he has, you will know that he has to be reasonably OK or he would not still be in business! And once you become a 'regular' customer, you will find most dealers pay attention to your specific interests and become very useful 'scouts' for locating material for your collection.

The singular most important effect on value is condition. This catalogue gives you detailed descriptions of the various numismatic grading terms. It is well worth taking time to study these. Never be afraid to ask a dealer about the condition of a coin. A good dealer will take time out to explain. It is a subjective matter and often one finds the condition of a coin goes up or down a grade depending on whether it is being sold or bought! The real problem comes when a coin has been cleaned. There is nothing basically wrong with a coin being cleaned. The world's museums have departments whose sole function is to restore, clean and preserve every type of artefact. Hammered coins found in the earth often need to be treated so that the inscriptions can be read. But there is a difference between cleaning to preserve and identify, and cleaning to make a coin look in better condition than it really is so as to get a higher price for it.

A beginner should never try to clean a coin. Leave it to the experts. Sound advice is to leave it altogether if it needs cleaning! Part of the skill of collecting coins is to select good examples. This means knowing when a bad-condition coin is worth having because it just does not turn up in better condition at an affordable price, and when a coin is easy to obtain in beautiful condition and therefore should be discarded in bad condition.

Collectors generally divide the English series into two halves. The first encompasses the hammered series, the second encompasses the milled series. Hammered coins get their name because they were literally hammered. The dies were similar to those used in ancient Greek and Roman times, but the lower die was now given a long spur, or tang, so that it would fit into a deep recess of the anvil. The upper die contained the reverse design and the lower die the obverse. Because the hammer blow directly impacted on the reverse die, it wore out more quickly than the lower, obverse die.

It follows that the quality of many of these coins was affected by the precision and strength of the hammer blow — and collectors pay more for a well struck and centred coin. In making the die itself, many different types of engraving instruments were used. Often two punches would be used to create one letter. Students can identify the use, on some coins, of the punch for the letter 'I' joined to a reversed 'C' to create the letter 'D'.

The 'milled' process has no connection with the milling round the edge of the coin. The name refers to the machinery which rolled silver to the right thickness and was driven by horse-power or water-power. It was Eloye Mestrelle of Paris who demonstrated to the Royal Mint the milled system and he was employed at the Mint to use his equipment which included a rolling-mill for making sheets of silver to an exact thickness, a cutter for the circular blanks and a press for even pressure when the die was stamped on to the coin blank.

As it happened, he did not last long because of opposition from the Mint authorities. The Warden of the Mint, Richard Martin, saw to it that he was sacked after holding a trial of skill between Mestrelle and the hammer-men. His lengthy report omitted all mention of the fact that Mestrelle was producing, for the first time, a coin of equal size, shape and with a perfect and uniform register of the die designs. Instead he reported that the hammer-men could work ten times faster and wrote: 'Wherefore neither the said engine nor any workmanship to be wrought thereby will be to the Queen's Majesty's profit.' Mestrelle went into business on his own account and was even less appreciated at Norwich where they hanged him and his three accomplices for making false money.

The hammered silver penny was the standard coin in England for around 500 years. The first recognisable portrayal of a king was that of King Offa. The inscription REX ANGLOR — King of the English, first appears on coins of King Alfred. But it was not until William the Conqueror that the English truly became one country and it is the last successful conquest of England, by William the Conqueror in 1066, that makes a good starting point for collectors of the English series. The Norman influence on design can be seen in the crosses.

When William I arrived he found that English coinage, which had once copied the French *denier* for its silver penny, was now superior to the continental coinage so he wisely left the system alone but introduced coins with his name. He inherited some 45 mints and by the close of his reign in 1087 England had about 70 mints working. Henry I re-introduced in 1108 the halfpenny — last struck by Eadgar — but only a few have come to light. The dies for coins were made in London and sent to the provincial mints. The name of moneyers was included on the reverse of the coin. This was not so much as an honour for them, as it was to ensure that the London authorities knew who made the actual coin. If it was not of the correct weight and fineness they knew who to see about it.

By the time Henry I came to the throne in 1100, forgers were operating very successfully. Merchants worried by the amount of forgery would cut into the coin to make sure it was silver. The general public then refused to take the coin because it was mutilated. To overcome this disastrous situation the government took the extraordinary step of requiring all coins to be cut.

Some of these official cuts extend a third of the way into a coin. While it may have overcome the problem of getting the public to use the coin, it did not stop forgery. Mint-masters were not above doing a bit of overtime on their own account and we learn from the Margam Annals that one Christmas Day on the King's orders, Bishop Roger of Sarum mutilated 94 moneyers at Winchester — about half the moneyers in England. It was not much of a Christmas for them as mutilation on that occasion involved the loss of their right hand and testicle. It did improve the coinage. Most people suspected of counterfeiting were found guilty because the initial examination involved placing their hands in fire. Innocent people were supposed to withstand the pain.

A foreign goldsmith, Philip Aimer of Tours, designed the short-cross coinage with the title HENRICUS REX which circulated from 1180 to 1247 — through the last eight years of Henry II, the reigns of Richard I and John and the first 30 years of Henry III. (Coins found named to King John were minted in Ireland). The short-cross was introduced to enable the coin to be divided into halves and quarters for small change. But clipping the edges to acquire the silver was so prevalent that a Council was held at Oxford to consider the matter in 1247. The result was the long-cross penny. The four ends of the cross were extended to the edge of the coin. Any coin which did not have the four ends of the cross clearly visible was an illegal coin. Despite the long cross, clipping continued and in 1290 the Jews were blamed for the practice and it was one of the reasons for their persecution and expulsion. Collectors who like the challenge of deep specialisation will find the short-cross or the long-cross coinages a real challenge with much research still needed, with the excitement of new hoard finds and possibly even new types.

Dating coins of the hammered period can be very difficult but one of the most important methods of attributing dates is the mintmark (also known as the 'privy mark' or the 'Initial'). These denote the place of issue and, by changing the mark, the period. These marks are usually found under the bust or by the legends. For most coins numismatists have been able to work out the date and place of issue to within a few years.

A new coinage was introduced by Edward I and he introduced the groat (a four-penny piece). The designs were improved to such an extent that they were copied on the Continent. He partly solved the problem of cutting pennies into halves and quarters by producing halfpennies and farthings.

Often coins tell us over which territories a king ruled. Edward III, for example, was shown as King of France on his coins from 1351–1361. Following the Treaty of Bretigny his coins show him as Lord of Aquitaine — and not King of France (1361–1369). Then, when the Treaty was broken, his coins show him as Lord of Aquitaine and King of France. Some of his coins name him as ruler of England, France, Ireland and Aquitaine. In the reign of Edward III an important numismatic event occurred with the introduction of the Trial of the Pyx. This was a random check on the quality of moneyers' coins and has been carried out ever since. The original law includes the passage '.. the Warden shall make a tryall of yt, and if yt shall not bee so good as yt is undertaken, yt shalbee retorned to the said Master to bee remolten at his owne proper costs.'

Although the silver penny was the standard coin for some 500 years, a gold currency was introduced in 1275 which included a pure gold penny, equal to 20 silver pennies. It was twice the weight of a silver penny but for various reasons soon disappeared from circulation.

Later the gold noble was issued. The design shows the king standing in a ship and there is a strong numismatic opinion that this represents the naval victory at Sluys in 1340. Angels and ryals were introduced in the succeeding years.

One of the great fascinations of coin collecting is that a collector can actually hold in his hand a coin minted, for instance, in the time of Henry V, victor of Agincourt, and it is surprising how inexpensive such items can be. The Wars of the Roses saw Henry VI removed from the throne in 1461 and captured at the Battle of St Albans in 1465. His place was taken by Edward IV but Henry VI was restored in 1470. His 'restored' coinage is scarce because the following year he was murdered and Edward IV began his second reign. There are many different varieties, mintmarks and mints in Henry VI's reign and the mintmarks enable us to date most of his coins to within a few years of issue.

For those who set out to obtain one specimen of each monarch there are problems with such historic figures as Richard III, who died in battle at Bosworth and had his crown picked up there and then and placed on the head of Henry VII. Coins of Richard III are scarce because of his short reign, from 1483 to 1485.

New denominations were brought in by Henry VII and the coinage saw the introduction of the famous gold sovereign in 1489. A wide range of coins were used including gold ryals, or nobles, angels, half-angels, silver testoons (shillings), groats, half-groats, pennies, halfpennies and farthings. Fortunately for collectors, the practice was resumed of giving the full title of the king. No longer was it just HENRICUS, it was now clearly HENRY VII. Another great improvement in the coinage was that the portrait ceased to be a stylistic impression of a king and became an actual likeness of the monarch.

These coins attract a lot of attention from collectors and such coins in superb condition command high prices. Yet very attractive examples can be bought quite inexpensively when one considers that the coin is a contemporary portrait produced by highly skilled engravers many centuries ago. Some collectors concentrate on portrait coins and the coinage of Henry VIII produces some very fine portraits.

Henry VIII soon debased the coinage that his father had kept at such a high standard. His subjects came to nickname him 'Old Coppernose' because the thin wash of silver on his coins soon wore off and the nose on the full-face portrait coins was the first to show the metal underneath. For some time certain people had been empowered to privately mint coins and one famous coin is Wolsey's groat, minted by Cardinal Thomas Wolsey while Archbishop of York. The coin depicts a cardinal's hat and the letters T and W. The Bill of Impeachment against Wolsey in 1530 included: 'of his pompous and presumptuous mind he hath enterprised to join and imprint the Cardinal's Hat under your Arms in your coin of groat made at your city of York, which like deed hath not yet been seen to have been done by any subject within your realm before this time.' It cost Wolsey his head and similar private ecclesiastical mints were curbed soon after.

Edward VI restored the fineness of the coinage and the famous silver crown was introduced in his reign. Crowns are very popular with collectors because the size allows greater freedom for the artist. The first crown shows the king on horseback. Shillings of this period are often found with the reverse worn completely smooth. This was because of the game, today known as shove-halfpenny. The shilling was in great demand for the game, so much so that the coin could on occasion fetch more than its face value.

Queen Mary came to the throne in 1553 and the following year a portrait of a Spanish king appears on English coins facing the portrait of Queen Mary, during the joint reign of Philip and Mary. The coin gave rise to the saying: 'Still amorous, cooing and billing, Like Philip and Mary on a Shilling.'

The regal portraits of Elizabeth I found on her coins are worthy additions to any collection. Some odd denominations were produced at this time, such as a three-halfpence and a three-farthings.

King James stopped the practice of private shopkeepers and traders issuing lead and pewter tokens and in its place he granted a licence to Lord Harrington to strike copper farthings. The licence was subsequently bought by the Duke of Lennox and later by Lord Maltravers. The king, of course, shared in the profits.

A tremendous variety of coins exist for Charles I and many collectors concentrate their attention on this one reign. The milled process was re-introduced by the French die-engraver Nicholas Briot. But although the coins were superior, they could not be issued fast enough and hand-hammering had to continue. The Civil War has left a multitude of emergency issues and siege money often cut from plate. When the king raised his standard at Nottingham in 1642, he introduced propaganda to his coinage with the 'Declaration' coins. On these he declared war on Parliamentary rebels and promised to defend the Protestant religion, the liberties of Parliament and the laws of England. His belief in divine right was expressed on many of the coins with the legend: CHRISTO AUSPICE REGNO — I reign under the auspices of Christ.

At this time coins exhibited very high quality workmanship, like the beautiful pattern coin produced for Charles by Thomas Rawlins and known as the Oxford crown — showing a view of the city below the king's horse.

Cromwell besieged Pontefract himself and there the royalists struck coins which read 'While I live I hope'. After Charles was beheaded the castle gamely carried on with the legend: 'For the son after the death of the father.' Cromwell's coinage became known as 'Breeches' money because of the shape of the joined shields on the reverse. Lord Lucas is supposed to have remarked to Charles II 'A fit name for the coins of the Rump'. During the Civil War the Parliamentarians continued to strike coins in the name of the king. This could be taken to mean that there was no intention at first to depose the king, just to curb his powers — or to mean that while the king lived the public would not use another coin. Often considered the greatest of all English die-engravers, Thomas Simon, was working at the Royal Mint when it was finally seized by Parliament in 1642.

He began to make his presence felt with a magnificent portrait of Cromwell. Milled experiments were gathering pace and the last hammered coinage was that hurriedly produced for the Restoration of Charles II in 1660. It is noteworthy that Charles II dated his coins with the regnal year on the edge, not from when he came to the throne but from the execution of his father.

It will be seen that a fascinating collection can be made to illustrate the great events of the Civil War. The importance of these coins as historical evidence cannot be underestimated, and often corroborates other source information.

Peter Blondeau, whose machinery had been used during the Commonwealth, retired on a pension. But he was brought back by Charles II and made Provost of the Moneyers and Engravers of the Mint and agreed to divulge 'his secrets in rounding the pieces before they are seized, and in marking the edges of monies.' It was to mark the end of coin clipping. Edges of crowns and halfcrowns were inscribed DECUS ET TUTAMEN (ornament and safeguard). The quality of the coins has never been higher and was in part due to the competition between very competent engravers. John Roettier, a brilliant engraver, had the advantage that his family had helped Charles during his exile. Thomas Simon, chief engraver, had to face a trial of skill. Both patterns produced by the engravers were magnificent. The Dutchman won and his coins were accepted. Many felt that Thomas Simon's were better and Roettier's had only been accepted in recognition of his family's service to the king. Simon certainly felt so and produced the now famous Petition Crown — a truly beautiful piece. The petition, inscribed in two lines on the edge reads 'Thomas Simon most humbly prays your Majesty to compare this, his tryall piece, with the Dutch, and if more truly drawn and emboss'd, more gracefully ordered and more accurately engraven, to relieve him.' His petition was not granted but he was allowed to design some of the smaller denominations. He died a few years later of the plague.

For those collectors who wish to limit their collecting interest, the milled series makes as clean break from the hammered. As we have seen, there were mill and screw-press coins as early as Elizabeth by Mestrelle and some by Nicholas Briot under Charles I. Cromwell portrait coins were struck on Peter Blondeau's newly invented machine. But now all coins were produced by the milled process. For some time, when Welsh silver was used to make coins, a mark had been placed on the coin to denote this. In the reign of Charles II the practice was extended to include an elephant, or elephant and castle, to represent the African Guinea Co. and a rose for silver from the West of England mines. Collectors who wish to restrict their collecting of the milled series often choose a coin, most popular being the crown or shilling, and try and put together as complete a collection as possible of all the dates and marks.

Coins of James II (1685–1688) show a strong face and are of high quality, the dies being engraved by Roettier. Very attractive are the coins of William and Mary and later William III. There is some difficulty in attributing engravers to coins in this reign which still gives scope for research. John Roettier, through age and probably arthritis could no longer use his hands properly and had to get his sons to do most of the work. So we have coins engraved by James and Norbert Roettier as well as by John himself. To make matters more complicated, Norbert had to flee to France and James was dismissed in 1697 for smuggling coin dies to France. Henry Harris and John Croker replaced them and also engraved coins during the reign.

With the death of Mary the elegant conjoined busts of the monarchs cease and coins show only the head of William III (1694–1702). During his reign a complete recoinage was undertaken. A total prohibition was placed on all clipped coins, which effectively demonetised the hammered coinage still circulating as most of it was now badly worn or clipped. An entry in Evelyn's diary tells us: 'Many executed at London for clipping money, now done to that considerable extent, that there was hardly any money that was worth about halfe the nominal value'. New mints were opened at Bristol, Chester, Exeter, Norwich and York and a prodigious output of coins was undertaken — recognised by numismatists because the coins are relatively common. Old coins were accepted at face by the government and replaced with the new coinage. The cost of this was borne by the introduction of a 'Window Tax' which raised well over a million pounds for the purpose. To avoid the tax, many people bricked up windows which can still be seen in many old houses today. The tax proved to be very effective so the government levied it right up to 1851.

History is well reflected on coins and major events during the reign of Queen Anne, (1702–1714) are commemorated. The union with Scotland in 1707 saw a change in the royal arms which, after the Act of Union, show the arms of Scotland and England joined in one shield instead of using separate shields as previously. In 1702 coins were made from silver taken from captured Spanish galleons at Vigo Bay. The name VIGO was placed under the queen's bust to indicate this. Collectors look for other such marks which are found on British coins, WCC for Welsh Copper Company and SSC for South Sea Company.

George I had the distinction of using one of the longest titles. The Latin abbreviations on his coins translate 'By the grace of God, King of Great Britain, France and Ireland, Defender of the Faith, Duke of Brunswick and Lüneburg, Archtreasurer and Elector of the Holy Roman Empire'.

Collectors who specialise in engravers' work find that George II portraits were first engraved by John Croker who had also produced the dies for Anne and George I. But the older portrait, produced in 1743, is the work of Tanner.

The early part of George III's reign saw very few coins minted but in 1787 an enormous issue of shillings and sixpences was put into circulation. Although many of these are still easy to obtain, there are some rarities like the Northumberland shilling. The Earl of Northumberland distributed £100 worth of these to mark his entry into Dublin as Lord Lieutenant.

The Spanish eight reales (the famous pirates' 'pieces of eight') was a universally used coin at this time and, as British supremacy at sea involved privateers relieving the Spanish of large quantities of coin, it was decided to make use of them. Silver coin was in short supply and in 1797 the Mint was instructed to countermark the pieces of eight with the head of George III in a small oval. Early examples were punchmarked with the 'duty paid' head used on silver hall marks.

Major changes came in the reign of Queen Victoria. Being a woman, she was not able to succeed to the Hanoverian throne so the Hanover shield had to be dropped from coins. A new piece, the florin, came into being as a result of campaigns for a decimal coinage. A motion before Parliament that silver coins of one-tenth and one-hundredth of a pound should be issued was withdrawn by agreement when the florin was produced. For some reason the normal lettering 'D.G.' for 'By the grace of God' was left out and the coin was quickly nicknamed 'the Godless florin'.

Numismatists interested in dies find Victoria's reign a treasure-trove. The die numbers were put on coins and after 1864 the die number can be seen at the base of the queen's portrait on florins, shillings and sixpences. This practice continued until 1879.

Edward VII had only one issue of coins and this was engraved by de Saulles. A very attractive coin is the florin which departs from the normal designs to show a standing Britannia.

George V's reign has many varieties but is perhaps most notable for the debasement of the coinage. In 1920 the price of silver rose so high that it was possible to melt silver coinage and make a profit. So coins were reduced to 50 per cent silver and 50 per cent alloy.

Although coin patterns exist for Edward VIII, his portrait coinage was never authorised for circulation and such pieces are very scarce. Coins of George V dated 1936 are generally regarded as posthumous issues of George V struck during the reign of Edward VIII.

The very attractive coins of George VI and Elizabeth II complete the series and give collectors much material for study. Coins of this period should be collected in mint condition where possible as they are comparatively easy to obtain. They are well worth studying and can lead to 'finds' of new varieties and errors. Modern coins have the advantage to collectors that they can examine large quantities. They may be common now but it is worth noting that all coins were 'new issues' once.

Colin Narbeth

An Introduction to Coin Collecting

I was a collector long before I became a dealer. I did not start dealing till 1956, by then I was already 12 years old. Coins have always fascinated me; the fact that the coin in my hand is so old has always excited me. Where has it been all these years, who owned it, who has handled it? The number one principle in collecting is: it must be something you do because you want to and because you enjoy it. Never believe that you are collecting for profit, you will be sadly disappointed. I do not sell coins for investments. Who can tell what is going to happen next? Not me, that's for sure. It is true that collectors who have stayed the course and have collected right along, when prices were high and when prices were low, have done very nicely when they sold their collections. But the reason they were collecting is that they enjoyed it and they learned about the coins in their collections. Someone who collects in a very narrow field will often know more than the dealers he buys from. After all, we dealers are like GPs, we know a little about a lot of things. You could well become the specialist in your chosen field, you just have to start somewhere.

The scarcer a coin is, the higher the price it will command, right? No! The price of a coin is determined in some unfathomable way by a combination of rarity, condition, desirability and collector interest. A common coin in choice condition will in many cases be more expensive than a rare coin in worn condition. In the old days collectors tried to obtain every variety that existed. Coin collecting tended to be an exclusive pastime which required disposable income and free time to study the coins. Today most collectors will try for a representative coin, a nice example of each major variety; we call this type collecting. What with the level of today's prices, it would be almost impossible to try and obtain one of everything. One nice coin is worth more than ten poor examples. A coin which is in choice Very Fine condition can have more 'eye appeal' than a coin that is in indifferent Extremely Fine quality.

Grading goes from the poorest to the finest as follows: Poor, Fair, About Good, Good, Very Good, Fine, Very Fine, Extremely Fine, Good Extremely Fine, About Uncirculated, Uncirculated, Choice Uncirculated and Gem Uncirculated. In this country Proof is a method of striking and not a condition, thus on the early proofs you can have an EF, Proof or even a Fine Proof. A Proof today is struck several times to get the best depth of design, on a polished planchet and with polished dies. The higher the grade, i.e. the less wear a coin has, the more expensive a coin will be. There are many coins in the hammered field which do not exist in grades higher than Very Fine, there are many milled coins which do not exist in Uncirculated condition. If you see a coin in a grade which is exceptional, than you can expect it to command an exceptional price. Novice collectors have to be aware that some dealers polish and/or over grade their coins to make them appear a better grade and thus sell for more money. If a coin looks too cheap there is something wrong, there is no Santa Claus! Polishing a coin, rather than increasing its value, in real terms decreases it and makes the coin harder to sell.

Coins with beautiful toning appeal to me because I know that they have lain undisturbed and no one has played with them for a long period of time. On the other hand, many collectors like their coins bright and shiny. Many new collectors regard a coin with toning as a 'dirty coin'. My sage advice to you is *do not clean your coins as you will hurt their value!* I have seen coins worth £500 which will bring only £50 after having been polished. Either learn to live with beautiful multi-coloured and hued toning or find untoned coins. Never clean your coins!

Coins cost much less today in terms of purchasing power then they did when they were originally issued. In the reign of Queen Anne a skilled craftsman working six days a week earned one shilling (5p) a week. Today a reasonable Queen Anne shilling sells for around £30 and a skilled craftsman earns £400 a week. The Queen Anne shilling is cheaper today, in terms of purchasing power, than it was when it was issued almost 300 years ago. In the time of Queen Anne one of her shillings would have been the equivalent of 60 hours' work today that same coin can be exchanged for only 3 hours' work. Coins today represent good value for money.

Getting back to how a coin is valued, the more people who collect a particular series, the more demand there will be for that series and the more people who will be willing to pay 'a price' for a particular coin from that series. There are some extremely rare hammered coins, but if there are only ten people who want an example and eleven coins on offer, prices will be low. On the other hand, if there were one hundred examples of an Edward VII coin and hundreds of collectors who wanted one, then prices would be high. Personally, I believe that when you know the history of hammered coins, then any coin which exists today is rare. There is no exact formula for determining what a coin will sell for, tastes change and with that prices also change. An educated collector is the best collector, so know your coins and get to know your dealer.

What should you collect? Rather than answer that, I would like to suggest a way that you might collect. Unless you have some specialist field which delights and consumes you, do not collect in too narrow a field to start. The mistake that many collectors make when first starting out is trying to decide immediately what they are going to collect. Buy whatever pleases and interests you, a little of this and a little of that. Over a period of time, nature will take its course and you will gradually narrow down your field of concentration. If you start collecting too narrowly in the beginning, you might well lose interest and stop collecting altogether. Let your imagination run wild. It is only after you have collected for a while and held and touched actual coins, that you will discover your true area of interest. I believe in the shotgun approach; a shotgun shell lets off many small pellets and one or more of them will usually find the target.

Some people collect by monarch, trying to get one coin from each reign, some by denomination such as shillings, halfcrowns or crowns. Others collect coins which are of historic significance to them, while yet others try to collect coins struck in and around their region. If you want to collect one coin of each monarch, then the penny is the only denomination which is listed continuously from the first to the last monarch in this book. I like to collect by type; when I show my collection to friends they find it more interesting. On the other hand, it is exciting to attempt to complete a date set of a series. The coinage since the Currency Reform Act of 1816 is possible to complete, but it will cost a bit of money, even in the lower grades.

Why do people collect? I guess it is a disease and, as a sufferer myself, I know the symptoms. You want to own, to possess something, in this case a piece of history. It is not something to be ashamed of, rather something to be proud of. You are helping retain a part of our cultural history. It is a disease with no suffering and patients have the delusion that they are enjoying themselves. Welcome to the clinic!

Coin books are important so that you can learn about your hobby. You have bought a copy of this book and for the time being, it will be all that you will need on the subject. Later on, if you start to specialise and go into the subject more deeply, you might well require a more specialised book. Books also tell the background and history about a particular coin or area, they make collecting fun!

Do not try to buy too many coins at the beginning, it is a temptation and as dealers we are here to tempt you — pass me that apple will you... The late J. William 'Bill' Ross told me, when I started in coins some 40 years ago, that 'there will always be more coins than there is money!'. By that he meant take your time, do not go in over your head when you start. There will come a time when you want a coin which costs more than you can afford. At that point you have three choices, one: selling something else in order to buy that new coin; two: talking to the dealer or auctioneer about perhaps spreading the purchase price over a few months; or three: forgetting it! Yes, you would like the coin, but there will be other coins around later, when you have the money available. There will always be more coins than there is money. Strange to hear a dealer say that, remember that I am a collector too; been there, done that...

Get to know a dealer and see what they have to offer, their best items will inevitably be offered to their favourite collectors and never go on display. We might have a nice coin and know that there are three collectors who need it. At that point your previous history comes into play; we will offer it to the collector who has been the least trouble or made himself most popular. If you haggle over the price, mess about over the arrangements or heaven forbid, bounce a cheque, it is to the back of the queue for you. Spend some time with your dealer, get to know them, let them get to know you. Remember that dealers make their living from coins, spend some money with them. There are few things that dealers hate more than a collector who takes up their time asking about a coin, only to reveal that they have used this free advice to buy that coin from another dealer. This may sound cold-hearted, but if you purchased a coin from another dealer, please do not show it to me. No dealer likes to see the 'bargains' that you bought from someone else. Would you make an appointment with your dentist to show him the work another dentist has done? I think not. Coin dealers are professionals who have put in long hours and many years studying our subject, treat us as professionals and we can make collecting fun for you.

The only way to get into coin collecting is to buy some coins. Many dealers have 'junk' boxes of low value coins, at Coincraft we even sell British and world coins by the kilo so the actual cost of coins can be in the pennies. Once you have seen and handled coins let your imagination run wild. Where has that coin been, who has handled it etc. Check with your local museum which may well have a coin collection, but it is no good studying coins if you have never actually handled them.

Collecting can be as inexpensive or as expensive as your budget will allow. The most important thing is to have fun! Do not let anyone tell you what to collect, buy a little of this and a little of that until you find what interests and excites you. Learn about the hobby and try and find a dealer or dealers that you are happy with and they are happy with you. Nothing gives a dealer a greater thrill than starting a new collector off and helping them build a nice collection. Take some time to look through this book, pick it up and open a page at random, let your eyes do the dancing. But most of all *enjoy yourself!*

Richard Lobel

Unique New Numbering System
The Number tells you what the Coin is

Coincraft's unique new numbering system for English coins is a key feature of this catalogue and one that we are particularly proud to be introducing. Although at heart it is a very simple idea, we think that it is quite revolutionary in its own way.

As dealers and collectors ourselves, we were appalled at the prospect of producing a numbering system that was yet another string of incomprehensible figures. Sorting out a collector's wants list, producing an inventory or even jotting down a buying list was time consuming and often needlessly complicated. We thought, perhaps if we shifted the emphasis away from the catalogue and on to the coins themselves, the results would make sense. By using a form of shorthand notation we found that it actually worked! We have tested the limits of the idea, refined its application and every so often, we would even question its very principle, to ensure that we were on the right track. The system was being refined right up to the time that this book went to press. At the last moment we decided that the coinage of Queen Victoria could and should be subdivided by major type, to give you an even more precise picture of what coin the number was actually describing.

Coincraft's new system has numbers which are composed of three distinct parts. The first part tells you which monarch struck the coin, the second part tells you which denomination the coin is and the third part tells you which variety it is. In conjunction with the Catalogue, the variety pinpoints the date if the coin is dated, the mint, type and variety, which will allow you to identify your coins. But at the very least, the first two sections allow a person reading the number to know which monarch struck the coin and what coin it is. If you have a wants list with KM-575 or Seaby-3686, what does the collector want? You cannot know without referring to the relevant book — providing you have one handy. But if the collector asked for G2CR-010, you would know at once that it was a George II (G2) crown (CR) and, by looking up the variety 010 under Crowns, George II, you would find that it is the 1732 issue. Note that the variety numbers jump by fives, so as to leave room for any varieties which might be discovered in the future without having to renumber your entire collection. As mentioned previously, the coinage of Victoria, denoted by 'V', includes a reference to the type of head on the obverse, 'Y' for Young, 'G' for Gothic, 'J' for Jubilee and 'O' for Old Head.

Of course, as with every rule there is an exception, and in this instance it is the decimal coinage. The principle remains the same, but the application has been modified slightly to take into account the peculiarities of the series. Decimal coins are denoted by a 'D', followed by the abbreviation for the denomination, a stroke and then the last two digits of the year they were issued. Because several different types are usually issued for each date of the decimal series, a suffix code is used to distinguish between them:

1: currency coin

2: specimen (nonproof) issue

3: proof issue in base metal

4: proof in silver

5: piedfort proof in silver

6: proof in gold

On some coins, a further coding is incorporated into the suffix on an ad hoc basis where further classification of a variety is necessary. The numbering system for cased sets consists of a prefix PS or (for decimal) DPS for proof sets; MS or DMS for mint sets; a suffix of the last two digits of the date or, in the case of sets before 1902, the four digits of the date; an optional suffix allocated on an ad hoc basis to distinguish different types of set of the same date.

This new numbering system is remarkably easy to use and is based on common sense. The names of the various monarchs are abbreviated to the first initial and number. A second letter of the name is only included when it is necessary to distinguish, as for example between Edward and Elizabeth. Thus for Edward I to Edward VIII all that is required is an 'E' for Edward followed by the numbers 1 to 8; Elizabeth I is abbreviated to EL and Elizabeth II to EL2. Following the same principle, the denominations are usually indicated by two letters. Thus crown becomes CR, halfcrown HC, halfpenny HP, etc. Try to think of monarchs and how you would put their names down in our shorthand. Now try it again with the denominations. Easy, isn't it? Check the charts below and see how well you did. I believe that in five minutes you will have mastered this new numbering system.

REIGN	REF
William I	W1
William II	W2
Henry I	H1
Stephen	S
Matilda	MA
Henry II	H2
Richard I	R1
John	JH
Henry III	H3
Edward I	E1
Edward II	E2
Edward III	E3
Richard II	R2
Henry IV	H4
Henry V	H5
Henry VI	H6
Edward IV	E4
Edward V	E5
Richard III	R3
Henry VII	H7
Henry VIII	H8
Edward VI	E6
Mary	M
Philip & Mary	PM
Elizabeth I	EL
James I	J1
Charles I	C1
Commonwealth	COM
Cromwell	CR
Charles II	C2
James II	J2
William & Mary	WM
William III	W3
Anne	A
George I	G1
George II	G2
George III	G3
George IV	G4
William IV	W4
Victoria	V
Edward VII	E7
George V	G5
Edward VIII	E8
George VI	G6
Elizabeth II	EL2

DECIMAL COINAGE	REF
Five Pounds	D5P
Two Pounds	D2P
One Pound	D1P
Fifty Pence	D50
Twenty Five Pence	D25
Twenty Pence	D20
Ten Pence	D10
Five Pence	D05
Two Pence	D02
One Penny	D01
Halfpenny	DHP

DENOMINATION	REF
Angel	AG
Broad	BR
Crown	CR
Double Crown	DC
Double Florin	DFL
Eighteen Pence Token	18D
Farthing	FA
Fifty Shillings	50S
Five Guineas	5G
Five Pounds	5P
Florin	FL
Fourpence, Maundy	4M
Groat	4D
Guinea	GN
Half Angel	HA
Half Crown	HC
Half Farthing	HF
Half Florin	HFL
Half Groat / Twopence, Copper	2D
Half Guinea	HG
Half Laurel	HL
Half Noble	HN
Half Pound	HP
Half Sovereign	HS
Half Unite	HU
Halfpenny	HD
Laurel	LA
Noble	NB
Penny, Copper/Bronze	1D
Penny, Maundy	1M
Pound	PD
Quarter Angel	QA
Quarter Farthing	QF
Quarter Florin	QFL
Quarter Guinea	QG
Quarter Laurel	QL
Quarter Noble	QN
Ryal	RY
Shilling	SH
Sixpence	6D
Sovereign	SV
Testoon	TS
Third Farthing	TF
Third Guinea	TG
Three Farthings	3F
Three Shillings	3S
Threehalfpence	3HD
Threepence	3D
Threepence, Brass	3DB
Threepence, Silver	3M
Triple Unite	TU
Twenty Pence	20D
Two Guineas	2G
Two Pounds	2P
Twopence, Maundy	2M
Unite	UN

Index Charts

The following two charts indicate which denominations were struck under which monarch and, by citing the relevant page numbers in this Catalogue, can also act as a 'quick index'.

Hammered Coins

	TU	SV	UN	LA	PD	RY	HS	DC	HL	HU	HP	NB	AG	FL	CR	CRR	HN	
William I																		W1
William II																		W2
Henry I																		H1
Stephen																		S
Matilda																		MA
Henry II																		H2
Richard I																		R1
John I																		JH
Henry III																		H3
Edward I																		E1
Edward II																		E2
Edward III												111		129			147	E3
Richard II												113					148	R2
Henry IV												114					149	H4
Henry V												115					149	H5
Henry VI												116	121				150	H6
Edward IV						118						117	121				151	E4
Edward V													122					E5
Richard III													122					R3
Henry VII		81				97							123					H7
Henry VIII		82					99					124	124		131	145		H8
Edward VI		83				100							125		132			E6
Mary I		84				97							125					M
Philip & Mary													126					PM
Elizabeth I		85			85	97	101						126		133			EL
James I		85	86	87		97	103	103	103				127		135			J1
Charles I	79		88		92			104		105	106		127		137			C1
Commonwealth		94						108							143			COM
Charles II		95						108							144			C2

Milled Coins

	5G	5P	50S	2G	2P	BR	GN	SV	HG	HS	TG	QG	CR	DFL	3S	HC	FL	
Cromwell			387			399							433			455		CR
Charles II	377			389		401		417					433			455		C2
James II	378			389		402		417					435			457		J2
William & Mary	379			390		402		418					436			457		WM
William III	379			390		403		418					436			458		W3
Anne	380			391		404		419					437			460		A
George I	381			391		405		419				431	438			461		G1
George II	381			392		406		420					439			461		G2
George III						407	409	420	423	429	431	440		453	462		G3
George IV		383		393			409		423				442			464		G4
William IV				393			410		423				443			464		W4
Victoria		383		394			410		424				444	451		465	471	V
Edward VII		384		394			413		426				446			466	473	E7
George V		385		395			413		426				446			467	474	G5
Edward VIII		385		395			415						447			468	475	E8
George VI		385		395			415		427				448			468	475	G6
Elizabeth II		386		396			415		427				448			469	476	EL2

	HA	HFL	HC	20D	QN	QA	QFL	SH	6D	4D	3D	2D	3HD	1D	3F	HD	FA		
William I														285					W1
William II														287					W2
Henry I														287		341			H1
Stephen														290					S
Matilda														291					MA
Henry II														292					H2
Richard I														294					R1
John I														295					JH
Henry III				187										296		341	357		H3
Edward I										233				299		341	357		E1
Edward II														306		343	359		E2
Edward III		159			189		197			233		261		308		343	359		E3
Richard II					190					235		262		313		345	360		R2
Henry IV					191					236		263		314		346	360		H4
Henry V					191					236		264		315		346	360		H5
Henry VI	153				192					237		264		316		347	361		H6
Edward IV	153				193					240		266		319		348	362		E4
Edward V	154									244		269		324					E5
Richard III	154									245		269		325		351			R3
Henry VII	154							199		245		269		325		351	362		H7
Henry VIII	155		161			195		199		247		271		327		352	362		H8
Edward VI	155		162					200	221	250	255	274		330		354	363		E6
Mary I	156									250		275		331					M
Philip & Mary	156							202	221	251		275		332					PM
Elizabeth I	156		163			195		203	222	251	255	275	283	332	339	354			EL
James I	157		164					205	224			277		333		354	363		J1
Charles I			166					206	225	252	256	277		334		355	364		C1
Commonwealth			184					218	230			281		337		355			COM
Charles II			184					218	231	254	259	281		337					C2

	18D	SH	6D	4M	4D	3M	3DB	2M	2D	3HD	1M	1D	HD	FA	HF	TF	QF	MS	
Cromwell		479	495																CR
Charles II		479	495	507		513		523			531		545	557				*	C2
James II		480	495	507		513		523			531		545	557				*	J2
William & Mary		481	496	507		513		523			531		546	558				*	WM
William III		481	496	508		514		524			532		547	558				*	W3
Anne		483	498	508		514		524			532			559				*	A
George I		484	498	508		514		524			532		548	560				*	G1
George II		486	499	509		514		524			533		549	560				*	G2
George III	477	487	500	509		515		525	527		533	535	550	561				*	G3
George IV		488	500	509		515		525			533	536	551	562	569	571		575	G4
William IV		489	501	510	511	516		525		529	534	536	551	562	569	571		575	W4
Victoria		489	501	510	511	516		526		529	534	537	552	563	569	571	573	575	V
Edward VII		491	503	510		517		526			534	540	554	565		572		576	E7
George V		491	504	510		518		526			534	541	554	565		572		577	G5
Edward VIII		492	504			518	521					542	555	566					E8
George VI		492	505	510		519	521	526			534	542	555	566				577	G6
Elizabeth II		493	505	510		519	522	526			534	543	556	567				578	EL2

* listed under individual coins

Acknowledgements

We would like to give special thanks to the following people who helped us put this book together:

Peter Gerald 'Maundy' Allen

Laurie Bamford

Joe Bispham

James Brown

Barry Clayden

Malcolm Coeshaw

Chris Comber

Michael Gouby

Peter Hicks

Peter Jackson

Claire Lobel

Dimitri Loulakakis

Nigel Mills

Peter Mitchell

Sylvia Mitchell

James Morton

Colin Narbeth

Paul Nicholson

William Paul

P. Alan Rayner

Peter Wallwork

Colin Whitear

Peter Wild

We would also like to thank the following for their help:

Denise Altman

Garry Charman

Adam Croton

Anthony Dowle

Daniel Fearon

Patrick Finn

Robert Ilsley

Mark Rasmussen

Douglas Savile

May Sinclair

Alan Ward

Chris Webb

Finally, we would also like to thank the following auction houses for their help:

Bonhams

Buckland Dix & Wood

Christies

Croydon Coin Auctions

Glendinings

Sothebys

Spink

To everyone THANK YOU !

Glossary

'0'	Privy or mintmark, see chapter 'Mintmarks'.
'1'	Privy or mintmark, see chapter 'Mintmarks'.
'2'	Privy or mintmark, see chapter 'Mintmarks'.
'A'	Privy or mintmark, see chapter 'Mintmarks'.
'B'	Privy or mintmark, see chapter 'Mintmarks'.
'Y'	Privy or mintmark, see chapter 'Mintmarks'.
Aberystwyth Mint	The first provincial mint to be established by Charles I. It was opened in Wales in 1638 by Sir Thomas Bushell, the lessee of the Welsh silver mines. His privy mark was an open book. Coins were struck at this mint from dies shipped in from London and their minting ceased before the Civil War started.
Acorn	Privy or mintmark, see chapter 'Mintmarks'.
Adjustment Marks	When a flan or planchet was too heavy for a particular denomination, an adjuster would scrape it by hand to bring it down to the correct weight.
AE	Symbol for 'aes', an abbreviation for copper or bronze.
After Union	Coins struck during the reign of Queen Anne after the Union of England and Scotland in 1707. Those struck at Edinburgh can be distinguished by an E or E* below the bust. Only silver coins are known with an E or E*.
Altered Date	Where the date on a coin has been changed. Sometimes mints reuse dies and punch or re-engrave a new date over an old date. In some cases a coin will be altered to increase its collector value. An example is the 1933 penny, altered from 1935 into 1933.
Annulet	Privy or mintmark, see chapter 'Mintmarks'.
Anchor	Privy or mintmark, see chapter 'Mintmarks'.
Anchor & B	Privy or mintmark, see chapter 'Mintmarks'.
Anchor & Mullet	Privy or mintmark, see chapter 'Mintmarks'.
Angel	An English gold coin first issued in 1465 with a value of 6 shillings and 8 pence. St Michael spearing a dragon is on the obverse and a ship on the reverse. This denomination was struck under every monarch until the reign of Charles I.
Anglo-Hanoverian Coinage	Coins struck during the reigns of George I up to and including William IV. These were struck for the use in Germanic duchies such as Hanover and Brunswick. The British monarchs are portrayed on many of these coins as their line originated in Hanover.
Annulet	A ring, usually very small, in many cases used as a privy mark. Henry VI's coinage can be dated according to the placement of the annulet.
Annulet	Privy or mintmark, see chapter 'Mintmarks'.
Ansell Sovereign	Sovereigns struck in 1859 by the Royal Mint, under G.F. Ansell to test the use of Australian gold. The gold proved too brittle for use in coinage. An Ansell sovereign can be distinguished by the line down the ribbon or tie in Victoria's hair; see under sovereigns.
Anson, Admiral	Admiral Anson circumnavigated the globe and brought back silver and gold which he had captured from the Spanish. The coins struck by George II with Lima below his bust might indicate that the coins captured carried the Lima mintmark.
AR	Denotes Argentum, i.e. silver.
Arrow	Privy or mintmark, see chapter 'Mintmarks'.
Assay	A test to determine the actual metal content of an object or coin, i.e. the fineness of the precious metal as a percentage of the total content.
AU	A grade which is designated as About Uncirculated.
Au	Denotes Aurum, i.e. gold.

Bag Marks	When coins are struck they are placed in bags and then moved to the place where they will be distributed to the public for everyday use. In that moving the coins rub up against each other and acquire small marks; these are called bag marks. The fewer the number and the less severity of the marks the higher the value of the coin.
Bank of England Dollar	Struck from 1804 until about 1814 but still retaining the date 1804. It was issued by the Bank of England to help alleviate the shortage of change. They were overstruck on eight reales of the Spanish world and were to replace the countermarked coins. Previously a punch which had been used to hallmark silver with George III's portrait was use to countermark and thus make Spanish and other world coins legal tender. A wit in those days said it was the head of an ass on the head of a fool. Very wisely we do not know who said it.
Bank Token	Issued by the Bank of England between 1811 and 1816, they were struck in silver with denominations of One Shilling and Sixpence and Three Shillings. The Bank's name does not appear on the coins, just the legend 'Bank Token'. There is also a pattern ninepence token known. From the condition of many of these Bank Tokens they saw considerable circulation and use.
Barton's Metal	A very thin layer of gold which is laminated or bonded to a copper blank.
Base Metal	A non-precious metal i.e. not silver, gold, platinum, or palladium. Usually copper or bronze but today it also includes aluminium, stainless steel and cupro-nickel.
Bath Metal	A mixture of zinc (24.7%), copper (75%) and silver (0.3%), it is named after the city of Bath where it was invented. It was used in the 1720s to make coins for the American Colonies.
Beading	The small dots sometimes found either around the rim of a coin or between the legend and a field.
Before Union	Coin struck in the reign of Queen Anne before the union of England and Scotland in 1707.
Bell	Privy or mintmark, see chapter 'Mintmarks'.
Bell Metal	Originally referred to coins struck from the melted church bells of France.
Bi-metallic	A coin which is made up of two separate metals. In modern coins, they are usually in concentric circles. The James II tin coinage had a brass plug inserted in it to help stop counterfeiting.
Billet	Privy or mintmark, see chapter 'Mintmarks'.
Billon	A mixture of silver and another metal where the silver makes up a maximum of 50% of the mixture. When first issued and still shiny from the mint, a billon coin will look like silver, but paler. After wear the other metal comes through and the coin will look coppery. The posthumous coinage of Henry VIII is a good example of what can happen and how he got the nickname of 'Copper Nose'.
Bird	Privy or mintmark, see chapter 'Mintmarks'.
Blacksmith Half Crown	A crude halfcrown struck in Kilkenny in Ireland during the Civil War. This is a very rare copy of the Tower Mint halfcrown.
Blank	The metal disc also called a planchet or flan upon which the design of the coin is impressed. The blank is fed into a press where extreme pressure causes the metal of the blank to flow into the reversed design of the dies so the design comes out raised.

Blondeau, Pierre	A French engraver who worked at the Tower Mint during the Commonwealth administration and Charles II's reign. He reintroduced the screw press for the making of milled or machine struck coins. It had not been used since Elizabeth I was on the throne. He also had the ability and he knew how to put inscriptions or lettering on a coin's edge. This lettering was first used by Blondeau on pattern coins of 1651. It was not until 1658 that this process was regularly used on crowns and, after 1668, on five guineas. A lettered edge stopped the clipping of coins.
Blundered Inscription	On a coin where it has been struck several times and the slight shifting has made the legend unreadable.
Boar's Head	Privy or mintmark, see chapter 'Mintmarks'.
Bob	Slang term for shilling.
Bonnet Piece	A gold coin issued under James V of Scotland, it was valued at one ducat (3.5 grams). It was struck in 1539 from gold found at Crawford Muir. It is the first Scottish coin to bear a date.
Book	Privy or mintmark, see chapter 'Mintmarks'.
Book on Lectern	Privy or mintmark, see chapter 'Mintmarks'.
Border	The outer part of a coin nearest to the edge and rim of that coin. Usually part of the design and used to ensure that the coin will wear better and longer.
Boulton, Matthew	1728-1809, from Birmingham and a manufacturer of coinage machinery. Most famous for his Soho Mint which issued many of the early copper coins of George III. He was the first person to use steam power to strike coins.
Brass Threepence	A denomination which was struck for circulation from 1937 until 1967 and then in the 1970 Proof Set. First designed for issue under Edward VIII. When he abdicated it bore the portrait of George VI. It had twelve sides and was struck in brass.
Breeches Money	A slang term for the coinage under the Commonwealth. The two shields looked like an inflated pair of men's breeches.
Brilliant Uncirculated	A condition of grading. On copper and bronze coins this means bright and shiny just like it came from the mint. On silver coins it means with little or no toning, perhaps the middle coins from a roll where the outer coins have toned.
Briot, Nicholas (1580-1646)	Arrived in England ca 1626 and believed in machine struck coinage. A superb engraver, perhaps the finest this country has ever known. His work was far superior to the crude coins that were being struck at that time. During the Civil War he was loyal to Charles I and worked at York and Oxford. His coinage is neat, precise and most attractive.
Britain Crown	A five shilling gold coin issued by James I in 1604. The legend reads HENRICUS ROSAS REGNA JACOBUS (Henry unites the roses, James the kingdoms)
Britannia	Her seated figure can first be seen on Roman coins under Hadrian and Antoninus Pius. These coins were struck to commemorate their victories in the British dominions. Britannia is now depicted seated on a rock with a shield and trident in her hand.
Britannia Groat	William IV reintroduced the groat as a denomination into general circulation. It had not been in regular use since Charles I. His new groat had the seated figure of Britannia on it; the final issue was the Jubilee issue of Victoria in 1888.
Broad	A gold piece to the value of twenty shillings struck with the portrait of Oliver Cromwell, engraved by Thomas Simon and dated 1656.
Brockage	When a coin is stuck in a die and another planchet is introduced, that first coin makes an incused impression into the second coin. It acts like a miniature die. The second coin ends up with the same impression raised and incused.

Bronzed	Copper coins which have been covered with a thin layer of bronze, usually on proof coins to make them more attractive.
Bull Head	The portrait depicting George III on the new halfcrown after the Currency Reform Act of 1816. It was only used in 1816 and 1817. While some collectors also use this term to describe the shilling and sixpence of this issue, I have my doubts. After all it was only the design of the halfcrown which was changed in 1817.
Bullion Coin	A coin which changes hands at or near its intrinsic value. Usually struck and sold for the hoarding of precious metal. They are of no numismatic value except curiosity value.
Bun Coinage	The bronze coinage of Queen Victoria with a youthful portrait and her hair tied up in a bun; it was issued from 1860-1894.
Bunch of Grapes	Privy or mintmark, see chapter 'Mintmarks'.
Bungtown Coppers	Imitations of British copper coins struck mainly in the United Kingdom and also the American Colonies. There were many counterfeits of copper halfpennies, a number with most amusing legends. Also known as *Regal evasions*.
Bushell, Thomas	The lessee of the North Wales silver mines. In 1637 Charles I gave him permission to strike coins at Aberystwyth. These coins have the Welsh plumes and a privy mark of an open book. The quality of the engraving is quite fine and the workmanship extremely neat. They are beautiful coins.
Cabinet Friction	In the old days coins were kept and displayed in wooden cabinets. The coins tended to move about when the tray was taken out and rubbing or friction often happened on the high points. These coins have not seen circulation but I am afraid that the cabinet friction does adversely affect their prices.
Calais	A French town under English rule from 1363-1412 and again from 1424 to about 1440. English silver and gold coins were struck there and either have the legend VILLA CALAIS or a 'C' mint mark; many varieties exist.
Carlisle, Siege	Carlisle is a town on the English Scottish borders and in the Civil War was under siege. During the period October 1644 to June 1645, octagonal shaped coins were struck from dinner plates made of silver. The coins were valued at one and three shillings.
Cartouche	A scroll-like ornamental design, usually containing some feature within it, e.g. the lion at the centre of the William III crown reverse.
Cartwheel	A slang name for the copper coinage of 1797. The Soho Mint issued one and two penny coins which weighed one (28.35 grams) and two ounces (56.7 grams) respectively. It was the only time a government tried to give value for money. As expected the people hated the heavy two pence and the famous Cartwheel twopence was never issued again. The penny was actually struck for a number of years but all the coins bear the date 1797.
Cased Set	A group of coins which is issued in some sort of casing or packaging. They are usually all of the same date and made other than for general circulation. They can be issued for a coronation, jubilee or the like.
Castle	Privy or mintmark, see chapter 'Mintmarks'.
Catherine Wheel	Privy or mintmark, see chapter 'Mintmarks'.
Chevron Milling	A 'V' shaped milling introduced to deter counterfeiting, on the gold coinage of George II and George III.
Choice Uncirculated	A grade. A coin is Uncirculated if it has never been in circulation and is without wear. But due to the vagaries of how coins are struck, how the dies were made and how the coins were treated after striking, there are different grades of Uncirculated. Choice Uncirculated is better than a normal Uncirculated coin with far fewer bag marks and is well struck with full and uninterrupted lustre.
Cinquefoil	Privy or mintmark, see chapter 'Mintmarks'.

Clash Marks	The marks made on one die when it is struck by the other die without a flan or blank in between. When coins are struck from that die, they will have a minor impression from both dies.
Clipped Coin	A coin where a small quantity of metal has been removed while still trying to retain the original value. People would take hammered coins, put them in a sack, then shake the sack vigorously for hours. The sack would then be melted down and any metal left would be the persons wages for the day. This was called sweating the coins. It was illegal, but in the reign of Elizabeth I as long as the inner circle was not broken, the coin was still legal tender.
Coin	A form of money, today the fractional part of a paper note. Usually round and struck in metal, but there have been square, triangular and other shapes also struck. In the 7th Century BC the first stamped piece of metal was issued in Lydia.
Coin Weight	A piece of metal which exactly reproduces the weight of a known coin. This is used to check if a coin is of the proper weight and fineness. The coin goes in one side of a balance scale and the weight in the other; if the coin is of the correct weight then the scale will balance.
Collar	The metal ring which retains the blank while a coin is being struck. A collar can also impart a lettering or design on the edge of a coin whilst it is being struck.
Commemorative	A coin struck to honour or commemorate an event or person. In the past many commemoratives were issued at or near their face value. Today they are issued for collectors and to produce revenue for the issuing country or marketer. Many of the commemoratives issued today are not issued for general circulation and thus are NCLT (Non Circulating Legal Tender).
Company for Melting Down Pitcoale and Seacoale	Roses and plumes on the reverse of coins Privy or mintmark, see chapter 'Mintmarks'.
Condor Token	Privately issued copper tokens to the value of a farthing, halfpenny or penny in the late 1700s. First issued by the Pyes Mining Company in Wales. Due to the shortage of small change they were readily accepted as money and rapidly spread all over the country. The merchants made a small profit on the manufacture of the tokens and they also advertised their wares for free on the tokens. The first book on this subject was written by James Condor and thus they are often referred to as Condor Tokens.
Conjoined	Two or more busts shown slightly overlapping and looking in the same direction. The only coins of this country to have conjoined busts was the coinage of William and Mary.
Contemporary Forgery	A copy of coin made during the time that the coin circulated and was in current use.
Copper Nose	A nickname given to Henry VIII. The posthumous coinage was so debased that when it was worn, the copper showed through on Henry's nose. Thus he became known as 'Old Copper Nose'.
Copper-nickel	See *Cupro-nickel*.
Copy	A reproduction of something, in this case a coin. Museums make copies, some for their own collection and some for sale in their shops. Over the years some copies have become very collectable. For example the Renaissance copies of Roman coins known as Paduans are highly collected. Modern copies are often made to deceive collectors.
Corbet Farthing	Andrew Corbet was granted a patent to strike farthings in 1693. This was almost immediately revoked, but a few pieces still exist.
Coronet	Privy or mintmark, see chapter 'Mintmarks'.

Counterfeit	Coins (or notes) made outside the relevant issuing authority to cheat someone. They may well have the same metal content as the original. The exception is when the sovereign was demonetised, Italian counterfeiters made sovereigns with slightly more gold than the originals. That way they could not be prosecuted. They made a living on the 44% premium over gold content that sovereigns sold for at that time.
Countermark	A mark or design placed on a coin either by an issuing authority or by a private individual. During the reign of George III a small bust of the king was counterstamped on silver coins to make them legal tender in the United Kingdom. An individual can counterstamp a coin with his or her name or initials. In the 1800s many companies counterstamped advertising slogans on coins to get free advertising. It was later made illegal to deface coins by stamping anything on them.
Cracked Die	When too much pressure is applied when striking coins or when the die is very worn it will start to crack. As the metal is pushed into the die it will also be pushed into the crack, so cracks will appear as raised lines on a coin. It is possible to estimate when during the life of a die the coin was made, by the state and length of the die crack on the coin. A famous example is the Cromwell Crown.
Crescent	Privy or mintmark, see chapter 'Mintmarks'.
Cross Calvary	Privy or mintmark, see chapter 'Mintmarks'.
Cross Fitchée	Privy or mintmark, see chapter 'Mintmarks'.
Cross Fleury	Privy or mintmark, see chapter 'Mintmarks'.
Cross Pattée	Privy or mintmark, see chapter 'Mintmarks'.
Cross-Crosslet	Privy or mintmark, see chapter 'Mintmarks'.
Crown	Privy or mintmark, see chapter 'Mintmarks'.
Crown	The first English coin of this denomination was issued by Henry VIII in 1526. It was a gold coin with a face value of 4 shillings and 6 pence. It is very rare because it was shortly replaced with the Crown of the Double Rose, which has a face value of five shillings. The first silver crown was issued in 1551 by Edward VI and the last crown to be issued was in 1981, for the wedding of Prince Charles & Lady Diana Spencer.
Crown Gold	Henry VIII set the standard for gold to be 916 2/3 fine, known as 22 carat gold. The Mint still uses this standard today.
Crowned Leopard's Head	Privy or mintmark, see chapter 'Mintmarks'.
Crosier	The hook shaped top part of a mitre, usually found as a mark in legends.
Cruciform Shields	Shields in the form of a cross.
Cupro-nickel	An alloy of copper and nickel. Today the usual ratio is 75% copper to 25% nickel.
Currency	From the Latin currentia, a stream. Thus anything that flows from one hand to another: coins, banknotes, pigs, shells or any medium of exchange which is acceptable. Today we use the term to refer to paper money.
Cut Money	In the early days when you wanted to pay someone a halfpenny and you only had a silver penny, you literally cut it in half. If you needed farthings then you cut the coin into quarters.
Debasement	When a government uses less precious metal in the coining of money, while still retaining its original face or exchange value. The prime example is the coinage of Henry VIII.
Decimalization	In 1971 the British system of money was finally changed to a system based on tens or decimals. The Pounds, Shillings and Pence or 'LSD' system stopped being used and a new system of New Pence was introduced. No longer was the pound broken up into 240d, now we had 100p.

Declaration Type	Coins of Charles I issued during the Civil War period, the reverse of which contained the official royalist declaration RELIGO PROTESTANTIUM LEGES ANGLIAE LIBERTAS PARLIAMENTI (The religion of the Protestants the laws of England the liberty of Parliament).
Demonetised	A currency which is deemed to be no longer legal tender for debts both public and private. Under the Currency Reform Act of 1816 all coins issued before that date were demagnetised, no longer legal tender. A period of grace was given during which you could turn your old money in for the new coins. After that period of grace the coins were only worth their metal or intrinsic value.
Denomination	The name given to value of the coin either real or implied. A florin is to the value of two shillings or ten pence.
Denticles	Design objects used to create a border on a coin, usually round or wedge shaped. They go all around the edge of a coin next to the rim.
Device	That part of the design which is not a portrait or lettering.
Die	The engraved metal piece which is used to strike coins and medallions. In the old days an engraver cut directly into and in reverse in the metal. Today a plaster is sculptured and a rubber is made which is then placed on a reduction machine. The end product is called a hub and is raised like coins. From this, dies are struck and then hardened before use.
Die Axis	There are two types of die axis: coin alignment and medal alignment. In coin alignment if you are looking at the heads' side and turn the coin over through a vertical axis 180 degrees to the reverse, the reverse will be upside down ↓ . If on the other hand the reverse is right side up ↑ then this is medal alignment.
Die Break	A raised line which is caused by the metal of the flan being forced into a small crack or break in the die.
Die Numbering on Coins	The Royal Mint used to number their dies between 1863 and 1880. It was for experimentation, the object of which has been lost. It has been mooted that the Mint was trying to see how long dies lasted.
Die Variety	Because different pairs of dies are used to strike similar coins, there may be small differences on the coins. These small differences caused by different dies are called die varieties. As obverse and reverse dies wear out at different times, it is possible to link the dies used by comparing die combinations. Museums spend a lot of time in trying to follow the sequence of dies used and many scholarly papers have been written on the subject.
Die Wear	Dies as they strike a vast number of coins start to show signs of wear; this causes the coins they strike to appear rather weakly struck. Coins can be as struck but appear to be only Very Fine.
Dorrien Magens Shilling	A shilling issued in 1798 by the Royal Mint for the banking firm of Dorrien Magens. The government refused to allow this private enterprise to have its own coinage struck and so had all but about six examples melted down.
Double Florin	A denomination of four shillings struck only three times in our history. The first was issued in 1887, the Jubilee year of Queen Victoria, and continued on in general circulation until 1890. It is also known as 'the barmaid's ruin'. When she had a few drinks she would often give change for a crown (5/-) instead of a double florin (4/-). This shortage would have to be made up out of her own wages. There were pattern issues in the reigns of George V, George VI and Elizabeth II. All these patterns are rare.
Dragon	Privy or mintmark, see chapter 'Mintmarks'.
Drapery	Clothing or cloth in folds.
Dump Issue	A name used for the thick copper farthings and halfpennies of George I in 1717 and 1718.

Durham	A town where coins were issued over a very long period of time. Regal coinage was issued under William I onwards. Episcopal coinage started under Edward I and continued until the reign of Henry VIII.
Durham House	This was the Palace of the Bishop of Durham in London. It was situated along what is now called The Strand. It was in operation as a mint in the reign of Edward VI from 1548-1549.
E.I.C.	See *East India Company*
Early Striking	When a new pair of dies is first used they are heavily polished and thus the first few coins struck will have a prooflike appearance. These coins tend to demand a premium price and in many cases are much rarer than proofs.
East India Company	These initials EIC were used on some gold coins issued from 1729-1739.
Edge Inscription	Lettering on the edge of a coin which makes up a motto, first used on Cromwell coins. The inscription made it impossible to clip a coin.
Edge Nicks	Because of the way coins are struck and then dumped into a bucket or some other receptacle, they fall on top of each other. The edge of the coins can sustain nicks some minute and some substantial. These nicks decrease the value of coins and some dealers will try to put the nick 'right'. Be careful.
Edge Ornament	A design on the edge of coin applied using a collar.
Edge Plain	Indicates no milling or design on the edge of a coin. Often early proof coins will have a plain edge to differentiate proof coins from circulation strikes.
EF (Extremely Fine)	A grade where there is little actual wear except on the high points. On copper and bronze original lustre might well still be in evidence. A most appealing and attractive grade, much undervalued by the market place in its inane seeking of the ultimate perfection.
Effigy	The bust or portrait on the coin or medallion.
Eighteen Pence Token	A silver token coinage issued by the Bank of England to help with a shortage of small change. Issued between 1811 and 1816.
Electrotype	A copy of a coin or medal which has been made by a process of electrolysis. These pieces are made in two parts and then glued or soldered together. They can be very deceptive. You have to look for the join or line around the edge of the coin.
Elephant & Castle	The Africa Company Privy or mintmark, see chapter 'Mintmarks'.
Emergency Money	Money which is issued outside the Mint during a time when the normal issuing authority can not strike coins. It could be because of a siege (Civil War) or a shortage of small coins (Bank of England tokens).
En Medaille	If holding a coin between your fingers with the head side is upright, you flip it over 180° and the reverse side is upright, then this is struck en medaille. If the reverse is upside down then this is struck in coin rotation.
Enamelled Coins	In Victorian days fine engravers and jewellers made current and older coins into attractive jewellery by enamelling them. The surface was scraped off and the design re-engraved into the surface which was then filled with enamel. The workmanship ranged from poor to excellent. The latest coins that I have seen properly enamelled were those of Edward VII. The coins that are being sold today as enamelled are just piled high with acrylic paint and fired in a kitchen stove. Collectors will never collect these modern examples which prostitute the craftsmanship of Victorian and Edwardian times.
English Shilling	When George VI came to the throne, to honour his wife Elizabeth Bowes Lyon, a Scottish shilling was made for the first time (1937). To balance this there was also a shilling with English representation. This continued until 1970 when the last shillings were struck.
Engrailing	The term for the type of lines on the edge of a coin.
Engraver	The person who actually cuts the dies from which coins or medallions will be struck. He engraves into the metal.

Engraver's marks	Sometimes the person who engraves the die for a coin is allowed to put their name or initials on that die. So every time a coin is struck, their name or mark will appear on the coin. Under William Wyon there were many varieties of his famous 'WW' engravers mark on our coinage.
Engraving	The action of cutting the dies from which coins are struck.
Ermine	Privy or mintmark, see chapter 'Mintmarks'.
Error	Something which has gone wrong either in the striking of a coin or the printing of a banknote. Maybe the coin is struck off centre, double struck or struck on the wrong flan. Collectors will pay extra for a major error on a common coin; on a rare coin they will usually pay less.
Escallop	Privy or mintmark, see chapter 'Mintmarks'.
Escutcheon	Shield bearing a coat of arms.
Essay	A proposed design for a coin which may or may not be accepted.
Exergue	That part of a coin's design which is separated by a line below the base.
Eye	Privy or mintmark, see chapter 'Mintmarks'.
F (Fine)	A grade when the coin or note has seen considerable wear, but is still a very collectable coin. Many collectors like a used coin because they feel that it has actually been somewhere. Collectors on a budget also like this grade.
Facing	When the portrait on a coin or medal is head on to the viewer.
Fair	A grade where the coin has seen much wear and it is only just discernible as to what the coin is. Collectors usually stay away from this grade unless the coin or note is especially rare or expensive.
Fantasy	A coin struck not to copy something else but rather to be something completely new out of someone's imagination. Over the years fantasy coins have the habit of becoming acceptable to collectors. Many have very low mintages and can be far more attractive than regularly issued coins.
Farthing	The quarter part of a penny which is in turn the 240th part of a pound. The farthing was first introduced in the reign of Henry III and was last struck in 1956. The former was silver and the latter bronze.
FDC	See *Fleur de Coin*
Fiat Money	A medium of exchange where we accept the value that a government or issuing body puts on something. Real money has an intrinsic or metal value, fiat money has the backing in principal of a government.
Field	That part of the coin where there are no portraits or devices.
Fifty Shillings	A rare gold coin of the Commonwealth period with Cromwell's portrait.
Filled Dies	From time to time a die will become filled with lint, grease or something else. When coins are struck from filled dies then part of the design will not be struck up at all. A good example is the Gothic Florin whose design was so fine that occasionally parts of the coin would appear changed. In the Roman Numeral dates this of this series caused havoc.
Fillet	Victoria's head band; it comes plain or ornamented.
Find	The locating of a group of coins and or artefacts which have been buried or hidden. Two examples of famous finds are the two Colchester Hoards of Henry III pennies and the Reigate Hoard of Henry VI coins.
Fine Work	William III's gold coinage of 1701 where the workmanship is especially good quality workmanship.
Fishtail Lettering	Style of lettering where the end of the letters resembles a fish tail, only used on the coinage of Richard II.
Flan	The piece of metal upon which the design of the coin will be struck, also called a planchet or blank.
Fleur de Coin	A French term which translates as 'flower of the die' and means Uncirculated. This term was used far more in times when coins were either mint or used. Today we use the term to represent a full mint state coin in impeccable condition (perfect Uncirculated of at least choice quality). Used far more on the Continent that it is used in Great Britain today.

Florin	Originally a gold and a silver coin issued in Florence, Italy in 1252. Issued by Victoria as the first attempt at decimalization in 1849. Equivalent to two shillings or the tenth part of a pound, today it is ten pence.
Flower of eight circles & circle centre	Privy or mintmark, see chapter 'Mintmarks'.
Forgery	A copy of a coin or note made to deceive when exchanged for goods or services. In the old days you were hanged for just possessing a counterfeit, later people were transported to Australia.
Fourpence	A denomination also called a groat, being one third of a shilling and one sixtieth of a pound. First issued under Edward I.
Frosting	Frosting can be the matting of the bust or lettering on a proof coin to show contrast with the brilliant field of the coin. Such a coin is the silver proof 1977 Crown, which has almost a 'Wedgwood' effect. Frosting can also be part of the design of a coin such as the William and Mary Halfcrown.
G (Good)	A grade which denotes a considerable amount of wear. The coin is discernible but the lettering may not be clearly visible.
Gem Uncirculated	A grade of a coin struck for circulation. I consider this to be the highest grade that a coin can achieve. There must be full and outstanding lustre, an exceptional strike, no nicks and only the smallest bag marks discernible under a strong glass. This quality is harder to achieve in larger sized coins than in smaller sized coins. Fewer than 2% of all Uncirculated coins can be called Gem.
George Noble	A rare denomination issued by Henry VIII, which had Saint George on it.
Ghosting	When dies come together without a flan in between, you may get a partial image of one die on the other. When coins are struck from this die the resulting coins will have one strong image and one weak image of the other die all on one side.
Gilt	Gold plating on either silver or copper. In the reign of George III many of the proof issues were gold plated to make them look like gold.
Godless	The first florins issued were in the reign of Victoria in 1849. They had left off DEI GRATIA in the legend and thus this issue became known as the Godless Florins. They were recalled and a new version was issued in 1851.
Gold	A precious metal and, for most of history, the precious metal *par excellance*.
Gothic Crown	A crown issued in 1847 for circulation with a very ornate design, gothic in nature and thus became known as the Gothic Crown. Patterns were issued of this same design in 1846 and examples dated 1853 were included in the proof set of that year. Considered by many to be the most attractive British coin ever struck. The mintage of the 1847 issue is between 7 and 8,000 pieces.
Grade	A verbal, or in the United States, a numerical way of trying to describing the quality of a coin. Because the price of a coin is in many ways dependent on the grade, some individuals will try to over state the grade of a coin. Remember there is no Santa Claus, you get what you pay for.
Grain	A weight where one grain equals 0.064799 grams.
Graining	The milled edge design of a coin originally slanting rather than straight up and down.
Grapes	Privy or mintmark, see chapter 'Mintmarks'.
Great Recoinage	There have been a number of Great Recoinages over the years. There comes a point in time where coins have a problem circulating because they are of different weights and finesses. Two recoinages which are very important are the Recoinage of William III in 1696 and George III of 1816. For the details of the Recoinage Act of 1816 see the addendum.
Greek Cross	Privy or mintmark, see chapter 'Mintmarks'.
Greyhound's Head	Privy or mintmark, see chapter 'Mintmarks'.

Groat	A coin to the value of four pence, first issued in the reign of Edward I and struck for use up until the time of Queen Victoria. The coin is being struck today for inclusion in the Maundy Set.
Guinea	The denomination of a gold coin which had a face value of twenty-one shillings or £1.05 in new money. It got its name originally because the gold used in striking the coins came from Guinea in Africa. First issued under Charles II in 1663.
Half Crown	A denomination made up of two shillings and six pence. The first silver issue was by Edward VI in 1551; before then it had been a gold coin.
Half Farthing	A denomination used more in the colonies than in this country. Issued by George IV, William IV and Victoria.
Half Groat	Two pence or half of a four pence groat.
Half-rose & Castle	Privy or mintmark, see chapter 'Mintmarks'.
Halfpenny	The half portion of a penny. The first halfpenny was issued by Henry I and the last predecimal coin was struck in 1970.
Halved Sun & Rose	Privy or mintmark, see chapter 'Mintmarks'.
Hammered	The striking of a coin by placing a flan or blank between two dies and then having someone swing a heavy hammer down on those dies to impress that piece of metal with the image on the dies. The other type of minting is called milled, which is a misnomer. The coins do not have to have milled edges, but rather be struck by machines.
Hand	Privy or mintmark, see chapter 'Mintmarks'.
Harp	Privy or mintmark, see chapter 'Mintmarks'.
Harp Strings	In the reign of Charles II the number of harp strings varied, possibly to indicate which dies were being used.
Harrington	A licence was issued to Lord Harrington to strike farthings by James I. These coins were legal tender.
Heart	Privy or mintmark, see chapter 'Mintmarks'.
Heaton Mint	A private mint situated in Birmingham. Famous for the 'H' mintmark and has struck coins for many countries including British Pennies in 1912, 1918 and 1919.
Helmet	Privy or mintmark, see chapter 'Mintmarks'.
Hoard	A group of coins which have been buried or hidden sometime in the past with the anticipation of coming back to dig them up. They usually, but not always, are the same generic type of coin .
Holed	Pierced, the making of a hole in a coin after it left the mint. Done to enable the coin to be worn or to demonetise it.
Hub	The positive pair of metal dies from which striking dies can be made. These reversed dies are then used to do the actual striking of the coins.
Imitation Money	Copies of coins made usually as play money rather than to deceive anyone. The most famous of the manufacturers was Lauer of Nuremberg.
Imitation Spade Guinea	A copy in brass of the George III gold guinea known as the spade guinea, because of the appearance of the shield on the reverse. There are many hundreds of different designs. The original pieces were struck by a company called Kettle. A Victorian actress was known to shower the audience with these at the end of her act. They are not valuable but make a wonderful area to attempt to collect.
Incuse	A design which is sunk in rather than raised. Some initials on the coinage of William IV exist with both raised and incused lettering under the bust.
Intrinsic	The actual metal value of the coin. In the past the intrinsic or metal value was very close to the face value of the coin. It had to be that way otherwise no one would accept the coins in payment. Today we are told that the piece of metal has a face value of £5 and we accept it although the intrinsic value might well be only a few pence. See *fiat money*.

Jeton	These are counters as used from the 12th to the 19th centuries, there are also later pieces which have advertising on them. Derived from the French, it is not a word that is used much in this country today. Jetons were used in mathematical calculations and later in games.
Joey	Slang name for a silver threepence, after Joseph Hume.
Jubilee Coinage	Queen Victoria finally allowed new coins to be issued with a portrait other than her young head. These young head coins were issued from 1838-1887. Her vanity was such that the coins carried her portrait as a 17 year old even when she was 67. On the Jubilee of her reign the new design was struck along with a new denomination (the double florin). The small crown placed on the back of the queen's head made her look a bit foolish and the jubilee head design was changed again in 1893 to old or widow head coinage.
Key	Privy or mintmark, see chapter 'Mintmarks'.
Key Date	The most difficult to obtain dates in a series. For example the 1952 sixpence and the 1950 and 1951 pennies. These are the dates which you would not find in your change no matter how hard you looked. You would then go to a dealer and buy these dates to complete your collection. They are the important and difficult dates to obtain in the series.
Kings Norton Mint	A private mint situated in Birmingham. Known for the 'KN' mintmark. Issued many coins for overseas governments, struck pennies for this country in 1918 and 1919.
Late Soho Striking	The dies which Matthew Boulton had used were later sold for scrap. These dies were used in the early 1800s to strike coins. Many of these later strikings were mules of earlier pieces.
Latin Cross	Privy or mintmark, see chapter 'Mintmarks'.
Laureate	A bust with a wreath of laurel on the head.
Laurel	The James I gold twenty shilling piece first struck in 1619. It gets its 'name' from the laurel wreath on the king's head.
Legend	The inscription found on a coin or medal. In many cases it will consist of a string of abbreviations of Latin words.
Lennox farthings	Farthings struck under the licence that James I gave to Lord Lennox.
Leopard	A rare gold coin issued by Edward III in 1344 with a value of three shillings. The figure shown is actually a lion and not a leopard.
Leopard's Head	Privy or mintmark, see chapter 'Mintmarks'.
Light Coinage	Weights of coins reduced to make them more in line with the weight of European coins, reigns of Henry IV and Edward IV.
Lima Coinage	Coins issued in 1745 and 1746 by George II from silver captured by Anson from the Spanish. It is thought by some that the silver had originally come from Lima Peru and it was George II way of thumbing his nose at the Spanish by placing the name Lima below his bust on the coins.
Lion	Privy or mintmark, see chapter 'Mintmarks'.
Lion of Nassau	The lion in the centre of the coins of William III.
Lis	Privy or mintmark, see chapter 'Mintmarks'.
Lombardic lettering	Old fashioned lettering used up to about the time of Edward VI.
Long Cross Coinage	The penny coinage first issued by Henry III where the cross on the reverse came to the outer edge of the coin. It is said that the cross came to the edge for either of two reasons, the first is to help with cutting the coin into halves or quarters, to help in making change. The second was that it hindered the clipping of coins. As both halfpennies and farthings were introduced by Henry III but are extremely rare, I tend to believe the latter!
Love Token	A coin which is engraved with a sentiment, picture or both to show tenderness from one person to another. In Victorian times a young lady might get any number of engraved threepences or sixpences thus. It was the custom at the time to wear them on a charm bracelet.

Low Relief	Dies which are cut with the design in relief which does not protrude from the surface a great deal.
Low Tide	A variety on the 1902 penny and halfpenny coinage of Edward VII.
Lustre	The brilliant rich colour that coins have when they have just been struck. It is impossible to replace this lustre once it has been lost, but some people will attempt to replace the colour, for profit. There is a certain swirl to the lustre. In copper and bronze coins, the more of the original orange brilliance a coin has, the more desirable it is.
Maltravers farthings	Farthings struck by Lord Matravers who had been licensed by Charles I.
Martlet	Privy or mintmark, see chapter 'Mintmarks'.
Mascle	A diamond shaped privy or mintmark, see chapter 'Mintmarks'.
Matt Proof	A special finish which leaves a dull surface on the coin. This country issued matt proofs only in 1902 as an experiment; it was not repeated.
Maundy Money	Comes from the Maundy Ceremony which is believed to go back to the reign of Edward II. The first 'sets' can be made up from the hammered coins of Charles II. In fact no real Maundy Sets were made until the end of the reign of George III. Mintages are low and the recipient gets one penny for every year that the monarch is alive. So when Elizabeth II was 60, each person got 60 pence (six sets of four coins of the denominations 1, 2, 3 and 4 pence). When she was 61, they got six sets plus a 1 penny piece. When she was 62 they got six sets plus a 2 pence and so on.
Medal	An award usually given for valour and to be worn. Given by the government or some official organisation.
Medalet	A small sized medallion.
Medallion	A commemorative piece struck to honour an individual, event, place, time or the like. May or may not be issued by a government. If the event is of importance, many different companies may issue many different pieces.
Mestrelle or Meystrell	A French engraver who introduced the method of striking coins that we call today 'milled coinage'. Elizabeth I experimented with coins struck on a screw press between 1561 and 1571. Very neat workmanship and of a vastly superior quality than hammered coins. The Mint employees feared that this new machinery would put them out of a job. Mestrelle was dismissed and in 1578 he was hung for counterfeiting!
Metal Transfer	During striking, metal flows from one side of the coin to the other to fill the die. A vague outline can be seen on the 'wrong' side of the coin. Not to be confused with clashed dies.
Military Guinea	The last gold guinea ever to be struck was dated 1813. It is called the Military Guinea not because of the design but because it was struck for paying troops rather than for general circulation.
Milled	A misnomer for machine struck coinage. In the beginning, one of the most important things about machine struck coins was that they could have their edge milled to prevent clipping. This was replaced with lettering and then reintroduced later. But the generic term milled means machine struck.
Milling	The actual lines or grooves around the edge of a coin. They can be perpendicular or slanting.
Mint	In grading terms it is the same as Uncirculated, a coin which has not seen circulation. It also refers to a place where coins are struck.
Mint abbreviation	On the early hammered coins the moneyer's name was spelled out in full, but due to lack of space on the reverse of a coin the name of the mint might have to be abbreviated.
Mint Set	A set of uncirculated coins specially issued by a mint. The coins will usually have a special packaging and/or quality of the surfaces to differentiate them from regular circulation issues. The Royal Mint first issued Mint Sets in 1982 and have done so every year since.
Mintage	Number of coins struck.

Mintmark	A symbol placed on a coin to differentiate it from other similar coins struck elsewhere. It could tell you the mint and/or who struck it. If something was wrong with the metal content of the coins then the monarch knew who to 'speak to'. In the early coins the moneyer spelt out his name on the coins. A mintmark was used for some hammered issues and on milled issues. It could help link dies to coins and sometimes undated coins can be dated accurately by their mintmark.
Mirror Finish	When the surface of the planchet or flan has the appearance of brightness without flaws. This surface is found on proof coins where both the flan and the dies are polished to achieve perfection.
Misstrike	A coin which in any of a number of ways is not struck correctly. It might be off centre, it might be double struck or it might even be a brockage.
Model Coins	The model penny was struck by Joseph Moore of Birmingham ca 1844. It was a copper outer ring with a silvered inner part. It caused confusion with the public and the Mint had to tell the public that it was not legal tender. Other coins struck in much smaller size are usually by Lower of Nuremberg; these were used as play money for children.
Modified Effigy	A change on the coinage of George V in 1926.
Moneyer	The man who actually struck the coins, his name would appear on the coins.
Mounting	A coin can be mounted in either of two ways. The first is by attaching a loop to the coin with solder. The second is the construction of a ring or bezel to fit around the coin; a chain is then placed through a ring in the bezel. Both will decrease the value of a coin, one rapidly the other slowly.
Mule	If you take one die from one coin and another die from a second coin and combine the two dies to make a third coin, this third coin is called a mule. When Taylor had the Soho Mint dies, he muled many different coins to come with an equal number of new varieties.
Mullet	Privy or mintmark, see chapter 'Mintmarks'.
NCLT	See *Non Circulating Legal Tender Coins*
Negro's Head	Privy or mintmark, see chapter 'Mintmarks'.
'New' Coins	An indication on the decimal coinage from 1968 to 1981 to show that these were New Pence, not old Pence.
New Style Calendar	In 1752 the calendar changed from Gregorian to Julian.
Newark	A town in the Midlands which during the Civil War was surrounded and held to siege. Emergency coinage was 'struck' from cut up pieces of silver dinner plates. As some of the plates were gold plated silver so are the coins. They are dated 1645 and 1646 and the denominations are halfcrown, shilling, 9 pence and 6 pence.
No Hearts	In the 1787 shillings and sixpences there are varieties with hearts in one of the quarters and another variety without hearts; this is known as the no hearts type.
Noble	First struck in 1344 in the reign of Edward III, a gold coin to the value of six shillings and eight pence.
Non Circulating Legal Tender	NCLT coins are the subject of much heated debate in the coin industry. Basically these are most of the commemorative and off metal strikes issued by the mints. They are made for collectors and to gain money for the issuing authority. But if you wanted to spend them in theory you could, thus they are legal tender.
Northumberland Shilling	George III had struck £100 (2,000 pieces) of a special shilling in 1763. It was to be used by the Duke of Northumberland when he entered Dublin, as the Lord Lieutenant of Ireland. It has a distinct bust.
Notaphily	The collecting of banknotes or financial instruments made of paper.

Numismatics	The study of coins, medals, tokens, banknotes and other means of exchange. The general view used to be that you studied them in the context of their social importance and influence. Today you might just study them for fun and perchance to learn.
Obsidonal Currency	From the Latin *obsedere*, to sit on. Thus it was used when a place was 'besieged'. In this country it refers to the issues of the Civil War and encompasses Carlisle, Colchester, Newark, Pontefract and Scarborough. These are crude coins which were struck under extreme outside pressures. They were in general struck from cut up silver ware.
Obverse	The 'heads' side of the coin or the one with the most important legend, which is considered the most important side of the coin. The 'tails' side is called the reverse.
Off Metal Strike	Sometimes a flan for one coin will accidentally be struck with the dies of another denomination. If these coins are issued in two different metals then the resulting coin will be known as an off metal striking. Today mints offer their coinage in both the original metal and in silver and gold strikings; there is confusion as to what to call these.
Old Head	The last coinage of Queen Victoria which is also known as the widow head coins. She is portrayed wearing the veil of widowhood.
One Year Type	A major variety which is only struck and issued for one year. Examples are the George IV 1821 shilling and 1849 florin of Victoria.
Ornamental Trident	On the copper coins of Victoria, Britannia is holding a trident; this comes both plain and ornamented.
Ostrich's Head	Privy or mintmark, see chapter 'Mintmarks'.
Overdate	When dies have to be reused at a later date, rather than engrave new ones, a new date or part thereof is punched over the existing date. The overdate can only really be seen properly on high quality coins. In the Commonwealth there are some coins where the date has been repunched two or even three times. This saved the making of new dies, money and time.
Overseas Mints	When English coins were struck at mints other than in Great Britain. Example Calais in the reign of Henry VI.
Overstrike	When a coin is struck over an already existing coin. Examples are the Bank of England Dollar which was overstruck on Spanish eight reales.
Oxford Crown	A now very rare silver crown issued for the City of Oxford during the Civil War. It is dated 1644, was designed by Thomas Rawlins and shows the City of Oxford below the king on horseback.
P in brackets, (P)	Privy or mintmark, see chapter 'Mintmarks'.
Pansey	Privy or mintmark, see chapter 'Mintmarks'.
Parliament, Tower Mint under	During the Civil War in the reign of Charles I, the Tower Mint fell under the control of Parliament and coins with the portrait of Charles I were struck.
Patina or Patination	The toning that a coin has built up over a number of years. Many collectors, especially those just starting out, do not like what they call 'dirty' coins. I believe that nice patination not only enhances the appearance of coins but actually increases their value. Patina is something which comes naturally and can not be reproduced artificially.
Pattern	A proposed design for a new coin. When a new coin is going to be issued a number of engravers will be asked to submit their designs, before the final design is chosen. Once the actual design is chosen a number of examples will be struck before the date of issue for circulation. Even though these have the same appearance as the coin to be struck, because of the date they are considered to be patterns. Example, the 1848 florin of Victoria which is the same design as the issued 1849 coin.
Pax	The word for Peace which appears on the pennies of William I and William II. It was a hope for peace in the country.

Pear	Privy or mintmark, see chapter 'Mintmarks'.
Peck, C. Wilson	The author of the standard work on the copper and bronze coins of England.
Pellet	Privy or mintmark, see chapter 'Mintmarks'.
Pellet in Annulet	Privy or mintmark, see chapter 'Mintmarks'.
Penny	The denomination is from Denarius a Roman coin, which then became a denier in Europe and penny here which is abbreviated as 'd'.
Petition Crown	Thomas Simon submitted the design for a crown to Charles II in 1663. The workmanship was excellent and Simon managed to get two lines of text on the edge of the coin. He petitioned the king to accept his designs, but was turned down. It is said that the king did that because he could not forgive Simon for the coins he engraved in Cromwell's time.
Pheon	Privy or mintmark, see chapter 'Mintmarks'.
Piedfort	A French word for a coin which is thicker than the usual striking. There can be double, triple and six times thickness piedforts. In 1983 the Royal Mint started to issue special collectors examples of the new pound coin in silver proof piedfort and it proved to be very popular.
Pierced Cross	Privy or mintmark, see chapter 'Mintmarks'.
Pierced Mullet	Privy or mintmark, see chapter 'Mintmarks'.
Pile	The lower die in the pair of dies used to strike hammered coins. It usually had a sharp pointed end which could be stuck into the wood to hold it in place.
Pinches Family	A family of medallists who became *the* engravers in the mid 1800s. Engraved coins and medallions and did some outstanding work.
Pinecone	Privy or mintmark, see chapter 'Mintmarks'.
Pingo, Lewis (1743-1830)	Assistant engraver at the Royal Mint from 1776 and chief engraver from 1779-1815. Engraved many coins and patterns.
Pinhole	On the edge of coins you will sometimes see two pin holes; these were made to hold the coin in a mount as jewellery.
Pistrucci, Benedetto (1784-1855)	Engraver of gems as well as of the St George and the dragon reverse still used on coins today. The design was originally used on the 'new' sovereign of George III, struck in 1817.
Pitting	Small holes in the surface of a coin or the die which is caused by oxidation. If the die is pitted, then the coins it is used to strike will have small raised bumps on their surfaces. Many restrike coins can be told from the originals by the pitting or lack of it on the coins.
Plain Cross	Privy or mintmark, see chapter 'Mintmarks'.
Plain Edge Proof	Proofs of George III, William IV and Victoria often have plain edges to differentiate them from circulating coins.
Planchet	The flan or blank that is used to strike coins.
Plaster	A sculptor will use a round piece of plaster to engrave his design. From this plaster a rubber will be made. The rubber will be placed on a reduction machine to make hubs from which a die is made. The plaster will be much larger than the finished coin; this is to enable the fineness of the design to be engraved without the use of magnifying glass.
Plug	Some coins have a plug in them to prevent counterfeiting such as the tin coins of James II. When a coin has been holed after striking a plug maybe placed in the hole to make the coin look more attractive.
Plugged Coin	A coin which has been holed and that hole has been filled to make the coin look more attractive and be more saleable.
Plume	Privy or mintmark, see chapter 'Mintmarks'.
Pomegranate	Privy or mintmark, see chapter 'Mintmarks'.
Pontefract	A Royalist strong hold in the Civil War, under siege from June 1648 until March 1649. Emergency moneys were issued struck from silver dinner plates.
Portcullis	Privy or mintmark, see chapter 'Mintmarks'.

Portcullis Coinage	These were coins issued by Elizabeth I for use overseas by the East India Company in 1600-1601. They were trade coins and were struck with the denominations of 8, 4, 2 and 1 terstern and weighed the same as 8, 4, 2, and 1 reale respectively. They get their name by the depiction of a portcullis or drop gate on them.
Post-Union	After the Union of England and Scotland in 1707.
Posthumous issue	Coins of a monarch struck after his/her death.
Pre-Union	Before the Union of England and Scotland in 1707.
Presentation Piece	A coin specially struck to be given to a very important person. Sometimes the coin will be struck to a higher than normal quality, sometimes it will be struck in a more precious metal and sometimes it will be struck with a commemorative reverse. Presentation pieces were often made to show a monarch the new coinage or new designs.
Prince Elector Guinea	The guinea of George I issued in 1714 where the legend reads PR EL in place of EL, it also has a very different head.
Privy mark	A symbol or mark on a coin which allows you to tell when a coin was struck and who struck it. These were used to control the quality of the coins being struck. In previous periods the whole name of the person striking the coin would actually be spelled out on the coin itself.
Proof	In this country proof is a method of striking and not a condition. A proof coin is struck most carefully with polished dies and a polished flan. It will be struck more than once to get the high relief to show all the fine details. Sometimes you will get a lead piece with half of a coin, this is done to proof the die before striking.
Proof Set	a set of coins issued in proof quality by a mint. The coins will, in modern times, come in a case or some sort of presentation packaging.
Prooflike	A condition when the coins are issued in a quality which is better than the normal circulation striking but not up to Proof quality. The surfaces will shimmer.
Provenance mark	A symbol or mark on a coin to identify where the metal that coin was struck on, Prince of Wales Feathers shows that the silver came from Welsh mines, EIC for East India Company etc.
Provenance marks	Elephant or elephant and castle: *Africa Company*. E.I.C.: *East India Company*. WCC and plumes or two intertwined 'C's: *Welsh Copper Co.*. Roses & plumes: *Company for Melting Down Pitcoale and Seacoale*. Plumes: *Welsh silver also silver from Welsh Copper Co.*. Roses: *Mines in the West of England*. VIGO: *from silver captured at the battle of Vigo 1702*. LIMA: *from silver captured by Anson*. Rose below bust (Charles II): *West of England Mines*. SSC: *South Seas Co.*. Plumes below bust (Charles II): *Welsh Copper Co.*
Provincial Mints	The Great Recoinage of 1696 caused so much work that provincial mints had to be opened again. They were B = Bristol, C = Chester, E = Exeter, N = Norwich and Y = York.
Pseudo Coin	A fantasy which purports to be a coin when in fact it is usually a medallic piece.
Punch or Puncheon	A design or lettering on a piece of metal which is then applied to make a portion of a die. The head of George III might be made as a punch so that every die made for that coin will have the same details. It could be for applying lettering or a mintmark.
Pyx, Trial of	From the Greek pyxis, a box or vase. The Trial of the Pyx is the testing of the quality of the metal of the coins. Coins are placed in boxes at the Goldsmith's Hall and samples are picked at random. Then the coins are assayed to test the purity of the metal, this is the Trial of the PYX.

Quarter Farthing	The smallest denomination ever struck in this country. There were 3,840 of these coins to the Pound. They were issued by Queen Victoria and struck in copper and are scarce.
Quarter Guinea	A gold coin with a face value of five shillings and three pence. Only issued by George I in 1718 and George III in 1762.
Quatrefoil	Four pellets close together
R in brackets, (R)	Privy or mintmark, see chapter 'Mintmarks'.
Radiant Star	Privy or mintmark, see chapter 'Mintmarks'.
Raised Edge Proof	On the 1935 George V crown the lettering on the edge of the coin was raised to differentiate it from the incuse lettering on the circulation strikes.
Rarity	An attempt to describe how many of a coin still exist. When an exact number are not known then a scale of rarity is used. A scale might go from EC (Extremely Common) to S (Scarce), or from R for Rare to R5 for Extremely Rare. This 'guess-timation' of the number available is usually based on knowledge rather than mint reports of the number struck.
Rawlins, Thomas	Charles I's chief coin and medal engraver during the Civil War. Worked at Oxford and did the beautiful Oxford Crown.
Re-issue	When a mint strikes more coins than was originally planned. It should be in the same year or they then become restrikes. An example is the 1965 Canadian Mint Set. The Canadian Mint had so many orders that it reopened the ordering and struck as many sets as they had call for.
Recoinage	When old coins are called in because they are no longer legal tender, melted down and then the metal is made into other coins. The last great recoinages were William III and George III.
Reddite Crown	A pattern crown by Thomas Simon for Charles II.
Reducing Machine & Reduction Process	Today when a coin is to be struck, an engraver carves his design in plaster. This plaster is used to make a metal or rubber master which is then placed on a reducing machine. This cuts an exact copy but in a size which is the same as the coin which is to be struck.
Reeding	The milling on the edge of a coin.
Regnal Date	Year on the edge of a coin which is taken from the date of the death of the proceeding monarch. As this may occur in the middle of the year, a single year's coins will often carry two different regnal years during their striking. On the coinage of Charles II, this dates from the death of Charles I, 30 January 1649.
Relief	The raised portion of the coin design.
Restrike	When coins are struck from the original dies at a later time. The coins from the Soho Mint were restruck when Taylor bought the old dies for scrap metal value. Until the 1960s the Indian government would strike coins going back to the period of Victoria for you if you gave them old rupees in their place. Collectors should be aware that restrikes exist and that they do not bring as much as the original strikes do. Restrikes also diminish the value of the original strikings.
Reverse	The 'tails' side of the coin, the opposite from the 'heads' side.
Ribbon Stain	In 1950 and 1951 proof sets the chemicals in the ribbon interacts with the coins and you often see stains on the coins. This cannot be removed.
Richmond Farthings	The Duchess of Richmond was licensed to issue farthings by Charles I.
Rim	The raised part of a coin, formed by the metal from the edge being extruded.
Rose Ryal	A gold coin issued by James I. The king is sitting on his throne and the reverse has the Tudor Rose.
Roses	Provenance mark for the West of England Mines
Roses & Plumes	Provenance mark for *Company for Melting Down Pitcoale and Seacoale*
Rosette	Privy or mintmark, see chapter 'Mintmarks'.
Ryal	Edward IV first struck this gold coin in 1465; it had a value of ten shillings.

Scarborough	A town which in the Civil War was besieged. It issued many different denominations, all cut from silver dinner plates. There are many known denominations and all are rare. Rather than try to have uniform denominations they cut the silver, weighed it and then stamped it with its value.
Sceptre	Privy or mintmark, see chapter 'Mintmarks'.
Scottish Shilling	First issued in 1937 to honour Elizabeth, the wife of George VI, who was born in Scotland. The last Scottish shilling was issued in the proof set of 1970.
Scratches	Marks which are incused in the field of a coin. These may have been caused by any number of things. They detract from the appearance and value of a coin.
Seignorage	The difference between the metal or intrinsic value of the planchet plus the cost of striking deducted from the face value of the coin. In the past this was a relatively small proportion of the value, today it is increasingly larger. It is interesting to note that some small denominations actually cost more to strike than their face value.
Shield Reverse	This refers in particular to the first type of Victorian sovereign which had a shield or coat of arms on the reverse of the coin.
Shilling	The first attempt at a shilling which was the twentieth part of a pound, was the Testoon of Henry VII introduced in 1504. The first actual shilling was issued by Edward VI. This is also the first dated English coin; the date was in Roman numerals.
Short Cross Coinage	The penny coinage where the cross on the reverse fell well short of the edge of the coin, issued by Henry II, Richard I, John and Henry III. Henry III had both short and long cross coinage.
Shrewsbury	The first Civil War mint to be opened to strike coinage for Charles I. Thomas Bushell was the mintmaster and took his privy mark of the Welsh plumes with him.
Siege Money	Money which is issued by a locality which is under siege. Because of the siege, the normal flow of money into and out of the location is impeded. Commerce must still go on so they create their own form of exchange or money.
Silver Token	Privately issued silver pieces struck around 1811. They were used to help with the shortage of small change. The Bank of England also issued silver tokens, at which point the private issuers ceased.
Sixpence	A denomination of half a shilling containing the value of six one penny coins; there are Victorian patterns with the denomination of half a shilling. The sixpence was first struck in 1551 for the currency reform of Edward VI. It continued to be struck until 1970 and was legal tender till 1980.
Snick	Small piece of metal, usually 'V' shaped, taken out of hammered coins to check their metal content.
Soho Mint	Matthew Boulton's minting facilities in Birmingham, 1786-1809. He struck coins under contract for the British government including the famous Cartwheel Twopence.
South Sea Company	The South Sea Company had special coins struck for them in 1723 under George I. The coins were silver issues of sixpence, shilling, halfcrown and crown. They can be distinguished by the letters SSC in the angles between the arms on the reverse.
Sovereign	A gold coin first struck by Henry VII in 1489, to the value of twenty shillings. In 1816 under the Currency Reform Act the guinea was abolished and the sovereign made the unit of gold currency.
Spade Guinea	A gold coin to the value of 21 shillings issued by George III. The shield on the reverse looks like the metal part of a garden spade and thus it acquired the nickname Spade Guinea.

Specimen	A specially struck coin for presentation purposes. The surface is usually prooflike.
Specimen Set	A set of coins struck for presentation purposes.
Spur Ryal	James I gold coin issued in 1604 with a face value of fifteen shillings. The sharp rays of the sun on the reverse look like a spur.
SSC	See *South Sea Company*.
Star	Privy or mintmark, see chapter 'Mintmarks'.
Sterling	When it refers to the fineness of silver it is the British standard of 925 parts silver per 1,000 parts total. British coins were struck in Sterling Silver until 1919, at which point the metal content was changed to 500 fine silver.
Striation	marks on the coin usually from the scraping off of the excess metal of a coin. Sometimes from an improperly manufactured flan.
Sun	Privy or mintmark, see chapter 'Mintmarks'.
Swan	Privy or mintmark, see chapter 'Mintmarks'.
Sword	Privy or mintmark, see chapter 'Mintmarks'.
Tanner	Slang name for a sixpence.
Tanner, John	Engraver of coins during the reign of George II and George III. A German who came to England in 1728 and died here in 1775, he was responsible for most of George II's coinage.
Taylor, William Joseph (1802-1885)	A medallist and die sinker who produced a number of coins and tokens, mainly for export. He is most famous for restriking of coins from the Soho Mint's dies.
Testoon	The forerunner of the shilling issued by Henry VII in 1504 and valued at twelve pence. It weighed 144 grains, twelve times the weight of a penny. A rare coin with his portrait and of artistic importance.
Third Farthing	A coin with the value of one third of a farthing, which in turn is a quarter of a penny which is again one 240th of a pound. Used in the colonies.
Third Guinea	A gold coin with the value of seven shillings (35p), three of which made up a guinea, only issued by George III.
Thistle	Privy or mintmark, see chapter 'Mintmarks'.
Three Farthings	A silver coin to the value of three quarters of a penny, struck only in the reign of Elizabeth I.
Three Halfpence	A coin to the value of one penny and a half issued by Elizabeth I and again by William IV and Victoria, when it was used in overseas colonies, Ceylon, Jamaica and British Guiana.
Three Shilling Token	Bank token, struck in silver and issued by the Bank of England from 1811 until 1816. There are two busts of George III, the first in Roman armour and the second with a laurel wreath.
Threepence	A coin to the value of three pennies.
Tie	The bit on the bottom of the ribbon at the back of the head. Undergoes much change over the issues.
Token	A privately issued piece which stands in for a regal coin of a stated value. Many times the token will have an advertisement for the merchant who issued it. These pieces have less metal and cost less to strike than their purported face value. When there is a shortage of small change these pieces become more readily acceptable by the general populace. The vast influx of issues was in the 17th Century and then again in the late 18th Century. At the end, tokens were being issued for collectors rather than to fill a need in the community.
Toning	A coin over a period of time will react to its environment. The metal in a coin will change colour many times to a magnificent series of hues, and this is what we call toning. A toned coin is in fact more desirable than an untoned coin and in many cases will bring more money from a collector.

Tooling	The enhancement of a coin by burnishing the fields and getting the design to stand out more. It can also be to alter a coin's value by changing the date or some other part of the coin.
Touch Piece	As a monarch ruled by divine right, it was believed that by touching them with a coin and then wearing it, you would be cured of what ever ailed you. A 'Touching Ceremony' took place first in the reign of Edward the Confessor and last took place in the reign of Queen Anne. Special gold medallets were struck for the ceremony, to 'touch' the monarch.
Tournai	French town were Henry VIII struck coins.
Tower Mint	The principal mint of England from Norman days, it was situated in and around the Tower of London. It was actually inside the Tower of London until the early 19th Century.
Trefoil	Privy or mintmark, see chapter 'Mintmarks'.
Triangle	Privy or mintmark, see chapter 'Mintmarks'.
Triangle within Circle	Privy or mintmark, see chapter 'Mintmarks'.
Triple Unite	Issued in the Civil War it is physically the largest gold coin ever struck and had a face value of sixty shillings. It was struck at Shrewsbury and Oxford from 1642–1644.
Troy Weight	A measure of weight for precious metals. Where an ounce of feathers is weighed avoirdupois at 28 grams an ounce of gold is weighed in troy weight at 31.1 grams.
Truncation	The bottom part of a bust or neck on a coin, often where the engraver signs his name.
Tun	Privy or mintmark, see chapter 'Mintmarks'.
Two Lions	Privy or mintmark, see chapter 'Mintmarks'.
Type	A major variety of a coinage such as Victorian crowns can be broken up into four different types: Young Head, Gothic, Jubilee Head and Old Head. A collector would attempt to gather one of each type of crown rather than to complete a date set of Victorian crowns.
Type Coin	A coin which represents a major variety of a coinage rather than a specific date. Collectors often try and obtain one example of each major type rather than one of each date of coin issued.
Type Set	A collection of coins put together which shows the different major varieties of the coinage rather than all the dates.
Una & the Lion	The design on the Victoria gold £5 issued in 1839.
Unc (Uncirculated)	A grade which indicates that a coin has never been released into circulation. Although a coin may be less than perfect when struck, with scratches and nicks, that does not mean that it is not Uncirculated. Over the years a coin may tone or a copper coin may change from bright to dark, again this does not mean that it is not Uncirculated. The term literally means a coin which has not seen circulation.
Uniface	Having a design on one side only.
Unite	A gold coin of James I, first issued in 1604 and with a face value of twenty shillings.
Unpublished Variety	An example with a difference, i.e. lettering differential, metal content, overdate or unknown date which has never been listed in numismatic writings or journal.
VF (Very Fine)	A grade of coin where there has been obvious but a small amount of wear on the highest portions of the coin.
VG (Very Good)	A grade where the coin has experienced a lot of wear and where the details are still discernible but worn.
Vigo Coinage	The coinage of Queen Anne struck from silver and gold captured from the Spanish in the battle of Vigo.
WCC	See *Welsh Copper Company*

Weak Strike	When not enough pressure is used to strike the coin, the design will appear to be weak and an Uncirculated coin will look like a used example.
Welsh Copper Company	Shillings were struck under George I with silver which came from the Welsh Copper Company. To distinguish these coins from the normal ones a small 'WCC' is under George's bust. These coins are all scarce and in higher grades are Rare.
Wire Money	Maundy money issued in 1792 by George III, where the shape of the numerals looked like a piece of wire. A one year type.
With Hearts	The shillings and sixpences of George III dated 1787 have hearts in one section of the shield. If they do not then it is the no hearts variety.
Wolsey	Cardinal Wolsey had a mint at York from 1514-1526 and struck coins with his initials 'T. W.' on them. He struck a groat which caused problems and a trial. In the past the clergy had only struck pennies. The king was incensed that he dared to strike groats and also that he had placed his initials on the coins.
Woolpack	Privy or mintmark, see chapter 'Mintmarks'.
Wreath Crown	A series of crowns issued from 1927 to 1936 excluding 1935, with a wreath on the reverse. This was the fourth coinage under George V; a proof set was issued in 1927 containing this coin. Mintages are low and it is also known as the Christmas Crown as it was given out as presents at that time of year.
Year Set	A collection or set of coins containing all the coins that were issued in a specific year.
Yeo, Richard	Engraver at the Royal Mint from about 1749. He produced the Northumberland Shilling and guineas of George III and died in 1779.
York	At this town there was an Episcopal mint from about 750 AD and it remained until Archbishop Wolsey struck his groats and the king closed him down. The inscription on coins struck in York is EBOR.
Young Head	This has been used for the coinage of George II, George III and Victoria and helps to differentiate the first coins issued during a long reign.

Richard Lobel

Hammered Coins
1066 to 1662

Introduction to Hammered Coinage

The pleasure and skill of discovering and collecting coins is greatly enhanced by an understanding of their underlying history, of the conflicts seen during various reigns and the inherent problems of producing hammered coinage. With this in mind, we will try to provoke your interest and understanding with the following brief historical summary.

Nearly all issues produced until 1662 were hammered. As the name suggests, they were made by placing the flan for the coin between two dies and striking the top die with a hammer so that the detail from the dies would be impressed on the flan of the coin. By law, the face value of the coin corresponded to its precious metal content and so, for example, a coin valued at twenty shillings would have to contain twenty shillings' worth of precious metal. If a coin was underweight or of low fineness it was in effect not worth its face value and, by issuing such inferior coins, a dishonest moneyer could make extra profit. This problem was addressed by having the name of the moneyer and mint included in the reverse legend so that any substandard coins could be attributed to their maker — a practice which continued up to the reign of Henry III and a few issues of Edward I. The details of all mints are to be found in the relevant chapters, but the collector might note that, as a general rule, the moneyer's name is found first on all issues and is usually followed by 'on' (meaning 'of') and the name of the mint. So, for example, the reverse legend might read 'Ricard on Lund', i.e. Richard (moneyer's name) of London (mint). It should also be stressed that in virtually all issues the mint names were not spelt as they are today and, to further complicate matters, the spelling often varied for each class or moneyer. Although we have listed all the mints and the known abbreviations and spellings with each issue, it is possible, particularly in the early issues, that some spellings and abbreviations have not been included. This is due primarily to the fact that many of these issues are rare and have not been recorded and, in such a case, a collector would need to use the process of elimination and possibly consult more specialist books.

In virtually all hammered issues the bust of the reigning monarch is to be found on the obverse with his or her name and, normally, title in the legend. The reverse usually bears some design and often the name of the town in which the coin was minted. We have enclosed the full obverse legend for all issues and accompanied it by a translation as, with the exception of the Commonwealth issues (1649–1660), the legends are in Latin. Again however, a considerable number of dies were produced for a single issue and this often resulted in discrepancies and irregularities in spelling. Collectors should bear in mind that in such a case a coin with a different spelling may not necessarily be any more rare or valuable than the issues we have listed.

The other problem which plagued the hammered coinage was *clipping*, the fraudulent practice of cutting small parts off the edge of the coin. Individuals would then pass the coin on, having made a profit for themselves and a loss to the Crown. Clipped coins are worth less to collectors too. As each coin is different, it is difficult to value but a badly clipped coin might be worth up to 75% less than an unclipped one. The inexperienced collector should use the information in this book to ascertain the correct size of a coin to avoid unknowingly buying a clipped coin.

During most reigns, hammered coins from other European countries circulated freely in England as they were used in trade. Although such issues were only worth their weight in silver, English coins were, for most reigns, very highly prized in Europe because of their superior quality in both production and fineness. Since this often meant that large quantities of English coins ended up in Europe, during many reigns it was actually illegal to export English coins although it would appear that the law was difficult to enforce. As the value of silver rose over the years, speculators and merchants were often one step ahead of the moneyers and mints who produced coins with a metal content higher than their value, something which obviously cost many monarchs dearly. But since most monarchs were keen to produce coins of good metal content and a high value, this particular problem was never satisfactorily resolved.

The historical period covered in this book begins in 1066 with the ascendancy to the English throne of William the Conqueror. Born in 1027 and the illegitimate son of Duke Robert the Devil and a tanner's daughter, William based his claim to the throne on a promise made to him by the then king, Edward the Confessor, who was his second cousin. However, upon Edward's death in 1066, a Council of barons appointed to designate a successor elected Edward's brother-in-law, Harold Godwinson, instead. William launched an invasion from Normandy and, in the ensuing battle of Hastings, Harold was killed and his army defeated, whereupon the Council prudently decided to offer the throne to William. Crowned on Christmas Day 1066, he reigned for twenty-one years until his death in 1087 and had four sons and five daughters from his marriage to Matilda of Flanders.

William I's coinage saw very little change from previous issues, with the silver penny being the only coin produced. But, as the penny had a fairly high value, there was need for smaller denominations, a problem that merchants and traders solved by legally cutting coins in half and quarters and thus producing halfpennies and farthings. Coins constituted a political statement for a monarch and William I, wishing the entire country to be aware that he was king, had over fifty mints producing coins. A total of eight main types were issued, the most popular and common being the Pax, or Peace, issue which was struck during the end of his reign and reflected his feelings and hopes for the country. Yet, because the dies used by the provincial mints for most hammered issues were made in London and despatched to the mints, considerable control was exercised over the entire country's coinage and a degree of conformity in style and issues prevailed.

William the Conqueror left the English throne to his third and favourite son, William II nicknamed Rufus because of his flaming red hair. Born in 1056, Rufus ascended the throne in 1087 and reigned until 1100 when he was killed by a stray arrow in what might have been a hunting accident or an act of murder.

In terms of style, William II's coins were very much a continuation from his father's issues. They are, however, much scarcer since fewer mints were active probably because enough coins had been struck during William I's reign.

William II never married, nor did he leave any offspring so when he died in 1100, the throne went to his brother, Henry I (b. 1068) the fourth son of William the Conqueror. Henry I reigned for thirty-five years and was married twice; his first wife, Matilda of Scotland, bore him a daughter while his second wife, Adela of Louvain, a son.

Henry I's reign was a problematic time for England's coinage. The strict controls enforced during the reign of William I were, for the most part, disregarded, and this resulted in many moneyers producing quantities of coins that were underweight or of low metal fineness. The public, always wary of undervalued coins, often clipped the edges of a coin to inspect the silver inside it and thus exacerbated the situation, as people would not accept coins with chipped edges. In 1108–1109 an extraordinary decision was taken, probably in desperation, to officially mutilate coins on the grounds that if they were clipped at the time of striking it would make them acceptable. But as this did not increase confidence in the coinage, in 1124 Henry I summoned all the moneyers to what became known as the 'Assize of the Moneyers' in Winchester.

They were required to explain their activities to him and many were severely punished for producing coins of inferior quality. During Henry I's reign a total of fifteen different issues were struck, the most common being the last two. This period also saw the introduction of the halfpenny which was produced at the Winchester mint and is extremely rare because very few coins were circulated.

After the death of his son and heir in 1120, Henry I nominated his daughter Matilda as his successor. But upon his death in 1135, the Council decided that a woman was unfit to rule and Stephen of Blois was offered the throne. Born in 1097, Stephen was Henry's nephew and William the Conqueror's grandson and reigned for nineteen years. It was a period of intense conflict as Henry I's daughter Matilda waged war on Stephen in a struggle for the throne. Meanwhile, Stephen married Matilda of Boulogne and had a son and two daughters. It was upon the death of this son in 1153 that an agreement was reached between Stephen and Matilda: Stephen would continue to reign until his death, whereupon Matilda's son would succeed him. He died in 1154.

The turbulence which marked Stephen's reign was reflected in the coinage, although some coins were produced, mainly from the South East mints which remained loyal to the king. These issues, which are all pennies, are very crude in style and design. At the same time Matilda, as well as some powerful barons, also produced coins. All issues are extremely rare and reflect the power struggle taking place at this time.

The death of Stephen saw the end of Norman rule as the throne passed to Henry of Anjou, the eldest son of Matilda and Geoffrey Plantagenet, Count of Anjou. Born in 1133 and ascending the throne in 1154 as Henry II, he became the first in a long line of fourteen Plantagenet kings whose name derives from 'planta genista', or yellow bloom, which Henry II's father wore in his helmet and was later incorporated in the family coat of arms. The Plantagenets consist of three related families: the Angevins (of Anjou), the Lancastrians (of Lancaster), and the Yorkists (of York).

Henry II, an Angevin, reigned for thirty-five years. Married to Eleanor of Aquitaine, he had five sons and three daughters. His reign saw the restoration of law and order amongst the population although the king lost his conflict with the Church in England. The church was determined to remain independent of royal power and the murder of Archbishop Thomas à Becket, with whom Henry had quarrelled bitterly over this issue, determined the outcome. Becket was murdered at Canterbury Cathedral in 1170 by men believing they were acting under Henry's instructions; the church gained a martyr and retained its independence.

Numismatically, Henry II's reign can be split into two main issues. Firstly there is the cross-and-crosslet coinage or Tealby issue — the name originating from a large hoard of these coins found at Tealby in Lincolnshire. There are six minor varieties of this issue. The obverse shows the king holding a sceptre and the reverse a large cross with a crosslet in each quarter. These coins were struck at some thirty mints but, being of very poor quality and strike, they were, as the issues from previous reigns, unacceptable. In an attempt to improve the quality, the short cross coinage was introduced in 1180. This issue lasted until 1247, being struck during the reigns of Richard I, John and part of Henry III's reign.

Upon Henry II's death in 1189 his second eldest son, Richard I (b. 1157), ascended the throne. Richard the Lionheart, 'Coeur-de-Lion', was a soldier, a crusader, and spent only ten months of his ten-year reign in England. He married Berengaria of Navarre but had no children. Control of England was left in the hands of Deputies who skilfully thwarted the intrigues of Richard's brother John. However, when Richard died in 1199, John, the fourth son of Henry II, ascended the throne and reigned for seventeen years. John's reign saw the loss of most of England's possessions in France, high taxation, misrule and finally a quarrel with the Church which led to the king's excommunication. The Church in Rome triumphed over John in its demand for rights for the people. In 1215, at Runnymede, the *Magna Carta*, stating these rights, was sealed by John. He broke his word. The nobility, with

aid from France organised an invasion. John died during the midst of this in 1216.

John's coinage showed the king's bust with a sceptre on the obverse and a small cross with four pellets in each quarter on the reverse and was very similar to the previous two reigns. For all four reigns the obverse legend reads HENRICUS — Henry. Possibly conformity had gone too far since as reigns changed the name of the king on the coin did not. Fewer mints were active during John's reign and it was the London and Canterbury mints which produced huge quantities of coins while provincial mints and dies for the coins were controlled from London. Constant improvement in transportation allowed for the easier distribution of coins around the country which meant that there was decreasing need for provincial mints. All short cross issues, because of the obverse legend and reverse cross, are fairly similar and the collector might find identifying the reign difficult. However, each reign had various issues, all of which are different. These minor varieties often consist of small differences in the lettering or style which was a form of quality control, allowing coins to be linked to specific dies should there be a problem with their weight or fineness. In the relevant chapters we have listed all the varieties, so the collector will be able to identify an issue.

King John was married twice and had two sons by his first wife, Isabelle of Gloucester, and three daughters by his second, Isabelle of Angouleme. John's son Henry III (b. 1207), ascended the throne in 1216 but, until he came of age in 1227, the government was controlled by deputies and it was they who succeeded in expelling the French invaders. Once again an unsatisfactory king ruled and from 1258 England saw the return of civil unrest. Henry III reigned for 56 years and married Eleanor of Provence with whom he had four sons and two daughters.

During the short cross coinage of Henry III the London mint produced silver halfpennies and farthings, which are now extremely rare. However, the need for smaller denominations was still met by cutting pennies into halves and quarters. The short cross coinage proved a tremendous success although its one flaw was that the cross on the reverse did not extend to the edge of the coin and so the public could not know how large the penny should be — which became especially confusing when the size was reduced during the reigns. This inconsistency allowed dishonest individuals to clip coins for profit with the inevitable result that underweight coins were in circulation, creating a dissatisfied public. In an effort to solve this problem, the long cross coinage was introduced in 1247. It was fairly similar to the short cross coinage, but had a long cross on the reverse that extended to the edge of the coin, breaking the legend, and this helped reduce clipping. This issue has many minor varieties. Also, for some time there had been a feeling in the country that a larger denomination was needed as, not only were several European states issuing gold coins during this period, but also gold Byzantine and Arabic coins, brought back from the Crusades, were in circulation. In response, Henry III instructed William of Gloucester to strike a gold twenty pence piece. The superb coin produced showed the king enthroned on the obverse and a long cross with a flower and pellets in each quarter on the reverse. Unfortunately, while beautifully designed, this issue was doomed because rising gold prices resulted in its gold content value outstripping its face value and so most of it was melted down on the Continent. The short and long cross coinages were popular and huge quantities of coins were produced. At last the population had coins they could trust and, when a coin was worn down, it could be exchanged at the mint for a new one and this further boosted public confidence in the coinage.

In 1272 Henry III died and his son Edward I (b. 1239) came to the throne. During his thirty-five year reign, Edward exhibited considerable abilities as a soldier, statesman and lawmaker, focusing particularly upon the workings of parliament and the judiciary. However, Edward's determination to rule an undivided nation was thwarted as both Wales and Scotland claimed independence. Wales was conquered but until his death in 1307 Edward waged an unsuccessful war against Scotland. Edward's first wife, Eleanor of Castile, gave him three sons and five daughters, while Margaret of France gave him two sons and one daughter.

Edward I's issues were a success, although clipping continued to be a major problem. For the first few years of Edward's reign, the long cross coinage was struck in Henry's name and, as well as being prone to clipping due to its crude strike, it was beginning to look old-fashioned. Various laws were again introduced to halt clipping but without much success so, in 1279, Edward I decided to introduce a totally new coinage, both in style and denomination. The penny was still the most important denomination, with millions of coins being produced at a total of twelve mints nationwide. At this time, the independent ecclesiastical privilege mints of York and Durham were established, coins being struck there under the control of the Archbishops who stood to make considerable profits out of such a rewarding enterprise as minting coins. Edward I's recoinage saw the introduction of the privy mark, a small detail or deformation of a detail that linked the coin to a particular die and moneyer as a form of quality control and replaced the moneyer's name, which is no longer found on the coins. With all the mints' dies except Berwick on Tweed being made in London, a conformity in style and design was achieved and there is a total of ten main types or classes, and several varieties within each class. The obverse of the coins carried the king's name and title, the reverse the mint's name — with the exception of some of the coins from Bury St Edmunds. The new denominations introduced by Edward's recoinage were the groat, halfpenny and farthing. The groat was an unpopular denomination because it was underweight; it had a value of fourpence, but four single pennies weighed more. As the public would not accept it in trade, the groat was discontinued and not reintroduced until the reign of Edward III, when it carried the correct weight and was finally a success. The farthing and halfpenny on the other hand were successful from the start, particularly as they facilitated trade and put an end to the inconvenience of having to cut coins in halves and quarters. The class system of these two denominations is slightly linked with that of the penny and both issues were struck mainly in London, although five provincial mints also produced them. Overall, Edward I's recoinage was superb in style and quality and determined the styling of coins until the reign of Henry VII. Also, the king's portrait for the first time attempted to be more of a true likeness. Yet the coinage became a victim of its own success due to its immense popularity abroad and the fact that several European countries, mainly the Low Countries, copied Edward's pennies using low grade silver. This resulted in the illegal trade of good English silver coins for inferior foreign imitations. Furthermore, clipping was rife once again in spite of various laws aimed at upholding the quality of the coins in circulation.

Edward I died in 1307 and was succeeded by his son Edward II (b. 1284) who, having inherited none of his father's qualities as a monarch, succeeded only in arousing opposition to his reign. His wife Isabella of France, who gave him two sons and two daughters, eventually deserted him; his opponents invaded England and finally, after a twenty-year reign, he abdicated in favour of his son Edward III (b. 1312). Edward II was imprisoned and, in 1327, murdered.

Edward II's coinage was very much a continuation from his father's reign. The class system of the recoinage was continued and all issues are very similar to those of Edward I. Edward III ascended the throne in 1327; married to Philippa of Hainault, they had six sons and five daughters. By 1337 he was at war with France, commencing a conflict that would span several reigns and become known as The Hundred Years War. Ostensibly the war was started in support of Edward III's claim to the French throne although controlling trade between the two countries was a decisive factor. Between 1348–1350 the bubonic plague, or Black Death, decimated England. The war could not be maintained under such conditions and the Treaty of Brétigny was signed in 1360. After fifty years on the throne, Edward III died in 1377; only five fortified towns and accompanying lands in France remained in England's possession.

Edward III's first coinage was very much a continuation from the previous reign and all issues are rare, reflecting the shortage of bullion during this period. During the second silver coinage, however, the fineness of some issues was reduced from .925 to .833, an unpopular measure that provoked concern that English coinage would begin to imitate inferior European standards. Nevertheless, as several European states had successfully introduced gold coinage, Edward wished to do likewise and in 1343 engaged two Florentine engravers, George Kirkyn and Lotte Nicholyn, for this purpose. They produced three superb gold coins: the double leopard, the leopard and the helm. But it was necessary to ensure that the face value and metal content of the new coins accurately reflected the difference in bullion value between gold and silver; thus, for example, a gold coin with a face value of twenty pence would have to have a gold content equivalent to the value of twenty silver pennies. Unfortunately the new issue had been overvalued, so the coins were not worth their weight in gold and they were a failure. Although fairly large quantities of coins had been produced, most were melted down and it is hardly surprising that they are now extremely rare. Yet despite this setback, Edward III still wanted to introduce some gold denominations because England was beginning to fall behind in Europe and gold coins would greatly facilitate trade. In 1344 Percival of Lucca joined the royal mint and as a result the gold noble and quarter noble were introduced later that year, to be followed by the gold half noble in 1346. The gold noble had a value of 6s 8d (or eighty pence), the half noble forty pence. These superb issues showed the king in a ship on the obverse, while the reverse carried an ornate design. The quarter noble, with a value of twenty pence, was a small coin and only showed the royal shield on the obverse. But, as the first two issues were overweight, in 1351 the weight of all three denominations was reduced bringing them in line with their face value. This eliminated the profitability of overweight coins being melted down. The gold noble was a great success and happily accepted in Europe; it was in use until the reign of Edward IV. The groat and halfgroat were successfully introduced in 1351 with a value of fourpence and twopence respectively. The moneyers had accurately gauged weights and fineness, so the discerning public happily accepted these new denominations. The obverse for both denominations shows a crowned bust of the king and the reverse a long cross with three pellets in each quarter and two legends, the outer legend being a religious statement, the inner one the mint. Although Edward III's reign is very complicated numismatically because there are many varieties within the issues, it also saw the full introduction of the mintmark which is a symbol, or depiction of an object and found on the obverse and/or reverse, at the beginning of the legends. Mintmarks were a form of quality control, linking dies to coins and, with documentary and hoard evidence, many issues can be accurately dated. The mintmark was a popular idea and was used on nearly all hammered coins until the reign of Charles II. Several mints were active during Edward III's reign, the most notable ones being York and Calais in France, which was under English rule. There are many varieties in the obverse legends reflecting the changing fortunes occurring in the war with France. As with all varieties and issues, they are dealt with in great detail in the relevant chapters.

Edward III's eldest son Edward the Black Prince died a year before his father, so his son Richard (b. 1367) ascended the throne in 1377 and reigned for twenty-two years as Richard II. However, until he came of age, the country was ruled by the Royal Council which was led by Richard's uncle, Edward III's son, John of Gaunt. Neither Edward's first wife, Anne of Bohemia, nor his second, Isabella of France, gave him a child. Richard's succession to the throne saw the start of the Wars of the Roses, otherwise known as the Cousins' War, a fierce struggle for the crown undertaken by John of Gaunt and, after his death, by his son Henry of Bolingbroke, who finally succeeded in deposing Richard II in 1399. The latter was imprisoned and, in 1400, murdered. This was merely the beginning of the Cousins' War; it was to affect the reigns of several English kings up to Henry VII.

Richard II's coinage was very much a continuation in style and denominations to that of Edward III. All issues are fairly scarce, if not rare, and very few coins were produced in any quantity, probably due to there being sufficient coins in circulation from the reign of Edward III while the continuing war with France caused a bullion shortage.

Henry IV, Henry Bolingbroke of Lancaster (b. 1367), ascended the throne in 1399 and with his coronation comes the end of the Angevin line and the start of the Lancastrian. Henry's first wife was Mary de Bohun, his second Joan of Brittany; he had four sons and two daughters. The dispute over the rightful heir to the throne continued during his reign and England saw rebellions and Civil War.

By the time Henry IV came to the throne England's coinage was in a serious situation. There was a severe shortage of bullion because, compared with European issues, the coinage was undervalued and so English coins were constantly been drained away into other countries to be melted down for profit. In 1412 it was decided to reduce the weight of all coins; the gold issues were reduced by ten per cent, the silver by about sixteen per cent. The two coinages for this reign are, therefore, called the Heavy and Light coinage. All issues from this reign are very rare.

By the time Henry IV died, in 1413, the rebellions had been quelled allowing his son Henry V (b. 1387) to inherit the throne. Henry V renewed the war with France and the defeat of the French at Agincourt led to further successes, culminating in Henry V's marriage to Catherine of Valois, daughter of Charles VI, King of France, who also acknowledged Henry as his rightful heir and thus denying his son, the Dauphin, the right of succession. In 1422 Henry V died, leaving his son Henry VI to inherit the thrones.

During Henry V's reign the coinage improved, both in quality and quantity. This was due, in part, to the reduced weight introduced in Henry IV's reign. The success England was enjoying in its conflict with France was also a factor. The mintmark system, as well as other marks, continued. This resulted in the enforcing of good quality control.

In 1422 Henry VI inherited the English and, within a few months, the French throne. He had not yet celebrated his first birthday. A Council, led by his uncle Humphrey of Gloucester, ruled until Henry came of age. Inevitably there was war with France, which finally ended in 1453 by which time England had lost all of its French possessions with the exception of Calais. In 1445 Henry VI married Margaret of Anjou, who gave him a son. Unfortunately Henry VI had inherited the madness that ran in his mother's family. The illness overtook him in 1454, whereupon Richard, Duke of York and next in line to the throne after Henry's baby son, was appointed Regent. This appointment reopened the old conflict for the throne. Henry VI's recovery after a year saw him in control once again but open hostilities now broke out between the Houses of York and Lancaster. During this period of conflict Richard, Duke of York was killed. It was Richard's son Edward (b. 1442) who defeated the Lancastrians. In 1461 Edward, Duke of York, deposed Henry VI and became king as Edward IV. Henry VI was restored to the throne in 1470 but his second reign only lasted until 1471.

The first few years of Henry VI's first reign saw a plentiful supply of gold and silver. This resulted in large quantities of gold and silver coins being produced. The denominations were very much a continuation from the previous reign. The Calais mint, still under English rule, produced large quantities of gold and silver coins. Calais was used for two reasons; firstly as a political statement, confirming that England ruled this part of France and secondly to facilitate trade between England and Europe. As with the previous issue, mintmarks, as well as other marks, can be found. These will help the collector identify, date and class this issue correctly.

Having deposed Henry VI, Edward IV became the first Yorkist king. Edward reigned between 1461–1470 and 1471–1483. He married Elizabeth Woodville, who gave him two sons and seven daughters. Between 1461–1470 Edward IV was occupied with various intrigues aimed at removing him from the throne and in

1470 his enemies prevailed, forcing him to flee the country. Henry VI returned to the throne.

Edward IV's first reign inherited the problem of a lack of bullion. So, in 1464, the weight of all silver coins was reduced by twenty per cent. The gold noble was replaced by a similar, but slightly heavier, coin called the rose noble or ryal. This coin had a lower metal content, and had a value of ten shillings. It was not to be a popular denomination. The gold angel, with a value of six shillings and eightpence, was introduced. The angel showed St Michael spearing a dragon on the obverse and a ship on the reverse. The reduction in the weights of the coins allowed the production of large quantities of coins. There was an urgent need for coinage, so several old mints were reopened.

Henry VI, imprisoned in the Tower of London from 1465, was restored to the throne in 1470. However, during this short reign, Henry was at war with Edward IV. This conflict resulted in the death of Henry VI's son, Prince Edward, and finally Henry's capture. Once again Henry VI was imprisoned in the Tower, where he was murdered in 1471.

The coinage of Henry VI's second reign was very much a continuation from Edward IV's. The unpopular rose noble, or ryal, had been discontinued. However, the angel, with the value of the old noble, was popular. Henry VI's second reign saw the introduction of the half angel. As one would expect, from such a short reign, very few coins were produced.

Edward IV's return to the throne, unsurprisingly, brought little change to the coinage. The angel and half angel were now important denominations and replaced the nobles and half nobles of previous reigns.

Upon Edward IV's death in 1483, his son, Edward V, inherited the throne. His was to be one of the shortest reigns. Edward V (b. 1470) was too young to rule so a Council, which included some of his uncles, took control. One of these uncles, Richard, Duke of Gloucester, seized the opportunity to usurp the Boy King. Richard crushed any opposition from the Queen-mother's family, imprisoned both Edward V and his only brother in the Tower of London and within a few months of Edward V's accession, had claimed the throne. Both Edward V and his brother were murdered in the Tower and Richard III was considered responsible for this infamous act.

Coins were issued during Edward V's brief reign. They are virtually identical to those of Edward IV. On the obverse of Edward IV's coinage is the mintmark boar's head, while the reverse had the mintmark halved sun and rose. It is thought that issues with the mintmark halved sun and rose on the obverse and reverse were struck during Edward V's reign.

Richard III (b. 1452) reigned between 1483–1485. He was married to Anne Neville, with whom he had one son. His usurpation of the throne alienated many nobles who had previously supported him and the murder of Richard's nephews in the Tower added to his unpopularity throughout the country. Henry, Earl of Richmond, to whom the Lancastrian claim to the throne had descended and who was exiled in Brittany, invaded. Richmond, and his supporters triumphed. This was to be the last important conflict in the War of the Roses. Richard III was killed in battle. Richmond became King Henry VII.

Richard III's coinage is very similar to previous reigns, but bears his own name.

Henry VII (b. 1457), the son of Edmund Tudor, ascended the throne in 1485. In 1486 Henry married Elizabeth of York, the eldest daughter of Edward IV. This marriage united the claims of Lancaster and York, the War of the Roses was over and the reign of Tudor kings began. Henry VII reigned for twenty-four years. From his marriage he had two sons and two daughters. Henry's aim was to bring peace and prosperity to England. Henry forged alliances with Spain and Scotland through the arranged marriages of his son and daughter. His son Arthur married the Spanish princess, Catherine of Aragon. His daughter Margaret married King James IV of Scotland. This reign was to see the end of medieval England and the beginning of the Renaissance.

During Henry VII's reign the gold sovereign, with a value of twenty shillings, was produced. This coin was the forerunner of the pound coin of today. The gold sovereign showed the king enthroned on the obverse. The reverse carried the royal arms over a rose. The gold Sovereign is rare. Gold angels and half angels were produced in large quantities. These denominations were the main gold coins circulating in England at this time. The first issues of Henry VII's silver coinage were very similar to previous reigns. This silver coinage included groats, halfgroats, pennies, halfpennies and farthings. Henry VII's early issues reflected the virtual uniformity seen since the reign of Edward III. On the Continent, however, the style of coinage was changing. It was decided that the English coinage should reflect this change in style. In 1494 Alexander of Brugsal, a German, was appointed as engraver to the mint in London. It was Alexander who developed the superb silver 'profile' issue. This issue showed a lifelike crowned portrait of the king on the obverse, while the reverse showed the royal arms over a cross. The testoon, with a value of twelve pence, was first produced during this reign. However, all specimens are very rare. The testoon was later to become known as the shilling. The groat and halfgroat were to be produced and in far larger quantities. All groats were struck at the Tower mint but the halfgroats were also struck at Canterbury and York. The style of the penny also changed as the obverse now showed the king enthroned and the reverse the royal shield. These pennies became known as sovereign pennies. In all issues the mintmark system continued, linking dies with a particular issue. This also means that the coins can be accurately dated, usually within a year or so.

The death of Henry VII in 1509 saw Henry VIII ascend the throne. Henry VII's eldest son Arthur had died in 1502. Henry VIII (b. 1491) was contracted to marry his brother's widow, Catherine of Aragon who thus became the first of Henry VIII's six wives. The fate of these wives reads as follows: divorced, beheaded, died, divorced, beheaded, survived (as the king died first), but only the first three marriages produced heirs, two daughters and a son in all. It was Henry VIII's first divorce which saw the beginning of the Reformation. The Pope refused to accept Henry's right to divorce. Henry broke ties with Rome. With the support of Parliament, Henry assumed the title of Protector and Supreme Head of the Church and Clergy of England. There followed the Dissolution of the Monasteries, which served two purposes, while further eradicating Roman jurisdiction, it stripped the monasteries of their wealth. Henry VIII reigned for thirty-eight years. The monarchy was technically constitutional, but Henry's power was practically absolute.

Henry VIII's first coinage, 1509–1525, hardly changed in style from his father's. The only slight differences being the obverse legend, and the mintmarks. In 1526, however, the value of all gold coins was increased by about ten per cent. This was in response to the rising price of bullion. It would prevent gold coins vanishing into Europe. The sovereign now had a value of twenty-two shillings and sixpence, the gold angel a value of seven shillings and sixpence. Several new denominations were also introduced. Firstly there was the George noble with a value of six shillings and eightpence, then the half-George noble, followed by the gold crown of the rose, with a value of four shillings and sixpence. All three issues were very unpopular and were not continued. During the second coinage the gold crown and gold halfcrown were introduced with a value of five shillings and two shillings and sixpence respectively. Each issue showed a rose with a crown above on the obverse; the reverse showed a crown above the shield. The style of the silver coins was changed for the second coinage. The groat and halfgroat had a new, more mature bust of the king. Once Henry was in control of the Church he closed the Church's privilege mints. From this point on all mints were to be controlled by the king. Towards the end of Henry VIII's reign the third coinage was introduced. It was probably the most unpopular coinage ever to be produced by a monarch. Henry VIII's finances were in a shambles, due mainly to his extravagances. To increase revenue it was decided to drastically reduce the silver content of all silver coins. By the end of the third coinage, the 'silver' coins had a two-thirds copper content. For the first time in England's history, the coins were not worth their metal content. It is not surprising, therefore, that this coinage was unpopular. This issue had a new style, older bust of the king. During this issue the testoon was successfully introduced. Gold issues were also struck, and the gold half sovereign was also successfully introduced. The weights, and gold content, of these issues varied. This was due to the devaluation of the gold content.

When Henry VIII died in 1547, his son, Edward VI, ascended the throne. Born in 1537, he was too young to rule and the Duke of Somerset, his uncle and 'Protector', virtually ruled the country. Edward reigned for six years, until his death in 1553 by which time, England was established as a Protestant state. This reign saw war with Scotland and general unrest.

Three main coinages were struck during Edward's reign. Firstly there was the posthumous coinage of his father Henry VIII which was very similar to Henry's third coinage, with base issue coins being produced. Secondly, there was the base issue coins bearing Edward VI's name, heraldic arms and portrait. Thirdly, there was the fine silver issue struck in 1551–1553 which included the first silver crown, halfcrown, sixpence and threepence. With good quality silver used, this was a major step in the improvement of English coins. The crown and halfcrown, which are both dated, show the Boy King on horseback. The shilling, sixpence and threepence show a crowned bust of the king. Edward VI's base issue silver coins were unpopular. However, the base shillings were the first English coins to be dated. Roman numerals were used for the dates. Several gold denominations were struck during Edward's reign. Most of these were a continuation from previous reigns. By the end of Edward VI's reign, good quality coins were being produced. These coins had a high metal content and weight as well as being superbly designed.

The next in succession to Edward VI was his sister, Mary who was a devout Catholic. This was used to persuade Edward to exclude Mary's claim and name Lady Jane Grey as his heir. Lady Jane's father-in-law led this plot to alter the succession. The right to the throne would now pass from the Tudors to the Dudley family. Upon Edward's death Lady Jane Grey was proclaimed queen. However, the plot failed. Within ten days Mary and her supporters had reclaimed the Tudor throne and Lady Jane's father-in-law was executed. Having originally spared Lady Jane, Mary eventually had both Jane and her husband executed. Mary I (b. 1516) ascended the throne in 1553, becoming the first queen to reign. A devout Catholic, Mary was determined to re-introduce Catholicism. And she insisted on marrying her cousin, Philip of Spain who was a fanatical Roman Catholic. Although her choice led to three insurrections, Mary was victorious and the marriage took place in 1554. During the rest of her reign Mary tried to enforce the conversion of England by ruthlessly persecuting Protestants, some of whom were burnt at the stake, and earned herself the nickname Bloody Mary. Once again England went to war against France and lost Calais.

For the first two years of Mary's reign, only her own portrait is to be found on the coins. After her marriage to Philip of Spain, both their busts are to be found on the shilling and sixpence, although only Mary's bust appears on other silver issues. However, both their names are in the legend.

When Mary died in 1558, Henry VIII's daughter from his second marriage, Elizabeth, ascended the throne. Born in 1533, she was the last of the Tudors. With Elizabeth came a return to Protestantism and by the end of her forty-four year reign England had been transformed; religious conflicts had all but disappeared, the Spanish Armada was defeated, Sir Francis Drake circumnavigated the globe. This was a period of voyage and discovery, when internal conflicts were controlled.

Elizabeth I's reign is notable for the large quantities of coins, of various denominations, produced. Initially base issue coins, from previous reigns, still circulated. Elizabeth recognised the importance of having a sound coinage. This meant coins of good weight, metal content and a variety of denominations. As an act of urgency, Elizabeth immediately ordered the base issue shillings of Edward VI to be countermarked, and then devalued. Elizabeth also ordered base issue coins to be taken in and melted down. This was an expensive exercise. However, confidence in English coins was restored. All of Elizabeth's coinage was struck in London and silver from the newly discovered Americas was often used. The silver denominations were crowns, halfcrowns, shillings, sixpences, groats, threepences, halfgroats, three-halfpence, pennies, three farthings and halfpence. Several silver issues were dated and as all issues had mintmarks on the obverse and reverse, the collector will be able to date the issue. The gold issues were very much a continuation from previous reigns. Sovereigns, now with a value of thirty shillings, pounds (twenty shillings), ryals (fifteen shillings), halfpounds, angels, half-angels, quarter-angels, crowns and halfcrowns were produced. This was the most prolific reign for the number of denominations and with this comprehensive denomination structure, Elizabeth had considered the needs of both the rich and poor.

In 1561, milled coins were issued for the first time. These coins were introduced by a Frenchman, Eloye Mostrelle, employed by the mint in London. They were struck using a screw press powered by horses and were the forerunner to the coins of today. These milled issues were superior to the hammered ones but their manufacture was slow and, moreover, Mostrelle's presence in the mint was unpopular partly because he was French but more significantly because he was seen as threatening the moneyers' employment. Mostrelle was dismissed in 1572 and the production of milled coins ceased. Mostrelle turned to counterfeiting, for which he was hanged in 1578.

In 1600, at the Tower mint, trade coins, otherwise known as portcullis money, were produced. These were struck for the company of merchants in London trading into the East Indies. These issues, which are all rare, were struck with the equivalent weight in silver to Spanish silver coins. These coins were not for circulation in England. They were issues for trade in the East Indies.

Throughout her reign Elizabeth refused to marry and in 1603 died childless. This meant that James VI of Scotland ascended the English throne as James I; he was the first Stuart king. James had married Anne of Denmark in 1589 and they had three sons and four daughters. As King of Scotland, James had had a troubled reign and he brought these troubles to the English throne so once again there was conflict between Protestant and Catholic. In the Gunpowder Plot of 1605, Catholic sympathisers attempted to blow up the king and Parliament and, although the plot failed, it caused even greater prejudice against Catholics and religious intolerance prevailed. In 1611 the authorised version of the Bible was published and in 1620 the Pilgrim Fathers set sail for the Americas, to establish a community where their beliefs could flourish.

With both England and Scotland ruled by one monarch, the design of the coins changed slightly as the Scottish title was incorporated in the legend and the Scottish arms appeared as part of the royal shield. Large quantities of coins were struck during James I's reign. The price of gold rose steadily during this period resulting in new denominations and changing values of coins. The most important denomination was the gold unite which had a value of either twenty or twenty-two shillings, depending upon when it was circulating. The name unite represents the uniting of England and Scotland. At the end of James I's reign the unite was replaced by the laurel, depicting the bust of the king wearing a laurel wreath. Other gold denominations produced were the rose ryal (thirty shillings), sovereign (twenty shillings), spur ryal (fifteen shillings), angel, half laurel, double crown (each ten shillings), Britain crown, quarter laurel, crown, half angel (each five shillings), thistle crown (four shillings) and the halfcrown (two shillings and sixpence). It is important to note that the values and weights, of some of these issues, varied with the fluctuating gold price. James I's silver coinage was also produced in some quantity and was very similar to the previous reign although fewer denominations were struck. Those produced were the crown, halfcrown, shilling, sixpence, halfgroat, penny and halfpenny. For many years the public had been demanding lower denominations. In large towns such as London the poor used lead tokens as coinage.

However, in 1613, James granted a licence to Lord Harrington, allowing him to produce copper farthings. These coins were very popular and profitable to produce. The licence was later taken over by the Duke of Lennox.

James I died in 1625 and his second son, Charles I ascended the throne. Born in 1600, Charles married Henrietta Maria of France and had four sons and five daughters. His reign saw a power struggle between king and parliament, which was dissolved three times. After the third time, in 1629, Charles proceeded to rule without Parliament. England was divided into supporters of parliament and royalists and this state of affairs lasted eleven years until Civil War erupted in 1642 and Oliver Cromwell, parliamentarian, formed an army. In 1645, Cromwell's forces crushed the royalists and a year later Charles I surrendered to the Scots who handed him over to the English. Finally in 1648, after facing a tribunal, Charles was sentenced to death; he was beheaded in 1649. The Commonwealth period extends from 1649 to 1660; Cromwell becoming Lord Protector in 1653.

Initially Charles I's coinage was very much a continuation from the previous reign. The gold angel was produced for the last time, and is very rare. The Tower mint struck the gold denominations unite, double crown and crown. The other main denominations struck at the Tower mint were crowns, halfcrowns, shillings, sixpences, halfgroats, pennies and halfpennies, as well as copper farthings. Many varieties of most issues exist. Some of the issues, particularly the shilling, were fairly poorly made. For the first time since the reign of Elizabeth I, milled coins were produced and once again it was a Frenchman, Nicholas Briot, who introduced this coinage. The Briot issues were superb in both design and production; however, the machinery was too slow in the production of the coin and the presence of Nicholas Briot in the Tower mint was unpopular. This unpopularity once again stemmed from the fact that he was a Frenchman and also because the moneyers were worried about their own employment. Mintmarks continued to be used for all issues, and the denomination for the coin could be found, for most issues, indicated in Roman numerals behind the bust. Before the Civil War, which was caused by Charles I's poor political judgement, high spending and constant arguments with Parliament, virtually all coins were struck at the Tower mint in London. However, huge quantities of farthings were struck under licence of which various varieties exist. Coins were also struck under licence at the Aberystwyth mint in Wales where large quantities of silver were being mined.

The Civil War, as one would expect, caused considerable difficulties in the production and supply of coinage. The Tower mint in London remained open but under the control of Parliament although the coins it struck still bore the portrait and name of Charles I. This shows an interesting political statement revealing the real wish for Cromwell's supporters to restore Charles I as king but with parliamentary control. Most provincial mints, such as York, Exeter, Truro, Shrewsbury, Oxford, Worcester, Chester and Bristol among others, reopened and most were in the west of England and loyal to the king. The dies for these issues were hurriedly made while several mints often shared a particular die, because the urgency of production was so great. These coins, of varying denominations, were needed to pay the troops loyal to the king as well as to supply local trade should communications with the Tower mint be cut off. Most denominations were struck at the provincial mints and this was the first time that the triple unite, with a value of sixty shillings, as well as the silver pound and halfpound were produced outside London. Most of these provincial issues carry an abbreviation of what is known as the Declaration on the reverse: RELIG PROT LEG ANG LIBER PAR, (varieties exist) which in translation reads: 'the religion of the Protestants, the laws of England, the liberty of Parliament'. During the Civil War several towns, such as Newark and Pontefract, were besieged by Cromwell and their occupants produced emergency or siege money, which usually consisted of silver plates cut into shapes, weighed and then hammered with a fairly crude design and value. Numismatically, Charles I's reign is the most complicated and possibly the most interesting. The stages of the

Civil War can almost be traced by the mints and the production of coins as the king and his army moved around the country.

During the Commonwealth dated hammered coins with legends in English were produced. All issues had the heraldic arms of St George and Ireland in them; they were very plain in style, reflecting the Puritan aesthetic values. Unites, double crowns and crowns were the gold denominations which were produced while the silver denominations were crowns, halfcrowns, shillings, sixpences, halfgroats, pennies and halfpennies. During this period, due to the shortage of small change, towns and traders issued copper and brass pennies, halfpennies and farthings in enormous quantities, to facilitate trade. Milled coins were struck with the bust of Oliver Cromwell on the coin. All issues are considered patterns; they were however produced in some quantity and many coins saw circulation. The denominations struck were fifty shillings, broad (twenty shilling) crown, halfcrown, shilling, sixpence and farthing. Many varieties of the farthing were struck. They are sometimes considered as tokens as well as patterns.

Following the death of Cromwell, Charles II, who had been living in exile during the Commonwealth period, was asked by Parliament to return and in 1660 he was restored to the English throne. Hammered coins in gold and silver were again produced in some quantity. However, with the advancement of the machinery for making milled coins, hammered coins were becoming obsolete and in 1662 hammered coins were produced for the last time.

From a personal point of view, I find the hammered coinage fascinating because of the complexities of the issues and also because of the very real links the coins had with political events and history. At the onset of this book, people asked me to make the hammered coinage easily comprehensible. This is by no means easy because the hammered coinage is so difficult to understand and also because I wanted to introduce more information into this book than has been previously published in any general book on the subject. The book also seeks to address itself both to the total beginner as well as to the advanced collector. We hope we have succeeded in keeping all collectors happy. To the new collector the whole hammered section might at first seem rather daunting and I have been asked on numerous occasions for advice on how to understand and learn about the issues. My advice is to read up as much as you can on the issues, but remember that there is no substitute for handling and looking at the actual coins. Dealers often have 'lots' of very worn hammered coins that they might sell cheaply and it might be useful as an educational exercise to identify such coins. Many previously published books recommend that collectors start with either one denomination or one reign. Such an approach does simplify some aspects of collecting but, if you are like me and find the whole series interesting, it can seem far too restrictive.

Through my research for this book I have been amazed to see how the information on and knowledge of some numismatic periods has changed over the years. This is mainly due to new hoards being found and more documentary evidence coming to light, and it is particularly true of the provincial mints of Charles I. Even while writing this book, new important issues have been found. In many respects the history of hammered coins is still being written and I am sure that there are many more issues to be discovered.

The last twenty years have been a fascinating period for hammered coinage due mainly to the use of metal detectors. With these now sophisticated machines, tens of thousands of coins have been found including very small denominations. This has produced a wealth of new information, stimulated collectors' interest and put many more coins on the market. With the redevelopment of much of London in the 1980s, huge quantities of coins were found around or in the river Thames. This has often caused problems with archaeologists, when metal detectors were illegally used on listed sites, or when finds of coins were not properly declared as treasure troves.

Finally, it should be stated that the information in this book is by no means complete. We look forward to hearing from collectors who have varieties which we have not listed. For the first time in any book we have listed all obverse and reverse legends. We know many varieties exist in these legends and we have, where possible, listed the most common.

I hope you, the collector, will find this book useful and informative and that it will bring you many happy years of collecting.

Mintmarks

The mintmark, or privy mark as it is sometimes known, evolved during the reign of Edward III. Since Anglo-Saxon times, the need to link coins to dies and therefore moneyers and mints was strongly felt by a population worried about underweight coins of low metal fineness. After Edward I's 1279 re-coinage, the moneyer's name was not placed on the coins but, instead, various marks or varieties in letters or the king's bust were deliberately included so a coin could be accurately linked to a die. The mintmark was very much a development of this idea and from the reign of Edward III a mark of a certain style was placed on virtually all hammered coins at the beginning of the obverse legend and usually at the beginning of the reverse legend. These marks are important as, not only do they help identify a coin, but also date it more accurately.

From the moneyers' point of view, dies could now be more easily checked for wear or damage and their production could be improved. Dies from various issues were sometimes swapped, especially if only half had been damaged, often resulting in the two sides of a coin having different mintmarks; we have listed most such cases when they occur. Moreover, it was not uncommon, particularly under James I and Elizabeth I, for one mintmark to be engraved over another, thus extending the life of a die.

Below we list the various mintmarks, with an indication of the reign(s) in which they occur. This is followed by a chronological listing, giving the specific years within each reign that a mintmark was used. The last list of mintmarks is of James I and Charles I farthings, which do not always conform to the gold and silver issues. Finally, we have illustrated all mintmarks, to help collectors with identification.

Mintmarks	Reign
cross 1 pommée	Edward III
cross 1 broken	Edward III
cross 2	Edward III
cross 3	Edward III
cross potent	Edward III
cross pattée	John, Henry III, Edward I, Edward II, Edward III, Richard II, Henry IV, Henry V, Henry VI, Edward IV, Charles I
plain or Greek cross	Edward III, Henry VI, Edward IV, Henry VII, Henry VIII, Elizabeth I, James I
cross patonce	Henry VI, Henry VIII
cross fleurée	Henry VI, Edward IV
cross cavalry	Charles I
long cross fitchée	Edward IV, Henry VII, Henry VIII
short cross fitchée	Henry VI, Edward IV
Restoration cross	Henry VI
Latin cross	Elizabeth I
voided cross	Henry VI, Henry VIII
saltire cross	James I
cross & four pellets	Edward IV
pierced cross	Henry V, Henry VI, Edward IV
pierced cross & pellet	Edward IV
pierced cross & central pellet	Henry V, Edward IV
cross crosslet	Henry VII, Elizabeth I
curved star	Henry VIII
star	Henry VIII, Elizabeth I, Charles I
spur rowel	Henry VIII, James I
mullet	James I, Charles I
eglantine	Elizabeth
sun	Edward IV
pansy	Edward IV, Henry VII, Henry VIII
heraldic cinquefoil	Edward IV
rose	Edward IV, Henry VI, Richard III, Henry VII, Henry VIII, Edward VI, Elizabeth I, James I, Charles I
rosette	Charles I
Catherine Wheel	Henry VIII
cross in circle	Edward IV
halved sun & rose	Edward IV, Edward V, Richard III, Henry VII
lis upon half rose	Henry VII
lis	Henry VI, Edward IV, Richard III, Henry VII, Henry VIII, Edward VI, Philip & Mary, Elizabeth I, James I, Charles I
lis upon sun & rose	Henry VII
lis rose dimidiated	Henry VII
lis issuant from rose	Henry VII
arrow	Henry VIII, Edward VI
A	Elizabeth I
anchor	Henry VII, Elizabeth I, Charles I, Commonwealth
anchor & B	Charles I
flower & B	Charles I
bell	Elizabeth I, James I, Charles I
book	James I, Charles I
boar's head	Richard III, Charles I
acorn	Henry VIII, Elizabeth I, Charles I
bow	Edward VI
BR	Charles I
castle	Henry VIII, Elizabeth I, James I, Charles I
castle with H	Henry VIII
crescent	Henry VIII, Elizabeth I, James I
pomegranate	Henry VIII, Mary I
coronet	Elizabeth I, James I
crown	Charles I, Charles II
ermine	Elizabeth I
escallop	Henry VII, Henry VIII, Edward VI, Elizabeth I, James I
eye	Charles I
radiate eye	Henry VII
gerb	Charles I
grapes	James I, Charles I
greyhound's head	Henry VII
hand	Elizabeth I
harp	Charles I
heart	Charles I
helmet	Charles I
key	Henry VIII, Elizabeth I, James I
leopard's head	Edward VI, Charles I
crowned leopard's head	Henry VII

lion	Edward VI, Elizabeth I, Charles I
lion rampant	Charles I
martlet	Henry VII, Henry VIII, Edward VI, Elizabeth I, Charles I
blackamoor's head	Charles I
ostrich's head	Edward VI
(P)	Charles I
pall	Edward IV
pear	Charles I
plume	Charles I
portcullis	Elizabeth I, Charles I
portcullis crowned	Henry VIII
sceptre	Charles I
sunburst	Henry VIII
swan	Edward VI
(R)	Charles I
sword	Elizabeth I
T	Henry VIII, Edward VI
TC	Henry VIII, Edward VI
WS	Henry VIII
y or Y	Edward VI
dragon	Henry VII
triangle	Charles I
triangle in circle	Charles I
sun	Charles I, Commonwealth
uncertain	Henry VIII
grapple	Henry VIII
tun	Henry VII, Edward VI, Elizabeth I, James I, Charles I
woolpack	Elizabeth I
thistle	James I
figure 6	Edward VI
floriated cross	Charles I
lozenge	Charles I
billet	Charles I
plume	Charles I
two lions	Charles I
clasped book	Charles I
bugle	Charles I
crown	Edward III, Edward IV
trefoil	Henry VI, Edward IV, Henry VIII, James I
annulet	Edward IV
pellet in annulet	Edward IV, Henry VIII
cinquefoil	Henry VII, James I
crozier	Henry VII
radiant star	Henry VIII
flower	Henry VIII
S	Henry VIII
E	Henry VIII, Edward VI
K	Henry VIII
pierced mullet	Edward VI
half rose	Mary
half rose & castle	Philip & Mary
0	Elizabeth I
1	Elizabeth I
2	Elizabeth I
pellets or pellet	Charles I
B	Charles I

Mintmarks for gold and silver coins

Edward III

cross pattée (6)	1334–1351
cross 1	1351–1352
cross 1 broken	1352–1353
cross 2	1354–1355
crown	1356
cross 3	1356–1361
cross potent	1361–1369

cross pattée	1369–1377
plain cross	uncertain

Richard II

cross pattée	1377–1399

Henry IV

cross pattée	1399–1413

Henry V

cross pattée	uncertain
pierced cross with pellet centre	uncertain
pierced cross	uncertain

Henry VI 1st Reign

plain cross	1422–1460
lis	uncertain
pierced cross	1422–1427
cross pommée	1422–1434
cross patonce	1427–1434
cross fleurée	uncertain
voided cross	1434–1435
lis	1460

Edward IV 1st Reign

lis	1461–1464
cross fleury	1461–1464
plain cross	1461–1464
rose	1464–1465
pall	1464–1467
sun	1465–1466
crown	1467–1469
lis	1467–1470
sun	1467–1468
rose	1468–1469
long cross fitchée	1469–1470
sun	1469–1470

Henry VI Restored

cross pattée	1470–1471
restoration cross	1470–1471
trefoil	1470–1471
rose	1470–1471
lis	1470–1471
short cross fitchée	1470–1471

Edward IV 2nd reign

rose	1471–1483
lis	1471–1483
short cross fitchée	1471
annulet	1471–1472
trefoil	1471–1472
pansy	1471–1473
small annulet	1472–1473
sun	1472–1473
pellet in annulet	1473–1477
cross and 4 pellets	1473–1477
cross in circle	1473–1477
cross pattée	1473–1477
pierced cross 1	1473–1477
pierced cross 1 and pellet	1477–1480
pierced cross 2	1477–1480
pierced cross and central pellet	1477–1480
heraldic cinquefoil	1480–1483
long cross fitchée	1480–1483

halved sun and rose	?

Edward IV or Edward V

halved sun and rose	1483 ?

Edward V

halved sun and rose	1483
boar's head	1483?

Richard III

halved sun and rose	1483–1485
boar's head	1483–1485
lis	1483–1485
rose	1483–1485

Henry VII

halved sun and rose	1485–1487
lis upon sun and rose	1485–1487
lis upon half rose	1485–1487
lis rose dimidiated	1485–1487
rose	1485–1487
lis	1487
cross fitchée	1487
plain cross	1487–1488
no marks	1488–1489
cinquefoil	1489–1493
crozier	1489–1493
cross fitchée	1492
escallop	1493–1495
dragon	1493–1495
lis	1493–1498
tun	1493–1498
pansy	1495–1498
crowned leopard's head	1498–1498
lis issuant from rose	1498–1498
tun	1498–1498
anchor	1499–1502
greyhound's head	1502–1504
lis	1502–1504
martlet	1502–1509
cross crosslet	1504–1505
rose	1504–1509
pheon	1505–1509

Henry VIII

pheon	1509–1544
castle	1509–1526
castle with H	1509–1526
crowned portcullis	1509–1526
rose	1509–1544
martlet	1509–1526
pomegranate	1509–1526
cross fitchée	1509–1526
lis	1509–1544
radiant star	1509–1523
crowned T	1513–1518
star	1514–1526
pansy	1514–1526
escallop	1514–1526
voided cross	1514–1526
spur rowel	1523–1526
sunburst	1526–1544
arrow	1526–1544
star	1526–1544
crescent	1526–1529
trefoil	1526–1529
flower 8 petals	1526–1529
cross	1526–1530
acorn	1526–1530

cross patonce	1526–1536
uncertain mark	1526–1536
radiant star	1529–1544
key	1530–1544
Catherine Wheel	1533–1544
pellet in annulet	1544–1547
S	1544–1547
E	1544–1547
WS monogram	1546–1549
annulet and pellet	1547
lis	1547–1549
arrow	1547–1549
K	1547–1549
Roman E	1547–1549
bow	1548–1549
TC monogram	1549
rose	1549
grapple	1549
t	1549–1550
martlet	1550–1551

Edward VI

bow	1548–1549
arrow	1549
grapple	1549
rose	1549–1551
TC monogram	1549
Roman E	1549
pheon	1549
t or T	1549
swan	1549–1550
Y	1549–1550
6	1549–1550
martlet	1550
leopard's head	1550
lion	1550–1551
lis	1550–1551
Y or y	1551
ostrich's head	1551
tun	1551–1553
escallop	1551–1553
pierced mullet	1552–1553

Mary

pomegranate	1553–1554
halfrose	1553–1554

Philip and Mary

lis	1554–1558
halfrose and castle	1554–1558

Elizabeth I

lis	1558–1560
cross crosslet	1560–1561
martlet	1560–1561
star	1560–1566
pheon	1561–1565
rose	1565
portcullis	1566
lion	1566–1567
coronet	1567–1570
lis	1567–1570
castle	1569–1571
ermine	1572–1573
acorn	1573–1574
eglantine	1573–1577
Greek cross	1578–1579
Latin cross	1580–1581
sword	1582

bell	1582–1583
A	1582–1584
escallop	1584–1586
crescent	1587–1589
hand	1590–1592
tun	1591–1595
woolpack	1594–1596
key	1595–1598
anchor	1597–1600
0	1600
1	1601–1602
2	1602

James I

thistle	1603–1604
lis	1604–1605
rose	1605–1606
escallop	1606–1607
grapes	1607
coronet	1607–1609
key	1609–1610
bell	1610–1611
mullet	1611–1612
tower	1612–1613
trefoil	1613
cinquefoil	1613–1615
tun	1615–1616
book on lectern	1616–1617
crescent	1617–1618
plain cross	1618–1619
saltire cross	1619
spur rowel	1619–1620
rose	1620–1621
thistle	1621–1623
lis	1623–1624
trefoil	1624

Charles I

lis	1625
cross calvary	1625–1626
blackamoor's head	1626–1627
castle	1627–1628
anchor	1628–1629
heart	1629–1630
plume	1630–1631
rose	1631–1632
flower and B	1631–1632
harp	1632–1633
portcullis	1633–1634
bell	1634–1635
crown	1635–1636
tun	1636–1638
anchor	1638–1639
anchor and B or mullet	1638–1639
triangle	1639–1640
star	1640–1641
triangle in circle	1641–1643
(P)	1643–1644
(R)	1644–1645
eye	1645
sun	1645–1646
sceptre	1646–1648
book	1638–1642
plume	1642–1646
pellets or pellet	1642–1646
rose	1642–1645
bugle	1642–1643
lion	1642–1644
lis	1642–1646
cross pattée	1643
acorn	1643

castle	1643
helmet	1643
leopard's head	1643–1644
two lions	1643–1644
lis	1643–1644
bunch of grapes	1643–1644
bird	1643–1644
boar's head	1643–1644
L in rampart	1643–1644
rosette	1643–1644
Br.	1643–1645
pellets	1643–1645
rosette	1643–1645
floriated cross	1643–1646
cross pattée	1644
lozenge	1644
billet	1644
mullet	1644
gerb	1644–1645
pear	1644–1645
castle	1644–1645
A	1645
B	1646
crown	1648–1649

Commonwealth

sun	1649–1657
anchor	1658–1660

Cromwell

none	

Charles II

crown	1660–1662
none	1660–1662

Mintmarks for James I and Charles I Farthings

As many of these mintmarks do not conform to the silver and gold issues, they have been listed separately. Accurate dating is uncertain and should the mintmarks be badly blundered or not listed here, the coin in question is probably a forgery.

James I Farthing

Harrington Type

ermine	1613–1614
millrind	1613–1614
pellet	1613–1614
trefoil	1613–1614
crescent	1613–1614
mullet	1613–1614
cinquefoil	1613–1614
cross saltire	1613–1614
lis	1613–1614
martlet	1613–1614

Lennox Type

	1614–1625 exact date uncertain
bell	
flower	
annulet	
ball	
coronet	
crescent	
cross fitchée	

72

cross pattée
dagger
eagle's head
grapes
lion passant
mascle
quatrefoil
rose
star
thistle head
trefoil
triangle
tun
woolpack
A
lion rampant
lis
stirrup

Charles I Farthing
Royal and Maltravers Issues 1625–1642

A
annulet
annulet with pellet centre
bell
book
cinquefoil
crescent
cross with pellets in angles
cross calvary
cross pattée
cross patonce
cross saltire
dagger
ermine

estoile
estoile pierced
eye
fish hook
fleece
fusil
two fusil
gauntlet
halberd
harp
heart
horseshoe
leaf
lion passant
lis
three lis
martlet
nautilus
rose
shield
spearhead
tower
trefoil
woolpack
woolpack over annulet
lion rampant
quatrefoil
cross pattée fitchée

Rose Farthing 1636–1644?

lis
martlet
mullet
cross pattée
crescent

Illustrations of mintmarks

lis

anchor

bell

acorn

coronet

hand

key

swan

triangle in circle

sun

0

1

cross 1 pommée

 cross 1 pommée broken

 cross 2

 cross 3

 cross potent

 cross pattée

 plain or Greek cross

 cross patonce

 cross fleurée

 cross calvary

 long cross fitchée

 short cross fitchée

 Restoration cross

 Latin cross

 voided cross

 saltire cross

 cross & four pellets

 pierced cross

 pierced cross & pellet

 pierced cross & central pellet

 cross crosslet

 curved star

 star

 spur rowel

 mullet

 eglantine

 sun

 pansy

 heraldic cinquefoil

 rose

 rosette

 Catherine Wheel

 cross in circle

 halved sun & rose

 lis upon half rose

 lis upon sun & rose

 lis rose dimidiated

 lis issuant from rose

 arrow

 A

 anchor & B

 flower & B

 book

 boar's head

 bow

 BR

 castle

 castle with **H**

 crescent

 pomegranate

Illustrations of mintmarks

 crown

 ermine

 escallop

 eye

 radiate eye

 gerb

 grapes

 greyhound's head

 harp

 heart

 helmet

 leopard's head

 crowned leopard's head

 lion

 lion rampant

 martlet

 blackamoor's head

 ostrich's head

 (P)

 pall

 pear

 plume

 portcullis

 portcullis crowned

 sceptre

 sunburst

 (R)

 sword

 T

 TC

 WS

 y

 Y

 dragon

 trianngle

 uncertain

 grapple

 tun

 woolpack

 thistle

 6

 floriated cross

 lozenge

 billet

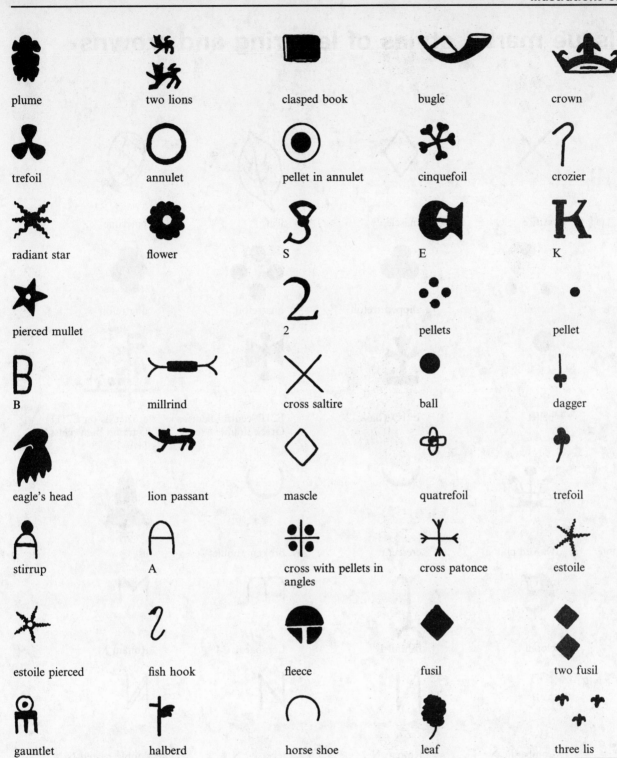

plume	two lions	clasped book	bugle	crown
trefoil	annulet	pellet in annulet	cinquefoil	crozier
radiant star	flower	S	E	K
pierced mullet	2	pellets	pellet	
B	millrind	cross saltire	ball	dagger
eagle's head	lion passant	mascle	quatrefoil	trefoil
stirrup	A	cross with pellets in angles	cross patonce	estoile
estoile pierced	fish hook	fleece	fusil	two fusil
gauntlet	halberd	horse shoe	leaf	three lis
nautilus	shield	spear head	tower	woolpack over annulet
		cross pattée fitchée		

Issue marks, styles of lettering and crowns

mullet

saltire

mascle

leaf

pinecone

trefoil, early style

trefoil

slipped trefoil

quatrefoil

quatrefoil

rosette

pellet

E21D Class 12

E21D central fleur as Greek double axe

crozier as on E21D Durham mint, classes 11A, 12, 13

Shrewsbury plume

Oxford plume

crescent

broken annulet

lis

open E

closed E

fishtail I

Lombardic M

Roman M

fishtail N

Lombardic N

Roman N

reversed N

double barred N

wedge shaped R

reversed S

S for E11D-C3F

S for E11D-C8A

cross for H31D-110

X in JH1D Class 5C

bifoliate crown

trifoliate crown

E21D Class 11A-11C

78

Triple Unite

Charles I 1625–1649

The triple-unite, with a value of sixty shillings, was the highest denomination to be produced during the hammered coinage. Issued by Charles I at the Shrewsbury and Oxford mints during the Civil War, they are undoubtedly magnificent coins. All issues are made of gold and show the king holding a sword on the obverse and the Declaration with the date below on the reverse. The two mints are easily identified since Shrewsbury has the Declaration in two lines and Oxford in three.

Shrewsbury Mint 1642

Collecting Hints

This issue is extremely rare.

Obverse Legend CAROLUS D.G. MAG BRIT FRAN ET HIBER REX — Charles by the grace of God King of Great Britain France and Ireland

Reverse Outer Legend EXURGAT DEUS DISSIPENTUR INIMICI — Let God arise and His enemies be scattered

Reverse Inner Legend RELIG PROT LEG ANG LIBER PAR — The religion of the Protestants the laws of England the liberty of Parliament

Obverse Crowned king holding sword, plume behind his head; no mintmark.

Reverse Three plumes and mark of value (III) above the two-line declaration, 1642 below.

C1TU-005 ex. rare

Oxford Mint 1642–1644

Collecting Hints

These issues are rare, but usually obtainable. Specimens exist in all grades from Fine to EF but not below Fine; most are undamaged and well struck.

Obverse Legend CAROLUS D.G. MAG BRIT FR ET HIB REX — Charles by the grace of God King of Great Britain France and Ireland

Reverse Outer Legend EXURGAT DEUS DISSIPENTUR INIMICI — Let God arise and His enemies be scattered

Reverse Inner Legend RELIG PROT LEG ANG LIBER PAR — The religion of the Protestants the laws of England the liberty of Parliament

Obverse Half-length bust of king holding sword, plume behind; mintmark plume.

Reverse Declaration on three lines, above it value (III) with three plumes, below it 1642.

C1TU-010 F £2,400 VF £4,500

As previous, but the Declaration on the reverse in one continuous scroll; dated 1642 or 1643.

C1TU-015 F £2,500 VF £4,800

As previous, but a larger bust of fine style of king holding a short olive branch; mintmark small lis. Reverse as previous but dated 1643 only.

C1TU-020 ex. rare

As previous, but taller bust of king with scarf behind his shoulder; mintmark plume, dated 1643.

C1TU-025 F £2,800 VF £5,200

As previous, but no scarf.

C1TU-030 F £2,500 VF £4,800

As previous, but OXON below date.

C1TU-035 ex. rare

A slightly smaller coin with minor varieties in the bust; reverse as previous, but dated 1644.

C1TU-040 F £2,500 VF £4,800

As previous, but OX instead of OXON below date.

C1TU-045 F £2,800 VF £5,200

Sovereign Unite Laurel Pound

The gold double-ryal, or sovereign as it became known, was introduced during the reign of Henry VII with a value of twenty shillings. It was the highest contemporary denomination and based on the *real d'or* of the Netherlands. While the coin's name reflected the sense of magnificence associated with it, its design and style complied with Renaissance rather than medieval aesthetic values. The sovereign was later named the unite and continued to be produced until 1662, when it was replaced by the guinea, a denomination of twenty-one shillings. However, it was reintroduced in 1817 and is still produced today although the coin was replaced by a banknote during World War I. In 1983 the pound note was discontinued and a pound coin with its old value of twenty shillings was introduced but, with this issue made of brass, it was a long way from the superb coins of Henry VII. The sovereign and pound coin might have an identical denomination value, but the sovereign is a bullion coin and valued at the price of its gold content. It remains popular in jewellery and with collectors.

Henry VII 1485–1509

Introduced in 1489, the sovereign had a value of twenty shillings. All issues were produced at the London mint and a mintmark can be found at the beginning of the obverse and reverse legends. Although varieties exist, the obverse always depicts the king enthroned and the reverse a Tudor rose with the royal shield in the centre. During this period, double and treble sovereigns were also produced using the sovereign dies (H7SV-025) but struck on flans two or three times thicker. These two issues are unique and were probably presentation pieces or patterns not intended for circulation; we have not, therefore, listed them as a separate denomination.

Collecting Hints

All issues are extremely rare as few specimens were struck. Coins are usually found in VF condition but other grades do exist.

Obverse Legend HENRICUS DEI GRATIA REX ANGLIE ET FRANCIE DNS IBAR (or HIB) (varieties exist) — Henry by the grace of God King of England and France Lord of Ireland

Reverse Legend IHESUS AUTEM TRANSIENS PER MEDIUM ILLORUM IBAT (varieties exist) — But Jesus passing through their midst went His way

Obverse Large figure of king sitting on a low-back throne, lis in background; mintmark cross fitchée.

Reverse Large Tudor rose with small shield in centre; mintmark cross fitchée.

H7SV-005 ex. rare

Legends As previous.

Obverse As previous, but no lis in background; mintmark cinquefoil.

Reverse As previous, but crown over royal shield; mintmark cinquefoil.

H7SV-010 ex. rare

Legends As previous.

Obverse King on high-backed ornamental throne with a greyhound and dragon on side pillars; mintmark dragon.

Reverse Shield on Tudor rose; mintmark dragon.

H7SV-015 F £6,000 VF £15,000

Legends As previous.

Obverse As previous, but the throne has a high canopy which breaks the legend; mintmark lis.

Reverse As previous; mintmark dragon.

H7SV-020 F £5,800 VF £14,500

Legends As previous.

Obverse King on narrow throne with portcullis below his feet; mintmark lis.

Reverse As previous, but mintmark cross crosslet or pheon.

H7SV-025 F £5,800 VF £14,500

Henry VIII 1509–1547

Gold sovereigns were struck throughout Henry VIII's reign and there was also the posthumous issue struck under Edward VI. The first two issues (1509–1544) are very similar to the last of Henry VII, the main difference being the mintmarks. During the third coinage, sovereigns were produced at the Southwark and Bristol mints as well as the Tower mint in London, with a new design of a lion and griffin holding the royal arms on the reverse; again, the mintmarks are most important for identification. The posthumous issue sovereigns, struck at the Bristol and Tower mints, are virtually identical to the third coinage apart from the use of Roman lettering instead of the more ornate Lombardic.

Collecting Hints

All issues of the first and second coinage are extremely rare. Coins, when available, are usually found undamaged in Fine to VF condition.

First Coinage 1509–1526

Obverse Legend HENRICUS DEI GRATIA REX ANGLIE ET FRANC DNS HIB — Henry by the grace of God King of England and France Lord of Ireland

Reverse Legend IHESUS AUTEM TRANSIENS PER MEDIUM ILLORUM IBAT — But Jesus passing through their midst went His way

Obverse King enthroned, portcullis below; mintmark portcullis.

Reverse Royal shield over Tudor rose; mintmark portcullis.

H8SV-005 VG £1,500 F £3,000 VF £6,000

Second Coinage 1526–1544

The value of the sovereign was raised to twenty-two shillings in 1526.
As previous, but mintmark sunburst or lis on the obverse and sunburst, lis or arrow on the reverse.

H8SV-010 VG £1,400 F £2,800 VF £5,800

Third Coinage 1544–1547

The weight of the sovereign was reduced, as was its value, from twenty-two to twenty shillings. All third coinage sovereigns have Lombardic lettering in the legends.

Collecting Hints

There is little doubt that this issue saw more circulation than the previous ones. While still very rare, coins are usually found in Fine condition and are often slightly creased. VF and EF examples do exist and some issues, especially in the lower grades, look rather brassy in colour due to the fluctuating fineness of the gold. Also, the weights of some issues vary.

Tower Mint

Obverse Legend HENRIC 8 DI GRA ANGL FRANCIE ET HIBER REX (varieties exist) — Henry VIII by the grace of God King of England France and Ireland

Reverse Legend IHESUS AUTEM TRANSIENS PER MEDIUM ILLORUM IBAT (varieties exist) — But Jesus passing through their midst went His way

Obverse Large figure of king enthroned, candlesticks on throne pillars; mintmark lis.

Reverse Crowned royal arms, lion and dragon either side; mintmark lis.

H8SV-015 VG £2,000 F £4,000 VF £10,000

Legends As previous.

Obverse Smaller figure of king enthroned, birds on throne pillars; mintmark lis, pellet in annulet.

Reverse As previous; mintmark lis.

H8SV-020 VG £800 F £1,600 VF £3,800

Southwark Mint

This mint was located on the South Bank of the River Thames in London. This issue is only identifiable by the mintmark and an 'E' sometimes found below the shield on the reverse.
Legends As previous.

Obverse As previous, but mintmark 'S' or 'E', often muled.

Reverse As previous, but sometimes 'E' below the royal shield; mintmarks as obverse.

H8SV-025 VG £800 F £1,500 VF £3,600

Reverse As previous, but mintmark lis.

H8SV-035 VG £1,800 F £4,200 VF £8,000

Bristol Mint

This issue is differentiated by the mintmark 'WS', usually found only on the obverse.

Legends As previous.

Obverse As previous; mintmark 'WS'.

Reverse As previous, but no 'E' below shield; mintmark none or, rarely, 'WS'.

Bristol Mint

Legends As previous.

Obverse As previous, but mintmark 'WS'.

Reverse As previous, but mintmark 'WS'.

H8SV-040 VG £1,200 F £2,400 VF £4,800

Edward VI 1547–1553

Edward VI issued four different gold sovereigns during his reign. After the posthumous issue in his father's name listed above, a similar style sovereign was produced at the London mint during Edward's second period (1549–1550). Then, during the third period (1550–1553) the fine sovereign was produced, with a value of thirty shillings. It is fairly similar in style to the issues of Henry VIII, with the king enthroned on the obverse and the royal arms over the Tudor rose on the reverse. Finally, the ordinary sovereign of twenty shillings was also produced during the third period bearing a half-length bust of the king facing right on the obverse and a crowned shield supported by a lion and dragon on the reverse. While the fine sovereign might well have commanded a separate denomination chapter, it was known as a sovereign and we feel that it should be listed here since the weight and gold content was the most important factor in valuing a coin at the time.

H8SV-030 VG £1,500 F £3,200 VF £6,500

Posthumous Coinage 1547–1551

These two rare issues were struck during the reign of Edward VI at the Tower and Bristol mints. They are virtually identical to the previous issues, with even the mintmarks remaining unchanged, but the legends are in Roman rather than Lombardic lettering.

Second Period Jan. 1549 — April 1550

Collecting Hints

These two issues are very rare. When available, coins are usually found in Fine condition and are sometimes creased although coins in the higher grades do exist.

Collecting Hints

This issue is very rare and when available usually found in Fine condition; VF examples do exist but they are extremely rare.

Tower Mint

Legends As previous, but Roman lettering.

Obverse As previous, but mintmark lis.

Obverse Legend EDWARD VI DEI GRA AGL FRAN ET HIBER REX (varieties exist) — Edward VI by the grace of God King of England France and Ireland

Reverse Legend IHS AUTEM TRANSIENS PER MED ILLOR IBAT — But Jesus passing through their midst went His way

Obverse King enthroned; mintmark arrow or 'Y'.

Reverse Crowned royal arms held by a lion and dragon, 'ER' below shield; mintmarks as obverse.

E6SV-005 VG £1,000 F £2,000 VF £4,000

Third Period 1550–1553

Fine Sovereign

This issue had a value of thirty shillings.

Obverse Legend EDWARD VI D G ANGLIE FRANCIE Z HIBERNIE REX — Edward VI by the grace of God King of England France and Ireland

Reverse Legend IHESUS AUTEM TRANSIENS PER MEDIUM ILLORUM IBAT — But Jesus passing through their midst went His way

Obverse King enthroned, portcullis below him and decoration around the inner circle; mintmark tun or ostrich head.

Reverse Royal arms over Tudor rose; mintmarks as obverse.

E6SV-010 F £10,000 VF £20,000

These dies were also used to strike the double sovereign. This coin, which was struck on a flan of double thickness, is probably unique and thought to be a presentation piece or pattern rather than a denomination for circulation. It has not, therefore, been listed here.

Sovereign

This issue had a value of twenty shillings.

Obverse Legend EDWARD VI D G AGL FRA Z HIBER REX — Edward VI by the grace of God King of England France and Ireland

Reverse Legend IHS AUTEM TRANSIE PER MEDI ILLORU IBAT — But Jesus passing through their midst went His way

Obverse Half-length bust of king facing right, holding orb and sword; mintmark 'Y' or tun.

Reverse Crowned royal arms with a lion and dragon on either side, 'E.R' below shield; mintmark as obverse.

E6SV-015 VG £500 F £1,000 VF £2,000

Mary 1553–1554

During the reign of Mary the gold fine sovereign, with a value of thirty shillings, was produced. It shows the queen enthroned on the obverse and sometimes has the date in Roman numerals at the end of the legend. The reverse bears the royal arms over a Tudor rose. This issue shows much decoration and ornamentation, especially on the obverse.

Obverse Legend MARIA D G ANG FRA Z HIB REGINA (sometimes followed by MDLIII or MDLIIII; varieties exist) — Mary by the grace of God Queen of England France and Ireland (1553 or 1554)

Reverse Legend A. DNO FACTU EST ISTUD Z EST MIRA IN OCUL NRIS — This is the Lord's doing and it is marvellous in our eyes

Obverse Queen seated on ornamental throne, a portcullis below and decoration within the inner circle; mintmark pomegranate or halved rose.

Reverse Royal arms over Tudor rose; mintmarks as obverse.

MSV-005 VG £1,000 F £2,200 VF £4,000

No sovereigns were struck during the reign of Philip and Mary.

Elizabeth I 1558–1603

During Elizabeth I's reign fine sovereigns with a value of thirty shillings were produced, as were gold pounds with a value of twenty shillings. The fine sovereign depicts the queen enthroned on the obverse and the royal arms over a Tudor rose on the reverse while the gold pound bears the bust of the queen on the obverse and a crowned shield on the reverse. All issues were struck at the Tower mint and have a mintmark on the obverse and reverse, at the beginning or end of the legend.

Fine Sovereign

Collecting Hints

All issues are very rare and are usually found undamaged in Fine or VF condition.

First — Third Issues 1559–1578

Obverse Legend ELIZABETH D G ANG FRA ET HIBE REGINA (minor varieties exist) — Elizabeth by the grace of God Queen of England France and Ireland

Reverse Legend A DNO FACTU EST ISTUD ET EST MIRAB IN OCULIS NRIS — This is the Lord's doing and it is marvellous in our eyes

Obverse Queen enthroned with a portcullis below; mintmark lis or cross crosslet.

Reverse Royal arms over a Tudor rose; mintmarks as obverse.

ELSV-005 VG £1,000 F £2,000 VF £4,000

No sovereigns or pounds were struck for the fourth issue (1578–1582).

Fifth Issue 1583–1600

Legends As previous.

Obverse As previous, but the throne is lower; mintmark 'A', escallop, crescent, hand, tun.

Reverse As previous; mintmarks as obverse.

ELSV-010 VG £1,000 F £2,000 VF £4,000

Gold Pound

Gold pounds were produced in some quantity during the fifth and sixth coinages (1592–1602). They had a value of twenty shillings.

Collecting Hints

These coins, while rare, are obtainable. They can be found in all grades from VG to EF but specimens are sometimes damaged. Collectors tend to pay particular attention to the obverse which bears a superb bust of the queen.

Obverse Legend ELIZABETH D G ANG FRA ET HIB REGINA — Elizabeth by the grace of God Queen of England France and Ireland

Reverse Legend SCUTUM FIDEI PROTEGET EAM — The shield of faith shall protect her

Obverse Crowned bust of queen; mintmark tun, woolpack, key, anchor, O, 1, 2.

Reverse Crown over royal arms and dividing 'E.R'; mintmarks as obverse.

ELPD-015 VG £400 F £750 VF £2,000

James I 1603–1625

During the reign of James I three types of sovereign were produced. The regular sovereign was struck during the first coinage. It was largely a continuation from previous reigns in style and value (twenty shillings) and, like all gold issues from this coinage, is rare due to a contemporary shortage of gold. The second coinage saw the introduction of the gold unite, so called because the legends on the coin proclaimed James I's intentions regarding the union of the two kingdoms of England and Scotland. The value of the unite was twenty shillings until 1612, when it was raised to twenty-two due to the rise of the value of gold across Europe. Finally, the gold laurel with a value of twenty shillings was introduced during the third coinage. Named after the laurel that the king is portrayed wearing on his head, this issue was produced in some quantity but its quality in style and design was comparatively poor. All issues were struck at the Tower mint in London and have mintmarks at the beginning of the obverse and usually the reverse legend.

First Coinage 1603–1604 Sovereign

Collecting Hints

This issue, which was only struck for two years, is very rare and usually found undamaged in Fine to VF condition. Specimens in the lower grades seem to be extremely rare.

Obverse Legend IACOBUS D G ANG SCO FRAN ET HIB REX — James by the grace of God King of England Scotland France and Ireland

Reverse Legend EXURGAT DEUS DISSIPENTUR INIMICI — Let God arise and His enemies be scattered

Obverse Half-length crowned bust of king holding orb and sceptre; mintmark thistle.

Reverse Royal arms with crown above dividing 'I.R.'; mintmark thistle.

J1SV-005 VG £450 F £900 VF £1,800

Legends As previous.

Obverse As previous, but the king is wearing decorated armour; mintmark thistle or lis.

Reverse As previous, but mintmark thistle or lis.

J1SV-010 VG £450 F £950 VF £1,850

Second Coinage 1604–1619 Unite

Collecting Hints

The gold unite is a superb, large, well designed coin and is usually available to collectors; it is an ideal coin to have from this period. It was produced in some quantity and collectors should have little difficulty obtaining an example. Unites can be found in all grades from poor to EF but many specimens are worn or damaged, reflecting considerable circulation. Also, many were made into jewellery or holed and then perhaps plugged at a later date. Collectors should beware of plugged or mounted coins when buying a specimen.

Second Bust

Obverse Legend IACOBUS D G MA BRI FRA ET HI REX (minor varieties exist) — James by the grace of God King of Great Britain France and Ireland

Reverse Legend FACIAM EOS IN GENTEM UNAM — I will make them one nation

Obverse Crowned king with pointed beard, holding orb and sceptre; mintmark lis or rose.

Reverse Crown above royal arms dividing 'I.R'; mintmark lis or rose.

J1UN-015 VG £170 F £300 VF £550

Fourth Bust

Legends As previous.

Obverse Crowned king with long beard not tucked into his armour and holding an orb and sceptre; mintmarks rose, escallop, grapes, coronet, key, bell, mullet, tower, trefoil and cinquefoil.

Reverse As previous; mintmarks as obverse.

J1UN-020 VG £160 F £280 VF £500

Fifth Bust

Legends As previous.

Obverse Crowned bust of king with short bushy beard and holding an orb and sceptre; mintmarks cinquefoil, tun, book, crescent, plain cross, saltire.

Reverse As previous; mintmarks as obverse.

J1UN-025 VG £160 F £280 VF £500

Scotland also produced coins which are very similar to the unite but with a different style bust, different reverse shield and mintmark thistle.

Third Coinage 1619–1625 Laurel

Collecting Hints

The gold laurel is scarcer than the gold unite and less popular with collectors as it is not as attractive. The laurel with the fifth bust is extremely rare, while the other two issues are usually found in Fine or VF condition. Like the unite, these issues are often found damaged in less than Fine condition and undoubtedly saw considerable circulation.

First Bust

Obverse Legend IACOBUS D G MAG BRI FRA ET HIB REX (minor varieties exist) — James by the grace of God King of Great Britain France and Ireland

Reverse Legend FACIAM EOS IN GENTEM UNAM — I will make them one nation

Obverse Large bust of king wearing a laurel, value (XX) behind his head; mintmark spur rowel.

Reverse Long cross fleury over crowned square shield; mintmark spur rowel at end of legend.

J1LA-030 VG £180 F £375 VF £650

Second Bust

Legends As previous.

Obverse As previous, but slightly smaller bust; mintmark spur rowel or rose.

Reverse As previous; mintmarks as obverse.

J1LA-035 VG £170 F £350 VF £625

Third Bust

Legends As previous.

Obverse Smaller, neater bust of king with his chin not protruding as much as the previous issue; mintmark rose or thistle.

Reverse As previous; mintmarks as obverse.

J1LA-040 VG £170 F £350 VF £625

Fourth Bust

Legends As previous.

Obverse Laureate bust of king wearing new-style cloak; mintmarks lis or trefoil.

Reverse As previous; mintmarks as obverse.

J1LA-045 VG £170 F £350 VF £625

Fifth Bust

Obverse Legend As previous, but HI instead of HIB.

Reverse Legend As previous.

Obverse Smaller, crude bust of king of very poor style wearing laurel, with value behind; mintmark trefoil.

Reverse As previous; mintmark trefoil.

J1LA-050 rare

Charles I 1625–1649

As mentioned earlier, the name of the denomination changed from 'sovereign' to 'unite' and 'laurel' although the values of the coins remained the same. During this period, the denomination was mainly referred to as twenty shillings, however, as today, coins of the same denomination had different names. During all of Charles I's reign gold unites were produced at the Tower mint. They depicted the crowned bust of the king on the obverse and a shield of varying styles, with a crown above, on the reverse. A mintmark can usually be found at the beginning of the obverse and reverse legends and issues struck while the mint was under the control of Parliament are easily identified by their mintmarks. Nicholas Briot also produced wonderful, machine-made unites in 1631–1632. These issues, which are very rare, are superb in style and design and are greatly superior to the hammered issues of the Tower mint.

During the Civil War at the end of Charles I's reign provincial mints struck coins, often to pay troops loyal to the king, and gold unites and superb silver pounds were produced at several locations. Most provincial gold unites are extremely rare or even unique, although the Oxford mint did produce a small quantity of specimens. These issues, which are very crude in style, differ greatly from the regular Tower issue specimens in that the bust of the king is very different and the reverse does not bear a shield, but only the Declaration with the date below. The silver pounds, which were produced at the Shrewsbury and Oxford mints, can easily be recognised by the XX (20 shillings) above the Declaration on the reverse but, as the two issues are extremely similar in style, both should be studied when identifying a coin.

The issues of Charles I are numerous and we have listed Collecting Hints for each. It is important to remember that Charles II also issued unites and that in all cases the obverse legend of Charles I starts CAROLUS, whereas Charles II starts CAROLUS II.

Tower Mint

Tower Mint under King 1625–1642

Collecting Hints

Most issues are fairly common and are usually available to the collector in VG to VF condition. Some issues are not fully round and although specimens may have been clipped, there is little doubt that moneyers sometimes paid little attention to the shape of a coin's flan. Furthermore, many issues are often damaged or worn, reflecting considerable circulation. Collectors should try to obtain an example with as good a portrait as possible.

First Bust

Obverse Legend CAROLUS D G MAG BR FR ET HI REX — Charles by the grace of God Great King of Britain France and Ireland

Reverse Legend FLORENT CONCORDIA REGNA — Through concord kingdoms flourish

Obverse King wearing ruff and double-arched crown, value behind his head; mintmark lis or cross calvary.

Reverse Crown over square shield; mintmark as obverse.

C1UN-005 VG £150 F £325 VF £550

As previous, but extra garnishing to shield on reverse; mintmark lis.

C1UN-010 VG £150 F £340 VF £570

As C1UN-005 but king is wearing a flat-topped single-arched crown.

C1UN-015 VG £150 F £325 VF £550

Second Bust

Obverse Legend As previous; minor varieties exist.

Reverse Legend As previous.

Obverse Smaller, thinner and neater bust of king with a smaller ruff; mintmark cross calvary, blackamoor's head, castle, anchor, heart.

Reverse Crown over square royal shield; mintmark as obverse.

C1UN-020 VG £150 F £300 VF £550

Obverse As previous, but larger bust with wider crown; mintmark heart or plume.

Reverse As previous; mintmarks as obverse.

C1UN-025 VG £150 F £300 VF £550

As previous, but with mintmark anchor below bust.

C1UN-030 VG £250 F £475 VF £900

Third Bust

Legends As previous.

Obverse King wears more visible armour; mintmark plume or rose.

Reverse Oval shield with crown above and dividing 'C.R'; mintmark as obverse.

C1UN-035 VG £140 F £280 VF £500

Fourth Bust

Legends As previous.

Obverse King with longer hair and smaller collar; mintmark harp, portcullis, bell, crown, tun.

Reverse Oval shield with crown above, 'C.R' with small crowns above divided by shield; mintmark as obverse.

C1UN-040 VG £140 F £280 VF £500

No unites were struck with the fifth bust.

Sixth Bust

Legends As previous.

Obverse King with pointed beard (Briot-style bust) and large lace collar; mintmark anchor, triangle, star, triangle in circle.

Reverse Crown over oval shield dividing crowned 'C R'; mintmark as obverse.

C1UN-045 VG £150 F £300 VF £550

Obverse As previous; mintmark anchor.

Reverse Crown over square-topped shield, dividing crowned 'C. R' (Briot-style reverse).

C1UN-050 v. rare

Tower Mint under Parliament 1643–1648

The mintmarks differentiate this issue from previous ones.

> ## Collecting Hints
>
> These issues are rarer than the previous ones. Specimens are usually found, often poorly struck, in Fine to VF condition.

Fourth Bust

Legends As previous.

Obverse & Reverse As C1UN-040, but mintmark 'P'.

C1UN-055 VG £180 F £375 VF £700

Sixth Bust

Legends As previous.

Obverse & Reverse As C1UN-045, but mintmark '(P)', '(R)' or triangle in circle.

C1UN-060 VG £200 F £400 VF £800

Seventh Bust

Obverse As previous, but bust of cruder style; mintmark eye, sun, sceptre.

Reverse Crown over royal shield, dividing crowned 'C R'; mintmark as obverse.

C1UN-065 VG £200 F £425 VF £850

Briot's Coinage 1631–1632

This issue is machine-made and easily identified by its mintmark and uniquely shaped reverse shield.

Collecting Hints

This is a superb issue and undoubtedly the finest unite struck under Charles I. It is also very rare, although specimens do exist in Fine to EF condition and are usually undamaged.

Obverse Legend CAROLUS D. G. MAGN BRITANN FRAN ET HIBER REX — Charles by the grace of God King of Great Britain France and Ireland

Reverse Legend FLORENT CONCORDIA REGNA — Through concord kingdoms flourish

Obverse Crowned bust of king, value (XX) behind; mintmark flower and 'B'.

Reverse Crown over square-topped shield which divides crowned 'CR'.

C1UN-070 F £1,000 VF £2,000

Provincial Issues

These rare unites were struck during the Civil War and were often used to pay royalist troops.

Chester Mint

This issue should not be confused with the Tower mint one; not only is it poorer in style but also on the Tower issue the 'C R' on the reverse is uncrowned.

Collecting Hints

This issue is extremely rare.

Obverse Legend CAROLUS D.G. MA BR FR ET HI REX — Charles by the grace of God Great King of Britain France and Ireland

Reverse Legend FLORENT CONCORDIA REGNA — Through concord kingdoms flourish

Obverse Crowned bust with value behind; mintmark plume.

Reverse Crown over oval shield which divides crowned 'CR'; mintmark plume.

C1UN-075 ex. rare

Oxford Mint

These issues are easily identified by the reverse design which has the Declaration with date below and plumes above; this is only shared by the extremely rare Bristol issue. Many varieties of the Oxford unite exist and we have listed them all.

Collecting Hints

All issues are very rare, but specimens for collectors do exist outside museums. The issues are extremely crude in style and often have weaknesses in the legends due to the poor strike. Specimens exist in VG to VF condition.

Obverse Legend CAROLUS D. G. MAG BRIT FR ET HIB REX (many minor varieties exist) — Charles by the grace of God King of Great Britain France and Ireland

Reverse Legend EXURGAT DEUS DISSIPENTUR INIMICI — Let God arise and His enemies be scattered

Reverse Inner Legend RELIG PROT LEG ANG LIBER PAR (many minor varieties exist) — The religion of the Protestants the laws of England the liberty of Parliament

Obverse Crowned bust of king holding olive branch, value (XX) behind; no mintmark.

Reverse The Declaration in two lines, three plumes above, date 1642 below.

C1UN-080 VG £300 F £600 VF £1,400

As previous, but the Declaration in three lines, dated 1642 or 1643 below.

C1UN-085 VG £300 F £600 VF £1,400

Obverse Larger bust of king holding sword.

Reverse As previous, but dated 1643 only.
C1UN-090 VG £325 F £650 VF £1,500

Obverse Shorter bust of king; mintmark plume.

Reverse As previous, but dated 1643 or 1645.

C1UN-095 VG £300 F £600 VF £1,400

As previous, but OX below date 1644.

C1UN-100 VG £300 F £600 VF £1,400

Obverse Tall new-style bust going to the edge of the coin, the legend starts near the bottom of the coin; no mintmark.

Reverse As previous, dated 1643.

C1UN-105 VG £300 F £600 VF £1,400

Obverse Smaller bust of king as C1UN-095.

Reverse The Declaration on three straight lines, dated 1644 OX.

C1UN-110 ex. rare

Obverse Longer, narrow bust and not as small as previous.

Reverse As previous.

C1UN-115 VG £325 F £650 VF £1,450

Obverse As previous.

Reverse A single plume above the Declaration instead of three; dated 1645 or 1646, OX.

C1UN-120 VG £325 F £650 VF £1,500

Bristol Mint

This issue is similar to C1UN-095 dated 1645, however, it has the mintmark 'BR' on the obverse.

Collecting Hints

This issue is extremely rare.

Obverse Legend CAROLUS D.G. MAG BR FR ET HIB REX — Charles by the grace of God Great King of Britain France and Ireland

Reverse Legend EXURGAT DEUS DISSIPENTUR INIMICI — Let God arise and His enemies be scattered

Reverse Inner Legend REL PROT LEG ANG LIB PAR — The religion of the Protestants the laws of England the liberty of Parliament

Obverse King holding sword, value (XX) behind; mintmark 'BR'.

Reverse Three plumelets over the Declaration, dated 1645 below.

C1UN-125 ex. rare

Truro Mint

This issue should not be confused with the more common Tower issue although both use the mintmark rose on the obverse and reverse. One Truro issue has a different reverse legend, while the other has a crowned 'C' and 'R' on either side of the shield on the reverse; the Tower issues are uncrowned.

Collecting Hints

The first issue is unique, the second extremely rare.

Obverse Legend CAROLUS D.G. MAG BR FR ET HI REX — Charles by the grace of God Great King of Britain France and Ireland

Reverse Legend FLORENT CONCORDIA REGNA — Through concord kingdoms flourish

Obverse Crowned bust with value (XX) behind; mintmark rose.

Reverse Crowned oval garnished shield; mintmark rose.

C1UN-130 unique

As previous, but reverse legend reads CULTORES SUI DEUS PROTEGIT — God protects His worshippers.

C1UN-135 ex. rare

Worcester Mint 1643–1644

This issue, which is extremely rare, can be identified by the lion paws on either side of the shield on the reverse.

Collecting Hints

This issue is extremely rare in any grade.

Obverse Legend CAROLUS D G MAG BR FR ET HI RE[X] — Charles by the grace of God King of Great Britain France and Ireland

Reverse Legend FLORENT CONCORDIA REGNO — Through concord kingdoms flourish

Obverse Crowned bust with value (XX) behind; no mintmark.

Reverse Crown over oval royal shield, a lion paw either side of the shield.

C1UN-140 ex. rare

Shrewsbury Mint 1644

The mints of Shrewsbury and Worcester were very closely connected. The Shrewsbury issue is identical to the Worcester one, except for the mintmark lis which can only be found on the obverse, and the fact that on the reverse there are no lion paws either side of the shield.

Legend As previous.

Obverse As previous, but mintmark lis.

Reverse As previous, but no lion paws and no mintmark.

C1UN-145 possibly unique

Shrewsbury and Oxford Silver Pounds

Silver pounds with a value of twenty shillings were produced at the Oxford and Shrewsbury mints between 1642 and 1644. Both these issues, which are very similar, show the king on horseback on the obverse with various designs below the horse and on the reverse the Declaration with plumes above and date below. The denomination, (XX) twenty shillings, can be found above the Declaration. These issues are very similar in style and design, and collectors will have to refer to both when identifying a coin. The main differences are as follows: the Shrewsbury mint has no mintmark at the beginning of the obverse legend, although most issues have a series of pellets; most Oxford issues use mintmark plume; all Shrewsbury issues are dated 1642, while Oxford issues are dated 1642–1644. Also, Oxford plumes have a 'tie' at the bottom, whereas Shrewsbury plumes do not.

Collecting Hints

These large coins are very rare although specimens exist in VG to VF condition. They must have been difficult to strike and this is sometimes reflected in their condition.

Shrewsbury Mint 1642

Obverse Legend CAROLUS D G MAG BRIT FRA ET HIB REX — Charles by the grace of God King of Great Britain France and Ireland

Reverse Legend EXURGAT DEUS DISSIPENTUR INIMICI — Let God arise and His enemies be scattered

Reverse Inner Legend RELIG PROT LEG ANGL LIBER PAR — The religion of the Protestants the laws of England the liberty of Parliament

Obverse King on horseback with plume behind.

Reverse Declaration in two lines, date 1642 below, value and three plumes above.

C1PD-150 VG £500 F £1,200 VF £2,500

As previous, but new-style, neater horseman walking over a pile of arms.

C1PD-155 VG £500 F £1,200 VF £2,500

As previous, but a cannon below king's horse on the obverse and only one plume above Declaration on the reverse.

C1PD-160 VG £650 F £1,500 VF £3,000

Oxford Mint 1642–1644

Obverse Legend CAROLUS D.G MAG BRIT FRA ET HIBER REX — Charles by the grace of God King of Great Britain France and Ireland

Reverse Outer Legend EXURGAT DEUS DISSIPENTUR INIMICI — Let God arise and His enemies be scattered

Reverse Inner Legend RELIG PROT LEG ANG LIBER PAR — The religion of the Protestants the laws of England the liberty of Parliament

Obverse Large horseman with king's sword breaking the inner circle, arms below horse; mintmark plume.

Reverse Declaration with date 1642 below, value (XX) and three Shrewsbury-style plumes above. This is a Shrewsbury die.

C1PD-165 VG £700 F £1,800 VF £3,500

As previous, but the reverse is an Oxford die with Oxford plumes.

C1PD-170 VG £700 F £1,800 VF £3,500

As previous, but new-style horseman on the obverse with horse trampling on arms, exergual line below horse.

C1PD-175 VG £500 F £1,200 VF £2,500

As previous, but cannon amongst arms, dated 1642 or 1643.

C1PD-180 VG £500 F £1,200 VF £2,500

As previous, but the space below groundline on the obverse is chequered, dated 1642 only.

C1PD-185 VG £800 F £2,000 VF £4,000

As previous but Briot-style horseman, dated 1643.

C1PD-190 VG £800 F £2,000 VF £6,000

Legends As previous.

Obverse As C1PD-165 obverse.

Reverse The Declaration in three lines in the form of a scroll, dated 1644 with OX below, value (XX) above and a single plume above value.

C1PD-195 VG £800 F £2,000 VF £6,000

Pontefract Siege Issue 1648–1649

These issues were struck inside Pontefract Castle during the siege by Cromwell's army.

Collecting Hints

These issues are extremely rare.

Obverse Legend DUM SPIRO SPERO — Whilst I live I hope

Reverse Legend CAROLUS SECUNDUS 1648 — Charles II 1648

Obverse Large crown over 'CR'.

Reverse Castle gateway with flag.

C1SV-200 ex. rare

Obverse Outer Legend CAROL II D.G. MAG B F ET H REX — Charles II by the grace of God King of Great Britain France and Ireland

Obverse Inner Legend HANC DEUS DEDIT — God has given this

Reverse Legend POST MORTEM PATRIS PRO FILIO — For the son after the death of his father

Obverse Large crown, 1648.

Reverse As previous.

C1SV-205 ex. rare

Commonwealth 1649–1660

Gold unites with a value of twenty shillings were produced during most of the Commonwealth period. These issues are very plain in style when compared to previous ones, reflecting contemporary Puritan values. The obverse shows the arms of St George and bears a mintmark, the reverse has the date and, just below it, the value (XX). For the first time, the legends are in English rather than Latin echoing anti-Catholic feeling.

Collecting Hints

The first issue with the mintmark sun is rare but obtainable. Coins are found, sometimes damaged, in all grades from VG to EF. All issues with mintmark anchor are very rare and tend to be found in lower grades.

Obverse Legend THE COMMONWEALTH OF ENGLAND

Reverse Legend GOD WITH US

Obverse St George's shield within wreath; mintmark sun.

Reverse St George's shield and Irish shield, value above, dated 1649–1657.

COMSV-005 VG £250 F £500 VF £1,000

As previous, but mintmark anchor, dated 1658 or 1660.

COMSV-010 VG £600 F £1,200

Charles II 1660–1685

Hammered Coinage 1660–1662

Gold unites with a value of twenty shillings were produced during Charles II's hammered coinage. These rare issues show the king's bust on the obverse and a crown above the royal arms on the reverse. The gold unite was replaced by the milled gold guinea in 1663, with a value of twenty shillings subsequently rising to twenty-one shillings. It was not until 1817, at the end of George III's reign, that the sovereign was reintroduced with a value of twenty shillings.

<table>
<tr><td>**Collecting Hints**

Both issues are very rare. Examples are usually found undamaged in Fine or VF condition.</td></tr>
</table>

Obverse Legend CAROLUS II D G MAG BRIT FRAN ET HIB REX — Charles II by the grace of God King of Great Britain France and Ireland

Reverse Legend FLORENT CONCORDIA REGNA — Through concord kingdoms flourish

Obverse Bust of king wearing a laurel; mintmark crown.

Reverse Crown above oval royal shield which divides 'CR'.

C2UNH-005 VG £350 F £650 VF £1,200

As previous, but value (XX) behind king's head.

C2UNH-010 VG £350 F £650 VF £1,200

Ryal

With a value of ten shillings, the ryal was a replacement for the noble during the reign of Edward IV but, as it proved unpopular, it was later replaced by the angel. The Edward IV ryal is listed under the Noble Chapter as it is such a continuation in style. Although the ryal was reintroduced in 1487 under Henry VII, very few coins were issued and it continued to be unpopular especially compared to the angel which was produced in some quantity. The ryal was not produced again until the reign of Mary, when its value was increased to fifteen shillings, or half a fine sovereign.

Henry VII 1485–1509

Collecting Hints

This coin is extremely rare in any grade.

Obverse Legend HENRIC D. GRA REX ANGL Z FRANC DNS IBAR — Henry by the grace of God King of England and France Lord of Ireland

Reverse Legend IHC AUTEM TRANSIENS PER MEDIU ILLORU IBAT — But Jesus passing through their midst went His way

Obverse King standing in a ship holding a sword and shield, two flags flying from ship.

Reverse French shield over large Tudor rose; mintmark cross fitchée.

H7RY-005 F £8,000 VF £16,000

Mary 1553–1554

Collecting Hints

With a value of fifteen shillings, this issue is extremely rare; specimens are usually found in VF condition. In fact, in 1985, a VF specimen sold at auction for £13,000. Collectors should be aware that very good Victorian forgeries exist and can be detected by the lack of detail on the rose on the reverse of the coin.

Obverse Legend MARIA DG. ANG FRA Z HIB REGINA MDLIII — Mary by the grace of God Queen of England France and Ireland 1553

Reverse Legend A DNO FACTU EST ISTUD Z EST MIRA IN OCULNRIS — This is the Lord's doing and it is marvellous in our eyes

Obverse Queen on a ship; mintmark pomegranate.

Reverse Radiate rose in centre of design.

MRY-005 ex. rare

Elizabeth I 1558–1603

Collecting Hints

This is an extremely rare denomination, struck only between 1584–1589. It is sought after as it is accepted as the last truly mediaeval English coin. Usually found in Fine to VF condition, it bears a mintmark only on the reverse.

Fifth Issue

Obverse Legend ELIZAB D G ANG FR ET HIB REGINA — Elizabeth by the grace of God Queen of England France and Ireland

Reverse Legend IHS AUT TRANSIENS PER MEIU ILLORUM IBAT — But Jesus passing through the midst of them went his way

Obverse Queen standing in a contemporary sailing ship.

Reverse Geometric design; mintmark 'A', escallop, crescent, hand.

ELRY-005 VG — F £8,000 VF £12,000

James I 1603–1625

Rose Ryal

This rare issue was struck during the second and third coinage of James I. It was really a two-ryal piece and should not be classed as a sovereign which was valued at either twenty or twenty-two shillings. The obverse of these extremely decorative coins is fairly similar in style to the Elizabeth I fine sovereign which, of course, had the same value as the rose ryal. A mintmark can be found on the obverse and reverse and the value of the coin, (XXX) thirty shillings, appears above the royal shield on the reverse of the third coinage.

Spur Ryal

This issue, so called because the sun and rose on the reverse resemble a spur, was introduced during the second coinage. Originally its value was fifteen shillings but, in line with all gold coins, it was raised in 1612 to sixteen shillings and sixpence. During the third coinage a new-style spur ryal was introduced with its value and weight reduced to fifteen shillings. On the obverse it shows a crowned lion above the royal arms dividing the value (XV), while the reverse remains similar to previous issues.

Second Coinage 1604–1619

Obverse Legend IACOBUS DG MAG BRIT FRAN ET HIBER REX — James by the grace of God King of Great Britain France and Ireland

Reverse Legend A DNO FACTUM EST ISTUD ET EST MIRAB IN OCULIS NRIS — This is the Lord's doing and it is marvellous in our eyes

Obverse King enthroned, a portcullis below his feet; mintmark rose, escallop, grapes, coronet, key, mullet, tower, trefoil, cinquefoil, tun, closed book.

Reverse Royal arms over a rose; mintmarks as obverse.

Second Coinage 1604–1619

Obverse Legend IACOBUS DG. MAG BRIT FRAN ET HIB REX — James by the grace of God King of Great Britain France and Ireland

Reverse Legend A. DNO FACTUM EST ISTUD ET EST MIRABILE — This is the Lord's doing and it is marvellous [in our eyes]

Obverse King in ship holding sword and shield; mintmark rose, escallop, coronet, mullet, tower, trefoil, cinquefoil, closed book.

Reverse Rose over radiant star, a lion and crown in each quarter; mintmarks as obverse.

J1RY-005 F £1,000 VF £2,000

J1RY-020 F £2,200 VF £4,500

Third Coinage 1619–1625

Obverse Legend IACOBUS DG MA BRI FR ET HI REX — James by the grace of God King of Great Britain France and Ireland

Reverse Legend As previous.

Obverse King enthroned, a portcullis below; mintmark spur rowel, rose, thistle, lis.

Reverse Royal shield, value (XXX) above circled by roses, lions and lis; mintmarks as obverse.

Third Coinage 1619–1625

Obverse Legend IACOBUS DG MAG BRIT FRA ET HI REX — James by the grace of God King of Great Britain France and Ireland

Reverse Legend A DNO FACTUM EST ISTUD ET EST MIRABILE — This is the Lord's doing and it is marvellous [in our eyes]

Obverse Lion holding sceptre above the royal shield which divides 'XV'; mintmark spur rowel, rose, thistle, trefoil (at end of legend).

Reverse Rose over radiate star, a lion and crown in each quarter; mintmarks as obverse.

J1RY-010 F £1,100 VF £2,200

J1RY-025 F £2,200 VF £4,500

As previous, but plain back to king's throne; mintmark trefoil.

J1RY-015 F £1,200 VF £2,400

Half Sovereign Double Crown Ten Shillings Halfpound Half Laurel

The half-sovereign with a value of ten shillings was introduced during the third coinage of Henry VIII. It was to become a popular and much needed denomination and was produced for circulation as a gold coin until 1915 at the Royal Mint in London and then until 1926 at the Empire mint in South Africa. Thereafter, it was issued as a banknote until decimalization, when it was replaced by the fifty pence piece. Undoubtedly, the introduction of the half-sovereign, along with the gold crown, marked the start of the long haul towards decimalization and conformity.

Charles II's reign saw the introduction of the guinea and half-guinea which for a while replaced the sovereign and half-sovereign until the latter were re-introduced towards the end of George III's reign.

Gold ryals, also known as rose nobles, were produced during several reigns prior to Henry VIII and most, albeit not all, issues had a value of ten shillings. We have listed these issues in a separate chapter as they were not called half-sovereigns or fall into a wider scheme of creating a better denomination structure. Also listed separately are the gold angels which did sometimes have a value of ten shillings. Double crowns, ten-shillings, halfpounds and half-laurels can be found here.

Henry VIII 1509–1547

Half-sovereigns were produced during Henry VIII's third coinage (1544–1547) at the Tower and Southwark mints in London and the Bristol mint. All issues are easily identified by the mintmarks found at the beginning of the legend, always on the obverse and sometimes on the reverse. After Henry VIII's death in 1547 and during the reign of his son Edward VI, half-sovereigns were produced in Henry's name at the Tower and Southwark mints. These issues are very similar to the third coinage and are included under Henry VIII. Collectors should refer to the third as well as the posthumous coinage when identifying an issue.

Collecting Hints

Both issues, while scarce, are obtainable. They are usually found in about Fine condition; VF and EF examples are very rare. Most coins are found unclipped and usually undamaged, but not well struck.

Third Coinage 1544–1547

Tower Mint

Obverse Legend HENRIC 8 DI GRA AGL FRANCI ET HIB REX (many varieties exist) — Henry VIII by the grace of God King of England France and Ireland

Reverse Legend IHS AUTEM TRANSIENS PER MEDIV ILLORUM IBAT (many varieties exist) — But Jesus passing through their midst went His way

Obverse King on throne holding orb and sceptre; mintmark lis or pellet in annulet.

Reverse Crown over shield, lion and dragon either side.

H8HS-005 VG £180 F £350 VF £700

Southwark Mint

Legends As previous.

Obverse As previous, but mintmark 'S' or 'E'.

Reverse As previous, but sometimes an 'E' below the shield; mintmarks as obverse, often muled.

H8HS-010 VG £180 F £350 VF £700

Bristol Mint

Legends As previous.

Obverse As previous, but mintmark 'WS'.

Reverse As previous, but no 'E' below shield; sometimes no mintmark.

H8HS-015 VG £300 F £550 VF £1,200

Posthumous Coinage 1547–1551

This issue closely resembles the previous one, but bears a youthful bust enthroned even though the obverse legend is the same.

Tower Mint

Legends As previous.

Obverse King with youthful bust sitting on the throne; mintmark arrow, annulet and pellet, lis, grapple, martlet.

Reverse Crown over royal arms, lion and dragon either side; mintmark annulet and pellet.

H8HS-020 VG £200 F £375 VF £700

As previous, but a 'K' below the shield on the reverse, mintmark none, 'E' or 'K' as reverse mintmark only.

H8HS-025 VG £200 F £385 VF £750

As H8HS-020, but a grapple below the shield on the reverse; mintmark grapple or none.

H8HS-030 VG £200 F £375 VF £700

Southwark Mint

Legends As previous.

Obverse As H8HS-020; mintmark 'E' or none.

Reverse As H8HS-020, but sometimes 'E' below royal shield.

H8HS-035 VG £170 F £325 VF £600

Edward VI 1547–1553

During Edward VI's reign a number of half-sovereigns of various styles were produced. The first issue was the posthumous Henry VIII, listed above. During the first period, half-sovereigns were produced very similar to the previous issue but with the obverse legend reading EDWARD 6 instead of HENRIC 8. During the second period, a variety of half-sovereigns were struck at the Tower mint as well as the Durham House mint, situated in London where the Strand is today. These issues show the bust of the Boy King, sometimes uncrowned, with a crown over the royal arms on the reverse. Finally, a half-sovereign was produced during the third period depicting a half-length figure of the king holding a sword and orb on the obverse and a crown over the royal arms on the reverse.

First Period April 1547 — Jan. 1549

Collecting Hints

These issues are quite rare and difficult to obtain. When available, they are usually in Fine condition.

Tower Mint

Obverse Legend EDWARD 6 DI GRA AGL FRANCI HIB REX — Edward VI by the grace of God King of England France and Ireland

Reverse Legend IHS AUTE TRANSIEN PER MEDIU ILLOR IBAT (minor varieties exist) — But Jesus passing through their midst went His way

Obverse King on throne holding orb and sceptre; mintmark arrow.

Reverse Crown over shield, lion and dragon either side.

E6HS-005 VG £300 F £580 VF £1,200

Southwark Mint

This issue is identical to the previous one except for the mintmark 'E' also, an 'E' of various styles can sometimes be found below the shield on the reverse.

E6HS-010 VG £350 F £700 VF £1,400

Second Period Jan. 1549 — April 1550

Collecting Hints

The issues from the Tower mint, while rare, are obtainable especially in Fine condition. However, all issues from Durham House are extremely rare and difficult to obtain in any grade. Collectors should pay particular attention to the obverse and reverse legend readings as this will help with identification.

Uncrowned Bust
Tower Mint

Obverse Legend TIMOR DOMINI FONS VITE MDXLIX — The fear of the Lord is the fountain of life 1549

Reverse Legend EDWARD VI D.G. AGL FRA Z HIB REX — Edward VI by the grace of God King of England France and Ireland

Obverse Uncrowned bust of king; mintmark arrow.

Reverse Crown over royal shield dividing 'E R' (EDWARD REX-Edward King).

E6HS-015 ex. rare

Obverse Legend SCUTUM FIDEI PROTEGET EUM — The shield of faith shall protect him

Reverse Legend As previous.

Obverse As previous, but mintmark arrow or 'Y'. There is also an extremely rare variety with mintmark '6'.

Reverse As previous.

E6HS-020 VG £300 F £650 VF £1,300

Durham House Mint

Obverse Legend As previous, but sometimes date MDXLVIII at end of legend.

Reverse Legend As previous.

Obverse As previous; mintmark bow.

Reverse As previous.

E6HS-025 probably unique

Obverse Legend LUCERNA PEDIBUS MEIS VERBUM TUUM — Thy word is a lamp unto my feet

Reverse Legend As previous.

Obverse As previous.

Reverse As previous.

E6HS-030 ex. rare

Crowned Bust

Tower Mint

Obverse Legend EDWARD VI DG AGL FRA Z HIBER REX — Edward VI by the grace of God King of England France and Ireland

Reverse Legend SCUTUM FIDEI PROTEGET EUM — The shield of faith shall protect him

Obverse Crowned bust of king; mintmark arrow, swan, grapple, 'Y', martlet.

Reverse Crown over royal shield which divides 'E.R.'.

E6HS-035 VG £270 F £500 VF £1,000

Durham House Mint

Obverse Legend As previous.

Reverse Legend As obverse legend.

Obverse Crowned bust of king; mintmark bow.

Reverse As previous.

Varieties in the legends exist in this extremely rare issue as it sometimes muled with E6HS-030.

E6HS-040 ex. rare

Third Period 1550–1553

Collecting Hints

This most attractive issue is rare and difficult to obtain. When available, it is usually found in Fine or VF condition.

Obverse Legend EDWARD VI DG AGL FRA Z HIB REX — Edward VI by the grace of God King of England France and Ireland

Reverse Legend IHS AUTEM TRANSIE PER MEDI ILLORU IBAT — But Jesus passing through their midst went His way

Obverse Half-length figure of the king holding orb and sword; mintmark 'Y', tun.

Reverse Crown over royal shield which divides 'E.R'.

E6HS-045 VG £300 F £600 VF £1,200

No half-sovereigns were produced during the reigns of Mary, and Philip and Mary.

Elizabeth I 1558–1603

During most of Elizabeth I's reign, hammered gold halfpounds with a value of ten shillings were produced. All issues show the bust of the queen on the obverse and a crown over the royal arms on the reverse while a mintmark can be found on the obverse and reverse at the beginning of the legends. During most of Elizabeth I's reign gold angels with the same value as halfpounds were also produced; these issues can be found under the angels chapter. Gold halfpounds were also produced during the milled issue but in very small quantities.

Hammered Coinage Halfpound

First — Third Issues 1559–1578

The halfpounds for the first three issues hardly varied in style at all and were all struck at the Tower mint.

Obverse Legend ELIZABETH DG ANG FR ET (or Z) HI REGINA — Elizabeth by the grace of God Queen of England France and Ireland

Reverse Legend SCUTUM FIDEI PROTEGET EAM — The shield of faith shall protect her

Obverse Youthful bust of queen crowned; wire-lined inner circles; mintmark lis.

Reverse Crown over royal shield, 'E R.' (ELIZABETH REGINA) divided by crown.

ELHS-005 VG £250 F £500 VF £1,000

As previous, but beaded inner circles and mintmark cross crosslet, rose, portcullis, lion, coronet, castle on the obverse.

ELHS-010 VG £200 F £400 VF £800

No halfpounds were struck for the fourth issue.

Fifth Issue 1583–1600

Obverse Legend ELIZAB(ETH) DG ANG FR ET HI REGINA — Elizabeth by the grace of God Queen of England France and Ireland

Reverse Legend As previous.

Obverse Older bust of queen with a more elaborate dress and a profusion of hair; mintmark tun, woolpack, key, anchor, 'O'.

Reverse As previous.

ELHS-015 VG £300 F £600 VF £1,200

Sixth Issue 1601–1602

As previous, but mintmark '1' or '2'.

ELHS-020 VG £350 F £800 VF £1,600

Milled Coinage Halfpound

This issue is easily differentiated from the hammered ones by style and the fact it has no inner circles. Minor varieties in the style and size of bust exist.

Obverse Legend ELIZABETH DG ANG FRA ET HIB REGINA — Elizabeth by the grace of God Queen of England France and Ireland

Reverse Legend SCUTUM FIDEI PROTEGET EAM — The shield of faith shall protect her

Obverse Crowned bust of queen; mintmark star or lis.

Reverse Crown over royal shield which divides 'E.R'.

ELHS-025 VG £450 F £1,000 VF £2,000

James I 1603–1625

The erratic supply and fluctuating price of gold during the reign of James I was largely responsible for the lack of a comprehensive monetary policy regarding the denominations of gold coins. Half-sovereigns were produced during the first coinage but in very small numbers. Then, during the second coinage, double crowns were produced with a value of ten shillings until 1612 and eleven shillings after that. To avoid the ensuing confusion, the half-laurel was introduced during the third coinage; so called because the king was wearing a laurel wreath on his head instead of a crown. It bore its value of ten shillings behind the bust. Nevertheless, angels, which are listed in a separate chapter, were also produced at this time and usually had a value of ten shillings.

First Coinage Half Sovereign 1603–1604

Collecting Hints

This issue, easily identified by its unique legends, is extremely rare in any grade and collectors may encounter great difficulty in obtaining a specimen.

Obverse Legend IACOBUS D G. ANGL SCO FRAN ET HIBER REX — James by the grace of God King of England Scotland France and Ireland

Reverse Legend EXURGAT DEUS DISSIPENTUR INIMICI — Let God arise and His enemies be scattered

Obverse Crowned bust of king; mintmark thistle.

Reverse Crown above royal shield dividing 'I R' (IACOBUS REX).

J1HS-005 VG — F £1,800 VF £4,000

Second Coinage Double Crown 1604–1619

Collecting Hints

These issues, while scarce, are obtainable. There are minor varieties in the bust which we have listed. Coins, usually found unclipped and undamaged, are mostly available in Fine condition and although VF examples exist, they are rare.

Obverse Legend IACOBUS DG. MAG BRIT FRAN ET HIB REX — James by the grace of God King of Great Britain France and Ireland

Reverse Legend HENRICUS ROSAS. REGNA IACOBUS — Henry united the roses James the kingdoms

Obverse Third bust of king with protruding, square-cut beard; mintmark lis, rose.

Reverse Crown over royal shield dividing 'I R'.

J1DC-010 VG £130 F £250 VF £450

As previous, but fourth bust with the king's hair brushed forward and plainer armour; mintmark rose, escallop, grapes, coronet, key, bell.

J1DC-015 VG £130 F £250 VF £450

As previous, but fifth bust with longer hair brushed back; several very minor varieties exist. Mintmark mullet, tower, trefoil, cinquefoil, tun, book, crescent, plain cross, saltire, key.

J1DC-020 VG £120 F £240 VF £430

Third Coinage Half Laurel 1619–1625

Collecting Hints

While scarce, this issue is obtainable especially in the lower grades. However, coins are sometimes found damaged and those in better than VF condition are extremely rare.

Obverse Legend IACOBUS DG. MAG BRI FRA ET HIB REX — James by the grace of God King of Great Britain France and Ireland

Reverse Legend HENRIC ROSAS REGNA IACOBUS — Henry united the roses, James the kingdoms

Obverse Large bust of king wearing a laurel on his head; value (X) behind head; mintmark spur rowel.

Reverse Cross over royal shield with crown above.

J1HL-025 VG £150 F £275 VF £550

As previous, but smaller, fourth bust; mintmark spur rowel, rose, thistle, lis, trefoil.

J1HL-030 VG £150 F £275 VF £550

Second Bust

Legends As previous.

Obverse Smaller bust of king wearing a ruff; mintmark cross calvary, blackamoor's head, castle, anchor, heart, plume.

Reverse As previous.

C1DC-010 VG £140 F £250 VF £500

Charles I 1625–1649

Both gold and silver coins with a value of ten shillings were issued under Charles I. The first issues struck at the Tower mint were gold and known as double crowns. Easily recognisable by the X for ten shillings found behind the king's bust, they were struck almost throughout Charles I's reign. The mintmarks and style of the bust and reverse shield differentiate the various issues. During 1631–1632 Nicholas Briot introduced a superb milled ten-shillings. The quality and design of this issue is excellent and clearly differentiates it from other issues. During the Civil War the provincial mints of Oxford and Bristol produced gold half unites. Oxford and Shrewsbury produced a superb silver halfpound with a value of ten shillings.

Tower Mint Double Crown

Collecting Hints

Most issues, while scarce, are obtainable. The ones struck under the king tend to be more common than those struck under Parliament. Very large numbers of minor varieties exist and collectors should check all issues when identifying a coin. Most specimens are found in Fine condition, those in VF or better being very rare. These issues saw much circulation and are sometimes found damaged or clipped.

Third Bust

Legends As previous.

Obverse Shorter bust of king wearing heavier armour; mintmark plume or rose.

Reverse Oval shield with crown above and dividing 'C.R.'.

C1DC-015 VG £140 F £250 VF £500

Fourth Bust

Legends As previous.

Obverse A slightly wider bust of king with a more pointed beard; several varieties of bust exist. Mintmark harp, portcullis, tun, bell, crown, anchor.

Reverse As previous, but a small crown over the 'C' and 'R'.

C1DC-020 VG £130 F £240 VF £500

Tower Mint under King 1625–1643

First Bust

Obverse Legend CAROLUS DG MAG BRIT FRA ET HIB REX (many minor varieties exist) — Charles by the grace of God King of Great Britain France and Ireland

Reverse Legend CULTORES SUI DEUS PROTEGIT — God protects His worshippers

Obverse Bust of king wearing large ruff with value behind his head; mintmark lis, cross calvary.

Reverse Crown above square-topped shield.

C1DC-005 VG £140 F £250 VF £500

Fifth Bust Aberystwyth Style

As previous, but large bust of good style; mintmark anchor, triangle.

C1DC-025 VG £150 F £300 VF £600

Sixth Bust Briot Style

As previous, but full, wide bust of king; mintmark triangle, star, triangle in circle.

C1DC-030 VG £150 F £300 VF £600

This issue is possibly a trial or pattern.

Legends As previous.

Obverse As previous; mintmark anchor.

Reverse Rectangular shield with crown above, 'C.R' at sides.

C1DC-035 ex. rare

Tower Mint under Parliament 1643–1648

Legends As previous.

Obverse As C1DC-020, but mintmark eye.

Reverse As C1DC-020.

C1DC-040 ex. rare

Legends As previous.

Obverse As C1DC-025, but mintmark sun or sceptre.

Reverse Oval shield.

C1DC-045 VG £250 F £500 VF £1,000

Legends As previous.

Obverse As C1DC-030, but mintmark '(P)'.

Reverse As C1DC-030.

C1DC-050 VG £250 F £500 VF £1,000

Seventh Bust

As previous, but cruder bust of king with large nose; mintmark sun.

C1DC-055 VG £300 F £600 VF £1300

As mentioned earlier, many varieties of most busts exist and it is important when identifying an issue to make sure the mintmark corresponds.

Briot's Milled Coinage 1631–1632

Collecting Hints

This superb issue is rare. When available, it is usually found undamaged in Fine to EF condition.

Obverse Legend CAROLUS DG MAG BRITAN FRAN ET HIB REX — Charles by the grace of God King of Great Britain France and Ireland

Reverse Legend CULTORES SUI DEUS PROTEGIT — God protects His worshippers

Obverse Detailed bust of king, value behind; mintmark 'B' and flower.

Reverse Crown over square-topped shield, 'C.' and 'R' with small crowns above on either side of the shield; mintmark 'B' in legend.

C1DC-060 VG — F £650 VF £1,600 EF £2,800

Provincial Mints

Oxford Mint

Oxford produced a gold half-unite, valued at ten shillings, and a silver halfpound. The gold half-unite bears the king's bust on the obverse and the Declaration in three lines on the reverse. The value of the coin can easily be distinguished by an X for ten shillings behind the king's bust. The only other gold half-unites were produced at the Tower mint and omit the Declaration on the reverse. The silver halfpound produced at Oxford is a superb, large coin. It shows the king on horseback on the obverse and, on the reverse, the Declaration in two lines with the date below it and the denomination X and three plumes above. This issue is very similar to the ones from Shrewsbury and collectors should refer to both mints for identification.

Gold Half Unite

Collecting Hints

This issue is very rare and usually found in Fine condition, sometimes damaged; it is very crude in style and production.

Obverse Legend CAROLUS DG MAG BR FR ET HI REX — Charles by the grace of God Great Britain France and Ireland King

Reverse Legend EXURGAT DEUS DISSIPERTUR INIMICI — Let God arise and His enemies be scattered

Reverse Inner Legend RELIG PROT LEG ANG LIBER PAR — The religion of the Protestants the laws of England the liberty of Parliament

Obverse Bust of king with value behind; no mintmark.

Reverse Declaration in three straight lines, 1642.

C1HU-065 VG — F £700 VF £1400

Obverse As previous.
Reverse Declaration in a scroll 1642 or 1643.

C1HU-070 VG £200 F £450 VF £800

Obverse New-style bust to bottom of coin; legend begins at 7 o'clock.
Reverse As previous, but dated 1643 only.

C1HU-075 VG £350 F £600 VF £1,350

As previous, but coin is dated 1644 with OX below date.

C1HU-080 ex. rare

Reverse Shrewsbury reverse die with three plumes without bands.

C1HP-085 VG £250 F £550 VF £1,000

As previous, but reverse has bands in the plumes; Oxford die.

C1HP-090 VG £200 F £450 VF £800

Silver Halfpound

The Oxford halfpounds are very similar to the Shrewsbury issues but have minor differences, especially on the obverse. Collectors should pay particular attention to any mintmark and plume behind the king's head, as well as to whether the horse is on a groundline. All Oxford horses have a groundline while some Shrewsbury issues do not. Oxford issues are dated 1642 and 1643, Shrewsbury ones 1642 only. Oxford plumes have a 'tie' which is absent in Shrewsbury plumes. Collectors should refer to every issue from Oxford and Shrewsbury when identifying a coin and bear in mind that minor varieties exist in the legends.

Shrewsbury Mint

These issues are very similar to the Oxford ones, where details on identification are given.

Collecting Hints

While rare, these issues are available and usually found in Fine or VF condition, often with striking flaws or cracks in the flan.

Collecting Hints

While rare, these issues are obtainable and usually found in Fine or VF condition, often with flaws or cracks in the flan due to striking.

Obverse Legend CAROLUS DG MAG BRIT FRAN ET HIB REX — Charles by the grace of God King of Great Britain France and Ireland

Reverse Legend EXURGAT DEUS DISSIPENTUR INIMICI — Let God arise and His enemies be scattered

Reverse Inner Legend RELIG PROT LEG ANG LIBER PAR — The religion of the Protestants the laws of England the liberty of Parliament

Obverse King on horseback with plume behind; mintmark plume.

Obverse Legend CAROLUS D.G. MAG BRI FRA ET HIB REX — Charles by the grace of God King of Great Britain France and Ireland

Reverse Legend EXURGAT DEUS DISSIPENTUR INIMICI — Let God arise and His enemies be scattered

Reverse Inner Legend RELIG PROT LEG ANGL LIBER PARL — The religion of the Protestants the laws of England the liberty of Parliament

Obverse King on horseback with plume behind, no groundline; mintmark nine pellets.

Reverse Three plumes without bands and value X (ten shillings) above Declaration, 1642 below.

Obverse King on horseback with groundline, plume behind.
Reverse As C1HP-095.

C1HP-095 VG £200 F £400 VF £1,000

C1HP-105 VG £200 F £400 VF £1,000

As previous, but only two plumes on reverse above Declaration.

As previous, but cannon and arms below horse; mintmark four pellets.

C1HP-100 VG £220 F £450 VF £1,100

C1HP-110 VG £200 F £400 VF £1,000

As previous, but just arms and no canon or plume on obverse.

C1HP-115 VG £200 F £400 VF £1,000

Colchester Siege Issue 1648

Made of gold with a value of ten shillings, there is doubt as to whether this is a contemporary siege issue or a later, fantasy one. Although no documentary evidence exists to support its authenticity, we have decided to list it here.

Collecting Hints

This issue is of the highest rarity.

Obverse Gateway to Colchester, 'C' and 'R' on either side, 'OBS COL 16SX48' in two lines; 'SX' stands for ten shillings.

Reverse Plain.

C1HS-120 ex. rare

Commonwealth 1649–1660

The Commonwealth double crown, struck in gold, is very similar to the other gold issues. The denomination is easily identifiable by an X for ten shillings above the two shields on the reverse. All issues are dated and have the mintmark sun or anchor on the obverse. Like all Commonwealth issues, the double crown is very plain in style and design, reflecting contemporary Puritan values.

Collecting Hints

The first issue is rare but obtainable, found in all grades from VG to EF. The issue with the mintmark anchor is extremely rare in all grades.

Obverse Legend THE COMMONWEALTH OF ENGLAND

Reverse Legend GOD WITH US

Obverse St George's cross in shield within wreath; mintmark sun.

Reverse Shields of St George and Ireland; value X above, dated 1649–1657.

COMDC-005 VG £200 F £450 VF £800

As previous, but mintmark anchor dated 1660.

COMDC-010 VG £600 F £1,200 VF £2,500

No double crowns were struck by Cromwell. The so-called half-broads of ten shillings are not contemporary.

Charles II 1660–1685

Hammered Coinage 1660–1662

This rare gold issue bears a bust of the king on the obverse and a crown above the royal shield on the reverse. Should the bust be very different in style, it is probably an issue of Charles I.

Collecting Hints

Both issues are very rare and difficult to obtain. When available, they are usually in Fine or VF condition.

First Issue

Obverse Legend CAROLUS II DG MAG BRIT FRAN ET HIB REX — Charles II by the grace of God King of Great Britain France and Ireland

Reverse Legend FLORENT CONCORDIA REGNA — Through concord kingdoms flourish

Obverse Bust of Charles II; mintmark crown.

Reverse Crown over royal shield which divides 'C.R'.

C2DCH-005 VG £350 F £700 VF £1,400

Second Issue

As previous, but mark of value X behind king's bust.

C2DCH-010 VG £300 F £600 VF £1,200

Noble

During the reign of Edward III gold coins were produced in some quantity for the first time. The gold twenty-pence had been introduced in Henry III's reign and the gold leopard or florin at the beginning of Edward III's, but these issues are extremely rare and saw no circulation. However, this changed with the introduction of the gold noble. These issues, which were produced in some variety and quantity, show the king in a ship on the obverse and a cruciform design on the reverse. The value of the noble was six shillings and eightpence, i.e. eighty pence. Smaller gold denominations, the half-noble and quarter-noble, complemented the monetary reform.

Edward III 1327–1377

Large quantities of gold nobles were produced with many varieties, all of which are minor. On Edward III's issues, the word EDWARD or EDWAR is found on the obverse legend and usually divided by the front of the ship. Although Edward IV also issued nobles, he used the mintmarks rose or lis, found on the obverse and/or reverse legends; and, should the coin have a rose on the king's ship, it is an Edward IV ryal. Many varieties of nobles exist, the main differences being the obverse legends which reflect the British monarch's claim to the sovereignty of all or part of France. During the second, third and fourth coinages Edward laid claim to the throne of France, so FRANC can be found in the obverse legend. Following the 1360 treaty (for details see relevant section of the Penny chapter) FRANC was replaced by ACQ on the coins. After the treaty broke down in 1369, FRANC was reintroduced on the obverse legend of the nobles. Two mints were active producing nobles under Edward III, London, and Calais in France. Until 1361, all issues were struck in London but the town of Calais also produced nobles thereafter. Calais was chosen as a mint for two reasons: the fact that an English king struck English coins in France contained a very powerful political statement, also, with the growth of European commerce, it was useful for English merchants trading on the continent to have a supply of good quality coins. Issues from Calais can usually be identified by a C in the middle of the obverse cross and sometimes a flag on the stern of the ship. There are exceptions which are all listed in the various issues.

Collecting Hints

Most issues, while scarce, are obtainable and usually found unclipped in Fine to VF condition. Coins sometimes have solder marks where they have been made into jewellery (mounted), in which case they are worth considerably less than unmounted examples.

Second Coinage 1344–1346

This issue weighs 138.5 grains (9.0 grams).
Obverse Legend EDWAR DGRA REX ANGL Z FRANC DNS HYB — Edward by the grace of God King of England and France Lord of Ireland
Reverse Legend IHC AUTEM TRANSIENS PER MEDIUM ILLORUM IBAT — But Jesus passing through their midst went His way
Obverse King holding sword and shield in ship, large lettering with Lombardic 'N'.

Reverse 'L' in centre of cross.

E3NB-005 ex. rare

Third Coinage 1346–1351

This issue weighs 128.5 grains (8.3 grams).
As previous, but a large 'E' in centre of the reverse cross.

E3NB-010 VG — F £1,200 VF £2,400

Fourth Coinage 1351–1377

All issues weigh 120 grains (7.8 grams).

Pre-Treaty Period 1351–1361

This issue was struck while Edward was laying claim to the French throne and FRANC can be found in the obverse legend. Many minor varieties exist and have been listed, however, no true gold nobles are known for series A as they are muled with series B.

Series B/A 1351

Obverse Legend EDWARD DEI GRA REX ANGL Z FRANC D HYB(E) — Edward by the grace of God King of England and France Lord of the Irish
Reverse Legend IHE AUTEM TRANSIENS PER MEDIUM ILLORUM IBAT — But Jesus passing through their midst went His way
Obverse King holding sword and shield on ship, open 'C' and 'E', Roman 'M' and 'N' in legend; mintmark cross I.
Reverse Lombardic 'M' and 'N' in legends, 'E' in centre of reverse cross.

E3NB-015 VG £225 F £450 VF £850

Series C 1351–1352

Similar to previous, but closed 'C' and 'E', Lombardic 'M', Roman 'N' and wedge-tailed 'R'; mintmark cross 1.

E3NB-020 VG £220 F £425 VF £800

Series D 1352–1353

As above, but mintmark cross 1 or broken cross 2 on reverse only.

E3NB-025 VG £250 F £550 VF £1,000

Series E 1354–1355

Mintmark cross 2 or cross 3 with broken letters in the legend, the 'V' often has a nick in the right limb.

E3NB-030 VG £220 F £425 VF £800

Series F 1356

Mintmark crown only; the 'C's and 'E's are often broken at the top.

E3NB-035 VG £250 F £500 VF £950

Series G 1356–1361

Mintmark cross 3 or cross 4; the 'E's in the legend are often broken and with an extra long middle bar.

E3NB-040 VG £210 F £400 VF £800

Many of the dies for these issues are muled. The following mules are very rare: B/A, C/D, E/F, G/F, F/G — the first letter refers to the obverse die, the second to the reverse.

Transitional Period 1361

This issue can be easily recognised by the obverse legend reading ACQ (many varieties exist) and omitting FRANC; mintmark cross potent.

Obverse Legend EDWARD DEI GRA REX ANGL DNS HIB Z ACQ (many varieties exist) — Edward by the grace of God King of England Lord of Ireland and Aquitaine

Reverse Legend IHC AUTE TRANSIES P MEDIUM ILLORR IBAT (many varieties exist and often entire words are missing) — But Jesus passing through their midst went His way

Obverse King with sword and shield in ship; mintmark cross potent, abnormal size 'I', 'H', 'P', 'F' or 'N' sometimes in legends.

Reverse 'E' in centre of cross, annulet or pellet at corner of central cross.

E3NB-045 VG £250 F £500 VF £1,000

Treaty Period 1361–1369

This issue is very similar to the previous one, with the mintmark cross potent and virtually identical obverse and reverse legends. However, in all cases a saltire or annulet can be found at the start of the obverse legend, just before EDWARD. During this period coins were also struck at Calais.

London Mint

Legends As previous.
Obverse As previous, but an annulet or saltire before EDWARD.

Reverse As previous, but the 'A' in IBAT is unbarred.

E3NB-050 VG £180 F £375 VF £700

Calais Mint

Legends As previous.

Obverse As previous, with saltire, quatrefoil or nothing before EDWARD, all 'A's in the legend are unbarred, flag at stern of ship.

Reverse 'C' in centre of cross.

E3NB-055 VG £200 F £420 VF £850

As previous, but no flag at stern of ship.

E3NB-060 VG £200 F £420 VF £850

Post-Treaty Period 1369–1377

During this period nobles were struck in London and Calais. Once again the obverse die has been changed and includes FRANC and also AQT (varieties). This legend is unique to the period and while many varieties exist, the words for France and Aquitaine always appear.

London Mint

Obverse Legend EDWARD DEI G REX ANG Z FRA DNS HYB Z AQT — Edward by the grace of God King of England and France Lord of Ireland and Aquitaine

Reverse Legend As previous.

E3NB-065 VG £200 F £400 VF £800

As previous, but a crescent on the forecastle of the king's ship.

E3NB-070 VG £200 F £400 VF £800

As ED3NB-065 with new-style thin, tall lettering, 'E' with a pellet in centre of reverse.

E3NB-075 VG £190 F £380 VF £800

As previous, but an 'E' with a saltire in the centre on the reverse.

E3NB-080 VG £200 F £425 VF £850

Calais Mint

Legends As previous.

Obverse Flag at stern of ship.

Reverse 'E' in centre of reverse.

E3NB-085 VG £200 F £400 VF £800

As previous, but an 'E' with pellet in centre of reverse.

E3NB-090 VG £200 F £400 VF £800

No flag on ship but a 'C' in centre of reverse.

E3NB-095 VG £225 F £500 VF £950

Richard II 1377–1399

During the reign of Richard II nobles were struck at the London and Calais mints. As with the previous reign, the obverse shows the king holding a sword and shield in a ship and the reverse an elaborate cross with decoration around it. The issues are fairly easy to identify as RICARD appears at the beginning of the obverse legend, broken by the bow of the ship. No other Richard issued gold coins so it can only be an issue of Richard II. The issues from the mint of Calais, which was under English rule at the time, are identified by the fact that the king's ship has a flag on it. The style of the letters in the legends of Richard II varies greatly and is important when identifying the issues.

Collecting Hints

All Richard II nobles are very rare and difficult to obtain. When available they are usually found in Fine to VF condition, unclipped and undamaged. These coins tend to have been found in hoards, hence the reasonable condition of the specimens.

London Mint

The first issue of Richard II's coinage used a reverse and/or an obverse die from an Edward III issue. On the obverse die Edward's name was altered to RICARD and an 'R' placed over the 'E' in the centre of the reverse. Various dies were used and the legends are the same as the issues of Edward III.

R2NB-005 VG £250 F £750 VF £1,500

Obverse Legend RICARD DI G REX ANGL Z FR DNS HIBS Z AQT (minor varieties in abbreviation exist) — Richard by the grace of God King of England and France Lord of Ireland and Aquitaine

Reverse Legend IHC AUTEM TRANSIENS PER MEDIUM ILLORR IBAT (many varieties exist) — But Jesus passing through their midst went His way

Obverse King in the ship with a lis over the sail, lettering in the style of Edward III.

Reverse Cross with 'R' in centre, decoration around cross.

R2NB-010 VG £300 F £600 VF £1,350

Obverse Legend As previous, but sometimes omits FRA.

Reverse Legend As previous.

Obverse As previous, but no lis, annulet above the sail, straight-sided lettering in the legends.

Reverse As previous.

R2NB-015 VG £250 F £500 VF £1,100

Obverse Legend RICARD DI GR REX ANGL DNS HIBS Z AQT — Richard by the grace of God King of England Lord of Ireland and Aquitaine (NB: French title omitted)

Reverse Legend As previous.

Obverse Fishtail lettering in legends, sometimes with a lis or lion on the ship's rudder and/or a trefoil by the king's shield.

Reverse As previous.

R2NB-020 VG £350 F £750 VF £1,500

Legends & Reverse As previous.

Obverse Dumpy style lettering with sometimes an escallop or crescent on the ship's rudder and/or a trefoil over the sail.

R2NB-025 VG £350 F £750 VF £1,500

Calais Mint

These issues can easily be identified by the flag on the stern.

Obverse Legend As R2NB-005 (altered dies with France in the legend).

Reverse Legend As previous.

Obverse The king in a ship with a flag at stern.

Reverse As previous.

R2NB-030 VG £350 F £750 VF £1,500

As R2NB-015 with straight-sided lettering and a quatrefoil over the sail.

R2NB-035 VG £350 F £750 VF £1,500

As R2NB-020, but with fishtailed lettering.

R2NB-040 VG £300 F £700 VF £1,450

As previous, but a lion on the ship's rudder.

R2NB-045 VG £380 F £900 VF £1,850

As R2NB-025 with small, dumpy-style lettering, sometimes a trefoil over sail or a crescent on the rudder.

R2NB-050 VG £300 F £700 VF £1,450

Henry IV 1399–1413

The gold nobles of Henry IV's reign can be divided into the heavy coinage (120 grains, 7.8 grams) and the light coinage (108 grains, 7.0 grams). The issue can be identified by several points; firstly HENRIC appears at the beginning of the obverse legend and is broken by the bow of the ship. But Henry IV was not the only Henry to produce nobles, Henry V and Henry VI (1st reign), also struck them. At a quick glance all issues look similar, but variations actually differentiate them from each other. It is important that collectors pay particular attention to the mintmark, which can sometimes be found clearly on the obverse and always on the reverse at the beginning of the legend. The only mintmark of Henry IV's issues was cross pattée. Minor marks and varieties are also found on all issues. If uncertain, collectors should check all issues from all reigns when identifying a noble. During the heavy coinage, London and Calais produced nobles. The Calais mint, like previous reigns, is identified by a flag at the stern of the king's ship.

Heavy Coinage 1399–1412

London Mint

Obverse Legend HENRIC DI GRA REX ANGL Z FRANC DNS HIB Z AQT (many varieties exist) — Henry by the grace of God King of England and France Lord of the Irish and Aquitaine

Reverse Legend IHC AUTEM TRANSIENS PER MEDIUM ILLORR IBAT — But Jesus passing through their midst went His way

Obverse The king standing in a ship, four lis on upper part of his shield, crescent on ship's rudder; mintmark cross pattée.

Reverse H in cross, sometimes over 'R', obviously a Richard II reverse die.

H4NB-005 VG — F — VF £8,000

As previous, but three lis on shield, a crescent, pellet or lis on ship's rudder.

H4NB-010 VG — F — VF £8,000

Calais Mint

As H4NB-005 but a flag at the stern of the ship, a crown on or to the left of the ship's rudder.

H4NB-015 ex. rare

As H4NB-010, but with a flag at the stern of the ship, a crown or saltire on the rudder.

H4NB-020 VG — F — VF £9,000

Light Coinage 1412–1413

This issue was only struck at the London mint.
Legends As previous.

Obverse New-style shield with three lis, trefoil or trefoil and annulet on side of ship; mintmark cross pattée.

Reverse Trefoil on quarter.

H4NB-025 VG — F £1,000 VF £2,000

Henry V 1413–1422

Henry V's issues closely resemble those of Henry IV and Henry VI. Collectors should refer to the general introduction to Henry IV to help identify the various issues and reigns. All of Henry V's issues were struck in London and the mintmarks used, which are unique to these issues, are cross pattée or pierced cross, both with central pellet. In all except class G, a quatrefoil can be found above the ship's sail and in one quarter of the reverse. These minor varieties are unique to these issues.

Collecting Hints

Most issues, while rare, are obtainable and are usually found undamaged in the higher grades. Nobles are rarely clipped, but sometimes the lettering is difficult to read due to the small flans.

Class A

Obverse Legend HENRIC DI GRA REX ANGL Z FRANC DNS HYB (often abbreviated) — Henry by the grace of God King of England and France Lord of the Irish (NB: the omission of 'and Aquitaine' is another small difference between Henry IV and Henry V issues)

Reverse Legend IHC AUTEM TRAN(S)IENS PER MEDIUM ILLORR IBAT (varieties exist) — But Jesus passing through their midst went His way

Obverse King on a ship with a quatrefoil over the ship's sail, short broad lettering.

Reverse Cross with 'H' in centre, quatrefoil in second quarter of cross.

H5NB-005 ex. rare

Class B

As previous, but ordinary lettering with barred 'H's, sometimes an annulet on the ship's rudder.

H5NB-010 VG £300 F £575 VF £1,100

Class C

New-style lettering, a mullet by the king's sword, sometimes an annulet on the ship's rudder or a broken annulet on the ship's side.

H5NB-015 VG £300 F £600 VF £1,100

Class D

Mullet and annulet by king's sword, a trefoil by the shield and a broken annulet on the ship's side.

H5NB-020 VG £250 F £450 VF £900

Class E

Pellet at king's sword point, annulet or trefoil on ship's side, trefoil by shield, unbroken annulet and sometimes a mullet by the king's sword-arm.

H5NB-025 VG £250 F £475 VF £950

Class F

Trefoil by king's shield, annulet or trefoil on ship's side, mullet and sometimes annulet by sword arm.

H5NB-030 VG £250 F £475 VF £950

Class G

No marks in field and no quatrefoil on obverse or reverse, annulet stops and mullet after HENRIC in obverse legend.

H5NB-035 VG £350 F £750 VF £1,400

Henry VI First Reign 1422–1461

Nobles were struck throughout the reign of Henry VI, but the decline in the supply of gold was reflected in the quantity of coins struck. Thus, while fairly large numbers were produced in the first part of the reign, very few were issued towards the end of the period and then only at the London mint. As with all of Henry VI coins, the nobles can be divided into issues differentiated by various marks, usually in the legends. These marks were a form of quality control, so that the dies could be linked to various issues. As was stated above, Henry VI issues are fairly similar to those of Henry IV and Henry V and collectors might have to refer to all three reigns when identifying a coin and pay particular attention to the different mintmarks and any unusual marks found on the coin or in the legend. No nobles were struck during Henry VI's second reign.

As with previous issues, the mintmark can be found on the reverse of the coin at the beginning of the legend. HENRIC can always be found on the obverse and is usually broken by the bow of the king's ship. Three mints, in London, Calais and York, were active during the first part of Henry VI's reign. The issues from Calais are easy to identify as they have a flag at the stern of the king's ship while those from York have no flag but a lis over the stern. The London issue have neither a flag nor a lis.

As England's European trade steadily increased from Edward I's reign onwards, large quantities of English coins, which were known for their quality, good weight and metal fineness, ended up in Europe despite various forms of currency control. Gold nobles in particular were so popular that they were imitated and produced in some quantity in the Low Countries. The style of these imitations however is different from the English issue.

Collecting Hints

All early issues of Henry VI, while scarce, are obtainable. All the later issues are extremely rare and in one case unique. Most coins, because they have been found in hoards, are in good condition with Fine to VF being the average grades. Coins are rarely found damaged and usually have clear legends and unclipped flans.

Annulet Issue 1422–1427

London Mint

Obverse Legend HENRIC DI GRA REX ANGL Z FRANC DNS HYB — Henry by the grace of God King of England and France Lord of the Irish

Reverse Legend IHC AUTEM TRANSIENS PER MEDIUM ILLORR IBAT — But Jesus passing through their midst went His way

Obverse King on ship holding sword and shield, annulet by his arm.

Reverse Annulets in legend and one annulet in the spandrel; mintmark lis.

H6NB-005 VG £200 F £400 VF £650

As previous, but the obverse die is from a Henry V issue and so bears no annulet.

H6NB-010 VG — F £800 VF £1,500

Calais Mint

As H6NB-005 but a flag at the stern of the king's ship, 'H' in the centre of the reverse.

H6NB-015 VG £250 F £450 VF £750

As previous, but 'C' in the centre of the reverse.

H6NB-020 VG £250 F £475 VF £800

York Mint

As H6NB-005, but a lis over the stern of the ship.

H6NB-025 VG £325 F £600 VF £1,200

Rosette Mascle Issue 1427–1430

London Mint

Legends As previous.

Obverse A lis by the sword arm, rosettes or rosettes and mascles in the legend.

Reverse Lis in second quarter, mintmark lis, rosettes or rosettes and mascles in the legend.

H6NB-030 VG £350 F £750 VF £1,500

Calais Mint

Obverse As previous, but a flag on the stern of the ship.
Reverse Mintmark lis.

H6NB-035 VG £350 F £775 VF £1,550

Pinecone Mascle Issue 1430–1434

Legends As previous.
Obverse Pinecone and mascle in legends.
Reverse A lis in one quarter, pinecones and mascles in the legend; mintmark lis.

H6NB-040 VG £325 F £700 VF £1,400

Leaf Mascle Issue 1434–1435

Legends As previous.
Obverse A leaf in the sea, saltires and a mascle in the legend.
Reverse Saltires with one leaf and one mascle in the legend; mintmark lis.

H6NB-045 VG — F £2,000 VF ex. rare

Leaf Trefoil Issue 1435–1438

Legends As previous.
Obverse & Reverse Leaves and trefoils in legends.

H6NB-050 VG — F £2,000 VF £4,000

Trefoil Issue 1438–1443

Legends As previous.
Obverse Trefoil to left of shield, saltires in legend.
Reverse Saltires, trefoils and a pellet in legend; mintmark lis.

H6NB-055 VG — F £2,000 VF ex. rare

Leaf Pellet Issue 1445–1454

Legends As previous.
Obverse An annulet, lis and leaf below the king's shield.
Reverse A pellet before the 'H' in centre reverse, annulets and saltires in legend.

H6NB-060 VG — F £2,000 VF ex. rare

Cross Pellet Issue 1454–1460

Legends As previous.
Obverse & Reverse Details unknown.

H6NB-065 unique

Edward IV First Reign 1461–1470

The gold noble, which had hardly changed in style, value or quality since the reign of Edward III, was produced for the last time during Edward IV's reign. The rise in the price of gold from the 1430s onwards meant that gold coins were worth more in Europe than in England and had resulted in a shortage in England, as gold coins were taken abroad for profit. The situation became particularly problematic during Edward IV's reign and only a small quantity of nobles was struck during the heavy coinage. Finally in 1464, to stop gold coins drifting to the Continent, the value of all gold nobles in circulation was raised from six shillings and eight pence to eight shillings and four pence and a new coin, the rose noble or ryal was introduced. With a value of ten shillings and weighing 120 grains (7.8 grams), the ryal is easily recognisable by the rose on the king's ship featured on the obverse and the different central design on the reverse. However, the new denomination proved unpopular and was discontinued after 1470. By contrast the angel, which was introduced in 1464 with a value of six shillings and eight pence as the original noble had been, soon became an important and popular denomination. Edward IV's heavy coinage nobles are fairly similar to those of Edward III except for the mintmarks which are unique to each issue; Edward III used various crosses, while Edward IV used mintmark rose or lis, sometimes muled.

Heavy Coinage 1461–1464

London was the only mint that produced gold coins during the heavy coinage.

> ## Collecting Hints
>
> All three issues are extremely rare; when available, examples are usually found in Fine to VF condition.

Obverse Legend EDWARD DI GRA REX ANGL Z FRANC DNS HYB — Edward by the grace of God King of England and France Lord of Ireland (legend starts at 11 o'clock)
Reverse Legend IHC AUTEM TRANSIENS PER MEDIUM ILLOR IBAT — But Jesus passing through their midst went His way
Obverse King with sword and shield in ship, a lis below the shield.
Reverse Central cross; mintmark lis.

E4NB-005 VG — F £4,000 VF £7,500

As previous, but quatrefoil below the sword arm; mintmark rose on the obverse, lis on the reverse.

E4NB-010 ex. rare

As previous, but rose in two spandrels on reverse; mintmark rose obverse and reverse.

E4NB-015 ex. rare

Light Coinage 1464–1470
Rose Noble or Ryal

During this period, large quantities of gold coins needed to be produced and the provincial mints of Bristol, Coventry, Norwich and York as well as, of course, London took an active part. The various mints can easily be identified by their initials, found in the waves below the king's ship. These are none for London, 'B' for Bristol, 'C' for Coventry, 'N' for Norwich and 'E' for York.

In style as well as value, the rose noble was a popular coin on the Continent and various copies were struck throughout the 16th century, mainly in the Low Countries. They are copies of the London mint only and very crude in style with coarse features.

Collecting Hints

All London issues, while scarce, are obtainable. They are usually found undamaged with full unclipped flans in Fine to VF condition. Coins from the provincial mints, in particular Coventry and Norwich, are much scarcer and more difficult to obtain.

London Mint

Obverse Legend EDWARD D. GRA REX ANG Z FRANC DNS (H)IB — Edward by the grace of God King of England and France Lord of Ireland

Reverse Legend IHC AUT TRANSIENS PER MEDIUM ILLOR IBAT — But Jesus passing through their midst went His way

Obverse King holding sword and shield, large rose on side of ship, banner with E on stern; mintmark rose, sun or crown, sometimes only on reverse.

Reverse Rose over radiate sun in centre, fleurs in spandrels.

E4NB-020 VG £225 F £400 VF £750

As previous, but small trefoils in spandrels on reverse; mintmark crown, sun over crown, long cross fitchée sometimes only on reverse.

E4NB-025 VG £225 F £400 VF £750

Bristol Mint

Legends As previous.

Obverse As E4NB-020, 'B' in waves below ship.

Reverse Large fleurs in spandrels; mintmark sun, crown.

E4NB-030 VG £250 F £450 VF £800

As previous, but small trefoils in spandrels; mintmark crown or sun only on reverse.

E4NB-035 VG £260 F £475 VF £825

Coventry Mint

Legends As previous.

Obverse As E4NB-020, but 'C' in waves below ship.

Reverse Mintmark sun.

E4NB-040 VG £400 F £850 VF £1,600

Norwich Mint

Legends As previous.

Obverse As E4NB-020, but 'N' in waves below ship.

Reverse Mintmark rose? or sun.

E4NB-045 VG £450 F £900 VF £1,800

York Mint

Legends As previous.

Obverse As E4NB-020, but 'E' in waves below ship; no mintmark.

Reverse Large fleurs in spandrels; mintmark sun, sun and lis, lis.

E4NB-050 VG £250 F £450 VF £800

As previous, but small fleurs in spandrels on reverse; mintmark lis or sun.

E4NB-055 VG £250 F £450 VF £800

Angel

During the reign of Edward IV the weights and values of coins had to be changed to bring them more in line with the fluctuating price of gold. The gold noble which had been a popular denomination, especially with merchants, with a value of six shillings and eight pence was replaced by the ryal or rose noble, with a value of ten shillings. Also, the value of all nobles from previous issues was raised to eight shillings and four pence, to prevent the export of coins from England. This, however, left an unwelcome gap in the denomination structure, so the gold angel was introduced with a value of six shillings and eight pence, the same as the earlier nobles. The design shows St Michael spearing a dragon on the obverse and a ship on the reverse. These issues were much more life-like in style when compared to earlier ones. The denomination was retained until the reign of Charles I and even though the value changed, the general design and style did not.

Edward IV First Reign 1461–1470

The gold angel from the first reign of Edward IV is fairly easy to identify. The king's name is found at the beginning of the obverse legend and reads EDWARD and although angels were struck in Edward IV's second reign and under Edward V, each reign used different styles and mintmarks. The mintmark is found at the beginning of the legends, but not always on both sides of the coin.

Collecting Hints

All issues are extremely rare. The few examples we have traced are in VF to EF condition.

Obverse Legend EDWARD D GRA REX . ANGL FRANC DNS HB — Edward by the grace of God King of England France Lord of Ireland

Reverse Legend PER CRUCE TUA SALVA NOS XPC REDEMPTOR (minor varieties exist) — By Thy Cross save us O Christ our Redeemer

Obverse St Michael spearing a dragon.

Reverse Ship with cross and arms at centre, rays of sun at masthead, large rose and sun by mast; mintmark rose.

E4AG-005 ex rare

As previous, but small rose and sun at mast; mintmark crown.

E4AG-010 ex rare

Henry VI Restored Oct. 1470 — April 1471

During this very short period gold angels were struck at the London and Bristol mints which stylistically were very much a continuation from the reign of Edward IV. Henry VII and Henry VIII also produced angels, however, all issues of Henry VI have a lis beside the mast of the ship on the reverse, while the issues of Henry VII and Henry VIII have a rose. If uncertain, collectors should check the coin's mintmark, usually found on the obverse at the beginning of the legend. Moreover, the Bristol issue is easily identified by a 'B' in the waves on the reverse.

Collecting Hints

Considering that these issues were produced for such a short period, it is not surprising that they are both very rare. When available, they are usually found in Fine or VF condition.

London Mint

Obverse Legend HENRIC DI GRA REX ANGL Z FRANC (minor varieties exist) — Henry by the grace of God King of England and France

Reverse Legend PER CRUCE TUA SALVA NOS XPC REDEMPTOR — By Thy Cross save us O Christ our Redeemer

Obverse St Michael killing a dragon; mintmark Restoration cross or none.

Reverse Ship with arms and mast in the shape of a cross, an 'H' and a lis divided by the cross; mintmark cross pattée, lis or Restoration cross.

H6AG-005 VG £300 F £600 VF £1,200

Bristol Mint

Legends As previous.

Obverse As previous, but no mintmark.

Reverse As previous, but 'B' in the waves below the ship; mintmark Restoration cross or none.

H6AG-010 VG £350 F £850 VF £1,600

Edward IV Second Reign 1471–1483

These two issues are very much a continuation from the reign of Henry VI. The style is not as detailed as that of Edward's first reign angel, but this issue is much more common. Mintmarks play an important part in identification and collectors should also refer to the Edward V angel where the issues are discussed. As with the previous reign, the Bristol mint was also active and can easily be identified by a 'B' in the waves below the ship on the reverse.

Collecting Hints

Issues from the London mint, while rare, are obtainable usually in Fine or VF condition; issues from the Bristol mint are very rare.

London Mint

Obverse Legend EDWARD DI GRA REX ANGL Z FRANC — Edward by the grace of God King of England and France

Reverse Legend PER CRUCEM TUAM SALVA NOS XPC REDEMPTOR (varieties exist) — By Thy cross save us O Christ our Redeemer

Obverse St Michael killing a dragon; mintmark short cross fitchée, annulet, pellet in annulet, cross and four pellets, heraldic cinquefoil, pierced cross, cross with pellet in one quarter.

Reverse Ship with arms and mast in the shape of a cross, an 'E' and a rose divided by the mast.

E4AG-015 VG £160 F £330 VF £500

Bristol Mint

Legends As previous.

Obverse As previous, but mintmark annulet only.

Reverse As previous, but a 'B' in waves below ship.

E4AG-020 VG — F £900 VF £1,800

Edward IV or V

Gold angels of the London mint with the mintmark of halved sun and rose are thought to have been struck under Edward V from dies made during the reign of Edward IV. These issues are identical to the Edward IV second reign angel except for the mintmark.

Collecting Hints

These coins are very rare and, when available, usually found in Fine or VF condition.

Obverse Legend EDWARD DI GRA REX ANGL Z FRANC — Edward by the grace of God King of England and France

Reverse Legend PER CRUCEM TUAM SALVA NOS CHRISTE REDEMPTOR — By Thy Cross save us O Christ our Redeemer

Obverse St Michael killing a dragon; mintmark halved sun and rose.

Reverse Ship with arms and mast in the shape of a cross, an 'E' and a rose divided by the mast.

E4AG-025 VG — F £1,200 VF £2,500

Edward V 1483

This issue is very much a continuation of the last one but again the mintmark is different. On the obverse there is the mintmark boar's head which was the personal emblem of Richard III who was Edward's 'Protector'; on the reverse the mintmark halved sun and rose is used again. This reverse die is from the previous issue, it is only the obverse die which is new.

Collecting Hints

This issue is extremely rare.

As previous, but mintmark boar's head on the obverse.

E5AG-005 ex. rare

Richard III 1483–1485

Very few coins were struck under Richard III and the gold angel was no exception. Several issues used altered dies from the previous reigns, all have an 'R' for Richard besides the ship's mast and in the two more common issues the king's name appears as RICARD or RICAD. All issues were struck at the London mint.

Obverse Legend EDWARD DI GRA REX ANGL Z FRANC — Edward by the grace of God King of England and France

Reverse Legend PER CRUCEM TUAM SALVA NOS CHRISTIE REDEMPTOR — By the Cross save us O Christ our Redeemer

Obverse St Michael killing dragon; mintmark halved sun and rose.

Reverse 'R' over 'E' by ship's mast on reverse; mintmark sun and rose. This die was originally from Edward IV/V.

R3AG-005 probably unique

As previous, but mintmark boar's head on obverse (Edward V die); reverse as previous.
R3AG-010 probably unique

Obverse Legend RICARD DI GRA REX ANGL Z FRANC — Richard by the grace of God King of England and France

Reverse Legend As previous.

Obverse St Michael killing a dragon; mintmark sun and rose or boar's head.

Reverse 'R' by ship's mast, sometimes over 'E' (Edward IV/V die); mintmark sun and rose or boar's head, sometimes muled.

R3AG-015 VG £500 F £1,000 VF £1,600

Obverse Legend RICA(R)D DI GRA REX ANGL Z FRANC — Richard by the grace of God King of England and France

Reverse Legend As previous.

Obverse As previous.

Reverse 'R' by mast, small cross on reverse; mintmark as previous.

R3AG-020 VG £500 F £1,100 VF £1,700

Henry VII 1485–1509

Throughout Henry VII's reign gold angels were produced at the London mint in some quantity. There are several varieties and we

have listed them all. The main differences in type is that St Michael, instead of being a feathered figure, is wearing armour on the later issues and there are two different reverse legends which we have listed. Henry VIII also produced angels during the first part of his reign but these issues can be identified by the eight in either Roman (VIII) or Arabic (8) numerals after the king's name. Similarly, angels were produced in Henry VI's second reign but are distinguishable from their mintmarks, style and various marks on the coin.

Class 1A

Obverse Legend HENRIC DI GRA REX ANGL Z FRANC — Henry by the grace of God King of England and France

Reverse Legend PER CRUCE TUA SALVA NOS XPC REDEMPTOR (many varieties) — By Thy Cross save us O Christ our Redeemer

Obverse A feathered St Michael with one foot on a dragon; mintmark sun and rose, lis upon sun and rose, lis upon half rose.

Reverse A ship with royal arms in centre and mast above, an 'H' and a rose divided by the mast.

H7AG-005 VG £180 F £375 VF £800

Class 1B

This is an altered die from the reign of Richard III. On the obverse RICARD has been altered to read HENRIC and on the reverse an Edward IV/V die has been altered with the 'H' over an 'E'. Mintmark rose on obverse only. It is possible other varieties exist.

H7AG-010 VG £300 F £650 VF £1,300

Class 2A

As Class 1A, but mintmark none, cinquefoil or escallop; often muled.

H7AG-015 VG £180 F £375 VF £800

Class 2B

Obverse Legend As H7AG-005.

Reverse Legend IHC AUTEM TRANSIENS PER MEDIUM ILLORUM IBAT — But Jesus passing through their midst went His way

Obverse As previous; mintmark none or cinquefoil.

Reverse As previous.

H7AG-020 VG £180 F £375 VF £800

Class 3A

Obverse Legend As previous.

Reverse Legend As Class 1A.

Obverse New-style St Michael wearing armour with two feet on a dragon, large straight lettering in legends; mintmark escallop, pansy, lis issuant from rose, anchor, greyhound's head, sometimes muled.

Reverse As previous.

H7AG-025 VG £160 F £325 VF £650

Class 3B

Obverse Legend As previous.

Reverse Legend IHC AUTEM TRANSIENS PER MEDIUM ILLORUM IBAT — But Jesus passing through their midst went His way

Obverse As previous; mintmark escallop.

Reverse As previous.

H7AG-030 VG £170 F £350 VF £700

Class 4A

Obverse Legend As previous.

Reverse Legend As Class 3A.

Obverse Small square lettering; mintmark greyhound's head.

Reverse As previous.

H7AG-035 VG £170 F £350 VF £700

Class 4B

Legends As previous, tall thin lettering.

Obverse As previous; mintmark cross crosslet or greyhound's head (mule from previous issue).

Reverse As previous; mintmark cross crosslet.

H7AG-040 VG £170 F £350 VF £700

Class 5

Legends As previous.

Obverse Large crook-shaped abbreviation after HENRIC; mintmark cross crosslet, pheon.

Reverse As previous, mintmark cross crosslet, pheon or none.

H7AG-045 VG £160 F £320 VF £600

Henry VIII 1509–1547

Gold angels were produced during Henry VIII's first, second and third coinages and are very much a continuation from the reign of Henry VII. The main difference is in the obverse legend, where Henry VII angels read HENRIC DEI GRA etc. while Henry VIII issues read HENRIC VIII (or 8) DI GRA or DG. The mintmarks are also different, with the exception of mintmark pheon which was used in both reigns.

During the second coinage Cardinal Wolsey introduced the George noble. This coin had a value of six shillings and eight

pence which, of course, was the same as the angel. However, during the second coinage the value of the angel was increased to seven shillings and six pence, due partly to the rising price of gold, but also to Henry VIII's extravagant spending. The George noble, which is extremely rare, is included here and was intended to continue as an important denomination but, with numerous other denominations being issued during this period, it was not really needed and the public preferred to use the more familiar angel.

Collecting Hints

All issues are rare but obtainable. Coins are usually found undamaged, but sometimes slightly clipped, in Fine or VF condition.

First Coinage 1509–1526

Obverse Legend HENR(I)C VIII DI GRA REX AGL Z FRA — Henry by the grace of God King of England and France

Reverse Legend PER CRUCE TUA SALVA NOS XPE RED (varieties exist) — By Thy Cross save us O Christ our Redeemer

Obverse St Michael killing a dragon; mintmark pheon, castle, castle with 'H', crowned portcullis.

Reverse Ship with royal arms, an 'H' and rose divided by the ship's mast; mintmarks as obverse, sometimes muled.

H8AG-005 VG £160 F £325 VF £600

As previous, but no rose by the ship's mast; mintmark portcullis.

H8AG-010 VG £200 F £425 VF £800

Second Coinage 1526–1544

The value of the angel was raised to seven shillings and sixpence.

Obverse Legend HENRIC VIII D G R AGL Z FRA — Henry VIII by the grace of God King of England and France

Reverse Legend As previous.

Obverse As previous; mintmark sunburst or lis.

Reverse As previous.

H8AG-015 F £300 VF £600

George Noble

This coin, with a value of six shillings and eight pence, was produced to replace the angel denomination. Two varieties exist, one of which is unique. The obverse shows a ship with a rose in the centre and, for the first time, the reverse depicts St George killing a dragon.

Obverse Legend TALI DICA SIGNO MES FLUCTUARI NEQUIT — Consecrated by such a sign the mind cannot waver

Reverse Legend HENRIC D G R AGL Z FRANC DNS HIBERNIE — Henry by the grace of God King of England and France Lord of Ireland

Obverse St George on horseback killing a dragon.

Reverse Ship with a rose on the mast,' H.K.' divided by the mast; mintmark rose.

H8AG-020 very rare

Obverse Legend TALI DICATA SIGNO MEN FLUCTUARE NEQUIT — Consecrated by such a sign the mind cannot waver

Reverse Legend HENRIC D G R AGL Z FRANC DNS HYB — Henry by the grace of God King of England and France Lord of Ireland

Obverse St George on horseback brandishing a sword, a dragon below; mintmark rose.

Reverse Ship with three masts, rose on centre mast.

H8AG-025 unique

Third Coinage 1544–1547

This angel is very much a continuation from the second coinage, the main difference being that the Roman numeral VIII after the king's name is replaced by an Arabic 8. The 'Collecting Hints' are similar to those of the earlier issues. The value of the angel was eight shillings for this issue.

Obverse Legend HENRIC 8 DG AGL FRA Z HIB REX — Henry VIII by the grace of God King of England France and Ireland

Reverse Legend PER CRUCE TUA SALVA NOS XPE REDE — By Thy Cross save us O Christ our Redeemer

Obverse St Michael killing a dragon, sometimes an annulet by St Michael's head; mintmark lis.

Reverse Ship with royal arms, 'H' and rose divided by mast, sometimes an annulet on the ship; mintmark lis.

H8AG-030 VG £150 F £340 VF £625

No angels were struck during the posthumous coinage.

Edward VI 1547–1553

This issue, struck under Edward's name, is very much a continuation from his father's reign. Due to the shortage of metal, inflation and debasement in other denominations, the value of the angel was ten shillings. The obverse legend starts with the king's name EDWARD VI. It is important to remember that Edward IV and V both produced angels, but the styles, legends and mintmarks are very different.

Obverse Legend EDWARD VI D.G. AGL FRA Z HIB REX — Edward VI by the grace of God England France and Ireland King

Reverse Legend PER CRUCE TUA SALVA NOS XPE REDE — By Thy Cross save us O Christ our Redeemer

Obverse St Michael killing dragon; mintmark ostrich head or tun over ostrich head.

Reverse Ship with royal arms in centre, a rose and an 'E' divided by the mast.

E6AG-005 VG — F £4,500 VF £9,000

Mary 1553–1554

The gold angel was produced in some quantity during Mary's reign. Its value remained ten shillings and the design was very similar to previous issues. Angels were also struck under Philip and Mary, but are much rarer. The main differences between the issues lie in the obverse legends which start MARIA and PHILIP Z MARIA respectively; the mintmarks also vary for each issue.

Obverse Legend MARIA D G ANG FRA Z HIB REGINA — Mary by the grace of God Queen of England France and Ireland

Reverse Legend A DNO FACTU EST ISTUD Z EST MIRABI — This is the Lord's doing and it is marvellous [in our eyes]

Obverse St Michael killing a dragon; mintmark pomegranate or half rose and castle.

Reverse Ship with royal arms in centre, an 'M' and a rose divided by the mast.

MAG-005 VG £250 F £600 VF £1,200

Philip and Mary 1554–1558

This issue, which is very rare, is differentiated from the previous one mainly by the obverse legend and the mintmarks.

Obverse Legend PHILIP Z MARIA DG. REX Z REGINA — Philip and Mary by the grace of God King and Queen

Reverse Legend A DNO FACTU EST ISTUD Z EST MIRABILE — This is the Lord's doing and it is marvellous [in our eyes]

Obverse St Michael killing a dragon, angel wings of varying size; mintmark lis.

Reverse Ship with royal arms in centre, 'P. M' divided by the mast; mintmark lis.

PMAG-005 VG — F £1,400 VF £2,400

Elizabeth I 1558–1603

The gold angel, still with a value of ten shillings, was produced in some quantity throughout Elizabeth's long reign. All issues are hammered with no milled specimens existing for this denomination. The angel was popular even if it might have appeared old-fashioned in style when compared to some of the new denominations such as the sovereign. Moreover the halfpound was introduced at this time with an identical value of ten shillings. These issues circulated alongside the angel and, while popular, were not as popular as the old-style angel, which had changed very little in style from the reign of Edward IV. As with coinage today, Elizabethan England did not like change and the angel was to stay until the reign of Charles I.

First-Third Issues 1559–1578

There is nothing for the angel issues to differentiate the first three issues, so they have all been listed together. Many minor varieties exist in the legends.

Obverse Legend ELIZABETH D G ANG FRAN Z HIB REGI — Elizabeth by the grace of God Queen of England France and Ireland

Reverse Legend A. DNO. FACTUM EST ISTUD ET EST MIRABI — This is the Lord's doing and it is marvellous [in our eyes]

Obverse St Michael killing a dragon, wire lined or beaded inner circles; mintmark lis.

Reverse Ship with royal arms, a rose and an 'E' divided by the ship's mast; mintmark as obverse.

ELAG-005 VG £200 F £450 VF £775

Legends As previous, except obverse legend reads FRA. ET. REGINA

Obverse As previous, but beaded inner circles; mintmark cross crosslet, lis, coronet, ermine, acorn and eglantine.

Reverse Ship facing right, royal arms and 'E' and rose divided by mast; mintmark as obverse.

ELAG-010 VG £190 F £425 VF £750

Legends As previous.

Obverse As previous, but mintmark ermine, acorn and eglantine.

Reverse Royal ship facing left; mintmark as obverse.

ELAG-015 VG £190 F £425 VF £750

Fourth Issue 1578–1582

This issue used gold of a slightly reduced fineness.
Legends As previous.

Obverse As previous; mintmark Greek cross, Latin cross or sword; beaded inner circles.

Reverse Ship facing right, royal arms and an 'E' and a rose divided by the mast; mintmark as obverse.

ELAG-020 VG £190 F £425 VF £750

Fifth Issue 1583–1600

The fineness of gold was raised for this issue.
Legends As previous.

Obverse As previous, but mintmark bell, 'A', escallop, crescent, hand, tun, key, anchor or 0.

Reverse As previous; mintmark as obverse.

ELAG-025 VG £180 F £425 VF £750

Sixth Issue 1601–1602

The weight for this issue was very slightly reduced. The mintmarks denoted the year, thus 1 is for 1601 and 2 for 1602.
As previous, but mintmark 1 or 2.

ELAG-030 VG £220 F £500 VF £1,000

James I 1603–1625

Gold angels were introduced in 1605 during the second coinage with a value of ten shillings which in 1612, with the price of gold rising, was raised to eleven shillings. The second coinage angel is very similar in style to earlier reigns but a new style angel of lighter weight was introduced in the third coinage. The value of this coin was again ten shillings, which was obviously a more practical denomination. The obverse is fairly similar to previous issues while the reverse shows a more modern ship in full sail. Many angels from these issues have large holes, which was done officially to make them into 'touch' pieces. Touch pieces were used at 'touching' ceremonies, where people suffering from scrof-

ula were brought to be cured. As under Elizabeth I, the gold angel circulated alongside denominations of similar value such as the double crown and half-laurel. The angel was a popular coin but now looked outdated in style when compared to issues such as the unite. It had lasted well since medieval times, but the coins were becoming much rarer and finally stopped being produced during the reign of Charles I.

Second Coinage 1604–1619

Obverse Legend IACOBUS D G MAG BRIT ET F ET H REX — James by the grace of God King of Great Britain and France and Ireland

Reverse Legend A DNO FACTUM EST ISTUD — This is the Lord's doing and it is marvellous in our eyes

Obverse St Michael killing a dragon; mintmark rose, escallop, grapes, coronet, bell, mullet, tower, trefoil, cinquefoil, tun, book, crescent, plain cross or saltire.

Reverse Ship with royal arms in centre, an 'I' and a rose divided by the ship's mast; mintmark as obverse.

J1AG-005 VG £225 F £500 VF £1,000

Third Coinage 1619–1625

Obverse Legend IACOBUS D G MAG BRI FRA ET HIB REX — James by the grace of God King of Great Britain France and Ireland

Reverse Legend ADOMINO FACTUM EST ISTUD — This is the Lord's doing and is marvellous in our eyes

Obverse St Michael killing a dragon; mintmark spur rowel, rose, thistle, lis or trefoil.

Reverse A ship in full sail, mintmark as obverse.

J1AG-010 VG £250 F £600 VF £1,150

Charles I 1625–1649

Under Charles I, angels were struck at the Tower mint until 1643. Although they were produced most years, they are a very rare denomination. Stylistically, they are very much a continuation from James I's third coinage, with St Michael killing a dragon on the obverse and a ship in full sail on the reverse. The main differences in the two reigns are in the obverse legends and mintmarks. The value of the angel was ten shillings and on most coins a mark of value X (10 shillings) can be found in the obverse field. Again, many of these coins can be found officially holed so they could be used in 'touching' ceremonies, where those who suffered from scrofula were brought to be cured. Known as 'touch pieces', these coins are interesting but worth less than undamaged specimens. The gold angel finally stopped being produced in 1643, having been superseded in style and quality by the double crown during the reign of Charles I, as well as by other denominations during the previous reign.

Collecting Hints

All issues are very rare and not usually found in better than Fine condition. VF examples exist but are extremely rare. Many coins, as mentioned earlier, are officially holed and some specimens are also damaged.

Obverse Legend CAROLUS D G MAG BRI FRA ET HIB REX (minor varieties exist) — Charles by the grace of God King of Great Britain France and Ireland

Reverse Legend AMOR POPULI PRAESIDIUM REGIS — The love of the people is the King's protection

Obverse St Michael killing a dragon; mintmark lis or cross calvary.

Reverse Ship in full sail; mintmark as obverse.

C1AG-005 VG £300 F £700 VF £1,500

Legends As previous.

Obverse As previous, but mark of value to right of St Michael; mintmark blackamoor's head, castle, anchor or heart.

Reverse As previous; mintmark as obverse.

C1AG-010 VG £250 F £600 VF £1,200

Legends As previous.

Obverse As previous, but mark of value to left of St Michael; mintmark blackamoor's head, heart, rose, harp, portcullis, bell, crown, tun, anchor, triangle star or triangle in circle.

Reverse As previous; mintmark as obverse.

C1AG-015 VG £250 F £700 VF £1,500

Florin or Double Leopard

Edward III 1327–1377

Instructed by Edward III to produce gold denominations for England in 1343, the two Florentines George Kirkyn and Lotte Nicholyn designed the florin or double leopard in 1344. The florin, based on the French gold issues and with a value of six shillings, was intended to be an issue for the whole of Europe, not just England. But as the gold used to strike the coins had been overvalued, the issue was unacceptable to merchants and had to be demonetised in August 1344. The coins were recalled, melted down and used to make the popular and acceptable gold noble. This issue is undoubtedly one of the most beautiful medieval English coins ever produced and it is a loss to collectors that virtually all specimens were destroyed.

Obverse Legend EDWR D GRA REX ANGL Z FRANC DNS HIB — Edward by the Grace of God King of England and France Lord of Ireland

Reverse Legend IHC TRANSIENS PER MEDIUM ILLORUM IBAT — But Jesus passing through their midst went His way

Obverse King enthroned beneath a canopy, two leopards' heads at sides.

Reverse Royal cross within a quatrefoil, a leopard in each spandrel.

E3FL-005 ex. rare

Crown

The crown, or the 'crown of the double rose' as it was known at the time, was introduced during Henry VIII's 1526 monetary reform. The first crowns were stuck in gold and it was not until Edward VI's reign that the silver crown was introduced. Many collectors believe that all crowns are silver but until the reign of Charles I gold crowns were produced in some quantity, except for the reign of Mary and Philip when no crowns were struck. However, silver crowns were also produced during the reigns of Elizabeth, James I and Charles I. With gold and silver in plentiful supply and the sizes of both coins being acceptable to the public, there was no reason why crowns could not be struck in silver as well as gold. Crowns were produced in all reigns from Elizabeth I to Elizabeth II and are still struck today but, despite being legal tender, they have become commemorative issues saved by collectors rather than being found in circulation. There has now been a move by the Royal Mint to produce five pound commemorative coins, which are the same size as the old crown and are referred to by many people as a 'crown'.

Henry VIII 1509–1547

Gold crowns were produced during the second, third and posthumous issues of Henry VIII; they were all made of good quality 22 carat gold and unlike some of the silver issues were never debased. All issues have a crown over a rose on the obverse and a crown over a shield on the reverse; they also bear initials on the obverse and, sometimes, the reverse which, together with the mintmark, serve to identify issues. The Bristol mint struck crowns which bear the mintmark WS on the obverse and/or reverse during the second coinage while the Southwark mint, London's second mint located just south of the River Thames, struck crowns during the third and posthumous coinage. The posthumous issue can be identified easily as it omits the 8 after the king's name.

Collecting Hints

Most issues, while scarce, are obtainable; the Southwark posthumous issue in particular is extremely rare. Coins are usually available unclipped in Fine or VF condition.

Second Coinage 1526–1544

All these issues were struck at the Tower mint. The various initials on the reverse refer to Henry VIII's various wives.

Obverse Legend HENRIC VIII RUTILANS ROSA SINE SPINA — Henry VIII a dazzling rose without a thorn

Reverse Legend DEI GR ANGLIE FRANC DNS HIBERNIE — By the grace of God King of England France Lord of Ireland

Obverse Rose with crown above, 'H.K' crowned initials; mintmark rose.

Reverse Crown above shield, no initials; mintmark rose.

H8CR-005 VG £180 F £275 VF £500

As previous, but 'HK' on obverse and reverse; mintmark rose (obverse) lis (reverse), lis or arrow.

H8CR-010 VG £180 F £290 VF £520

As previous, but 'HK' on obverse, 'HA' on reverse or vice versa; mintmark arrow.

H8CR-015 VG £200 F £320 VF £600

As previous, but 'HR' on obverse, 'HK' on reverse or vice versa; mintmark arrow.

H8CR-020 ex rare

As previous, but 'HA' on reverse; mintmark arrow.

H8CR-025 VG £200 F £320 VF £600

As previous, but 'HA' on obverse, 'HR' on reverse; mintmark arrow.

H8CR-030 ex. rare

As previous, but 'HI' on obverse and reverse; mintmark arrow.

H8CR-035 VG £200 F £320 VF £600

As previous, but 'HK' on obverse, 'HI' on reverse; mintmark arrow.

H8CR-040 VG £200 F £340 VF £650

As previous, but 'HR' on obverse, 'HI' on reverse; mintmark arrow.

H8CR-045 VG £200 F £340 VF £650

As previous, but 'HR' on reverse; mintmark arrow.

H8CR-050 VG £180 F £320 VF £600

As previous, but reverse legend reads DEI GR ANGLIE DNS HIBERNIE REX; mintmark pheon.

H8CR-055 VG £200 F £500 VF rare

Third Coinage 1544–1547

This issue while similar to the previous one, has 8 instead of VIII in the obverse legend and different mintmarks.

Tower Mint

Obverse Legend HENRIC 8 RUTILANS ROSA SINE SPINA — Henry VIII a dazzling rose without a thorn

Reverse Legend DEI GRA ANGLIE FRANC HIBERNIE REX — By the grace of God King of England France and Ireland

Obverse Rose with crown above initials H.R; mintmark pellet in annulet.

Reverse Crown above shield initials 'HR'.

H8CR-060 VG £140 F £250 VF £500

As previous, but omits RUTILANS in obverse legend.

H8CR-065 VG £150 F £260 VF £500

As previous, but an annulet is found on the inner circle in the obverse legend.

H8CR-070 VG £160 F £270 VF £520

Southwark Mint

This issue can be identified by the mintmark only.
Legends As H8CR-065.
Obverse As H8CR-065; mintmark 'S', 'E', sometimes muled.
Reverse As H8CR-065.

H8CR-075 VG £180 F £300 VF £600

Bristol Mint

The mintmark WS, which is unique for Bristol, can always be found on the obverse and/or reverse.

Obverse Legend HENRIC VIII RUTILANS ROSA SINE SPINA — Henry VIII a dazzling rose without a thorn

Reverse Legend DEI GRA ANGLIE FRANC HIBERNIE REX — By the grace of God King of England France Ireland

Obverse As previous, but mintmark 'WS' or none.

Reverse As previous, but mintmark 'WS' or none.

H8CR-080 VG £140 F £250 VF £500

As previous, but legend reads HENRIC 8 instead of HENRIC VIII.

H8CR-085 VG £140 F £250 VF £500

Posthumous Coinage 1547–1551

This issue is very similar to the third coinage except for the legends and sometimes the mintmark. Produced during the reign of Edward VI, it should really be under Edward VI coinage but, as these issues are so similar to the issues of Henry VIII, they have been classed under Henry VIII for the convenience of the reader.

Tower Mint

Obverse Legend HENRIC 8 RUTILANS ROSA SINE SPINA — Henry VIII a dazzling rose without a thorn

Reverse Legend DEI GRA ANGLIE FRAN Z HIB REX — By the grace of God King of England France and Ireland

Obverse Crown over rose, 'HR' initials; mintmark arrow, none (with 'K' on reverse), grapple, martlet.

Reverse Crown over shield, 'HR' initials; mintmark as obverse.

H8CR-090 VG £200 F £400 VF £800

As previous, but the legend is in a different order with several varieties and omits the '8'.

H8CR-095 VG £250 F £500 VF £1,000

Southwark Mint

As H8CR-075 but mintmark 'E', with transposed legends; varieties exist.

H8CR-100 VG £250 F £500 VF £1,000

Edward VI 1547–1553

During the reign of Edward VI there were three main issues of crowns. After the posthumous issue struck in Henry VIII's name and listed above, the second main issue consists of the gold crowns produced in Edward's name throughout all three periods of coinage; they are all very rare and the first issue is thought to be unique. The third main issue under Edward VI was the silver crown. Dated between 1551 and 1553, these coins are superb in style and production, with the obverse showing the Boy King on horseback and the reverse the royal arms over a cross.

Gold Issue

Collecting Hints

All issues are extremely rare and the first issue is presumed unique. When available, the second and third period coins are usually found in fine and VF condition, but collectors will have difficulty in obtaining a specimen.

First Period April 1547 — Jan. 1549

Obverse Legend RUTILANS ROSA SINE SPINA — A dazzling rose without a thorn

Reverse Legend EDWARD 6 DG AGL. FRA Z HIB REX — Edward VI by the grace of God King of England France and Ireland

Obverse Crown over rose dividing 'ER'.

Reverse Crown over shield dividing 'ER'; mintmark arrow.

E6CR-005 ex. rare, probably unique

Second Period Jan. 1549-April 1550

Obverse Legend SCUTUM FIDEI PROTEGET EUM — The shield of faith shall protect him

Reverse Legend EDWARD VI DG AGL FR Z HIB REX — Edward VI by the grace of God King of England France and Ireland

Obverse Uncrowned bust of king; mintmark arrow, '6', 'Y'.

Reverse Crown over royal shield dividing 'E.R.'.

E6CR-010 VG £400 F £900 VF £1,600

Obverse Legend EDWARD VI DG AGL FR Z HIB REX — Edward VI by the grace of God King of England France and Ireland

Reverse Legend SCUTUM FIDEI PROTEGET EUM — The shield of faith shall protect him

Obverse Crowned bust of king; mintmark arrow, grapple, swan and 'Y'.

Reverse Crown over royal shield dividing 'ER'.

E6CR-015 VG £250 F £600 VF £1,100

Third Period 1550–1553

Obverse Legend EDWARD VI DG ANGL FRA Z HIB REX — Edward VI by the grace of God King of England France and Ireland

Reverse Legend SCUTUM FIDEI PROTEGET EUM — The shield of faith shall protect him

Obverse Half length bust of king holding orb and sword; mintmark 'Y' or tun.

Reverse Crown over royal shield dividing 'ER.'.

E6CR-020 VG £400 F £900 VF £1,800

Silver Issue 1551–1553

This coin was struck during Edward VI's fine silver issue. Unlike some other earlier denominations, it was struck in good quality silver and was popular since it once again provided the public with silver coins which were worth their metal weight. Many of these crowns are overstruck dates. We have noted 1551/52 and 1553 over 1552 or 1551.

Collecting Hints

While these crowns are scarce they are obtainable in VG to VF condition; some however are found gilded and this detracts from their value. Being the first numerically dated English coin (Edward VI base shillings used Latin numbering) it is an historical issue and an important acquisition for any collection.

Obverse Legend EDWARD VI DG AGL FRA Z HIBER REX — Edward VI by the grace of God King of England France and Ireland

Reverse Legend POSUI DEUM ADIVITOREM MEUM — I have made God my helper

Obverse Boy King on horseback, date 1551–1553 below; mintmark 'Y' or tun. Crowns dated 1552 are much scarcer than those of the other two dates.

Reverse Royal arms over cross; mintmark 'Y' or tun.

E6CR-025 VG £160 F £300 VF £600

No crowns were struck during the reign of Mary or Philip and Mary.

Elizabeth I 1558–1603

Hammered gold crowns were struck during most of Elizabeth's reign. All issues had a bust of the queen on the obverse, a crowned shield dividing 'E R' (ELIZABETH REGINA) on the reverse and a mintmark at the beginning of both obverse and reverse legend. Issues are fairly easily identifiable by the various mintmarks and minor varieties in style. Milled gold crowns were also issued at the time and are very different in style from the gold hammered issues, mainly because they omit the inner circles. Finally, a silver crown, which is probably the best-known Elizabeth I crown, was struck during the last two years of her reign. Produced in some quantity, it is the most common issue, as well as the most popular with collectors. The obverse shows a superb bust of the queen and the reverse the royal shield over a cross, and a mintmark can be found at the beginning of the obverse and reverse legend.

Hammered Gold Issue

Obverse Legend ELIZABETH DG ANG FR ET HI REGINA — Elizabeth by the grace of God Queen of England France and Ireland

Reverse Legend SCUTUM FIDEI PROTEGET EAM — The shield of faith shall protect her

Obverse Crowned bust of queen in plain dress, no inner circles; mintmark lis.

Reverse Crown over royal shield dividing 'E.R.', wire lined inner circles.

ELCR-005 ex. rare, only two known

Obverse Legend As previous, minor varieties exist.

Reverse Legend As previous.

Obverse As previous, but beaded inner circles; mintmark cross crosslet, rose, portcullis, lion, coronet or castle.

Reverse As previous.

ELCR-010 VG £170 F £320 VF £700

Obverse Legend ELIZAB DG ANG FRA ET HIB REGI — Elizabeth by the grace of God Queen of England France and Ireland

Reverse Legend As previous.

Obverse Crowned bust of queen with long hair and decorative dress; mintmark tun, woolpack, key, cypher, '1' or '2'. N.B. Sixth issue mintmark '1' and '2' are very rare.

Reverse As previous.

ELCR-015 VG £170 F £320 VF £700

Milled Gold Issue

Obverse Legend ELIZABETH DG ANG FRA ET HIB REGINA — Elizabeth by the grace of God Queen of England France and Ireland

Reverse Legend SCUTUM FIDEI PROTEGET EAM — The shield of faith shall protect her

Obverse Crowned bust of queen of various styles, no inner circle; mintmark star or lis.

Reverse Crown over royal arms dividing 'E.R.'.

ELCR-020 VG £600 F £1,000 VF £2,200

Hammered Silver Issue

Obverse Legend ELIZABETH DG ANG FRA ET HIBER REGINA — Elizabeth by the grace of God Queen of England France and Ireland

Reverse Legend POSUI DEUM ADIUTOREM MEUM — I have made God my helper

Obverse Crowned bust of queen holding sceptre and orb; mintmark '1' or '2'.

Reverse Royal arms in shield over long cross.

ELCR-025 VG £250 F £450 VF £900

James I 1603–1625

Gold as well as silver crowns were produced under James I, but fluctuations in the supply and price of gold meant that many denominations were devalued and this lack of consistency is reflected in the way coins have been listed. In the second coinage the value of a half angel was, for a period, five shillings but as it was not called a crown it is listed separately. Also during the second coinage, the thistle crown was introduced with a value of only four shillings, as was the Britain crown with a value of five shillings; they are both included here. The Britain crown derives its name from the MAG BRIT (Great Britain) in the obverse legend. During the third coinage, gold quarter-laurels were produced with the value of a crown and V for five shillings behind the bust of the king; they are included in this chapter. There is little doubt that the varieties of gold coins during this reign are confusing, but with erratic gold prices and the coins worth their weight in gold the government was compelled to vary the denominations and values.

Silver crowns were also produced during most of James's reign. They all have the king on horseback on the obverse, the royal shield, sometimes with a plume above, on the reverse and a mintmark at the beginning of the obverse and reverse legends. As the silver sixty-shillings produced in Scotland during this period is very similar in style and design to the English crown, collectors should carefully compare the two. First check the reverse legend; only the second and third coinages have the same legend readings as the Scottish issue. Then check the mintmark; on the Scottish issue it is thistle only, the second issue did not use mintmark thistle, the first one did but had a different reverse legend and the third coinage used the mintmark thistle but the style of the coin is different. In particular, the English issue has, in nearly all cases, a bird-headed harp in the royal shield as well as colon stops in the obverse legend while the Scottish issue has a very plain harp and single pellet stops in the legend. No issue from Scotland has a plume over the royal shield and, furthermore, on the obverse legend the English issue uses 'ET' and the Scottish issues '&'.

Gold Issue

First Coinage 1603–1604

The first coinage can easily be distinguished from other issues by the reverse legend and mintmarks.

Obverse Legend IACOBUS DG ANG SCO FRA ET HI REX — James by the grace of God King of England Scotland and Ireland

Reverse Legend TUEATUR UNITA DEUS — May God guard these United [Kingdoms]

Obverse Bust of king; mintmark thistle or lis.

Reverse Crown above royal arms and dividing 'IR' (IACOBUS REX); mintmark thistle.

J1CR-005 VG — F £1,000 VF £2,200

Second Coinage 1604–1619

Large quantities of gold crowns were produced during this period. The first issue, known as the Britain crown, has a bust of the king of various styles on the obverse and a crown above the royal arms and dividing 'IR' (IACOBUS REX) on the reverse. The reverse legend is also different from the first coinage. The second issue, the thistle crown, had a denomination of only four shillings but is classed as a crown and easily identified as it omits the king's bust on the obverse and bears a thistle on the reverse.

Britain Crown

First Bust

Obverse Legend IACOBUS D.G. MAG BRI FRA ET H. REX. — James by the grace of God King of Great Britain France and Ireland

Reverse Legend HENRICUS ROSAS REGNA IACOBUS — Henry united the Roses, James the kingdoms

Obverse Crowned bust of king with a rounded bust and a square beard; mintmark lis, rose, escallop, grapes and coronet.

Reverse Crown over royal shields and dividing 'I.R.'.

J1CR-010 VG £95 F £170 VF £300

Third Bust

As previous, but crowned bust of king with square cut beard which projects; mintmark key, bell, mullet, tower, trefoil, cinquefoil.

J1CR-015 VG £95 F £170 VF £300

135

Fifth Bust

As previous, but crowned bust of king with longer hair brushed back and a beard that is not neat; mintmark cinquefoil, tun, book, crescent, plain cross, saltire.

J1CR-020 VG £95 F £170 VF £300

Thistle Crown

Obverse Legend IA DG MAG BRIT ET H REX — James by the grace of God King of Great Britain and Ireland

Reverse Legend TUEATUR UNITA DEUS — May God guard these United [Kingdoms]

Obverse Crown above rose, 'I R' usually divided by rose; mintmark lis, rose, escallop, grapes, coronet, key, bell, mullet, tower, trefoil, cinquefoil, tun, book, crescent, plain cross.

Reverse Crown above thistle dividing 'I.R'.

J1CR-025 VG £100 F £180 VF £300

Third Coinage 1619–1625

With gold prices and denomination values fluctuating, public faith in the coinage was severely shaken, so major monetary reforms were introduced with the third coinage in 1619. For the first time on gold crowns, the denomination V for five shillings can be found on the coin, behind the king's head. The bust is also very different, depicting the king uncrowned and wearing a laurel. This laurel actually gave the whole issue its name and the gold crown is known as the quarter-laurel.

Second Bust

Obverse Legend IACOBUS DG MAG BRI FR ET HIB REX — James by the grace of God King of Great Britain France and Ireland

Reverse Legend HENRICUS ROSAS REGNA IACOBUS — Henry united the Roses, James the kingdoms

Obverse Bust of king with large face wearing a laurel, value behind bust; mintmark spur rowel, rose, thistle, lis.

Reverse Crown over royal arms.

J1CR-030 VG £100 F £180 VF £320

Fourth Bust

There is no inner circle on the reverse of some issues.
As previous, but the king's bust is smaller and neater; mintmark lis, trefoil.

J1CR-035 VG £100 F £180 VF £320

First Coinage 1603–1604

Obverse Legend IACOBUS DG ANG SCO FRAN ET HIBER REX — James by the grace of God King of England Scotland France and Ireland

Reverse Legend EXURGAT DEUS DISSIPENTUR INIMICI — Let God arise and His enemies be scattered

Obverse King on horseback; mintmark thistle, lis.

Reverse Royal arms in square garnished shield.

J1CR-040 VG £225 F £450 VF £1,000

Second Coinage 1604–1619

Obverse Legend IACOBUS DG MAG BRIT FRAN ET HIB REX — James by the grace of God King of Great Britain France and Ireland

Reverse Legend QUAE DEUS CONIUNXIT NEMO SEPARET — What God hath joined let no man put asunder

Obverse As previous; mintmark lis, rose, escallop, grapes.

Reverse As previous.

J1CR-045 VG £200 F £350 VF £800

Third Coinage 1619–1625

Legends As previous.

Obverse As previous, but colon dots in obverse legend as opposed to single stops; mintmark rose, thistle, lis, trefoil.

Reverse As previous, but no stops in reverse legend and the harp on the shield in most cases has a bird's head at the end.

J1CR-050 VG £170 F £300 VF £600

Legends As previous.

Obverse As previous; mintmark thistle, lis, trefoil.

Reverse As previous, but large plume (denoting silver mined in Wales) over the royal shield.

J1CR-055 VG £180 F £350 VF £800

Charles I 1625–1649

During the reign of Charles I both gold and silver crowns were produced. With fairly plentiful supplies of gold and silver there was no reason why crowns could not be produced in both metals. These issues gave the public a choice and also helped when trading on the Continent. All gold crowns were struck at the Tower mint in London and have a bust of the king with the value V (five shillings) behind the king's head on the obverse and the royal shield on the reverse. A mintmark can be found in nearly all cases at the beginning of the obverse and reverse legends. During the early part of the reign the silver issues were also stuck at the Tower mint and then at provincial mints during the Civil War.

Gold Issue 1625–1642

Collecting Hints

Most issues are fairly common, however there are exceptions which we have listed. They are sometimes found damaged in Fine condition, but VF and EF examples do exist. These crowns tend to be slightly less popular with collectors who prefer the larger silver issues.

First Bust

Obverse Legend CAROLUS DG MAG BR FR ET HI REX — Charles by the grace of God King of Great Britain France and Ireland

Reverse Legend CULTORES SUI DEUS PROTEGIT — God protects His worshippers

Obverse Crowned bust of king wearing a ruff, value behind; mintmark lis, cross calvary.

Reverse Square-topped shield with crown above; minor varieties in the style of the shield exist.

C1CR-005 VG £100 F £170 VF £320

Second Bust

Legends As previous.

Obverse As previous, but a thinner bust of the king; mintmark cross calvary, blackamoor's head, castle, anchor, heart, plume.

Reverse As previous, but sometimes no mintmark.

C1CR-010 VG £100 F £165 VF £310

Legends As previous.

Obverse As previous, but larger bust; mintmark plume, rose.

Reverse As previous; mintmark plume over rose sometimes on reverse, crown above shield.

C1CR-015 VG £100 F £165 VF £310

Third Bust

Legends As previous.

Obverse Slightly wider bust of king wearing a larger crown; mintmark plume.

Reverse Crowned oval shield; mintmark plume.

C1CR-020 VG £160 F £300 VF £600

Fourth Bust

Several very minor varieties of this issue exist. It was produced both under the king (1632–1641) and under Parliament (1643–1648) but, as only the mintmark differentiates the two, we have included them here together. Mintmarks (P), (R), eye, sun and sceptre were used under Parliament.

Legends As previous.

Obverse Larger bust of king not wearing a ruff; mintmark harp, portcullis, bell, crown, tun, anchor, triangle, star, triangle in circle, '(P)', '(R)' eye, sun, sceptre.

Reverse Oval shield dividing crowned 'C.R'.

C1CR-025 VG £100 F £170 VF £320

Fifth Bust — Aberystwyth Style

This issue is known as the Aberystwyth bust because it is the style of bust used on the provincial issues of the Aberystwyth mint.

Legends As previous.

Obverse Smaller, neater bust of king without a ruff; mintmark anchor.

Reverse As previous, but mintmark anchor.

C1CR-030 VG £150 F £240 VF £500

Sixth Bust — Briot Style

This issue, which is unique and possibly a pattern, was probably not by Briot but copied the bust of some of Briot's machine-made issues.

As previous, but new-style bust of king with more hair and wider crown; mintmark anchor.

C1CR-035 unique

Briot's Coinage

This gold issue was machine made.

Collecting Hints

This issue is excessively rare and very difficult to obtain.

Obverse Legend CAROLUS D.G. MAG BRIT FR ET HIB REX — Charles by the grace of God King of Great Britain France Ireland

Reverse Legend CULTORES SUI DEUS PROTEGIT — God protects His worshippers

Obverse Bust of king with value behind; mintmark 'B'.

Reverse Crown over royal shield which divides 'C.R.'

C1CR-040 ex. rare

Silver Issue

Tower Mint under King 1625–1642

These issues show the king on horseback on the obverse and the royal arms on the reverse. When identifying a coin collectors should also refer to the provincial mints and pay particular attention to the mintmark, which is found on the obverse and reverse at the beginning or the end of the legend, the shape of the reverse shield and the style of the horseman. Also note that all issues from the Tower Mint are undated.

Collecting Hints

Most issues, while scarce, are fairly easy to obtain in VG to Fine condition but rare and desirable in VF and EF. They tend not to be chipped or damaged, but some coins have areas on them that are particularly worn.

Class 1A

Obverse Legend CAROLUS DG MAG BRIT FRA ET HIB REX — Charles by the grace of God King of Great Britain France and Ireland

Reverse Legend CHRISTO AUSPICE REGNO — I reign under the auspices of Christ

Obverse Horse with plume on head, king with sword raised; mintmark lis or cross calvary.

Reverse Square-topped, garnished shield of royal arms.

C1CR-045 VG £125 F £250 VF £550

Class 1B

As previous, but plume over shield on reverse; mintmarks lis, cross calvary, castle.

C1CR-050 VG £300 F £600 VF £1,200

Class 2A

Obverse Legend As previous, minor varieties exist.

Reverse Legend As previous.

Obverse As previous, but smaller horseman, the king holds his sword on his shoulder; mintmark harp.

Reverse Oval shield with 'C.R' above shield, no plume.

C1CR-055 VG £125 F £250 VF £500

Class 2B.1

As previous, but a plume dividing C.R; mintmark plume or rose.

C1CR-060 VG £135 F £275 VF £550

Class 2B.2

As previous, but the royal arms are over a cross fourchée; mintmark harp, plume.

C1CR-065 VG £200 F £400 VF £800

Class 3A

Obverse Legend As previous, minor varieties exist.

Reverse Legend As previous.

Obverse King on horseback holding his sword in the air; mintmark bell, crown, tun, anchor, triangle, star.

Reverse Oval shield with no plume or CR.

C1CR-070 VG £140 F £280 VF £580

Class 3B

As previous, but plume over shield on the reverse; mintmark portcullis, crown, tun.

C1CR-075 VG £150 F £300 VF £600

Briot Style Horseman

The obverse is fairly similar to contemporary Scottish issues. If a coin's reverse is different from the one described here, collectors should refer to issues of Scotland.

Obverse Legend CAROLUS DG MAG BRIT FR ET HIB REX — Charles by the grace of God King of Great Britain France and Ireland

Reverse Legend CHRISTO AUSPICE REGNO — I reign under the auspices of Christ

Obverse King on horseback on small neater horse, there is a groundline below the horse and the king's sword is very long; mintmark triangle in circle.

Reverse Royal arms in oval shield.

C1CR-080 ex. rare

Tower Mint under Parliament 1642–1648

This issue is very much a continuation of the Tower mint under the king although the style of the king's horse is slightly different and the issues can easily be identified by their unique mintmarks. The 'Collecting Hints' are similar to the previous issues except that these two classes are scarcer and tend to be found in the lower grades.

Class 4

Obverse Legend CAROLUS D.G. MAG BRI FRA ET HIB REX — Charles by the grace of God King of Great Britain France and Ireland

Reverse Legend CHRISTO AUSPICE REGNO — I reign under the auspices of Christ

Obverse Foreshortened king on horseback; mintmark '(P)', '(R)', eye and sun.

Reverse Royal arms in oval garnished shield.

C1CR-085 VG £150 F £300 VF £600

Class 5

As previous, but larger, spirited horse and the king holding a long sword; mintmark sun. These coins are usually struck on larger flans than those of Class 4.

C1CR-090 VG £170 F £325 VF £650

Briot's Coinage 1631–1639

Unlike Charles I's other issues which were all hammered, this superb, rare coin was milled and very different in style. The whole coin is very well proportioned and elegant and the issue can easily be identified by the mintmark flower on the obverse and a 'B' on both obverse and reverse. The 'B' stood for Briot and could be classed as an engraver's mark.

Collecting Hints

This issue is rare and usually found undamaged in Fine to VF condition; rarely found in the low grades due to the qualities of strike, it is also extremely rare in EF.

Obverse Legend CAROLUS D.G. MAGN BRITAN, FRAN ET HIBER REX — Charles by the grace of God King of Great Britain France and Ireland

Reverse Legend CHRISTO AUSPICE REGNO — I reign under the auspices of Christ

Obverse King on horseback with groundline; mintmark 'B' and flower.

Reverse Crown over royal arms which divide crowned 'C R'.

C1CR-095 VG £180 F £350 VF £800

Reverse Three plumes and value V (five shillings) above Declaration, 1642 below.

C1CR-100 VG £250 F £450 VF £900

Aberystwyth Style Horseman

As previous, but Aberystwyth-style horseman with longer sword and king's scarf catching in the wind.

C1CR-105 ex. rare

Provincial Issues

Crowns were struck during the Civil War at Shrewsbury, Oxford, Truro and Exeter. The Shrewsbury and Oxford issues are fairly similar and have the Declaration on the reverse. They can be distinguished by the dates, as Shrewsbury issues were only struck in 1642 while most Oxford issues were struck during 1643, and by the style of the horseman and the plumes. The Truro and Exeter issues are fairly similar to those of the Tower mint except that many are dated. Those that are undated also use the mint-mark rose found on the Tower mint issue 2B, however the obverse and reverse are very different in style.

Oxford Mint

Shrewsbury Mint

> # Collecting Hints
>
> The Shrewsbury-style horseman issue is rare and usually found undamaged in Fine or VF condition but the Aberystwyth-style horseman issue is extremely rare.

> # Collecting Hints
>
> All crowns from the Oxford mint are rare; nearly all are dated 1643 and there are very many minor varieties. Coins are usually found unclipped and undamaged in Fine condition although VF examples exist. One excessively rare issue shows the king on horseback with the City of Oxford in the distance on the obverse but collectors should be aware that many forgeries and electrotype copies (made by R. Ready) of this stunning and extremely rare coin exist.

Shrewsbury Style Horseman

Obverse Legend CAROLUS D.G. MAG BRIT FRAN ET HIBER REX — Charles by the grace of God King of Great Britain France and Ireland

Reverse Outer Legend EXURGAT DEUS DISSIPENTUR INIMICI — Let God arise and His enemies be scattered

Reverse Inner Legend RELIG PROT LEG ANG LIBER PAR — The religion of the Protestants the laws of England the liberty of Parliament

Obverse King on horseback with groundline, plume without band behind king's head. Many minor varieties of the Shrewsbury style horseman exist.

Shrewsbury Obverse Die Issue

This issue used the obverse die from the Shrewsbury crown and the Oxford reverse, which has a different style in the three plumes above the Declaration.

Obverse Legend CAROLUS DG MAG BRIT FRAN ET HIBER REX — Charles by the grace of God King of Great Britain France and Ireland

Reverse Outer Legend EXURGAT DEUS DISSIPENTUR INIMICI — Let God arise and His enemies be scattered

Obverse Inner Legend RELIG PROT LEG ANG LIBER PAR — The religion of the Protestants the laws of England the liberty of Parliament

Obverse King on horseback with plume behind head.

Reverse Three Oxford-style plumes with denomination (V) above Declaration, dated below 1642 or 1643; N.B. Shrewsbury struck crowns are dated 1642 only.

C1CR-110 VG £225 F £450 VF £900

Oxford Style Horseman

This issue, dated 1643, is easily identified by the grass that is depicted on the groundline on the obverse. Minor varieties exist, particularly in the number and position of stops in the legend.
Legends As previous.

Obverse King on horseback with plume behind him; mintmark plume at beginning of obverse legend. The king's horse walks on groundline of grass.

Reverse Three plume and denomination above the Declaration, 1643 below.

C1CR-115 VG £275 F £550 VF £1,100

Rawlins Style Crown

The dies for this issue were made by Thomas Rawlins.
Legends As previous, but PARL instead of PAR in the Declaration.

Obverse King on horseback, view of Oxford behind.

Reverse Three plumes and denomination above floral scrolls, the Declaration in the centre with date 1644 below and OXON (Oxford) below date.

C1CR-120 ex. rare

Truro Mint 1642–1643

All coins for this mint have the mintmark rose at the beginning of the obverse and reverse legends which, as mentioned earlier, was also used in the Tower mint class 2B. The two issues are easy to differentiate by the style of horseman and the reverse shield. All issues are undated; if a coin is dated collectors should refer to the Exeter mint.

Collecting Hints

Truro crowns, while scarce, are obtainable and usually found undamaged and unclipped but fairly worn in VG to Fine condition; VF examples exist but are very rare.

Obverse Legend CAROLUS D.G. MAG BRI FRA ET HI REX — Charles by the grace of God King of Great Britain France and Ireland

Reverse Legend CHRISTO AUSPICE REGNO — I reign under the auspices of Christ

Obverse King on horseback with no groundline; mintmark rose.

Reverse Royal arms in garnished oval shield.

C1CR-125 VG £125 F £250 VF £500

As previous, but the royal shield is garnished with twelve scrolls.

C1CR-130 VG £130 F £270 VF £520

As C1CR-125, but with king looking sideways instead of forwards as on previous issues.

C1CR-135 VG £125 F £250 VF £500

Other very minor issues exist, mainly with different styles in horseman and the garniture of the royal shield.

Exeter Mint

Exeter crowns are fairly easy to identify as they are all dated (1644 or 1645) at the end of the reverse legend and have the mintmark rose or castle. Many minor varieties of this issue exist, particularly in the style of the king's sash and the variety of mintmarks. The minor styles and varieties are all fairly common and make little difference to rarity or value.

Collecting Hints

Crowns from the Exeter mint while scarce are obtainable. They are usually found in VG to Fine condition often with weaknesses in the legend and irregularities in the flan which are due to poor production rather than clipping. The whole style of the issue tends to be rather poor and crude and there is no doubt that the dies were made hurriedly.

Obverse Legend CAROLUS D.G. MAG BRI FRA ET HI REX — Charles by the grace of God King of Great Britain France and Ireland

Reverse Legend CHRISTO AUSPICE REGNO — I reign under the auspices of Christ

Obverse King on horseback; mintmark castle or rose.

Reverse Royal arms in garnished shield, dated 1644 or 1645 at end of legend; mintmark rose, castle, sometimes in legend, or EX.

C1CR-140 VG £125 F £250 VF £500

Scarborough Siege Issue

Scarborough was the only siege town to produce a crown. The denomination can be identified because below the castle on the obverse it is stamped 'S' then 'V' below followed by S.C.

Collecting Hints

This issue is extremely rare and collectors should be aware of forgeries.

Obverse View of castle, counterstamped 'S.' with 'V' below SC.
Reverse Plain.

C1CR-145 ex. rare

Commonwealth 1649–1660

During the Commonwealth both gold and silver crowns were produced. They are very similar in style, having the date on the reverse and, for the first time, the legends in English. The coins are attractive but very plain in style with the obverse of both issues showing a St George cross within a wreath and the reverse the arms of Ireland with St George cross.

Gold Issue

Collecting Hints

All gold issues are rare, particularly that with the anchor mintmark dated 1658 or 1660. Coins tend to be available in the higher grades from Fine to EF and are usually undamaged, but collectors might have difficulty obtaining an example.

Obverse Legend THE COMMONWEALTH OF ENGLAND
Reverse Legend GOD WITH US
Obverse Shield of St George within wreath; mintmark sun.
Reverse Shield of St George and Ireland with date above 1649, 1650, 1651, 1652, 1653, 1654, 1655, 1656 or 1657.

COMCR-005 VG £200 F £350 VF £700

As previous, but mintmark anchor and date 1658 or 1660.

COMCR-010 VG £500 F £1,000 VF £2,000

Silver Issue

Obverse Legend THE COMMONWEALTH OF ENGLAND

Reverse Legend GOD WITH US

Obverse Shield of St George within wreath; mintmark sun.

Reverse Shield of St George and Ireland with value and date above 1649, 1651, 1652, 1652 over 1, 1653, 1654, 1656 minor varieties in the size of this date exist.

COMCR-015 VG £200 F £375 VF £750

Coins dated 1649, 1651 and 1654 are extremely rare.

Charles II 1660–1685
Hammered Issue 1660–1662

During the hammered coinage of Charles II only gold crowns were struck. Two varieties were produced, both showing the bust of Charles II on the obverse and the royal shield with a crown above on the reverse. These issues were replaced in 1662 by the silver milled issue which is fairly common and listed in the milled section of this book.

Obverse Legend CAROLUS II D.G. MAG BRIT FR ET HIB REX — Charles II by the grace of God King of Great Britain France and Ireland

Reverse Legend FLORENT CONDORDIA REGNA — Through concord kingdoms flourish

Obverse Bust of king wearing laurel; mintmark crown.

Reverse Crown above oval shield dividing 'C.R'.

C2CRH-005 VG £250 F £650 VF £1,500

As previous, but value (V) behind king's bust.

C2CRH-010 VG £400 F £750 VF £1,700

Crown of the Rose

Henry VIII 1509–1547

The crown of the rose, with a value of four shillings and sixpence, was introduced for a short period during the second coinage of Henry VIII. It was made of 23 carat gold but was soon succeeded by a gold crown made of 22 carat gold and with a value of five shillings.

Collecting Hints

These issues are extremely rare.

Obverse Legend HENRIC 8 DEI GRA REX ANGL Z FRAC — Henry VIII by the grace of God King of England France

Reverse Legend HENRIC RUTILANS ROSA SINE SPINA — Henry a dazzling rose without a thorn

Obverse Crown over royal shield; mintmark rose.

Reverse Rose in centre of cross, two crowned 'H's and two lions in angles; mintmark rose.

H8CRR-005 ex. rare

As previous but reverse legend reads DNS HIB RUTILANS ROSA SINE SPINA — Lord of Ireland a dazzling rose without a thorn

H8CRR-010 ex. rare

Half Noble

The half-noble was introduced during the reign of Edward III as part of the 1346 monetary reform, and the extension of the denominations in circulation. It was exactly half the weight of the full noble and had a value of three shillings and fourpence. In virtually all issues, half-nobles are very similar in style, appearance and quality to nobles, depicting the king with a sword and a shield in a ship on the obverse and a cross surrounded by decoration on the reverse. A mintmark, which is important for identification, can be found in all cases on the obverse, either at the beginning or end of the legend.

Edward III 1327–1377

The half-noble was first introduced during the third coinage (1346–1351) and produced more widely during the fourth (1351–1377), becoming an important denomination both in England and with merchants in Europe. The obverse shows the king with a sword and shield in a ship; EDWARD is always broken by the ship's bow. Half-nobles are divided into several issues according to their obverse legends, which reflect Edward's territorial aspirations in France (for details, see the relevant section of the Penny chapter). Until 1361, half-nobles included FRANC on the legend; this was replaced by AQU until 1369 but FRANC returned in the final, post-treaty period. Two mints produced gold half-nobles during Edward III's reign, London and Calais. The issues from Calais can easily be identified by a flag at the ship's stern or a 'C' in the cross in the centre of the reverse. Calais, in Northern France, was under the control of Edward III and was used as a mint firstly to show English sovereignty in the area and secondly to supply English merchants trading in Europe.

Collecting Hints

Edward III's half-nobles are scarce but obtainable, however, although they are as scarce as the gold noble, this is not reflected in their value since collectors prefer to own a gold noble rather than a half-noble. With many half-nobles found in hoards, the condition of specimens is often very good and the average grade Fine to VF. Nevertheless, recent examples found by metal detectors indicate that many half-nobles saw considerable circulation and may be worn or clipped.

Third Coinage 1346–1351

Obverse Legend EDWAR D GRA REX ANGL Z FRA D — Edward by the grace of God King of England and France Lord (of the Irish)

Reverse Legend DOMINE NE IN FURORE TUO ARGUAS ME — O Lord rebuke me not in Thine anger

Obverse King on ship holding sword and shield, large lettering in legends with Lombardic 'N'.

Reverse Mintmark cross pattée, closed 'E' in centre of reverse cross.

E3HN-005 VG — F £1,500 VF £3,000

Fourth Coinage 1351–1377

Pre Treaty Period 1351–1361

We have listed the main varieties although, with muling, there is little doubt that other minor varieties do exist.

Obverse Legend As previous; minor varieties.
Reverse Legend As previous.

Obverse King on ship holding sword and shield; Roman 'M' and 'N' ('N' sometimes reversely barred or unbarred), annulet stops in legend.

Reverse As previous, actually with the last issue's reverse die, making this one a mule; Lombardic 'M' or 'N' in reverse legend.

E3HN-010 VG £150 F £300 VF £550

As previous, but a closed 'E' and 'C' and a Lombardic 'M' in legends.

E3HN-015 VG £150 F £325 VF £575

Broken letters in the legends with the 'V' often having a nick in the right arm.

E3HN-020 VG £300 F £500 VF £1,000

Transitional Period 1361

Obverse Legend EDWARDUS DEI G REX ANGL D or E D DEI GRA REX ANGL DNS HIB Z ACQ (several varieties exist) — Edward by the grace of God King of England Lord of Ireland and Aquitaine

Reverse Legend DOMINE NE IN FURORE TUO ARGUAS ME — O Lord rebuke me not in Thine anger

Obverse King on ship holding sword and shield, irregular sized lettering.

Reverse 'E' in centre of reverse, pellets or annulets in centre of cross; mintmark cross potent.

E3HN-025 VG £150 F £275 VF £475

Treaty Period 1361–1369

These issues were struck at London and Calais. They had new-style letters of uniform size and a curule-shaped 'X' in the legends.

London Mint

Obverse Legend EDWARD DEI G REX ANGL D HYB Z AQT — Edward by the grace of God King of England Lord of the Irish and Aquitaine

Reverse Legend DOMINE NE IN FURORE TUO ARGUAS ME — O Lord rebuke me not in Thine anger

Obverse King in ship holding sword and shield; a saltire before EDWARD.

Reverse As previous; mintmark cross potent.

E3HN-030 VG £150 F £275 VF £475

As previous, but an annulet before EDWARD.

E3HN-035 VG £175 F £350 VF £600

Calais Mint

Legends As previous.

Obverse As previous, but a saltire before EDWARD, a flag at the ship's stern.

Reverse 'C' in centre on reverse.

E3HN-040 VG £180 F £360 VF £600

As previous, but no marks before EDWARD. Sometimes without a flag at the ship's stern.

E3HN-045 VG £200 F £400 VF £700

As previous, but a quatrefoil before EDWARD.

E3HN-050 VG £200 F £400 VF £700

Post Treaty Period 1369–1377

London Mint

Obverse Legend EDWARD DI GRA REX ANGL Z FRANC D — Edward by the grace of God King of England and France Lord (of the Irish)

Reverse Legend As previous.

Obverse As previous, but annulet before EDWARD.

Reverse 'E' in centre with pellet; mintmark cross potent.

E3HN-055 F £900 VF £1800

Calais Mint

Legends As previous.

Obverse King on ship with a flag at the stern.

Reverse 'E' in centre of reverse.

E3HN-060 VG £200 F £400 VF £800

As previous, but a 'C' on reverse. This issue is a mule using the reverse die from the Treaty issue (E3HN-040 to -050).

E3HN-065 VG £200 F £400 VF £800

Should your coin have a rose in the side of the king's ship it is a rose half-noble of Edward IV's first reign.

Richard II 1377–1399

During the reign of Richard II half-nobles were produced at the London and Calais mints. All issues have RICARD at the beginning of the obverse legend, broken by the ship's bow. Richard II was the only Richard to produce half-nobles. The issues are very similar in style to those of Edward III except for the obverse legend and an 'R' on the centre cross of the reverse, which however is sometimes omitted in the first issue. As mentioned earlier, Calais was an active mint producing gold coins during the reign of Richard II and its issues are easily identified by a flag at the ship's stern.

Collecting Hints

All issues are very rare but, when available, usually found in Fine to VF condition because most specimens in collections today have been found in hoards and are therefore usually neither damaged nor badly worn.

London Mint

Obverse Legend RICARD DI GRA REX ANGL Z FR D HIBS Z AQT (many varieties exist usually with abbreviations or FR omitted altogether) — Richard by the grace of God King of England and France Lord of the Irish and Aquitaine

Reverse Legend DOMINE NE IN FURORE TUO ARGUAS ME — O Lord rebuke me not in Thine anger

Obverse This issue is an altered die of Edward III and RICHARD is struck over EDWARD; king on ship holding sword and shield.

Reverse This again is sometimes an altered die of Edward III, an 'R' is struck over the 'E' in the central cross.

R2HN-005 VG £300 F £600 VF £1,200

In some cases only one die has been altered. These coins were struck right at the beginning of Richard II's reign while new dies were being prepared.

The following three issues for London are true issues of Richard II and the style of their lettering is different.

Legends As previous.

Obverse King in ship holding sword and shield, straight-sided lettering with an annulet over the sail.

Reverse 'R' in centre of cross; mintmark cross pattée. Straight-sided lettering in legends.

R2HN-010 VG £280 F £550 VF £1,100

Legends As previous.

Obverse Lion on rudder of ship, fishtailed lettering in legends.

Reverse As previous, but fishtailed lettering in legends.

R2HN-015 VG £280 F £550 VF £1,100

Legends As previous.

Obverse Crescent on ship's rudder, small dumpy lettering in legends.

Reverse As previous, but dumpy lettering.

R2HN-020 VG £300 F £600 VF £1,200

Calais Mint

All issues have a flag at the ship's stern to differentiate them from London issues.

Legends As previous.

Obverse As R2HN-005 (Edward III's die).

Reverse As R2HN-005 (Edward III's die).

R2HN-025 VG £325 F £700 VF £1,400

Legends As previous.

Obverse Quatrefoil over sail, straight-sided lettering.

Reverse 'R' in centre of cross, straight-sided lettering; mintmark cross pattée.

R2HN-030 VG £325 F £700 VF £1,400

Legends As previous.

Obverse Lion on ship's rudder, fishtailed lettering in legend.

Reverse As previous, but fishtailed lettering in legend.

R2HN-035 VG £300 F £600 VF £1,200

Legends As previous.

Obverse Crescent on ship's rudder, or trefoil over sail or saltire behind rudder; dumpy style lettering.

Reverse As previous, but dumpy style lettering.

R2HN-040 VG £350 F £800 VF £1,600

Henry IV 1399–1413

All issues of Henry IV are rare and the half-noble is the rarest of them all. It is fairly similar to issues of Henry V and VI who also produced half-nobles. In Henry IV's case, HENRIC is found at the beginning of the obverse legend broken by the ship's bow and the mintmark cross pattée is found in all issues except Calais, at the start of the reverse legend. Of the three Henrys that produced half-nobles the cross pattée mintmark was used for Henry IV and Henry V. All issues of the three Henrys had various marks, such as annulets and mascles, on the coin that can differentiate the various issues and reigns. If uncertain, collectors should check all three reigns when trying to identify an issue, paying particular attention to mintmarks and other marks on the coins

With the value of gold and silver rising and the scarcity of bullion, the mints faced increasing difficulty producing coins, and those that were struck were often smuggled abroad for sale as their metal content was so high. So in 1412 the metal content of gold coins was reduced by 10% and the so-called light coinage replaced the heavy. A half-noble in particular, instead of weighing 60 grains (3.9 grams), now weighed 54 grains (3.5 grams).

London and Calais both produced half-nobles but the issues from Calais were only struck during the heavy coinage and are easily identified by a flag at the ship's stern.

Collecting Hints

All issues are extremely rare and collectors will have great difficulty in obtaining an example. The very few specimens we have seen have been in Fine to VF condition.

Heavy Coinage 1399–1412

London Mint

Obverse Legend HENRIC DI G REX ANGL Z FR DNS HIB AQT — Henry by the grace of God King of England and France Lord of the Irish and Aquitaine (often abbreviated)

Reverse Legend DOMINE NE IN FURORE TUO ARGUAS ME — O Lord rebuke me not in Thine anger

Obverse King in ship holding sword and shield with four lis in the two French quarters; this is known as the 'old arms' type.

Reverse 'H' in centre of cross; mintmark cross pattée.

H4HN-005 ex. rare

As previous, but three lis in the two French quarters on the king's shield; known as the 'new arms' type.

H4HN-010 F £5,000 VF —

Calais Mint

As previous, but a flag on the ship's stern; mintmark crown.

H4HN-015 ex. rare

Light Coinage 1412–1413

This issue was only struck at the London mint. Should your coin have a quatrefoil above the ship's sail refer to Henry V.

Legends As previous.

Obverse King in ship holding sword and shield with new style arms, an annulet on the side of the ship.

Reverse 'H' in centre of reverse cross.

H4HN-020 F £3,000 VF —

Henry V 1413–1422

During the reign of Henry V half-nobles were produced at the London mint in some quantity. All issues used the mintmark cross pattée with pellet in centre or pierced cross, except for the first very rare issue which uses the Henry IV reverse die. Many coins can also be identified by a quatrefoil above the ship's sail on the obverse. Many issues are fairly similar to those of Henry VI and, if uncertain, collectors should refer to this chapter.

Collecting Hints

Most issues of Henry V are very rare and the first issue is extremely so. Coins when available are usually undamaged in Fine to VF condition as they have been found in hoards and rarely saw much circulation.

Obverse Legend HENRIC DI GRA REX ANGL Z F — Henry by the grace of God King of England and France

Reverse Legend DOMINE NE IN FURORE TUO ARGUAS ME — O Lord rebuke me not in Thine anger

Obverse King on ship holding sword and shield, a quatrefoil above the sail.

Reverse Mintmark cross pattée; this is a Henry IV die.

H5HN-005 ex. rare

Legends As previous.

Obverse As previous, but quatrefoil below sail, broken annulet on ship.

Reverse 'H' in centre of cross; mintmark cross pattée or pierced cross.

H5HN-010 VG £250 F £450 VF £900

Legends As previous.

Obverse Broken annulet on ship's side and a mullet above the shield.

Reverse Broken annulet in upper right quarter of coin, the rest as previous.

H5HN-015 VG £240 F £425 VF £900

Legends As previous.

Obverse Mullet above shield, trefoil usually between shield and prow.

Reverse As previous, usually using previous die.

H5HN-020 VG £270 F £500 VF £1,000

Legends As previous.

Obverse Quatrefoil over ship's sail, mullet sometimes after first word of legend.

Reverse Mullet or annulet stops after first word of legend.

H5HN-025 VG £250 F £450 VF £900

Henry VI First Reign 1422–1461

During the first few years of Henry VI's reign half-nobles were produced in some quantity. All issues bear HENRIC at the beginning of the obverse legend broken by the ship's bow while mintmarks and various other marks can class coins into issues. This form of quality control linked each coin to a particular die but it was particularly complex and as there is no easy way of

identifying issues collectors might find it necessary to refer to all issues, even those of Henry IV and Henry V.

During Henry VI's reign three mints produced half-nobles: London, Calais and York. The Calais mint is identifiable by a flag at the stern of the ship and sometimes a 'C' instead of an 'H' in the centre of the reverse cross. The issues of York are identified by a lis over the ship's stern.

Collecting Hints

All issues are rare and the later issues extremely so. Coins are usually undamaged in Fine to VF condition as many have been found in hoards and so saw little circulation.

Annulet Issue 1422–1427
London Mint

Obverse Legend HENRIC DI GRA REX ANGL Z FRANC — Henry by the grace of God King of England and France

Reverse Legend DOMINE NE IN FURORE TUO ARGUAS ME — O Lord rebuke me not in Thine anger

Obverse King holding shield and sword on ship, annulet by sword, lis after HENRIC.

Reverse Annulet in one spandrel on reverse, a mullet in legend, 'H' in centre cross.

H6HN-005 VG £180 F £300 VF £650

This issue is a mule and used the obverse die from issues of Henry V.

Obverse Legend HENRIC DI GRA REX ANGL Z F (varieties exist) — Henry by the grace of God King of England and France

Reverse Legend As previous.

Obverse As (London) issues of Henry V, usually H5HN-025

Reverse As previous.

H6HN-010 VG £250 F £450 VF £900

Calais Mint

Obverse Legend As H6HN-005.

Reverse Legend As previous.

Obverse As H6HN-005 with a flag at the ship's stern.

Reverse As H6HN-005, but sometimes 'C' instead of 'H' in centre of cross.

H6HN-015 VG £300 F £550 VF £1,100

York Mint

Legends As previous.

Obverse As previous, but a lis over ship's stern instead of a flag.

Reverse As previous, but 'H' in centre of cross.

H6HN-020 VG £300 F £550 VF £1,100

Rosette Mascle Issue 1427–1430
London Mint

Legends As previous.

Obverse King with sword and shield on ship, rosettes and mascle stops in legend.

Reverse Lis in one quarter of reverse, rosette and mascle stops in legend; mintmark lis.

H6HN-025 F £900 VF £1,800

Calais Mint

Legends As previous.

Obverse King with sword and shield on ship, flag at stern, rosette stops in legend.

Reverse Lis in one quarter of reverse, rosette stops in legend; mintmark lis.

H6HN-030 F £950 VF £1,900

Pinecone Mascle Issue 1430–1434

This issue was struck in the London mint and is found only as a mule, using the obverse die from the previous issue.

Legends As previous.

Obverse King on ship holding sword and shield, rosettes and mascle stops.

Reverse Mintmark lis; pinecones and mascle stops in legend.

H6HN-035 ex. rare

Leaf Mascle Issue 1434–1435

Legends As previous.

Obverse / Reverse No details available.

H6HN-040 ex. rare

Leaf Trefoil Issue 1435–1438

This issue is only found as a mule using the reverse die from the annulet issue.

Legends As previous.

Obverse King in ship with sword and shield, leaves and trefoils in legend.

Reverse As H6HN-005.

H6HN-045 probably unique

No other half-nobles were produced during the later issues of Henry VI.

Edward IV First Reign 1461–1470

The gold half-noble had hardly changed in style, value or quality since the previous century when it was first introduced. However, Henry VI's reign was the last period in which the true half-noble, with a value of three shillings and four pence, was to be issued. During the first period of Edward IV's reign, from 1461–1464, few nobles and no half-nobles were produced as the high gold price meant that the coins' metal value was higher than their intrinsic face value. In 1464, in response to this crisis the value of all half-nobles in circulation was increased to four shillings and twopence and a new coin of higher value and weight was introduced. Known as the rose half-noble or half-ryal, it had a value of five shillings. The half-ryal is fairly similar to the old-style half-nobles except for a rose on the ship on the obverse and a different central design on the reverse. However, the new denomination was unpopular and ceased at the end of Edward IV's first reign. Then, during Henry VI's second reign, the gold half-angel was introduced with a value of three shillings and fourpence which, of course, was the old value for the half-noble.

A total of five mints were actively producing the new half rose ryal during the reign of Edward IV and may be distinguished by a letter found in the waves below the ship. They were London (none), Bristol (B), York (E), Coventry (C) and Norwich (N).

Collecting Hints

While the London issue is rare, the provincial ones are very rare. Coins are usually found undamaged in Fine or VF condition.

London Mint

Obverse Legend EDWARD DI GRA REX ANGL Z FRANC — Edward by the grace of God King of England and France

Reverse Legend DOMINE NE IN FURORE TUO ARGUAS ME — O Lord rebuke me not in Thine anger

Obverse King holding sword and shield on ship; mintmarks rose, crown, sun, long cross fitchée or none. Various combinations of mintmarks and muling exist.

Reverse Rose upon a sun.

E4HN-005 VG £170 F £320 VF £600

Bristol Mint

Legends As previous.

Obverse As previous, but 'B' in waves below ship; no mintmark.

Reverse As previous, but mintmark sun, crown, none, sun and crown.

E4HN-010 VG £200 F £420 VF £800

Coventry Mint

Legends As previous.

Obverse As previous, but 'C' below ship.

Reverse As previous, but mintmark sun.

E4HN-015 ex. rare

Norwich Mint

Legends As previous.

Obverse As previous, but an 'N' below ship.

Reverse As previous, but mintmark rose.

E4HN-020 F £1,500 VF —

York Mint

Legends As previous.

Obverse As previous, but 'E' (for EBORACI, Latin for York) below ship.

Reverse As previous, but mintmark sun, lis, sun over crown, rose and lis.

E4HN-025 VG £170 F £320 VF £600

As previous, but a lis in the ship's side instead of 'E'.

E4HN-030 ex. rare

Half Angel

Even though the angel was introduced during the first reign of Edward IV the half-angel, or angelet as it was sometimes called later, was not introduced until the second reign of Henry VI. It had a value of three shillings and four-pence but was never produced in any quantity. The issues are virtually identical in style to the larger and more popular full angel, with St Michael killing the dragon on the obverse and a ship with arms in centre on the reverse. The mintmark, which is helpful in identification, is usually found at the beginning of the obverse and/or reverse legends.

Henry VI Restored Oct. 1470 — April 1471

These coins were struck at the London and Bristol mints and bear a mintmark only on the reverse. Henry VII and Henry VIII also struck half-angels, but in most cases the mintmark is different, the style and various marks which are found on the issues of Henry VIII can also help with identification. The king's name in all cases is found at the beginning of the obverse legend, and it should read HENRIC, HENRICU or HERIC — Henry.

The Bristol mint struck half-angels, however, it is thought only one specimen exists. This issue is identified by a 'B' in the waves below the ship.

> ### Collecting Hints
>
> Coins from the London mint are extremely rare, and when available are usually in Fine or VF condition. The issue from the Bristol mint, as mentioned earlier, is unique.

London Mint

Obverse Legend HE(N)RIC(U) DI GRA REX ANGL Z FRA (many varieties exist) — Henry by the grace of God King of England and France

Reverse Legend O CRUX AVE SPES UNICA (minor varieties exist) — Hail thou cross my only hope

Obverse St Michael killing a dragon; mintmarks none.

Reverse Ship with royal arms in centre, a mast in the shape of a cross above, an 'H' and lis either side of the royal arms; mintmark cross pattée, Restoration cross or lis.

H6HA-005 F £1,750 VF £3,500

Bristol Mint

Obverse Legend HENRIC DI GRA REX ANGL Z FRA — Henry by the grace of God King of England and France

Reverse Legend As previous.

Obverse As previous.

Reverse As previous, but mintmark Restoration cross only, 'B' in the waves below the ship.

H6HA-010 unique

Edward IV Second Reign 1471–1483

These issues, which were all struck at the London mint, are very much a continuation from the previous reign. In all cases the mintmark can be found on the obverse and sometimes the reverse. The varieties of these three issues lie in the arrangement of the legends.

Edward V also produced half-angels which have the mintmark halved sun and rose on the obverse and reverse, or sometimes a boar's head on the obverse and a halved sun and rose on the reverse. When identifying an issue collectors should refer to these issues if necessary.

> ### Collecting Hints
>
> These issues are very rare and are usually found undamaged in Fine to VF condition.

Obverse Legend EDWARD DEI GRA REX ANG — Edward by the grace of God King of England

Reverse Legend O CRUX AVE SPES UNICA — Hail thou cross my only hope

Obverse St Michael killing the dragon; mintmark pierced cross and pellet, annulet, pierced cross central pellet, heraldic cinquefoil.

Reverse Ship with royal arms above, the mast in the shape of a cross, 'E' and rose either side of the mast; mintmarks as previous.

E4HA-005 VG £150 F £250 VF £500

Obverse Legend As E4HA-005 reverse.

Reverse Legend As E4HA-005 obverse.

Obverse As previous; mintmark short cross fitchée.

Reverse As previous; no mintmark.

E4HA-010 VG £200 F £400 VF £750

Obverse Legend As E4HA-005 obverse legend.

Reverse Legend As above.

Obverse As previous; mintmark annulet.

Reverse As previous; no mintmark.

E4HA-015 VG £180 F £375 VF £700

Edward IV or V

There is uncertainty whether half-angels were struck during the reign of Edward V using the mintmark halved sun and rose. It is now thought that the dies were made during the reign of Edward IV, but were used to strike coins during the short reign of Edward V. Only the mintmark can differentiate these issues.

Collecting Hints

This issue is extremely rare.

Obverse Legend EDWARD DI GRA REX ANG — Edward by the grace of God King of England

Reverse Legend O CRUX AVE SPES UNICA — Hail thou cross my only hope

Obverse St Michael killing the dragon; mintmark halved sun and rose.

Reverse Ship with royal arms in centre, a mast in the shape of the cross above, 'E' and a rose either side of the cross; mintmark halved sun and rose.

E4HA-020 ex. rare

Edward V 1483

This issue, which is unique, has the mintmark boar's head on the obverse and mintmark halved sun and rose on the reverse.

Collecting Hints

This coin is unique.

Obverse Legend EDWARD DI GRA REX ANG — Edward by the grace of God King of England

Reverse Legend O CRUX AVE SPES UNICA — Hail thou cross my only hope

Obverse St Michael killing the dragon; mintmark boar's head.

Reverse Ship with royal arms in centre, a mast in the shape of a cross with 'E' and a rose either side of the cross; mintmark halved sun and rose.

E5HA-005 unique

Richard III 1483–1485

This issue is very much a continuation from the previous one. RICARD is found at the beginning of the obverse legend and the mintmark boar's head on the obverse and reverse. This issue was struck at London only.

Collecting Hints

This issue is extremely rare.

Obverse Legend RICARD DI GRA REX ANG — Richard by the grace of God King of England

Reverse Legend O CRUX AVE SPES UNICA — Hail thou cross my only hope

Obverse St Michael killing the dragon; mintmark boar's head.

Reverse Ship with royal arms in centre, a mast in the shape of a cross, 'R' and rose either side of mast; mintmark boar's head.

R3HA-005 ex. rare

Henry VII 1485–1509

Half-angels were struck during most of Henry VII's reign; they were all struck at London and again are very much a continuation from the last reign. The first issue uses altered dies from Edward IV or V and the mintmark halved sun and rose; it is extremely rare. The next issues show a slightly more life-like St Michael with both feet, instead of just one, on the dragon.

Henry VIII also struck half-angels but used different mintmarks so coins can be easily identified. Should the mintmarks be unclear, we have listed minor varieties which will enable collectors to identify the issue. Henry VI's restored reign also produced half-angels but they show St Michael with just one foot on the dragon.

Collecting Hints

The first issue is extremely rare, the others rare. Coins are often found slightly damaged in Fine condition. However, VF and EF examples do exist but are very rare.

Obverse Legend HENRIC DI GRA REX ANG (altered dies) — Henry by the grace of God King of England

Reverse Legend O CRUX AVE SPES UNICA — Hail thou cross my only hope

Obverse St Michael with one foot on the dragon killing it; mintmark halved sun and rose or lis over halved sun and rose?

(altered die)

Reverse Ship with royal arms in centre, mast in shape of cross above, 'H' and rose either side.

H7HA-005 VG £180 F £400 VF £750

Obverse Legend HENRIC DI GRA REX ANGL — Henry by the grace of God King of England

Reverse Legend As previous.

Obverse St Michael with both feet on the dragon; mintmark pansy or anchor.

Reverse As previous; mintmark pansy or greyhound's head.

H7HA-010 VG £160 F £300 VF £600

As previous, but small square lettering; mintmark rose on obverse and reverse.

H7HA-015 VG £180 F £400 VF £750

As H7HA-010, but tall, thin lettering; mintmark rose (obverse), cross crosslet (reverse).

H7HA-020 VG £165 F £375 VF £700

As H7HA-010, but large crook-shaped abbreviation after HENRIC on the obverse; mintmark pheon.

H7HA-025 VG £150 F £275 VF £550

Henry VIII 1509–1547

Gold half-angels were struck during all three issues of Henry VIII's reign although not during the posthumous coinage. All issues are very much a continuation from the reign of Henry VII except for the mintmarks and, in some cases, the obverse legend; also the third issue often has annulets on the ship. We have listed all the varieties, but collectors should pay particular attention to the mintmark and, if uncertain, refer back to the reign of Henry VII.

During the first coinage the value of the half-angel remained three shillings and four pence. However, because English coins were being exported abroad where they had a higher value, the value of the half-angel was increased to three shillings and nine pence in 1526.

All half-angels were struck at the London mint.

Collecting Hints

Half-angels from the first coinage while rare are obtainable; from the second coinage they are very rare. Coins are usually found in Fine condition, while VF and even EF examples do exist. There is no doubt that many of these coins saw considerable circulation and this is reflected in their condition.

First Coinage 1509–1526

Obverse Legend HENRIC DI GRA REX AGL Z or HENRIC VIII DI GRA REX AL (many minor varieties exist) — Henry (VIII) by the grace of God King of England (and)

Reverse Legend O CRUX AVE SPES UNICA — Hail thou cross my only hope

Obverse St Michael killing the dragon; mintmark castle, castle with 'H' or portcullis crowned.

Reverse Ship with royal arms in centre, a mast in the shape of a cross, 'H' and rose either side; mintmarks as obverse but also rose muled.

H8HA-005 VG £150 F £300 VF £500

Second Coinage 1526–1544

Legends As previous but HENRIC VIII in obverse.

Obverse As previous, but mintmark lis.

Reverse As previous, but mintmark lis.

H8HA-010 VG £250 F £500 VF £1,000

Third Coinage 1544–1547

Obverse Legend HENRIC 8 D G AGL FR Z HIB REX — Henry VIII by the grace of God King of England France and Ireland

Reverse Legend O CRUX AVE SPES UNICA — Hail thou cross my only hope

Obverse As previous, but annulet on ship; mintmark lis.

Reverse As previous.

H8HA-015 VG £150 F £275 VF £500

As previous, but no annulet on ship. This issue should not be confused with the second coinage; the only difference is the obverse legend.

H8HA-020 VG £160 F £300 VF £550

As previous, but three annulets on ship.

H8HA-025 VG £140 F £250 VF £500

Edward VI 1547–1553

Half-angels were produced during the third period of Edward VI's reign but only one specimen survives. The issue, which now had a value of five shillings, was produced at the Tower mint in London.

Obverse Legend EDWARD VI D G AGL F Z HI REX — Edward VI by the grace of God King of England France and Ireland

Reverse Legend PER CRU TUA SALVA NOS XPE — By Thy cross save us O Christ our Redeemer

Obverse St Michael killing the dragon; mintmark ostrich's head.

Reverse Ship with royal arms in centre, a mast in the shape of a cross, 'E' and a rose either side of mast.

E6HA-005 unique

Mary 1553–1554

Half-angels were struck during Mary's reign, however, they are rare. They were also struck during the reign of Philip and Mary, the main differences being the obverse legend. The style of the coin, with the exception of the legends, is very much a continuation of previous reigns.

Obverse Legend MARIA D G A FR Z HIB REGINA — Mary by the grace of God Queen of England France and Ireland

Reverse Legend A DNO FACTU EST ISTVD Z — This is the Lord's doing and it is marvellous in our eyes (abbreviated)

Obverse St Michael killing the dragon; mintmark pomegranate.

Reverse Ship with royal arms in centre, a mast in the shape of a cross, 'M' and rose either side of the cross.

MHA-005 F £2,000 VF £4,500

Philip and Mary 1554–1558

This issue, which is extremely rare, is very much a continuation from Mary's reign, the main difference being the obverse legend and the mintmark.

Obverse Legend PHILIP Z MARIA D G REX Z REGI — Philip and Mary by the grace of God King and Queen

Reverse Legend A DNO FACTU EST ISTUD Z EST MIR — This is the Lord's doing and it is marvellous in our eyes

Obverse St Michael killing the dragon; mintmark lis.

Reverse Ship with royal arms in centre, a mast with PM either side.

PMHA-005 ex. rare

Elizabeth I 1558–1603

During the first five issues of Elizabeth I's reign half-angels were produced with a value of five shillings. They circulated alongside the crown of similar value, however, by now the half-angel's style, which had changed very little from the reign of Henry VI, was looking tired and old-fashioned, especially when compared to many of the other contemporary English gold coins.

First — Third Issues 1559–1578

Obverse Legend ELIZABETH D G A FR ET HI REGINA — Elizabeth by the grace of God Queen of England France and Ireland

Reverse Legend A DNO FACTUM EST ISTUD ET EST MIRA — This is the Lord's doing and it is marvellous in our eyes

Obverse St Michael killing the dragon; mintmark lis, wire lined inner circles.

Reverse Ship with royal arms in centre, a mast in the shape of a cross above, 'E' and rose either side, wire lined inner circles; mintmark lis.

ELHA-005 ex. rare

Legends As previous.

Obverse As previous, but beaded inner circles; mintmark lis, cross crosslet, coronet, ermine, acorn, eglantine.

Reverse As previous, but beaded inner circles, the ship now faces right.

ELHA-010 VG £150 F £250 VF £500

Fourth Issue 1578–1582

The fineness of gold for this issue was slightly reduced.
Legends As previous.

Obverse As previous, but mintmark Greek cross or sword.

Reverse As previous; mintmarks as obverse.

ELHA-015 VG £150 F £250 VF £500

As previous, but no 'E' or rose by mast of ship; mintmark Latin cross.

ELHA-020 VG £250 F £500 VF £1,000

Fifth Issue 1583–1600

The fineness of gold for this issue was raised slightly.

Legends As previous.

Obverse As ELHA-015; mintmark bell, 'A', escallop, crescent, hand, key, anchor.

Reverse As ELHA-015; mintmarks in obverse.

ELHA-025 VG £150 F £250 VF £500

James I 1603–1625

Gold half-angels were struck for a very short time during James I's second coinage. In 1612 the value of all half-angels was raised to five shillings and sixpence, and this included all coins from previous reigns and issues. However, the half-angel had become obsolete in denomination and style from medieval England, and production of the half-angel finally ceased in 1619.

Collecting Hints

All issues are extremely rare.

Obverse Legend IACOBUS D G MA BRI FRA ET HI REX — James by the grace of God King of Great Britain France and Ireland

Reverse Legend A DNO FACTUM EST ISTUD — This is the Lord's doing and it is marvellous in our eyes

Obverse St Michael killing the dragon; mintmark tower, trefoil, cinquefoil, tun, closed book, plain cross, saltire cross.

Reverse Ship with royal arms in centre, 'I' and rose either side of shortened mast; mintmarks as obverse.

J1HA-005 F £1,500 VF £3,000

Half Florin or Leopard

Edward III 1327–1377

In 1344, a year after Edward III had instructed the Florentines George Kirkyn and Lotte Nicholyn to produce gold denominations for England, the half-florin or leopard was created. Largely based on the European gold issues, it was intended to be not just for England but for the whole of Europe. Its value was three shillings but as the gold used to strike the coins had been overvalued, the coins were unacceptable to the public. By August of that year the issue was demonetised and the coins recalled, melted down and used to make the popular and more acceptable noble issues. Nevertheless, this issue is undoubtedly one of the most beautiful medieval English coins ever produced and it is a loss to collectors that virtually all specimens were destroyed.

Collecting Hints

This issue is extremely rare; however, most specimens exist in the higher grades.

Obverse Legend EDWAR D GRA REX ANGL Z FRANC DNS HIB — Edward by the grace of God King of England and France Lord of Ireland

Reverse Legend DOMINE NE IN FURORE TUO ARGUAS ME — O Lord rebuke me not in Thy anger

Obverse A leopard with a cloak of the royal arms.

Reverse Royal cross in a quatrefoil, a leopard in each quarter.

E3HFL-005 ex. rare

Halfcrown

Henry VIII's monetary reform of 1526 introduced the halfcrown which, like most new denominations, was struck in some quantity. It was made of 22 carat gold and had the value of two shillings and sixpence. However, although the gold issue was important to the monetary reform it was really too small in size and could easily get lost. Furthermore, having a coin of such high value this small was unpopular so the silver halfcrown was introduced during Edward VI's fine silver issue. Made of good quality silver and beautifully designed, it was an important and acceptable denomination. Probably because there were enough numbers in circulation, halfcrowns were not struck again until the end of Elizabeth I's reign, except for some gold issues. However, during all future reigns and until 1967, large quantities of halfcrowns were produced for circulation.

Henry VIII 1509–1547

Under Henry VIII gold halfcrowns were produced from 1526, during the second and third coinages as well as the posthumous coinage struck under Edward VI. All these issues are fairly similar. Halfcrowns were struck at the Tower mint during the second coinage, then also at Bristol and Southwark during the third coinage and finally at the two London mints, Tower and Southwark, during the posthumous coinage. To identify the mint and issue, collectors should pay particular attention to the mint-mark at the beginning of the obverse and, in most cases, the reverse legend.

Collecting Hints

These issues are fairly scarce but tend to be unpopular with collectors as there is no bust of the king on the coin. Rarely found in better than Fine condition, they are sometimes damaged. Nevertheless, they are the first halfcrown struck and no serious collection of halfcrowns would be complete without an example.

Second Coinage 1526–1544

Obverse Legend RUTILANS ROSA SINE SPINA — A dazzling rose without a thorn
Reverse Legend HENRIC 8 DI GRA REX AGL Z FRA — Henry VIII by the grace of God King of England and France
Obverse Crown above a rose; mintmark rose.
Reverse Crown over royal shield.

H8HC-005 VG £100 F £220 VF £500

As previous, but rose dividing 'HK' on both sides of the coin, uncrowned on obverse.

H8HC-010 VG £90 F £200 VF £420

As previous, but HK on the obverse only; mintmark rose on obverse and lis on reverse (the dies of this issue are muled), or lis, or arrow.

H8HC-015 VG £100 F £220 VF £500

As previous, but HI both sides of coin; mintmark arrow.

H8HC-020 VG £120 F £250 VF £550

As previous, except that the mintmark is a pheon, there is 'HR' on both sides of coin and the reverse legend reads HENRIC 8 D G AGL FR Z HIB REX (varieties exist) — Henry VIII by the grace of God King of England France and Ireland

H8HC-025 VG £200 F £400 VF £850

Third Coinage 1544–1547

Unlike the silver issues of the third coinage, the gold issues were never debased.

Tower Mint

Obverse Legend RUTILANS ROSA SINE SPINA — A dazzling rose without a thorn
Reverse Legend HENRIC 8 DG AGL FR Z HIB REX — Henry VIII by the grace of God King of England France and Ireland
Obverse Crown above a rose; mintmark pellet in annulet, initials H.R.
Reverse Crown over shield, H.R.

H8HC-030 VG £90 F £180 VF £375

As previous, but an annulet on the inner circle.

H8HC-035 VG £95 F £190 VF £380

Southwark Mint

This was London's second mint and operated just south of the river Thames. This issue used Roman and Lombardic lettering.
Legends As previous.
Obverse As H8HC-030 but mintmark 'S'.
Reverse As H8HC-030 but mintmark 'S'.

H8HC-040 VG £110 F £230 VF £475

Obverse Legend HENRIC 8 ROSA SINE SPIN — Henry VIII a rose without a thorn
Reverse Legend DEI GRA AGL FR Z HIB REX — By the grace of God King of England France and Ireland
Obverse As previous, but mintmark 'E'.

Reverse As previous, but mintmark 'E'.

H8HC-045 VG £150 F £300 VF £600

Bristol Mint

Obverse Legend HENRIC 8 ROSA SINE SPINA — Henry VIII a rose without a thorn

Reverse Legend DEI GRA AGL FRA Z HIB REX — By the grace of God King of England France and Ireland

Obverse As previous, but mintmark 'WS' monogram.

Reverse As previous, but no mintmark.

H8HC-050 VG £150 F £350 VF £700

Posthumous Coinage 1547–1551

Tower Mint

On each issue a mintmark is found on the obverse and/or reverse.

Obverse Legend RUTILANS ROSA SINE SPINA — A dazzling rose without a thorn

Reverse Legend HENRIC 8 D GR AGL FRA HIB REX — Henry VIII by the grace of God King of England France and Ireland

Obverse Crown over rose dividing 'H.R.'; mintmark arrow, none, 'K', grapple, or martlet.

Reverse Crown over royal shield; mintmark arrow, none or martlet.

H8HC-055 VG £150 F £300 VF £600

Southwark Mint

As previous, but legends all in Roman lettering and mintmark 'E' or none.

H8HC-060 VG £150 F £300 VF £600

Edward VI 1547–1553

Three main types of halfcrown were produced during Edward VI's reign. Firstly there was Henry VIII's posthumous issue listed above. Then, gold halfcrowns were produced during the first, second and third periods (1547–1553); the first being similar in style to that of Henry's except for bearing the king's own name and initials and the next two having the bust of the Boy King on the obverse and a crowned shield on the reverse. The third main issue of the reign is the fine silver issue and the halfcrown for this, struck in fine silver, is a superb coin depicting the Boy King on horseback with the date below on the obverse and the royal arms on the reverse. All of these issues were produced at the Tower mint.

Gold Issue

First Period 1547–1549

Obverse Legend RUTILANS ROSA SINE SPINA — A dazzling rose without a thorn

Reverse Legend EDWARD 6 D GR AGL FR Z HIB REX — Edward VI by the grace of God King of England France and Ireland

Obverse Crowned rose dividing 'ER'.

Reverse Crowned shield dividing 'ER'; mintmark arrow.

E6HC-005 ex. rare

Second Period 1549–1550

Obverse Legend EDWARD VI DG AG FR Z HI REX — Edward VI by the grace of God King of England France and Ireland

Reverse Legend SCUTUM FIDEI PROTEGET EUM — The shield of faith shall protect him

Obverse Uncrowned bust of king; mintmark 'Y' or arrow.

Reverse Crown over shield; mintmark 'Y' or none.

E6HC-010 VG £300 F £700 VF £1,400

As previous, but the king is crowned; mintmark arrow, swan, grapple or 'Y' — sometimes a different mintmark on the obverse and reverse.

E6HC-015 VG £275 F £550 VF £1,100

As E6HC-010, but mintmark arrow or grapple and the obverse and reverse legends are transposed:

Obverse Legend SCUTUM FIDEI PROTEGET EUM-The shield of faith shall protect him

Reverse Legend EDWARD VI DG AG FR Z HI REX-Edward VI by the grace of God King of England France and Ireland

E6HC-020 VG £275 F £600 VF £1,200

Third Period 1550–1553

Collecting Hints

This issue is very rare in any grade and when available is usually in Fine to VF condition.

Obverse Legend EDWARD VI DG AG FR Z HI REX — Edward VI by the grace of God King of England France and Ireland

Reverse Legend SCUTUM FIDEI PROTEGET EUM — The shield of faith shall protect him

Obverse Crowned king holding orb and sceptre; mintmark 'Y' or tun.

Reverse Crown over shield, dividing 'ER'.

E6HC-025 VG £400 F £800 VF £2,000

Fine Silver Issue 1551–1553

Collecting Hints

This issue while scarce is obtainable usually undamaged in Fine condition; VF and even EF examples exist but are rare.

Obverse Legend EDWARD VI DG AGL FRA Z HIB REX — Edward VI by the grace of God King of England France and Ireland

Reverse Legend POSUI DEUM ADIVITORE MEUM — I have made God my helper

Obverse Boy King on walking horse, a plume on the horse's head, the date 1551 below the horse; mintmark 'Y'.

E6HC-030 VG £140 F £220 VF £500

As previous, but the horse is galloping and there is no plume on its head; mintmark tun, dated 1551–1553.

E6HC-035 VG £150 F £250 VF £550

As previous, but large walking horse; mintmark tun, dated 1553 only.

E6HC-040 VG £200 F £450 VF £1,200

No halfcrowns were struck during the reign of Mary or Philip and Mary.

Elizabeth I 1558–1603

Gold halfcrowns were produced during most of Elizabeth's reign; they were all hammered except for one very rare milled issue. Silver halfcrowns were only produced during the last two years of the reign, albeit in large quantities. The gold halfcrowns on the other hand were struck in fairly small numbers not only because many silver ones had been produced under Edward VI but also because the public disliked a small coin with such a high value. All halfcrowns were struck at the Tower Mint.

Hammered Gold Issue 1559–1602

First — Third Issues 1559–1578

Collecting Hints

Gold halfcrowns are rare. They are usually found in Fine condition, sometimes creased or holed; VF and even EF examples exist but are rare. However, the value of this issue does not reflect its rarity due to the fact that most collectors prefer to own either a silver halfcrown or a gold coin of larger value; a gold halfcrown may be rather difficult to obtain.

Obverse Legend ELIZABETH DG ANG FRA ET HI REGINA (minor varieties exist) — Elizabeth by the grace of God Queen of England France and Ireland

Reverse Legend SCUTUM FIDEI PROTEGET EAM — The shield of faith shall protect her

Obverse Crowned bust of queen facing left, wire-line inner circles; mintmark lis.

Reverse Crowned royal arms in shield which divides 'E.R.' (ELIZABETH REGINA).

ELHC-005 ex. rare only three known

As previous, but beaded inner circles; mintmark cross crosslet, rose, portcullis, lion, coronet, castle.

ELHC-010 VG £200 F £350 VF £750

No halfcrowns were struck for the fourth issue.

Fifth Issue 1583–1600

As previous, but older bust of queen; mintmark tun, woolpack, key, anchor (which is unique) and 0.

ELHC-015 VG £200 F £350 VF £750

Sixth Issue 1601–1602

As previous, but mintmark 1 or 2. This issue was struck alongside the silver halfcrown.

ELHC-020 ex. rare

Milled Gold Issue 1561–1570

This extremely rare issue can easily be identified by the completely different style of the coin and the mintmark star and lis.

Collecting Hints

While all milled gold issues of Elizabeth I are rare, the milled halfcrown is by far the rarest. It will be extremely difficult for collectors to obtain this coin in any grade.

Obverse Legend ELIZABETH D.G. ANG FRA (ET or Z) HIB REGINA — Elizabeth by the grace of God Queen of England France and Ireland

Reverse Legend SCUTUM FIDEI PROTEGET EAM — The shield of faith shall protect her

Obverse Crowned bust of queen facing left; mintmark star or lis.

Reverse Crowned royal arms in shield which divides 'E.R.'.

ELHC-025 VG £700 F £1,500 VF £3,000

Hammered Silver Issue 1601–1602

Even though the silver halfcrown was struck for only two years during the sixth coinage, it is more common than the gold issues due firstly to the fact that large quantities of silver were coming

in to Europe mainly from the Americas and secondly to the popularity of the coin's size and quality. The obverse shows a superb bust of the queen holding a sceptre and the reverse the royal shield over a cross. The mintmark '1' or '2' denotes the year (1601 or 1602) and can be found at the beginning of the obverse and reverse legend.

Collecting Hints

Silver halfcrowns are available in most grades, the most common being about Fine. However, rare and desirable VF and EF examples exist. Similarly, worn specimens can be found, often with a very flat portrait and a much clearer shield on the reverse which is due to the quality of strike. These issues while rare are usually obtainable and are sought after by collectors. Coins of mintmark '2' (1602) are extremely rare, less than a dozen are known.

Obverse Legend ELIZABETH D.G ANG FRA ET HIBER REGINA — Elizabeth by the grace of God Queen of England France and Ireland

Reverse Legend POSUI DEUM ADIUTOREM MEUM — I have made God my helper

Obverse Bust of queen holding sceptre; mintmark 1 or 2.

Reverse Royal shield over cross.

ELHC-030 VG £170 F £320 VF £600

James I 1603–1625

Both gold and silver halfcrowns were produced during James I's reign; all have the king's bust on the obverse.

Gold Issue

Collecting Hints

The first coinage is very rare in any grade. The second coinage issues, while rare are usually available in Fine condition; VF examples also exist but are very rare. Many issues are pierced and there is speculation that this was officially done to devalue the coins in later reigns. However, the scarcity of these coins is not reflected in their value as collectors prefer the silver halfcrowns or a larger but more common gold denomination.

First Coinage 1603–1604

Obverse Legend IACOBUS DG. AN SCO ET HI REX — James by the grace of God King of England Scotland and Ireland

Reverse Legend TUEATUR UNITA DEUS — May God guard these United [Kingdoms]

Obverse Crowned bust of king; mintmark thistle or lis.

Reverse Crown over royal shield, 'I R' divided by crown.

J1HC-005 VG £150 F £250 VF £600

Second Coinage 1604–1619

The main differences between the first and second coinage are the obverse legend readings and the mintmarks. The busts of the king on the second and third type are also different.

Obverse Legend I DG ROSA SINE SPINA — James by the grace of God a rose without a thorn

Reverse TUEATUR UNITA DEUS — May God guard these United [Kingdoms]

Obverse Crowned bust of king of similar style to the first coinage (first bust); mintmark lis, rose, escallop, grapes, coronet, key.

Reverse Crown over royal shield, 'I R' at sides of crown.

J1HC-010 VG £100 F £175 VF £350

As previous, but the king has a square beard that projects (third bust); mintmark key, bell, mullet, tower or trefoil.

J1HC-015 VG £110 F £180 VF £360

As previous, but the king has longer hair brushed back (fifth bust); mintmark cinquefoil, tun, book, crescent or plain cross.

J1HC-020 VG £100 F £175 VF £350

No gold halfcrowns were produced during the third coinage.

Silver Issue

Silver halfcrowns were produced during all three of James I's coinages. All issues show the king on horseback on the obverse and the royal arms on the reverse, and a mintmark can be found at the beginning of the obverse and reverse legend. These mintmarks are important for identification, particularly since Scotland struck coins that were very similar to the halfcrowns. All Scottish issues are mintmark thistle, while none of the second coinage English halfcrowns and only some of the first and third coinages used that mintmark. To distinguish these coins collectors need to look at the beginning of the reverse legend, which is QUAE DEUS for the Scottish coins and the second and third coinages, and EXURGAT for the first coinage, and then at the Irish harp on the reverse shield which in the English issue has a bird's head on the edge and on the Scottish one the end of the harp is turned in. The only English issue with a bird's head is the third coinage. It is important to check that the mintmarks correspond to the issue.

First Coinage 1603–1604

Obverse Legend IACOBUS D.G. ANG SCO FRAN ET HIB REX — James by the grace of God King of England Scotland France and Ireland

Reverse Legend EXURGAT DEUS DISSIPENTUR INIMICI — Let God arise and His enemies be scattered

Obverse King on horseback; mintmark thistle or lis.

Reverse Royal shield.

J1HC-025 VG £225 F £400 VF £1,000

Second Coinage 1604–1619

Obverse Legend IACOBUS DG MAG BRIT FRAN ET HIB REX — James by the grace of God King of Great Britain France and Ireland

Reverse Legend QUAE DEUS CONIUNXIT NEMO SEPARET — What God has joined together let no man put asunder

Obverse As previous, but mintmark lis, rose or escallop.

Reverse As previous.

J1HC-030 VG £200 F £350 VF £700

Third Coinage 1619–1625

Legends As previous.

Obverse As previous, but mintmark rose, thistle, lis or trefoil.

Reverse Shield with bird-headed Irish harp.

J1HC-035 VG £120 F £200 VF £450

As previous, but there is no groundline on the obverse; mintmark rose.

J1HC-040 VG £150 F £300 VF £600

As previous, but plume over shield on reverse; mintmark thistle, lis or trefoil.

J1HC-045 VG £120 F £220 VF £450

Charles I 1625–1649

During Charles I's reign large quantities of silver halfcrowns were produced, mainly at the Tower mint in London, although most provincial mints and several siege towns also struck them. Like many of Charles's other issues, the halfcrowns are very complex with many varieties and styles existing. In general the most common issues are those struck under the king at the Tower mint and if collectors are unsure of a coin they should refer to the Tower issues first and then the provincial ones. All except the siege pieces depict the king on horseback on the obverse and either the royal arms in a shield (Tower issues), or the royal arms or a legend in the centre (provincial issues) on the reverse. As stated earlier, many varieties exist. Unlike many of the provincial issues, all Tower halfcrowns are undated; also all except the siege issues have mintmarks, usually on the obverse and reverse legend. In identifying coins, collectors should always check that a mintmark ties in with a particular issue. They should also look carefully at the shapes and style of the royal arms on the reverse and at the king on horseback on the obverse as again many varieties exist, particularly regarding how the horse is walking, the position of the king's sword and the king's scarf. Unlike the smaller denominations, virtually all halfcrowns have no mark of value, however, all the smaller denominations did not have the king on horseback. The next higher denomination which used the king on horseback

was the crown which is much bigger, with a diameter of about 43 mm compared to the approximately 34 mm of the halfcrown.

Many forgeries of Charles I halfcrowns exist, most of them being good contemporary forgeries of the Tower mint issue, usually with a silvered layer over a copper or brass core. Although the style of these forgeries is usually good, the silver flakes off in most cases revealing the base metal underneath. The other main forgeries of halfcrowns that exist are nineteenth century 'museum' copies of the provincial mints. These were usually not produced as forgeries, however many have found there way into the market and can easily deceive an inexperienced collector. They are usually bright and untoned and often have very smooth edges whilst original coins tend to have rather ragged edges. Also some forgeries tend to be underweight and small in size. It is important, therefore, that collectors buy coins from these issues from a reputable dealer who has considerable knowledge.

Tower Mint

Tower Mint under King 1625–1642

Collecting Hints

Most Tower issues are fairly common, particularly the later ones. All issues are hammered, with the later ones often being poorly struck on flans of irregular size so perhaps not all of the legend will be clear. Collectors should try to obtain an example with a clear king on horseback, a clear mintmark and as much of the legend as possible. Many of these issues have been found in large hoards, often buried during the Civil War; they are usually available in VG to VF condition and, although EF examples exist, coins often left the mint in only VF condition. Moreover, many are found clipped, some so badly that they have no legend at all left. Also some coins are found with what look like deliberate nasty scratches and while the reason for this remains open to speculation, it could well have been the work of a contemporary ardent anti-royalist.

Obverse Legend CAROLUS D.G. MAG BRI FRA ET HI REX — Charles by the grace of God King of Great Britain France and Ireland

Reverse Legend CHRISTO AUSPICE REGNO — I reign under the auspices of Christ

Obverse King riding decorated horse on a groundline, a rose on the horse's coat; mintmark lis.

Reverse Square-topped garnished shield over a cross.

C1HC-005 VG £75 F £150 VF £350

As previous, but no rose on horse's coat.

C1HC-010 ex. rare

As previous, but no groundline.

C1HC-015 VG £75 F £150 VF £350

Obverse Legend As previous; minor varieties exist.

Reverse Legend As previous.

Obverse As previous, but a rather clumsier-looking horse; mintmark cross calvary, blackamoor's head, castle.

Reverse Royal arms not over a shield.

C1HC-020 VG £60 F £120 VF £250

As previous, but the horse is on a groundline; mintmark lis.

C1HC-025 VG £250 F £500

As previous, but with a plume over the shield on the reverse; mintmark lis, cross calvary, blackamoor's head, castle or anchor.

C1HC-030 VG £300 F £500 VF £1,200

As previous, but a smaller horse with a rose on its coat on the obverse; mintmark heart or plume.

C1HC-035 ex. rare

Obverse Legend As previous; many minor varieties exist.

Reverse Legend As previous.

Obverse King on horseback with no groundline or rose on the horse's coat; mintmark lis over rose or lis.

Reverse Royal arms in an oval garnished shield with C.R. (CAROLUS REX) above it.

C1HC-040 VG £50 F £90 VF £180

As previous, but a rose between 'C.R' on the reverse.

C1HC-045 ex. rare

As previous, but a large plume dividing 'CR' on the reverse.

C1HC-050 VG £80 F £160 VF £320

As C1HC-040, but differently garnished oval shield which divides 'C.R'; mintmark harp or portcullis.

C1HC-055 VG £45 F £75 VF £150

As previous, but a plume over the shield on the reverse; mintmark harp.

C1HC-060 VG £200 F £350 VF £700

Obverse Legend As previous, many varieties exist.

Reverse Legend As previous.

Obverse New-style king on horseback, the horse is undecorated, the king's sword is upright and his scarf flies out from the waist; mintmark anchor, bell, crown or tun.

Reverse Round garnished shield.

C1HC-065 VG £40 F £60 VF £135

As previous, but plume over the shield on the reverse; mintmark portcullis, bell, crown or tun.

C1HC-070 VG £70 F £140 VF £280

As previous, but the king's scarf flies from the shoulder; mintmark tun, anchor, triangle and star.

C1HC-075 VG £40 F £60 VF £130

As previous, but rough ground under the horse; mintmark triangle and star.

C1HC-080 VG £40 F £60 VF £135

Obverse This issue has a foreshortened horse with its mane in front of its chest and its tail between its rear legs; the king's scarf is flying from his shoulder; mintmark star and triangle in a circle.

Reverse As previous.

C1HC-085 VG £40 F £65 VF £135

Tower Mint under Parliament 1642–1648

With the Civil War dividing the country, this issue was struck under the orders of Parliament and it is interesting to note that the king still appeared on the coins. These issues are very much a continuation of the Tower mint under the king issues, but can easily be identified by their unique mintmarks.

Collecting Hints

Two of these issues are fairly common while one is rare. They are all slightly scarcer than the Tower mint under the king issues and often found poor in style and production. Collectors should be able to obtain an example in VG or Fine condition, although VF is quite rare, due to the poor strikings. Remember to try to obtain an example with a clear mintmark. These issues do not tend to be so badly clipped as some of the later royal ones.

Obverse Legend CAROLUS D.G. MAG BRI FRA ET HIB REX — Charles by the grace of God King of Great Britain France and Ireland

Reverse Legend CHRISTO AUSPICE REGNO — I reign under the auspices of Christ

Obverse King on horseback with sword pointing upwards and scarf flying from his shoulder; mintmark '(P)', '(R)', eye, sun.

Reverse Royal arms in a round shield.

C1HC-090 VG £40 F £70 VF £140

As previous, but the king is on a foreshortened horse with its mane in front of its chest and its tail between its rear legs; mintmark '(P)'.

C1HC-095 VG £100 F £200 VF £400

The king is on a tall horse with a long bushy tail; mintmark sun, sceptre.

C1HC-100 VG £60 F £110 VF £220

Briot's Coinage

Milled Issues 1631–1639

These milled or machine-made issues are superb in design and quality and probably the finest halfcrowns produced under Charles I. The obverse has the king on horseback while the reverse has an oval shield below a crown; also a mintmark can be found on the obverse of the first issue and on both sides of the second issue. These mintmarks, which both incorporate the letter B for Briot, are specific to these issues.

Collecting Hints

These issues are rare but when obtainable usually available in Fine or VF condition. They are rarely found clipped and are usually on full round flans.

First Milled Issue 1631–1639

Obverse Legend CAROLUS D.G. MAGN BRITAN FRAN ET HIB REX — Charles by the grace of God King of Great Britain France and Ireland

Reverse Legend CHRISTO AUSPICE REGNO — I reign under the auspices of Christ

Obverse King on horseback holding sword; mintmark flower and 'B'.

Reverse Crown over shield which divides 'C.R'.

C1HC-105 VG £140 F £300 VF £650

Second Milled Issue 1638–1639

Legends As previous.

Obverse As previous, except with mintmark anchor and 'B'.

Reverse As previous, except with mintmark anchor and 'B' also on reverse.

C1HC-110 VG £120 F £280 VF £600

Hammered Issue 1638–1639

While there is no doubt that the dies for this very rare issue were made by Briot, there is considerable evidence that the coins were not struck by him. The obverse has a Briot-style horse and the reverse a square-topped oval shield. In some cases, a reverse die from a common Tower issue was used and in all cases mintmark triangle has been used with a Briot obverse die.

Obverse Legend CAROLUS DG MAG BRIT FR ET HIB REX — Charles by the grace of God King of Great Britain France and Ireland

Reverse Legend CHRISTO AUSPICE REGNO — I reign under the auspices of Christ

Obverse King on horseback holding sword; mintmark anchor.

Reverse Square-topped shield; mintmark anchor.

C1HC-115 VG £300 F £600 VF £1,200

Obverse As previous, but mintmark triangle over anchor.

Reverse Round shield; mintmark triangle. This die is from a Tower mint issue.

C1HC-120 rare

Provincial Mints

York Mint 1643–1644

These scarce but obtainable issues are easily recognisable by the mintmark lion which is specific to this issue and found at the beginning of the obverse and reverse legend. Also in many of the issues EBOR (short for EBORACUM, Latin for York) is found under the horse. Many issues appear to be very slightly oval in shape and are sometimes very slightly bent. This appears to be the way they were made and does not affect their value.

Obverse Legend CAROLUS DG MAG BRI FR ET HI REX — Charles by the grace of God King of Great Britain France and Ireland

Reverse Legend CHRISTO AUSPICE REGNO — I reign under the auspices of Christ

Obverse King on horseback holding sword, groundline below horse; mintmark lion.

Reverse Square-topped shield dividing 'C.R'; mintmark lion.
C1HC-125 VG £130 F £220 VF £550

As previous, but oval shield and no C.R. on reverse.

C1HC-130 VG £100 F £170 VF £400

Obverse As previous, but no groundline below the horse.

Reverse A somewhat flattened shield.

C1HC-135 VG £90 F £170 VF £400

As previous, but EBOR below the horse on obverse.

C1HC-140 VG £85 F £160 VF £320

Obverse Legend CAROLUS DG MAG BRIT FRAN ET HIB REX — Charles by the grace of God King of Great Britain France and Ireland

Reverse Legend CHRISTO AUSPICE REGNO — I reign under the auspices of Christ

Obverse King on tall horse, EBOR below horse; mintmark lion.

Reverse Square-topped shield with crown above, flowers in legend, 'C.R' divided by shield.

C1HC-145 VG £80 F £140 VF £320

As previous, but oval shield on reverse.

C1HC-150 VG £80 F £140 VF £300

As previous, but the horse's tail is between its rear legs and on the reverse instead of 'CR' there are two lion's paws either side holding the shield.

C1HC-155 VG £80 F £140 VF £300

Aberystwyth Mint 1638–1642

This issue can easily be identified by the mintmark open book which can be found at the beginning of the obverse and reverse legends. The obverse die from this mint was used with reverse dies from other provincial mints to produce coins for other provincial mints. Therefore, check that the mintmark open book can be found on both obverse and reverse. If it is only found on the obverse, check the Shrewsbury mint issues.

> # Collecting Hints
>
> This issue is very rare in any grade and usually available in Fine condition although VF examples do exist. Most specimens are usually unclipped and undamaged. Should collectors just want an example from the Aberystwyth mint, they should consider a groat or threepence as they are fairly common and easily obtainable in good condition.

Obverse Legend CAROLUS DG MAG BRIT FRA ET HI REX — Charles by the grace of God King of Great Britain France and Ireland

Reverse Legend CHRISTO AUSPICE REGNO — I reign under the auspices of Christ

Obverse King on horseback holding sword, small plume behind king; mintmark open book.

Reverse Oval shield with large plume above; mintmark open book.

C1HC-160 VG £300 F £450 VF £900

As previous, but a more spirited horse. Obverse legend reads FRAN ET HIB.

C1HC-165 VG £320 F £480 VF £1,000

As C1HC-160, but ground below horse.

C1HC-170 VG £350 F £550 VF £1,200

Aberystwyth Furnace Mint 1648–1649

This issue, while fairly similar to the Aberystwyth ones, is differentiated by the mintmark crown found on the obverse and reverse. As it also has a plume behind the king, it can easily be distinguished from Tower mint issues which also used the mintmark crown.

Collecting Hints

This issue is very rare in any grade. Rarely found in better than Fine condition, it is much cruder in style than the Aberystwyth issues.

Obverse Legend CAROLUS DG MAG BRIT FRAN ET HI REX — Charles by the grace of God King of Great Britain France and Ireland

Reverse Legend CHRISTO AUSPICE REGNO — I reign under the auspices of Christ

Obverse King holding sword on horseback, plume behind king; mintmark crown.

Reverse Plume over royal arms.

C1HC-175 VG £600 F £1,200 VF £2,500

Hereford Mint

While documentary evidence exists that silver for coins was brought to Hereford, there is no other conclusive source establishing that this extremely rare issue was actually produced in Hereford. It used to be attributed to the Combe Martin mint. So, although there is no doubt that it was made in the area, the site of the actual mint cannot be confirmed. After all, with the Civil War raging, the dies for this issue could have been moved from town to town.

Collecting Hints

All coins from this issue are very rare and always found very worn, usually in less than Fine condition; VF examples probably do not exist.

Obverse Legend CAROLUS DG MAG BRI FRA ET HI REX — Charles by the grace of God King of Great Britain France and Ireland

Reverse Legend CHRISTO AUSPICE REGNO — I reign under the auspices of Christ

Obverse King holding sword on horseback; mintmark small lis.

Reverse Royal arms with lion and unicorn either side, crown above dividing C.R., dated 1645.

C1HC-180 VG £800 F £2,000

As previous, but undated.

C1HC-185 VG £800 F £2,000

Shrewsbury Mint 1642

During the Civil War it was intended to open mints at the king's temporary capitals of York and Shrewsbury. The Aberystwyth mint which had been run under royal licence by Thomas Bushell before the conflict erupted was moved to Shrewsbury where it could be better protected by local royalists and produce money for royal troops. It was only active in 1642 and, due to a shortage of gold, virtually all coins were struck in silver which was mainly supplied by the universities and wealthy royalists. Various dies were used for the issues including odd ones from the Aberystwyth mint, others smuggled out of London and also locally-made dies. By the end of 1642 the king had established himself at Oxford so Bushell moved there to open a new mint and Shrewsbury was closed. Because dies from other provincial mints, notably Aberystwyth and Oxford, were often interchanged, these issues are fairly difficult to identify. Nevertheless, all Shrewsbury coins have the king on horseback on the obverse, the Declaration on the reverse and are dated 1642. This makes identification somewhat easier as most Oxford issues are dated 1643.

Collecting Hints

All Shrewsbury issues are scarce and the halfcrowns are no exception; they are usually available undamaged in Fine to VF condition.

Obverse Legend CAROLUS DG MAG BRIT FRAN ET HIB REX — Charles by the grace of God King of Great Britain France and Ireland

Reverse Outer Legend EXURGAT DEUS DISSIPENTUR INIMICI — Let God arise and His enemies be scattered

Reverse Centre Legend RELIG PROT LEG ANGL LIBERT PAR — The religion of the Protestants the laws of England the liberty of Parliament

Obverse King on horseback, plume behind him; mintmark open book. This is the obverse Aberystwyth die.

Reverse Single plume above Declaration, 1642. This is a Shrewsbury die.

C1HC-190 ex. rare

Obverse As previous, but fat plume behind king on horseback (Aberystwyth die).

Reverse Three plumes above Declaration (Shrewsbury die).

C1HC-195 VG £150 F £250 VF £600

The following are all Shrewsbury dies except C1HC-215, but in certain cases the obverse or reverse die was used later to produce coins at Oxford.

Obverse Legend CAROLUS DG MAG BR FR ET HIB REX — Charles by the grace of God King of Great Britain France and Ireland

Reverse Legends As previous; minor varieties exist.

Obverse New-style Shrewsbury horseman with plume behind.

Reverse Single plume over Declaration and 1642 below.

C1HC-200 VG £180 F £300 VF £700

Obverse As previous.

Reverse The digits '2' and '6', for halfcrown, divided by a plume, over the Declaration.

C1HC-205 VG £300 F £600

As previous, but groundline below horse.

C1HC-210 VG £250 F £550 VF £1,100

Obverse As previous.

Reverse Plume above shield; mintmark open book (Aberystwyth die).

C1HC-215 VG £160 F £300 VF £600

Obverse As previous.

Reverse As C1HC-210, but three plumes above the Declaration and no denomination.

C1HC-220 VG £120 F £220 VF £500

As previous, but no plume behind the king.

C1HC-225 VG £140 F £280 VF £600

Undoubtedly, other varieties exist due to the muling of dies and those issues would be much scarcer than the ones listed.

Oxford Mint 1642–1646

As stated above, the Shrewsbury mint closed and moved to Oxford at the end of 1642. Thomas Bushell and William Parkhurst were in charge of the Oxford mint which produced large quantities of gold and silver coins with metal supplied mostly by the universities and wealthy royalists. Several of the old dies from the Aberystwyth and Shrewsbury mints were used alongside new dies made locally, some by the young talented engraver Thomas Rawlins. Coins were struck at Oxford until the city finally surrendered to Cromwell's army in June 1646. The Oxford issues are fairly complex; all have the king on horseback on the obverse and the Declaration with the date below on the reverse and a number of issues also have 'OX' for Oxford below the date. Although many of the Oxford issues are similar to those of Shrewsbury, an identification problem should only arise with coins dated 1642; Oxford coins bear the mintmark plume at the beginning of the obverse legend. For coins dated 1643, however, collectors should also bear in mind that the Bristol mint used Oxford dies.

Obverse Legend CAROLUS DG MAG BRIT FRAN ET HIB REX — Charles by the grace of God King of Great Britain France and Ireland

Reverse Outer Legend EXURGAT DEUS DISSIPENTUR INIMICI — Let God arise and His enemies be scattered

Reverse Inner Legend RELIG PROT LEG ANG LIBER PAR — The religion of the Protestants the laws of England the liberty of Parliament

Obverse King on horseback, no plume behind king (Shrewsbury die); mintmark plume. All other Oxford halfcrowns have a plume behind the king.

Reverse Three small plumes of different style above the Declaration, 1642.

C1HC-230 VG £100 F £190 VF £400

Obverse Oxford horse with plume behind; mintmark plume.
Reverse Three plumes over Declaration, dated 1642.

C1HC-235 VG £80 F £160 VF £320

Obverse Shrewsbury-style horse walking on groundline, plume behind king; mintmark plume.
Reverse As C1HC-230.

C1HC-240 VG £70 F £130 VF £260

As previous, but no groundline.

C1HC-245 VG £75 F £150 VF £300

Oxford Style Horseman

Legends As previous.
Obverse New-style horse walking on groundline, plume behind king; mintmark plume.
Reverse Three plumes above the Declaration, 1643.

C1HC-250 VG £80 F £160 VF £320

As previous, but without groundline, dated 1643.

C1HC-255 VG £80 F £150 VF £300

Briot Style Horseman

Legends As previous, (minor varieties).
Obverse New Briot-style horseman with grass under horse and plume behind king; mintmark plume.
Reverse Three plumes above Declaration, dated 1643, 'OX' below date.

C1HC-260 VG £80 F £150 VF £300

Obverse As previous.
Reverse Three plumes, the central one being the largest; 1643 or 1644, 'OX' below date.

C1HC-265 VG £80 F £150 VF £300

Obverse As previous, but lumpy ground under horse.

Reverse As C1HC-260 dated 1643, sometimes with 'OX'.

C1HC-270 VG £80 F £150 VF £300

Obverse As previous.
Reverse As C1HC-265, dated 1643 or 1644, 'OX' below date.

C1HC-275 VG £80 F £150 VF £300

Obverse As previous, but plain ground under horse.
Reverse As previous, dated 1644, 'OX' below date.

C1HC-280 VG £80 F £150 VF £300

Obverse As previous.
Reverse As C1HC-270, 1644 or 1645, 'OX' below date.

C1HC-285 VG £80 F £150 VF £300

Obverse As previous.
Reverse As C1HC-280, but large date.

C1HC-290 VG £100 F £180 VF £380

Obverse As previous.
Reverse As previous, but two small plumes either side of small date.

C1HC-295 VG £120 F £200 VF £400

Larger Briot Style Horseman

The horseman in this issue is large and clumsy and much poorer in style, but the legends and mintmarks remain the same.
Obverse Larger Briot-style horseman on plain ground, plume behind king; mintmark plume.
Reverse Three plumes over Declaration, 1644 or 1645 and 'OX' below.

C1HC-300 VG £80 F £160 VF £340

As previous, but lumpy ground under horse on obverse.

C1HC-305 VG £80 F £160 VF £340

Obverse As previous.
Reverse Large central plume between two small ones, dated 1644, 'OX' below.

C1HC-310 VG £80 F £160 VF £340

Obverse As previous, but pebbly ground under horse.
Reverse As C1HC-305, dated 1645–1646, 'OX' below.

C1HC-315 VG £80 F £160 VF £340

Obverse As previous.
Reverse Pellets or annulets by plumes and by date, 1645–1646, 'OX' below.

C1HC-320 VG £80 F £160 VF £340

Obverse As previous, but grass below horse.

Reverse As C1HC-315, but pellets at date.

C1HC-325 VG £80 F £160 VF £340

Reverse Three Bristol plumes above Declaration, 1643.

C1HC-335 VG £90 F £160 VF £300

Obverse As previous.

Reverse Rosettes by plumes and by date 1645, 'OX' below.

C1HC-330 VG £100 F £200 VF £500

As previous, but mintmark 'BR' on reverse and plume on obverse.

C1HC-340 VG £80 F £150 VF £300

Bristol Mint 1643–1645

Most issues from the Bristol mint are fairly easy to identify as they have 'BR' either on the obverse below the horseman or on the reverse bellow the date or in the legend. Although some of the issues used the Oxford obverse die, they can easily be distinguished as they bear the mintmark 'BR' on the reverse. If an issue does not have a clear mintmark, the three plumes on the reverse are distinctive, especially on the 1643 issues, being very different in style to the plumes of the other mints. To identify a coin, collectors should also check it against the Shrewsbury and Oxford issues, paying particular attention to the date, the mintmark on the obverse and reverse, the number and size of the plumes on the reverse and the style of the horseman.

Obverse As previous, but Shrewsbury plume behind king; mintmark plume.

Reverse 'BR' mintmark, 1643 or 1644.

C1HC-345 VG £80 F £145 VF £280

As previous, but 'BR' below date 1644 and below horseman; no mintmark on reverse.

C1HC-350 VG £80 F £150 VF £300

Collecting Hints

Most issues from the Bristol mint, while scarce, are obtainable. They are usually found in about Fine condition and VF examples are rare. Many issues tend to be slightly clipped, possibly due to an irregular flan, or have a small piercing in the centre, which appears to have been done officially, possibly to devalue the coin at the end of the seventeenth century. Also, hammered coins were holed through the centre at the time of the recoinage of 1697–1698 to signify that they might circulate at face value for a limited time.

As previous, but 'BR' below horse and date 1644 or 1645, and horseman of slightly different style.

Obverse Legend CAROLUS DG MAG BRIT FR ET HIB REX — Charles by the grace of God King of Great Britain France and Ireland

Reverse Outer Legend EXURGAT DEUS DISSIPENTUR INIMICI — Let God arise and His enemies be scattered

Reverse Inner Legend RELIG PROT LE AN LI PA — The religion of the Protestants the laws of England the liberty of Parliament

Obverse King on horseback with plume behind; mintmark plume or pellet. This is an obverse Oxford die, several minor varieties exist.

C1HC-355 VG £80 F £160 VF £300

As previous, but 'BR' mintmark on reverse 1644 or 1645.

C1HC-360 VG £90 F £160 VF £300

Late Declaration Issues 1645–1646

These very rare issues can easily be recognised by the various markings found on the coins, however, many used altered dies from other provincial mints, particularly Bristol. They were previously ascribed to Lundy mint.

Collecting Hints

All issues are extremely rare and difficult to obtain in any grade.

Obverse Legend CAROLUS DG MAG BR FR ET HIB REX — Charles by the grace of God King of Great Britain France and Ireland

Reverse Legend EXURGAT DEUS DISSSIPENTUR INIMICI — Let God arise and His enemies be scattered

Reverse Inner Legend REL PROT LE AN LI PA — The religion of the Protestants the laws of England the liberty of Parliament

Obverse King on horseback, plume behind king, letter 'A' below horse; mintmark plume.

Reverse Letter 'A' below date (sometimes over 'BR', Bristol die), 1645; mintmark 'A'.

C1HC-365 VG £500 F £1000

As previous, but no 'A' below date and no 'BR'. This is not a Bristol die.

C1HC-370 VG £400 F £700 VF £1500

Obverse As previous.

Reverse Scroll above Declaration, 'B' below date 1646.

C1HC-375 ex. rare

Obverse Plumelet below horse; mintmark plume.

Reverse Scroll above Declaration; mintmark plume, 1646.

C1HC-380 VG £250 F £500 VF £1200

As previous, but plumelet below date.

C1HC-385 VG £270 F £550 VF £1,100

Truro Mint 1642–1643

In November 1642 Sir Richard Vyvyan was commissioned to strike gold and silver coins at Truro and deliver them to Sir Ralph Hopton, the royalist Commander in Cornwall. Very few issues were dated but all used the mintmark rose and are fairly easy to distinguish. Although the Exeter mint also used the mintmark rose, Exeter coins are all dated after 1644; similarly, the Tower mint used the same mintmark, but the style of the coins is very different.

Collecting Hints

Most Truro halfcrowns are rare and in fact much rarer than crowns; they are usually found undamaged in about Fine condition.

Obverse Legend CAROLUS DG MAG BR FR ET HI REX — Charles by the grace of God King of Great Britain France and Ireland

Reverse Legend CHRISTO AUSPICE REGNO — I reign under the auspices of Christ

Obverse King galloping over arms; mintmark rose.

Reverse Oval shield, dated 1642 below shield in cartouche.

C1HC-390 ex. rare

Obverse As previous, but no arms below horse.
Reverse Oblong shield dividing 'C.R', undated.

C1HC-395 VG £550 F £1,000

As previous, but king is holding a sword.

C1HC-400 VG £450 F £900

As previous, but 'CR' above the shield on the reverse.

C1HC-405 VG £450 F £900

Obverse The horse is trotting.

Reverse 'C.R' at side of shield.

C1HC-410 VG £200 F £400 VF £1,000

Obverse The horse is walking, the king's head is in profile.
Reverse As previous.

C1HC-415 VG £200 F £375 VF £1,000

As previous, but 'CR' above shield.

C1HC-420 VG £220 F £450 VF £1,200

Truro or Exeter Mint

The following issues, which are all undated and have a mintmark rose, are very much a continuation of the Truro mint's production but historical records indicate that they might also have been struck in nearby Exeter. In the constantly changing conditions of the war, moneyers might well have travelled with their dies from one town to another, supplying coins for the troops.

Obverse Legend As previous, (minor varieties exist).

Reverse Legend As previous.

Obverse King on horseback, sash tied in a bow behind him; mintmark rose.

Reverse Oblong shield dividing 'C.R'.

C1HC-425 VG £100 F £180 VF £420

Obverse As previous.

177

Reverse Round shield with six or eight scrolls around it and no CR.

C1HC-430 VG £85 F £150 VF £340

Obverse King's sash flies out behind him.
Reverse Round shield.

C1HC-435 VG £100 F £200 VF £450

As previous, but reverse has an oblong shield.

C1HC-440 ex. rare

Obverse Briot-style horseman on a groundline.
Reverse Round shield.

C1HC-445 VG £100 F £200 VF £450

As previous, but with oblong shield.

C1HC-450 unique

Exeter Mint 1643-1646

The city of Exeter was captured by the royalist Prince Maurice in September 1643. The commission of Sir Richard Vyvyan, who had produced the previous Truro mint coinage, was renewed, he was placed in charge of the mint and commanded to hand the coinage produced over to Sir John Berkeley. After a dispute with Berkeley, Vyvyan was sent to prison for a time. Exeter finally surrendered to Cromwell in April 1646. Most Exeter issues use the mintmark rose, with only a few using mintmark castle or EX, and all are dated on the reverse either in the legend or below the Declaration. Thus, although the mintmark rose makes them very similar to the Truro issues, they can be distinguished since all Truro halfcrowns were undated except for a rare 1642 issue, and all Exeter ones were struck during 1644 or 1645. To identify an undated coin with mintmark castle or rose, collectors should refer to the Truro section as well as the Tower issues which also used these mintmarks but are very different in style.

Obverse Legend CAROLUS DG MAG BR FR ET HI REX — Charles by the grace of God King of Great Britain France and Ireland
Reverse Legend CHRISTO AUSPICE REGNO — I reign under the auspices of Christ
Obverse King galloping over arms; mintmark rose. This appears to be the Truro obverse die.
Reverse Oval shield, 1644 in legend.

C1HC-455 ex. rare

As previous, but 1645; mintmark castle on reverse.

C1HC-460 ex. rare

Obverse Short ill-proportioned horse; mintmark rose.
Reverse Oval shield, dated 1644, sometimes intercepted by a rose.

C1HC-465 VG £150 F £300 VF £600

Obverse Briot-style horse on groundline; mintmark rose.

Reverse Oval shield, 1644 in legend.

C1HC-470 VG £120 F £200 VF £420

Obverse New-style horse with twisted tail; mintmark rose.
Reverse Oval shield, dated 1644 or 1645 in legend.

C1HC-475 VG £120 F £200 VF £420 EF £800

Obverse As previous.
Reverse Mintmark castle, 1645 in legend.

C1HC-480 VG £150 F £320 VF £650

As previous, but mintmark EX, 1645 in legend.

C1HC-485 VG £150 F £320 VF £650

Declaration Type

Should the mintmarks of C1HC-490 and C1HC-495 not tie in, collectors should refer to other provincial mints, remembering that the obverse must have the mintmark rose.

Obverse Legend As previous.

Reverse Legend EXURGAT DEUS DISSIPENTUR INIMICI — Let God arise and His enemies be scattered

Reverse Inner Legend REL PRO LE ANG LIB PAR (varieties) — The religion of the Protestants the laws of England the liberty of Parliament

Obverse King on horseback; mintmark rose.

Reverse Mintmark EX sometimes in legend, 1644 or 1645 below Declaration.

C1HC-490 VG £600 F £1,200

As previous, but EX below date 1644.

C1HC-495 VG £500 F £1,100

Worcester Mint 1643–1644

Very little is known about the Worcester mint. Numismatists even debate whether these rare and crude issues were struck at Worcester at all or, possibly, Weymouth as there is no hard evidence linking a mint with the Worcester area. All these issues are crude in style, design and production. While similar to other issues of Charles I they are all very different in the style of the reverse shield and legend. Collectors should pay particular attention to any marks under the horse.

Obverse Legend CAROLUS DG MAG BRIT FRAN ET HIB REX — Charles by the grace of God King of Great Britain France and Ireland

Reverse Legend EXURGAT DEUS DISSIPENTUR INIMICI — Let God arise and His enemies be scattered

Reverse Inner Legend RELIG PROT LE AN LIB PA — The religion of the Protestants, the laws of England, the liberty of Parliament

Obverse King on horseback; mintmark two lions, W below horse.

Reverse Three plumes above Declaration, 1644 below.

C1HC-500 VG £250 F £500 VF £1,200

Obverse Legend As previous.

Reverse Legend CHRISTO AUSPICE REGNO — I reign under the auspices of Christ

Obverse As previous, but mintmark castle or helmet, 'W' below horse.

Reverse Square-topped shield with crown above.

C1HC-505 VG £175 F £350 VF £800

As previous, but oval shield with crown above on reverse; mintmark helmet.

C1HC-510 VG £200 F £400 VF £900

Obverse Grass under horse, 'W' above grass; mintmark castle.

Reverse Square-topped shield with crown above; mintmark helmet or none.

C1HC-515 VG £175 F £350 VF £800

As previous, but oval shield with crown above; lis or lions in legend.

C1HC-520 VG £200 F £400 VF £900

As previous, but oval shield dividing CR, roses in legend.

C1HC-525 VG £220 F £450 VF £1,000

Obverse Legend As previous.

Reverse Legend FLORENT CONCORDIA REGNA — Through concord kingdoms flourish

Obverse As previous.

Reverse Oval shield with a lion's paw either side and a crown above; no mintmark.

C1HC-530 VG £250 F £500 VF £1,200

Obverse Legend As previous.

Reverse Legend CHRISTO AUSPICE REGNO — I reign under the auspices of Christ

Obverse Tall horseman with no marks below bust; no mintmark.

Reverse Oval shield with crown above, lis, roses, lions or stars in legend.

C1HC-535 VG £200 F £400 VF £900

As previous, but square-topped shield with crown above; mintmark helmet.

C1HC-540 VG £250 F £500 VF £1,200

Obverse Legend As previous.

Reverse Legend FLORENT CONCORDIA REGNA — Through concord kingdoms flourish

Obverse As previous.

Reverse Oval shield with crown above; no mintmark.

C1HC-545 VG £200 F £400 VF £900

Obverse Legend As previous.

Reverse Legend CHRISTO AUSPICE REGNO — I reign under the auspices of Christ

Obverse Briot-style bust of king with sword slanting forwards, no or uncertain mintmark.

Reverse Oval shield with crown above roses in legends.

C1HC-550 VG £200 F £400 VF £900

As previous, but shield dividing 'CR' on the reverse.

C1HC-555 VG £200 F £400 VF £900

Legends As previous.
Obverse A fat, portly king on a crude horse; mintmark uncertain or none.
Reverse Oval shield with crown above, stars, lions, roses or lis in the legend.

C1HC-560 VG £180 F £375 VF £900

Obverse Thin king on rather scraggy horse; no or uncertain mintmark (leopard's head?).
Reverse Crown above oval royal shield; stars in the legend.

C1HC-565 VG £170 F £350 VF £800

Salopia or Shrewsbury Mint 1644

Very little is known about these issues and there is even uncertainty about whether they were struck in Shrewsbury at all. Several issues bear SA below the horse which would correspond to Salopia, the town's Latin name; on the other hand, the coins have little in common with the Shrewsbury 1642 issues which is unusual and puzzling considering that they were produced less than two years later. Stylistically, they are linked to the Worcester mint, and the geographic proximity of these two towns allows for a 'transit-mint' interpretation which was common at the time. However, in the absence of more concrete evidence, we have listed these rare issues separately and not under Shrewsbury.

Obverse Legend CAROLUS DG MAG BR FRAN ET HI(B) REX — Charles by the grace of God King of Great Britain France and Ireland

Reverse Legend CHRISTO AUSPICE REGNO — I reign under the auspices of Christ

Obverse King on horseback, SA below.

Reverse Crown over oval shield; mintmark helmet.

C1HC-570 ex. rare

Reverse Legend FLORENT CONCORDIA REGNA — Through concord kingdoms flourish
Obverse As previous.
Reverse As previous, but no mintmark.

C1HC-575 ex. rare

Obverse As previous, but SA replaced by a large cannon ball.
Reverse As C1HC-570; mintmark lis in legend or helmet.

C1HC-580 VG £800 F £1,500 VF —

Obverse Tall horse with no marks below it; mintmark lis.
Reverse Crown above large round shield; mintmark helmet.

C1HC-585 VG £380 F £700 VF £1,500

Obverse As previous.

Reverse Small, uncrowned, square-topped shield with lion's paw above and at either side; mintmark helmet.

C1HC-590 VG £450 F £800 VF £1,700

Obverse As previous.

Reverse Small oval shield with crown above; mintmark lis, helmet or none.

C1HC-595 VG £380 F £700 VF £1,500

Reverse Legend FLORENT CONCORDIA REGNA — Through concord kingdoms flourish

Obverse As previous.

Reverse Oval shield with crown above; no mintmark.

C1HC-600 VG £450 F £800 VF £1,700

Obverse A much cruder horse, often with both eyes showing; mintmark lis.

Reverse Round shield with crown above; mintmark lis.

C1HC-605 VG £450 F £800 VF £1,700

Obverse As previous, but grass under horse; mintmark lis.

Reverse As previous; mintmark rose or lis.

C1HC-610 VG £475 F £900 VF £2,000

Reverse Legend FLORENT CONCORDIA REGNA — Through concord kingdoms flourish

Obverse As previous, but a line under horse and no grass; mintmark lis.

Reverse Oval shield with crown above; no mintmark.

C1HC-615 VG £450 F £800 VF £1,700

Hartlebury Castle Mint 1646

Hartlebury Castle in Worcester was a royalist garrison from 1643 to 1646 and the only coin produced at its mint was the halfcrown. Virtually nothing is known about this issue although some numismatists believe it could have been a Chester issue. It is also known as the HC issue from the initials found at the base of the reverse shield.

> ## Collecting Hints
>
> This issue is extremely rare in any grade.

Obverse Legend CAROLUS DG MAG BRIT FRAN ET HIB REX — Charles by the grace of God King of Great Britain France and Ireland

Reverse Legend CHRISTO AUSPICE REGNO — I reign under the auspices of Christ

Obverse King on horseback; mintmark pear.

Reverse Oval shield, 'HC' in garniture below shield; mintmark three pears.

C1HC-620 VG £800 F £1,400 VF £3,000

Chester Mint 1644

Records indicate that during 1644 the Chester mint was active producing mainly halfcrowns, but also some other denominations. These issues are easily distinguished by their mintmarks while in some cases CHST, the town name abbreviated, can be found below the horse. These issues are similar to the ones from Hartlebury Castle and, as mentioned previously, the two mints could have been linked.

Collecting Hints

All issues are very rare in any grade. They are usually found in Fine condition but VF examples do exist. Many issues were struck on flans of irregular size, which may lead to legends being unclear. While the style of some of the issues is good with many resembling those from York, the actual production of the coins was poor.

Obverse Legend CAROLUS DG MAG BRI FR ET HIB REX — Charles by the grace of God King of Great Britain France and Ireland

Reverse Legend CHRISTO AUSPICE REGNO — I reign under the auspices of Christ

Obverse King on horseback, plume behind; mintmark three gerbs and sword, CHST below horse.

Reverse Oval shield; mintmark as obverse.

C1HC-625 VG £300 F £550 VF £1,200

Obverse As previous; mintmark prostrate gerb, cinquefoil or none.

Reverse Crown over royal shield; mintmark triangle of pellets, cinquefoil.

C1HC-630 VG £300 F £600 VF £1,400

Obverse As previous; mintmark cinquefoil, three pellets or prostrate gerb. No plume behind king or CHST below horse.

Reverse As previous; mintmark as obverse.

C1HC-635 VG £320 F £650 VF £1,500

Obverse As previous; mintmark cinquefoil.

Reverse Square-topped shield with crown above, a rose in the legend.

C1HC-640 VG £320 F £650 VF £1500

Obverse Legend As previous.

Reverse Outer Legend EXURGAT DEUS DISSIPENTUR INIMICI — Let God arise and His enemies be scattered.

Reverse Legend RELIG PRO ANG LIBER PAR — The religion of the Protestants the laws of England the liberty of Parliament

Obverse King on horseback, no plume behind or inscription below horse; mintmark three gerbs and a ?sword.

Reverse Three plumes over Declaration, dated 1644 below.

C1HC-645 VG £300 F £600 VF £1,400

Coventry or Corfe Castle

An incredibly rare issue with the mintmark interlinked 'C's was attributed to Coventry or Corfe Castle, near Swanage. Although listed in many reference books, it appears that this coin is a forgery.

Siege Issues

Newark 1645–1646

This denomination may be distinguished by the XXX, for 30 pence or halfcrown, found below the crown on the obverse.

Obverse Crown dividing CR, denomination below.

Reverse OBS NEWARK[E], 1645 or 1646 on three lines.

C1HC-650 VG £250 F £500 VF £850

Scarborough 1644–1645

Obverse Castle with gateway to left, value punched below.

Reverse None.

C1HC-655 VG — F £6,000 VF —

Commonwealth 1649–1660

Halfcrowns were struck during most of the Commonwealth period. The denomination is easily identifiable by the markings XXX found above the two shields on the reverse. All issues are dated and have the value (XXX for 30 pence i.e. halfcrown) on the reverse and bear a mintmark at the beginning of the obverse legend. In keeping with Puritan values, the legends are in English and the style of the coins, which were hammered, is very plain. Many varieties exist with misspellings in the legend and overdates.

Obverse Legend THE COMMONWEALTH OF ENGLAND

Reverse Legend GOD WITH US

Obverse Shield of St George within wreath; mintmark sun.

Reverse The arms of St George and Ireland, value and date above 1649, 1651–1656. Coins dated 1651 are rare, while issues dated 1655 are very rare.

COMHC-005 VG £100 F £200 VF £400

1658, 1659, 1660: As previous, but mintmark anchor.

COMHC-010 VG £180 F £500 VF £1,000

Charles II 1660–1685

Hammered Issue 1660–1662

Three main types of hammered halfcrowns were struck under Charles II, from 1660 to 1662. All are undated and have a crowned bust of the king on the obverse, the king's arms on the reverse and mintmark crown on the obverse and, sometimes, the reverse. Unlike other denominations from this series, they cannot be confused with issues of Charles I which show the king on horseback.

Obverse Legend CAROLUS II DG MAG BRIT FRAN ET HIB REX — Charles II by the grace of God King of Great Britain France and Ireland

Reverse Legend CHRISTO AUSPICE REGNO — I reign under the auspices of Christ

Obverse Crowned bust of king with no inner circles or mark of value; mintmark crown.

Reverse Royal shield over cross; no mintmark or inner circles.

C2HCH-005 VG £300 F £500 VF £1,200

Obverse Legend As previous, (minor varieties).
Reverse Legend As previous.
Obverse As previous, but mark of value XXX behind the bust.
Reverse As previous.

C2HCH-010 VG £350 F £600 VF £1,400

Obverse Legend As previous, (minor varieties).
Reverse Legend As previous.
Obverse As previous, but inner circles.
Reverse As previous, but inner circles and mintmark crown.

C2HCH-015 VG £70 F £120 VF £400

Twenty Pence

Henry III 1216–1272

Before Henry III's reign the need for higher denominations had been met, at least partly, by Byzantine and Arabic gold and silver issues that circulated among merchants and traders. But as commerce increased the monetary system also had to grow so in 1257 the king instructed his goldsmith, William of Gloucester, to prepare a coinage of pure gold. The twenty-pence was one of the issues introduced, with an obverse depicting the king enthroned and a reverse bearing a long cross with a flower in each quarter and the moneyer's name in the legend. A total of four different dies were made, producing three minor varieties and indicating that the issue was not a pattern but a denomination intended for circulation. As, however, the issue had been undervalued and, by 1265, was worth twenty-four rather than twenty pennies in gold, it is thought that the majority of coins were melted down by unscrupulous individuals for profit. Consequently, the coinage was not a success and few specimens have survived. It was not until the reign of Edward III that gold coins would be minted again.

Obverse Legend HENRICUS REX III — King Henry III

Reverse Legend WILLEM ON LUND — William of London

Obverse King holding sceptre and orb seated on a throne.

Reverse Long cross with rose in each quarter.

H320D-005 ex. rare (VF example in June 1985 sold for £65,000)

Quarter Noble

With a value of one shilling and eightpence, the gold quarter-noble was introduced under Edward III as part of the new denomination restructure. All issues have the king's arms in a shield on the obverse and a small cross surrounded by a design of arches, lis and lions and often a letter in the centre on the reverse. Many quarter-nobles have been found in hoards but, more recently, a great number have also been located with the help of metal detectors. This indicates that, unlike the nobles which were used primarily by wealthy merchants to trade with their European counterparts and are subsequently found in hoards, quarter-nobles were in general circulation at the time. Gold coins found with the help of metal detectors are usually dull in appearance with a matt surface and, under a magnifying glass, they show scratches and nicks due to movement in the soil where they lay. Coins with a dull, matt surface should not be cleaned or buffed up.

Edward III 1327–1377

The gold quarter-noble was first introduced in 1344, during the second coinage. This issue weighed 34.5 grains (2.2 grams) but was subsequently reduced to 32 grains (2.1 grams) in the third coinage (1346–1351). The second period issue, which is very rare, can be identified by an L for London in the centre of the reverse cross whereas most other issues bear an E for Edward instead. Most quarter-nobles were produced during the fourth coinage and can be identified by their obverse legends which reflect Edward III's claim to the throne of France (for details, see the relevant section of the Penny chapter). Being a popular and much needed denomination, the quarter-noble was produced during several reigns. The king's name can always be found at the beginning of the obverse legend and will read EDWARD, EDWARR or EDWAR; although Edward IV also struck quarter-nobles, only one example exists and can be distinguished by its mintmark at the beginning of the reverse legend, which was not used by Edward III. The obverse legend might also read RICARD or HENRIC, whereupon the coin is an issue of Richard II or Henry IV, V or VI. Two mints produced quarter-nobles under Edward III, London and Calais in France. The issues for Calais, which was used as a mint not only because coins were needed by English merchants in Europe but also as a political statement, were all struck during the treaty period of 1361–1369 and bear various marks differentiating them from the more common London issues.

Collecting Hints

Most quarter-nobles, while scarce, are obtainable. Many varieties exist and collectors should not have too much difficulty in obtaining a more common variety. Quarter-nobles are found in all grades from VG to EF but are sometimes clipped, damaged or very worn, reflecting their considerable circulation.

Second Coinage 1344–1346

Obverse Legend EDWAR REX ANG Z FRANC D HYB — Edward King England and France Lord of the Irish

Reverse Legend EXALTABITUR IN GLORIA — He shall be exalted in glory

Obverse King's arms in arches.

Reverse 'L' in centre of cross (this identifies the issue).

E3QN-005 F £1,500 VF £3,000

Third Coinage 1346–1351

Obverse Legend EDWAR R ANGL Z FRANC D HYB — Edward King of England and France Lord of the Irish

Reverse Legend As previous.

Obverse As previous, but large lettering and a Lombardic 'N' and 'M'.

Reverse 'E' in centre of reverse cross.

E3QN-010 VG £150 F £300 F £600

Many varieties of this issue exist, often with muling but all issues have mintmark cross 3.

Obverse Annulet stops in legend.

Reverse Saltire stops in legend.

E3QN-015 VG £100 F £200 VF £350

As previous, but muled with E3QN-025.

E3QN-020 VG £100 F £200 VF £350

Saltire stops in legend, a pellet either side of one lis on the reverse.

E3QN-025 VG £100 F £200 VF £350

Large 'E' in centre of the reverse.

E3QN-030 VG £100 F £220 VF £375

Fourth Coinage 1351–1377

Pre Treaty Period 1351–1361

Many varieties exist for the three issues produced during this period but all include the French title in the legend.

Class A

Obverse Legend EDWAR D G REX ANGL Z FRAE or EDWARR ANGL Z FRANC D HYBER or EDWAR D G REX ANGL Z FRANC — Edward King of England and France

Reverse Legend As previous.

Obverse Royal shield.

Reverse 'E' in centre cross.

E3QN-035 VG £100 F £200 VF £350

Class B

Legends As previous.
Obverse Royal shield with pellet below.
Reverse Closed 'E' in centre of cross; mintmark cross I.

E3QN-040 VG £100 F £200 VF £350

Class C

Obverse As previous.
Reverse Wedge-tailed 'R' and annulet stops in the legend; mintmark cross I.

E3QN-045 VG £110 F £220 VF £375

Transitional Period 1361

Obverse Legend EDWAR DEI GRAC REX ANGL D — Edward by the grace of God King of England Lord [of Ireland]
Reverse Legend As previous.
Obverse Royal shield, often with trefoils or annulets at cusps.
Reverse 'E' in centre cross; mintmark cross potent.

E3QN-050 VG £100 F £220 VF £375

Treaty Period 1361–1369

London Mint

Obverse Legend EDWARD DEI GRA REX ANGL — Edward by the grace of God King of England
Reverse Legend As previous.
Obverse Royal arms.
Reverse Lis in centre of reverse cross; mintmark cross potent.

E3QN-055 VG £85 F £180 VF £320

As previous, but an annulet before EDWARD.

E3QN-060 VG £85 F £180 VF £320

Calais Mint

As previous, but annulet in centre of cross on the reverse.

E3QN-065 VG £100 F £180 VF £320

As previous, but a cross in a circle after the royal shield on the obverse.

E3QN-070 VG £100 F £220 VF £375

As previous, but a quatrefoil in the centre cross on the reverse and just a cross over the shield on the obverse.

E3QN-075 VG £120 F £250 VF £400

As previous, but a crescent over the shield on the obverse.

E3QN-080 VG £135 F £275 VF £450

No quarter-nobles were produced during the post-treaty period.

Richard II 1377–1399

Fairly large quantities of quarter-nobles were produced under Richard II, all at the London mint. They were very similar in style and design to the previous, Edward III issues and one (R2QN-015) even used an altered die of that reign. They are, however, easy to distinguish as all bear RICARD at the beginning of the obverse legend and some also have an 'R' for Richard in the centre cross on the reverse. Moreover, no other Richard produced quarter-nobles.

Obverse Legend RICARD DEI GRA REX ANGL (varieties exist) — Richard by the grace of God King of England
Reverse Legend EXALTABITVR IN GLORIA — He shall be exalted in glory
Obverse Royal arms.
Reverse 'R' in centre of reverse; mintmark cross pattée.

R2QN-005 VG £170 F £350 VF £650

As previous, but a lis or pellet in centre cross on reverse.

R2QN-010 VG £160 F £300 VF £600

Obverse die altered from an Edward III issue; reverse has pellet in centre of shield.

R2QN-015 VG £160 F £320 VF £600

As R2QN-010, but escallop over shield.

R2QN-020 VG £160 F £320 VF £600

As R2QN-010, but three annulets over shield.

R2QN-025 VG £160 F £320 VF £600

As R2QN-010, but quatrefoil, cross or trefoil over shield.

R2QN-030 VG £160 F £300 VF £600

Henry IV 1399–1413

Henry IV, V and VI all produced very similar gold quarter-nobles, with the royal shield on the obverse and a cross surrounded by decoration on the reverse. A differentiating mintmark can usually be found at the beginning of the obverse and reverse legends but, as it is not clear on some coins, collectors should also look for any unusual marks or designs and refer to all three monarchs. All Henry IV quarter-nobles have HENRIC at the beginning of the obverse legend.

Henry IV's issues are divided into the heavy and the light coinage. In 1412 following a shortage of coins in circulation, which was brought about when rising gold prices resulted in bullion coins being smuggled abroad to be melted down and sold for profit, it was decided to reduce the weight of gold coins by ten percent and align it with their value. Thus, towards the end of Henry's reign the light coinage was produced. It should also be noted that during the heavy coinage new royal arms were introduced which only lasted for this reign and are easily identified by an extra lis in the upper quarter of the shield. Finally, the two mints that produced quarter-nobles under Henry IV were London and Calais in France. The issue from Calais, which is very rare, has the mintmark crown to distinguish it from the London issues, which used the mintmark cross pattée.

> ## Collecting Hints
>
> Quarter-nobles are the most common gold issues of Henry IV; however, they are all very rare and difficult to obtain. Coins are usually found in Fine or VF condition.

Heavy Coinage 1399–1412

London Mint

Obverse Legend HENRIC DI GRA REX ANGL Z FRANC (varieties exist) — Henry by the grace of God King of England and France

Reverse Legend EXALTABITUR IN GLORIA — He shall be exalted in glory

---

Obverse Old-style royal arms with crescent above; mintmark cross pattée.

Reverse Pellet in centre of reverse cross.

H4QN-005 VG £400 F £1,000 VF £2,000

As previous, but new-style royal arms on obverse with an extra lis in the top quarter.

H4QN-010 VG £375 F £900 VF £1,850

Calais Mint

Obverse As previous.

Reverse As previous, but mintmark crown.

H4QN-015 F £1,100 VF £2,200

Light Coinage 1412–1413

Legends As previous.

Obverse New-style royal arms with trefoils or trefoils and annulets at side.

Reverse Lis in centre of reverse cross.

H4QN-020 VG £250 F £500 VF £1,000

Henry V 1413–1422

Under Henry V, quarter-nobles were only struck at the London mint. As mentioned earlier, they are very similar in style to the issues of Henry IV and Henry VI, but can be distinguished apart. Only Henry V used the mintmark cross pattée with pellet in centre or the mintmark pierced cross, moreover all his issues have a lis above the royal arms and in the centre cross on the reverse. Also in most issues, one or more mullets can be found somewhere on the coin and this is a mark that only Henry V used on quarter-nobles.

> ## Collecting Hints
>
> All quarter-nobles are rare but obtainable and usually found in Fine or VF condition.

Obverse Legend HENRIC DI GRA REX ANGL — Henry by the grace of God King of England

Reverse Legend EXALTABITVR IN GLORIA — He shall be exalted in glory

Obverse Lis over royal shield, quatrefoil and annulet beside shield; the legend is in short, broad lettering.

Reverse Lis in centre of reverse.

H5QN-005 VG £150 F £300 VF £500

Obverse Royal shield and lis above, quatrefoil to the left and quatrefoil and mullet to the right; ordinary style lettering.

Reverse As previous.

H5QN-010 VG £130 F £225 VF £425

Obverse Royal shield and lis above, annulet to left and mullet to right of shield.
Reverse As previous.

H5QN-015 VG £130 F £225 VF £425

Obverse Royal shield and lis above, trefoil to left, mullet to right of shield.
Reverse As previous.

H5QN-020 VG £135 F £250 VF £450

Obverse Lis over royal arms, mullet after king's name, no other marks.
Reverse As previous.

H5QN-025 VG £135 F £250 VF £450

Henry VI First Reign 1422–1461

During the first part of Henry VI's reign, quarter-nobles were produced in some quantity. All are fairly similar to previous reigns, with the royal arms on the obverse and a lis in the centre of the reverse. The various Henry VI issues can be identified by the marks or stops, such as annulets, which are found in the legends and are specific to each issue. Again if collectors are uncertain when trying to identify a coin, they should refer to the issues of Henry IV and Henry V. Three mints produced quarter-nobles under Henry VI, London, Calais and York. They can be identified by the number of lis found over the royal shield on the obverse as London had one lis or none, York two and Calais either three or one and a small mintmark lis.

Collecting Hints

All issues, especially the provincial ones, are scarce, but collectors should be able to obtain a more common variety. Coins are usually found in Fine or VF condition.

Annulet Issue 1422–1427

London Mint

Obverse Legend HENRIC DI GRA REX ANGL — Henry by the grace of God King of England

Reverse Legend EXALTABITUR IN GLORIA — He shall be exalted in glory

Obverse Lis over royal arms; mintmark large lis.
Reverse Lis in centre; annulets in reverse legend.

H6QN-005 VG £100 F £225 VF £400

As previous, but a trefoil below the shield.

H6QN-010 VG £100 F £225 VF £400

As previous, but a pellet below the shield. If the mintmark lis is very small refer to H6QN-030.

H6QN-015 ex. rare

Calais Mint

Legends As previous.
Obverse Three lis over royal shield, mintmark large lis.
Reverse Lis in centre, annulets in legend.

H6QN-020 VG £120 F £260 VF £480

As previous, but the three lis on the obverse are around the royal shield.

H6QN-025 VG £120 F £240 VF £450

Only one lis above shield, but the mintmark lis is very small on the obverse and reverse; annulets in reverse legend.

H6QN-030 VG £120 F £240 VF £450

York Mint

As previous, but two lis over the royal shield; mintmark lis.

H6QN-035 VG £140 F £300 VF £550

Rosette Mascle Issue 1427–1430

London Mint

Legends As previous.
Obverse A lis over the royal shield, rosette stops on legend; mintmark lis.

Reverse Lis in centre, rosette and mascle stops in legend.

H6QN-040 VG £150 F £350 VF £600

As previous, but no lis over royal shield.

H6QN-045 VG £140 F £300 VF £550

Calais Mint

Legends As previous.

Obverse Lis over royal shield, a rosette either side of shield; mintmark lis.

Reverse Lis in centre, rosette stops in legend.

H6QN-050 VG £180 F £400 VF £700

Pinecone Mascle Issue 1430–1434

Legends As previous.

Obverse Lis over royal shield; mintmark lis.

Reverse Lis in centre, pinecone and mascle stops in legend.

H6QN-055 ex. rare

Leaf Mascle Issue 1434–1435

Legends As previous.

Obverse Lis above royal shield; mintmark lis.

Reverse A leaf below the 'R' in GLORI, saltire and mascle stops in legend.

H6QN-060 F £1,000 VF £2,000

Leaf Trefoil Issue 1435–1438

Legends As previous.

Obverse Lis over royal shield; mintmark lis.

Reverse Lis in centre. Leaf and trefoil stops in legend.

H6QN-065 probably unique

No quarter-nobles were struck for the rest of Henry VI's reign.

Edward IV First Reign 1461–1470

During the early part of Edward IV's reign the rising price of gold created a shortage in the supply to the mint which in turn led to a decrease in the number of gold coins in circulation. The situation was exacerbated by merchants exporting English gold coins to the Continent to melt and sell at a profit. To counteract this practice, the value of every noble in circulation was raised from six shillings and eightpence to eight shillings and fourpence in 1464 and, the following year, the gold ryal or rose noble was introduced with a value of ten shillings. This 1465 issue, which

included half-ryals and quarter-ryals, was a continuation of the noble series, so we have included the quarter-ryal here. The heavy coinage (1461–1464) quarter-noble is unique; and although more would undoubtedly have been produced, they were probably melted down at the time. The new quarter-ryal was very close to the quarter-noble in style, bearing the royal shield on the obverse and a rose over a radiate sun over a centre cross on the reverse. Mintmarks can be found on obverse and reverse, and dies are often muled. All issues were struck at the London mint only, and the quarter-ryal had a value of two shillings and sixpence.

Heavy Coinage 1461–1464

Collecting Hints

Only one coin survives.

Obverse Royal arms mintmark.

Reverse and Legends Details unknown.

E4QN-005 unique

Light Coinage 1464–1470

Collecting Hints

The first issue listed is probably unique and is considered by some numismatists to be a Continental copy or forgery. The next two issues are rare and, when available, usually found undamaged in Fine to VF condition.

Obverse Legend EDWARD DI GRA REX ANG — Edward by the grace of God King of England (and France)

Reverse Legend EXALTABITUR IN GLORIA — He shall be exalted in glory

Obverse Royal arms with rose above; mintmark sun.

Reverse A rose over a radiate sun over the centre reverse cross; mintmark rose.

E4QN-010 unique

Legends As previous.

Obverse E over royal shield, rose left of shield, sun to right; mintmark rose, sun, crown (often muled).

Reverse As previous.

E4QN-015 VG £175 F £350 VF £650

As previous, but rose to right of shield and sun to left; mintmark crown, sun, rose, long cross fitchée, lis. Sometimes muled.

E4QN-020 VG £185 F £370 VF £700

Quarter Angel

The gold quarter-angel was introduced in Henry VIII's third coinage (1544–1547), with a value of two shillings, as part of the new denomination structure. All issues show St Michael killing the dragon on the obverse and a ship with the royal arms in the centre on the reverse. Quarter-angels were only struck again under Elizabeth I but the two reigns are easily identified by the monarch's name at the beginning of the obverse legend. However, as the denomination proved unpopular, it was superseded by the popular shilling and halfcrown. This coin is also known as the angelet.

Henry VIII 1509–1547

This rare issue was struck at the London mint. Only one variety exists, always with the mintmark lis at the beginning of the obverse and reverse legend.

Collecting Hints

This issue is rare but obtainable. Coins are usually found in Fine condition, sometimes damaged or badly worn, reflecting considerable circulation. The style is not as good as the angel or half-angel as the die engraver would probably have found it difficult to put all the detail onto such a small die.

Obverse Legend HENRICUS VIII D GRA AGL — Henry VIII by the grace of God [of] England

Reverse Legend FRANCIE ET (or Z) HIBERNIE REX — France and Ireland King

Obverse St Michael killing the dragon; mintmark lis.

Reverse Ship with royal arms in centre, a mast in the shape of a cross above, 'H' and a rose either side.

H8QA-005 VG £150 F £275 VF £600

Elizabeth I 1558–1603

The gold quarter-angel was produced during most of Elizabeth's reign. As the angel had risen to ten shillings under Edward VI, the value of the quarter-angel was exactly two shillings and sixpence, the same as the gold halfcrown. These denominations circulated alongside each other; however, the quarter-angel was obsolete in design and value and stopped being produced in 1600 being replaced by the silver halfcrown, a denomination which was to be produced for circulation until 1967.

Collecting Hints

All Elizabeth's quarter-angels are rare. They are usually found in Fine condition, but VF examples do exist. The denomination is fairly unpopular with collectors as it is very small and poor in design when compared to large denomination gold coins.

First — Third Issues 1559–1578

Obverse Legend ELIZABETH DG ANG FRANCIE — Elizabeth by the grace of God [of] England France

Reverse Legend ET HIBERNIE REGINA FIDEI — and Ireland Queen [defender] of the Faith

Obverse St Michael killing the dragon; mintmark lis, ermine, acorn and eglantine.

Reverse Ship with royal arms in centre, a mast in the shape of a cross, 'E' and a rose either side; mintmark as obverse.

ELQA-005 VG £150 F £275 VF £500

Fourth Issue 1578–82

The gold used for this issue was of a slightly lower fineness.
Legends As previous.

Obverse As previous, but mintmark Greek cross, Latin cross or sword.

Reverse As previous; mintmarks as obverse.

ELQA-010 VG £140 F £260 VF £480

Fifth Issue 1583–1600

The coins for this issue had a slightly higher fineness of gold.
Legends As previous.

Obverse As previous, but mintmarks bell, 'A', escallop, crescent, hand, tun, woolpack, key or anchor.

Reverse As previous; mintmarks as obverse.

ELQA-015 VG £140 F £260 VF £480

No quarter-angels were struck for the sixth issue.

Quarter Florin or Helm

Edward III 1324–1377

Acting on instructions that Edward III had issued in 1343 regarding the production of gold denominations for England, the Florentines George Kirkyn and Lotte Nicholyn designed the quarter-florin or helm in 1344. With a value of one shilling and sixpence and based largely on the European gold issues, it was intended to be not only for England but also for the whole of Europe. However, the gold used to make the coins had been overvalued so the issue was unacceptable to merchants and had to be demonetised in August 1344. The coins were recalled, melted down and used to make the popular and more acceptable nobles.

Obverse Legend EDWR R ANGL Z FRANC D HIB — Edward King of England and France Lord of Ireland

Reverse Legend EXALTABITUR IN GLORIA — He shall be exalted in glory

Obverse Royal helmet surmounted by a lion and cap.

Reverse Floriated cross with a quatrefoil in centre.

E3QFL-005 ex. rare

Shilling

The shilling or testoon was first introduced in the profile issue of Henry VII. Documentary evidence is scarce but it is thought that few issues were originally struck because, like so many new denominations, the shilling did not become popular for some time. It was reintroduced in Henry VIII's third coinage, when fairly large quantities were produced but the entire coinage was unpopular. Finally, the shilling was successfully introduced during the reign of Edward VI and was subsequently produced during every reign except Mary's. The combination of rising inflation and general prosperity in Europe, due mainly to large quantities of silver and gold coming from the Americas, meant that the shilling, together with other larger denominations, became more important in English everyday transactions.

Henry VII 1485–1509

The shilling, known as the testoon, was introduced during Henry VII's profile issue but, with no documentary evidence surviving, little is known about it. It has been argued that the issues were trials or patterns but this seems unlikely since a total of three different dies were made. It is more probable that the shilling took some time to become popular as a denomination. It is important to remember that large quantities of European as well as English coins circulated in England at the time and merchants were in a position to choose which coins they would accept for their goods.

Profile Issue 1502–?1504

> ## Collecting Hints
>
> All three issues are extremely rare. When available they are usually found in Fine or VF condition.

Obverse Legend HENRIC DI GRA REX ANGLIE Z FRAN — Henry by the grace of God King of England and France

Reverse Legend POSUI DEUM ADIVTOE MEU — I have made God my helper

Obverse Crowned bust of king to right; mintmark lis.

Reverse Royal shield over cross.

H7TS-005 F £4,500 VF £8,500

As previous, but obverse legend reads HENRIC SEPTIM DI GRA REX ANGL Z FRA.

H7TS-010 F £5,000 VF £9,500

As previous, but obverse legend reads HENRIC VII DI GRA REX ANGL Z FRA.

H7TS-015 F £5,500 VF £10,000

Henry VIII 1509–1547

The shilling, still known as the testoon, was reintroduced during Henry VIII's third coinage (1544–1547) and continued to be produced in the posthumous coinage (1547–1551) when coins bearing Henry's name and portrait were struck while his son Edward VI was on the throne and producing coins in his own name. As both Henry's issues were made of base silver (i.e. silver mixed with a metal of little value, usually copper, to produce a coin of low fineness), they were extremely unpopular because the public was accustomed to, and expected, bullion coins. The three mints producing testoons during the two coinages were London, now known as Tower mint, Southwark and Bristol. They can easily be distinguished by their reverse legends which read as follows: Tower — POSUI ADIVITOREM MEUM (minor varieties exist); Southwark — CIVITAS LONDON; Bristol — CIVITAS BRISTOLLIE.

> ## Collecting Hints
>
> All Henry VIII's testoons are fairly rare and usually available in less than Fine condition, often badly worn and scratched. The edges of the coin are often chipped, usually due to the poor striking and metal content rather than clipping. Coins in VF and EF condition are very rare.

Third Coinage 1544–1547

Tower Mint

Obverse Legend HENRIC VIII DG AGL FR Z HIB REX — Henry VIII by the grace of God King of England France and Ireland

Reverse Legend POSUI DEUM ADIVTOREM MEUM (minor varieties) — I have made God my helper

Obverse Crowned bust of facing king; mintmark lis, two lis or pellet in annulet.

Reverse Crown over rose with crowned 'H' and 'R' at sides.

H8TS-005 Poor £75 VG £135 F £300 VF £800

As previous, but obverse legend starts HENRIC 8; mintmark lis or pellet in annulet.

H8TS-010 Poor £70 VG £135 F £300 VF £800

Southwark Mint

This issue was also produced during the posthumous coinage using the same or identical dies.

Obverse Legend HENRIC 8 DG AGL FR Z HIB REX — Henry VIII by the grace of God King of England France and Ireland

Reverse Legend CIVITAS LONDON — City London

Obverse As previous, but mintmark 'S' or 'E'; varieties in muling.

Reverse As previous.

H8TS-015 Poor £75 VG £140 F £350 VF £850

Bristol Mint

This issue was probably also struck during the posthumous coinage.

Obverse Legend As previous.

Reverse Legend CIVITAS BRISTOLLIE — City Bristol

Obverse As previous, but no mintmark.

Reverse As previous, but mintmark 'WS'.

H8TS-020 Poor £80 VG £160 F £375 VF £1,000

Posthumous Coinage 1547–1551

Obverse Legend HENRIC 8. DG AGL FR Z HIB REX — Henry VIII by the grace of God King of England France and Ireland

Reverse Legend POSUI DEUM ADIVTOREM MEUM — I have made God my helper

Obverse Crowned bust of facing king; mintmark none or pellet in annulet.

Reverse Crown over rose with 'H' and 'R' at sides, sleeve or lozenge shaped stops usually either side of legend; mintmark pellet in annulet.

H8TS-025 Poor £100 VG £200 F £600 VF £1,450

Edward VI 1547–1553

From this period onwards, the shilling was no longer known as a testoon. The shillings struck under Edward VI fall into three categories, the posthumous coinage mentioned above, the base issue and finally the fine silver coinage. The base issue, struck in Edward's name, was very much a continuation from the previous reign and again made of low grade, base silver. The superb coins of the fine silver issue, on the other hand, were made of good quality silver and became extremely popular with the public who had coins worth their weight in silver once more. All of these silver issues were struck at the Tower mint in London.

Base Issue

Many varieties in styles of bust and lettering exist but, due to the poor condition of most coins, they are very difficult to detect and we have only listed the main ones.

Collecting Hints

Most of these issues are fairly rare and very difficult to obtain in Fine or better condition. Often they are either clipped or have ragged edges due to striking and metal content; also they appear dull in colour and should never be cleaned. Collectors should pay particular attention to a clear portrait and, if seeking an example from the reign, might prefer a more attractive and easily obtainable fine silver issue. They should also note that contemporary forgeries struck in brass are quite common and appear to have seen some circulation, especially in Ireland and, finally, that the weights of some issues vary considerably although it would appear that the silver content remains the same.

First Period April 1547–1549

Durham House Year MDXLVIII (1548)

This rare issue was struck in brass alloy at the Durham House mint. It has been considered a possible forgery or pattern and no records exist.

Obverse Legend EDWARD VI DG AGL. FR Z HIB REX — Edward VI by the grace of God King of England France and Ireland

Reverse Legend TIMOR DOMINI FONS VITE MDXLVIII — The fear of the Lord is the fountain of life 1548

Obverse Crowned bust of king right.

Reverse Oval shield dividing 'ER'; mintmark bow.

E6SH-005 ex. rare

Second Period Jan. 1549 — April 1550

Three London mints (Tower, Southwark and Durham House) and two provincial ones (Bristol and Canterbury) were active in the second period. Although coins are fairly hard to identify correctly because of their poor condition, the various issues can be distinguished by the date which is found on the obverse and/or reverse. Should a coin be undated but with a reverse legend beginning INIMICOS, it is from Durham House mint. Coins with a clear date and mintmark are worth more than those without.

For convenience, issues are listed here by date, with the mint-marks to distinguish the various mints.

Year MDXLIX 1549

Struck in January and February 1549, these coins all bear bust 1.

Transposed Legends

Obverse Legend TIMOR DOMINI FONS VITE MDXLIX (varieties in order) — The fear of the Lord is the fountain of life 1549

Reverse Legend EDWARD VI DG AGL FRA Z HIB REX (varieties in order) — Edward VI by the grace of God King of England France and Ireland

Obverse Crowned bust of king to right.

Reverse Oval shield dividing 'ER'. The order of the legend might change in various issues.

Durham House Mintmark Bow on reverse.

E6SH-010 VG £60 F £150 VF £350

Tower Mintmark Arrow. There is also an extremely rare variety which bears bust 2 and mintmark arrow only on the reverse.
E6SH-015 VG £70 F £175 VF £400

Southwark Mintmark Obverse 'Y' or 'EY'; reverse 'Y'.

E6SH-020 VG £150 F £300 VF £650

Canterbury Mintmark Obverse none; reverse rose.

E6SH-025 ex. rare

Regular Legends

Obverse and reverse are as previous, but the legends are always in their correct order.

Obverse Legend EDWARD VI DG AGL FRA Z HIB REX (varieties in order) — Edward VI by the grace of God King of England France and Ireland

Reverse Legend TIMOR DOMINI FONS VITE (varieties in order) — The fear of the Lord is the fountain of life

Durham House Mintmark Bow.

E6SH-030 VG £150 F £300 VF £650

Tower Mintmark Obverse arrow, arrow over 6, grapple, grapple over '6',

pheon, swan, swan over Y; reverse swan. One die omits the 'ER' beside the shield.

E6SH-035 VG £60 F £150 VF £350

Southwark Mintmark Obverse 'Y', 'Y' over '6', 'Y'; reverse 'Y' over grapple.

E6SH-040 VG £80 F £180 VF £400

Bristol Mintmark Obverse 'TC' over 'G'; reverse 'TC'.

E6SH-045 VG £300 F £600 VF —

Canterbury Mintmark 't', 't' over 'G', 'T'.

E6SH-050 VG £80 F £180 VF £400

Year MDL 1550

Obverse, reverse and legends are as previous.

Tower Mintmark Obverse pheon and reverse swan, swan, martlet. There is also an extremely rare variety with mintmark crowned leopard's head.

E6SH-055 VG £60 F £150 VF £350

Southwark Mintmark 'Y'.

E6SH-060 VG £80 F £180 VF £400

Undated Issue

This issue, struck at the Durham House, has no date and a different reverse legend. Varieties exist, with the main difference being the order of the legends; the mintmark for all issues is bow.
Obverse Legend As previous.

Reverse Legend INIMICOS EIUS INDUAM CONFUSIONE — As for His enemies I shall clothe them with shame

Obverse & Reverse As previous; mintmark bow.

E6SH-065 VG £100 F £200

Third Period 1550–1551

Year MDL 1550

Obverse Legend As previous.

Reverse Legend As E6SH-015.

Obverse & Reverse As previous.

Tower Mintmark Lion over rose, or lis.

E6SH-070 VG £60 F £130 VF £300

Southwark Mintmark Obverse lis; reverse 'Y'.

E6SH-075 VG £60 F £130 VF £300

Year MDLI 1551

Legends As previous.

Obverse & Reverse As previous.

Tower Mintmark Obverse rose, lion, lion; reverse rose over lion.

E6SH-080 VG £100 F £200 VF £400

Southwark Mintmark Obverse 'Y'; reverse lis.

E6SH-085 VG £100 F £200 VF £400

Fine Silver Issue 1551–1553

This high grade silver issue of good quality and style was extremely popular. Struck at the Tower mint, it has a superb portrait of the Boy King on the obverse and the royal arms on the reverse. However, it was struck alongside the base issue thus producing two standards of coins. This was mainly due to the fact that many of the members of the Council that governed the country until Edward became of age had an interest in keeping the base coinage in production because it was so profitable. The king himself was in fact instrumental in restoring the coinage.

Collecting Hints

Edward VI fine silver shillings are fairly common, usually available in about Fine condition but sometimes scratched or holed. Examples in VF and even EF condition exist and are very desirable. Compared to the contemporary base issues, these coins are superb with clear design and legible legends.

Obverse Legend EDWARD VI DG AGL. FRA Z HIB REX — Edward VI by the grace of God King of England France and Ireland

Reverse Legend POSUI DEU ADIUTORE MEUM — I have made God my helper

Obverse Facing bust of crowned king, rose to left, value XII to right; mintmark 'Y' or tun.

Reverse Royal shield over long cross, mintmark 'Y' or tun.

E6SH-090 Poor £20 VG £40 F £65 VF £165

Philip and Mary 1554–1558

No shillings were struck during Mary's brief reign; however, large quantities were produced between 1554 and 1558 when, after an Act of Parliament pronouncing that a woman was unfit to rule alone, Mary reigned jointly with her husband Philip of Spain. To indicate duel sovereignty and boost Philip's popularity, both their busts are found on the coins. All issues were struck at the Tower mint and many were dated.

Collecting Hints

Philip and Mary shillings are fairly rare, especially in Fine or better condition. They are usually found, undamaged but worn, in less than Fine condition and although coins in VF and EF exist, they are very expensive and desirable. Forgeries, primarily modern ones, exist for most issues and include coins dated 1554 below the obverse busts and others dated 1557. Collectors should take care to buy from a reputable source.

Spanish Title

Obverse Legend PHILIP ET MARIA DG R ANG FR NEAP PR HISP — Philip and Mary by the grace of God King and Queen of England France and Naples Prince [and Princess] of Spain

Reverse Legend POSUIMUS DEUM ADIUTOREM NOSTRUM — We have made God our helper

Obverse Busts of Philip and Mary facing each other with large crown above.

Reverse Oval royal shield with crown above which divides the mark of value.

PMSH-005 VG £80 F £180 VF £450

As previous, but date below bust 1554 or 1555. This coin is rarely found in better than VG condition.

PMSH-030 VG £200 F — VF —

As previous, with no mark of value.

PMSH-010 VG £100 F £200 VF £500

As previous, but without ANG in obverse legend, dated 1555.

PMSH-035 VG £250 F — VF —

As PMSH-005, but dated 1554 on the obverse.

PMSH-015 VG £75 F £150 VF £350

English Title

Obverse Legend PHILIP ET MARIA DG REX ET REGINA ANGL — Philip and Mary by the grace of God King and Queen of the English

Reverse Legend As previous, but mark of value on the reverse.

Obverse As previous, dated 1554 or 1555.

Reverse As previous.

PMSH-020 VG £100 F £220 VF £450

As previous, but without mark of value on the reverse. The issue dated 1555 is extremely rare.

PMSH-025 VG £100 F £220 VF £450

Elizabeth I 1558–1603

Although a large quantity of shillings were produced under Elizabeth, there was a twenty year break in production between 1562 and 1582, probably because originally sufficient numbers were in circulation from Edward VI, Philip and Mary and the Great Recoinage of 1560–1562. Nevertheless, several varieties of hammered shilling were struck during the early part of the reign while milled shillings were also produced in the 1560s. All issues show a bust of the queen on the obverse and the royal shield over a cross on the reverse; they are undated and have no mark of value. However, they cannot be confused with other issues, because no other denomination is at all like the shilling in style and, most importantly, size. All issues have a mintmark on the obverse and reverse, found at the top of the coin at the beginning of the legends. And, since mintmarks were a form of quality control linking coins with dies, all Elizabeth I shillings can be dated very accurately with the help of the mints' records and historical data. The mintmark and the date struck are here listed with each issue.

First Issue 1559–1560

Collecting Hints

This issue is, for some reason, always found very worn and is fairly rare especially in better than VG condition.

Obverse Legend ELIZABET(H) DG ANG FRA(N) Z HIB REGINA — Elizabeth by the grace of God Queen of England France and Ireland

Reverse Legend POSUI DEUM ADIVTOREM MEUM — I have made God my helper

Obverse Crowned bust to left; mintmark lis. Wire-line inner circles.

Reverse Royal arms over cross.

ELSH-005 VG £80 F £200 VF £500

As previous, but wire-line and beaded inner circles.

ELSH-010 VG £50 F £100 VF £450

Second Issue 1560–1561

The main differences from the previous issue are the mintmarks and that the 'Z' in the obverse legend has been replaced by 'ET'. Both issues have large thin flans.

> ## Collecting Hints
>
> This is more common than the first issue but is again nearly always found in the lower grades, rarely clipped or deliberately damaged but nearly always worn. Coins in VF and EF condition are rare and desirable.

Obverse Legend ELIZABETH DG ANG FRA ET HIB REGINA — Elizabeth by the grace of God Queen of England France and Ireland

Reverse Legend POSUI DEU ADIUTOREM MEU — I have made God my helper

Obverse Bust of queen; mintmark cross crosslet or martlet (both 1560–1561).

Reverse Long cross over royal shield.

ELSH-015 VG £30 F £70 VF £200

Milled Coinage 1560–1561

During Elizabeth's reign the Frenchman Eloye Mestrelle was commissioned to produce machine-made coins using horsepower. First made in 1561 at the Tower mint, these milled issues are the predecessors of our modern coins and were of fine quality, well struck and fully round. The smaller denominations tend to be rare because of the difficulty in making small milled coins. However, although superior in quality, the milled issues took longer to produce than the hammered ones. Furthermore, Mestrelle was unpopular at the mint firstly because he was French and secondly because the workers who produced hammered coins feared that the new technique would make them redundant. The disputes and animosity between Mestrelle and his fellow workers eventually

resulted in his dismissal in 1572 and six years later he was hanged for counterfeiting. Under Elizabeth, milled issues were last struck in 1571; they were not introduced again until Nicholas Briot's issues of the 1630s.

Shillings were among the denominations that Mestrelle produced at the Tower mint using horsepower, but it is thought they were only made in 1560–1561, alongside the hammered issue. All milled issues have the mintmark star on both sides and are very different in style to the hammered.

> ## Collecting Hints
>
> Most milled shillings appear to have been weakly struck, especially when compared to the sixpence. The obverse in particular is very weak and this is probably due to the striking techniques and the thickness of the silver. Coins are usually found in less than Fine condition and those in VF and EF are rare and desirable. Shillings, like sixpences, are often found gilded and it appears that they were popular as jewellery pieces. Milled shillings are rarely found clipped.

The diameter of the coin is over 31 mm.

Obverse Legend ELIZABETH D.G. ANG FRA ET HIB REGINA — Elizabeth by the grace of God Queen of England France and Ireland

Reverse Legend POSUI DEUM ADIVTOREM MEUM — I have made God my helper

Obverse Bust of queen with plain dress; mintmark star.

Reverse Royal arms over long cross.

ELSH-020 VG £175 F £350 VF £800

As previous, but the queen's dress is decorated.

ELSH-025 VG £80 F £150 VF £400

As previous, but the diameter of the coin is 30–31mm.

ELSH-030 VG £50 F £120 VF £300

As previous, but the diameter of the coin is under 30 mm.

ELSH-035 VG £50 F £120 VF £300

Fifth Issue 1582–1600

The fifth and sixth issues are by far the most common of Elizabeth's shillings and, with a new portrait and different obverse legend, the whole style of the coin was changed. The two issues can be distinguished by the different mintmarks which are once more found on both sides of the coin.

> ## Collecting Hints
>
> The fifth issue is fairly easy to obtain, especially in VG to Fine condition; VF and EF examples exist but are quite rare. The coins are rarely found clipped or damaged and collectors should try to obtain one with a reasonable portrait and clear mintmark.

Obverse Legend ELIZAB DG ANG FR ET HIB REGI — Elizabeth by the grace of God Queen of England France and Ireland

Reverse Legend POSUI DEU ADIVTOREM MEU — I have made God my helper

Obverse Bust of queen.

Reverse Royal shield over long cross.

Mintmark Bell (1582–1583), 'A' (1582–1584), escallop (1584–1586), crescent (1587–1589), hand (1590–1592), tun (1592–1595), woolpack (1594–1596), key (1595–1598), anchor (1597–1600) or cypher (1600).

ELSH-040 VG £20 F £45 VF £120

Sixth Issue 1601–1602

This issue is virtually identical to the previous one except for the mintmarks and a very small reduction in the weight of the coins.

> ## Collecting Hints
>
> The 'Collecting Hints' are the same as for the previous issue except that the sixth is slightly scarcer.

As previous, but mintmark '1' (1601) or '2' (1602).

ELSH-045 VG £25 F £50 VF £140

James I 1603–1625

By the early seventeenth century, the shilling was established as an important denomination. All James I's issues are undated and have the bust of the king with the denomination behind on the obverse and the royal arms on the reverse. The various issues can be distinguished by the reverse legend, the mintmark at the beginning of the obverse and reverse legends, as well as by the style of the bust. However, should the bust be difficult to identify, some mintmarks are specific to particular issues and may be used to identify a coin. One scarce issue also has a large plume above the

reverse shield. It should be noted that several Scottish issues, produced during the reigns of James VI and Charles I, are fairly similar to James I's English shillings, except for differences in the royal shield and, sometimes, the legends. However, should a coin have a large harp on the reverse only, it is an Irish issue.

> ## Collecting Hints
>
> Most James I shillings are fairly common and usually found in less than Fine condition, often with a very worn portrait. Although collectors should have little difficulty obtaining an example in Fine or VF, EF specimens are rare and desirable. Shillings are rarely clipped but often found with deliberate scratches on them for which there does not seem to be a plausible explanation. Because of the quality of the strike, the reverse of the coin is usually in better condition than the obverse.

First Coinage 1603–1604

Obverse Legend IACOBUS DG. ANG SCO FRA ET HIB REX — James by the grace of God King of England Scotland France and Ireland

Reverse Legend EXURGAT DEUS DISSIPENTUR INIMICI — Let God arise and His enemies be scattered

Obverse Bust of the king with square-cut beard; mintmark thistle.

Reverse Royal arms.

J1SH-005 VG £25 F £60 VF £200

As previous, but the king's beard merges with his collar; mintmark thistle or lis.

J1SH-010 VG £22 F £55 VF £180

Second Coinage 1604–1619

This issue can be easily differentiated from the first coinage by the reverse legend.

Obverse Legend As previous.

Reverse Legend QUAE DEUS CONIUNXIT NEMO SEPARET — What God hath joined together let no man put asunder

Obverse Bust of king with projecting, square-cut beard; mintmark lis (1604–1605) or rose (1604–1606).

Reverse As previous.

J1SH-015 VG £22 F £45 VF £150

Obverse As previous, but the king's hair is brushed forward and his armour is plainer; mintmark rose (1605–1606), escallop (1606–1607), grapes (1607), coronet (1607–1609).

Reverse As previous.

J1SH-020 VG £20 F £45 VF £150

Obverse As previous, but slightly larger bust with longer hair brushed back; mintmarks coronet (1607–1609), key (1609–1610), mullet (1611–1612), tower (1612–1613), trefoil (1613), tun (1613–1615), closed book (1615–1616), plain cross (1617–1618), cinquefoil (1613–1615).

Reverse As previous.

J1SH-025 VG £20 F £45 VF £150

Third Coinage 1619–1625

Legends As previous.

Obverse Bust of king with long, very curly hair; mintmarks spur rowel (1619–1620), rose (1620–1621), thistle (1621–1623), lis (1623–1624), trefoil (1624)

Reverse Royal arms in shield.

J1SH-030 VG £22 F £50 VF £160

As previous, but plume over shield on reverse; mintmark thistle (1621–1623), lis (1623–1624), trefoil (1624).

J1SH-035 VG £30 F £60 VF £200

Charles I 1625–1649

Shillings were struck in large quantities and many varieties and styles during the reign of Charles I. The majority were produced at the Tower mint in London and have the king's portrait with the denomination (XII for twelve pence or shilling) behind on the obverse, the royal shield on the reverse and a mintmark at the beginning of the obverse and reverse legends. However, provincial mints were also active, especially during the Civil War when they produced money for the royal troops. Also, shillings were among the coins struck by royalists in besieged towns like Newark. These siege pieces are crude issues without a portrait and were produced, usually out of silver plate, to pay the troops defending the town from Cromwell's army. Although the denomination itself cannot be confused with any other because of the Roman numerals XII behind the king's bust, it is often only small marks and slightly different styles that differentiate the many issues of this reign. When identifying a coin, collectors should refer to the more common Tower mint issues first and bear in mind that mintmarks are in many cases specific to particular issues; also, collectors might also want to refer to the hammered issues of Charles II.

Tower Mint 1625–1648

The issues of the Tower mint in London may be subdivided into the hammered issue struck under royal authority, the hammered issue struck under Parliament and Briot's distinctive milled issue. The Parliament issue is clearly distinguished by a different style bust and specific mintmarks while Briot's milled coins are superb in design and detail, and easily identified by their distinctive style.

Tower Mint under King 1625–1642

Huge quantities of coins were produced at the Tower mint during this period and they have many styles and varieties, which we have listed. However many issues, due either to poor striking or clipping, have irregular sized flans and illegible or even non-existent legends.

Collecting Hints

Most issues are fairly common and usually found in about Fine condition; although VF and EF examples exist they are often on poor flans. Coins with full round flans and legible legends are much more desirable and collectors should also try to obtain a specimen with a good portrait and clear mintmark. Contemporary forgeries of some of the Tower mint issues exist, especially of the later classes. They can usually be identified by the coin's silver plating flaking off to reveal the copper or brass core underneath. These issues are also rather crude in style and judging by their condition were obviously in circulation for some time.

Class 1

Obverse Legend CAROLUS DG. MAG BRIT FRA ET HIB REX — Charles by the grace of God King of Great Britain France and Ireland

Reverse Legend CHRISTO AUSPICE REGNO — I reign under the auspices of Christ

Obverse Crowned bust of king wearing ruff with value behind; mintmark lis or cross calvary.

Reverse Royal shield with square top over a cross.

C1SH-005 VG £30 F £60 VF £120

Class 1B

As previous, but the coin is underweight at 81.5 grains (5.3 grams); mintmark cross calvary. All issues should weigh over 90 grains (5.8 grams).

C1SH-010 VG — F £80 VF £200

Class 1C

As C1SH-005, but the ruff and the armour are concealed by a scarf; mintmark cross calvary, castle.

C1SH-015 VG £25 F £50 VF £100

Class 1D

As C1SH-005, but plume over shield on the reverse, no cross on the reverse; mintmark lis, cross calvary.

C1SH-020 VG £30 F £60 VF £120

Class 1E

As C1SH-015, but the coin is underweight at 81.5 grains (5.3 grams); mintmark cross calvary. All issues should weigh over 90 grains (5.8 grams).

C1SH-025 VG — F £120 VF £275

Class 1F

As C1SH-015, but plume over shield with no cross on the reverse; mintmark cross calvary, blackamoor's head, castle, anchor, heart, plume.

C1SH-030 VG £30 F £60 VF £100

Class 1G

As previous, but with cross over the shield on the reverse; mintmark blackamoor's head.

C1SH-035 VG £200 F £400

Class 2

Obverse Legend CAROLUS D.G. MA(G) BRI(T) FR ET HIB REX (varieties exist) — Charles by the grace of God King of Great Britain France and Ireland

Reverse Legend CHRISTO AUSPICE REGNO — I reign under the auspices of Christ

Obverse Bust of king wearing ruff with more armour visible; mintmark plume or rose.

Reverse Oval royal shield, with 'C.R.' (CAROLUS REX) above.

C1SH-040 VG £25 F £40 VF £80

Class 2A

As previous, but plume over shield on reverse dividing the 'C' and 'R'; mintmark plume or rose.

C1SH-045 VG £60 F £120 VF £250

Class 3

Obverse Legend CAROLUS D.G. MA(G) BR(IT) FR(A) ET HIB REX (many varieties exist) — Charles by the grace of God King of Great Britain France and Ireland

Reverse Legend CHRISTO AUSPICE REGNO — I reign under the auspices of Christ

Obverse Crowned bust of king with lace collar; mintmark harp or portcullis.

Reverse Royal arms in oval shield which divides 'C.R'.

C1SH-050 VG £20 F £35 VF £70

Class 3A

As previous, but a plume over the shield on the reverse; mintmark harp.

C1SH-055 VG £100 F £200 VF £400

Class 3B

Legends As previous.

Obverse Crowned bust of king with no inner circles; mintmark bell, crown or tun.

Reverse Royal arms in round shield, no inner circle.

C1SH-060 VG £20 F £35 VF £70

Class 3C

As previous, but a plume over the royal shield on the reverse.

C1SH-065 VG £30 F £65 VF £130

Class 4

This issue has a bust similar in style to that produced at the Aberystwyth mint but it has a different mintmark.

Obverse Legend CAROLUS DG MA(G) BR(IT) FR(A) ET HI(B) REX (many varieties exist) — Charles by the grace of God King of Great Britain France and Ireland

Reverse Legend CHRISTO AUSPICE REGNO — I reign under the auspices of Christ

Obverse Large Aberystwyth-style bust of king with small value (XII) behind the bust; mintmark tun.

Reverse Square-topped shield over cross.

C1SH-070 VG £30 F £65 VF £130

Class 4A

As previous, but the king has rounder shoulders and the denomination (XII) is larger than in the previous issue; mintmark anchor or triangle.

C1SH-075 VG £25 F £40 VF £80

Class 4B

As previous, but the bust is smaller, the king is wearing a double-arched crown, small denomination (XII) behind bust; mintmark tun.

C1SH-080 VG £25 F £40 VF £80

Class 4C

As previous, but single-arched crown and large denomination behind bust; mintmark tun, anchor or triangle.

C1SH-085 VG £25 F £40 VF £80

Class 4D

As previous, but an older-style bust with a very pointed beard; mintmark anchor or triangle. This issue is often struck on flans of irregular size.

C1SH-090 VG £25 F £45 VF £100

Tower Mint under Parliament 1642–1648

When London came under the control of Parliament during the Civil War, the shillings produced at the Tower mint were very similar in style to those previously struck under the king and it is interesting to note that the king's portrait, heraldic arms and royal inscription continued to be on the coins. Still, these issues can easily be identified by their unique mintmarks. It would, however, appear from the striking of many issues that little care was taken in producing these coins, which are often badly struck on irregular shaped pieces of metal. Because of the great similarity with the previous Tower mint issues, classes are numbered consecutively.

Collecting Hints

Shillings struck under Parliament are fairly common, especially in the lower grades, but due to the poor quality of production coins in VF and EF condition are rare.

Class 4E

Obverse Legend CAROLUS DG MAG BRI FRA ET HIB REX — Charles by the grace of God King of Great Britain France and Ireland

Reverse Legend CHRISTO AUSPICE REGNO — I reign under the auspices of Christ

Obverse Crowned bust of king with pointed beard and value behind; mintmark '(P)', '(R)', eye, sun.

Reverse Royal arms in square-topped shield over small cross.

C1SH-095 VG £30 F £60 VF £140

Class 4F

As previous, but long narrow bust; mintmark sun, sceptre.

C1SH-100 VG £32 F £60 VF £140

Class 4G

As previous, but short, broad older bust; mintmark sceptre. Varieties of king's crown exist.

C1SH-105 VG £32 F £65 VF £150

Briot's Coinage 1631–1639

Milled Issues

These issues were milled producing a coin of better quality and are easily identifiable in both style and production. Furthermore the mintmark, which is similar to some issues, is nonetheless unique.

First Milled Issue 1631–1632

Obverse Legend CAROLUS DG. MAGN BRITANN FRAN ET HIB REX — Charles by the grace of God King of Great Britain France and Ireland

Reverse Legend CHRISTO AUSPICE REGNO — I reign under the auspices of Christ

Obverse Crowned bust of king with pointed beard and wearing a lace collar, value (XII) behind bust; mintmark flower and B/B.

Reverse Royal arms in square-topped shield over cross.

C1SH-110 VG £70 F £140 VF £325

Second Milled Issue 1638–1639

Obverse As previous, with the king's bust and clothing of slightly different style and minor differences in legend; mintmark anchor and 'B' and anchor.

Reverse As previous, but the cross over the shield is smaller and does not extend across the flan.

C1SH-115 VG £45 F £85 VF £180

Hammered Issue 1635–1639

This very rare hammered issue is virtually identical to the milled. There is uncertainty as to why it was made at all but evidence suggests that, while Briot's dies were used, the production was not actually under his control. Collectors should pay particular attention to the mintmark and obverse bust so as to avoid confusing this issue with the more common Tower mint ones that also use mintmark triangle.

Legends As previous.

Obverse As previous; mintmark anchor, triangle over anchor.

Reverse Several varieties exist. Square-topped shield over cross; sometimes mintmark triangle (Tower mint Class 4 die).

C1SH-120 VG £200 F £400

Provincial Mints

York Mint 1643–1644

Although there is considerable uncertainty regarding when the York mint was opened, it is thought that it became active in early 1642 and ceased production after the royalist defeat at Marston Moor in July 1644. The dies, which were probably styled or made by Nicholas Briot, were sent to York from London at the beginning of the Civil War but were captured by the Roundheads for a time. The York issues were not hammered but machine-struck on a rotary press and punched out by a mechanical cutter; this resulted in many coins being slightly bent. The issue is easily identified by the mintmark lion at the beginning of the obverse and reverse legend, while some issues also bear the word EBOR (for EBORACUM, York's Latin name) above or below the royal shield. It is important to note that several very minor varieties of the bust exist.

Obverse Legend CAROLUS D G. MAG BRI FRA ET HIB REX (minor varieties exist) — Charles by the grace of God King of Great Britain France and Ireland

Reverse Legend CHRISTO AUSPICE REGNO — I reign under the auspices of Christ

Obverse Crowned bust of king, value behind; mintmark lion.

Reverse EBOR over square-topped shield of the royal arms.

C1SH-125 VG £50 F £100 VF £200

As previous, but the bust is coarse in style and the armour plain.

C1SH-130 VG £60 F £120 VF £220

Obverse As previous.
Reverse EBOR below an oval shield of the royal arms.

C1SH-135 VG £60 F £120 VF £220

As previous, but a crown over an oval shield.

C1SH-140 VG £50 F £100 VF £200

As previous, but the royal shield has lion-skin garniture around the edges.

C1SH-145 VG £50 F £100 VF £200

Aberystwyth Mint 1638–1642

The various varieties of this scarce issue can easily be identified by the mintmark book at the beginning of the obverse and reverse legend; also, a plume can be found both in front of the king's face and above the royal shield. When identifying a coin, collectors should refer to the Shrewsbury issues as well, because the obverse Aberystwyth die was sometimes used at Shrewsbury.

Obverse Legend CAROLUS DG. MA(G) BR FR ET HI REX — Charles by the grace of God King of Great Britain France and Ireland

Reverse Legend CHRISTO AUSPICE REGNO — I reign under the auspices of Christ

Obverse Bust with large lace collar, plume before face and small XII behind bust, no inner circle; mintmark book.

Reverse Oval shield of royal arms with plume above, no inner circle.

C1SH-150 VG £100 F £200 VF £425

As previous, but with inner circle on the reverse.
C1SH-155 VG £80 F £160 VF £350

As C1SH-150, but large XII behind bust and inner circles on both sides of the coin.

C1SH-160 VG £80 F £160 VF £350

As previous, but a smaller bust with a more rounded lace collar.

C1SH-165 VG £80 F £160 VF £350

Obverse Briot's older bust (Tower mint class 4D), with a plume in front of the king's face. This obverse die was also used at the Shrewsbury mint but with a totally different reverse.

Reverse Plume over oval shield.

C1SH-170 VG £100 F £200 VF £425

Aberystwyth Furnace Mint 1648–1649

In 1648, at the end of the Civil War, Edmund Goore took control of the Welsh silver mines and, because Aberystwyth Castle had been badly damaged, the mint was moved to the silver mills. Although no accounts survive regarding the number of coins struck, it appears that very few were and the mint was closed in 1649. This extremely rare issue is similar to the Aberystwyth mint except for the mintmark crown, which is found on both sides of the coin, and the fact that the plume in front of the king's face is much smaller.

Collecting Hints

This issue is extremely rare in any grade and collectors may have great difficulty obtaining an example.

Obverse Legend CAROLUS D G MAG BRI FRA ET HIB REX — Charles by the grace of God King of Great Britain France and Ireland

Reverse Legend CHRISTO AUSPICE REGNO — I reign under the auspices of Christ

Obverse Crowned bust of king with value behind and plume in front of face; mintmark crown.

Reverse Plume over oval shield of royal arms.

C1SH-175 ex. rare

Shrewsbury Mint 1642

This rare issue had two different obverse dies; one is from the Aberystwyth shilling with the mintmark book and the plume in front of the king's face and the other is Shrewsbury mint's own crude issue with the mintmark plume at the beginning of the obverse legend. In both cases the reverse has the Declaration on three lines, the date 1642 below and three plumes above the Declaration. Collectors should note that the second Shrewsbury die was also used for an Oxford issue.

Collecting Hints

Both these coins are rare and difficult to obtain in better than Fine condition. The Shrewsbury die issue in particular is usually found in less than Fine condition, due to rather inferior dies.

Obverse Legend CAROLUS DG MAG BRIT FRA ET HI REX — Charles by the grace of God King of Great Britain France and Ireland

Reverse Outer Legend EXURGAT DEUS DISSIPENTUR INIMICI — Let God arise and His enemies be scattered

Reverse Inner Legend RELIG PROT LEG ANG LIB PAR — The religion of the Protestants the laws of England the liberty of Parliament

Obverse Bust of king, value behind, plume in front of face; mintmark book (Aberystwyth die).

Reverse Three plumes over the Declaration in three lines, date 1642 below.

C1SH-180 VG £250 F £500

Obverse Legend CAROLUS D.G. MAG BR FR ET HIB REX — Charles by the grace of God King of Great Britain France and Ireland

Reverse Legends As previous.

Obverse Crude bust of king with denomination behind (XII); mintmark plume.

Reverse As previous.

C1SH-185 VG £300 F £550

Oxford Mint 1642–1646

There are many varieties of this scarce issue. The first variety used the second Shrewsbury obverse die (C1SH-185) but a less crudely styled, Oxford reverse die. In particular, note the differences in the three plumes on the reverse which easily differentiate the two mints. All the other issues were struck using Oxford dies. However, collectors should note that the obverse Oxford die was also used at the Bristol mint. Most Oxford issues may be easily identified by the abbreviation 'OX' found below the date on the reverse.

Collecting Hints

Even though this issue is scarce it is obtainable, especially in the lower grades; many specimens are weakly struck and bent. Coins in VF and EF condition are rare and desirable.

Shrewsbury Obverse Die

Obverse Legend CAROLUS D.G. MAG BR FR ET HIB REX — Charles by the grace of God King of Great Britain France and Ireland

Reverse Outer Legend EXURGAT DEUS DISSIPENTUR INIMICI — Let God arise and His enemies be scattered

Reverse Inner Legend RELIG PROT LEG ANG LIBER PAR — The religion of the Protestants the laws of England the liberty of Parliament

Obverse Crowned bust of king with value behind; mintmark plume.

Reverse Three plumes over the Declaration, 1642 below.

C1SH-190 VG £60 F £110 VF £225

As previous, with 'OX' below date, 1644 which sometimes reads 1044 in error.

C1SH-220 VG £65 F £120 VF £250

Oxford Dies

Obverse Legend As previous, but varieties exist, especially in the spelling of the Irish title.

Reverse Legends As previous.

Obverse Small crowned bust of king with value behind; mintmark plume.

Reverse As previous, dated 1642 or 1643.

C1SH-195 VG £60 F £110 VF £225

As previous, but coarser style of bust, dated 1643.

C1SH-200 VG £60 F £110 VF £225

As previous, but large bust of fine work, dated 1643.

C1SH-205 VG £60 F £110 VF £225

As previous, but 'OX' below the date on the reverse, dated 1644 and 1646.
C1SH-210 VG £65 F £120 VF £250

Bust with bent crown, no 'OX' on reverse and dated 1643.

C1SH-215 VG £65 F £120 VF £250

Rawlins Issue

This issue used Rawlins' dies and can easily be identified by the 'R' on the truncation of the king's bust.

Obverse As previous, but with an 'R' on the truncation.

Reverse Dated 1644, no 'OX' below date.

C1SH-225 VG £100 F £200 VF £400

As previous, but 'OX' below date.

C1SH-230 VG £100 F £200 VF £400

Bristol Mint 1643–1645

Bristol was an important seaport and soon after it became a royalist stronghold in July 1643, Thomas Bushell established a mint there using silver from the various Welsh mines. Cromwell's forces took the city in August 1645. The Bristol issues are quite similar to the Oxford ones except that many have a plume in front of the king's face and a 'BR' below the date on the reverse; moreover, the size of the date on the reverse is different, fairly large on Oxford issues and small and neat on Bristol ones. Most Bristol issues bear the mintmark plume at the beginning of the obverse legend and this, along with the reverse design, serves to distinguish them from the Aberystwyth issues that also have a plume in front of the face.

Collecting Hints

While all Bristol mint denominations are scarce, the shilling is probably the least so and coins are usually found in about Fine condition on full unclipped flans, sometimes creased. They are difficult to obtain in VF or EF condition, but collectors should not have too much difficulty finding the lower grades.

Obverse Legend CAROLUS DG MAG BR FR ET HIB REX — Charles by the grace of God King of Great Britain France and Ireland

Reverse Outer Legend EXURGAT DEUS DISSIPENTUR INIMICI — Let God arise and His enemies be scattered

Reverse Inner Legend RELIG PRO LEG ANG LIB PAR — The religion of the Protestants the laws of England the liberty of Parliament

Obverse Crowned bust of king with value behind; mintmark plume. This is an Oxford die.

Reverse Three plumes of the same size and level over the Declaration, the date 1643 below. The only difference from the Oxford reverse is in the size and spacing of the plumes.

C1SH-235 VG £65 F £120 VF £240

Obverse As previous, using the Oxford obverse die.

Reverse New reverse with mintmark 'BR' in the legend; dated 1643 or 1644.

C1SH-240 VG £60 F £110 VF £240

Obverse As C1SH-235, but ?Oxford bust of crude style. There is uncertainty whether this is a Bristol or Oxford obverse die.

Reverse As C1SH-235.

C1SH-245 VG £70 F £140 VF £280

Obverse As previous.

Reverse As C1SH-240, with 'BR' below date, dated 1644.

C1SH-250 VG £60 F £115 F £240

Legends As previous.

Obverse Crowned bust of king of good style, small plume in front of face; no mintmark in legend.

Reverse The Declaration with three plumes above and dated 1644 or 1645; mintmark 'BR' in the legend.

C1SH-255 VG £65 F £130 VF £260

As previous, but with 'BR' below the date instead of in the reverse legend; dated 1644.

C1SH-260 VG £70 F £140 VF £280

As previous, but the king is wearing a round collar; 'BR' on its side below the date; dated 1644–1645.

C1SH-265 F £70 F £140 VF £280

As previous, but the king is wearing a square collar; 'BR' in the reverse legend, dated 1645.

C1SH-270 VG £75 F £150 VF £300

Late Declaration Issues 1645–1646

With documentary evidence scarce, very little is known about these issues which were thought to have been struck in Lundy Island, Appledore, Barnstaple or Bideford. However, recent research suggests that coins marked 'A' may have been struck in Ashby de la Zouch and those marked 'B' or with plumes in Bridgnorth-on-Severn. These mints were active in 1645 and 1646 and, with dies easy to transport, it is possible that the mint could have been moved either for safety or to produce urgently needed coinage in an area. These rare issues can easily be distinguished from those of Oxford or Bristol; they are the only ones to bear the date 1646 while the coins dated 1645 also bear the mintmark A in the reverse legend and an 'A' below the date.

Obverse Legend CAROLUS DG MAG BR FR ET HIB REX — Charles by the grace of God King of Great Britain France and Ireland

Reverse Legend EXURGAT DEUS DISSIPENTUR INIMICI — Let God arise and His enemies be scattered

Reverse Inner Legend REL PRO LEG ANG LIB PAR — The religion of the Protestants the laws of England the liberty of Parliament

Obverse Crowned bust of king, value behind and mintmark plume.

Reverse Mintmark 'A' in legend at the top of the coin; three plumes over the Declaration, dated 1645 with an 'A' below the date.

C1SH-275 VG £200 F £400 VF £1,000

As previous, but small plume before the king's face.

C1SH-280 VG £200 F £400 VF £1,000

As previous, but scroll above Declaration on reverse, dated 1646.

C1SH-285 VG £120 F £250 VF £550

As previous, but larger plume in front of face; the reverse has mintmark pellet and is dated 1646.

C1SH-290 VG £100 F £200 VF £400

Obverse Legend CAROLUS DG MAG BR FRA ET HI REX (varieties exist) — Charles by the grace of God King of Great Britain France and Ireland

Reverse Legend CHRISTO AUSPICE REGNO — I reign under the auspices of Christ

Obverse Small crowned bust of king with value behind; mintmark rose.

Reverse Royal arms in an oblong shield; mintmark rose.

C1SH-295 ex. rare

As previous, but the shield is round.

C1SH-300 VG £275 F £600

As previous, but oval shield dividing 'C.R'.

C1SH-305 VG £275 F £600

Obverse Larger bust of king with lank hair, value behind; mintmark rose.

Reverse As previous.

C1SH-310 VG £250 F £550

Truro Mint

All issues from the Truro mint have mintmark rose and although some of the common Tower issues also use the same mintmark, they are different in style and design.

Obverse As previous.

Reverse Royal arms in round shield surrounded by eight scrolls.

C1SH-315 VG £300 F £600

As previous, but only six scrolls around shield.

C1SH-320 VG £200 F £400

Exeter Mint 1643–1646

The first issue from the Exeter mint is quite similar to the ones from Truro and also uses the mintmark rose but may be distinguished as it is dated in the reverse legend. There is, however, another rarer Exeter issue with a reverse Declaration similar to that of Oxford and Bristol issues and it is probable that this reverse die actually came from the Oxford mint; but as the obverse has the rose mintmark, the issue can easily be differentiated.

Obverse Legend CAROLUS DG MA BR FRA ET HI REX — Charles by the grace of God King of Great Britain France and Ireland

Reverse Legend CHRISTO AUSPICE REGNO — I reign under the auspices of Christ

Obverse Bust of king with value behind; mintmark rose.

Reverse Round shield with six scrolls, dated 1644 or 1645; mintmark rose, often splitting the date.

C1SH-325 VG £85 F £175 VF £350

Declaration Type

Obverse Legend As previous.

Reverse Outer Legend EXURGAT DEUS DISSIPENTUR INIMICI — Let God arise and His enemies be scattered

Reverse Inner Legend RELIG PRO LEG ANG LIB PAR — The religion of the Protestants the laws of England the liberty of Parliament

Obverse As previous.

Reverse Three plumes above the Declaration, dated 1645; no mintmark.

C1SH-330 VG £250 F £500

Worcester or Shrewsbury Mint

This issue is very easy to recognise by the very crude style of the design. It was probably made in a considerable hurry and little attention has been paid to the quality of dies or the striking. It should be noted that because the issues of this mint are so rare and in such poor condition, additional mintmarks might exist which we have not listed.

Obverse Legend CAROLUS DG MAG BRIT FR ET HI REX (varieties exist) — Charles by the grace of God King of Great Britain France and Ireland

Reverse Legend CHRISTO AUSPICE REGNO — I reign under the auspices of Christ

Obverse Bust of king to left; mintmark castle.

Reverse Square-topped shield.

C1SH-335 VG £225 F £450

As previous, but 'C.R' above shield on reverse; mintmark helmet or pear.

C1SH-340 VG £225 F £450

As previous, but oval shield on reverse with no 'C.R'; mintmark lion, pear.

C1SH-345 VG £200 F £400

Legends As previous.

Obverse As C1SH-335, but an even cruder copy; mintmark boar's head, helmet.

Reverse As C1SH-335, but cruder in style.

C1SH-350 VG £250 F £500

As previous, but 'CR' above the royal shield on the reverse.

C1SH-355 VG £250 F £500

As previous, but an oval shield on the reverse; mintmark lis.

C1SH-360 VG £225 F £450

As previous, but a round shield on the reverse; mintmark bird, lis.

C1SH-365 VG £250 F £500

Obverse Bust to right, value behind king's head; mintmark pear.
Reverse Oval shield dividing 'CR', rose and lis in legends.

C1SH-370 ex. rare

Chester Mint 1644

This extremely rare issue can be differentiated by its unique mint-mark three pellets, found on the obverse.

Collecting Hints

This issue is extremely rare in any grade, and collectors may have great difficulty obtaining an example in any condition.

Obverse Legend CAROLUS DG. [uncertain] REX — Charles by the grace of God King [of Great Britain France and Ireland]. The only example that we have seen had an unclear legend.
Reverse Legend CHRISTO AUSPICE REGNO — I reign under the auspices of Christ
Obverse Crowned bust of king with value behind; mintmark triangle of pellets.
Reverse Crowned oval shield.

C1SH-375 ex. rare

As previous, but square shield over long cross on reverse.

C1SH-380 ex. rare

As previous, but shield without cross.

C1SH-385 ex. rare

Siege Issues
Carlisle 1644–1645

These extremely rare issues are either round or oval in shape.

Collecting Hints

Rarely found in better than Fine condition, coins are sometimes damaged and collectors may have great difficulty obtaining an example.

Obverse Crown above 'C.R'; denomination XII below.
Reverse OBS CARL 1645 — Siege Carlisle 1643; on three lines.

C1SH-390 VG £600 F £1,200 VF £3,000

As previous, but the reverse legend and date are on two lines.

C1SH-395 VG £600 F £1,200 VF £3,000

Newark 1645–1646

Newark was besieged several times between 1645 and 1646 and finally surrendered to Cromwell's army in May 1646. The shillings are easily identified by the value XII below the crown on the obverse.

Collecting Hints

Shillings can be found in most grades with even VF specimens being obtainable. Many coins are found gilded, but this does not greatly detract from their value because the gilding comes from the original plate from which the coins were made.

Obverse Flat-shaped crown dividing 'C.R' and denomination below.
Reverse OBS NEWARKE 1645 on three lines.

C1SH-400 VG £150 F £300 VF £550

As previous, but high-arched crown.

C1SH-405 VG £140 F £280 VF £525

As previous, but NEWARK omits last 'E'; dated 1645 or 1646.

C1SH-410 VG £135 F £260 VF £500

Pontefract 1648–1649

Pontefract, besieged from June 1648 to January 1649, was the last town to fall to Cromwell's troops. These rare issues can be found on flans of varying shapes but all have a crowned 'C.R' on the obverse and a castle gateway on the reverse. Most Pontefract issues do not bear a denomination, but as they weigh about the same as a shilling, it is presumed that this is what they were. Nevertheless, the weight of each coin varies, probably due to the haste in which they were produced. The last two issues were struck after the execution of Charles I and bear the name of his son, Charles II.

Collecting Hints

These issues are rare and difficult to obtain in any grade; collectors should beware of forgeries in this series. These issues were made in a variety of shapes.

Obverse DUM SPIRO SPERO — Whilst I live I hope (around 'C.R' crowned).
Reverse Castle surrounded by OBS, 'P.C.', sword and 1648.

C1SH-415 VG £320 F £700 VF £1,500

As previous, but no sword and 'P.C' on reverse divided by the value XII.

C1SH-420 VG £320 F £700 VF £1,500

Obverse As previous.
Reverse CAROLUS SECUNDUS — Charles II and 1648 around castle gateway with flag flying.

C1SH-425 VG £300 F £650 VF £1,400

Obverse Outer Legend CAROL II DG MAG BR H REX — Charles II by the grace of God King of Great Britain Ireland
Obverse Centre Legend HANC DEUS DEDIT — God has given this (i.e. the crown)
Reverse Legend POST MORTEM PATRIS PRO FILIO — For the son after the death of the father
Obverse Crown above inscription, date 1648 below.

Reverse Castle gate.

C1SH-430 VG £300 F £600 VF £1,350

Scarborough 1644–1645

Like other siege issues, these coins were made from silver plate; the denomination is counterstamped on the coin.

Collecting Hints

Scarborough shillings are extremely rare in any condition and collectors should be aware that numerous forgeries exist.

Obverse Castle gateway, value punched below.

Reverse None.

C1SH-435 ex. rare

Obverse Castle with two turrets, value punched below.

Reverse None.

C1SH-440 ex. rare

Commonwealth 1649–1660

Shillings were struck in some quantity during the Commonwealth. They are very plain in style and design but for the first time the inscriptions are in English, rather than Latin. All coins are dated and have a mintmark above the single shield, while the denomination XII is clearly found above the two shields. Collectors should beware of contemporary forgeries which were usually made of silver plated brass or copper and although the silver plate usually flakes off, good forgeries also exist. Various minor varieties for both issues exist, often with misspelled words in the legends and overdates; they are all rare.

Collecting Hints

While scarce, Commonwealth shillings are obtainable, especially in the lower grades. They are often clipped but unlike other denominations rarely holed. Coins in Fine condition are obtainable but those in VF and EF are rare and desirable. Issues with mintmark anchor are all very rare.

Obverse Legend THE COMMONWEALTH OF ENGLAND

Reverse Legend GOD WITH US

Obverse Shield of St George; mintmark sun above surrounded by palm and laurel.

Reverse Shield of St George and Ireland with denomination and date 1649, 1651–1657 above. Issues dated 1655 are rare, those dated 1657 are extremely rare.

COMSH-005 VG £60 F £120 VF £250

As previous, but mintmark anchor, dated 1658–1660. Issues dated 1659 are extremely rare.

COMSH-010 VG £120 F £300 VF rare

Charles II 1660–1685

Hammered Issue 1660–1662

During this short period three issues produced three different types of shilling. All are undated and have the king's bust on the obverse, the royal shield on the reverse and mintmark crown at the beginning of the obverse and sometimes the reverse legend. If a coin is hard to identify, collectors should check whether it is an issue of Charles I and bear in mind that all of Charles II's issues have mintmark crown and an obverse legend starting CAROLUS II DG.

Collecting Hints

The first two issues are rare, but usually found in Fine to VF condition, the third is fairly common in less than Fine condition and rare in VF or EF.

First Issue

Obverse Legend CAROLUS II DG MAG BRIT FR ET HIB REX — Charles II by the grace of God King of Great Britain France and Ireland

Reverse Legend CHRISTO AUSPICE REGNO — I reign under the auspices of Christ

Obverse Bust of king; mintmark crown.

Reverse Royal arms; no mintmark.

C2SHH-005 VG £90 F £150 VF £350

Second Issue

Obverse Legend As previous, but with several minor varieties.

Reverse Legend As previous.

Obverse As previous, but mark of value (XII) behind the king's bust.

Reverse As previous.

C2SHH-010 VG £150 F £300 VF £600

Third Issue

Legends As previous.

Obverse As previous, but with inner circles.

Reverse As previous, but with inner circles and mintmark crown.

C2SHH-015 VG £45 F £100 VF £250

Sixpence

First introduced under Edward VI, the sixpence soon became one of the most popular denominations. During the reign of George II, it was also known as the tanner after Sigismund Tanner who designed some issues. Sixpences were struck during most reigns and last produced for circulation in 1967. Under Elizabeth I, sixpences were bent and given to ladies on their engagement if the gentleman could not afford a ring.

Edward VI 1547–1553

The sixpence was introduced into circulation during Edward VI's fine silver coinage and quickly established as a popular denomination. Usually it was some time before new denominations won the English public over but, with the sixpence being made of good quality silver of a high fineness, it was eagerly accepted and much more desirable than either Henry VIII's later issues or Edward's own base coinage. The coins were produced at the Tower and York mints; they can be distinguished by the reverse legend, which reads POSUI DEUM ADIVTOREM MEUM for the Tower and CIVITAS EBORACI for York.

Collecting Hints

Tower mint sixpences are fairly common, especially in the lower grades, and are usually available in about Fine condition. Coins are often badly cracked, probably due to the striking, sometimes holed or creased but rarely clipped; those in VF and EF are rare and desirable. The issue from the York mint is rare and difficult to obtain in any grade.

Tower Mint

Obverse Legend EDWARD VI DG AGL FRA Z HIB REX — Edward VI by the grace of God King of England France and Ireland

Reverse Legend POSUI DEUM ADIVTOREM MEUM — I have made God my helper

Obverse Facing bust of king with rose to the left and denomination (VI) to the right; mintmark 'Y' or tun at start of legend.

Reverse Long cross over royal shield; mintmark as obverse.

E66D-005 Poor £20 VG £40 F £70 VF £200

York Mint

Obverse Legend As previous.

Reverse Legend CITIVAS EBORACI — City of York

Obverse As previous, but mintmark mullet.

Reverse As previous; mintmark mullet.

E66D-010 Poor £50 VG £100 F £160 VF £400

Philip and Mary 1554–1558

Sixpences were not produced during the reign of Mary 1553–1554 but reintroduced, with important new features, under Philip and Mary. The first novel feature of this issue was that the sixpences were dated, continuing a practice that was inaugurated with Edward VI's fine silver crown and halfcrown and of course still used today. As mentioned in previous chapters, undated coins can still be dated with considerable accuracy by the mintmark in conjunction with historical evidence. Some issues from the reign of Philip and Mary do not have mintmarks, but all later hammered issues have mintmarks with or without a date. The second novel feature of these sixpences was particular to the reign and shared by the other contemporary denominations; the coins had the busts of both Philip and Mary on the obverse. This had never been done before and was necessitated as much by the Act of Parliament that proclaimed Mary unfit to rule alone because she was a woman as by the hope that the popularity of her husband, Philip of Spain, might be boosted if his portrait was on the coins. Finally, sixpences were only struck at the Tower mint in London, a practice that would continue during the next two reigns.

Collecting Hints

Philip and Mary sixpences are fairly rare but obtainable, usually in about Fine condition although often damaged or creased; coins in VF and EF are very difficult to obtain and desirable. If collectors just want an example of this new-style coinage, they might consider obtaining a shilling instead, which is much more common. They should not however confuse the English sixpence with the more common Philip and Mary Irish groat, which has a large harp on the reverse.

Spanish Title

Obverse Legend PHILIP ET MARIA D G R ANG FR NEAP PR HISP — Philip and Mary by the grace of God [King and Queen] of England France and Naples Prince [and Princess] of Spain

Reverse Legend POSUIMUS DEUM ADIUTOREM NOSTRUM — We have made God our helper

Obverse Facing busts of monarchs, crown above separating date 1554; no mintmark.

Reverse Crown over royal shield and dividing mark of value VI.

PM6D-005 VG £70 F £150 VF £500

English Title

Obverse Legend PHILIP ET MARIA DG REX ET REGINA AN — Philip and Mary by the grace of God King and Queen of England

Reverse Legend As previous.

Obverse As previous, but dated 1555; no mintmark.

Reverse As previous.

PM6D-010 VG £75 F £175 VF £550

As previous, but dated 1557 with mintmark lis at start of obverse legend.

PM6D-015 VG £75 F £175 VF £550

As PM6D-010 but the obverse has a heavy-beaded inner circle between the legend and the busts. It is accepted that the obverse die from the Philip and Mary Irish groat was used to produce this coin. The reverse is as previous.

PM6D-020 ex. rare

This extremely rare issue is usually only obtainable in less than Fine condition.

Obverse Legend As PM6D-010.

Reverse Legend As PM6D-010.

Obverse As PM6D-010 with no mintmark; the date (1554 or 1557) is below the busts.

Reverse As PM6D-010.

PM6D-025 VG £200 F — VF —

Elizabeth I 1558–1603

The sixpence became an important and well-established denomination under Elizabeth I and although none was produced in the short period of her first two issues, large quantities were struck in the third issue. The sixpence is easily identified as a denomination since, with one extremely rare exception, all issues are dated and, again with one extremely rare exception, all have a rose behind the queen's bust. Also, all sixpences have mintmarks at the beginning of the obverse and reverse legend which we have listed with the dates, as the poor condition of some coins results in unclear dates. Moreover, some dates, in particular 1568/1567, are overdates — i.e. a die has been altered from one year to another so as to avoid the expense of a new die. In rare cases the date is not complete on the coin, usually with the last number missing. With huge quantities of coins being produced from numerous dies, variations in style exist and there are particularly many styles of bust in the third coinage. Finally, milled sixpences

were also produced under Elizabeth and are very different in style from the hammered issue.

Hammered Coinage

Collecting Hints

No collection should be without an Elizabeth I sixpence. They are fairly common, especially in VG to about Fine condition but VF and EF examples also exist and are desirable and obtainable. Sixpences are sometimes clipped, creased or holed. Collectors should try to obtain an example with a clear date, mintmark and portrait.

Third Issue 1561–1577

Many slight varieties of bust exist; several issues have been found undated and were probably die trials, as it is known that the date was engraved last on the die. All undated sixpences are extremely rare.

Large Flan Issue

This issue was only struck in 1561 with a flan measuring 27mm or more in diameter as compared to the less than 26mm flan of regular issues.

Obverse Legend ELIZABETH DG. ANG FRA ET HIB REGINA (varieties exist) — Elizabeth by the grace of God Queen of England France and Ireland

Reverse Legend POSUI DEU ADIVTOREM MEU — I have made God my helper

Obverse Large bust of queen with hair swept back, rose behind bust; mintmark pheon.

Reverse Cross over royal shield, 1561 above shield.

EL6D-005 VG £80 F £180 VF £400

As previous, but smaller bust; mintmark pheon.

EL6D-010 Poor £15 VG £30 F £60 VF £180

Regular Issue

Legends As previous.

Obverse Bust of queen with rose behind; mintmark at beginning of legend.

Reverse Cross over royal shield, date above shield; mintmark at beginning of legend: *Mintmark* Pheon (1561–1565), rose (1565), portcullis (1566), lion (1566–1567, undated), coronet (undated, 1567–1570), castle

(1569–1571), ermine (1572–1573, undated), acorn (1573–1574), eglantine (1573–1577)

EL6D-015 Poor £10 VG £18 F £35 VF £80

Another variety exists without a rose on the obverse, dated 1561; mintmark pheon. This issue is extremely rare and possibly a pattern or trial.

EL6D-020 ex. rare

Fourth Issue 1578–1582

Sixpences for this and the following issues tend to have slightly larger busts.

Legends As previous.

Obverse As previous, but with larger bust.

Reverse As previous.

Mintmark Plain cross (1578–1579), long cross (1580–1581), sword (1582).

EL6D-025 Poor £10 VG £18 F £35 VF £80

Fifth Issue 1582–1600

This issue is fairly similar to the previous one except for the obverse legend.

Obverse Legend ELIZAB D G ANG FR ET HIB REGI — Elizabeth by the grace of God Queen of England France and Ireland

Reverse Legend, Obverse & Reverse As previous.

Mintmark Bell (1582–1583), A (1582–1584), escallop (1584–1586), crescent (1587–1589), hand (1590–1592), tun (1592–1595), woolpack (1594–1595), key (1595–1598), anchor (1598–1600), cypher (1600).

EL6D-030 Poor £10 VG £18 F £35 VF £80

Sixth Issue 1601–1602

This issue is similar to the previous one and a continuation in style and design.

As previous, but mintmark '1' (1601–1602), '2' (1602).

EL6D-035 Poor £12 VG £20 F £40 VF £95

Milled Coinage

Elizabeth's milled sixpence, struck for eleven years at the Tower mint, can easily be distinguished from the hammered by its style and absence of inner circles. All issues are dated and have a rose behind the queen's bust, unlike the groat which has neither. For more details on Elizabeth's milled coinage, please refer to the Shilling Chapter.

Collecting Hints

Most types of milled sixpence are fairly common. They are usually available in about Fine condition, creased and often mounted or gilded as the coin was popular as jewellery. Coins in VF or EF, especially if uncreased, are obtainable and very desirable. This issue is never clipped and, because of the way the coins were produced, details are usually clear.

Obverse Legend ELIZABETH D G ANG FRA ET HIB REGINA — Elizabeth by the grace of God Queen of England France and Ireland

Reverse Legend POSUI DEUM ADIVITOREM MEUM — I have made God my helper

Obverse Small bust of queen, large rose behind; mintmark star.

Reverse Cross over royal shield, 1561 above shield.

EL6D-040 VG £25 F £50 VF £130

As previous, but tall narrow bust with plain dress; 1561 or 1562.

EL6D-045 VG £25 F £50 VF £130

As previous, but the dress is decorated; 1562.

EL6D-050 VG £25 F £50 VF £130

As previous, with large broad bust, small rose behind bust; 1562.

EL6D-055 VG £25 F £50 VF £130

As previous, but cross pattée on reverse over royal shield; 1562–1564.

EL6D-060 VG £30 F £60 VF £150

As previous, but the queen has a low ruff, with a visible ear; the border of the coin is made up of pellets; dated 1564 or 1566.

EL6D-065 VG £40 F £90 VF £180

Smaller bust of queen; mintmark lis on obverse and reverse. Dated 1567 or 1568.

EL6D-070 VG £35 F £70 VF £160

Large crude bust of queen breaking the legend in lower half of coin. Dated 1570 with mintmark lis, or 1571/0 with mintmark castle.

EL6D-075 VG £60 F £120 VF rare

James I 1603–1625

The sixpences produced under James I were a continuation in style and quality from those of Elizabeth, except that the Scottish arms are to be found on the shield on the reverse. Struck at the Tower mint, all sixpences are dated on the reverse above the shield and have a mintmark at the beginning of the obverse and reverse legend. Issues are distinguished chiefly by the style of the king's bust. As James VI of Scotland, James I also produced a Scottish six-shilling piece which is similar to the English sixpence, but cruder in style. To ensure correct identification, collectors should always check that the mintmark corresponds to the date of a sixpence.

Collecting Hints

Most James I sixpences are fairly common and collectors will have little difficulty obtaining an example. They are usually found in less than Fine condition, often clipped and in some cases the coin appears weakly struck, with a rather faint portrait. Coins in Fine and VF condition are fairly common, but those in EF are very rare and desirable. As James I shillings tend to be found in better condition than sixpences, collectors who just want an example from this reign might consider a shilling.

First Coinage 1603–1604

First Bust

Obverse Legend IACOBUS D.G ANG SCO FRA ET HIB REX — James King of England Scotland France and Ireland

Reverse Legend EXURGAT DEUS DISSIPENTUR INIMICI — Let God arise and His enemies be scattered

Obverse Bust of king with small neat beard, value VI behind bust; mintmark thistle.

Reverse Royal arms, 1603 above shield.

J16D-005 VG £20 F £40 VF £150

Second Bust

Legends As previous.

Obverse Bust of king with long pointed beard; mintmark thistle or lis.

Reverse As previous, but dated 1603 or 1604.

J16D-010 VG £18 F £38 VF £140

Second Coinage 1604–1616

Third Bust

Obverse Legend IACOBUS D.G. MAG BRIT FRA ET HIB REX — James by the grace of God King of Great Britain France and Ireland

Reverse Legend QUAE DEUS CONIUNXIT NEMO SEPARET — What God hath joined let no man put asunder

Obverse Bust of king with square-cut beard; mintmark lis or rose.

Reverse As previous, but dated 1604–1605.

J16D-015 VG £18 F £35 VF £100

Fourth Bust

Legends As previous.

Obverse King's bust similar to previous one except that the beard is bushier and unkempt, and the armour is plainer in style.

Reverse As previous, but dated 1605–1618.

Mintmark Rose (1605–1606), escallop (1606–1607), grapes (1607), coronet (1607–1609), key (1609–1610), bell (1610), mullet (1610–1611), tower (1611–1612), trefoil (1613), cinquefoil (1614–1615), tun (1615), plain cross (1618).

J16D-020 VG £18 F £35 VF £100

Fifth Bust

The king's bust is larger than the previous one and the hair is brushed back; the mintmark is a plain cross and the date 1618. This issue should not be confused with the sixth bust.

J16D-025 unique

Third Coinage 1619–1625

Sixth Bust

Legends As previous.

Obverse Bust of king with long curly hair.

Reverse Royal arms, date above.

Mintmark Rose (1621), thistle (1621–1623), lis (1623–1624), trefoil (1624).

J16D-030 VG £18 F £35 VF £100

Charles I 1625–1649

Charles I's reign was as complicated numismatically as it was turbulent politically. Large quantities of sixpences were produced mainly, but not exclusively, at the Tower mint; provincial mints also struck sixpences and there are a number of siege pieces. The early issues were dated and fairly similar in style to those of James I, but the later and more common Tower issues were undated. The denomination is easily identified as the mark of value (VI) can always be found behind the king's head.

Tower Mint

Most Tower mint issues are fairly common. The early ones, up to class 4B, were struck under the king and from 1642 onwards under Parliament. They can easily be identified by the mintmark, which is different in the earlier issues and found at the beginning of the obverse and reverse legend. In some, mostly later, issues

mintmarks have been altered so that dies could be used for another year and this often results in the mintmark looking blundered.

Tower Mint under King 1625–1642

Class 1

Obverse Legend CAROLUS D.G. MAG BRI FRA ET HI REX — Charles by the grace of God King of Great Britain France and Ireland

Reverse Legend CHRISTO AUSPICE REGNO — I reign under the auspices of Christ

Obverse Bust of king wearing ruff, value behind; mintmark lis or cross calvary.

Reverse Royal shield over a cross with date above, 1625 or 1626.

C16D-005 VG £40 F £60 VF £200

Class 1A

Legends As previous.

Obverse As previous, but the king's armour is concealed; mintmark cross calvary, blackamoor's head, castle, anchor, heart.

Reverse As previous, dated 1625–1629.

C16D-010 VG £40 F £60 VF £200

Class 1B

As previous, but no crown over royal shield on the reverse, dated 1629 or 1630; mintmarks heart or plume.

C16D-015 VG £60 F £80

Class 2A

Obverse Legend As previous, but minor varieties exist.

Reverse Legend As previous.

Obverse Bust of king with more armour visible; mintmark plume or rose.

Reverse Oval shield, no date, 'C.R.' above shield.

C16D-020 VG £30 F £50 VF £100

Class 2B

As previous, but a plume divides the 'C.R.' on the reverse.

C16D-025 VG £40 F £60 VF £120

Class 3

Legends As previous.

Obverse Bust of king with lace collar; mintmark harp or portcullis.

Reverse Oval shield dividing 'C.R'.

C16D-030 VG £20 F £40 VF £80

Class 3A

Legends As previous.

Obverse Bust of king without the inner circles usually found between the legend and the king's bust; mintmark bell, crown or anchor.

Reverse Oval shield, without either 'C.R' to sides or the inner circles usually found between the legend and shield.

C16D-035 VG £20 F £40 VF £80

Class 4

The size of the VI varies in this issue.

Legends As previous.

Obverse Bust of king within inner circles; mintmark tun or anchor.

Reverse Square-topped shield with inner circle.

C16D-040 VG £20 F £40 VF £80

Class 4A

As previous, but a slightly different Aberystwyth bust, the king's crown sometimes has a single or double arch; mintmark anchor or triangle.

C16D-045 VG £20 F £40 VF £80

Class 4B

As previous, but older-looking bust of king; mintmark triangle or triangle in circle.

C16D-050 VG £20 F £40 VF £80

Tower Mint under Parliament 1642–1648

This issue is easily identified by the unique mintmarks.

Class 4C

Legends As previous.

Obverse Bust of king similar to previous issue; mintmarks '(P)', '(R)', eye or sun.

Reverse Square-topped shield over cross.

C16D-055 VG £25 F £55 VF £125

Class 4D

Similar to class 4A (C16D-045); mintmark '(R)', eye, sun or sceptre.

C16D-060 VG £25 F £55 VF £125

Class 4E

As previous, but large, squat bust of king; mintmark eye or sun.

C16D-065 VG £100 F £250 VF —

Briot's Milled Coinage 1631–1639

Nicholas Briot joined the Tower mint in 1628 and was made sole designer for the bust of the royal coinage. In 1631 he introduced his milled, or machine-made, coinage which was high in quality, style and design and greatly superior to the hammered issues. Its main drawback appears to have been the length of time needed to produce the coins. Moreover, hammered coins were more popular with the moneyers at the mint, who were worried that machines would take over their jobs.

Collecting Hints

As with the other denominations, the quality of Briot's coins was much higher than that of contemporary hammered issues and this is reflected in the quality of the coins available today. Both issues are fairly scarce but obtainable, usually in Fine or VF condition. Due to the striking there is occasionally a weakness in parts of the legend, but the coins are usually round with complete legends unlike the Tower mint's hammered issues.

First Milled Issue 1631–1632

Obverse Legend CAROLUS D G MAGN BRITANN FR ET HIB REX — Charles King of Great Britain France and Ireland

Reverse CHRISTO AUSPICE REGNO — I reign under the auspices of Christ

Obverse Bust of king with value behind; mintmark flower and 'B'.

Reverse Square-topped shield over cross, small 'B' sometimes at top of cross.

C16D-070 VG £35 F £70 VF £150 EF £300

Second Milled Issue 1638–1639

Legends As previous.

Obverse Bust of slightly different style from last issue; mintmark anchor or mullet.

Reverse Royal arms over smaller cross, the edges of which just go to the inner circle.

C16D-075 VG £25 F £60 VF £135 EF £260

Provincial Mints

York Mint 1643–1644

This issue is fairly easy to distinguish by the mintmark lion.

Collecting Hints

York sixpences, unlike the other denominations, are fairly scarce especially in better than Fine condition.

Obverse Legend CAROLUS D.G. MAG BRIT FRAN ET HIB REX — Charles by the grace of God King of Great Britain France and Ireland

Reverse Legend CHRISTO AUSPICE REGNO — I reign under the auspices of Christ

Obverse Bust of king with pointed beard, denomination behind the bust; mintmark lion.

Reverse Oval shield with crown above.

C16D-080 VG £80 F £200 VF £450

As previous, but 'C.R' divided by shield on the reverse.
C16D-085 VG £70 F £180 VF £400

Aberystwyth Mint

This issue can easily be identified by the plume in front of the king's face and the mintmark book.

Collecting Hints

Sixpences from the Aberystwyth mint are fairly rare and difficult to obtain; when available, they are usually undamaged in Fine or VF condition.

Obverse Legend CAROLUS D.G. MAG BR FR ET HI REX (minor varieties exist) — Charles by the grace of God King of Great Britain France and Ireland

Reverse Legend CHRISTO AUSPICE REGNO — I reign under the auspices of Christ

Obverse Bust of king with plume in front of face, value behind and no inner circle; mintmark book.

Reverse Oval shield with plume above, no inner circle.

C16D-090 VG £80 F £160 VF £325

As previous, but inner circle on obverse.

C16D-095 VG £85 F £175 VF £350

As previous, but inner circle on obverse and reverse.

C16D-100 VG £80 F £160 VF £325

As previous, but on reverse the plume is square in shape.

C16D-105 VG £80 F £160 VF £325

As previous, but on obverse the king's crown breaks the inner circle.

C16D-110 VG £100 F £200 VF £400

Aberystwyth Furnace Mint 1648–1649

This issue is fairly similar to the Aberystwyth one but has mint-mark crown, and is a little cruder in style.

Collecting Hints

This issue is extremely rare in any grade.

Obverse Legend CAROLUS D.G. MAG BRI FRA ET HIB REX — Charles by the grace of God King of Great Britain France and Ireland

Reverse Legend CHRISTO AUSPICE REGNO — I reign under the auspices of Christ

Obverse Bust of king, value behind and small plume in front of face; mintmark crown.

Reverse Oval shield, plume above shield.

C16D-115 ex. rare

Oxford Mint 1642–1646

This rare issue used the Aberystwyth obverse die, probably because coins needed to be struck urgently; the reverse has the Declaration in three lines with a date below.

Collecting Hints

All issues are fairly rare but, when available, usually found in Fine or VF condition.

Obverse Legend CAROLUS D G. MAG BRIT FR ET HI REX — Charles by the grace of God King of Great Britain France and Ireland

Reverse Legend EXURGAT DEUS DISSIPENTUR INIMICI — Let God arise and His enemies be scattered

Reverse Centre Legend RELIG PROT LEG ANG LIBER PAR — The religion of the Protestants the laws of England the liberty of Parliament

Obverse Aberystwyth bust of king with inner circle, value behind bust and plume in front of face; mintmark book.

Reverse The Declaration in three lines, three plumes above and the date 1642 or 1643 below.

C16D-120 VG £75 F £150 VF £300

As previous, but smaller plumes of different style, known as Shrewsbury plumes, on the reverse; 1643.

C16D-125 VG £75 F £150 VF £300

As previous, but only one plume on reverse and a lis either side; dated 1644 with OX by date.

C16D-130 ex. rare

Bristol Mint 1643–1645

Obverse Legend CAROLUS D.G. MAG B F ET H REX — Charles by the grace of God King of Great Britain France and Ireland

Reverse Legend EXURGAT DEUS DISSIPENTUR INIMICI — Let God arise and His enemies be scattered

Reverse Inner Legend RELIG PRO LEG ANG LIB PAR — The religion of the Protestants the laws of England the liberty of Parliament

Obverse Coarse bust of king of poor style, value behind.

Reverse Three small plumes over the Declaration, 1643 below.

C16D-135 VG £80 F £160 VF £400

As previous, but plumelet in front of face.

C16D-140 VG £70 F £150 VF £380

Late Declaration Issues 1645–1646

These issues are different in style from the other provincial issues. The mintmarks 'B' and 'A' are specific to this issue. Although unconfirmed, it is thought that the mintmark might stand for the town that issued the coin, 'A' being for Appledore or Ashby de la Zouch and 'B' for Barnstaple, Bideford or Bridgnorth-on-Severn.

Obverse Legend CAROLUS D G MAG BR FR ET HI REX — Charles by the grace of God King of Great Britain France and Ireland

Reverse Legend EXURGAT DEUS DISSIPENTUR INIMICI — Let God arise and His enemies be scattered

Reverse Inner Legend REL PRO LEG ANG LIB PAR — The religion of the Protestants the laws of England the liberty of Parliament

Obverse Bust of king with value behind, plumelet in front of face; mintmark sideways 'A'.

Reverse Three plumelets above Declaration, 1645 below.

C16D-145 VG £100 F £200 VF £400

Obverse Legend CAROLUS D.G. MAG B F ET H REX — Charles by the grace of God King of Great Britain France and Ireland

Reverse Legend As previous.

Reverse Inner Legend As previous, but sometimes beginning TIN PRO instead of REL PRO which might be a die error.

Obverse Bust of king with value behind, plume in front of face; mintmark 'B'.

Reverse Scrolls and plumes above Declaration, 1646 below.

C16D-150 VG £70 F £125 VF £225

Exeter Mint

This rare issue has the date 1644 in the reverse legend and mintmark rose. The date in the legend is specific to this issue.

Obverse Legend CAROLUS DG. MA BR FR ET HI REX — Charles by the grace of God King of Great Britain France and Ireland

Reverse Legend CHRISTO AUSPICE REGNO — I reign under the auspices of Christ

Obverse Bust of king, value behind in varying sizes; mintmark rose.

Reverse Oval garnished shield, dated 1644; mintmark rose. Two reverses exist, on one the rose divides the date, on the other it does not.

C16D-155 VG £80 F £160 VF £400

Worcester or Shrewsbury Mint

Very little is known about this very rare and crudely produced coin. Its style of production is unique and so are the mintmarks castle and boar's head, usually muled.

Collecting Hints

This coin is rare in any grade and probably does not exist in better than Fine condition.

Obverse Legend CAROLUS DG MAG BR FR ET HI RX — Charles by the grace of God King of Great Britain France and Ireland

Reverse Legend CHRISTO AUSPICE REGNO — I reign under the auspices of Christ

Obverse Crude bust of king, value behind; mintmark castle.

Reverse Square-topped shield; mintmark boar's head.

C16D-160 VG £300 F £600

Siege Issues

Newark 1646

Newark was besieged several times between 1645 and 1646 and finally surrendered to Cromwell's army in May 1646. This issue can be easily identified from other denominations by the VI for sixpence below the crown on the obverse.

Collecting Hints

Only struck in 1646, the sixpence is one of the rarer denominations, usually obtainable in Fine condition and often holed. Some specimens are gilded, with the gilding coming from the article which was the original source of the coin. While interesting, gilded coins can be worth less because they are often unsightly where the gilding has worn.

Obverse Crown dividing 'CR', denomination below.

Reverse OBS NEWARK 1646 in three lines.

C16D-165 VG £125 F £250 VF £500

Scarborough 1644–1645

Scarborough produced two differently styled sixpences. The value was stamped on the coins, which are roughly square in shape.

Collecting Hints

All issues are extremely rare in any grade and collectors should beware of forgeries.

Obverse Castle with gateway to left, value (VI) punched below.
Reverse Plain.

C16D-170 ex. rare

Obverse Castle with two turrets, value (VI) punched below.
Reverse Plain.

C16D-175 ex. rare

Commonwealth 1649–1660

Hammered sixpences, fairly plain in style, were struck during the Commonwealth. The issue is similar to the other denominations with the shield of St. George on the obverse and the shield of St George and Ireland with the denomination VI above on the reverse. All issues were dated.

Collecting Hints

The early issue (with mintmark sun) is fairly common, especially in the lower grades, but the later issue (mintmark anchor) is rare in all grades. Many coins are badly worn, bent or damaged and those in better than Fine condition are rare for both issues. Coins dated 1657 are extremely rare.

Obverse Legend THE COMMONWEALTH OF ENGLAND

Reverse Legend GOD WITH US

Obverse St George's arms in wreath; mintmark sun.

Reverse Arms of St George and Ireland, value above and date in legend, 1649, 1651–1657.

COM6D-005 VG £40 F £90 VF £180

As previous, but mintmark anchor, dated 1658–1660.

COM6D-010 VG £150 F £350 VF —

Charles II 1660–1685

Hammered Issue 1660–1662

During this short period three different types of sixpence were produced, all of them undated with mintmark crown on the obverse.

Obverse Legend CAROLUS II D.G. MAG BRIT FRAN ET HIB REX — Charles by the grace of God King of Great Britain France and Ireland

Reverse Legend CHRISTO AUSPICE REGNO — I reign under the auspices of Christ

Obverse Bust of king with no mark of value; mintmark crown.

Reverse Royal shield over cross.

C26DH-005 VG £75 F £150 VF £300

As previous, but mark of value behind the king's head.

C26DH-010 VG £300 F £600 VF —

As previous, but inner circles on obverse and reverse.

C26DH-015 VG £40 F £80 VF £200

Groat

The groat, with a value of fourpence, was first introduced during the recoinage of Edward I in 1279. Its name, which was derived from the French *gros* and the Italian *grosso*, roughly translated means great or thick. The groat constituted an important part of Edward's recoinage to introduce more denominations into circulation. In the 1260s the French had successfully introduced a large silver coin with a fairly similar value to the groat — the *gros tournois*. With England being involved in increasing trade with Europe, Edward I realised the importance of larger denominations. Although Edward's issues did not succeed, the groat was successfully introduced under Edward III and was produced by most monarchs for circulation until the reign of Queen Victoria. Even now, the groat is produced as a Maundy fourpence and distributed by the monarch every year.

Edward I 1272–1307

Until the reign of Edward I the only coins produced, except for a few rare exceptions, were pennies. Increased trade in a more prosperous England and Europe required a variety of both smaller and larger denominations and the need was met by Edward I's recoinage, when the groat or fourpence was also introduced. Many consider this rare issue to have been an experiment or pattern, but as a total of eight different varieties were issued, it would appear that it was intended for circulation. Its introduction, however, was not a success not only because the public was accustomed to the penny and wary of change, but also because the groat was underweight with four single pennies weighing more. Merchants, especially those trading on the Continent, preferred payment in pennies so the groat became unpopular and was not successfully introduced into circulation until Edward III's reign. All Edward I issues were struck at London; in total, eight slight varieties exist. The prices are the same for all, depending upon whether they are mounted or not :

mounted VG £800 F £1,200

unmounted VG £1,000 F £1,600 VF £3,000

Collecting Hints

Edward I groats are rare. Most specimens show traces of gilding and solder marks and appear to have been made into jewellery at some period. Undamaged coins are extremely rare and most of the damaged ones are in Fine condition.

Obverse Legend EDWARDUS DI GRA REX ANGL — Edward by the grace of God King of England

Reverse Legend DNS HIBNE DUX AQUT — Lord of Ireland Duke of Aquitaine

Reverse Inside Circle Legend LONDONIA CIVI — City of London

Obverse Facing bust of crowned king within a quatrefoil, a flower either side of his hair.

Reverse Long-cross with three pellets in each angle, reverse legend in two circles.

E14D-005

Obverse Triple pellet stops in legend, spearheads to king's crown; the king's drapery in two wedges and a trefoil below bust.
Reverse As previous.

E14D-010

As previous, but a pellet either side of the king's bust.

E14D-015

Double pellet stops in legend, pearls on crown and a trefoil below bust.

E14D-020

Double or triple pellet stops in legend, spearheads to crown, curved drapery on king, trefoil below bust.

E14D-025

Double pellet stops in legend, small pearls on crown, king's drapery in two wedges, small flower below bust.

E14D-030

Triple pellet stops in legend, pearls on crown, the king has foreshortened circle, and a small flower below bust.

E14D-035

Double pellet stops, spearheads on crown, the rest as previous.

E14D-040

Edward III 1327–1377

The groat was successfully introduced into circulation during Edward III's fourth coinage (1351–1377). Like the groats of Edward I and Edward IV, which are all similar in style, Edward III issues bear the king's name at the beginning of the obverse legend but are distinguishable either by small particularities in the face, hair or legends or, in the case of Edward IV, by various marks in the legends and often in the field beside the king. However, collectors should note that there are many minor varieties of Edward III groats. The various issues based on the monarch's aspirations in France that are detailed in the relevant section of the Penny chapter also apply to the groat.

Collecting Hints

Edward III groats are fairly common; they can be found in VG to VF condition, EF specimens being rare. Many coins are clipped and some have weak areas where the legend is unclear. Collectors should try to obtain an example in Fine condition with good eye appeal and as round as possible.

Pre Treaty Period 1351–1361

London Mint

Varieties exist in most classes, especially E34D-040. Letters are often missed out or words misspelt in the legends and London is sometimes spelt LONDOM. In most cases these varieties are not rare.

1351

Obverse Legend EDWARD D G REX ANGL Z FRANC D HYB — Edward by the grace of God King of England and France Lord of Ireland. This is known as the French title.

Reverse Legend POSVI DEUM ADIVTOREM MEUM — I have made God my helper

Reverse Inside Circle Legend CIVITAS LONDON — City of London

Obverse Facing bust of king, with Roman 'M', open 'C' and 'E' in legend; mintmark cross '1'.

Reverse Large cross with three pellets in each quarter.

E34D-005 VG £60 F £125 VF £300

As previous, but crown in each quarter of the reverse instead of pellets.

E34D-010 unique

1351–1352

Legends As previous.

Obverse Facing bust of king with French title; Lombardic 'M', closed 'C' and 'E', 'R' with wedge-shaped tail.

Reverse Large cross with three pellets in each quarter.

E34D-015 VG £20 F £45 VF £95

1352–1353

As previous, but 'R' with normal tail; mintmark cross 1 or cross 1 broken.

E34D-020 VG £22 F £50 VF £100

1354–1355

As previous, but broken letters in legend, 'V' with nick in right limb; mintmark cross 2.

E34D-025 VG £20 F £45 VF £95

As previous, but a lis on the king's breast.

E34D-030 VG £25 F £60 VF £120

1356

As previous, but no lis on breast; mintmark crown.

E34D-035 VG £25 F £60 VF £120

1356–1361

Legends As previous.

Obverse Facing bust of king, usually with annulet under it; mintmark cross 3.

Reverse An annulet usually in one quarter.

E34D-040 VG £22 F £50 VF £100

York Mint

Obverse Legend EDWARD D G REX ANGL Z FRANC D HYB — Edward by the grace of God King of England and France Lord of Ireland

Reverse Legend POSVI DEUM ADIVTOREM MEUM — I have made God my helper

Reverse Inner Circle Legend CIVITAS EBORACI — City of York

Obverse Facing bust of king; mintmark cross 1 or cross 1 broken.

Reverse Large cross, three pellets in each quarter.

E34D-045 VG £30 F £75 VF £150

As previous, but broken letters in the legend and 'V' has a nick in the right limb.

E34D-050 VG £25 F £55 VF £130

Transitional Period 1361

In this scarce issue the French title in the obverse legend is missing and the letters are of irregular size.

Obverse Legend EDWAR DEI GRAC REX ANGL — Edward by the grace of God King of England

Reverse Inner Legend POSVI DEUM ADIVTOREM MEUM — I have made God my helper

Reverse Legend CIVITAS LONDON — City of London

Obverse Facing crowned bust of king, annulet each side of crown, irregular size lettering; mintmark cross potent.

Reverse Large cross, three pellets in each quarter.

E34D-055 VG £60 F £140 VF £400

Treaty Period 1361–1369

London Mint

This issue can be differentiated by the different obverse legend. Also the 'X' in REX is distinct. As with previous issues, there are several varieties which include various stops and marks in the legend, also the A in ADIVTOREM is sometimes unbarred. None of these varieties are particularly rare.

Obverse Legend EDWARD D(EI) G REX ANGL D(NS) HYB Z AQT — Edward by the grace of God King of England Lord of Ireland and Aquitaine

Reverse Legend POSVI DEUM ADIVTOREM MEUM — I have made God my helper

Obverse Facing bust of king; mintmark cross potent.

Reverse Large cross with three pellets in each quarter.

E34D-060 VG £22 F £50 VF £100

As previous, but annulet before EDWARD in obverse legend.

E34D-065 VG £25 F £60 VF £120

As previous, but annulet on king's breast.

E34D-070 VG £30 F £65 VF £130

Calais Mint

Obverse Legend EDWARD D G REX ANGL D HYB Z AQT — Edward by the grace of God King of England Lord of Ireland and Aquitaine

Reverse Legend POSVI DEUM ADIVTOREM MEUM — I have made God my helper

Reverse Inside Circle Legend VILLA CALESIE — Town of Calais

Obverse Facing bust of king, annulet on breast.

Reverse Large cross, three pellets in each quarter.

E34D-075 VG £70 F £150 VF £300

Post Treaty Period 1369–1377

These issues were all struck at the London mint. The French title has been resumed in the obverse legend. Saltire stops are found in the legends. Also, the word or abbreviation for 'and' in the obverse legend is omitted, probably by mistake.

Obverse Legend EDWARD DI GRA REX ANGL FRANC — Edward by the grace of God King of England [and] France

Reverse Legend POSVI DEUM ADIVTOREM MEUM — I have made God my helper

Obverse Facing bust of king, 'F' in legend usually reversed with varieties in readings; mintmark cross pattée.

Reverse Large cross, three pellets in each quarter.

E34D-080 VG £50 F £100 VF £300

Obverse Legend EDWARD DI G REX ANGL F DNS HIB A (varieties exist)-Edward by the grace of God King of England [and] France Lord of Ireland [and] Aquitaine

Reverse Legend POSVI DEUM ADIVTOREM MEUM — I have made God my helper

Obverse Facing bust of king, row of annulets under bust that resembles chain mail; mintmark cross potent with four pellets around it.

Reverse Cross with three pellets in each quarter.

E34D-085 VG £100 F £225 VF rare

Obverse Legend EDWARD DI G REX ANGL FRANC D HIB — Edward by the grace of God King of England [and] France Lord of Ireland

Reverse Legend As previous.

Obverse Row of pellets across king's breast; mintmark as previous issue.

Reverse As previous.

E34D-090 VG £130 F £250 VF rare

Richard II 1377–1399

Richard II's coinage continued in the style of Edward III's and all groats are rare. After checking that RICARD, rather than EDWARD or HENRI, is found at the top of the obverse legend and to distinguish it from a Richard III groat, collectors should pay particular attention to the face, hair and crown. Moreover, the two monarchs used different mintmarks; Richard II only used the cross pattée and Richard III used other mintmarks. Richard II issued four distinct types of groat and they were all struck at London.

Obverse Legend RICARD DI GRA REX ANGL(IE) Z FR(ANC) — Richard by the grace of God King of England and France

Reverse Legend POSVI DEUM ADIVTORE(M) MEU(M) — I have made God my helper

Obverse Facing bust of king; mintmark cross pattée. Pay particular attention to the ET or 'Z' in the legend.

Reverse Large cross with three pellets in each quarter.

R24D-005 VG £200 F £400 VF £1,000

As previous, but new-style lettering, particularly the 'Z' before FRANC in the obverse legend.

R24D-010 VG £150 F £300 VF £650

As previous, but a slightly different style of bust and fishtail serifs to lettering.

R24D-015 VG £200 F £400 VF £1,000

As previous, but slightly different style to bust, a crescent on the king's breast.

R24D-020 VG £750 F £1,200 VF rare

Henry IV 1399–1413

All issues from the reign of Henry IV are rare and groats are no exception. No groats were struck in the heavy coinage (1399–1412) but three main varieties were issued during the light coinage of 1412–1413. However, Henry IV's coins are fairly difficult to distinguish from the much more common issues of Henry V, VI and VII, all of which read HENRIC in the obverse legend — the first three Henrys (I — III) not having struck groats and those of Henry VIII being easily distinguishable. Henry VII's issues are also very different, particularly on the king's crown. Henry IV groats may be identified by the mintmark cross pattée (6) found above the crown in the legend (the only other Henry to use this mintmark is Henry VI Restored), the mint (London, found on the reverse inner circle legend) and the portraits, which have different style crown, hair and facial expressions. Having correctly identified the reign that a coin belongs to, collectors should look for any unusual marks on it such as annulets etc., to establish the issue.

Obverse Legend HENRIC DI GRA REX ANGL (Z FRANC) — Henry by the grace of God King of England (and France)

Reverse Legend POSVI DEUM ADIVTOREM MEUM — I have made God my helper

Reverse Inside Circle Legend CIVITAS LONDON — City of London

Obverse Facing crowned bust of king, pellet to the left of crown, annulet to the right; the French title has been omitted on some issues; mintmark cross pattée (6). This is an altered Richard II die with HENRIC struck over RICARD and signs of the old lettering coming through.

Reverse Large cross, three pellets in each quarter.

H44D-005 VG £800 F £1,600 VF £4,000

Obverse Legend HENRIC DI GRA REX ANGL Z FRANC — Henry by the grace of God King of England and France

Reverse Legend As previous.

Obverse Facing bust of king, annulet to the left and pellet to the right of crown, eight or ten arches in tressure; mintmark cross pattée.

Reverse As previous.

H44D-010 VG £700 F £1,400 VF £3,000

Obverse Legend HENRIC DI GRA REX ANGL Z FRANC (IE) — Henry by the grace of God King of the English and France

Reverse Legend As previous.

Obverse As previous, but nine arches in tressure.

Reverse As previous.

H44D-015 VG £700 F £1,400 VF £3,000

Henry V 1413–1422

As mentioned above, there are many similarities between the coinages of Henry IV, V and VI. However, Henry V used the mintmarks cross pattée or pierced cross, both with a central pellet. He also issued new marks, such as mullets or quatrefoils, which are usually found in the legends or the field of the coin; also the portrait, of which there are four main types, is different. Nevertheless, several of Henry V issues are muled using Henry IV dies. All Henry V groats were minted in London.

Obverse Legend HENRIC DI GRA REX ANGL Z FRANC — Henry by the grace of God King of England and France

Reverse Legend POSVI DEUM ADIVITOREM MEUM — I have made God my helper.

Reverse Inner Circle Legend CIVITAS LONDON — City of London

Obverse Emaciated bust of king with no neck, short, broad letters in the legend, quatrefoil after HENRIC, fleurs over crown; mintmark cross pattée with central pellet.

Reverse Long cross with three pellets in each quarter, quatrefoil after POSVI.

H54D-005 VG £300 F £500 VF £1,300

This issue is sometimes muled with a Henry IV reverse whereupon it does not have a quatrefoil nor is the lettering short and broad. However, it may also be muled with later issues of Henry V, whereupon the reverse lettering will again be different. All three varieties that make up this class are of equal rarity.

Legends As previous.

Obverse Scowling bust of king, ordinary lettering in legend, some issues have a quatrefoil after HENRIC; mintmark pierced cross with pellet in centre.

Reverse Large cross with three pellets in each quarter, ordinary lettering.

H54D-010 VG £150 F £300 VF £600

A variety exists that has a mullet in the centre of breast.

H54D-015 VG £130 F £260 VF £500

As with the previous issue, the obverse was sometimes muled with either a Henry IV issue or a later Henry V issue.

As previous, but frowning bust of king, usually with a mullet on the right shoulder, sometimes a quatrefoil is found after HENRIC; mintmark pierced cross with pellet centre.

H54D-020 VG £40 F £85 VF £220

On one very rare variety, the obverse legend ends FRANIE instead of FRANC.

H54D-025 VG £35 F £80 VF £200

As previous, but the obverse legend ends FRANC and there are no marks such as mullet on the obverse.

H54D-030 VG £60 F £130 VF £250

Henry VI First Reign 1422–1461

Henry VI's issues are fairly easy to distinguish by their style, mintmark and various other marks even though the obverse legend reads, like on the issues of the other Henrys, HENRIC. To differentiate this reign from the groats of other Henrys, collectors should bear in mind that on Henry IV's issues the face and crown are different. Henry V's bust is distinct and a number of marks such as mullet on right shoulder differentiate these issues. Henry VI Restored is usually identified by the king's name on the obverse, which reads HENRICV instead of HENRIC. The style, particularly of the crown, of Henry VII's issues is different, while Henry VIII's coins have a totally different style.

As with all Henry VI's denominations, the groat can be classified into various issues depending on the marks, such as annulets or pinecones and mascles, found on it. Three mints were active producing groats under Henry VI, London, Calais and York (which is rare). The mint's name can be found on the reverse of the coin in the inner circle and reads CIVITAS LONDON for London, VILLA CALISIE for Calais or, for the annulet issue, CIVITAS EBORACI for York. However, as many of these issues have similar markings it is important that collectors check all markings when attributing a coin to a class.

Annulet Issue 1422–1427

London Mint

Obverse Legend HENRIC DI GRA REX ANGL Z FRANC — Henry by the grace of God King of England and France

Reverse Legend POSVI DEUM ADIVTOREM MEUM — I have made God my helper

Reverse Inner Circle Legend CIVITAS LONDON — City of London

Obverse Facing bust of king.

Reverse Annulet in two quarters.

H64D-005 VG £20 F £45 VF £80 EF £140

Calais Mint

Obverse & Reverse Legend As previous.
Reverse Inner Circle Legend VILLA CALISIE — Town of Calais
Obverse Facing bust of king with an annulet either side of neck.
Reverse An annulet in two quarters on reverse.

H64D-010 VG £20 F £45 VF £80 EF £140

As previous, but no annulets on reverse.

H64D-015 VG £30 F £60 VF £120 EF £250

York Mint

Obverse & Reverse Legend As previous.
Reverse Inside Circle Legend CIVITAS EBORACI — City of York
Obverse Facing bust of king with lis either side of neck.
Reverse Annulet in two quarters.

H64D-020 VG £350 F £700 VF £1,400 EF rare

Annulet Trefoil Sub-Issue

London Mint

Obverse & Reverse Legend As previous.
Reverse Inside Circle Legend CIVITAS LONDON — City of London
Obverse Facing bust of king with trefoil of pellets to left of crown.
Reverse As previous.

H64D-025 VG £90 F £150 VF £300 EF rare

Calais Mint

Obverse & Reverse Legend As previous.
Reverse Inside Circle Legend VILLA CALISIE — Town of Calais
Obverse As previous, with an annulet either side of neck.
Reverse As previous.

H64D-030 VG £40 F £80 VF £160 EF £300

Rosette Mascle Issue 1427–1430

This issue has rosettes or rosettes and mascles in the legends.

London Mint

Obverse & Reverse Legend As previous.
Reverse Inside Circle Legend CIVITAS LONDON — City of London

Obverse Facing bust of king with no marks, but rosettes or rosettes and mascles in legend.
Reverse Rosettes or rosettes and mascles in legends.

H64D-035 VG £35 F £90 VF £180 EF £350

Calais Mint

Obverse & Reverse Legend As previous.
Reverse Inside Circle Legend VILLA CALISIE — Town of Calais
Obverse As previous.
Reverse As previous.

H64D-040 VG £25 F £50 VF £100 EF £200

There is a variety where a mascle is found in the spandrels.

H64D-045 VG £35 F £70 VF £140 EF £280

Pinecone Mascle Issue 1430–1434

This issue has pinecones and mascles in the legend.

London Mint

Obverse & Reverse Legend As previous.
Reverse Inside Circle Legend CIVITAS LONDON — City of London
Obverse Facing bust of king, no marks but pinecone and mascles in legend.
Reverse Pinecones and mascles in legend.

H64D-050 VG £25 F £60 VF £125

Calais Mint

As previous, but reverse inside circle legend reads VILLA CALISIE — Town of Calais.

H64D-055 VG £25 F £60 VF £125

Leaf Mascle Issue 1434–1435

This issue has a mascle in the legends and a leaf somewhere in the design.

London Mint

This issue is sometimes muled with other London issues, so the reverse often has different marks in the legend from its obverse class.

Obverse & Reverse Legend As previous.

Reverse Inside Circle Legend CIVITAS LONDON (or DONDON) — City of London

Obverse Facing bust of king with leaf below bust and mascles in legend.

Reverse Mascles in legend.

H64D-060 VG £50 F £100 VF £200

Calais Mint

Obverse & Reverse Legend As previous.

Reverse Inside Circle Legend VILLA CALISIE — Town of Calais

Obverse Facing bust of king, leaf on breast and mascles in legend.

Reverse Leaf usually below MEUM in legend.

H64D-065 VG £35 F £70 VF £150

Leaf Trefoil Issue 1435–1438

This issue usually has leaves and trefoil of pellets in the legends.

London Mint

Obverse & Reverse Legend As previous.

Reverse Inside Circle Legend CIVITAS LONDON — City of London

Obverse Facing bust of king, leaf on breast, leaves and trefoil of pellets in legend.

Reverse Leaves and trefoil of pellets usually in legends.

H64D-070 VG £35 F £70 VF £150

As previous, but no leaf on breast.

H64D-075 VG £40 F £80 VF £160

Calais Mint

Obverse & Reverse Legend As previous.

Reverse Inside Circle Legend VILLA CALISIE — Town of Calais

Obverse Facing bust of king, leaf on breast; leaves and trefoil usually in legend.

Reverse As previous.

H64D-080 ex. rare

Trefoil Issue 1438–1443

This issue usually has trefoil of pellets either side of neck and in the legends, as well as a leaf on the king's breast.

London Mint

Obverse & Reverse Legend As previous.

Reverse Inside Circle Legend CIVITAS LONDON — City of London

Obverse Facing bust of king, leaf on breast and trefoils by neck; trefoil of pellets in legend.

Reverse A leaf sometimes found before LON in legend.

H64D-085 VG £40 F £80 VF £160

Obverse & Reverse Legend As previous.

Obverse As previous, but fleurs in spandrels.

Reverse There are sometimes extra pellets in the quarters.

H64D-090 VG £40 F £80 VF £160

As previous, but sometimes trefoils instead of fleurs.

H64D-095 VG £35 F £75 VF £150

Calais Mint

Obverse & Reverse Legend As previous.

Reverse Inside Circle Legend VILLA CALISIE — Town of Calais

Obverse Facing bust of king, leaf on breast and trefoils by neck, trefoils in legend.

Reverse Trefoils in legend.

H64D-100 VG £60 F £150 VF rare

Trefoil Pellet Issue 1443–1445

This issue was only struck at the London mint.
Obverse & Reverse Legend As previous.

Reverse Inside Circle Legend CIVITAS LONDON — City of London

Obverse Facing bust of king, trefoils by neck, pellets by crown and small leaf on breast; trefoils in legend.

Reverse Sometimes an extra pellet in two quarters.

H64D-105 VG £35 F £70 VF £200

Leaf Pellet Issue 1445–1454

This issue usually has a leaf on breast and a pellet either side of the crown. It was only struck at the London mint.
Obverse & Reverse Legend As previous.

Reverse Inside Circle Legend CIVITAS LONDON — City of London

Obverse Facing bust of king, leaf on breast and pellets by crown.

Reverse An extra pellet in two quarters on reverse.

H64D-110 VG £30 F £65 VF £150

Similar to previous, but obverse legend reads ANGLI instead of ANGL and sometimes has a trefoil.

H64D-115 VG £30 F £65 VF £150

Obverse Legend As H64D-110, usual reading of ANGL.

Reverse Legends As previous.

Obverse Facing bust of king, leaf on neck and pellets by crown.

Reverse An extra pellet in two quarters.

H64D-120 VG £40 F £80 VF £180

As previous, but four pellets instead of two in the obverse field (two by the crown and two by the hair).

H64D-125 VG £45 F £100 VF £225

Unmarked Issue 1445–1454

This issue was only struck at the London mint.

Obverse & Reverse Legend As previous.

Reverse Inside Circle Legend CIVITAS LONDON — City of London

Obverse Facing bust of king, no marks.

Reverse Two or four extra pellets.

H64D-130 VG £125 F £300 VF rare

Cross Pellet Issue 1454–1460

This issue has a variety of markings and was struck at the London mint.

Obverse & Reverse Legend As previous.

Reverse Inside Circle Legend CIVITAS LONDON — City of London

Obverse Saltire either side of neck, pellets by crown, leaf and fleur on breast.

Reverse Two extra pellets in quarters.

H64D-135 VG £60 F £120 VF £250

Legends As previous.

Obverse Saltire on neck, pellets by crown, a mullet is usually found after HENRIC and FRANC.

Reverse Usually two extra pellets in design, sometimes a mullet in legend.

H64D-140 VG £55 F £110 VF £230

As previous, but mascles instead of mullets in legend.

H64D-145 VG £60 F £120 VF £250

As previous, but the pellets are by the king's hair instead of the crown.

H64D-150 VG £80 F £140 VF £300

Lis Pellet Issue 1454–1460

This issue was struck at the London mint.

Obverse & Reverse Legend As previous.

Reverse Inside Circle Legend CIVITAS LONDON — City of London

Obverse Facing bust of king, lis on neck, pellets by crown; sometimes a mascle after HENRIC.

Reverse Sometimes two extra pellets in quarters.

H64D-155 VG £100 F £200 VF £450

Edward IV First Reign 1461–1470

As with all Edward IV issues, groats can be divided into the heavy and the light coinage, so called because of a 20% reduction in the weight of the coins in 1464 when groats changed from weighing 60 grains (3.9 grams) to 48 grains (3.1 grams). Edward IV groats are fairly distinctive and EDWARD is found at the top of the obverse legend. To distinguish these issues from those of other Edwards, collectors should bear in mind the following points: Edward I's portrait is quite distinct from any other issue. Edward III's portrait, hair, crown and style of lettering are different. Edward IV's heavy coinage is slightly larger and, of course, heavier than the light coinage and the style is slightly different. Edward IV's second reign coinage is fairly similar to that of Edward IV's light coinage but may be distinguished, either by various small differences or marks, or by the mintmarks which tend to be different. The coins classed as Edward IV or V have a mintmark of halved sun and rose and it is uncertain whether they were an issue of Edward IV or V.

Heavy coinage groats were all struck at London and all varieties are scarce. The light coinage issue is far more prolific and, as the demand for coins increased, Bristol, Coventry, Norwich and York as well as London became active mints; Coventry and Norwich however ceased by Edward IV's second reign. The mint's name is found on the reverse of the coin in the inner circle and reads CIVITAS LONDON for London; VILLA BRESTOLL, BRISTOLL, BRESTOW, BRISTOW for Bristol; CIVITAS COVETRE for Coventry; CIVITAS NORWIC, NORVIC for Norwich or CIVITAS EBORACI for York.

Collecting Hints

Edward IV's heavy coinage issue is fairly rare, but sometimes available in Fine or VF condition. Light coinage groats from the London mint are fairly common and usually found in about Fine condition, although VF and even EF examples are not uncommon. However, the issues of the provincial mints, with the exception of York, are fairly scarce and desirable, especially in better than Fine condition. Nevertheless, collectors should have little difficulty obtaining an Edward IV groat and many of the issues tend to be unclipped with few problems and readable legends.

Heavy Coinage 1461–1465

These issues were all produced at the London mint.

Obverse Legend EDWARD DI GRA REX ANGL Z FRANC — Edward by the grace of God King of England and France

Reverse Legend POSVI DEUM ADIVTOREM MEUM — I have made God my helper

Reverse Inside Circle Legend CIVITAS LONDON — City of London

Obverse Facing bust of king with a lis on neck and pellets by crown; mintmark cross fleury, plain cross, lis. Sometimes muled.

Reverse Plain with three pellets in each quarter.

E44D-005 VG £40 F £80 VF £200

As previous, but no pellets either side of crown; mintmark plain cross or lis.

E44D-010 VG £60 F £100 VF £250

As previous, but facing bust of king, crescent on breast, quatrefoils by neck; mintmark rose.

E44D-015 VG £55 F £95 VF £220

As previous, but trefoil on king's breast; mintmark rose.

E44D-020 VG £40 F £80 VF £200

As previous, but an eye in the reverse inner circle legend.

E44D-025 VG £45 F £90 VF £210

As previous, but no quatrefoils by bust; mintmark rose.

E44D-030 VG £60 F £100 VF £250

As previous, but no trefoil on breast; mintmark rose.

E44D-035 VG £55 F £95 VF £220

Legends As previous.

Obverse Annulet at either side of king's neck; mintmark rose.

Reverse Eye in reverse legend after TAS.

E44D-040 VG £60 F £120 VF £300

Light Coinage 1464–1470

London Mint

This coin was struck with dies from the last heavy coinage issue (E44D-040) and can only be differentiated by its weight, 48 grains (3.1 grams).

Obverse Legend EDWARD DI GRA REX ANGL Z FRANC — Edward by the grace of God King of England and France

Reverse Legend POSVI DEUM ADIVTOREM MEUM — I have made God my helper

Reverse Inside Circle Legend CIVITAS LONDON — City of London

Obverse Facing bust of king, annulets at neck; mintmark rose.

Reverse Eye after TAS.

E44D-045 VG £40 F £75 VF £150

As previous, but new dies with a slightly different style; eye on reverse after DON or TAS.

E44D-050 VG £45 F £85 VF £200

This issue, like E44D-045, was struck with heavy coinage dies of E44D-020 and may only be distinguished by its weight.

Legends As previous.

Obverse Facing bust of king with quatrefoils either side of neck; mintmark rose.

Reverse Eye after TAS in legend.

E44D-055 VG £40 F £75 VF £150

As previous, but new dies are used; mintmark rose.

E44D-060 VG £35 F £65 VF £140

As previous, but no marks by neck and an eye in reverse legend; mintmark rose.

E44D-065 VG £50 F £100 VF £250

Legends As previous.

Obverse Facing bust of king, quatrefoils at neck; mintmark rose, sun, crown and long-cross fitchée. The mintmarks of this issue are sometimes muled so there is a different mintmark on each side of the coin.

Reverse No marks (such as eyes in legend).

E44D-070 VG £25 F £45 VF £100

As previous, but a rose or quatrefoil on the king's breast; mintmark rose, crown and sun. Sometimes muled.

E44D-075 VG £25 F £45 VF £100

As previous, but no marks by neck; mintmark sun, crown and long-cross fitchée. Sometimes muled.

E44D-080 VG £25 F £45 VF £100

As previous, with trefoils or crosses at neck; mintmark long-cross fitchée, rose and sun. Sometimes muled.

E44D-085 VG £25 F £45 VF £100

Bristol Mint

Obverse Legend EDWARD DI GRA REX ANGL Z FRANC — Edward by the grace of God King of England and France

Reverse Legend POSVI DEUM ADIVTOREM MEUM — I have made God my helper

Reverse Inside Circle Legend VILLA BRESTOLL or BRISTOLL or BRESTOW or BRISTOW — Town of Bristol

Obverse Facing bust of king, 'B' on breast, quatrefoils at neck; mintmark sun, rose and crown. Usually muled.

Reverse Long-cross; no unusual marks in legends.

E44D-090 VG £40 F £80 VF £160

As previous, but without 'B' on king's breast; mintmark sun.

E44D-095 VG £40 F £80 VF £160

As E44D-090 with 'B' on breast but trefoils at neck; mintmark sun.

E44D-100 VG £35 F £60 VF £140

As previous, 'B' on king's breast but no marks by neck; mintmark sun.

E44D-105 VG £35 F £60 VF £140

Coventry Mint

Obverse & Reverse Legend As previous.

Reverse Inside Circle Legend CIVITAS COVETRE — City of Coventry

Obverse Facing bust of king with 'C' for Coventry on king's breast and quatrefoils at neck; mintmark sun or rose. Sometimes muled.

Reverse No marks on reverse.

E44D-110 VG £45 F £75 VF £160

There is a noticeable difference in style and engraving expertise between the previous issue (E44D-110) and the two subsequent ones.

As previous, but coins produced from local, crude, poor quality dies; mintmark rose.

E44D-115 VG £50 F £85 VF £200

As previous, but no 'C' or quatrefoils.

E44D-120 VG £55 F £100 VF £300

Norwich Mint

Obverse & Reverse Legend As previous.

Reverse Inside Circle Legend CIVITAS NORWIC or NORVIC — City of Norwich

Obverse Facing bust of king with N for Norwich on his breast and quatrefoils at neck; mintmark rose or sun. Sometimes muled.

Reverse No marks.

E44D-125 VG £50 F £100 VF £225

York Mint

Obverse & Reverse Legend As previous.

Reverse Inside Circle Legend CIVITAS EBORACI — City of York

Obverse Facing bust of king with 'E' for EBORACI on his breast and quatrefoils at neck; mintmark sun, lis or crown. Sometimes muled.

Reverse No marks.

E44D-130 VG £35 F £60 VF £130

As previous, but trefoils at neck; mintmark lis and sun. Sometimes muled.

E44D-135 VG £35 F £60 VF £130

As E44D-130 but no 'E' on the king's breast; mintmark lis.

E44D-140 VG £40 F £70 VF £150

Henry VI Restored Oct. 1470 — April 1471

This scarce issue is very similar to Henry VI's first reign groats, especially those from the London mint, but has no other marks except the mintmark which in some cases is actually unique to the Restored coinage. Although this fact alone distinguishes this issue from the majority of earlier ones, collectors should also bear in mind that on some of the obverse legends of the Restored coinage HENRIC reads HENRICV. Nevertheless, there is no easy way of identifying this issue and a process of elimination based on the marks, mintmarks and obverse legend readings of every Henry VI class may have to be employed to identify a coin accurately.

Collecting Hints

All groats from this reign are rare due to the fact that it only lasted a few months. Most coins are available in Fine condition, although VF examples are obtainable. Collectors should try to ensure that a specimen is of good enough condition to be safely attributed to this rare issue.

London Mint

Obverse Legend HENRIC(V) DI GRA REX ANGL Z FRANC — Henry by the grace of God King of England and France

Reverse Legend POSVI DEUM ADIVTOREM MEUM — I have made God my helper

Reverse Inside Circle Legend CIVITAS LONDON — City of London

Obverse Facing bust of king, no marks; mintmark cross pattée, Restoration cross, lis, short cross fitchée. Often muled.

Reverse Long cross, three pellets in each quarter.

H64D-160 VG £100 F £175 VF £300

Bristol Mint

This issue is easily identified, being the only one to be struck by a Henry at the Bristol mint.

Obverse & Reverse Legend As previous.

Reverse Inside Circle Legend VILLA BRISTOW — Town of Bristol

Obverse Facing bust of king, 'B' on his breast; mintmark Restoration cross, rose, trefoil, short cross fitchée. Sometimes muled.

Reverse As previous.

H64D-165 VG £110 F £200 VF £350

York Mint

This issue is again easily identified as it is the only issue of a Henry struck at York that has an E for EBORACUM (York) on the king's breast.

Obverse & Reverse Legend As previous.

Reverse Inside Circle Legend CIVITAS EBORACI — City of York

Obverse Facing bust of king, 'E' on king's breast; mintmark lis and sun. Sometimes muled.

Reverse As previous.

H64D-170 VG £100 F £175 VF £300

Edward IV Second Reign 1471–1483

The groats from Edward IV's second reign are very similar to the first reign light coinage issues, which is hardly surprising as the two periods were only seven months apart. In identifying a second reign groat, collectors should check firstly, that the mint on the reverse inner circle reads CIVITAS LONDON for London, VILLA BRISTOW (varieties) for Bristol or CIVITAS EBORACI for York. Secondly, that any marks, such as pellets or roses, correspond to those listed under the various classes, And thirdly, that the mintmark, found above the king's head on the obverse and at the beginning of the outer circle legend on the reverse, ties in with the appropriate class. However, in some cases dies were muled so a different mintmark appears on each side of the coin; this situation is not uncommon for coins from this period.

Collecting Hints

Most of these issues are fairly common and coins are usually found in Fine condition although VF and EF examples are not uncommon. Most coins tend to be unclipped with full, readable legends.

London Mint

Obverse Legend EDWARD DI GRA REX ANGL Z FRANC — Edward by the grace of God King of England and France

Reverse Legend POSVI DEUM ADIVTOREM MEUM — I have made God my helper

Reverse Inside Circle Legend CIVITAS LONDON — City of London

Obverse Facing bust of king, no marks by bust, trefoils on cusps; mintmark short cross fitchée, annulet, trefoil, sun, pellet in annulet, cross and four pellets, cross in circle.

Reverse Long cross, three pellets in each quarter.

E44D-145 VG £25 F £45 VF £100

As previous, but a rose either side of the bust; mintmark pellet in annulet.

E44D-150 VG £25 F £50 VF £110

Legends As previous.

Obverse Facing bust of king, no marks by bust, fleurs on cusps; mintmark pierced cross, pierced cross and pellet, pierced cross with central pellet.

Reverse As previous.

E44D-155 VG £25 F £45 VF £100

As previous, but a pellet either side of the bust; mintmark pierced cross.

E44D-160 VG £40 F £80 VF £200

As E44D-155, but rose on breast; mintmark heraldic cinquefoil.

E44D-165 VG £25 F £45 VF £100

Bristol Mint

This issue is very similar to the one from Edward IV's first reign. Check mintmarks on both sides of the coin for accurate identification.

Obverse & Reverse Legend As previous.

Reverse Inside Circle Legend VILLA BRISTOW (possible varieties) — Town of Bristol

Obverse Facing bust of king, 'B' for Bristol on his breast; mintmark rose, annulet, sun, or none on reverse. Sometimes muled.

Reverse As previous.

E44D-170 VG £40 F £90 VF £200

York Mint

Both Edward IV reigns use mintmark lis but the earlier issues from the first reign have marks by the king's neck or no 'E' on the king's breast.

Obverse & Reverse Legend As previous.

Reverse Inside Circle Legend CIVITAS EBORACI — City of York

Obverse Facing bust of king, 'E' for EBORACI on his breast; mintmark lis.

Reverse As previous.

E44D-175 VG £40 F £90 VF £200

Edward IV or V

It is uncertain whether this issue was struck for Edward IV or Edward V but most numismatists consider that the dies were made for Edward IV and used for the production of coins under Edward V. This issue can only be differentiated from the more common issues of Edward IV by the mintmark halved sun and rose which is found on both sides of the coin.

Collecting Hints

This issue is very rare in any grade but Fine and VF examples do exist. It is most important that collectors obtain an example with a clear mintmark which could not be confused with mintmark rose or heraldic cinquefoil of the more common earlier issues of Edward IV.

Obverse Legend EDWARD DI GRA REX ANGL Z FRANC — Edward by the grace of God King of England and France

Reverse Legend POSVI DEUM ADIVTOREM MEUM — I have made God my helper

Reverse Inside Circle Legend CIVITAS LONDON — City of London

Obverse Facing bust of king, no marks, fleurs on cusps; mintmark halved sun and rose.

Reverse Long cross, three pellets in each quarter; mintmark halved sun and rose.

E44D-180 VG £200 F £425 VF £900

Edward V 1483

This extremely rare issue can be distinguished from the previous, more common ones of Edward IV only by the mintmark boar's head. The boar's head was the personal emblem of Richard II who was the young king's 'protector', even though he was later considered responsible for the boy's murder. On this rare issue, the boar's head mintmark is found on the obverse, and the halved sun and rose mintmark from the previous issue is found on the reverse.

Collecting Hints

This issue is extremely rare in any grade; Fine and VF examples exist, but rarely appear on the market. Collectors should ensure a specimen has clear mintmarks to avoid confusion with coins from the reign of Edward IV.

Obverse Legend EDWARD DI GRA REX ANGL Z FRANC — Edward by the grace of God King of England and France

Reverse Legend POSVI DEUM ADIVTOREM MEUM — I have made God my helper

Reverse Inside Circle Legend CIVITAS LONDON — City of London

Obverse Facing bust of king, fleurs on cusps, no marks by king; mintmark boar's head.

Reverse Long cross, three pellets in each quarter; mintmark halved sun and rose.

E54D-005 ex. rare

Richard III 1483 -1485

Richard III's coinage is easily identified by the obverse legend which starts RICARD; the only other Richard to issue groats was Richard II but they are very different in style and mintmarks.

Collecting Hints

Richard III groats are rare but obtainable and usually found in Fine condition, mostly unclipped with clear legends. VF and even EF examples exist, but are very rare.

London Mint

Obverse Legend RICARD DI GRA REX ANGL Z FRANC — Richard by the grace of God King of England and France

Reverse Legend POSVI DEUM ADIVTOREM MEUM — I have made God my helper

Reverse Inside Circle Legend CIVITAS LONDON — City of London

Obverse Facing bust of king; mintmark halved sun and rose, or boar's head, or none. Often muled, with varieties in style of mintmark.

Reverse Long cross, three pellets in each quarter; mintmark as obverse.

R34D-005 VG £180 F £300 VF £600

As previous, but pellet below bust.

R34D-010 VG £200 F £320 VF £620

York Mint

Obverse & Reverse Legend As previous.

Reverse Inside Circle Legend CIVITAS EBORACI — City of York

Obverse Facing bust of king without pellet; mintmark halved sun and rose.

Reverse No mintmark.

R34D-015 VG £250 F £500 VF £1,000

Henry VII 1485–1509

Numismatically, Henry VII's reign can be divided into two sections, the facing bust issue and the profile issue. The first is in many respects similar to that of previous reigns, but the superb profile issue depicts a lifelike portrait of the king and is wonderful in detail and manufacture. The dies were engraved by Alexander of Brugsal and the coins of this period reflect Renaissance aesthetic values and the change that was sweeping through Europe. The only mint that produced groats during Henry VII's reign was London and CIVITAS LONDON is found on the reverse inner circle legend of the facing bust issues.

Facing Bust Issue 1485–1505

As stated above, Henry VII's facing bust issue is similar to other reigns and the obverse legend begins HENRIC. However, not only is the crown quite distinct, being taller with arches and often jewelled, but also the king's portrait is different in style, and so is his hair. Finally, although the mintmarks used for this issue are also found on coins of other kings, such as Edward IV, they were not often used for any other Henry.

Collecting Hints

Facing bust groats, except for the first two classes, are fairly common and usually available unclipped in Fine or VF condition. Coins of lower grades are often damaged; EF examples are rare, but occasionally obtainable. The mintmarks on some of the issues, such as the greyhound's head, are often very bold and this makes the coin more desirable.

Obverse Legend HENRIC DI GRA REX ANGL Z FRANC — Henry by the grace of God King of England and France

Reverse Legend POSVI DEUM ADIVTOREM MEUM — I have made God my helper

Reverse Inside Circle Legend CIVITAS LONDON — City of London

Obverse Facing bust of king, old-style open crown; mintmarks halved sun and rose, lis upon halved sun, lis upon sun and rose, lis-rose dimidiated. Sometimes muled.

Reverse Long cross, three pellets in each quarter.

H74D-005 VG £40 F £100 VF £200

As previous, but crosses or saltires by neck; mintmark rose, cross fitchée or lis.

N.B. This issue shares the same mintmarks as Henry VI both reigns.

H74D-010 VG £45 F £110 VF £220

New Crown Type

Obverse & Reverse Legend As previous.

Obverse Facing bust of king, the crown has two plain arches either side; mintmark none or cinquefoil.

Reverse As previous.

H74D-015 VG £35 F £70 VF £140

As previous, but crosses either side of neck; mintmark lis or none.

H74D-020 VG £38 F £75 VF £150

An extremely rare variety has a portcullis in the centre of the reverse; mintmark none on the obverse, lis on the reverse.

H74D-025 ex. rare

Obverse Legend HENRIC DI GRA REX ANGL Z FRA (varieties in abbreviation) — Henry by the grace of God King of England and France

Reverse Legends As previous.

Obverse Facing bust of king, crown has two jewelled arches; mintmark cinquefoil.

Reverse As H74D-020.

H74D-030 VG £38 F £75 VF £150

Similar but with more realistic hair; mintmark escallop, pansy.

H74D-035 VG £32 F £65 VF £130

As previous, but crown has one plain and one jewelled arch; mintmark pansy, crowned leopard's head, lis issuant from rose, anchor, greyhound's head. Sometimes muled.

H74D-040 VG £38 F £75 VF £150

As previous, but the crown is arched with a single bar rather than four separate arches; mintmark greyhound's head, rose, cross-crosslet. Sometimes muled.

H74D-045 VG £38 F £75 VF £150

As previous, but the single arch is now a double bar made up of two lines; mintmark greyhound's head, cross-crosslet. Sometimes muled.

H74D-050 VG £38 F £75 VF £150

Profile Issue 1502–1509

With this issue Tudor England left its medieval past and entered the Renaissance, an exciting time of learning and discovery. The profile issue caused considerable interest at the time not least because the general style of coins had not changed much during the last two centuries. Notably, the practice of life-like portraits still continues today. This issue is unlike any previous ones apart from Henry VIII's first issue, but can easily be distinguished by the obverse legend which reads HENRIC VII (or variations) for Henry VII, and HENRIC VIII for Henry VIII. Although there is no mention on the design of where the coin was struck, the only mint used for the profile issue was London.

Collecting Hints

While there are several varieties, some of which are rare, collectors should have little difficulty obtaining an example in Fine condition. Rarely clipped, coins are usually well struck, with legible legends on a full flan. VF or even EF examples are obtainable, if rare, and show the beauty and quality of production.

Tentative Issue 1502–1505

These issues were trials using various dies and styles but, as most were issued into circulation, they cannot really be considered patterns. With such a new style and design and a fairly uneducated public, it took time to introduce new coins into circulation and, like today, there was a general dislike of change and hesitation in accepting new coins.

Obverse Legend HENRIC VII DI GRA REX ANGL Z F — Henry VII by the grace of God King of England and France

Reverse Legend POSVI DEUM ADIVTOE MEU — I have made God my helper

Obverse Crowned bust right; mintmark none, lis, crosslet, greyhound's head. Sometimes muled.

Reverse Royal shield over cross fourchée which divides the legend.

H74D-055 VG £60 F £125 VF £250

Obverse Legend HENRIC DEI GRA REX ANGLI Z FRA — Henry by the grace of God King of England and France

Reverse Legend As previous.

Obverse As previous; mintmark lis, none, greyhound's head. Sometimes muled.

Reverse As previous.

H74D-060 VG £120 F £250 VF £600

Obverse Legend HENRIC SEPTIM DI GRA REX ANGL Z FR — Henry Seventh by the grace of God King of England and France

Reverse Legend As previous.

Obverse As previous; no mintmark.

Reverse As previous; mintmark lis.

H74D-065 ex. rare

Obverse Legend HENRIC VII DI GRA REX ANGL Z F — Henry VII by the grace of God King of England and France

Reverse Legend As previous.

Obverse As previous, but the king's crown has tressures in the arches; mintmark crosslet.

Reverse As previous; mintmark crosslet.

H74D-070 ex. rare

Regular Issue

This issue is by far the most common; it was in no way a trial or pattern.

Legends & Reverse As previous.

Obverse Crowned bust facing right, triple band to king's crown; mintmark crosslet, pheon/crosslet, pheon. Slightly different in style from previous issues and sometimes muled.

H74D-075 VG £40 F £80 VF £150

Henry VIII 1509–1547

Henry VIII groats may be classed in four main types, the first, second, third and posthumous issues. The first coinage (1509–1526) was virtually identical to Henry VII's profile issue except for different mintmarks and the obverse legend reading HENRIC VIII instead of HENRIC VII, but still with the previous king's portrait. The portrait changed to that of Henry VIII in the second coinage (1526–1544), which has several varieties and was minted in London and York. The third coinage (1544–1547) was made of very base metal; it was struck with three slightly different styles of bust at the Tower mint, Southwark, Bristol,

Canterbury and York. Finally, the posthumous issue of 1547–1551 was produced during the first few years of Edward VI's reign but with Henry VIII's portrait and titles in the legends; three different busts were used for this issue with coins struck at the Tower mint, Southwark, Durham House, Bristol, Canterbury and York.

From the third coinage onwards two new London mints became active, Southwark and Durham House, and to avoid confusion, what was previously known as the London mint is henceforth referred to as Tower mint, from its location in the Tower of London. Coins may be linked to specific mints because they bear either the name of a mint or a legend exclusively attributed to one. They are the following: CIVITAS LONDON (City of London) for Southwark; POSVI DEUM ADIVTORE MEU(M) (I have made God my helper) for the Tower mint; REDDE CVIQUE QVOD SVVM EST (Render to each that which is his own) for Durham House; CIVITAS CANTOR for Canterbury; CIVITAS EBORACI for York and CIVITAS BRISTOLI for Bristol.

Collecting Hints

Most Henry VIII groats are fairly common. The first and second coinages, being made of good quality silver, are more attractive and usually obtainable unclipped with full legible legends on round flans in Fine condition, although VF examples are not uncommon; EF examples also exist and are extremely desirable. By comparison, the third and posthumous issues are, in most cases, extremely ugly coins. Not only is the old bust of the king less attractive, but also the low quality of the metal often produced a poor striking with weak legends and features and made the coins look dull, often with more mixed colours in the surface. Collectors should never attempt to clean coins of these issues, not even with a light duster, because they will appear copper in colour. Nevertheless, the groat is one of the most desirable coins of this reign and no collection should be without several examples.

First Coinage 1509–1526

London Mint

Obverse Legend HENRIC VIII DI GRA REX AGL Z FRA — Henry VIII by the grace of God King of England and France

Reverse Legend POSVI DEU ADIVTORE MEU — I have made God my helper

Obverse Crowned bust of Henry VII facing right; mintmark pheon, castle, portcullis crowned.

Reverse Royal shield over cross fourchée which divides legend.

H84D-005 VG £45 F £85 VF £180

Tournai Mint

This mint was in France but under English control.

Obverse Legend As previous.

Reverse Legend CIVITAS TORNACEN — City of Tournai

Obverse As previous, but mintmark crowned 'T'.

Reverse As previous.

H84D-010 VG £100 F £200 VF £600

Second Coinage 1526–1544

London Mint

Obverse Legend HENRIC VIII DI GRA REX AGL Z FR — Henry VIII by the grace of God King of England and France

Reverse Legend POSVI DEU ADIVTORE MEU — I have made God my helper

Obverse Youthful bust of king facing right with hair not touching the collar, Roman lettering except for the Lombardic 'H' in HENRIC; mintmark rose.

Reverse Long-cross fourchée over royal shield.

H84D-015 VG £80 F £150 VF £320

As previous, but Lombardic lettering; mintmark rose.

H84D-020 VG £50 F £100 VF £200

As previous, but the king's hair touches his collar, the lettering is mainly Lombardic; mintmark rose.

H84D-025 VG £50 F £90 VF £180

As previous, but the king's hair is over his collar, mostly Lombardic lettering; mintmark rose.

H84D-030 VG £35 F £75 VF £150

As previous, but all Lombardic lettering; mintmark lis, sunburst, arrow, pheon. Sometimes muled.

H84D-035 VG £35 F £75 VF £150

As previous, but the king's bust has slightly different features, with the hair above the collar and all the letters in the legend are Lombardic; mintmark lis, arrow, pheon, sunburst.

H84D-040 VG £35 F £70 VF £140

Irish Title

Obverse Legend HENRIC VIII DI GRA HIB REX AGL Z F — Henry VIII by the grace of God King of Ireland England and France

Reverse Legend As previous.

Obverse As previous; mintmark pheon, lis; often muled.

Reverse As previous.

H84D-045 VG £100 F £250 VF £500

York Mint

The ecclesiastical mint of York was under Archbishop Thomas Wolsey.

Obverse Legend HENRIC VIII DI GRA AGL Z FRA — Henry VIII by the grace of God King of English and France

Reverse Legend CIVITAS EBORACI — City of York

Obverse Youthful bust of king facing right; mintmark voided cross, acorn, sometimes muled.

Reverse Long-cross fourchée over royal shield dividing 'T.W.' (Thomas Wolsey) and cardinal's hat below the shield.

H84D-050 VG £50 F £100 VF £200

As previous, but omits T.W.; mintmark voided cross, acorn.

H84D-055 VG £200 F £450 VF £900

Third Coinage 1544–1547

Made of base silver, these coins are usually dull in colour. The different styles of bust all depict an ageing king and were used for most of the provincial mints.

Tower Mint

Obverse Legend HENRIC 8 D G AGL FRA Z HIB REX — Henry VIII by the grace of God King of England France and Ireland

Reverse Legend POSVI DEUM ADIVTORE MEU — I have made God my helper

Obverse Crowned bust of king; mintmark lis.

Reverse Royal shield over long-cross.

H84D-060 VG £35 F £70 VF £160

As previous, but with an annulet on the inner circle.

H84D-065 VG £45 F £90 VF £200

Southwark Mint

Obverse Legend As previous.

Reverse Legend CIVITAS LONDON — City of London

Obverse Crowned bust of varying styles; mintmark none, lis, 'S' or 'S' and 'E'.

Reverse As previous.

H84D-070 VG £40 F £80 VF £180

Bristol Mint

Obverse Legend As previous.

Reverse Legend CIVITAS BRISTOLI — City of Bristol

Obverse As previous; no mintmark.

Reverse As previous, but mintmark 'W S'.

H84D-075 VG £45 F £90 VF £200

Canterbury Mint

Obverse Legend As previous.

Reverse Legend CIVITAS CANTOR — City of Canterbury

Obverse As previous; no mintmark.

Reverse As previous, but no mintmark.

H84D-080 VG £45 F £90 VF £200

York Mint

Obverse Legend As previous.

Reverse Legend CIVITAS EBORACI — City of York

Obverse As previous; no mintmark.

Reverse As previous.

H84D-085 VG £45 F £90 VF £200

Posthumous Coinage 1547–1551

These issues were again of base silver. Three new busts were used, although busts from the third coinage were also employed, albeit

rarely, in the Tower and Bristol mints; these issues may be distinguished by the mintmarks.

Tower Mint

Obverse Legend HENRIC 8 DG AGL FRA Z HIB REX — Henry VIII by the grace of God King of England France and Ireland

Reverse Legend POSVI DEUM ADIVTORE MEU — I have made God my helper

Obverse Crowned busts of king of varying styles; mintmark lis, arrow, 'K', grapple, martlet or none. Often muled.

Reverse Royal arms over cross.

H84D-090 VG £35 F £75 VF £160

Southwark Mint

Obverse Legend As previous.

Reverse Legend CIVITAS LONDON — City of London

Obverse As previous; mintmarks lis, 'E' or none.

Reverse As previous.

H84D-095 VG £40 F £80 VF £180

Durham House Mint

Obverse Legend As previous.

Reverse Legend REDDE CVIQUE QVOD SVVM EST — Render to each that which is his own

Obverse Crowned bust of king; mintmark bow.

Reverse As previous.

H84D-100 VG £75 F £150 VF £350

Bristol Mint

Obverse Legend As previous.

Reverse Legend CIVITAS BRISTOLI — City of Bristol

Obverse As H84D-075; no mintmark.

Reverse As previous, but mintmark 'WS' or 'TC'.

H84D-105 VG £40 F £80 VF £180

Canterbury Mint

Obverse Legend As previous.

Reverse Legend CIVITAS CANTOR — City of Canterbury

Obverse Crowned bust of king; mintmark none or rose.

Reverse Royal arms over cross.

H84D-110 VG £40 F £80 VF £180

York Mint

Obverse Legend As previous.

Reverse Legend CIVITAS EBORACI — City of York

Obverse As previous; mintmark lis or none.

Reverse As previous.

H84D-115 VG £45 F £90 VF £200

Edward VI 1547–1553

The groat was only produced during Edward's first coinage (1547–1549) at the same time as Henry VIII's posthumous issue. In fact the posthumous issue groat seems to have been more acceptable to the public, probably because Edward was just a boy with virtually no power in the country. Moreover, very few Edward VI groats were struck, at first because large quantities had been produced under Henry and in the posthumous coinage, and then because the production of the sixpence and threepence in the later part of the reign made this denomination appear redundant. All Edward VI groats were struck in base silver; they look dull in colour and often have a porous surface.

Collecting Hints

Edward VI groats are very rare in any grade; the average condition they are found in is Poor to VG, but Fine and VF examples exist. Many coins tend to flake small amounts of silver, often from the edges, usually due to the poor metal content.

Tower Mint

Obverse Legend EDWARD D.G.

Reverse Legend POSVI

Obverse Crowned bust right; mintmark arrow.

Reverse Royal arms over cross.

E64D-005 VG £100 F £250 VF rare

As previous, but obverse legend reads EDOARD 6.

E64D-010 ex. rare

Southwark Mint

Obverse Legend As E64D-005.

Reverse Legend CIVITAS LONDON — City of London

Obverse As previous; mintmark 'E' or none.

Reverse As previous.

E64D-015 VG £120 F £300 VF rare

Mary 1553–1554

The coinage of Mary falls into two distinct categories. Firstly there is her own issue, which can be easily identified by the obverse legend which starts MARIA. The second category is for the period when Mary shared the throne with her husband Philip, and the obverse reads PHILIP Z MARIA. The groat was reintroduced as a denomination during Mary's reign. Although Edward VI and his council seem to have favoured the shilling, sixpence and threepence, the increased volume of groats struck under Mary indicate a desire to return to it as a principal silver denomination. Very large quantities of groats were produced throughout her reign and all bear a superb detailed portrait of the queen: Philip's portrait was only included on the shilling and sixpence.

Collecting Hints

Groats of Mary and Philip and Mary are fairly common, especially in less than Fine condition. However, coins in VF or better are far more difficult to obtain and many are creased.

Obverse Legend MARIA D G ANG FRA Z HIB REGI — Mary by the grace of God Queen of England France and Ireland

Reverse Legend VERITAS TEMPORIS FILIA — Truth is the daughter of time

Obverse Crowned left-facing bust of queen; mintmark pomegranate after queen's name.

Reverse Cross over royal shield; mintmark as obverse after VERITAS.

M4D-005 Poor £20 VG £40 F £85 VF £180

Philip and Mary 1554–1558

Obverse Legend PHILIP Z MARIA D G REX Z REGINA — Philip and Mary by the grace of God King and Queen

Reverse Legend POSUIMUS DEUM ADIVTO NOS — We have made God our helper

Obverse As previous, but mintmark lis at start of legend.

Reverse As previous; mintmark lis at start of legend.

PM4D-005 Poor £20 VG £45 F £95 VF £200

Elizabeth I 1558–1603

Groats continued to be struck in quite large numbers during the first few years of Elizabeth's reign but a desire to return to the predominance of the threepence, sixpence and shilling as the main silver denominations meant there was no further need for the groat. All groats, including the rare milled issue, were produced at the Tower mint. Due to their similar size and weight, groats might easily be confused with sixpences, but whereas none of the groats are dated, all sixpences are — except for some extremely rare examples; also all sixpences, except again for a few very rare issues, bear a large rose behind the queen's head.

Hammered Coinage

> ### Collecting Hints
> Groats are fairly common and usually available in about Fine condition; VF and EF examples are rare, but obtainable. Most coins are unclipped with clear legends.

First Issue 1559–1560

Obverse Legend ELIZABETH D G ANG FRA Z HIB REGI — Elizabeth by the grace of God Queen of England France and Ireland

Reverse Legend POSUI DEU ADIUTOREM MEU — I have made God my helper

Obverse Crowned left-facing bust, wire-line inner circles; mintmark lis.

Reverse Royal shield over cross.

EL4D-005 VG £60 F £120 VF £300

As previous, but wire-line and beaded inner circles.

EL4D-010 VG £25 F £70 VF £140

There is a rare variety with a very small bust, using the half-groat die.

EL4D-015 ex. rare

Second Issue 1560–1561

Obverse Legend ELIZABETH D G ANG FRA ET HIB REGINA — Elizabeth by the grace of God Queen of England France and Ireland

Reverse Legend POSUI DEU ADIUTOREM MEU — I have made God my helper

Obverse Crowned left-facing bust, beaded circles; mintmarks cross crosslet or martlet.

Reverse Royal shield over cross.

EL4D-020 VG £20 F £50 VF £100

Milled Coinage

This rare issue was struck in 1561; it is distinguishable from the sixpence by being undated and omitting the rose behind the queen's head. Milled coins are different in style from hammered, with the detail and striking usually clearer.

> ### Collecting Hints
> This issue is usually found in the lower grades, sometimes damaged. Elizabeth milled groats are considerably scarcer than the milled sixpences.

Obverse Legend ELIZABETH D G ANG FRA ET HIB REGINA — Elizabeth by the grace of God Queen of the English France and Ireland

Reverse Legend POSVI DEUM ADIVTOREM MEUM — I have made God my helper

Obverse Crowned left-facing bust, no inner circles; mintmark star.

Reverse Queen's shield over cross.

EL4D-025 VG £60 F £120 VF £300

Charles I 1625–1649

No groats were issued under James I, being replaced by the two-pence, sixpence and shilling. The denomination was reintroduced under Charles I and, although no groats were produced at the Tower mint, several provincial mints were active. They can all be easily distinguished from other denominations by the Roman numerals IIII by the king's bust.

Aberystwyth Mint

The mint in the royal castle of Aberystwyth was created in 1637 by indenture between the king and the moneyer Thomas Bushell so as to utilise the locally-mined silver. All Aberystwyth issues use the mintmark open book which symbolised Bushell's accountability to the king. The dies for these issues were made in London and the mint closed in 1642.

Collecting Hints

This issue can be found in all grades from VG to EF. They are well struck and the quality of coins found is higher than other issues.

Obverse Legend CAROLUS D G M B F ET H REX — Charles by the grace of God Great King of Britain France and Ireland

Reverse Legend CHRISTO AVSPICE REGNO — I reign under the auspices of Christ

Obverse Large left-facing bust with lace collar, no armour on shoulder and a plume in front of the king's face, value behind; mintmark book.

Reverse Plume over oval shield with royal arms.

C14D-005 VG £30 F £45 VF £90 EF £200

As previous, but smaller bust.

C14D-010 VG £30 F £45 VF £90 EF £200

Larger bust and the king has armour on shoulder.

C14D-015 VG £30 F £50 VF £100 EF £220

Aberystwyth Furnace Mint

Collecting Hints

This issue is rare in any grade. Coins are often found holed, which was probably done officially at a later date. Most coins appear to have seen considerable circulation.

Obverse Legend CAROLUS D G MAG BR FRA ET HIB REX — Charles by the grace of God King of Great Britain France and Ireland

Reverse Legend CHRISTO AVSPICE REGNO — I reign under the auspices of Christ

Obverse Bust of king on the left with IIII behind the head and small plume in front of the face; mintmark crown.

Reverse Oval shield with plume above it.

C14D-020 VG £70 F £150 VF £300

Oxford Mint

Collecting Hints

While scarce, these issues are obtainable, especially in the lower grades. Coins are sometimes found bent, damaged or holed.

Obverse Legend CAROLUS D G M B F ET H REX — Charles by the grace of God King of Great Britain France and Ireland

Reverse Outer Legend EXURGAT DEUS DISSIPENTUR INIMICI — Let God arise and His enemies be scattered

Reverse Centre Legend RELIG PRO LEG ANG LIBER PA(R) — The religion of the Protestants the laws of England the liberty of Parliament

Obverse Bust of king with IIII behind head and plume in front of face; mintmark book. This die was from the Aberystwyth mint.

Reverse Declaration in centre, plume above, dated 1644, 'OX' below date; the outer legend starts three-quarters of the way around the coin.

C14D-025 VG £40 F £60 VF £200

As previous, but three plumes above Declaration.

C14D-030 VG £45 F £80 VF £250

As previous, but lion's head on shoulder.

C14D-035 VG £35 F £60 VF £200

As previous, but large bust with the king's crown reaching to the top of the coin.

C14D-040 VG £45 F £80 VF £250

Large bust to the bottom of the coin and obverse legend starting two-thirds of the way around coin instead of at the top.

C14D-045 VG £45 F £90 VF £260

Similar to previous, but no inner circles. This issue uses a Rawlins die and there is an 'R' on the king's shoulder.

C14D-050 VG £50 F £100 VF £280

As C14D-035 but dated 1645.

C14D-055 VG £55 F £100 VF £280

As C14D-045 but dated 1645.

C14D-060 VG £45 F £80 VF £250

Similar to C14D-050 with large single plume over Declaration which is in cartouche; dated 1645 or 1646.

C14D-065 VG £45 F £100 VF £250

Bristol Mint

These issues are very similar to the Oxford ones except that they sometimes have 'BR' instead of 'OX' below the date and the Declaration is between two straight lines with three plumes above. Because groats are often in poor condition, collectors might have to check through all Charles I issues to find the correct type.

Collecting Hints

While scarce, these issues are obtainable, especially in the lower grades. Coins are sometimes found bent, damaged or holed.

Obverse Legend CAROLUS D G MAG BR FR ET HI REX — Charles by the grace of God King of Great Britain France and Ireland

Reverse Legend EXURGAT DEUS DISSIPENTUR INIMICI — Let God arise and His enemies be scattered

Reverse Centre Legend REL PROT LEG ANG LIB PAR — The religion of the Protestants the laws of England the liberty of Parliament

Obverse Crowned left-facing bust, value behind, nothing in front of face; mintmark pellet.

Reverse Three plumes above Declaration; 1644 below.

C14D-070 VG £85 F £190 VF £400

As previous, but plumelet before face.

C14D-075 VG £85 F £190 VF £400

As previous, but 'BR' for Bristol below date.

C14D-080 VG £80 F £180 VF £360

Late Declaration Issue 1645–1646

There is considerable debate regarding where these coins were struck. Previously attributed to Lundy Island or Barnstaple, it is now thought that they may have been struck at Bridgnorth or Ashby de la Zouch. The main difference from previous issues is the date.

> ## Collecting Hints
>
> The first issue is of the highest rarity; the second is rare but obtainable, usually in the lower grades.

Obverse Legend CAROLUS D G MAG BR FR ET HIB REX — Charles by the grace of God King of Great Britain France and Ireland

Reverse Legend EXURGAT DEUS DISSIPENTUR INIMICI — Let God arise and His enemies be scattered

Reverse Inner Legend REL PRO LEG ANG LIB PAR — The religion of the Protestants the laws of England the liberty of Parliament

Obverse Bust of king, value behind the head and plumelet in front.

Reverse Three plumelets above Declaration, dated 1645.

C14D-085 ex. rare

As previous, but upper Declaration line is in two scrolls; dated 1646.

C14D-090 VG £60 F £100 VF £200

Exeter Mint

> ## Collecting Hints
>
> While scarce, this issue is obtainable and usually found undamaged in VG to Fine condition.

Obverse Legend 1644 CAROLUS D G M B F ET H REX — 1644 (date) Charles by the grace of God King of Great Britain France and Ireland

Reverse Legend CHRISTO AUSPICE REGNO — I reign under the auspices of Christ

Obverse Bust of king, value behind; mintmark rose.

Reverse Oval shield.

C14D-095 VG £50 F £90 VF £220

Worcester, Salopia (Shrewsbury) or possibly Hereford Mint

There is great uncertainty regarding which mint struck this issue, especially as dies could have been transported to all three mints.

> ## Collecting Hints
>
> This issue is very rare and the coins were struck with extremely crude dies.

Obverse Legend CAROLUS D G M B F ET H REX — Charles by the grace of God King of Great Britain France and Ireland

Reverse Legend CHRISTO AUSPICE REGNO — I reign under the auspices of Christ

Obverse Crowned left-facing bust in very crude style, value behind; mintmark rose over lis.

Reverse Oval shield; mintmark helmet.

C14D-100 VG £220 F £450 VF rare

No groats were issued during the Commonwealth.

Charles II 1660–1685

Hammered Issue 1660–1662

The hammered groat was only struck once during Charles II's reign, in the third issue.

> ## Collecting Hints
>
> This issue is fairly common especially in Fine or less condition; VF and even EF examples are not uncommon. Many of the coins lack some of the legends due either to a small flan or clipping.

Obverse Legend CAROLUS D G MAG BRIT FR ET HIB REX — Charles by the grace of God King of Great Britain France and Ireland

Reverse Legend CHRISTO AVSPICE REGNO — I reign under the auspices of Christ

Obverse Left-facing bust of king, mark of value behind, inner circles; mintmark crown.

Reverse Shield over cross; mintmark crown.

C24DH-005 VG £18 F £35 VF £70

Threepence

First introduced in Edward VI's fine silver coinage, the threepence was of good quality silver and formed part of a new set of denominations. But as with most newly introduced denominations it was not very popular and the next two reigns reverted back to the groat. Although it was an easier denomination to work with in the context of pounds and shillings, the public preferred the groat which had, of course, been in circulation since the reign of Edward I.

Edward VI 1547–1553

The threepence, introduced during the fine silver issue and made of good quality silver, is easily distinguished from the other denominations by the Roman numeral III for threepence found to the side of the king's head. Threepences were struck at London and York.

Collecting Hints

Edward VI threepences are fairly rare, especially in a good grade, and many are very badly cracked. This cracking does not appear to have been a fault of striking but, for some reason, deliberate vandalism. Coins are usually available in about Fine condition and VF and EF examples are extremely rare.

London Mint

Obverse Legend EDWARD VI D G ANG FRA Z HIB REX — Edward VI by the grace of God King of England France and Ireland

Reverse Legend POSUI DEUM ADIUTOREM MEUM — I have made God my helper

Obverse Facing bust of king with rose to the left and III to the right; mintmark tun.

Reverse Long cross over royal shield.

E63D-005 VG £70 F £150 VF £350

York Mint

Obverse Legend As previous.

Reverse Legend CIVITAS EBORACI — City of York

Obverse As previous, but mintmark mullet.

Reverse As previous.

E63D-010 VG £100 F £200 VF £450

No threepences were struck during the reigns of Mary or Philip and Mary.

Elizabeth I 1558–1603

The threepence was reintroduced under Elizabeth I, who realised the importance of smaller denominations, and it played an important part in a varied structure of denominations. With a 21 mm diameter for most 1561 issues and 19 mm for all other, the threepence is fairly similar in size to the groat and halfgroat but may easily be distinguished as, unlike them, it is dated and has a rose behind the queen's bust. The coins also have mintmarks on both sides which facilitates dating when the date itself is weak. Milled threepences were also produced and although they too are dated and have a rose behind the queen's bust, they differ from the hammered issue in style, being more ornate and lacking inner circles to divide the legend from the bust or shield. Three-halfpences were also introduced under Elizabeth but, although they are fairly similar in style to the threepence, they are much smaller with a maximum diameter of 17 mm on some 1561 issues and 16 mm on all others.

Hammered Coinage

No threepences were struck during the first or second issues.

Collecting Hints

Hammered threepences are fairly common in Fine condition, while even VF or EF examples are desirable but not very rare. Issues are usually unclipped, but sometimes slightly bent. Collectors should try to obtain an example in at least Fine condition, with a clear date and reasonable portrait.

Third Issue 1561–1577

Large Flan Issue (21 mm)

Obverse Legend ELIZABETH D G. ANG FR ET HIB REGINA — Elizabeth by the grace of God Queen of England France and Ireland

Reverse Legend POSUI DEU ADIUTOREM MEU — I have made God my helper

Obverse Crowned bust of queen, rose behind head; mintmark pheon.

Reverse Shield over long cross, dated 1561.

EL3D-005 VG £30 F £60 VF £120

Regular Flan Issue (19 mm)

Legends As previous.

Obverse Crowned bust of queen, rose behind; mintmark as listed below.

Reverse Shield over long cross, date (listed below) over shield.

Mintmark & Date Pheon (1561–1565), rose (1565), portcullis (1566), lion (1566–1567), coronet (1567–1570), castle (1570–1571), ermine (1572–1573), acorn (1573–1574) eglantine (1573–1577).

EL3D-010 VG £20 F £40 VF £80

As previous, but omitting rose behind the queen's head on the obverse, dated 1568; mintmark coronet.

EL3D-015 unique

Fourth Issue 1578–1582

This issue is identical to the third issue except that its silver content is fractionally lower.

As previous, but mintmark and date as listed below.

Mintmark & Date Plain cross (1578–1579), long cross (1580–1581), sword (1582).

EL3D-020 VG £20 F £40 VF £80

No threepences were issued during the fifth or sixth issues.

Milled Coinage 1561–1564

Collecting Hints

The milled issue is fairly rare, especially in Fine or better condition and many coins are creased. Issues are often pierced or gilded as this coin was obviously later popular as a jewellery piece.

Obverse Legend ELIZABETH D G. ANG FRA ET HIB REGINA — Elizabeth by the grace of God Queen of England France and Ireland

Reverse Legend POSUI DEUM ADIUTOREM MEUM — I have made God my helper

Obverse Small bust of queen with plain dress, rose behind bust; mintmark star.

Reverse Shield over long cross, dated 1561.

EL3D-025 VG £50 F £100 VF £220

As previous, but tall narrow bust with large rose, dated 1562; mintmark star.

EL3D-030 VG £45 F £90 VF £200

As previous, but short bust with small rose.

EL3D-035 VG £60 F £120 VF £240

As previous, but the long cross on the reverse is a cross pattée; dated 1563 or 1564.

EL3D-040 VG £80 F £160

No threepences were struck during the reign of James I.

Charles I 1625–1649

Under Charles I, no threepences were struck at the Tower mint but most provincial mints were active producing them, sometimes in considerable quantities. The denomination is identified by the Roman numeral III behind the king's bust.

Aberystwyth Mint 1638–1642

Bristol and Oxford often used obverse or reverse dies from the Aberystwyth threepence, so collectors should also refer to those issues when identifying a coin which may be from Aberystwyth.

Collecting Hints

Aberystwyth threepences are by far the most common and usually available in Fine or VF condition; EF examples are rare but obtainable.

Obverse Legend CAROLUS DG M(A)B. F(R) ET H(I)(B) REX — Charles by the grace of God King of Great Britain France and Ireland

Reverse Legend CHRISTO AUSPICE REGNO — I reign under the auspices of Christ

Obverse Bust of king with plumes in front of face and the denomination behind his head; mintmark book.

Reverse Large oval shield with plumes above.

C13D-005 VG £25 F £45 VF £90 EF £180

As previous, but the king's crown cuts the inner circles.

C13D-010 VG £25 F £45 VF £90 EF £180

Aberystwyth Furnace Mint 1648/1649

Collecting Hints

This issue is rare in any grade and very difficult to obtain.

Obverse Legend CAROLUS D.G. MAG BR FR ET HI REX — Charles by the grace of God King of Great Britain France and Ireland

Reverse Legend CHRISTO AUSPICE REGNO — I reign under the auspices of Christ

Obverse Crowned bust, plumelet in front of face, value behind; mintmark crown.

Reverse Small oval shield with large plumes above.

C13D-015 VG £100 F £200 VF £375

Oxford Mint

Collecting Hints

Oxford threepences are fairly common, especially in the lower grades, but the urgency to strike coins was such that many issues used an Aberystwyth die. Coins in better than Fine condition are rare. Many coins from this issue are often damaged and holed.

Obverse Legend CAROLUS D G MAG BR FR ET H. REX — Charles by the grace of God King of Great Britain France and Ireland

Reverse Legend EXURGAT DEUS DISSIPENTUR INIMICI — Let God arise and His enemies be scattered

Reverse Inner Legend RELI PRO LEG ANG LIB PAR. 1644 OX — The religion of the Protestants the laws of England the liberty of Parliament. 1644 Oxford

Obverse Aberystwyth die; plume in front of king's face with value behind.

Reverse The Declaration in three lines.

C13D-020 VG £40 F £80 VF £160

Obverse Legend CAROLUS D.G. M BR F ET H REX — Charles by the grace of God King of Great Britain France and Ireland

Reverse Legend CHRISTO AUSPICE REGNO — I reign under the auspices of Christ

Obverse Bust of king with denomination behind bust and 'R' (for Rawlins, the die maker of the obverse) below the king's shoulder.

Reverse Aberystwyth die with large oval shield and plumes above; mintmark book.

C13D-025 VG £35 F £75 VF £150

Obverse Legend As previous.

Reverse Legend As C13D-020 but sometimes omits 'OX'.

Obverse As previous, but without 'R' on the king's shoulder.

Reverse As C13D-020, dated 1644 or 1646.

C13D-030 VG £35 F £75 VF £150

Bristol Mint

Collecting Hints

This issue is rare in any grade and particularly difficult to obtain in better than Fine, while coins are often damaged or holed.

Obverse Legend CAROLUS D G. MAG B F ET H REX — Charles by the grace of God King of Great Britain France and Ireland

Reverse Outer Legend EXURGAT DEUS DISSIPENTUR INIMICI — Let God arise and His enemies be scattered

Reverse Inner Legend REL PRO LEG AN LIB PA 1644 — The religion of the Protestants the laws of England the liberty of Parliament. 1644

Obverse This is an Aberystwyth die, with a plume in front of the king's face and denomination behind; mintmark book.

Reverse Three small plumes above the Declaration, date below.

C13D-035 VG £70 F £150 VF £300

As previous, but plume with bands before face, denomination behind king's head; mintmark pellet (local die).

C13D-040 VG £70 F £150 VF £300

Legends As previous.

Obverse As previous, but plumelet before king's face.

Reverse Only one plumelet above the declaration, 1645.

C13D-045 ex. rare

Exeter Mint

Collecting Hints

This issue is obtainable but fairly scarce, particularly in better than Fine condition and is often holed or damaged.

Obverse Legend CAROLUS D.G. MA BR F ET H RE — Charles by the grace of God King of Great Britain France and Ireland

Reverse Legend CHRISTO AUSPICE REGNO — I reign under the auspices of Christ

Obverse Bust of king with denomination behind the head; mintmark rose.

Reverse Royal arms with date 1644 above.

C13D-050 VG £60 F £100 VF £200

Worcester or Shrewsbury Mint

Collecting Hints

This issue is very crude in style but extremely rare and difficult to obtain in any grade.

Obverse Legend CAROLUS DG. MB F ET H REX — Charles by the grace of God King of Great Britain France and Ireland

Reverse Legend CHRISTO AUSPICE REGNO — I reign under the auspices of Christ

Obverse Crude bust of king with denomination behind; mintmark lis.

Reverse Oval shield.

C13D-055 VG £150 F £300 VF —

Chester Mint

It is not certain that this issue is from the Chester mint at all and until a hoard or documentary evidence appears, it will not be possible to class it correctly.

Collecting Hints

This issue is extremely rare in any grade and collectors may have great difficulty obtaining an example.

Obverse Legend CAROLUS. D.G. MAG. BRIT. FRAN. ET HIB REX. — Charles by the grace of God King of Great Britain France and Ireland

Reverse Legend CHRISTO AUSPICE REGNO — I reign under the auspices of Christ

Obverse Bust of king with denomination behind; no mintmark.

Reverse Square shield undated; mintmark prostrate gerb.

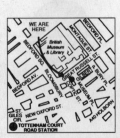

Late Declaration

Obverse Legend CAROLUS D G M B F ET HI REX — Charles by the grace of God King of Great Britain France and Ireland

Reverse Legend EXURGAT DEUS DISSIPENTUR INIMICI — Let God arise and His enemies be scattered

Reverse Inner Legend REL PRO LEG AN LIB PA 1646 — The religion of the Protestants the laws of England the liberty of Parliament

Obverse Crowned bust, plumelet before bust, value behind; mintmark plume.

Reverse Declaration, one plume above and a scroll either side.

C13D-065 VG £100 F £200 VF £350

As previous, but no scroll, 1645.

C13D-070 VG £100 F £200 VF rare

No threepences were struck under the Commonwealth or Cromwell.

Charles II 1660–1685

Hammered Coinage 1660–1662

Threepences were only struck during the third issue of the hammered coinage (1660–1662).

Obverse Legend CAROLUS II D G. MAG BRI F ET H REX — Charles by the grace of God King of Great Britain France and Ireland

Reverse Legend CHRISTO AUSPICE REGNO — I reign under the auspices of Christ

Obverse Bust of king within an inner circle, mark of value behind bust; mintmark crown.

Reverse Royal shield over cross.

C23DH-005 VG £20 F £40 VF £80 EF £150

Halfgroat

Introduced under Edward III in 1351, the halfgroat or twopence was stylistically very similar to the groat with only its size and weight reduced. It was a popular denomination and issued by all monarchs until George III, when it was continued as a Maundy coin. The halfgroat was also issued as legal tender in several British colonies during the 19th century.

Edward III 1327–1377

Edward III realised the importance of having varied denominations in circulation to facilitate trade and the halfgroat, introduced in 1351 during the fourth coinage, became one of the most important. Although Edward's halfgroat closely resembles the contemporary groat, its design and style are fairly different from later issues of Edward IV, Richard II or the Henrys (IV, V, VI and VII). The halfgroat bears the king's name, EDWARDUS, at the top of the obverse legend and although Edward III was not the only Edward to issue halfgroats, the ones from Edward IV's two reigns are very different in style, slightly smaller and lighter. Three mints produced halfgroats during Edward III's reign, London, York and Calais, which was under English rule at the time and was used for political as well as monetary reasons. The mint name can be found on the reverse inner legend and reads CIVITAS LONDON for London, CIVITAS EBORACI for York and VILLA CALESIE for Calais. The various issues based on Edward's aspirations in France that are detailed in the relevant section of the Penny chapter also apply to the halfgroat.

Collecting Hints

Edward III halfgroats are fairly common and usually obtainable in about Fine condition, often clipped; VF examples are rare, but exist. Coins tend to be found in lower grades than the groat, where large hoards are available in slightly better condition. However, all Edward III coins from the Calais mint are rare.

Pre Treaty Period 1351–1361

These issues have the French title in the obverse legend.

London Mint
1351

Obverse Legend EDWARDUS REX ANGL Z FRAN — Edward King of England and France

Reverse Outer Legend POSVI DEUM ADIVTOREM MEUM — I have made God my helper

Reverse Inner Legend CIVITAS LONDON — City of London

Obverse Facing crowned bust of king, Roman 'M', open 'C' and 'E' in legend; mintmark cross 1.

Reverse Long cross, three pellets in each quarter.

E32D-005 VG £40 F £70 VF £150

1351–1352

As previous, but a Lombardic 'M', closed 'C' and 'E', and the 'R' has a wedge-shaped tail.

E32D-010 VG £15 F £30 VF £60

1351–1353

As previous, but 'R' with normal tail; mintmarks cross 1 or cross 1 broken.

E32D-015 VG £15 F £30 VF £60

As previous, but the letters in the legends are broken, often with parts missing, the 'V' usually has a nick in the right arm; mintmark cross 2.

E32D-020 VG £15 F £30 VF £60

As previous, but mintmark crown.

E32D-025 VG £18 F £35 VF £70

As previous, but mintmark cross 3.

E32D-030 VG £18 F £35 VF £70

As previous, but an annulet in one quarter and sometimes under the king's bust; mintmark cross 3.

E32D-035 VG £20 F £40 VF £80

York Mint

Obverse & Reverse Outer Legend As previous.

Reverse Inner Legend CIVITAS EBORACI — City of York.

Obverse Facing crowned bust of king, similar to E32D-015.

Reverse Large cross, three pellets in each quarter.

E32D-040 VG £25 F £50 VF £110

As E32D-020 with reverse inner legend as previous.

E32D-045 VG £25 F £50 VF £110

As previous, but with a lis on the king's breast.

E32D-050 VG £30 F £60 VF £120

Transitional Period 1361

This issue, which omits the king's French title, was only struck at the London mint.

Obverse Legend EDWARD REX ANGLIE DNS HIB — Edward King of England Lord of Ireland

Reverse Outer Legend POSVI DEUM ADIVTOREM MEUM — I have made God my helper

Reverse Inner Legend CIVITAS LONDON — City of London

Obverse Facing crowned bust of king with an annulet either side of crown, the letters of the legend are irregular in size and there are only seven arches in the tressure; mintmark cross potent.

Reverse Large cross, three pellets in each quarter.

E32D-055 VG £60 F £130 VF £250

Treaty Period 1361–1369

London Mint

Obverse Legend EDWARDUS REX ANGL DNS HYB — Edward King of the English Lord of Ireland

Reverse Outer Legend POSVI DEUM ADIVTOREM MEUM — I have made God my helper

Reverse Inner Legend CIVITAS LONDON — City of London

Obverse Facing bust of king, new-style 'X' in REX.

Reverse Large cross, three pellets in each quarter.

E32D-060 VG £20 F £40 VF £80

As previous, but annulet before EDWARDUS in the obverse legend and an unbarred 'A' in ADIVTOREM in the reverse legend.

E32D-065 VG £20 F £40 VF £80

As previous, but annulet on the king's breast and barred 'A' in ADIVTOREM.

E32D-070 VG £35 F £70 VF £140

Calais Mint

Obverse & Reverse Outer Legend As previous.

Reverse Inner Legend VILLA CALESIE — Town of Calais

Obverse Facing bust of king, annulet on his breast.

Reverse Large cross, three pellets in each quarter.

E32D-075 VG £60 F £130 VF £250

Post Treaty Period 1369–1377

This issue has the French title in the obverse legends once more; also the 'X' in REX resembles a St Andrew's cross while the abbreviation for ET (and) is a reversed 'F'.

Obverse Legend EDWARD DI GRA REX ANGL F (reversed) FR — Edward by the grace of God King of England and France

Reverse Outer Legend POSVI DEUM ADIVTOREM MEUM — I have made God my helper

Reverse Inner Legend CIVITAS LONDON — City of London

Obverse Facing bust of king, row of pellets across one side of his breast (this is called chain mail); mintmark cross pattée.

Reverse Large cross, three pellets in each quarter.

E32D-080 VG £100 F £200 VF —

Obverse Legend EDWARDUS REX ANGL F (reversed) FRANC — Edward King of England and France

Reverse Legends As previous.

Obverse Facing bust of king, a pellet either side of crown's central lis.

Reverse As previous.

E32D-085 VG £60 F £120 VF £250

Obverse Legend EDWARD REX ANGL F (reversed) FRANC(IE) — Edward King of England and France

Reverse Legends As previous.

Obverse Facing bust of king; the size of the bust sometimes varies.

Reverse As previous.

E32D-090 VG £60 F £120 VF £250

This issue was probably struck at the time of Edward III's death.

Obverse Legend EDWARDUS REX ANGL F(reversed) FRAC — Edward King of England and France

Reverse Legends As previous.

Obverse Facing bust of king, possibly Richard II, with small head and long neck.

Reverse As previous.

E32D-095 ex. rare

Richard II 1377–1399

All of Richard II's halfgroats are rare. They were only struck in London, often using altered Edward III dies so that the king's name reads RICARD instead of EDWARD, thus facilitating identification. However, as Richard III also issued halfgroats, it is important to check the mintmarks which constitute the main difference between the two reigns although there are also differences in the style of the halfgroats too. Richard II only used mintmark cross pattée, while Richard III used either a halved sun and rose, or boar's head.

Obverse Legend RICARD DI GRA REX ANGLI — Richard by the grace of God King of England (varieties exist).

Reverse Outer Legend POSVI DEUM ADIVTOREM MEUM — I have made God my helper

Reverse Inner Legend CIVITAS LONDON — City of London

Obverse Facing bust of king, new-style lettering in legend; mintmark cross pattée.

Reverse Long cross, three pellets in each quarter.

R22D-005 VG £175 F £300 VF £650

Legends As previous.

Obverse Facing bust of king with bushy hair, fishtail lettering in legends; mintmark cross pattée.

Reverse As previous, but fishtail lettering.

R22D-010 VG £185 F £330 VF £675

Several of Richard II's issues were muled with those of Edward III. The obverse die was changed to read RICARD instead of EDWARD, and often the original name can be seen underneath.

There are several varieties due to the muling of dies in this very rare issue.

Obverse Legend RICARD DI GRA REX ANGL Z FRANC (varieties) — Richard by the grace of God King of England and France

Reverse Legends As previous.

Obverse Facing bust of king, which is often Edward III depending on which die has been muled.

Reverse Long cross, three pellets in each quarter. This is often a Edward III die.

R22D-015 VG £250 F £500 VF £900

Obverse Legend RICARD DI GRA REX ANGLI — Richard by the grace of God King of England

Reverse Legends As previous

Obverse New-style bust and crown of king.

Reverse Long cross with three pellets in each quarter.

R22D-020 VG £350 F £600 VF —

Henry IV 1399–1413

All Henry IV issues are very rare and the halfgroat is no exception. Numismatically the reign can be divided into the heavy and the light coinage; the latter being introduced in 1412, when the weight of the halfgroat dropped from 36 grains 2.3 grams to 30 grains 1.9 grams. London was the only mint to produce halfgroats during this reign.

Like Henry IV's other denominations, the halfgroat is fairly difficult to identify because, although it bears the king's name HENRIC at the start of the obverse legend, a number of Henrys issued halfgroats. Nevertheless, those struck under Henry VI and Henry VII are very different in style from Henry IV's. Furthermore, despite the existence of numerous varieties for the issues of these two reigns, most of Henry V's coins have mullets somewhere in their design while none of Henry IV's halfgroats bear this mark.

Heavy Coinage 1399–1412

Obverse Legend HENRIC DI GRA REX ANGL Z FRANC — Henry by the grace of God King of England and France

Reverse Outer Legend POSVI DEUM ADIVTOREM MEUM — I have made God my helper

Reverse Inner Legend CIVITAS LONDON — City of London

Obverse Facing bust of king with star on his breast; mintmark cross pattée.

Reverse Long cross with three pellets in each corner, unbarred 'N's in LONDON.

H42D-005 VG £600 F £1,200 VF £2,400

Light Coinage 1412–1413

Obverse Legend As previous, but omitting FRANC.

Reverse Legends As previous.

Obverse Altered Richard II dies with facing bust of king, pellet to left and annulet to right of crown; mintmark cross pattée.

Reverse Long cross with three pellets in each quarter.

H42D-010 VG £500 F £750 VF £1,600

Obverse Legend As H42D-005 with full French title.

Reverse Legends As previous.

Obverse Henry IV's own dies with facing bust of king, annulet to left and pellet to right of crown; mintmark cross pattée.

Reverse As previous.

H42D-015 VG £450 F £700 VF £1,500

Henry V 1413–1422

Henry V halfgroats, which were only minted in London, are rare particularly compared to the groat or penny. They are also fairly difficult to identify as they closely resemble Henry IV's issues. Apart from the details listed under Henry IV on how to distinguish the various reigns apart, we should add that Henry V's issues have various marks which are specific to their particular class. Also, a close study of the bust reveals that the neck is often much slimmer than that of other monarchs and many of the facial expressions are specific to this reign. Collectors should ensure that every detail on a coin is meant to be there and, if something is missing or added, check through both reigns to identify the specimen correctly.

Collecting Hints

Henry V halfgroats are rare and usually obtainable in about Fine condition, although VF examples exist. The lower grade coins are often damaged, making it difficult to identify the issue and collectors should try to obtain a coin in Fine condition, which is easily identifiable. If collectors merely want a coin from Henry V's reign, it would perhaps be wiser to consider a groat or penny.

Obverse Legend HENRIC DI GRA REX ANGL (or ANGLIE) Z F — Henry by the grace of God King of England and France

Reverse Outer Legend POSVI DEUM ADIVTOREM MEUM — I have made God my helper

Reverse Inner Legend CIVITAS LONDON — City of London

Obverse Facing bust of king with no neck, annulet or pellet sometimes by crown, short broad lettering in legend.

Reverse Long cross, three pellets in each corner.

H52D-005 VG £200 F £400 VF rare

As previous, but ordinary lettering, no marks by crown; this issue is sometimes muled with a Henry IV reverse.

H52D-010 VG £80 F £150 VF £300

As previous, but facing bust with neck which has an oval swelling, there is a broken annulet to left of crown and sometimes a mullet on the right shoulder or in the centre of the king's breast. One variety has a broken annulet either side of crown. Also a mule with a Richard II reverse is known.

H52D-015 VG £50 F £100 VF £200

As previous, but facing bust of king with trefoil to right and annulet to left of crown and mullet on breast.

H52D-020 VG £50 F £100 VF £200

Legends As previous.

Obverse Facing bust of king, neat in style with a hollow neck, no marks by neck or crown.

Reverse As previous, but sometimes muled with a Henry VI reverse.

H52D-025 VG £60 F £120 VF £240

Henry VI First Reign 1422–1461

Like all silver Henry VI denominations, halfgroats may be categorised into issues according to the marks on the coin which may be by the king's head or in the legends. All halfgroats bear the king's name, HENRIC, in the obverse legend and have a different, more lifelike bust than the issues of the two previous Henrys. Collectors should also pay particular attention to the mintmark, found above the king's head at the beginning of the obverse legend; Henry IV and Henry V used only three mintmarks between them but Henry VI used a total of seven different mintmarks. A total of three mints were active during Henry VI's reign; London and Calais were by far the most prolific but the York mint did produce some very rare issues during the early part of the reign. The mint's name can be found in the inner legend on the reverse and reads CIVITAS LONDON for London, CIVITAS EBORACI for York and VILLA CALISIE for Calais.

Collecting Hints

Henry VI's halfgroats are fairly common, but not as common as groats. They are usually obtainable unclipped and undamaged in Fine condition, VF examples are not uncommon while those in EF are rare.

Annulet Issue 1422–1427
London Mint

Obverse Legend HENRIC DI GRA REX ANGL Z FR — Henry by the grace of God King of England and France

Reverse Outer Legend POSVI DEUM ADIVTOREM MEUM — I have made God my helper

Reverse Inner Legend CIVITAS LONDON — City of London

Obverse Facing bust of king.

Reverse Long cross, three pellets in each quarter and with an annulet in two quarters.

H62D-005 VG £20 F £40 VF £75 EF £150

Calais Mint

Obverse & Reverse Outer Legend As previous.

Reverse Inner Legend VILLA CALISIE — Town of Calais

Obverse Facing bust of king, an annulet either side of his neck.

Reverse Long cross with pellets in each quarters with two annulets in quarters.

H62D-010 VG £20 F £40 VF £65 EF £125

As previous, but only one annulet on reverse.

H62D-015 VG £35 F £55 VF £120 EF £200

As previous, but no annulets on reverse.

H62D-020 VG £20 F £40 VF £65 EF £125

York Mint

Obverse & Reverse Outer Legend As previous.

Reverse Inner Legend CIVITAS EBORACI — City of York

Obverse Facing bust of king, a lis either side of neck.

Reverse Long cross with three pellets in each quarter, an annulet in two quarters.

H62D-025 VG £400 F £800 VF £1,800 EF rare

Annulet Trefoil Sub Issue

This issue was only struck at the Calais mint.
Obverse & Reverse Outer Legend As previous.

Reverse Inner Legend VILLA CALISIE — Town of Calais

Obverse Facing bust of king, annulets either side of neck, trefoil to left of crown.

Reverse Long cross with three pellets in each quarter, an annulet in two quarters.

H62D-030 VG £40 F £80 VF £160

Rosette Mascle Issue 1427–1430

This issue has rosettes and mascles in the legends.

London Mint

Obverse & Reverse Outer Legend As previous.

Reverse Inner Legend CIVITAS LONDON — City of London

Obverse Facing bust of king, rosettes and mascles somewhere in the legend.

Reverse Rosettes and mascles in legends.

H62D-035 VG £25 F £50 VF £110

Calais Mint

As previous, but reverse inner legend reads VILLA CALISIE — Town of Calais.

H62D-040 VG £20 F £40 VF £90

A mascle is sometimes found between the inner curves and the beaded circle.

H62D-045 VG £30 F £60 VF £120

Pinecone Mascle Issue 1430–1434

This issue has pinecones and mascles in the legend.

London Mint

Obverse & Reverse Outer Legend As previous.

Reverse Inner Legend CIVITAS LONDON — City of London

Obverse Facing bust of king, pinecones and mascles in legend.

Reverse Pinecones and mascles in legend.

H62D-050 VG £20 F £40 VF £80

Calais Mint

As previous, but reverse inner legend reads VILLA CALISIE — Town of Calais.

H62D-055 VG £20 F £40 VF £80

Leaf Mascle Issue 1434–1435

This issue has a mascle in the legend and a leaf below the bust.

London Mint

Obverse & Reverse Outer Legend As previous.

Reverse Inner Legend CIVITAS LONDON — City of London

Obverse Facing bust of king, leaf under bust.

Reverse Mascle in legend; pellet under TAS and DON in reverse legend.

H62D-060 VG £30 F £70 VF £150

Calais Mint

Obverse & Reverse Outer Legend As previous.

Reverse Inner Legend VILLA CALISIE — Town of Calais

Obverse Leaf below facing bust of king.

Reverse Leaf sometimes on reverse, mascle in legend.

H62D-065 VG £20 F £45 VF £100

Leaf Trefoil Issue 1435–1438

Mostly with leaves and trefoils in the legends, this issue was only struck at the London mint.
Obverse & Reverse Outer Legend As previous.

Reverse Inner Legend CIVITAS LONDON — City of London

Obverse Facing bust of king, leaf on breast, leaves in obverse legend.

Reverse Long cross, three pellets in each quarter, no leaves or trefoil.

H62D-070 VG £25 F £50 VF £120

As previous, but trefoils in legends on obverse and reverse.

H62D-075 VG £35 F £70 VF £140

As previous, but no leaf on breast but leaves and/or trefoils in legends.

H62D-080 VG £50 F £100 VF £200

No halfgroats were struck for the trefoil issue of 1438–1443.

Leaf Pellet Issue 1445–1454

This issue was only struck at the London mint and usually has a leaf on the king's breast and a pellet on either side of the crown.

Obverse & Reverse Outer Legend As previous.

Reverse Inner Legend CIVITAS LONDON — City of London

Obverse Facing bust of king, pellets either side of crown and leaf on his breast.

Reverse Long cross with an extra pellet in two quarters, making a total of fourteen.

H62D-085 VG £20 F £40 VF £100

As previous, but sometimes no leaf on the king's breast and no stops or marks in the reverse legend.

H62D-090 VG £20 F £40 VF £100

Unmarked Issue 1453–1454

This issue, which was only struck at the London mint, has no marks in the field or in the legends except for one saltire stop on the reverse. It also has two extra pellets on the reverse, making a total of fourteen.

Obverse & Reverse Outer Legend As previous.

Reverse Inner Legend CIVITAS LONDON — City of London

Obverse Facing bust of king.

Reverse An extra pellet in two quarters.

H62D-095 VG £150 F £250 VF £500

Cross Pellet Issue 1454–1460

This issue was only struck at the London mint and has a saltire (small cross) on neck and a pellet either side of crown.

Legends As previous

Obverse Facing bust of king, saltire by neck, a pellet either side of crown.

Reverse An extra pellet in two quarters, making a total of fourteen, mullets in legends.

H62D-100 VG £150 F £250 VF £500

No halfgroats were struck for the rare lis pellet issue of 1456–1460.

Edward IV First Reign 1461–1470

This reign can be divided into the heavy and the light coinages. Heavy coinage halfgroats were struck between 1461 and 1464; the light coinage was issued from 1464 to 1470. Halfgroats from the

heavy coinage weigh 30 grains (1.9 grams), which at the time was heavier than their actual value. This was due to the increasing price of silver which in turn was caused by a shortage and high demand in Europe. To address this problem, the weight of the coins was reduced by 20% in 1464. Many heavy coinage halfgroats were melted down, either officially or unofficially, producing a 20% profit.

Heavy Coinage

All these issues were struck at the London mint.

Obverse Legend EDWARD DI GRA REX ANGL Z FRAN — Edward by the grace of God King of England and France

Reverse Outer Legend POSUI DEUM ADIUTOREM MEUM — I have made God my helper

Reverse Inner Legend CIVITAS LONDON — City of London

Obverse Facing crowned bust of king, lis on his breast, a pellet either side of crown; mintmark cross fleury or plain cross.

Reverse Long cross, four pellets in two quarters.

E42D-005 VG £100 F £250 VF £600

Legends As previous.

Obverse Facing bust of king, crescent on his breast, quatrefoil either side of neck; mintmark rose.

Reverse Long cross, three pellets in each quarter.

E42D-010 VG £120 F £300 VF £650

Legends As previous.

Obverse Crowned bust of king, trefoil on breast, quatrefoils either side of neck; mintmark rose.

Reverse As previous, but an eye in the inner legend.

E42D-015 VG £120 F £300 VF £650

As previous, but no marks on king's breast.

E42D-020 VG £120 F £300 VF £650

Legends As previous.

Obverse Crowned bust of king, an annulet either side of neck; mintmark rose.

Reverse As previous, but sometimes omits eye in legend.

E42D-025 VG £110 F £280 VF £550

Light Coinage

London Mint

This issue uses the same dies as the previous one; the only difference in the coins is the weight.
As previous, but no eye in the reverse legend.

E42D-030 unique

Legends As previous.

Obverse Crowned bust of king, quatrefoils at neck; mintmark rose, sun, crown, none, sometimes muled.

Reverse Long cross, three pellets in each quarter.

E42D-035 VG £40 F £80 VF £160

As previous, but saltires at neck; mintmark sun, crown, sometimes muled.

E42D-040 VG £40 F £80 VF £160

As previous, but trefoils at neck; mintmark sun, crown, long cross fitchée, sometimes muled.

E42D-045 VG £35 F £70 VF £150

As previous, but no marks by neck; mintmark sun and long cross fitchée always muled.

E42D-050 VG £60 F £150 VF £300

Bristol Mint

Obverse Legend As previous.

Reverse Outer Legend As previous.

Reverse Inner Legend VILLA BRISTOW (or BRESTOW or BRISTOLL) — Town of Bristol

Obverse Crowned bust of king, crosses or saltires either side of neck; mintmark rose, sun or crown, often muled.

Reverse Long cross, three pellets in each quarter.

E42D-055 VG £60 F £140 VF £300

As previous, but quatrefoils by neck.

E42D-060 VG £60 F £140 VF £300

As previous, but trefoils by neck; mintmark crown.

E42D-065 VG £70 F £160 VF £350

As previous, but no marks at neck; mintmark crown obverse, sun reverse.

E42D-070 VG £70 F £160 VF £350

Canterbury Mint
Ecclesiastical Mint under Archbishop Bourchier

Obverse Legend As previous.

Reverse Outer Legend As previous.

Reverse Inner Legend CIVITAS CANTOR — City of Canterbury

Obverse Crowned bust of king, a knot below the bust, quatrefoils either side of neck; mintmark pall.

Reverse Long cross, three pellets in each quarter, mintmark none, rose, sun.

E42D-075 VG £18 F £35 VF £80

As previous, but no quatrefoil at neck; mintmark pall.

E42D-080 VG £18 F £35 VF £80

As previous, but saltires by neck; mintmark pall, sometimes sun on reverse.

E42D-085 VG £20 F £40 VF £85

As previous, but trefoils by neck; mintmark pall.

E42D-090 VG £40 F £90 VF £180

As previous, but wedges by hair or neck; mintmark pall, sometimes rose or sun on reverse.

E42D-095 VG £20 F £40 VF £85

As E42D-075 or E42D-080 but no knot below king's bust.

E42D-100 VG £25 F £50 VF £120

Royal Mint

Legends As previous.

Obverse Crowned bust of king, quatrefoils at neck; mintmark crown.

Reverse As previous; mintmark crown or none.

E42D-105 VG £20 F £40 VF £90

As previous, but saltires by neck; mintmark as previous.

E42D-110 VG £20 F £40 VF £90

As previous, but trefoils by neck; mintmark crown, rose, sometimes sun on reverse.

E42D-115 VG £22 F £45 VF £100

As previous, but no marks at neck; mintmark sun.

E42D-120 VG £40 F £90 VF £200

Coventry Mint

Obverse Legend As previous.

Reverse Outer Legend As previous.

Reverse Inner Legend CIVITAS COVETRE — City of Coventry

Obverse Crowned bust of king, crosses either side of neck; mintmark sun.

Reverse Long cross, three pellets in each quarter.

E42D-125 unique

Norwich Mint

As previous, but reverse inner legend reads CIVITAS NORVIC — City of Norwich; and there are saltires instead of crosses by king's neck on the obverse.

E42D-130 ex. rare

York Mint

Obverse Legend As previous.

Reverse Outer Legend As previous.

Reverse Inner Legend CIVITAS EBORACI — City of York

Obverse Crowned bust of king, quatrefoils by neck; mintmark sun or lis.

Reverse Long cross, three pellets in each quarter, mintmark sun, lis or none.

E42D-135 VG £40 F £90 VF £180

As previous, but saltires by neck; mintmark lis.

E42D-140 VG £40 F £90 VF £180

As previous, but trefoils by neck; mintmark lis or none (reverse).

E42D-145 VG £40 F £90 VF £180

As E42D-135 but an E on the king's breast; mintmark lis, none on reverse.

E42D-150 VG £35 F £85 VF £170

Henry VI Restored Oct. 1470 — April 1471

During this very short period, London and York produced half-groats. The London issue is very similar to the first reign ones except that it is lighter in weight, it has no marks such as annulets or mascles, and uses the mintmark Restoration cross which was not used at all during the first reign. The extremely rare York issue is easily identified by the 'E' (for EBORACUM) on the king's breast as no other Henry used this mark on halfgroats.

> ## Collecting Hints
>
> Coins from this period are all rare and the halfgroat is no exception. The coins from the London mint are difficult to obtain in any condition but Fine and VF examples exist. The issues from York are extremely rare in any grade.

London Mint

Obverse Legend HENRIC (V) DI GRA REX ANGL Z FR(A)(NC) — Henry by the grace of God King of England and France

Reverse Outer Legend POSVI DEUM ADIVTOREM MEUM — I have made God my helper

Reverse Inner Legend CIVITAS LONDON — City of London

Obverse Facing bust of king; mintmarks Restoration cross, Restoration cross and none.

Reverse Long cross, three pellets in each quarter.

H62D-105 VG £150 F £300 VF £600

York Mint

Obverse & Reverse Outer Legend As previous.

Reverse Inner Legend CIVITAS EBORACI — City of York

Obverse Facing bust of king, 'E' on breast; mintmark lis.

Reverse As previous, but mintmark lis or sun.

H62D-110 ex. rare

Edward IV Second Reign 1471–1483

Numismatically, Edward IV's second reign is a continuation from his first, which is hardly surprising given there is only a seven month gap between them. There are however minor distinguishing differences mainly in the mintmarks and other marks.

Collecting Hints

Coins from the second reign tend to be slightly scarcer than those of the first although the most common mints (London and Canterbury) are usually obtainable in Fine condition, sometimes clipped; VF and EF examples exist but are not common. Collectors should try to obtain an unclipped example with a clear mintmark.

London Mint

Obverse Legend EDWARD DI GRA REX ANGL Z FRA — Edward by the grace of God King of England and France

Reverse Outer Legend POSVI DEUM ADIVTOREM MEUM — I have made God my helper

Reverse Inner Legend CIVITAS LONDON — City of London

Obverse Facing bust of king, trefoils on cusps; mintmark short cross fitchée, annulet, trefoil, pellet in annulet, cross and four pellets, cross in circle, cross pattée, pierced cross (varieties), rose or heraldic cinquefoil.

Reverse Long cross, three pellets in each quarter.

E42D-155 VG £20 F £40 VF £80

Bristol Mint

Obverse & Reverse Outer Legend As previous.

Reverse Inner Legend VILLA BRISTOW — Town of Bristol

Obverse Facing bust of king, 'B' on breast; mintmark rose, short cross fitchée.

Reverse As previous.

E42D-160 ex. rare

Canterbury Royal Mint

Obverse & Reverse Outer Legend As previous.

Reverse Inner Legend CIVITAS CANTOR — City of Canterbury

Obverse Facing bust of king, trefoils on cusps; mintmark rose, long cross fitchée, long cross fitchée and heraldic cinquefoil, or heraldic cinquefoil.

Reverse As previous.

E42D-165 VG £20 F £40 VF £80

As previous, but a 'C' on king's breast; mintmark rose.

E42D-170 VG £18 F £38 VF £75

As previous, but 'C' also in centre of reverse; mintmark rose.

E42D-175 VG £18 F £38 VF £75

As previous, but 'C' on the king's breast and a rose in the centre of the reverse; mintmark rose.

E42D-180 VG £18 F £38 VF £75

York Mint

Obverse & Reverse Outer Legend As previous.

Reverse Inner Legend CIVITAS EBORACI — City of York

Obverse Facing bust; mintmark lis.

Reverse As previous.

E42D-185 VG £70 F £140 VF £280

Edward V 1483

While it is believed that halfgroats were produced for this reign, it appears that none have survived. This issue would, however, be easily identified by the mintmark halved sun and rose, or boar's head. The obverse legend would be similar to that of Edward IV and the coin would only have been struck at London.

Richard III 1483–1485

During this short reign, halfgroats were only produced at the London mint. They bear the king's name, RICARD, on the obverse and may be distinguished from Richard II's issues by differences in style and weight, as well as by the mintmark which is cross pattée for Richard II and either halved sun and rose or boar's head for Richard III.

Collecting Hints

Richard III halfgroats are very rare in any condition; Fine and VF examples exist but are extremely rare. The groat from this reign, while rare, is much more common than the halfgroat.

Obverse Legend RICARD DI GRA REX ANGL Z FRA — Richard by the grace of God King of England and France

Reverse Outer Legend POSVI DEUM ADIVTOREM MEUM — I have made God my helper

Reverse Inner Legend CIVITAS LONDON — City of London

Obverse Facing bust of king; mintmark halved sun and rose.

Reverse Long cross, three pellets in each quarter.

R32D-005 VG £500 F £1,000 VF £2,000

As previous, but pellet below bust; mintmarks halved sun and rose on obverse and boar's head on reverse.

R32D-010 VG £600 F £1,200 VF £2,200

Henry VII 1485–1509

The so-called profile issue divides Henry VII's reign in two distinct numismatic styles. Until its introduction in 1502, the king's bust was in the standard medieval style with a rather unrealistic portrait; but the new design, by the German Alexander of Brugsal, was a product of the Renaissance and showed a lifelike profile portrait in incredible detail.

Henry's first issue is fairly easy to distinguish from earlier examples by the crown which, except for a few cases, has arches going over the top, and by the bust, especially the neck and rather unkempt hair. Although a few halfgroat issues have the early crown and might easily be confused with earlier issues of Henry VI, they also have specific mintmarks. The king's name, HENRIC, is found at the beginning of the obverse legend on all issues. Three mints were active during this period, London, Canterbury (ecclesiastical) and York (ecclesiastical and royal) and their name is found in the inner reverse legend: CIVITAS LONDON for London, CIVITAS CANTOR for Canterbury and CIVITAS EBORACI for York.

Collecting Hints

In the facing bust issues, most classes and all mints are fairly common and easy to obtain, usually in Fine condition. VF examples are not rare but EF ones are both rare and desirable. Many issues tend to be clipped or struck on rather small flans. Unclipped coins with full legible legends are more desirable.

London Mint

Obverse Legend HENRIC D(E)I GRA REX ANGL Z FR — Henry by the grace of God King of England and France

Reverse Outer Legend POSVI DEUM ADIVTOREM MEUM — I have made God my helper

Reverse Inner Legend CIVITAS LONDON — City of London

Obverse Facing bust of king, open crown similar to previous issues; mintmark lis on rose.

Reverse Long cross, three pellets in each quarter.

H72D-005 VG £200 F £400 VF £800

As previous, but facing bust of king with double-arched crown, rosettes on tressures; mintmark escallop.

H72D-010 ex. rare

As previous, but no rosettes on tressure, lozenge panel in centre of reverse; mintmark lis.

H72D-015 VG £25 F £50 VF £100

As previous, with a lis on the king's breast; mintmark lis.

H72D-020 VG £25 F £50 VF £100

Legends As previous.

Obverse Facing bust of king, unarched crown; mintmark lis.

Reverse Lozenge panel in centre of reverse.

H72D-025 VG £20 F £40 VF £80

As previous, but struck on a smaller die with smaller lettering.

H72D-030 VG £20 F £40 VF £80

Canterbury Mint

Ecclesiastical Mint under Archbishop Morton 1486–1490

Obverse & Reverse Outer Legend As previous.

Reverse Inner Legend CIVITAS CANTOR — City of Canterbury

Obverse Facing bust of king wearing an open crown, crosses either side of neck; mintmark tun.

Reverse 'M' in centre of cross.

H72D-035 VG £20 F £40 VF £80

As previous, with a double-arched crown; no mintmark.

H72D-040 VG £20 F £40 VF £80

Under King and Archbishop Jointly 1490–1500

As previous, but without 'M' on the reverse; mintmarks lis, tun, pansy. Several minor varieties exist with different style lettering and various marks and stops in the legend.

H72D-045 VG £18 F £35 VF £70

York Mint

Royal Mint

Obverse & Reverse Outer Legend As previous.

Reverse Inner Legend CIVITAS EBORACI — City of York

Obverse Facing bust of king wearing a double-arched crown, lis on his breast; mintmark lis.

Reverse Lozenge panel in centre.

H72D-050 VG £20 F £40 VF £80

As previous, but no lis on king's breast; mintmark lis.

H72D-055 VG £20 F £40 VF £80

As H72D-050 but unarched crown.

H72D-060 VG £18 F £38 VF £75

Ecclesiastical Mint under Archbishop Savage

Several varieties of this coin exist, with different style lettering. *Legends* As previous.

Obverse Facing bust of king wearing double arched crown, keys either side of neck; mintmark martlet.

Reverse Long cross with three pellets in each quarter.

H72D-065 VG £18 F £38 VF £75

Sede Vacante Issue 1507–1508
As previous, but with no keys by bust; mintmark martlet.

H72D-070 VG £22 F £45 VF £90

Profile Issue
The stunning profile issue shows superb craftsmanship in design and production. It is easily recognisable but, because Henry VIII used the same portrait in his first coinage, it is important to ensure that the obverse legend reads HENRIC VII or HENRIC for Henry VII rather than HENRIC VIII. There are also several differences in the mintmarks and reverse legends. Unlike previous issues, Henry VII's mints are not marked by names but by symbols, such as keys below the reverse shield for York, and collectors should check all classes when identifying a coin.

> ## Collecting Hints
> No collection should be without a coin from the profile issue and, although the groat is larger and shows off the diemaker's work better, the halfgroat is still an attractive coin. Specimens are usually unclipped and obtainable in Fine condition; VF and EF examples are rare, but exist. Often the coins were in circulation for a considerable time and are therefore very worn.

London Mint
Obverse Legend HENRIC VII DI GRA REX AGL Z — Henry by the grace of God King of England and [France]

Reverse Legend POSVI DEUM ADIVTOREM MEUM — I have made God my helper

Obverse Profile bust of king; mintmark lis and pheon, sometimes muled.

Reverse Cross over royal arms.

H72D-075 VG £35 F £70 VF £150

As previous, but the obverse legend reads HENRIC omitting the VII.

H72D-080 ex. rare

Canterbury Mint
As H72D-075, but mintmark martlet or rose.

H72D-085 VG £30 F £60 VF £120

York Mint under Archbishop Bainbridge
As H72D-075, but two keys below shield on reverse; mintmark martlet or rose.

H72D-090 VG £30 F £60 VF £120

As previous, but 'X.B.' either side of reverse shield and no keys below; mintmark rose obverse and martlet reverse.

H72D-095 VG £35 F £65 VF £130

Henry VIII 1509–1547
There were three main coinages during Henry VIII's reign and the posthumous coinage which bears Henry's portrait but was struck under his son. Henry's own first coinage bears the portrait of his father, Henry VII, but has HENRIC VIII in the obverse legend as well as different mintmarks and reverse legends; the second coinage shows the young portrait of the king. The third and posthumous coinages, which are very similar in style, were both struck in base silver and proved very unpopular. Base silver is produced when copper is added to silver, resulting in poor quality coins of a low fineness and Henry VIII introduced this coinage in an effort to relieve the financial troubles caused by overspending.

First Coinage 1509–1526
Four mints produced halfgroats during the first coinage, London, Canterbury, York and Tournai in France. Some issues are just marked with symbols, such as keys, to differentiate the mint but others bear its name in full.

> ## Collecting Hints
> First coinage halfgroats are fairly common and usually obtainable unclipped in Fine condition. VF examples are desirable and exist, as do EF examples. Many coins from this issue appear to have been in circulation for a long time and are often very worn.

London Mint
Obverse Legend HENRIC VIII DI GRA REX AGL Z — Henry VIII by the grace of God King of England and [France]

Reverse Legend POSVI DEV ADIVTOE MEV — I have made God my helper

Obverse Profile bust of Henry VII; mintmark portcullis crowned.

Reverse Royal arms over cross.

H82D-005 VG £60 F £130 VF £220

Canterbury Mint under Archbishop Warham

As previous, but mintmark rose on the obverse. The only difference between this and the previous issue is the mintmark.

H82D-010 VG £50 F £100 VF £200

As previous, but 'WA' above shield on reverse; mintmark martlet.

H82D-015 VG £45 F £90 VF £170

As previous, but 'W.A.' divided by shield; mintmark cross fitchée.

H82D-020 VG £35 F £70 VF £140

Obverse Legend As previous.

Reverse Legend CIVITAS CANTOR — City of Canterbury

Obverse As previous; mintmarks pomegranate, lis, cross fitchée and lis.

Reverse 'W.A.' divided by shield.

H82D-025 VG £35 F £70 VF £140

York Mint

Ecclesiastical Mint under Archbishop Bainbridge 1508–1514

Obverse Legend As previous.

Reverse Legend POSVI DEV ADIVTOE MEU — I have made God my helper

Obverse Profile bust of Henry VII; mintmark martlet.

Reverse Cross over royal arms, keys below shield.

H82D-030 VG £35 F £70 VF £140

As previous, but 'X.B' divided by shield; mintmark martlet.

H82D-035 VG £40 F £80 VF £160

Ecclesiastical Mint under Archbishop Wolsey 1514–1530

As previous, with keys, but no 'X.B' by shield, Cardinal's hat below shield; mintmarks martlet or radiant star.

H82D-040 VG £60 F £120 VF £250

Royal Mint

Obverse Legend As previous.

Reverse Legend CIVITAS EBORACI — City of York

Obverse Profile bust of king; mintmark radiant star, star, pansy, escallop or voided cross.

Reverse Cross over royal shield, keys either side and Cardinal's hat below shield.

H82D-045 VG £40 F £80 VF £160

As previous, with 'T.W' divided by shield; mintmark voided cross.

H82D-050 VG £45 F £90 VF £180

Tournai Mint

Only groats and halfgroats were produced at this mint, which was located in France.

Collecting Hints

This issue is probably unique.

Obverse Legend As previous.

Reverse Legend CIVITAS TORNACEN — City of Tournai

Obverse As previous; mintmark crowned 'T'.

Reverse Cross over royal arms.

H82D-055 probably unique

Second Coinage 1526–1544

The second coinage (1526–1544) bears a youthful portrait of Henry VIII and was struck at London, Canterbury and York. Either the mint's name or an identifying legend on the reverse distinguishes the three; for London it is POSVI DEV ADIVTOE MEU (I have made God my helper) and CIVITAS CANTOR for Canterbury, CIVITAS EBORACI for York.

Collecting Hints

Halfgroats from the second coinage are fairly common. They are usually obtainable in Fine condition; VF examples are not uncommon but EF ones are rare and desirable. Most coins are unclipped but the legends can sometimes be slightly weak in places due to poor striking.

London Mint

Obverse Legend HENRIC VIII D.GR AGL Z FR — Henry VIII by the grace of God of England and France

Reverse Legend POSVI DEV ADIVTOE MEU — I have made God my helper

Obverse Youthful bust of king; mintmarks, rose, lis, sunburst, arrow.

Reverse Cross over royal shield.

H82D-060 VG £30 F £60 VF £120

Obverse Legend HENRIC D.G. AGL Z HIB REX — Henry by the grace of God King of England and Ireland

Reverse Legend As previous.

Obverse As previous, but mintmark pheon.

Reverse As previous.

H82D-065 VG £200 F £400 VF —

Canterbury Mint
Royal Mint

Obverse Legend HENRIC VIII D GR AGL Z FR — Henry VIII by the grace of God of England and France

Reverse Legend CIVITAS CANTOR — City of Canterbury

Obverse Youthful bust of king; mintmark uncertain, rose, cross patonce, or 'T', sometimes muled.

Reverse 'W.A' divided by shield.

H82D-070 VG £20 F £45 VF £90

As previous, but nothing beside the shield; mintmark uncertain.

H82D-075 VG £30 F £60 VF £120

Ecclesiastical Mint under Archbishop Cranmer

As previous, but T.C beside shield; mintmark Catherine Wheel.

H82D-080 VG £25 F £50 VF £100

York Mint
Ecclesiastical Mint under Archbishop Wolsey

Obverse Legend As previous.

Reverse Legend CIVITAS EBORACI — City of York

Obverse Youthful bust of king; mintmark voided cross.

Reverse Cross over shield, 'T.W' divided by shield with Cardinal's hat below.

H82D-085 VG £20 F £50 VF £100

Sede Vacante Issue 1530–1531

As previous, but no marks such as letters or Cardinal's hat on the reverse; mintmark key.

H82D-090 VG £30 F £60 VF £120

Ecclesiastical Mint under Archbishop Lee

As previous, but 'E.L' or 'L.E' divided by the reverse shield; mintmark key.

H82D-095 VG £20 F £50 VF £100

Third Coinage 1544–1547

As mentioned earlier, the third coinage was made from base silver and coins from this issue are usually dull in appearance but should not be cleaned, because they will then look as if they have been made of copper. A total of five mints produced halfgroats during this period: Bristol, Canterbury and York and two London-based mints. The second London mint was Southwark mint, just south of the River Thames and, to avoid confusion, what was previously referred to as London mint is henceforth the Tower mint. The mint can be found by referring to the reverse legends which read POSUI DEVM ADIVTOE MEU (I have made God my helper) for the Tower Mint, CIVITAS LONDON for Southwark, CIVITAS CANTOR for Canterbury, CIVITAS EBORACI for York and CIVITAS BRISTOLI for Bristol.

Tower Mint

Obverse Legend HENRIC 8 D.G. AGL F Z HIB REX (many varieties) — Henry VIII by the grace of God of England France and Ireland King

Reverse Legend POSVI DEUM ADIVTOE MEU — I have made God my helper

Obverse Bust of ageing king; mintmark lis or nothing.

Reverse Cross over royal shield.

H82D-100 VG £40 F £80 VF £180

Southwark Mint

Obverse Legend As previous.

Reverse Legend CIVITAS LONDON — City of London

Obverse Bust of ageing king, Roman and Lombardic lettering; mintmark 'S' or 'E' in forks or none.

Reverse As previous.

H82D-105 ex. rare

Bristol Mint

Obverse Legend As previous.

Reverse Legend CIVITAS BRISTOLI — City of Bristol

Obverse As previous, but mintmark on reverse only.

Reverse As previous; mintmark 'WS'.

H82D-110 VG £35 F £70 VF £180

Canterbury Mint

Obverse Legend As previous.

Reverse Legend CIVITAS CANTOR — City of Canterbury

Obverse & Reverse As previous, no mintmark.

H82D-115 VG £35 F £65 VF £180

York Mint

Obverse Legend As previous.

Reverse Legend CIVITAS EBORACI — City of York

Obverse & Reverse As previous, no mintmark.

H82D-120 VG £40 F £80 VF £180

Posthumous Coinage 1547–1551

After Henry VIII's death in 1547, his son Edward ascended the throne but until 1551 continued to issue coins with Henry VIII's portrait and name. This is known as the posthumous coinage. Although very similar to Henry's third coinage, these issues have different mintmarks, and some of the York mint have a different style bust. Moreover, a third mint opened in London during this coinage at Durham House, a former palace on the Strand owned by the Bishop of Durham. The reverse reading for this mint is REDD CUIQ QD SUUM EST (Render to each that which is his own); the other mints remain as in the previous issue.

Collecting Hints

Most coins are usually dull in appearance due to their low silver content. Coins are usually found in VG or F condition while coins in VF and EF do exist from the common mints.

Tower Mint

Obverse Legend HENRIC 8 D G AGL FR Z HI REX (many varieties) — Henry VIII by the grace of God King of England France and Ireland

Reverse Legend POSVI DEUM ADIUTOE MEU — I have made God my helper

Obverse Ageing bust of king, Roman lettering; mintmarks arrow, 'K', grapple, lis, martlet, none, often muled.

Reverse Cross over royal arms.

H82D-125 VG £35 F £65 VF £180

Southwark Mint

Obverse Legend As previous.

Reverse Legend CIVITAS LONDON — City of London

Obverse As previous; mintmark 'E', pheon, 'K' and none, often muled.

Reverse As previous.

H82D-130 VG £35 F £65 VF £180

Durham House Mint

Obverse Legend As previous.

Reverse Legend REDD CUIQ QD SUUM EST — Render to each that which is his own

Obverse As previous, but mintmark bow, often just on reverse.

Reverse As previous.

H82D-135 VG £200 F £400 VF rare

Bristol Mint

This issue can be identical to H82D-110.

Obverse Legend As previous.

Reverse Legend CIVITAS BRISTOLI — City of Bristol

Obverse As previous, no mintmark.

Reverse As previous; mintmark 'T.C' or 'WS'.

H82D-140 VG £35 F £70 VF £180

Canterbury Mint

Obverse Legend As previous.

Reverse Legend CIVITAS CANTOR — City of Canterbury

Obverse As previous; mintmark none, or 'T'.

Reverse As previous; mintmark none, or 'T'.

H82D-145 VG £35 F £65 VF £150

York Mint

Obverse Legend As previous.

Reverse Legend CIVITAS EBORACI — City of York

Obverse As previous, but two styles of bust; no mintmark.

Reverse As previous.

H82D-150 VG £35 F £65 VF £180

Edward VI 1547–1553

Halfgroats were produced in considerable quantities during Edward VI's reign but all the common issues were in the name of his father, Henry VIII (the posthumous coinage listed above), and those struck in his own name are rare. The latter were produced for only a short period (April 1547 to January 1549) and in very base silver; no halfgroats were struck during Edward's fine silver issues. The three mints that produced halfgroats, the Tower and Southwark in London and the Canterbury mint, are distinguished by the reverse legends which read POSUI etc. (I have made God my helper) for the Tower, CIVITAS LONDON for Southwark and CIVITAS CANTOR for Canterbury.

Tower Mint

Obverse Legend EDOARD [uncertain]

Reverse Legend POSUI [uncertain]

Obverse Crowned bust to right; mintmark arrow.

Reverse Royal shield over cross.

E62D-005 VG £175 F £350 VF £750

Southwark Mint

Obverse Legend As previous.

Reverse Legend CIVITAS LONDON — City of London

Obverse Crowned bust to right; mintmark arrow or 'E'.

Reverse As previous.

E62D-010 VG £175 F £350 VF £750

Canterbury Mint

Obverse Legend EDOARD [uncertain]

Reverse Legend CIVITAS CANTOR — City of Canterbury

Obverse Crowned bust to right; no mintmark.

Reverse As previous.

E62D-015 VG £125 F £225 VF £500

Mary 1553–1554

Although large quantities of groats were produced during Mary's reign, very few halfgroats were struck, probably due to there being sufficient numbers in circulation from previous reigns. Also, because of inflation and the falling value of silver, there was a need at this time for larger denominations. Unlike several of the previous issues, Mary's halfgroats were struck in good quality silver; they were only produced at the Tower mint and can easily be distinguished from Philip and Mary's 1554–1558 issue by the legends.

Obverse Legend MARIA D.G. ANG FRA Z HIB REGI — Mary by the grace of God Queen of England France and Ireland

Reverse Legend VERITAS TEMPORIS FILIA — Truth is the daughter of time

Obverse Crowned bust left of queen; mintmark pomegranate.

Reverse Royal shield over long cross.

M2D-005 ex. rare

Philip and Mary 1554–1558

Philip and Mary halfgroats are not as rare as Mary's issue and were again only struck at the Tower mint. They can easily be differentiated from the previous issue as both the obverse and reverse legends are different.

Obverse Legend PHILIP ET MARIA D.G. REX ET REGINA — Philip and Mary by the grace of God King and Queen

Reverse Legend POSUIM DEUM ADIUTO NOS — We have made God our helper

Obverse Crowned bust of Mary left; mintmark lis.

Reverse Royal shield over cross.

PM2D-005 VG £150 F £350 VF £800

Elizabeth I 1558–1603

Elizabeth I and her government recognised the importance of having a large number of small denominations in the coinage and the halfgroat was produced during most of her reign, circulating together with other denominations which were very close in value, such as the threepence. Each denomination was produced in quantity and helped to facilitate trade. Under Elizabeth, halfgroats were only struck at the Tower mint in London.

Identifying Elizabeth's coinage is not in itself difficult as in virtually all silver issues, including the halfgroats, the queen's distinctive bust appears on the obverse with her name in the legend. But distinguishing the various denominations is sometimes more complicated and collectors should bear in mind that none of the halfgroats but all threepences and three-halfpence from this reign are dated and that threepences and three-halfpence, with one exception, have a rose behind the queen's bust which is omitted in the halfgroat. Moreover, in the fourth and sixth issue halfgroats, two pellets denoting two pence can be found behind the queen's bust. Finally, accurately to identify a particular issue, collectors should locate the mintmark, which is specific to each issue. Collectors will also find that the earlier issues tend to be slightly larger than the later ones.

Collecting Hints

Elizabeth's halfgroat is fairly common with the exception of the first issue and the milled coinage. Fine and VF examples are not uncommon while EF examples also exist and are desirable. The portrait on the coin is usually reasonable but the legends are sometimes a little weak.

First Issue 1559–1560

Obverse Legend ELIZABETH D.G. ANG FRA Z HIB REG — Elizabeth by the grace of God Queen of England France and Ireland

Reverse Legend POSUI DEU ADIUTOREM MEU — I have made God my helper

Obverse Crowned bust of queen facing left, a wire-line inner circle; mintmark lis.

Reverse Shield over long cross.

EL2D-005 VG £100 F £200 VF £400

Second Issue 1560–1561

Apart from the mintmark, there is a slight difference between the first and second issue obverse legend where Z, denoting 'and', is replaced by ET.

Obverse Legend ELIZABETH D.G. ANG FRA ET HIB REGINA — Elizabeth by the grace of God Queen of England France and Ireland

Reverse Legend As previous.

Obverse As previous, but beaded inner circle, mintmark cross-crosslet or martlet.

Reverse As previous, beaded inner circle.

EL2D-010 VG £20 F £40 VF £80

Third Issue 1561–1572

As previous, but a slightly different style in bust; mintmarks portcullis, lion, coronet or castle.

EL2D-015 VG £25 F £50 VF £100

No halfgroats were struck for the fourth issue.

Fifth Issue 1582–1600

Obverse Legend E.D.G. ROSA SINE SPINA — Elizabeth by the grace of God a rose without a thorn

Reverse Legend CIVITAS LONDON — City of London

Obverse Crowned bust of queen facing left, two pellets behind the bust; mintmark bell, 'A', escallop, crescent, hand, tun, woolpack, key, anchor or cypher. Some very early issues of mintmark bell omit the pellets or have the pellets struck over II.

Reverse As previous.

EL2D-020 VG £18 F £35 VF £70

Sixth Issue 1601–1602

Legends As previous

Obverse Bust of queen with two pellets behind; mintmark '1' or '2'.

Reverse As previous.

EL2D-025 VG £25 F £50 VF £100

Milled Coinage

Although milled halfgroats were produced during Elizabeth's reign, it is thought that they were not a success due to the difficulties in producing such a small coin. Like the hammered issue, they can be differentiated from the threepence by the absence of a date and of the rose behind the queen's bust.

Collecting Hints

They are rare and are usually found in VG or F condition often damaged.

Obverse Legend ELIZABETH D.G. ANG FRA ET HIB REGINA — Elizabeth by the grace of God Queen of England France and Ireland

Reverse Legend POSUI DEUM ADIUTOREM MEUM — I have made God my helper

Obverse Crowned bust of queen left; mintmark star.

Reverse Square shield over cross, no inner circles.

EL2D-030 VG £60 F £125 VF £400

Reverse Thistle with small crown above.

J12D-015 VG £18 F £35 VF £60 EF £120

James I 1603–1625

Although James I issued fewer denominations than Elizabeth, the halfgroat continued to be struck throughout his reign and falls in two main types according to design. In the first coinage, the halfgroat bore the king's bust on the obverse and the royal shield with no legend on the reverse. But in the second and third coinages it omitted the bust and depicted a crowned rose on the obverse and a crowned thistle on the reverse. This was the first halfgroat to omit the monarch's portrait since the denomination was introduced under Edward III and was probably intended as a political statement, stressing, in combination with the reverse legend, the link that England had achieved with Scotland.

Collecting Hints

James I's first issue is fairly scarce, especially in the better grades; the average condition in which it is found is less than Fine, although Fine and VF examples exist and are obtainable. The later issues are fairly common; Fine and VF examples are fairly easy to obtain while EF examples also exist but are rare and desirable.

First Coinage 1603–1604

Obverse Legend I.D.G ROSA SINE SPINA — James by the grace of God a rose without a thorn

Reverse Legend None.

Obverse Crowned bust of king right with II behind; mintmarks thistle or lis.

Reverse Royal shield with mintmark above.

J12D-005 VG £20 F £40 VF £100

Second Coinage 1604–1619

Obverse Legend I.D.G ROSA SINE SPINA — James by the grace of God a rose without a thorn

Reverse Legend TUEATUR UNITA DEUS — May God guard these united (kingdoms)

Obverse Rose with large crown above; mintmark lis, rose, escallop, grapes or coronet.

Reverse Thistle with large crown above and stops or dots in legend.

J12D-010 VG £15 F £30 VF £50 EF £100

Legends As previous.

Obverse Rose with small crown above; mintmark coronet, key, bell, mullet, tower, trefoil, cinquefoil, tun, book or plain cross.

Third Coinage 1619–1625

Legends As previous.

Obverse Rose with small crown above; mintmark spur rowel, none, rose, thistle, lis, trefoil or trefoil and lis.

Reverse Thistle with small crown above, no stops in legend.

J12D-020 VG £15 F £30 VF £50 EF £100

Charles I 1625 1649

Halfgroats were struck in great quantities and numerous varieties during Charles I's reign. Most were produced at the Tower mint in London, either from hand-hammered dies or under Nicholas Briot's supervision from milled dies; the two issues being struck alongside each other. Many provincial mints also opened, especially during the Civil War when the Roundheads gained control of the capital and the Tower mint. Most of Charles' halfgroats have the Roman numeral II by the king's bust, denoting the denomination. Finally, many halfgroats are found holed and this was probably done officially at the end of the 17th century, to devalue the coin.

Tower Mint

Tower Mint under King 1625–1642

There are two main types but many varieties of this issue; the first has a crowned rose on either side of the coin. This design only occurs in Charles I's reign and should not be confused with James I's second and third coinages, which have a crowned rose on the obverse and a crowned thistle on the reverse.

Collecting Hints

All the varieties from this issue are fairly common, the average grade being less than Fine although VF or even EF examples exist. The legends are often weak, usually due to poor striking and considerable circulation.

Crowned Rose Issue

Obverse Legend C D G ROSA SINE SPINA — Charles by the grace of God a rose without a thorn

Reverse Legend IUS THRONUM FIRMAT — Justice strengthens the throne

Obverse Crowned rose with inner circles; mintmarks lis, cross calvary, blackamoor's head.

Reverse Crowned rose with inner circles.

C12D-005 VG £20 F £40 VF £100

Legends As previous.

Obverse Crowned rose with no inner circles; mintmark blackamoor's head, castle, anchor, heart or plume.

Reverse Crowned rose with no inner circles.

C12D-010 VG £15 F £30 VF £60

Bust Issue

Many varieties in the obverse legend exist but all issues will read one of the following: CAROLUS D G MAG B F ET H REX— — CAROLUS D G MA B F ET H REX — CAROLUS D G MB F ET H REX — CAROLUS D G M B FRA ET HIB REX— — CAROLUS D G M A B F ET H REX. Due to the muling of the various issues and the many varieties, the obverse legend is only listed once.

Obverse Legend CAROLUS D G M(A)(G) B F(RA) ET H(IB) REX — Charles by the grace of God King of Great Britain France and Ireland

Reverse Legend IUSTITIA THRONUM FIRMAT — Justice strengthens the throne

Obverse Bust of king wearing ruff and mantle; mintmark plume or rose.

Reverse Oval shield.

C12D-015 VG £15 F £28 VF £50

As previous, but plume over reverse shield.

C12D-020 VG £20 F £35 VF £60

Obverse Bust of king wearing lace collar; mintmark harp, crown or portcullis.

Reverse 'C.R' divided by oval shield, no inner circles.

C12D-025 VG £15 F £28 VF £50

As previous, with inner circles on obverse and reverse; mintmark harp or portcullis.

C12D-030 VG £20 F £35 VF £60

As previous, but inner circle on reverse only.

C12D-035 VG £15 F £35 VF £60

As previous, but inner circle on obverse only.

C12D-040 VG £15 F £28 VF £50

Bust and shield as previous, but no 'C.R' divided by shield, inner circles on both sides; mintmark portcullis.

C12D-045 VG £15 F £28 VF £50

As previous, but inner circle only on obverse.

C12D-050 VG £15 F £28 VF £50

Obverse New style bust of king, no inner circles; mintmark bell, crown, tun, anchor, triangle, star or triangle in circle.

Reverse Rounder shield, no inner circle.

C12D-055 VG £15 F £28 VF £50

As previous, but inner circle on obverse; mintmark triangle.
C12D-060 VG £15 F £28 VF £50

As previous, but inner circles on both sides; mintmark triangle, star or triangle in circle.

C12D-065 VG £15 F £28 VF £50

Obverse New-style bust similar to the Aberystwyth mint issues, no inner circles; mintmark anchor.

Reverse Rounder shield, no inner circles.

C12D-070 VG £20 F £35 VF £60

As previous, but inner circles on reverse; mintmark anchor.

C12D-075 VG £20 F £35 VF £60

Obverse Very small bust of king, no inner circles; mintmark anchor.

Reverse Rounder shield, no inner circles.

C12D-080 VG £20 F £35 VF £60

Tower Mint under Parliament 1642–1648

London and the Tower mint came under the control of Parliament in 1642. The halfgroats produced during this period are fairly similar to the previous issues except for the mintmark and it is interesting to note that the Roundheads retained the king's portrait and emblems on the coins.

Collecting Hints

Both varieties from this period are slightly scarcer than the previous issues. They are usually obtainable in about Fine condition but better grade coins do exist. It is important that a coin bears a clear mintmark for accurate identification.

Obverse Legend CAROLUS D G M B F ET HIB REX — Charles by the grace of God King of Great Britain France and Ireland

Reverse Legend IUSTITIA THRONUM FIRMAT — Justice strengthens the throne

Obverse Bust of king, inner circles on obverse and reverse; mintmarks '(P)', '(R)', eye, sun, sceptre.

Reverse Rounder shield of royal arms.

C12D-085 VG £25 F £50 VF £100

Obverse Legend CAROLUS D G M B F ET H REX — Charles by the grace of God King of Great Britain France and Ireland

Reverse Legend IUSTITIA THRONUM FIRMAT — Justice strengthens the throne

Obverse Older, shorter bust of king with pointed beard; mintmarks eye, sun, sceptre. Inner circles both sides.

Reverse Rounder shield.

C12D-090 VG £25 F £50 VF £100

Briot's Milled Issue 1631–32

Collecting Hints

The halfgroat from this issue is fairly scarce but, due to the good quality of production, is often found in better grades than the hammered. Specimens are usually obtainable in Fine to VF condition and even EF examples are not rare.

Obverse Legend CAROLUS D.G MAG BRIT FR ET HIB R — Charles by the grace of God [King of] Great Britain France and Ireland

Reverse Legend IUSTITIA THRONUM FIRMAT — Justice strengthens the throne

Obverse Bust of king, II behind and 'B' below bust; no mintmark.

Reverse Square topped shield of royal arms over cross; no mintmark.

C12D-095 VG £30 F £50 VF £100 EF £200

Provincial Mints

Halfgroats were produced at several provincial mints and many issues look fairly similar. When identifying a coin, collectors should check through all the provincial mints, ensuring that the mintmark corresponds to the issue. Also, in every issue the halfgroat as a denomination can be identified by the Roman numeral II behind the bust of the king.

Aberystwyth Mint

This issue, which had four varieties, can be identified by the large plume on the reverse and mintmark open book.

Collecting Hints

This issue is fairly scarce but usually obtainable undamaged in VG or Fine condition.

Obverse Legend CAROLUS D.G. M B F ET H REX — Charles by the grace of God King of Great Britain France and Ireland

Reverse Legend IUSTITIA THRONUM FIRMAT — Justice strengthens the throne

Obverse Bust of king with lace collar, no inner circles, value behind.

Reverse Large plume, no inner circles.

C12D-100 VG £40 F £70 VF £140 EF £250

Similar to last, but the king's lace collar is square.

C12D-105 VG £35 F £65 VF £130 EF £230

As C12D-100, but inner circles on both sides of the coin.

C12D-110 VG £30 F £60 VF £120 EF £220

Briot-style bust, similar to that of the Tower mint's first coinage, inner circles on both sides of the coin. This issue was hammered.

C12D-115 VG £35 F £65 VF £130 EF £230

Aberystwyth Furnace Mint 1648–1649

This issue is very similar to the Aberystwyth one except for the mintmark crown and the slightly different design of the plume on the reverse.

Collecting Hints

The coin is very rare in any grade.

Obverse Legend CAROLUS D G MA BR FR ET HIB REX — Charles by the grace of God King of Great Britain France and Ireland

Reverse Legend IUSTITIA THRONUM FIRMAT — Justice strengthens the throne

Obverse Bust of king and inner circles; mintmark crown.

Reverse Large plume with band inscribed ICH DIEN — I serve, inner circles.

C12D-120 VG £100 F £220 VF £450

Oxford Mint

Two very different issues were produced at the Oxford mint. The first resembles the Aberystwyth issue with a large plume on the reverse which, however, is of a different style; it also has mintmark lis or cross. The second issue has a very distinct reverse, with the Declaration in three lines, the date 1644 and OX (for Oxford) below the date.

Collecting Hints

Both Oxford issues are rare; often found holed or damaged, they are rarely available in VF condition.

Obverse Legend CAROLUS D G M B F ET H(IB) REX — Charles by the grace of God King of Great Britain France and Ireland

Reverse Legend IUSTITIA THRONUM FIRMAT — Justice strengthens the throne

Obverse Bust of king; mintmark lis or cross, value behind head.

Reverse Large plume in centre.

C12D-125 VG £60 F £120 VF £250

Obverse Legend As previous.

Reverse Outer Legend EXURGAT DEUS DISSIPENTUR INIMICI — Let God arise and His enemies be scattered

Reverse Inner Legend RELIG PROT LEG ANG LIBER — The religion of the Protestants the laws of England the liberty of Parliament

Obverse Bust of king.

Reverse Declaration on three lines, three fleur-de-lis above, date 1644 below and OX below that; the outer legend does not start at the top of the coin.

C12D-130 VG £80 F £150 VF £300

Bristol Mint

Only one issue was produced at the Bristol mint and has a very different style reverse.

Collecting Hints

This issue is rare in any grade and is often damaged.

Obverse Legend CAROLUS D G M B F ET H REX — Charles by the grace of God King of Great Britain France and Ireland

Reverse Outer Legend EXURGAT DEUS DISSIP INIMICI — Let God arise and His enemies be scattered (abbreviated)

Reverse Centre Legend RE PR LE AN LI PA — The religion of the Protestants the laws of England the liberty of Parliament

Obverse Bust of king; no mintmark.

Reverse Declaration on three lines, undated, BR for Bristol below declaration.

C12D-135 VG £150 F £300 VF —

Late Declaration Silver

Very little is known about this issue which is often known as the Plumes mint and easily identifiable, being the only halfgroat issued with the date 1646.

Collecting Hints

Coins from this issue are very rare in any grade and are often damaged.

Obverse Legend CAROLUS D G M B F ET H REX — Charles by the grace of God King of Great Britain France and Ireland

Reverse Legend IUSTITIA THRONUM FIRMAT — Justice strengthens the throne

Obverse Bust of king; no mintmark.

Reverse Large plume dividing date 1646.

C12D-140 VG £150 F £300

Exeter Mint

Two issues were struck at Exeter. The first resembles the common Tower mint issues except that that it is dated (1644) and has mintmark rose. The second issue is easily identifiable; it is also dated 1644 and has a large rose in the centre of the reverse.

Obverse Legend CAROLUS D G M B F ET HI REX — Charles by the grace of God King of Great Britain France and Ireland

Reverse Legend THRO IUSTI FIRMAT 1644 — Justice strengthens the throne 1644

Obverse Bust of king; mintmark rose.

Reverse Royal shield.

C12D-145 VG £60 F £100 VF £300

As previous, but large rose in the centre of the reverse.

C12D-150 VG £80 F £140 VF £350

Worcester or Salopia (Shropshire)

This issue is very crude in style with a tall bust of little detail. It is easily identified by its design, the mintmark lis and the reverse legend.

Obverse Legend CAROLUS D G M B F ET H REX — Charles by the grace of God King of Great Britain France and Ireland

Reverse Legend CHRISTO AUSPICE REGNO — I reign under the auspices of Christ

Obverse Crude bust of king; mintmark lis.

Reverse Crude round shield.

C12D-155 VG £200 F £400 VF —

During Charles I's reign Briot struck a pattern two twopence, with the king's bust on the obverse and two 'C's joined with a crown on the reverse. While classed as a pattern, this issue is fairly common and obviously saw circulation. As collectors may come across this issue we have noted it.

Commonwealth 1649–1660

Halfgroats were struck throughout the Commonwealth period; all bearing no legends, date or mintmark. The halfgroat is virtually identical to the penny except for the Roman numeral II above the reverse shields denoting the denomination.

Obverse Legend None.

Reverse Legend None.

Obverse Arms of St George within wreath.

Reverse Arms of St George and Ireland with II above.

COM2D-005 VG £22 F £35 VF £70 EF £125

Charles II 1660–1685

Hammered Issue 1660 -1662

Charles II's hammered and machine-made issues are fairly common. While they were only struck for a few years, large quantities and several varieties were produced. All issues have the denomination in Roman numerals (II) behind the king's bust but are easily distinguished from Charles I's issues by the distinct portrait of Charles II and the obverse legend reading CAROLUS II instead of just CAROLUS. They were all struck at the Tower mint.

First Issue

Obverse Legend CAROLUS II DG MAG BRIT FR ET H REX — Charles II by the grace of God King of Great Britain France and Ireland

Reverse Legend CHRISTO AUSPICE REGNO — I reign under the auspices of Christ

Obverse Bust of king with no mark of value and no inner circles; mintmark crown.

Reverse Royal shield over cross; no mintmark.

C22DH-005 VG £15 F £30 VF £60 EF £120

Second Issue

As previous, but with mark of value behind the king's bust and mintmark crown on obverse, none on reverse.

C22DH-010 VG £80 F £200 VF £400 EF rare

As previous, but mintmark also on reverse. This issue was machine-made and is usually much rounder than others.

C22DH-015 VG £14 F £30 VF £60 EF £120

This issue was also machine-made.

Legends As previous.

Obverse Bust of king to edge of coin, the crown has a single arch and the legend starts at bottom left of coin.

Reverse As previous.

C22DH-020 VG £16 F £35 VF £70 EF £140

Third Issue

This issue was hammered and coins were often fairly badly struck.

Legends As previous.

Obverse Bust of king in an inner circle, value behind the head and the legend starts at the top of the coin; mintmark crown.

Reverse As previous.

C22DH-025 VG £15 F £30 VF £60 EF £120

Three Halfpence

Elizabeth I 1558–1603

The penny-halfpenny, or three-halfpence, was introduced in Elizabeth I's third and fourth issues as part of a plan to produce large quantities of coins of varying denominations and high metal content. It depicts the bust of the queen with a rose behind on the obverse and the royal shield with the date above on the reverse; a mintmark can be found at the beginning of the obverse and reverse legend. All three halfpence issues were struck at the Tower mint. Although this denomination may easily be confused with the threepence or three-farthings which were both produced at the time, the diameters of the coins vary and, for unclipped specimens, are as follows:

threepence: 1561 large flan 21 mm, all others 19 mm

three-halfpence: 1561 large flan 17 mm, all others 16 mm

three-farthings: 14 mm flan

However, halfgroats and pennies were also struck under Elizabeth. To distinguish the three-halfpence from these, collectors should bear in mind that the halfgroat and penny omit the rose behind the queen's bust and the date except for an extremely rare 1558 penny which is dated but can easily be identified since no three-halfpences were issued that year.

Obverse Legend E. D. G. ROSA SINE SPINA — Elizabeth by the grace of God a rose without a thorn

Reverse Legend CIVITAS LONDON — City of London

Obverse Crowned bust of queen with rose behind; mintmark as listed below.

Reverse Royal arms with date above; mintmark at start of legend.

Mintmark Pheon (1561–1562, 1564), rose (1565), portcullis (1566), lion (1567), coronet (1567–1569), castle (1570), ermine (1572–1573), acorn (1572–1574), eglantine (1573–1577), plain cross (1578–1579), long cross (1581) or sword (1582).

EL3HD-005 VG £25 F £50 VF £100

No three-halfpences were struck after 1582 and the denomination was discontinued because both James I and Charles I produced large quantities of halfpennies and farthings.

Penny

The silver penny probably was first introduced in England during the reign of Offa in 757 AD. The origin of the word is uncertain but possibly comes from the German *pfennig* which was a German denomination. The issues were similar in size and weight to the continental *deniers* of this period. The abbreviation 'd' came from the Roman denomination *denarius* and was used up until the 1970s. The penny up until the reign of Edward III was the most important denomination and from then on was produced during every reign and is in circulation today.

William I 1066–1087

William I continued the previous, Anglo-Saxon system of coinage with the silver penny being the only denomination struck. As it was a fairly large denomination at the time, when smaller monetary units were needed, pennies were cut in half or even quarters. Most pennies have a facing bust of the king on the obverse, which was a departure from the sideways bust of most earlier Anglo-Saxon coins, and a design surrounded by the legend with the moneyer's name and the mint on the reverse. Of the eight major types of pennies, the most famous and popular is the Pax (Peace) penny, produced at most mints in 1086–1087 and thought to reflect the peace that prevailed after the conquest, as powerful notables pledged their allegiance to the king.

To satisfy the demand for coinage, some 70 mints were active during William's reign, but it was the moneyers who were personally responsible for maintaining the weight (20 to 22 grains, 1.3 to 1.4 grams for pennies) and the silver fineness of the coins they produced. So although there was only a small amount of space on the reverse for the 'identification details', the moneyer's name was considered more important than the mint and rarely abbreviated, albeit often 'misspelled'. The moneyer's name begins the legend after a small cross and is usually followed by ON and then the town's name; for example '+ GODRIC ON LEMRE' i.e. 'Godric of Leicester'. One should note that letters are sometimes unintelligible due to the poor cutting of dies while certain letters, such as 'N', are often reversed and 'U' is written as a 'V'. In cases where the legend is particularly bad, a coin might be traced through the moneyer's name, specialist books and an elimination process. Below we list the various mints and the abbreviations of their name that are most commonly found on the coins, although it should be stressed that more varieties could very possibly exist — and we have listed the coins of William I and William II together as the two reigns are so similar in this respect.

William I & William II Mints

Rarity	Mints	Abbreviations
RR	Barnstaple	BARD — BARDI
RR	Bath	BADN
RR	Bedford	BED — BD — BEDEFO
RRR	Bedwyn	BEDEWIND
RRR	Bridport	BRDPHT –BRIPUT — BRID
RR	Bristol	BRIGCTSO — BRICSI — BRICA — BRI
RR	Bury St Edmunds	EDM DM
RR	Cambridge	GRINNT — GRANT
R	Canterbury	CATPAI –CNT –C — CANTO — EANT — CNTLI
RRR	Cardiff	CAIRDI — CARITI
RR	Chester	LECI — CESTRE — LEGECE — CESTR
RR	Chichester	CISSAN — CICEST

Rarity	Mints	Abbreviations
RRR	Christchurch	TWIN — TPIN
RR	Colchester	CO — COLE — COLEC — COLI — COEC
RRR	Cricklade	CRIC
RR	Derby	DRBI — DERBI
RRR	Devitum (probably St Davids, Wales)	DEVITUM
RR	Dorchester	DORECES
R	Dover	DOF R — DOI — DOVOR
RR	Durham	DUNE — DUN
RR	Exeter	IEXEC — IEXE — EXECSI — EXECI — EXCI
RR	Gloucester	GLPEC — GEP — GLE — GLEPI
RRR	Guildford	GILDEF — GLDF
RR	Hastings	AESTI — HIEST
RR	Hereford	HEREFORI — HRF
RR	Hertford	HRTFR — RETEF
RR	Huntingdon	HVNTEN — HVTD — H — HVT — HV
RRR	Hythe	HIDEN
RR	Ilchester	GIVELCSTI — GIF
R	Ipswich	GIP — GIPE — GIPSP
RRR	Launceston	STEFNI
RR	Leicester	LEMRE — LEGRI
RR	Lewes	LIEWIE — LAEPES
R	Lincoln	LINCOLNE — LINCOLN — LINC — LINI
R	London	LVNDN –LVNDNE — LVNDENI — LVN — LI — LVNI — LVI — LOUN
RR	Maldon (Essex)	MIEL — MLD
RRR	Malmesbury	MALME
RRR	Marlborough	MIERLEBH
RRR	Maint	MAINT
RR	Northampton	HMTVI — HATVI
RR	Norwich	NORI — N — NORDPI — NODP — NORDI –NORDPIC — NORD
RR	Nottingham	SNOTINGI — SNOTI
R	Oxford	OXSN — OXNE — OXSI — OXI — OXNEF
RRR	Peterborough	BURI
RRR	Pevensey	PEFNESE
RRR	Rhuddlan	RUDILI
RRR	Rochester	ROF ECS
RRR	Romney	RV — RVME — RUMN
RR	Salisbury	SIER — SIERBI — SEBR
RRR	Sandwich	SANDP
RRR	Shaftesbury	SCF — SCIEF — S
RRR	Shrewsbury	SCRUB
RR	Southwark	SDEP — SVDE — SVDEP
RRR	Stafford	STEFFOR — STAEF
R	Stamford	STN — STI
RRR	Steyning	STNI — STNIG
RRR	Sudbury	SVBR — SVD — SVDI
RRR	Tamworth	TAMP
RRR	Taunton	TV — TANT — TNT
RR	Thetford	DEOTFORI — DEOTF — DTFI — DTFRDI
RRR	Totnes	TOTN
RR	Wallingford	PALL — P — PAL — PALI — PALLIG — PA
RRR	Wareham	PERE
RRR	Warwick	PERI — VERI — PERP

Rarity	Mints	Abbreviations
RRR	Watchet	PICEDI
RR	Wilton	PILTV — PILTUNAP
RRR	Winchcombe	WINCL — PNCL
RR	Winchester	PINC — PICES — PNCE — PINCE
RRR	Worcester	PIH — PIHR
RR	York	EOF ERP — EOF I — EOI — IIIFERP — EFR — EFRPI — EFRP — EOF E — EFRPICI

Rarity of Mints

We have listed all main issues of William I and II. The prices given refer to common mints. All mints with a single 'R' would fall under this pricing. As a rule mints with 'RR' would be worth approximately 50% more. Mints with 'RRR' are extremely rare and could be worth twice as much as the prices given. This rarity system however is only a guide because with the use of metal detectors more coins are being found and the rarity of a mint can quickly change. Also demand for various mints can change with collectors' interest.

Collecting Hints

William I pennies can usually be found in Fine to VF condition and, as most have come from hoards, they will have an attractive appearance. However, all coins are fairly fragile and should be handled with care as it is not uncommon for them to break when mistreated; bent coins should never be straightened. In some cases the legends may be blundered or damaged but collectors should ensure that the moneyer's name and mint are legible. Many of the provincial mints are reasonably plentiful and some collectors collect by mint, others try to obtain representative examples of all eight major types.

Profile, Cross Fleury Issue 1066–1068

Obverse Legend PILLEMUS REX (I or A) — King William

Reverse Legend Moneyer's name and mint.

Obverse Left profile of king crowned, with sceptre.

Reverse Cross fleury with annulet at centre.

W11D-005 VG £125 F £275 VF £475

Bonnet Issue 1068–1071

Obverse Legend PILLEMUS REX (I or A) — King William

Reverse Legend Moneyer's name and mint.

Obverse Crowned facing bust of king with two fillets falling from crown each side of head, looking like a bonnet.

Reverse Cross voided with annulet in centre, pellet (or dot) between two crescents at end of each limb.

W11D-010 VG £110 F £250 VF £450

Canopy Issue 1071–1074

Obverse Legend PILLEMUS REX (I) — King William

Reverse Legend Moneyer's name and mint.

Obverse Crowned facing bust within canopy supported by two columns.

Reverse Double quadrilateral with incurved sides, fleur at the angles, annulet in centre.

W11D-015 VG £140 F £300 VF £500

Two Sceptres Issue 1074–1077

Obverse Legend PILLEM REX ANGLOR — William King of the English

Reverse Legend Moneyer's name and mint.

Obverse Crowned facing bust of king with sceptre either side of bust.

Reverse Cross fleury with annulet in centre over saltire botonnée.

W11D-020 VG £140 F £275 VF £475

Two Stars Issue 1077–1080

Obverse Legend PILLEM REX AN. — William King of the English

Reverse Legend Moneyer's name and mint.

Obverse Crowned facing bust of king with a star at either side.

Reverse Cross botonnée over quadrilateral with incurved sides, annulet in centre.

W11D-025 VG £140 F £275 VF £475

Sword Issue 1080–1083

Obverse Legend PILLELM REX I. — King William I

Reverse Legend Moneyer's name and mint.

Obverse Crowned facing bust of king holding sword in his right hand.

Reverse Cross pattée over quadrilateral with incurved sides, fleury at angles.

W11D-030 VG £150 F £300 VF £500

Right Profile, Cross and Trefoils Issue 1083–1086

This issue, which was only produced at the London mint, has recently been found struck in lead. The original dies were used and it is uncertain whether this issue is a trial striking or, more likely, a forgery.

Obverse Legend PILLELM REX — King William

Reverse Legend Moneyer's name and mint.

Obverse Crowned bust to right facing sceptre.

Reverse Cross pattée with annulet in centre with a voided trefoil in each angle.

W11D-035 VG £150 F £325 VF £550

Pax Issue 1086–1087

Obverse Legend PILLELM REX — King William

Reverse Legend Moneyer's name and mint.

Obverse Crowned facing bust of king holding sceptre; there are three different styles of crown in this issue.

Reverse Cross pattée, in each angle an annulet containing one letter of PAXS (peace).

W11D-040 VG £100 F £200 VF £325

William II 1087–1100

William II was the second son of William I and succeeded him in 1087. He continued to strike pennies but standards of production progressively deteriorated, with badly produced dies being used and the resultant coins often having blundered legends and weak flat parts. This can make it difficult to decipher the mint and moneyer's name. There are five main designs of William II's coins which, like those of his father, were struck throughout the country despite the fact that many mints closed during his reign so that only 34 remained active at his death, as opposed to over fifty during the earlier part of his reign.

Collecting Hints

All William II coins are rare and usually of poor quality. Collectors should try to obtain a Fine example, with lettering clear enough to make out the mint name.

Profile Issue 1087–1090

Obverse Legend PILLEM R. — King William

Reverse Legend Moneyer's name and mint.

Obverse Crowned bust right, holding a sword.

Reverse Cross pattée with annulet at centre over cross fleury.

W21D-005 VG £200 F £375 VF £700

Cross in Quatrefoil Issue 1090–1093

Obverse Legend PILLELM RE (X or sometimes I) — King William

Reverse Legend Moneyer's name and mint.

Obverse Crowned bust facing, holding sword.

Reverse Quatrefoil with pellet at each angle enclosing a cross pattée with annulet at centre.

W21D-010 VG £200 F £375 VF £700

Cross Voided Issue 1093–1096

Obverse Legend PILLELM R(I, A, EX or sometimes EI) — King William

Reverse Legend Moneyer's name and mint.

Obverse Facing crowned bust between two stars; except for the Dover, Hastings, Northampton and Norwich mints which omit the stars.

Reverse Voided cross pattée with annulet in centre over a cross annulettée.

W21D-015 VG £200 F £375 VF £700

Cross Pattée and Fleury Issue 1096–1099

Obverse Legend PILLELM RE(X or sometimes I) — King William

Reverse Legend Moneyer's name and mint.

Obverse Facing crowned bust of king holding sword.

Reverse Cross pattée over a cross fleury.

W21D-020 VG £200 F £400 VF £800

Cross Fleury and Piles Issue 1099–1100

The coins of this issue are very blundered.

Obverse Legend PILLELM (I) RI — King William

Reverse Legend Moneyer's name and mint.

Obverse Crowned facing bust holding a sceptre in right hand and a star to right of bust.

Reverse Cross fleury with a pile surmounted by a pellet in each angle.

W21D-025 VG £200 F £400 VF £800

Henry I 1100–1135

The penny continued to be the main denomination during Henry's relatively long reign because although the halfpenny was introduced, it proved very unpopular and only three or four specimens are known today. Fifteen major types of pennies were issued yet the quality of production continued to be poor. Coins were struck at various mints countrywide and it is obvious from the early issues that little central control could be imposed on the activities of the moneyers who made a very large seniorage or profit by producing coins that were underweight and below fineness. In 1124, Henry finally summoned the moneyers to Winchester and called them to account for their activities; a number of them were even mutilated for issuing coins of inferior quality. As a result, the coinage did improve in fineness and weight, although not always in production.

Around 54 mints were intermittently active during this period and, as previously, the mint and moneyer's name were included in the coin's reverse legend which usually starts with a small cross followed by the moneyer's name, the word ON and the mint. Again, the moneyer's name was written in full even if long but the town name might well be abbreviated, often to a few letters. Thus for example, a coin may read '+ AHGEMVND:ION:C', i.e. + moneyer's name of C (Canterbury, abbreviated due to a long name), or '+ RODBERT:ON:CAN', i.e. + moneyer's name of CAN (Canterbury, not abbreviated as much due to the moneyer's shorter name). Words are usually separated by two pellets (:) and it should be noted that letters were often left out or legends were blundered because of bad dies. Owing to the originally poor quality of the coin, it is often impossible to identify the mint. The mints are listed below, with some of the abbreviation often found on the coin.

Henry I Mints

Rarity	Mints	Abbreviations
RR	Barnstaple	BARD
RRR	Bath	BA — BADA
RRR	Bedford	
RR	Bristol	BRIS — BRISTO
RR	Bury St Edmunds	SAN EDMN — SEDM
RRR	Cambridge	
R	Canterbury	C — CAN — CATN — CANTLEI
RRR	Cardiff	
RRR	Carlisle	CARLI — CARD
RR	Chester	CESTRE — LEGL
RR	Chichester	CIC — CICES
RRR	Christchurch (Twynham)	TVEHAM — TPN
RR	Colchester	COLE — COL
RRR	Derby	DERBIP — DERBEREI
RR	Dorchester	DOREC
RR	Dover	DOI — DOF
RR	Durham	DVRHAM
RRR	Exeter	EX
RRR	Gloucester	GLOWA — GLE
RRR	Hastings	HIEST — HAS
RRR	Hereford	HEREF
RRR	Huntingdon	HUN
RRR	Ilchester	IVELCE
RRR	Ipswich	GIPE
RRR	Launceston	LANTSA
RRR	Leicester	LE — LEI — LECE
RRR	Lewes	LIEIP — LEP
RR	Lincoln	LINC
R	London	LVN — LVND — LVNDEN
RR	Northampton	NORH — NORHAM
RR	Norwich	NORPIC — NOR — NORPI — NORDE
RRR	Nottingham	NO —NOT —SNOT — SNOTI
RR	Oxford	OXENN — OX
RRR	Pembroke	PEI
RRR	Pevensey	
RRR	Rochester	ROFI
RR	Romney	RUME
RR	Salisbury	SEBR — SERR
RR	Sandwich	SAN
RRR	Shaftesbury	S — SEFTE
RRR	Shrewsbury	
RRR	Southampton	
RR	Southwark	SVDPE — SVTP
RRR	Stafford	
RR	Stamford	
RRR	Sudbury	SVD — SUTB
RRR	Tamworth	
RRR	Taunton	TANTV
RR	Thetford	TET — TETF — DTF
RRR	Totnes	
RRR	Wallingford	WALL
RRR	Wareham	PERA — WARE
RRR	Warwick	WAR — PARPIC
RRR	Watchet	
RRR	Wilton	PILTV — PIL
RRR	Winchcombe	
RR	Winchester	PINCE — PIN
RRR	Worcester	PIRE — PIRECES
RR	York	EVER — EBO

Rarity of Mints

The most common mints are 'R' while the rarest are 'RRR'. We have listed prices for each issue and these refer to the most common mints (R). It is often difficult to identify mints due to the poor condition of the coins. As a general rule, issues with 'RR' are worth approximately 50% more and those with 'RRR' 100% more of the prices given. The rarities of issues will change as more coins come on to the market with the help of metal detectors, and the varying demands of collectors.

Collecting Hints

As previously noted, most of Henry I's coinage is of fairly poor quality. Collectors wishing to obtain an example of this reign might well choose a class XIV or XV penny as, being struck after 1124, they tend to be of better quality and have clearer mints. Many Henry I pennies have a small cut in the edge, produced by contemporaries checking the fineness of the coin, which sometimes makes them unsightly and a bad cut reduces the coin's value. Furthermore, a fair number of coins turn up cracked, often because of the small clip in the edge, and those with bad cracks should be avoided as they can break easily. Dealers have been known to send out a cracked coin in one piece, only to have it arrive in two or more.

Annulet Issue 1101–1102

Obverse Legend HENRI (CUS) REX N — King Henry

Reverse Legend Moneyer's name and mint.

Obverse Crowned facing bust with an annulet either side of neck.

Reverse Cross fleury with annulet in centre and in each angle three pellets on a pile which rests on the inner circle.

H11D-005 VG £200 F £450 VF £900

Profile Issue 1102–1103

Obverse Legend HENRI REX — King Henry

Reverse Legend Moneyer's name and mint.

Obverse Crowned bust facing left holding sceptre.

Reverse Cross fleury with annulet at centre.

H11D-010 VG £200 F £450 VF £900

Pax Issue 1103–1104

The PAX (peace) issue is thought to refer to the Alton treaty which marked Henry's success in negotiating peace with his brother Robert and quelling a rebellion amongst Robert's supporters.

Obverse Legend HENRY REX (EI) — King Henry

Reverse Legend Moneyer's name and mint.

Obverse Facing crowned bust of king with an annulet on right shoulder and a trefoil on the left.

Reverse PAX between two beaded lines, two annulets above and below.

H11D-015 VG £250 F £500 VF £900

Annulets and Piles Issue 1104–1105

Obverse Legend HENRIC RE — King Henry

Reverse Legend Moneyer's name and mint.

Obverse Facing crowned bust with sceptre over right shoulder.

Reverse Four annulets between four piles.

H11D-020 VG £250 F £500 VF £900

Voided Cross and Fleurs Issue 1105–1106

Obverse Legend HENRIC REX. — King Henry

Reverse Legend Moneyer's name and mint.

Obverse Facing crowned bust with sceptre over right shoulder and star in field.

Reverse Voided cross with fleur in each angle.

H11D-025 VG £325 F £700 VF £1,400

Pointing Bust and Stars Issue 1106–1107

Obverse Legend HENRI REX. — King Henry

Reverse Legend Moneyer's name and mint.

Obverse Crowned bust three quarters right holding sceptre in right hand and pointing with left; three stars in the right part of the field.

Reverse Cross pattée over saltire with a star in each angle.

H11D-030 VG £400 F £1,000 VF £2,000

Quatrefoil and Stars Issue 1108–1109

Obverse Legend HENRI RE (X) — King Henry

Reverse Legend Moneyer's name and mint.

Obverse Crowned facing bust.

Reverse Quatrefoil with piles, annulet and pellet in centre.

H11D-035 VG £200 F £450 VF £800

Larger Profile, Cross and Annulets Issue 1109–1110

Obverse Legend HENRI REX. — King Henry

Reverse Legend Moneyer's name and mint.

Obverse Crowned bust facing left, facing sceptre.

Reverse Cross with annulet in each angle.

H11D-040 VG £400 F £800 VF £1,600

Cross in Quatrefoil Issue 1107–1108

Obverse Legend HENRI REX. — King Henry

Reverse Legend Moneyer's name and mint.

Obverse Crowned facing bust with a sceptre in right hand and a star and a quatrefoil of annulets to the right of bust. A quatrefoil of annulets is four annulets next to each other touching in a diamond shape.

Reverse Cross in quatrefoil.

H11D-045 VG £300 F £650 VF £1,300

Full Face, Cross Fleury Issue 1114–1119

Obverse Legend HENRICUS REX A (N) — Henry King of England

Reverse Legend Moneyer's name and mint.

Obverse Crowned facing bust.

Reverse Cross fleury with annulet in centre.

H11D-050 VG £175 F £375 VF £650

Double Inscription Issue 1110–1114

Obverse Legend HENR (IR). — King Henry

Reverse Legend In most cases the outer circle has the name of the moneyer and the inner circle the mint from which the coin was issued.

Obverse Crowned bust facing left, holding sceptre.

Reverse Double inscription between three beaded circles, the outer one divided by four quatrefoils, small cross in centre.

H11D-055 VG £400 F £800 VF £1,600

Smaller Profile, Cross and Annulet Issue 1119–1120

Obverse Legend HENRICUS — Henry

Reverse Legend Moneyer's name and mint.

Obverse Small crowned bust facing left, a rosette in the field.

Reverse Cross pattée with an annulet enclosing a pellet in each angle.

H11D-060 VG £250 F £450 VF £900

Star in Lozenge Fleury Issue 1120–1122

Obverse Legend HENRICUS — Henry

Reverse Legend Moneyer's name and mint.

Obverse Crowned bust left holding sceptre.

Reverse Quadrilateral with incurved sides, fleur at each angle, trefoil of annulets between each pair of fleurs, star in centre.

H11D-065 VG £250 F £450 VF £900

Pellets in Quatrefoil Issue 1122–1124

Obverse Legend HENRICUS R(EX) — King Henry

Reverse Legend Moneyer's name and mint.

Obverse Crowned facing bust holding sceptre, a star to the right of bust and in a few cases an annulet on the king's shoulder.

Reverse Quatrefoil with star in centre and pellets on limbs, a lis in each angle.

H11D-070 VG £130 F £260 VF £450

Quadrilateral on Cross Fleury Issue 1125–1136

Obverse Legend HENRICUS — Henry

Reverse Legend Moneyer's name and mint.

Obverse Crowned bust three quarters facing left, holding sceptre.

Reverse Quadrilateral with incurved sides over cross fleury.

H11D-075 VG £100 F £225 VF £400

Stephen 1135–1154

Stephen's reign was a period of almost dual monarchy, as well as civil war and anarchy. Henry I had wanted his daughter Matilda to succeed him but both she and his nephew Stephen claimed the throne when he died. The cousins arrived in England from France almost simultaneously and set up rival courts, in Bristol and London respectively. The location of their courts was reflected in the minting of their coins, with Stephen's coins being struck mostly in the east and south of the country while Matilda's were in the west. However, with the prevalent uncertainty a number of powerful Earls, especially those in the Northern Border region, started to strike coins in their own names. All the coins produced at this time were pennies and although the quality was very poor, numerous designs and styles were used since there were so many issuers, die makers and mints. We have listed the five main types of Stephen pennies and although there are many variants of each type, particularly the 'Watford' one, the variants themselves are rare, often unique, albeit in appalling condition. As with Henry I's coins, the moneyer's name and the mint, often abbreviated, are found on the reverse, but as the legends are very blundered it is often impossible to decipher the mint even on a Fine condition coin. Listed below are the mint names with their usual abbreviation but it is important to remember that letters were often omitted or joined together by their vertical stem to save space, especially if the moneyer's name was long. In fact, many of the mints for Stephen pennies can not be worked out.

Stephen Mints

Rarity	Mints	Abbreviations
RRR	(possibly Peterborough)	BUR
RRR	Bedford	BED
RRR	Bramber	BRAN
RRR	Bristol	BRIST
RR	Bury St Edmunds	EDM
RRR	Cambridge	
R	Canterbury	CANT
RRR	Cardiff	CARDI
RRR	Carlisle	CARDI
RR	Castle Rising	RIS
RR	Chester	CES
RRR	Chichester	CICES
RRR	Cipen (possibly Ipswich)	CIPEN
RRR	Colchester	COLE
RRR	Corbridge	
RRR	Derby	DURBI
RRR	Dorchester	
RRR	Dover	DOFVER

Rarity	Mints	Abbreviations
RRR	Durham	DVNHO
RRR	Eden (possibly Carlisle)	EDEN
RRR	Exeter	EXE
RRR	Gloucester	GLO
RR	Hastings	HAS
RRR	Hendon (near Hull)	HEDON
RRR	Hereford	HERE
RRR	Huntingdon	HUN
RRR	Ipswich	GIP
RRR	Launceston	LANSA
RRR	Leicester	LEREC
RRR	Lewes	LEPE —LEV —LEP — LIEIP
R	Lincoln	LINCOL — NIC
R	London	LUND
RRR	Newcastle	NI —NE —NEVCAS — NIVCA
RRR	Northampton	NORHAN
RRR	Norwich	NORPT
RRR	Nottingham	SNOT
RR	Oxford	OXEN
RRR	Pembroke	PAN
RRR	Pevensey	PEVEN
RRR	Rye	RIE
RRR	Salisbury	SAL
RRR	Sandwich	SAN
RRR	Shaftesbury	SCIEFT
RRR	Shrewsbury	SALOPES
RRR	Southampton	
RRR	Southwark	SUTHGEW
RRR	Stafford	STAFO
RR	Stamford	STANF
RRR	Steyning	(S)TEN
RRR	Sudbury	SUD
RRR	Swansea	SWENSI — SVENSHI
RRR	Tamworth	
RRR	Taunton	TANTVN
R	Thetford	FORT — TETFOR
RRR	Tutbury	
RRR	Wareham	PARHAM
RRR	Warwick	PAR
RRR	Watchet	WACET
RR	Wilton	PILT
RR	Winchester	PINCE
RRR	Worcester	PIREC
RRR	York	EVER

Rarity of Mints

As with previous reigns, we have listed rarities of mints. As mentioned however, it is impossible to identify most coins' mints. A clear, identifiable mint adds value to a coin and mints with 'RR' are very rare while those with 'RRR' are extremely rare. An issue with 'RRR' could be worth twice as much as the price given while an issue with 'RR' could be worth up to 50% more. Rarity of these issues is always changing due to more coins being found.

Collecting Hints

Stephen's pennies are always popular and not as rare as one might expect, especially the Watford type. By contrast, coins of Matilda or the Earls are very rare and infrequently appear on the market although the advent of metal detectors may alter the situation dramatically at any time. Should collectors require just one example from the reign, they should look for a Watford type as, with patience, these coins can be found in Fine even though their average condition is only fair. Collectors should also try to obtain a coin with a clear mint, keeping in mind that the mint's name is often obliterated in coins of even Fine condition, because like Henry I's pennies, those of Stephen are crude, frequently struck on irregular shaped flans and often off-centre. Specimens with a round flan and a centred strike are more desirable and rare. Collectors interested in coins of Matilda and the Earls should be prepared for a long wait and plenty of searching. These coins are all very rare, very desirable and rarely come on to the market.

Watford Issue

The issue derives its name from a hoard found in Watford and contains several minor varieties including no inner circle on the obverse, annulets in the crown or crescents before the nose.

Obverse Legend STIEFNE (R, RE or REX) — King Stephen

Reverse Legend Moneyer's name and mint.

Obverse Crowned bust facing right holding sceptre.

Reverse Cross moline with a fleur in each angle.

ST1D-005 VG £100 F £220 VF £450

Watford Issue with different Obverse Legend

The obverse legend of this issue, PERERIC(M), cannot actually be translated and is thought to have been constructed to look like HENRICUS, the name of the previous monarch. Wishing to extricate themselves from the conflict over the throne and realising the importance of supplying adequate quantities of coinage during this turbulent period, the moneyers seem to have adopted this novel solution which, in part, was acceptable because the vast majority of the population were illiterate.

Obverse Legend PERERIC(M)

Reverse Legend Moneyer's name and mint.

Obverse Crowned bust facing right holding sceptre

Reverse Cross moline with a fleur in each angle.

ST1D-010 VG £200 F £450 VF —

Voided Cross Issue

Obverse Legend STIEFNE — Stephen

Reverse Legend Moneyer's name and mint.

Obverse Crowned bust, three-quarters left holding sceptre.

Reverse Plain cross voided with a mullet in each angle.

ST1D-015 VG £150 F £300 VF £600

Profile, Cross and Piles Issue

There is also a variety where the bust faces right rather than left.

Obverse Legend STIEFNE — Stephen

Reverse Legend Moneyer's name and mint

Obverse Crowned bust facing left holding sceptre.

Reverse Cross fleury with a pile and a trefoil of annulets in each angle.

ST1D-020 VG £200 F £450 VF £900

Awbridge or Cross Pommée Issue

So named because many coins of this type were found in a hoard in Awbridge.

Obverse Legend STIEFNE — Stephen

Reverse Legend Moneyer's name and mint.

Obverse Bearded crowned bust facing three quarters left and holding sceptre in right hand.

Reverse Voided cross pommée with a lis in angles.

ST1D-025 VG £150 F £300 VF £600

Matilda

The style of Matilda's issues tended to be cruder than that of the regular issues of Stephen, reflecting the production of dies and coins in the provincial mints.

Matilda Mints

Mints	Abbreviations
Bristol	BRIS
Calne ?	CA
Canterbury ?	CA
Gloucester	GLO
Oxford	OX
Wareham	

Collecting Hints

All Matilda pennies are exremely rare and it is very difficult to obtain an example in any condition.

The design of this style is quite similar to Stephen's Watford type penny, but there is also a variety of the reverse with cross pattée over cross fleury.

Obverse Legend MATILDI IMP. — Empress Matilda

Reverse Legend Moneyer's name and mint.

Obverse Crowned bust facing right holding a sceptre.

Reverse Cross moline with a fleur in each angle.

MT1D-005 VG £1,000 F £2,000 VF £3,500

Henry II 1154–1189

Peace was restored in England under Henry II, who ascended the throne in 1154 as the first Plantagenet king, but at first Stephen's coinage continued to be minted and retained its poor quality, with many coins being underweight and of low silver fineness. To restore public confidence in the currency a new standard and type of coin, the cross and crosslets penny, was introduced in 1158 and is often referred to as the Tealby penny, after the hoard in which many of these coins were found. A total of thirty-one mints was employed in the recoinage but, once the new issue was complete, only twelve mints were allowed to remain active and this reduction began the gradual decline in the number of mints used to strike English coins.

The Tealby coinage was acceptable in terms of weight and silver fineness but the overall quality of production was appalling so in 1180, Henry II introduced a new style of coinage, the short-cross penny, with better made dies. Despite being fairly ugly, the style remained more or less unaltered until 1247 which was quite a departure from the past practice of changing it every few years. However, retaining a single style gave a sense of greater stability both to the currency and the country itself. Greater uniformity was also achieved by the further reduction in the number of mints. As with previous coinages, the moneyer's name and mint, often abbreviated, were on the reverse which also bore a small cross in the centre with four pellets in each quarter. This enabled merchants to make halfpennies and farthings out of the pennies by simply cutting along the lines of the cross, thus producing an abundance of change since the penny was still the only denomination produced throughout Henry's reign.

Tealby Issue

Although six different designs were used on the obverse of the Tealby penny, the layout of the reverse remained unchanged. The legend consists of a small cross preceding the moneyer's name which is given in full and followed by ON (for 'of') and the mint name, often abbreviated. For example, a coin might read 'ROBERD ON GIPE', Roberd of Ipswich or 'RICARD ON LERE', Ricard of Leicester. In identifying the mints it is important to bear in mind that, apart from being misspelled on occasion, town names were often different from their modern equivalents and were sometimes shortened or even lengthened, often by an additional E at the end, so as to accommodate the size of the die; in general, the longer a moneyer's name, the shorter the mint abbreviation. Collectors should also remember that varieties of some mints exist. Owing to the poor quality of striking, the mint is often unclear but if the moneyer's name is legible it is possible to identify the mint with reference to specialist books and a process of elimination aided by the fact that in some cases there was only one moneyer of that name working in the country.

Henry II Tealby Issue Mints

Rarity	Mint	Abbreviation
RRR	Bedford	BED
RRR	Bristol	BRIS
R	Bury St Edmunds	S.EDM
R	Canterbury	CANTO
R	Carlisle	CARDU
RR	Chester	CESTE
RRR	Colchester	COLE
RRR	Durham	DVNHOL
RRR	Exeter	EXC
RRR	Gloucester	GLOECE
RRR	Hereford	HEREFOR
RRR	Ilchester	IVELCE
R	Ipswich	GIPES
RRR	Launceston	LANST
RR	Leicester	LERE
RRR	Lewes	LEVAS
R	Lincoln	LINC
R	London	LUND
RR	Newcastle	NIV
RR	Northampton	NORHA
R	Norwich	NORED
RR	Oxford	OXENE
RRR	Pembroke	PAIN
RRR	Salisbury	SALEB
RRR	Shrewsbury	SALOPES
RRR	Stafford	STA
R	Thetford	TED
RRR	Wallingford	WELL
RRR	Wilton	PIL
RR	Winchester	WINC
RR	York	EVERWI

Rarity of Mints

We have given rarities of all the mints. 'R' is rare, 'RR' very rare and 'RRR' extremely rare. As mentioned, many coins even in Fine condition will not show the mint name due to poor striking. Prices for 'RR' coins are approx. 50% above those listed while those with 'RRR' are up to twice the value.

Collecting Hints

Tealby pennies are relatively easy to obtain but many suffer from weak striking, so the mint and moneyer's name may not be clear. Also, coins are often irregular in shape with parts of the legend struck off-centre resulting in flat areas untouched by a die. Collectors should try to obtain an example with a clear mint and reasonable portrait.

A: 1158–1161

Obverse Legend HENRI REX ANG — Henry King of England

Obverse Crowned facing bust with no hair, wearing armour with sceptre in right hand.

H21D-005 VG £50 F £90 VF £180

B: 1161–1165

Obverse Legend HENRY REX AN — Henry King of England

Obverse Crowned facing bust with no hair, wearing armour with sceptre in right hand. Mantle design slightly different from previous issue.

H21D-010 VG £50 F £90 VF £180

C: 1161–1165

Obverse Legend HENRI R ANG — Henry King of England

Obverse Crowned facing bust with single curl of hair. Wearing armour designed of sweeping lines. Sceptre in right hand and collar decorated.

H21D-015 VG £50 F £90 VF £180

D: 1165–1168

Obverse Legend HENRI REX — King Henry

Obverse Crowned facing bust, sceptre in right hand. Similar to H21D-015 with decorated collar and H21D-020 has a decorated shoulder.

H21D-020 VG £50 F £90 VF £180

E: 1168–1170

Obverse Legend HENRI REX A — Henry King of England

Obverse Crowned facing bust, sceptre in right hand. Mantle sweeps from left shoulder across body with shoulder not decorated.

H21D-025 VG £50 F £100 VF £200

F: 1170–1180

Obverse Legend HENRI REX — King Henry

Obverse Crowned facing bust, holding sceptre in right hand, with the king's hair in a bunch of curls to the right of his head.

H21D-030 VG £50 F £100 VF £200

Short Cross Coinage

As stated above, the short-cross coinage was introduced in 1180 and continued to be struck, virtually unchanged, for nearly 70 years, thus covering not only Henry II's reign but also those of Richard I, John I and the early part of Henry III. Furthermore, all the coins look fairly similar with identical obverse legends of HENRICUS REX. It was therefore necessary to break the short-cross coinage into classes based on small differences in, for example, the hair, lettering or facial features, so that a coin can be attributed to a particular reign by identifying its class. Collectors should bear in mind that Henry II pennies depict the king with a sceptre and tend to be larger than those of the other three monarchs while Richard I's issues tend to be more blundered. It is also important to pay particular attention to the 'X' on the obverse legend of John and Henry III pennies as a number of classes depend mainly on this one letter.

Short Cross Coinage Classes by Reign

Henry II	Richard I	John I	Henry III
1A	2	4C	6B
1B	3A	5A	6C
1C	3B	5B	7
	4A	5C	8A
	4B	6A.1	8B.1
		6A.2	8B.2
		6A.2A	8B.3

Henry II Short Cross Coinage Mints

Below we have listed all the mints which struck coins for Henry II, the mint name or abbreviation, as it is found on the coins, the moneyer and finally the class and subsection in which the moneyer struck coins. Often however a moneyer was active through several reigns and this has to be taken into account when identifying a coin's class. And once again, the mint's and moneyer's names were often misspelled and abbreviated while letters were sometimes pushed together to share the same vertical stem.

Mints	Abbreviations	Moneyers	Classes
London	LUND	Aimer	1A B C
		Alain	1A B C
		Alainv	1A B
		Alward	1B
		Davi	1B C
		Fil Aimer	1A B
		Gilebert	1C
		Godard	1B
		Henri	1A B
		Henri Pi	1A B
		Iefrei	1A 1B 1C
		Iohan	1A 1B
		Osber	1B
		Pieres	1A 1B 1C
		Pieres M	1A 1B
		Randul	1A 1B
		Raul	1B C
		Reinald	1B
		Willelm	1A B C
Carlisle	CARDI	Alain	1B C
Exeter	EXERI	Asketil	1A B
		Iordan	1A B
		Osber	1A B
		Raul	1B
		Ricard	1B C
		Roger	1B
Lincoln	NICOLE	Edmund	1B C
		Girard	1B
		Hugo	1B
		Lefwine	1B C
		Rodbert	1B
		Walter	1B
		Will.D.F.	1B
		Willelm	1B C
Northampton	NOR	Filipe	1A B
		Hugo	1A B
		Raul	1A B C
		Reinald	1A B
		Simund	1B
		Walter	1A B C
		Willelm	1A B
Norwich	NOR (possibly Northampton)	Reinald	1B C
		Willelm	1B
Oxford	OXEN	Asketil	1B
		Iefrei	1B
		Owein	1B
		Ricard	1B C
		Rodbert	1B
		Rodbt.F.B.	1B
		Sagar	1B
Wilton	WILT	Osber	1A B
		Rodbert	1A B
Winchester	WINCE	Adam	1B C
		Clement	1A B
		Gocelm	1A B C
		Henri	1A
		Osber	1A B
		Reinier	1B
		Ricard	1B
		Rodbert	1A B
Worcester	WIREC	Edrich	1B
		Godwine	1B C
		Osber	1B

Mints	Abbreviations	Moneyers	Classes
York	EVERWIC	Alain	1A B
		Efrard	1A B C
		Gerard	1B
		Hugo	1B C
		Hunfrei	1A B
		Isac	1A B
		Turkil	1A B C
		Willelm	1A B

Collecting Hints

Short-cross pennies are fairly easy to obtain and collectors should aim for an example in at least Fine condition, with a clear mint and moneyer's name.

Classes

Class 1A

Obverse Legend HENRICUS REX — King Henry

Obverse Facing crowned bust of king holding sceptre, the face is narrow and there is a square 'E' and sometimes a square 'C' in the legend, as well as pellets.

Reverse Small cross, four pellets in each quarter.

H21D-035 VG £100 F £225 VF £450

Class 1B

Obverse Legend As previous.

Obverse Facing crowned bust of king holding sceptre, his hair has two curls to left and five curls to right; pellets in the legend and the 'E' and 'C' are more rounded.

Reverse As previous.

H21D-040 VG £40 F £80 VF £160

Class 1C

Obverse Legend As previous.

Obverse Facing crowned bust of king holding sceptre. The style is becoming a little blundered now, with no stops or pellets in the legend.

Reverse As previous.

H21D-045 VG £40 F £80 VF £160

Pricing

We have priced all the coins in their classes in VG, Fine and VF condition; these prices are for the most common mints, usually London and Canterbury. We have also priced coins by mint and these prices are for the most common class of each mint; coins of a rare class would be valued at higher prices.

Mint	VG	F	VF
London	40	80	160
Carlisle	70	140	280
Exeter	65	130	260
Lincoln	60	120	220
Northampton	60	120	220
Norwich	60	120	220
Oxford	75	150	300
Wilton	70	140	280
Winchester	40	80	160
Worcester	75	150	300
York	40	80	160

Richard I 1189–1199

The pennies of the short-cross coinage continued throughout Richard I's reign and, although the quality of production became cruder, the style remained fairly similar. The obverse legend of all Richard's pennies reads HENRICUS REX (King Henry) and the reverse continued to have a small cross with four pellets in each quarter and a legend with the moneyer's name and mint; what changed from one class to another was the bust of the king. All of Richard I's issues are very much a continuation from the short cross coinage of Henry II but the classes, while similar in style, are different to those of Henry I, John and Henry II. Collectors might need to refer to all reigns when identifying a coin. The reverse legend on the coin gives the moneyer's name and the mint. The legend starts with the moneyer's name, followed by ON (of) and then the mint, which is usually abbreviated. We have listed the mint, mint abbreviation and moneyer's name and the classes which each struck to help identification.

Richard I Mints

Mints	Abbreviations	Moneyers	Classes
Canterbury	CANT	Goldwine	2–4B
		Hernaud	4B
		Io(h)an	4B
		Meinir	2–4B
		Reinald	2–4B
		Reinaud	2–4A
		Roberd	2–4B
		Samuel	4B
		Ulard	2–4B
Carlisle	CARDI	Alein	3–4B
Durham	DURE — DUNO	Adam	4A
		Alein	4A B
Exeter	EXEN	Ricard	3B
Lichfield	LIHEFE	Ioan	2
Lincoln	NICOLE	Edmund	2
		Lefwine	2
		Willelm	2
London	LUND	Aimer	2–4B
		Fulke	4A–B
		Goldwine	4A
		Henri	4A–B
		Raul	2
Northampton	NOR	Geferi	4A
		Roberd	3
		Waltir	3
Norwich	NOR	Randul	4A–B
		Willelm	4A–B
Shrewsbury	SALOP	Ive	4B
		Reinald	4A B
		Willelm	4A
Winchester	WINCE	Adam	3A
		Gocelm	2–3
		Osbern	3–4A
		Pires	4A
		Willelm	2–4
Worcester	WIREC	Osbern	2
York	EVERIC	Davi	4B
		Everard	2–4B
		Hue	2–4A
		Nicole	4B
		Turkil	2–4B

Collecting Hints

These coins while scarce are obtainable and always popular with collectors. They tend to be slightly crude in style and when available are usually found in VG to Fine condition. Several of the mints are rare and difficult to obtain. Collectors should remember when identifying a mint that the letters are sometimes blundered or missing.

John 1199–1216

The short-cross coinage continued through John's reign, with the obverse legend still reading HENRICUS REX (King Henry) and the reverse having the moneyer's name and mint around a small cross with four pellets in each quarter. The first class is fairly similar to Richard's coinage but the rest of John's pennies are of a higher standard, with neater work and a slightly more lifelike portrait. The later issues are very similar to those of Henry III. The mints and moneyers are very much a continuation from the previous reign where they have been discussed in greater detail.

Class 2

Round facing face, curls both sides of head, large pellets for eyes and a bushy beard, sceptre in hand and five or more curls in crown.

R11D-005 VG £60 F £125 VF £250

Class 3A

Long thin face with pellet eyes, seven pearls in crown with a beard of small curls, sceptre in hand.

R11D-010 VG £60 F £125 VF £250

Class 3B

Similar to above but annulet instead of pellet eyes.

R11D-015 VG £45 F £90 VF £180

Class 4A

This class includes a variety that has colon stops instead of a single stop on the reverse of the coin.
Similar to above, but beard of pellets rather than curls.

R11D-020 VG £45 F £90 VF £180

Class 4B

Very crude facing bust, the hair represented by a couple of crude curves and the beard by just a few pellets; sceptre in hand.

R11D-025 VG £45 F £90 VF £180

Pricing

Prices are for the most common type

Mint	VG	F	VF
London	45	90	180
Canterbury	45	90	180
Carlisle	100	220	400
Durham	110	250	450
Exeter	90	200	380
Lichfield	ex. rare		
Lincoln	80	150	300
Northampton	90	200	380
Norwich	90	200	380
Shrewsbury	130	250	450
Winchester	50	100	200
Worcester	ex. rare		
York	50	100	200

John Mints

Mints	Abbreviations	Moneyers	Classes
Bury St Edmunds	S.EDM — SANTEA	Fulke	5B C
Canterbury	CANT	Arnaud	5A-C
		Coldwine	4C-5C
		(H)Ernaud	4C-5C
		Hue	4C-5C
		Io(h)an	4C-5C
		Iohan B	5B-C
		Iohan M	5B-C
		Rauf	5C
		Roberd	4C-5C
		Samuel	4C-5C
		Simon	5A or 5C
		Simun	4C-5B
Carlisle	CARDI	Tomas	5B
Chichester	CICST	Pieres	5B
		Rauf	5A-B
		Simon	5A-B
		Willelm	5B
Durham	DURO — DUNO	Pieres	4C-6A
Exeter	EX	Gilebert	5A-B
		Iohan	5A-B
		Ricard	5A-B
Ipswich	GIPE	Alisandre	5B C
		Iohan	5B-C
King's Lynn	LIHEFE	Iohan	5B
		Nicole	5B
		Willelm	5B
Lincoln	NICOLE	Alain	5A
		Andreu	5A-C
		Hue	5B-C
		Iohan	5A
		Rauf	5A-B
		Ricard	5A
		Tomas	5A B
London	LUND	Abel	5C-6A
		Adam	5B-C
		Arnaud	5B
		Beneit	5B-C
		Fulke	4C-5A
		Henri	4C-5B
		Ilger	5B-6A
		Iohan	5B
		Rauf	5C-6A
		Rener	5B-C
		Ricard	4C-5B
		Ricard B	5B-C
		Ricard T	5B
		Walter	5C-6A
		Willelm	4C-5C
		Willelm B	5B-C
		Willelm L	5B-C
		Willelm T	5B-C
Northampton	NORHT	Adam	5B-C
		Randul	4C
		Roberd	5B
		Roberd T	5B
Norwich	NOR	Gifrei	5A-C
		Iohan	5A-C
		Renald	5A
		Renaud	5A-C
Oxford	OXEN	Ailwine	5B
		Henri	5B
		Miles	5B
Rhuddlan	RULA — RUTLAN — RULAN RUTN — RULTN	Halli	
		Henricus	
		Tomas	
		Simond	
Rochester	ROFE	Alisandre	5B

Mints	Abbreviations	Moneyers	Classes
Winchester	WIN	Hurfrei	5B
		Adam	5A-C
		Andreu	5B-C
		Bartelme	5B-C
		Henri	5A
		Iohan	5A-C
		Lukas	5B-C
		Miles	5A-C
		Rauf	5B-C
		Ricard	5A-B
York	EVERIC	Davi	4C-5B
		Nicole	4C-5C
		Renaud	5B
		Tomas	5B

The Rhuddlan mint, which is believed to have been active during John's reign, does not conform to the normal classes in this series. The dies are of local manufacture and so the coins are crude in style.

Collecting Hints

The coins while scarce are obtainable in all grades. They are sometimes clipped or damaged and there is no doubt that many of them saw considerable circulation. Many of these issues are very similar to those of Richard I and Henry III. Collectors might need to refer to both reigns when identifying a coin.

Class 4C

Crude facing bust, sceptre in hand. Similar to previous issues of Richard I except that the letter S in the obverse legend is reversed.

JH1D-005 VG £45 F £90 F £180

Class 5A

Facing bust holding sceptre; new neater style, 'S' is reversed, cross pommée in reverse legend. Some coins of this class have ornamented letters, with extra and often more exaggerated curves, which gives the impression that the whole legend is more ornate.

JH1D-010 VG £40 F £75 VF £150

Class 5B

Similar to above except that the 'S' is not reversed and the cross pommée has been replaced by a cross pattée.

JH1D-015 VG £40 F £75 VF £150

Class 5C

Similar to above but 'X' in obverse legend composed of four strokes in the form of a St Andrew's cross.

JH1D-020 VG £45 F £90 VF £180

Class 6A.1

Slightly coarser style with slightly taller face, 'X' in legend is composed of two strokes in the form of a St Andrew's cross.

JH1D-025 VG £40 F £75 VF £150

Class 6A.2

Similar to above but a very slightly rounder face and the 'X' in the obverse legend has arms at right angles with rounded ends.

JH1D-030 VG £40 F £75 VF £150

Class 6A.2A

Similar to above but the 'X' has arms at right angles and more rounded edges looking almost as if it is made up of four pellets.

JH1D-035 VG £35 F £70 VF £145

Muling of obverses and reverses of different classes was not uncommon during this period, particularly in Class 5.

Pricing

The prices below are for the most common types.

Mint	VG	F	VG
London	40	70	145
Bury St Edmunds	50	100	200
Canterbury	40	70	145
Carlisle	85	170	320
Chichester	60	120	240
Durham	70	140	280
Exeter	50	100	200
Ipswich	50	100	200
King's Lynn	100	200	400
Lincoln	50	100	200
Northampton	50	100	200
Norwich	50	100	200
Oxford	50	100	200
Rhuddlan	100	200	400
Rochester	90	180	360
Winchester	45	80	150
York	50	90	160

Henry III 1216–1272

The short-cross coinage continued under Henry III until 1247 and, although the mints issuing coins were reduced to six, London and Canterbury were extremely prolific. Having lasted for 67 years, the short-cross coinage was undoubtedly a success. Being of reasonable quality, acceptable design and good fineness, it was popular with the public and brought a much needed stability to the country. The only problem was that many of the coins in circulation were underweight through no fault of the moneyers, because of the illegal practice of clipping. This was facilitated by the cross on the reverse not extending to the edge of the coin, which meant that the public often could not know exactly how large the coin should be. So, in 1247, the short cross was replaced by a longer one that reached to the very edge of the coin, the rest of the design remaining mainly unaltered. Because of the introduction of the new coinage, many of the old mints were reopened to supply sufficient quantities of coins. As with the short-cross penny, the long-cross one could be cut along the lines of the cross to produce halfpennies and even farthings.

Short Cross Coinage

Henry's short-cross coinage is similar in style to that of previous reigns, especially John's, and the same system of classification is continued. The obverse legend of all classes still reads HENRICUS REX and the reverse bears the moneyer's name and mint in the legend, with a small cross in the centre and four pellets in each angle.

Henry III Short Cross Coinage Mints

Mints	Abbreviations	Moneyers	Classes
Bury St Edmunds	S.EDM — SANTEA	Io(h)an	7–8
		Norman	7
		Rauf	6B-7
		Simund	7
		Willelm	7
Canterbury	CANT	Arnold	6C

Mints	Abbreviations	Moneyers	Classes
		Henri	6B-7
		Hiun	6B-7
		Iun	7
		Io(h)an	6B-8
		Ioan Chic	7
		Ioan F.R.	7
		Nicole	7–8
		Norman	7
		Osmund	7
		Roberd	6B
		Robert	7
		Robert Vi	7
		Roger	6B-7
		Roger of R	7
		Salemun	6C-7
		Samuel	6B-7
		Simon	7
		Simun	6B-7
		Tomas	6C-7
		Walter	6B-7
		Willelm	7–8
		Willem Ta	7
Durham	DURO — DUNO	Pieres	7
London	LUND	Abel	6B-7
		Adam	7
		(H)elis	7
		Giffrei	7
		Ilger	6B-7
		Ledulf	7
		Nichole	7–8
		Rau(l)f	6B-7
		Ricard	7
		Terri	7
		Walter	6B-6C
Winchester	WIN	Henri	6C
York	EVERIC	Iohan	6C
		Peres	6C
		Tomas	6C
		Wilam	6C

Collecting Hints

These are the most common of all the short-cross coinages. They are available, often clipped, in all grades and there is no doubt that many of these coins saw considerable circulation.

Class 6B

Obverse Very tall lettering in legends with the king's face often thin.

Reverse Cross with four pellets in each quarter.

H31D-005 VG £18 F £35 VF £65

Class 6C

Obverse The king has a very pointed face with larger staring eyes. There is also a fairly scarce variety of this type with ornamental lettering in the legend.

Reverse As previous.

H31D-010 VG £18 F £35 VF £65

Class 7

Obverse The bust of the king has no neck. There are various styles of hair and eyes in this class.

Reverse As previous, but without stops between the words in the legend.

H31D-015 VG £18 F £35 VF £65

Class 8A

Obverse New style with large bust, 'X' in REX curule shaped.

Reverse As previous, mintmark cross pattée.

H31D-020 ex. rare

Class 8B.1

Obverse Similar to Class 8A.

Reverse As previous, but mintmark cross pommée.

H31D-025 VG £20 F £40 VF £75

Class 8B.2

Obverse Similar to 8B.1 but the bust is cruder with the beard being made of just a few sharp lines; wedge shaped 'X' in legend.

Reverse As previous.

H31D-030 VG £20 F £40 VF £75

Class 8B.3

Obverse As above, but very crude bust with two large pellets for eyes and four large curls for hair, 'X' in legend is a cross pommée.

Reverse As previous.

H31D-035 VG £20 F £40 VF £75

Pricing

The prices below are for the most common types.

Mint	VG	F	VG
London	18	35	65
Bury St Edmunds	25	50	100
Canterbury	18	35	65
Durham	100	200	350
Winchester	25	50	100
York	100	200	350

Long Cross Coinage 1247–1272

There are two main varieties of long-cross pennies, depending on whether a sceptre is found on the obverse or not; but within these varieties, the long-cross coinage is again broken up into classes according to slight differences of style. The reverse legend is similar to that of the short-cross coinage, bearing the moneyer's name and mint, often abbreviated, except for Class 1A which omits both moneyer and mint, and Class 1B which only omits the moneyer. This however was highly unpopular because it reduced the moneyers' accountability and it was precisely this absence of control that had allowed the production of underweight, low fineness coins in previous reigns. When the moneyer's name and mint were reintroduced, the same considerations regarding abbreviation applied and the legend again started with the moneyer's name, followed by ON (of) and the mint name. We have listed the mint names, their abbreviations, the moneyer's names and the class in which each moneyer was active.

Henry III Long Cross Coinage Mints

Mints	Abbreviations	Moneyers	Classes
Bristol	BRUSTOV	Elis	3A-C
		Henri	3B
		Iacob	3A-C
		Roger	3A-C
		Walter	3B-C
Bury St Edmunds	SANTED	Ion or Iohs	2–5A, 5G-I
		Randulf	5A-F
		Renand	5G
		Stephane	5G
Canterbury	CANT	Alein	5G-H
		Gilbert	2–5D, F, G
		Ion or Ioh or	3E-5D, F, G
		Iohanes	
		Nicole or Nichole	1B, 2–5H
		Ricard	5G, H
		Robert	5C-H
		Walter	5C-H
		Willem(e)	1B, 2–5D, F, G
Carlisle	CARLEL	Adam	3A, B
		Ion	3A, B
		Robert	3A, B
		Willem	3A, B
Durham	DVRH	Philip	3B
		Ricard	5B-C

Mints	Abbreviations	Moneyers	Classes
		Roger	5G
		Willem	5G
Exeter	ECCETRE	Ion	2–3C
		Philip	2–3C
		Robert	2–3C
		Walter	2–3B
Gloucester	GLOECES	Ion	2–3C
		Lucas	2–3C
		Ricard	2–3C
		Roger	2–3C
Hereford	HERE	Henri	3A–B
		Ricard	3A–C
		Roger	3A–C
		Walter	3A–C
Ilchester	IVELCE	Huge	3A–C
		Ierveis	3A–C
		Randulf	3A–C
		Stephe	3A–C
Lincoln	NICOLE	Ion	2–3C
		Ricard	2–3C
		Walter	2–3C
		Willem	2–3C
London	LUND	Davi(d)	3C, 5F
		Henri	3A–5D, F, G
		Ion, Ioh, Iohan, Iohs	5C–G
		Nicole	1B/2mule, 2–5C
		Renaud	5G–I
		Ricard	3C–5G
		Robert	5G
		Thomas	5G
		Walter	5C–G
		Willem	5C–G
Newcastle	NEVECA	Adam	3A–B
		Henri	3A–C
		Ion	3A–C
		Roger	3A–C
Northampton	NORHA	Lucas	2–3B
		Philip	2–3C
		Tomas	2–3C
		Willem	2–3C
Norwich	NORWIC	Huge	2–3C
		Jacob	2–3C
		Ion	2–3C
		Willem	2–3C
Oxford	OXON	Adam	2–3C
		Gefrei	2–3C
		Henri	2–3C
		Willem	2–3C
Shrewsbury	SROSEB	Lorens	3A–C
		Nicole	3A–C
		Peris	3A–C
		Ricard	3A–C
Wallingford	VALI — WALI	Alisandre	3A–B
		Clemert	3A–B
		Ricard	3A–B
		Robert	3A–B
Wilton	WILT	Huge	3B–C
		Ion	3A–C
		Willem	3A–C
Winchester	WINT	Huge	2–3C
		Iordan	2–3C
		Nicole	2–3C
		Willem	2–3C
York	EVERWIC	Alain	2–3B
		Ieremire	2–3B
		Ion	2–3C
		Rener	2–3C
		Tomas	3B, C

Collecting Hints

Henry III's long-cross coinage is plentiful due to the discovery of hoards, the most notable of which was found in Colchester. It is relatively easy to find coins in Fine or VF condition and even EF coins appear occasionally. Collectors should aim for a coin in the best possible condition, with a fully readable legend. Examples from many of the regional mints, however, are fairly scarce and may take some time and effort to obtain, They also tend to come in slightly lesser grades than, for instance, the London issue. Finally, the last two classes of the long-cross coinage tend to be crude and are usually found in the lower grades.

Obverse without Sceptre

Class 1A

This issue omits both the moneyer's name and the mint but is considered to have been struck in London and Canterbury.

Obverse Legend HENRICUS REX — King Henry

Reverse Legend ANGLIE TERCI — Third of England

Obverse King's bust.

Reverse Long-cross with three pellets in each quarter.

H31D-040 VG £125 F £250 VF £500

Class 1B

Due to lack of space the obverse legend is broken halfway through the word ANGLIE and continued on the reverse which then bears the mint name abbreviated to LON, CAN or AED.

Obverse Legend HENRICUS REX ANG — Henry King of England

Reverse Legend LIE TERCI LON (or CAN or AED) — the Third London (Canterbury or Bury St Edmunds)

Obverse Bust of king facing.

Reverse As previous.

H31D-045 VG £45 F £90 VF £180

Class 2

The new reverse legend with the moneyer's name and mint is continued through all the rest of Henry III's classes.

Obverse Legend HENRICUS REX TERCI — King Henry the Third

Reverse Legend Moneyer's name and mint.

Obverse Bust of king.

Reverse As previous.

H31D-050 VG £22 F £45 VF £90

Class 3A

Obverse Legend HENRICUS REX III — King Henry III

Obverse The king has a thinner face.

H31D-055 VG £20 F £38 VF £70

Class 3B

Obverse Legend HENRICUS REX III — King Henry III

Obverse The king has a smaller, rounder face.

H31D-060 VG £20 F £38 VF £70

Class 3C

Obverse Legend As Class 3B.

Obverse More pointed chin on bust with the neck indicated by two lines and the eyes by pellets in annulets.

H31D-065 VG £20 F £38 VF £70

Obverse with Sceptre

The design of the reverse remained unaltered.

Class 4A

Obverse Legend HENRICUS REX III — King Henry III

Obverse Similar to Class 3C but king is holding a sceptre.

H31D-070 VG £50 F £100 VF £200

Class 4B

Obverse Legend As Class 4A.

Obverse The king has a slightly larger face and a crown of a slightly different design.

H31D-075 VG £55 F £110 VF £220

Class 5A

The obverse legend does not stop at the top of the coin, but just after the sceptre and this position is retained on all the rest of Henry III's classes.

Obverse Legend HENRICUS REX III — King Henry III

Obverse The bust is similar to Class 4B except that the king has rounder eyes.

H31D-080 VG £20 F £40 VF £80

Class 5B

As Class 5A but the king has a narrower face, round eyes and the tails of the 'R's in the legends are wedge shaped.

H31D-085 VG £20 VF £38 VF £75

Class 5C

As Class 5B but the king has oval eyes.

H31D-090 VG £20 F £38 VF £75

Class 5D

New-style portrait with a different crown with correctly-shaped fleur, and the tails of the 'R's in the legend are not wedge shaped.

H31D-095 VG £35 F £70 VF £140

Class 5E

As Class 5D but the crown is decorated by beads.

H31D-100 VG £90 F £180 VF £350

Class 5F

The king has a slightly larger face and the crown is of a different style, with a double band along it.

H31D-105 VG £20 F £40 VF £80

Class 5G

As Class 5F but the crown has a flatter base and a single band. Curule 'support to a chair' shaped 'X' in obverse legend.

H31D-110 VG £20 F £40 VF £80

Class 5H

As Class 5G but much cruder in style and with pellets instead of fleur in crown.

H31D-115 VG £20 F £40 VF £80

Class 5I

Even cruder than Class 5H and the king has a triple line of pellets for a beard.

H31D-120 ex. rare

Pricing

The prices below are for the most common types.

Mint	VG	F	VF
London	20	38	75
Bristol	25	50	100
Bury St Edmunds	25	50	100
Canterbury	20	38	75
Carlisle	50	100	225
Durham	60	120	250
Exeter	40	80	150
Gloucester	30	60	120
Hereford	40	80	150
Ilchester	70	140	280
Lincoln	30	60	120
Newcastle	30	60	120
Northampton	30	60	120
Norwich	30	60	120
Oxford	35	70	140
Shrewsbury	45	90	180
Wallingford	45	90	180
Wilton	45	90	180
Winchester	25	50	100
York	25	50	100

Cut Pennies from William I to Henry III

As mentioned earlier, for over 200 years the penny was the sole denomination to be struck, except for a couple of very rare issues of Henry I and Henry III. As it was such a large denomination, traders met the need for small change by cutting coins in half or quarters. Cut pennies of the earlier reigns are fairly scarce because many coins come from large hoards which were probably set aside as savings rather than exchanged for goods. However, with the advent of metal detecting more cut coinage has been found, especially from the short and long-cross series. Every collection should have a few of these fractional pennies and for collectors on a limited budget they can provide an inexpensive example of an early coin.

Edward I 1272–1307

Edward I succeeded his father, Henry III, in 1272 although he was absent on a crusade at the time of Henry's death. Obviously, coin production could not be arrested until Edward's return, so the long-cross coinage was continued in a similar style. Two types were produced during these seven years; the first is very crude but the second is of better quality. Most of the examples from these classes that are on the market today come from the Colchester Hoard, found in 1969.

As Edward crossed Europe on his return from the crusades in 1279, he was able to conclude an important wool trade treaty with the Low Countries, an indication of the steady increase in Anglo-European commerce. The king acknowledged the need to improve the style and fineness of English coinage and avoid the inferior quality coins that had occasionally been produced under previous reigns and shaken public confidence in the economy. There was also a need for both larger and smaller denominations than the penny, which had not changed much for about five hundred years, and so the groat (fourpence), halfpenny and farthing were introduced. Finally, there was the problem of clipping for which the Jews were unfairly blamed, often being either killed or forced to flee abroad. Their unpopularity stemmed from the fact that many were money-lenders and even Edward owed them money; by persecuting them for clipping, powerful individuals avoided paying their debts.

In response to these pressures, a new coinage was introduced in 1279 with a different design. Millions of coins were struck, mostly in London and Canterbury, and the public could take their old, underweight long or short-cross pennies to the mints and exchange them for new coins of correct weight and fineness. These new-style pennies soon became the envy of Europe and were copied extensively, although often in low fineness silver. But as this only made Edward's coins even more popular and severely drained the local supply, exporting English coins abroad became illegal in 1299. The strong, good quality currency helped strengthen the economy and England enjoyed considerable prosperity. Moreover, although clipping still occurred and the relevant penalties continued to be enforced during Edward's reign, the new design made it much easier to detect if a coin had been clipped.

Edward I's coinage was prolific in both numbers and varieties, with many of these issues looking very similar, especially to a new collector. After checking that the reverse bears the long cross, collectors should look at the portrait paying attention to the size (earlier issues tend to be larger than later ones), as well as the design of the crown, eyes, hair style and garments, and ensure that a specimen is not from Edward II or Edward III. If a coin looks very crude in style it could an issue from the Berwick mint and if it has a major discrepancy, such as no crown or a different legend, it could be a Continental imitation. When reading the reverse legend for the mint, it is important to remember that not only did die-makers often make mistakes but also the script was slightly different to today's, letters such as N might be reversed and, to save space, a comma might replace a letter or two letters might share the same stem.

Long Cross Coinage

The class numbering is continued from Henry III's reign as Edward's coins are so similar. The obverse legend still reads HENRICUS REX III and the reverse bears a long cross and the moneyer's name and mint in the legend; we have listed the relevant details below. It should be noted that only three mints were active at the time.

Edward I Long Cross Coinage Mints

Mint	Abbreviations	Moneyers	Class
London	LUND	Phelip	7
		Renaud	7
Bury St Edmunds	SANTED	Ioce	7
		Ion or Ioh	6 7
Durham	DURH	Roberd	6
		Robert	7

Collecting Hints

As mentioned earlier, Edward's Class 6 long-cross penny is very crude and even VF coins often look very ugly. The second type is of better quality but examples are rare. Of the three mints London and Durham are rare, Bury St Edmunds is common especially in Class 6. Collectors who simply want an example of this interesting type might well opt for a Bury St Edmunds Class 6 in the best grade possible.

Below we list the two classes, followed by the mints and prices.

Class 6

Obverse Crude bust of king holding sceptre. The king has large eyes and long realistic curly hair.

Reverse Long cross, three pellets in each quarter.

Class 7

Similar to the previous design, but of much better quality with smaller eyes and sharper features.

Pricing

Number	Mint	Class	VG	F	VF
E11D-005	Bury St Edmunds	Class 6	25	45	100
E11D-010		Class 7	50	100	200
E11D-015	Durham	Class 6	150	300	—
E11D-020		Class 7	150	300	—
E11D-025	London	Class 7	50	100	200

The 1279 Recoinage

The 1279 coinage differed from previous issues in many ways. There is a more realistic, lifelike facing bust of the crowned king on the obverse and the legend is longer, usually reading EDW REX ANGL DNS HYB (Edward King of England Lord of Ireland). The reverse has a large cross, going from the middle to the edge of the coin with three pellets in each quarter; the moneyer's name is omitted from the legend (except in one issue from Bury St Edmunds), but the mint name is usually given in full, e.g. CIVITAS LONDON (City of London) or VILLA NOVI CASTRI (Town of Newcastle). The new coinage also contained a privy mark, a slight difference such as a rose on the king's breast, or an alteration in the size of the king's eyes or the style of a letter, that distinguished each issue. These differences were not due to lack of care in producing dies but done deliberately, replacing the moneyer's name as a form of quality control; any coin appearing underweight or of low fineness could be returned to the moneyer and compared to the original die. Excluding a few provincial issues, there are about 34 different styles of Edward I penny which look fairly similar to an untrained eye since, after all, they only needed to be distinguishable to moneyers and mint officials. The various types are categorised into classes and to identify a coin correctly, collectors should pay particular attention to the hair style, any marks on the king's breast and the shape of the king's eyes as well as to the general style of lettering. The later classes tend to be slightly smaller than the earlier issues.

Classes

All issues have a crowned bust of the king. The reverse bears a long cross with three pellets in each quarter. The reverse legend shows the mint name.

Class 1 1279

Class 1A

This coin was only struck at the London mint.

Obverse Legend EDW REX ANGL DNS HYB — Edward King of England Lord of Ireland

Reverse Legend The mint's name.

Obverse Crowned bust of king with plain band to crown, Lombardic 'N' in legend.

Reverse Long cross with three pellets in each quarter.

Class 1B

Obverse Legend ED REX ANGLIE DNS HYBN — As above

Similar to Class 1A, but no drapery on bust and Roman 'N' reversed on obverse and reverse legends.

Class 1C

Obverse Legend EDW REX ANGL DNS HYB — As above

Similar to Class 1A, but the lettering is smaller and there is a Roman 'N', often reversed, in the obverse legend.

Class 1D

Obverse Legend EDW R ANGL DNS HYB — As above

The face and lettering are larger than Class 1C although the same in terms of style.

Class 2 1280

With very few exceptions, which we have listed, the obverse legend for the rest of Edward's pennies reads EDW R ANGL DNS HYB.

Class 2A

Obverse Legend EDW R ANGL DNS HYB — As above

Large face and short neck similar to Class 1D but the crown is slightly different in style with the right hand side of the central lis normally broken.

Class 2B

Similar to Class 2A, but the king has a high neck and narrower face; 'N' in legend reversed.

Class 3 1280–1281

Class 3A

This issue was only struck in London. Crescent shape to base of neck; there are more facial features, and pearls (or dots) in the crown.

Class 3B

Similar to Class 3A, but the king's neck and drapery on bust looks like a segment of a circle.

Class 3C

Similar to Class 3A, but no pearls on crown; the king's drapery is in one piece and hollowed in centre.

Class 3D

Normal crown and bust, but the drapery is in two pieces and the king's face is broad.

Class 3E

Long narrow face. This issue was only struck in Durham, Newcastle and both of the York mints; the York ecclesiastical issue often has a quatrefoil in the centre on the reverse and, sometimes, on the breast.

Class 3F

Broad bust with a large nose. This issue tends to be poorer in style and some of the lettering is made up to look like wedges; on the reverse the 'S' is different in style.

Class 3G

Smaller, neater bust with a narrow face, the fleurs on the edge the of crown have a slightly different design.

Class 4 1282–1289

Class 4A

Fairly similar to Class 3G, but the drapery is in the shape of two wedges; the 'C' and 'E' in the lettering are open.

Class 4B

Similar to Class 4A, but shorter face and hair.

Class 4C

Similar to Class 4A, but larger face and more hair; unbarred 'A' in legend.

Class 4D

Similar to Class 4C, but pellet or dot at the beginning of obverse and/or reverse legend.

Class 4E

Similar to Class 4D, but three pellets on king's breast and a pellet in reverse legend.

Class 5 1290–1291

Class 5A

Similar to Class 4, but the coin is well spread out and there is a pellet on the king's breast.

Class 5B

Similar to Class 5A, but with taller lettering and narrower face.

Class 6 1292–1296

Class 6A

This issue was only minted at London and is somewhat smaller in size. The cross above the king's crown is almost plain in style and the crown is slightly different in style.

Class 6B

Obverse Legend EDWR (or EDWA) ANGL DNS HYB — As before

Similar but slightly better style; cross pattée above king's crown, closed 'E' in legend and the 'N' on the reverse is usually double barred.

Class 7 1294–1296

Class 7A

Obverse Legend As Class 2A.

Similar to Class 6B, but with a rose on breast and almond shaped eyes; double barred 'N' in legend.

Class 7B

Very similar to 7A, but king has longer hair and a slightly different crown.

Class 8 1294–1300

Class 8A

Obverse legend as Class 6B; smaller crown, no rose on bust with an unusual shaped 'S'; the king also has a longer neck.

Class 8B

Similar to Class 9A but still has unusual shaped 'S' in legend and nothing on breast.

Class 9 1300–1302

Class 9A

Obverse Legend EDWR (or EW or EDW) ANGL DNS HYB — As before

Similar to Class 8B, but the drapery is in two wedges and the king has a narrow face; there usually is a star on the breast and the crown is flatter.

Class 9B

These coins tend to be slightly smaller in size. The 'N' in the legend is of various styles, barred, unbarred or pothook; often there is also a star or pellet on the breast.

Class 10 1302–1310

Class 10A

Obverse Legend EDWARD R ANGL DNS HYB — As before

Very narrow lettering with concave sides and narrow face.

Class 10B

All classes onwards have a bifoliate crown, with two leaves at each end instead of three.

Obverse Legend EDWARR ANGL DNS HYB — As before

Similar to Class 10A, but some issues have an earlier style crown.

Class 10C

Obverse Legend EDWA R — King Edward

Identical to 10B except for the obverse legend; new-style crown as standard.

Class 10D

Obverse Legend EDWAR ANGL DNS HYB — As before

Similar to Class 10C, but with a slightly wider face and more ornate letters in legend.

Class 10E

Obverse Legend EDWAR ANGL DNS HYB — As before

Similar to 10D, but the king's face is squarer and has a shorter neck.

Class 10F

Obverse Legend EDWAR ANGL DNS HYB — As before

Similar to Class 10E, but the cross above the king's crown is dumpier in shape.

Mints

Although most of Edward I's coins were struck at London and Canterbury, dies were also made for various provincial mints. The coins from provincial mints conform in almost every detail to the 10 major classes laid out previously but there are a few exceptions where small marks or a slightly different design were added to the coin to distinguish them. The mint is found on the reverse, usually preceded by CIVITAS (city) or VILLA (town). Below we have listed all the mints that issued coins and the inscriptions found on the reverse legend, with slashes marking where the long-cross breaks the legend. We have also given the class in which the coins were issued and any unusual marks found on them.

Bristol Mint

VILL/ABR/ISTO/LLIE — Town of Bristol	2B, 3B, 3D, 3F, 3G
VILL/BRI/STO/LIE	9B

Bury St Edmunds Mint

This mint is the one exception that had a moneyer's name, Robert de Hadelie, rather than the mint name on some issues.

ROBE/RTU/SDEH/ADL — Robert de Hadelie	3C
ROBE/RTUS/DEH/ADL	4A
ROBE/RTDE/HADE/LEIE	3C, 3D, 3G, 4A, 4B, 4C
VIL/LAS/EDM/VDI — Town of Bury St Edmunds	4E, 5B
VIL/LAS/EDM/VNDI	5B
VILA/SCI/EDM/VDI	6B
VILL/ASCI/EDM/VNDI	7A, 8A
VILL/ASCI/EDM/VDI	7A
VILA/SCIE/DMV/NDI	8A, 8B, 9A
VILL/SCIE/DMV/NDI	9B
VILL/SCIE/DMV/NDI	10A, 10B

Canterbury Mint

CIVI/TAS/CAN/TOR — City of Canterbury	2A, 2B, 3B, 3C, 3D, 3F, 3G, 4A, 4B, 4C, 4E, 5A, 5B, 6A, 6B, 7A, 7B, 9A, 9B, 10A, 10B
CIVI/TAS/CAN/TVR	2A or sometimes 2B

Chester Mint

CIVI/TAS/CES/TRIE — City of Chester	3G, 9B
CIVI/TAS/CEST/RIE	3G sometimes

Durham Mint

Durham was an ecclesiastical privilege mint, having a 'favour' from the king that allowed coins to be struck there under the watchful eye of the powerful Bishops — an important source of revenue for the Church. Several Bishops introduced small marks on their coin using their family crests.

Regular Issue	CIV/TAS/DVR/ EME — City of Durham	9B, 10A, 10B, 10E, 10F	King's receiver, no distinguishing marks
Bishop de Insula	CIV/TAS/DVR/ EME	2B, 3B, 3C, 3E, 3G, 4A	No distinguishing marks
Bishop Bec	CIV/ITAS/DVR/ EME	4B, 4E, 5B, 6B, 7B	Cross moline as initial mark on both sides of coin.
	CIV/ITAS/DVR/ ENE	9A	
	CIV/ITA/SDVR/ ENE	9A	
			There is also a variety where a cross moline is found in one quarter on the reverse.
	CIV/ITAS/DVR/ EME	4B	

Exeter Mint

CIV/TAS/EXO/NIE — City of Exeter	9B

Kingston upon Hull Mint

VILL/KYN/CES/TON — Town of Kingston upon Hull (abbreviated).	9B
VIL'/KYN/CES/TON	9B

London Mint

CIVI/TAS/LON/DON — City of London	all classes except 3E

Lincoln Mint

CIVI/TAS/LIN/COL' — City of Lincoln	3C, 3D, 3F, 3G

Newcastle Mint

VIL/ANO/VICA/STRI — Town of Newcastle	3E
VILL/NOVI/CAS/TRI	10A, 10B
VILL/NOV'/CAS/TRI	9B, 10A, 10B
VIL'/NOV'/CAS/TRI	9B, 9C

Reading Mint

VIL/LAR/ADI/NGY — Town of Reading	1D

York Mint

As well as a royal mint, York had an ecclesiastical privilege mint like Durham. The two types of coins had to look different so, although the legends remained the same, a quatrefoil was placed in the centre of the reverse cross of those struck at the ecclesiastical mint.

CIVI/TAS/EBO/RACI — City 2A, 2B, 3B, 3C, 3E, 3F, 9B Royal mint
of York
CIVI/TAS/EBO/RACI   3E, 3G, 9B   Ecclesiastical mint

Pricing

Mint	Class	Number	VG	F	VF
Bristol	2B	E11D-030	30	50	100
	3B	E11D-035	35	60	120
	3D	E11D-040	25	45	90
	3F	E11D-045	35	60	120
	3G	E11D-050	25	50	100
	9B	E11D-055	25	50	100
Bury St Edmunds. Robert de Hadelie reverse	3C	E11D-060	40	80	160
	3D	E11D-065	40	80	160
	3G	E11D-070	40	80	160
	4A	E11D-075	40	90	180
	4B	E11D-080	40	80	160
	4C	E11D-085	40	80	160
Mint name reverse	4E	E11D-090	25	50	100
	5B	E11D-095	40	100	—
	6B	E11D-100	40	100	-
	7A	E11D-105	40	100	-
	8A	E11D-110	25	50	100
	8B	E11D-115	30	60	120
	9A	E11D-120	25	50	100
	9B	E11D-125	25	50	100
	10A	E11D-130	25	55	110
	10B	E11D-135	25	50	100
Canterbury	2A	E11D-140	22	40	80
	2B	E11D-145	20	35	70
	3B	E11D-150	25	55	100
	3C	E11D-155	20	30	60
	3D	E11D-160	20	30	60
	3F	E11D-165	30	70	120
	3G	E11D-170	30	30	60
	4A	E11D-175	22	35	70
	4B	E11D-180	20	30	60
	4C	E11D-185	20	30	60
	4D	E11D-190	20	40	75
	4E	E11D-195	20	40	75
	5A	E11D-200	30	75	150
	5B	E11D-205	30	75	150
	6A	E11D-210	60	140	300
	6B	E11D-215	40	100	200
	7A	E11D-220	40	100	200
	7B	E11D-225	40	100	200
	9A	E11D-230	22	35	75
	9B	E11D-235	20	30	60
	10A	E11D-240	20	30	60
	10B	E11D-245	60	30	60
Chester	3G	E11D-250	40	80	150
	9B	E11D-255	35	70	140
Durham	2B	E11D-260	25	50	100
	3B	E11D-265	30	60	120
	3C	E11D-270	25	50	100
	3E	E11D-275	25	50	100
	3G	E11D-280	25	50	100
	4A	E11D-285	25	50	100
	4B	E11D-290	25	50	100
	4E	E11D-295	25	50	100
	5B	E11D-300	30	70	125
	6B	E11D-305	40	100	200
	7B	E11D-310	40	100	200
	9A	E11D-315	25	50	100
	9B	E11D-320	25	50	100
	10A	E11D-325	25	50	100
	10B	E11D-330	25	50	100
	10E	E11D-335	25	50	100
	10F	E11D-340	25	50	100
Exeter	9B	E11D-345	35	70	140
Kingston upon Hull	9B	E11D-350	40	80	150
London	1A	E11D-355	200	450	—
	1B	E11D-360	200	500	—
	1C	E11D-365	25	45	90
	1D	E11D-370	25	45	90
	2A	E11D-375	20	30	60
	2B	E11D-380	20	30	60
	3A	E11D-385	30	70	120

Mint	Class	Number	VG	F	VF
	3B	E11D-390	30	60	100
	3C	E11D-395	20	30	60
	3D	E11D-400	20	30	60
	3F	E11D-405	22	50	100
	3G	E11D-410	20	30	60
	4A	E11D-415	20	35	65
	4B	E11D-420	20	30	60
	4C	E11D-425	20	30	60
	4D	E11D-430	20	30	60
	4E	E11D-435	20	35	65
	5A	E11D-440	30	70	120
	5B	E11D-445	30	70	120
	6A	E11D-450	60	140	220
	6B	E11D-455	40	100	200
	7A	E11D-460	40	100	200
	7B	E11D-465	40	100	200
	8A	E11D-470	25	50	100
	8B	E11D-475	25	50	100
	9A	E11D-480	20	30	60
	9B	E11D-485	20	30	60
	10A	E11D-490	20	30	60
	10B	E11D-495	20	30	60
	10C	E11D-500	20	30	60
	10D	E11D-505	20	30	60
	10E	E11D-510	20	30	60
	10F	E11D-515	20	35	80
Lincoln	3C	E11D-520	25	45	90
	3D	E11D-525	25	45	90
	3F	E11D-530	30	60	110
	3G	E11D-535	25	45	90
Reading	1D	E11D-540	120	250	—
Newcastle	3E	E11D-545	25	45	90
	9B	E11D-550	25	45	90
	9C	E11D-555	25	45	90
	10A	E11D-560	25	45	90
	10B	E11D-565	25	45	0
York	2A	E11D-570	25	50	100
	2B	E11D-575	25	50	100
	3C	E11D-580	20	40	90
	3E	E11D-585	25	50	100
	3F	E11D-590	30	60	120
	3G	E11D-595	20	40	80
	9B	E11D-600	20	40	80

Berwick on Tweed Mint

The coins of Berwick on Tweed have not been included in the previous listing because they do not conform to the classes of Edward I. As mentioned earlier, dies were usually made in London and sent out to the provincial mints, thus ensuring conformity both in production and style. But the dies used at Berwick were of local manufacture, because, due to its proximity to Scotland, the town was a constant battle-ground between Scots and English and often changed hands as battles progressed. So, although Berwick was hardly the safest location for a royal mint, there was a need for coinage not least for the payment of the English troops and local dies were made to strike it. The coins produced were all pennies and can be divided into four classes.

Collecting Hints

Berwick coins tend to be crude in style and a portrait with large staring eyes. Many seem to have a lower silver content than the regular issues. Berwick pennies are common, but nice VF examples are hard to find. Collectors should try to obtain an example in at least Fine condition and visually attractive.

Class 1

Obverse Legend EDW R ANGL DNS HYB — Edward King of England and Lord of Ireland

Reverse Legend VILLA BEREVVICI — Town of Berwick

Obverse Facing bust of king wearing crown.

Reverse Similar to all reverses on Edward I pennies.

E11D-605 VG £20 F £50 VF £120

Class 2

Obverse Legend EDW(A), R ANGL DNS HYB — As before

Reverse Legend VILLA BERREWYCI (or BERREVICI) — Town of Berwick

Obverse As above, but very crude in style; the king's crown is also ornamented with large pellets

Reverse As previous.

E11D-610 VG £20 F £50 VF £120

Class 3

This is identical to Class 1, except that the obverse legend reads EDWA instead of EDWR.

E11D-615 VG £20 F £50 VF £120

Class 4

Obverse Legend EDWA R ANGL DNS HYB — As before

Reverse Legend VILLA BEREVVICI — Town of Berwick

Obverse Neater bust with large eyes and a pellet on the breast.

Reverse As previous.

E11D-620 VG £22 F £60 VF £60 EF £130

Edward II 1307–1327

Edward II succeeded Edward I in 1307 and although his reign was neither as prosperous nor as peaceful as his father's, there is very little difference in their coinage. The penny continued as the main denomination, and the halfpennies and farthings that were also struck are now scarce. Stylistically, the two reigns are also similar, with virtually identical reverses and only minor differences on the obverse. The obverse legend reads EDWA(R) R ANGL DNS HYB, which is different from most of Edward I's pennies except for some of the later classes. The crown on Edward II's pennies is bifoliate, having two prongs on each end, while most Edward I issues have a crown with three prongs — except for Class 10 which also has a bifoliate crown. However, the most common Edward II pennies are those of Class 11, which have a broken pearl to the left of the crown; the later classes (12 to 15) omit the broken pearl but all have a bifoliate crown and the same legend. Most of these later classes differ from the previous ones in the style of the crown. Finally, many of Edward II's pennies tend to be a little smaller than those of Edward I.

Classes

Classes are numbered consecutively from the previous reign because the coins are so similar.

Class 11 1310–1314

Class 11A

Obverse Legend EDWAR ANGL DNS HYB — Edward King of England and Lord of Ireland

Obverse Facing crowned bust of king; crown with broken pearl to left of centre, straight-sided 'N' in legend.

Reverse Similar to all Edward I reverses.

Class 11B

Similar to Class 11A, but face slightly smaller, large serifs to 'N's in legend, 'E' with an angular back.

Class 11C

Similar to Class 11B, but 'A' of legend is double-barred at vertical side and flat topped.

Class 12 1314

The crown has its central fleur formed of three wedges, rather than a curved lis style as previous classes.

Class 13 1315–1318

Very similar to previous issues, but the central fleur of crown is in the form of a Greek double-axe.

Class 14 1318–1320

Very similar to Class 13 but the central fleur is taller and the king has a slightly larger face with leering eyes.

Class 15 1320–1335

Class 15A

The bust is similar to Class 14, but the crown is smaller and flatter and its spearheads or points are often bent to the left.

Class 15B

Similar to Class 15A, but a slightly smaller face.

Class 15C

Similar to previous issues, but the king has a larger face and the 'E' in the legend is large.

Mints

Only five mints were active under Edward II, probably because large quantities of coins had been produced in the previous reign and the need for new coinage was not acute. We have listed the mints below, along with their inscriptions with slashes marking where the long cross breaks the legend, the classes in which the issues were struck and, where appropriate, any distinguishing marks.

Bury St Edmunds Mint

VILL/SCIE/DMV/NDI — Town of Bury   all Edward II classes
St Edmunds

Canterbury Mint

CIVI/TAS/CAN/TOR — City of   all Edward II classes
Canterbury

London Mint

CIVI/TAS/LON/DON — City of   all Edward II classes
London

Durham Mint

Durham continued as an ecclesiastical privilege mint, producing coins under the control of the Bishops. However, the first issue is known as the King's Receiver Issue because it was struck by a Receiver under strict instructions from Edward II who had been displeased with Bishop Bec for putting his own small marks on the coins.

King's Receiver	CIVI/TAS/DVN/ ELM CIVI/TAS/ DVR/EME — City of Durham	11A, 14	a plain cross mintmark
Bishop Bec	CIVI/TAS/DVR/ EME	11A	a cross moline mintmark on the obverse
Bishop Kellawe	CIVI/TAS/DVN/ ELM	11A, 12, 13	a crozier end to the long-cross on the reverse
Bishop Beaumont	CIVI/TAS/DVN/ ELM	13, 14, 15A, B, C	a lion and lis mintmark on the obverse
Sede Vacante	CIVI/TAS/DVN/ ELM	15C	plain cross on the obverse*

* There is confusion as to when and why this issue was produced. The coins were struck under the authority of the king rather than the Bishop and some experts consider them to be London-Durham mules. There are several varieties.

Pricing

Mint	Class	Number	VG	F	VF
Bury St Edmunds	11A	E21D-005	22	45	90
	11B	E21D-010	22	45	90
	11C	E21D-015	25	50	100
	12	E21D-020	22	45	90
	13	E21D-025	22	45	90
	14	E21D-030	22	45	90
	15A	E21D-035	22	45	90
	15B	E21D-040	22	45	90
	15C	E21D-045	25	50	100
Canterbury	11A	E21D-050	22	45	90
	11B	E21D-055	22	45	90
	11C	E21D-060	25	50	100
	12	E21D-065	22	45	90
	13	E21D-070	22	45	90
	14	E21D-075	22	45	90
	15A	E21D-080	22	45	90
	15B	E21D-085	22	45	90
	15C	E21D-090	25	50	100
London	11A	E21D-095	22	35	70
	11B	E21D-100	22	35	70
	11C	E21D-105	25	30	100
	12	E21D-110	22	40	80
	13	E21D-115	20	35	70
	14	E21D-120	20	30	60
	15A	E21D-125	20	32	65
	15B	E21D-130	20	32	65
	15C	E21D-135	20	32	65
Durham	11A	E21D-140	25	50	100
	11B	E21D-145	25	50	100
	11C	E21D-150	25	50	100
	12	E21D-155	25	50	100
	13	E21D-160	25	50	100
	14	E21D-165	25	50	100
	15A	E21D-170	25	55	110
	15B	E21D-175	25	55	110
	15C	E21D-180	40	90	180

Berwick on Tweed Mint

The Berwick pennies of Edward II continue from the previous reign and again form a separate category (please see above for details). Like the previous issues, coins tend to be crude, often made of rather base metal and found in fairly poor condition. In all of the classes the obverse legend translates as 'Edward King of England and Lord of Ireland' and the reverse as 'Town of Berwick', while the reverse design is a long cross with three pellets in each quarter.

Class 5 1310

Obverse Legend EDWA(R) ANGL DNS HYB — Edward King of England and Lord of Ireland

Reverse Legend VIL/LAB/ERE/WICI (or /WYCI) — Town of Berwick

Obverse Facing bust of king with bifoliate crown with a broken spearhead.

E21D-185 VG £30 F £80 VF £180

Class 6

Obverse Legend EDWAR ANGL DNS HYB

Reverse Legend VIL/LAB/ERE/WICI (or /WYCI or /WYC')

Obverse As above, but the king has a trifoliate (three pronged) crown.

E21D-190 VG £35 F £90 VF £200

Class 7

Obverse Legend EDWAR ANGL DNS HYB

Reverse Legend VILL/ABE/REV/VICI (or /ICI)

Obverse As above, the face often has squinting eyes and the whole coin is very crude.

E21D-195 VG £40 F £100 VF £220

There is also a very rare variety which has a bear's head in one quarter of the reverse.

E21D-200 very rare

Edward III 1327–1377

Edward III succeeded his father at the age of fourteen and reigned for fifty years, although during the early period the country was in fact ruled by his mother, Queen Isabella. Edward's reign was a period of conflict, not only with the Scots but also with France as he laid claim to the French throne and the vicissitudes of that enterprise are reflected in the legends of his coins. Moreover, when the town of Calais became English after a treaty with France, coins were also struck there partly for convenience and partly as a political statement.

During the first part of Edward's reign only a small quantity of pennies was produced, similar in style to those of his father. However, a new series of coins was introduced when increasing trade with Flanders necessitated the production of good quality gold currency and a variety of denominations. The gold noble, half-noble, and quarter-noble were introduced to be followed later by the groat, or fourpence, which became very popular and eventually superseded the penny in importance, and the halfgroat, which again proved popular. The penny itself changed in style, with a bust that was very different from that on the issues of the two preceding monarchs, while halfpennies and farthings were also produced. There was, at last, an adequate supply of varying denominations, which benefited both the internal market and trade with Europe, where English coins of all denominations were readily acceptable.

Edward's long reign resulted in numerous varieties in the coinage but identifying an Edward III penny is fairly easy, except for the first coinage of 1327–1335. As with the other four Edwards who struck pennies, the obverse legend begins with EDWARDUS or some abbreviation which in this case will read at least EDWA; the portrait is quite distinct however as, in contrast to the other

four, Edward III, who is depicted with long hair, kept his youthful looks on all his coins. A total of five mints were active from 1344 to 1377 and their legends, found on the reverse of the coin, read as follows: CIVITAS LONDON for London, CIVITAS DUREME (varieties) for Durham, VILLA CALESIE for Calais, VILLA RADINGY for Reading and CIVITAS EBORACI for York. Once the above details have been identified, the obverse legend will help indicate the particular issue and it often helps to write a coin's legend out in full before attempting to match it. Finally, look for any unusual marks such as annulets or saltires, which are often in the legend or on or below the king's breast and constituted a form of quality control by being individual to a particular die. In this way, if there was a problem with a coin, it could have been traced back to the original die and moneyer. The main varieties of marks are:

An annulet, usually in the legend or king's breast and sometimes in the four quarters on the reverse.

An escallop in one quarter on coins from the Reading mint.

A quatrefoil usually in the centre of the reverse on coins from York.

A crown found at 12 o'clock on the obverse legend.

A crozier on the reverse of coins from Durham.

A trefoil of pellets sometimes on the king's breast.

A quatrefoil enclosing a pellet in the centre of the reverse from some coins of York.

A double annulet sometimes found in the legends.

A pellet sometimes found in the legend, or an extra one in the quarters on the reverse.

A voided quatrefoil sometimes on the king's breast.

A lis sometimes on the king's breast.

Collecting Hints

Except for the first coinage and certain varieties and mints, Edward III pennies are available but usually found in a lower grade than those of the first two Edwards. Although coins in EF condition tend to be rare, it should not be difficult to find an example in Fine or even VF. Many of the lower grade coins tend to be clipped and, due to poor striking, parts of the legend are often flat. Collectors should try to obtain an unclipped example with as much detail showing as possible.

First Coinage 1327–1335

Because of the extensive similarities in style, the class numbering system continues from the previous reign. This small and scarce issue is very similar to Class 15 of Edward II but has Lombardic 'N's in the legend. The reverse of the coin is determined by the mint and the various details are listed below.

Class 15D

Obverse Legend EDWAR ANGL DNS HYB — Edward King of England and Lord of Ireland

Obverse Facing bust of king as Class 15 but Lombardic 'N's in legend.

Mints

As well as London, five provincial mints were active during the first coinage, four of which have the Class 15D obverse. The provincial issues are all scarce or rare and have Lombardic 'N's in legend; the points where the long cross breaks the legend are represented below by slashes. Collectors should also cross reference with the provincial mints of Edward I and Edward II to ensure that they have the correct issue.

London Mint

Reverse Legend CIVITAS LONDON — City of London

Reverse Long cross, three pellets in each quarter.

E31D-005 VG £200 F £400 VF £800

Bury St Edmunds Mint

Reverse Legend VILL/SCIE/DMV/NDI — Town of Bury St Edmunds

E31D-010 ex. rare

Canterbury Mint

Reverse Legend CIVI/TAS/CAN/TOR — City of Canterbury

Reverse Two varieties exist, both with mintmark cross pattée on the obverse but one has a pellet in the centre of the reverse, the other an extra three pellets in a quarter.

E31D-015 VG £175 F £350 VF £750

Durham Mint

Reverse Legend CIVI/TAS/DVN/ELM — City of Durham

Reverse A small crown can be found on the reverse.

E31D-020 VG £300 F £600 VF v. rare

York Mint

Reverse Legend CIVI/TAS/EBO/RACI — City of York

Reverse Four varieties exist:

1. a quatrefoil in the centre of the reverse cross;

2. a small pellet in each quarter of the obverse mintmark;

3. three extra pellets in one quarter;

4. sometimes a Roman 'N' only on the obverse legend.

E31D-025 VG £150 F £275 VF £550

Berwick on Tweed Mint

As with the previous two reigns, the Berwick issues do not conform to the regular classes. This type was issued around 1344.
Obverse Legend EDWARDUS ANGL HIB

Reverse Legend VIL/LAB/ERW/ICI

Obverse Crowned bust of king.

Reverse A bear's head in one quarter.

E31D-030 VG £200 F £400 VF £800

No pennies were produced during the second coinage (1335–1343). This was probably because there were adequate reserves in circulation from the previous two reigns since, by con-

trast, large quantities of halfpennies were struck to satisfy demand.

Third or Florin Coinage 1344–1351

The third, or florin coinage, spans the period from 1344 to 1351 and derived its name from the fact that the dies were made by two Florentine craftsmen. Because the new style for the penny is so different, the class numbering system is discontinued after the first coinage. The obverse still bears a facing bust of the king but the main difference is in the style of hair, Edward III's being long and unkempt while Edward I's is much neater; also, the neck and shoulders differ in style, as does the lettering. As with previous issues, the mint can be found on the reverse and, of the five mints that were active at the time, London was the most prolific.

London Mint

Obverse Legend EDW R ANGL DNS HYB — Edward King of England and Lord of Ireland

Reverse Legend CIVITAS LONDON — City of London

Obverse Facing bust with bushy hair and broad neck and shoulders; Lombardic 'N's in the legend, as well as annulets.

E31D-035 VG £18 F £38 VF £80

As above, but the obverse legend reads EDWAR ANGL DNS HYB.

E31D-040 VG £16 F £35 VF £80

Similar to E31D-040, but a Roman 'N', sometimes reversed, is found on the obverse legend.

E31D-045 VG £16 F £35 VF £80

As above, but there are no annulet stops in the legend and a variety of 'N's are used.

E31D-050 VG £16 F £35 VF £80

Canterbury Mint

Obverse Legend As E31D-040.

Reverse Legend CIVI/TAS/CAN/TOR — City of Canterbury

Obverse As previous.

E31D-055 VG £35 F £75 VF £150

Obverse Legend EDWR ANGL DNS HYB. Reversed Roman 'N' in legend.

E31D-060 VG £35 F £75 VF £150

Durham Mint

All the coins from the Durham mint are rare. Many varieties of the reverse legend exist and we have listed the major ones below.

Obverse Legend EDWARDUS REX AIN — Edward King of England

Reverse Legend CIV/ITAS/DUN/ELM or DUN/OLME — City of Durham. Crozier in reverse.

E31D-065 VG £75 F £175 VF £350

Obverse Legend EDWR ANGL DNS HYB — Edward of England Lord of Ireland

Reverse Legend CIVITAS DUN/ELM or DUN/OLM — City of Durham

E31D-070 VG £35 F £75 VF £150

Obverse Legend EDWR ANGL DNS YB — Edward of England Lord of Ireland. Usually one Lombardic and one Roman 'N'.

Reverse Legend As previous.

E31D-075 VG £35 F £75 VF £150

Obverse Legend EDWAR R ANG DNS HYB. — Edward of England Lord of Ireland. Lombardic Ns.

Reverse Legend CIVI/TAS DUN/ELM, CIVI/TAS DUN/OLM, CIVI/TAS DUN/OLME, VIL/ADU/NOL/MIE, VIL/LAD/UR/REM — City or Town of Durham

E31D-080 VG £75 F £175 VF £350

Obverse Legend EDWARDUS REX ANGLIE — Edward King of England

Reverse Legend VILA DUNO LMIE — Town of Durham

E31D-085 VG £75 F £175 VF £350

Reading Mint

Obverse Legend EDWR ANGL DNS HYB

Reverse Legend VIL/LA R/ADI/NGY — Town of Reading

An escallop can be found in one quarter of the reverse instead of the usual three pellets.

E31D-090 VG £175 F £350 VF £750

York Mint

Obverse Legend EDWR ANGL DNS HYB

Reverse Legend CIVI/TAS/EBO/RACI — City of York

Obverse Variety of 'N's in legends.

Reverse Long cross, quatrefoil in centre, three pellets in each quarter.

E31D-095 VG £25 F £50 VF £100

Fourth Coinage 1351–1377

Edward III's fourth coinage is an important turning point in English numismatic history, involving the successful introduction of the groat and halfgroat as well as the gold noble, half-noble and quarter-noble. It constitutes the beginning of the modern varied denomination system. However, as well as being a historical landmark, the fourth coinage was itself influenced by contemporary events and is classified according to the obverse legend which charts the progress of Edward's claim to the French throne. Based on the 1360 Treaty of Brétigny that granted Edward land in France, the coinage is subdivided into the pre-treaty, transitional, treaty and post-treaty periods. During the pre-treaty and post-treaty periods, when Edward's claims were not recognised, FRANC (France) appeared in the legends of most of his coins. It was omitted for the six years that the treaty was upheld. In some cases, but not on the penny, FRANC was replaced by AQT for Aquitaine, the French territory granted to Edward. After the treaty was repudiated by the French in 1369, the two counties went to war again and England lost most of its French possessions except Calais and Bordeaux. However, the one feature of the coinage that remained constant was the king's portrait with the result that even at the age of sixty, Edward retain his youthful looks on the coins.

Pre Treaty Period 1351–1361

Many of the coins produced between 1351 and 1361 bear the word FRANC, but the penny does not. Three mints were active in the production of coins during this decade.

London Mint

Minor varieties of this issue exist.

Class B

Obverse Legend EDWARDUS REX ANGLI — Edward King of England

Reverse Legend CIVI/TAS/LON/DON — City of London

Obverse Facing bust with round eyes.

Reverse Lombardic 'M' and 'N' in legend with an annulet in each quarter; mintmark cross pattée.

E31D-100 VG £40 F £100 VF £200

Class C

As above, but closed 'C' and 'E', and 'R' with wedge-shaped tail in legend; an annulet in each quarter of the reverse.

E31D-105 VG £18 F £35 VF £75

Class D

As above, but 'R' with normal tail.

E31D-110 VG £18 F £35 VF £75

Class E

The legend has broken letters and an annulet can not always be found in each quarter.

E31D-115 VG £18 F £35 VF £75

Class F

The mintmark crown can be found on the obverse of the coin.

E31D-120 VG £20 F £38 VF £75

Class G

Annulet in one quarter on reverse.

E31D-125 VG £18 F £35 VF £75

An annulet can be found below the bust.

E31D-130 VG £22 F £45 VF £90

A saltire can be found in one quarter on the reverse.

E31D-135 VG £30 F £60 VF £120

Durham Mint

This issue was struck under Bishop Hatfield.

Obverse Legend EDWARDUS REX ANGLI — Edward King of England

Reverse Legend VILLA DURREM — Town of Durham

There is an extra pellet in each quarter and a crozier in the reverse legend.

E31D-140 VG £100 F £200 VF £400

Obverse Legend As previous.

Reverse Legend CIVITAS DUNELMIE — City of Durham

Obverse As E31D-105.

E31D-145 VG £30 F £60 VF £120

Legends As previous.

Obverse As E31D-110.

E31D-150 VG £30 F £60 VF £120

Legends As previous.

Obverse As E31D-115.

E31D-155 VG £25 F £50 VF £100

Obverse Legend As previous.

Reverse Legend CIVITAS DVREME — City of Durham

Obverse As E31D-120.

E31D-160 VG £30 F £60 VF £120

Legends As previous.

Obverse As E31D-125.

E31D-165 VG £22 F £45 VF £90

Legends As previous.

Obverse As E31D-130.

E31D-170 VG £20 F £40 VF £80

Legends As previous.

Obverse As E31D-135.

E31D-175 VG £20 F £40 VF £80

Legends As previous.

Obverse An annulet can be found on each of the king's shoulders.

E31D-180 VG £20 F £40 VF £80

Legends As previous.

Obverse A trefoil of pellets can be found on the king's shoulders.

E31D-185 VG £22 F £45 VF £90

Obverse Legend As previous.

Reverse Legend CIVITAS DVRELMIE — City of Durham

Obverse Plain bust of king.

Reverse Crozier in legend.

E31D-190 VG £22 F £45 VF £90

York Mint

Royal Mint

Obverse Legend EDWARDUS REX ANGLI — Edward King of England

Reverse Legend CIVITAS EBORACI — City of York

Obverse As E31D-110.

Reverse Plain cross to centre.

E31D-195 VG £30 F £60 VF £120

As above, but some letters in legend are broken.

E31D-200 VG £20 F £38 VF £75

Episcopal Mint under Archbishop Thorsby

Obverse Legend EDWARDUS REX ANGLI — Edward King of England

Reverse Legend CIVITAS EBORACI — City of York

Obverse Similar to E31D-110.

Reverse Cross with quatrefoil in centre.

E31D-205 VG £25 F £50 VF £100

Similar to above but sometimes annulet in one quarter on the reverse and sometimes under bust of king.

E31D-210 VG £20 F £38 VF £80

As previous, but an annulet or saltire on breast.

E31D-215 VG £22 F £45 VF £90

Transitional Period 1361–1363

This small and scarce issue can be easily identified as it omits REX (king) from the obverse legend. Most of the lettering in this issue is of irregular size. The same three mints were active during this period.

London Mint

Obverse Legend EDWAR(D)ANGLIE DNS HIB — Edward of England and Lord of Ireland

Reverse Legend CIVITAS LONDON — City of London

Obverse Facing bust of king; annulet in two upper quarters of mintmark cross.

E31D-220 VG £60 F £120 VF £240

York Mint

At the time, York was an ecclesiastical mint under the control of Archbishop Thorsby.

Obverse Legend As previous.

Reverse Legend CIVITAS EBORACI — City of York

Reverse Quatrefoil enclosing pellet in centre of reverse.

E31D-225 VG £45 F £90 VF £180

Durham Mint

At the time, Durham was an ecclesiastical mint under the control of Bishop Hatfield.

Obverse Legend As previous.

Reverse Legend CIVITAS DORELME or DURENE — City of Durham

Reverse The reverse legend is preceded by a crozier.

E31D-230 VG £55 F £110 VF £220

Treaty Period 1361-1369

During this short period of peace, coins were also struck at Calais which became an important mint and continued to be active intermittently until Henry VI's reign.

London Mint

Obverse Legend EDWARD ANGL R DNS HYB — Edward of England and Lord of Ireland

Reverse Legend CIVITAS LONDON — City of London

Obverse Double annulet stops in legend and unbarred 'A' in CIVITAS.

E31D-235 VG £20 F £40 VF £85

There is also a variety similar to the above. It has a barred 'A' on the reverse legend, and a pellet before EDWARD.

Calais Mint

Obverse Legend As previous.

Reverse Legend VILLA CALESIE — Town of Calais

Obverse Double annulet stops in legend.

Reverse Pellet after LA in legend.

E31D-240 VG £60 F £125 VF £250

York Mint

Obverse Legend EDWARDUS REX ANGLI — Edward King of England

Reverse Legend CIVITAS EBORACI — City of York

Obverse Pellet stops in legend.

Reverse As previous.

E31D-245 VG £60 F £125 VF £250

Similar to above, but the king has a voided quatrefoil on his breast. Most of this issue appears to have been made with locally produced, poor quality dies.

E31D-250 VG £70 F £150 VF £300

Similar to E31D-245, but with an annulet before EDWARDUS.

E31D-255 VG £60 F £125 VF £250

Obverse Legend EDWARD ANGL R DNS HYB — Edward King of England Lord of Ireland

Reverse Legend As previous.

Obverse & Reverse Similar to the London issue, but sometimes with a pellet before EDWARD.

E31D-260 VG £60 F £125 VF £250

Many varieties of the obverse legend exist.

Obverse Legend EDWARDUS DEI G REX AN — Edward by the grace of God King of England (abbreviated)

Reverse Legend CIVITAS EBORACI — City of York

Obverse Single annulet stops in legend.

Reverse Quatrefoil in centre of reverse.

E31D-265 VG £30 F £60 VF £120

Durham Mint

Obverse Legend EDWARDUS REX ANGLI — Edward King of England

Reverse Legend CIVITAS DUREME — City of Durham

Obverse Single annulet stops in legend.

Reverse Crozier at the beginning of legend.

E31D-270 VG £40 F £80 VF £160

Obverse Legend As previous.

Reverse Legend CIVITAS DUNELMIS — City of Durham

This issue has no crozier in the legend.

E31D-275 VG £45 VG £90 VF £180

Post Treaty Period 1369–1377

Three mints were active during this period and, for the first time, FRANC (France) can be found in some of the legends. In many cases the 'F' of FRANC is reversed, probably due to an error in the die production.

London Mint

Obverse Legend EDWARD R ANGL FRANC or EDWARDUS REX ANGLIE FR — Edward King of England and France

Reverse Legend CIVITAS LONDON — City of London

Obverse The king sometimes has a pellet on his breast.

Reverse Roman 'N' in reverse legend is sometimes reversed.

E31D-280 VG £40 F £80 VF £160

Obverse Legend EDWARDUS REX ANGLIE — Edward King of England

Reverse Legend CIVITAS LONDON — City of London

Obverse A cross, annulet or quatrefoil or nothing on the king's breast.

Reverse Usually extra pellets on the reverse.

E31D-285 VG £45 F £90 VF £180

York Mint

York was an ecclesiastical mint under the control of Archbishops Thorsby or Neville.

Obverse Legend EDWARD REX ANGL FR (ANC sometimes) — Edward King of England and France

Reverse Legend CIVITAS EBORACI — City of York

Obverse A double annulet, large pellet or saltire stops in legend. Some coins have a cross or annulet on breast.

Reverse Quatrefoil in centre of reverse. Sometimes a plain cross at the start of the legend.

E31D-290 VG £25 F £50 VF £100

Obverse Legend EDWARD DI GRA REX ANG — Edward by the grace of God King of England

Reverse Legend As previous.

Obverse Saltire stops in the legend.

Reverse As previous.

E31D-295 VG £30 F £60 VF £120

Obverse Legend EDWARDUS REX ANGLIE (ET) — Edward King of England (and)

Reverse Legend As previous; crozier in legend.

Obverse There is usually an annulet, lis or cross on the king's breast. This issue usually has saltire stops in the legend.

Reverse As previous.

E31D-300 VG £25 F £50 VF £100

Durham Mint

Durham was an ecclesiastical mint under the control of Bishop Hatfield.

Obverse Legend EDWARDUS REX ANGL FR — Edward King of England [and] France

Reverse Legend CIVITAS DUNOLM — City of Durham

Obverse Double annulets and saltires in legend.

Reverse Long cross, three pellets in each quarter, crozier in legend.

E31D-305 VG £45 F £90 VF £180

Obverse Legend EDWARDUS REX ANGLIE — Edward King of England

Reverse Legend As previous.

Obverse Annulet, lis or nothing on king's breast.

Reverse As previous.

E31D-310 VG £50 F £100 VF £200

Richard II 1377–1399

The last quarter of the fourteenth century was a time of problems and difficulties for England and this was reflected in the quantity and quality of the coins produced. Because Edward III's son the Black Prince died in 1376, when the king himself died a year later the throne went to his eleven year old grandson, Richard II. During Richard's reign, England continued to lay claim to the French throne and was at war with France until 1396. High taxation was imposed to meet the costs of the war and this caused several peasant uprisings.

Moreover during this period, large quantities of poor quality European coins, inferior in both weight and fineness, circulated alongside England's high quality coinage. Large profits could be made by smuggling English coins to the Continent where they would be melted down and, after other valueless metals had been added to the alloy, the coinage would be produced and returned to England. To an uneducated eye, the baser coins looked just the same. This not only made small change scarce, but caused a problem for the mints which were also having difficulties obtaining sufficient quantities of silver for the production of more coins. The situation was in fact a good illustration of Gresham's law that bad money drives good money out of circulation.

The 'new' denominations of Edward III continued into Richard II's reign. Pennies were produced at London, York and Durham.

Collecting Hints

Richard II's pennies are fairly easy to obtain in the lower grades and the average condition in which they are found is Poor to Fair. Often clipped or damaged, they tend not to be attractive coins. York pennies are much more common than those of London and Durham, but many of the York coins were struck from poor quality, locally produced dies and often look very blurred and crude. Collectors should try to obtain an example in at least VG, if not Fine condition but may find it very difficult to obtain specimens in VF or better condition.

London Mint

Obverse Legend RICARDUS REX ANGLIE — Richard King of England

Reverse Legend CIVITAS LONDON — City of London

Obverse Facing bust of king.

Reverse Reversed 'N's in legend.

R21D-005 VG £150 F £300 VF £600

Obverse Legend RICARDUS REX ANGLE Z FRANC — Richard King of England and France

Reverse Legend As previous.

Obverse As previous, but the king has a lis on his breast.

R21D-010 VG £150 F £300 VF £600

Obverse Legend RICARD REX ANGLIE — Richard King of England

Reverse Legend As previous.

Obverse Facing bust with bushy hair; the legend's lettering is fishtailed in shape at the ends.

R21D-015 VG £200 F £400 VF £750

York Mint

A quatrefoil can be found on the reverse in all cases.

Obverse Legend RICARDUS REX ANGLIE — Richard King of England

Reverse Legend CIVITAS EBORACI — City of York

Obverse Lis, cross or nothing on breast.

Reverse Quatrefoil in centre of reverse.

R21D-020 VG £50 F £100 F £200

Obverse Legend RICARDUS REX ANGLIE Z — As previous.

Reverse Legend As previous.

Obverse Pellets by shoulders, cross on breast.

R21D-025 VG £50 F £100 F £200

Obverse Legend RICARDUS REX ANGLIE — As previous.

Reverse Legend As previous.

Obverse No marks on bust or in the field; a breastline is indicated.

R21D-030 VG £45 F £85 VF £170

Similar to previous, but without breastline.

R21D-035 VG £55 F £110 VF £220

Obverse Legend RICARD REX ANGL Z FRANC — Richard King of England and France

Reverse Legend As previous.

Obverse Coarse, rather crude bust.

Reverse As previous, but scallop after TAS.

R21D-040 VG £55 F £110 VF £220

Similar to previous, but the bust is of fine work.

R21D-045 VG £60 F £120 VF £240

Obverse Legend RICARD REX ANGLIE or RICARDUS REX ANGL Z F — Richard King of England (and France)

Reverse Legend As previous, no marks.

Obverse The king has bushy hair.

Reverse 'R' in centre of quatrefoil.

R21D-050 VG £200 F £400 VF —

Durham Mint

Obverse Legend RICARDUS REX ANGLIE — Richard King of England

Reverse Legend CIVITAS DUNOLM — City of Durham

Obverse Facing bust of king with a lis or cross on breast.

Reverse Long cross, three pellets in each quarter.

R21D-060 VG £200 F £350 VF —

Henry IV 1399–1413

Henry Duke of Lancaster, who also was a grandson of Edward III, usurped Richard II in 1399 and ruled as Henry IV. He encountered serious opposition, however, and it was a time of problems and conflict in the country with various attempts being made against the king's life. Also, England was at war with both Scotland and Wales. Henry IV inherited the coinage problems of Richard II. As noted earlier, the price of silver and gold was low in England compared with Europe and, although it was illegal, coins were smuggled out of England to be melted down on the Continent and sold at a profit. This caused major problems for England as not only were there insufficient coins in circulation, but also, the mints could not obtain enough bullion to issue more.

Henry IV's pennies are divided into the heavy and the light coinages. The heavy coinage is so called because the weight of the coins had not been changed in line with the Continental silver price. These coins tend to be somewhat similar to Richard II's issues and cruder in style. The light coinage was issued in 1412 when the weight was reduced to correspond with Continental silver pieces and so put an end to the illegal export of English coinage. This issue was a great success even though it lasted less than two years. The style of the coins was much better, with a more lifelike portrait.

Collecting Hints

All of Henry IV's coins are rare and the penny is no exception. The average condition is VG to about Fine; coins in Fine or better are rare. Many coins tend to be clipped, have flattened legends or creases in the flan. All these features make it difficult to differentiate Henry IV's coins from other more common issues of earlier or later reigns. Using the information listed, collectors should check that a coin is correctly identified. When buying a Henry IV penny from a dealer, collectors should also ensure that the dealer guarantees not only the authenticity of the coin, but also the description. To identify these coins it is necessary to pay particular attention to the obverse legend and to the various marks found on the obverse and reverse of the coin. The mintmark is found at the start of the obverse legend and all issues only used the mintmark cross pattée.

Heavy Coinage 1399–1412

London Mint

Obverse Legend HENRIC DI GRA REX ANGL — Henry by the grace of God King of England

Reverse Legend CIVITAS LONDON — City of London

Obverse Facing bust of king with long hair and a long neck. This die was originally used for a Richard II penny as HENRIC appears to have been struck over RICARDUS. A cross pattée can be found at 12 o'clock in the legend.

Reverse Large cross in centre breaking legends, four pellets in two quarters and three pellets in the two remaining quarters. The reverse die was for Henry IV issues only.

H41D-005 VG £325 F £750 VF £1,500

Similar to the previous issue, but a star can be found on the breast and there are two pellets above the central fleur on the crown. On the reverse some varieties have either 12 or 14 pellets in the quarters.

H41D-010 VG £325 F £750 VF £1,500

Obverse As H41D-005, but the king has a short neck.

Reverse As previous, but Lombardic 'N'.

H41D-015 VG £325 F £750 VF £1,500

York Mint

Reverse Legend CIVITAS EBORACI — City of York

Obverse Similar to H41D-005 with the king having a long neck.

Reverse Quatrefoil in centre of reverse cross.

H41D-020 VG £200 F £400 VF £800

As above, but the king has a broader face and rounder chin.

H41D-025 VG £200 F £400 VF £800

Light Coinage 1412–1413

London Mint

Obverse Legend HENRIC REX ANGLIE — Henry King of England

Reverse Legend CIVITAS LONDON — City of London

Obverse Facing bust of king, pellet to left and annulet to right of crown and a trefoil on breast.

Reverse As previous issues, with three pellets in each quarter, trefoil at beginning of legend and Lombardic 'N's in LONDON.

H41D-030 VG £300 F £600 VF £1,200

As above, but with annulet to left and pellet to right of crown.

H41D-035 unique

Similar, but the obverse legend reads HENRIC DI GRA REX ANGL — Henry by the grace of God King of England.

H41D-040 VG £300 F £600 VF £1,200

Similar to H41D-035, but the king has a small bust with short hair.

H41D-045 ex. rare

York Mint

Obverse Legend HENRIC REX ANGLIE — Henry King of England

Reverse Legend CIVITAS EBORACI — City of York

Obverse Facing bust of king with an annulet on breast and after HENRIC.

Reverse Quatrefoil in centre and annulet stops in legend.

H41D-050 VG £200 F £400 VF £800

Durham Mint

Obverse Legend As previous.

Reverse Legend CIVITAS DVNOLM — City of Durham

Obverse Facing bust of king, trefoil on breast.

Reverse Plain cross.

H41D-055 VG £180 F £375 VF £750

Collectors may wonder why we have given no weights to help to differentiate the two coinages. This is because most specimens tend to be clipped, damaged or worn, making it difficult to give an accurate weight.

Henry V 1413–1422

Henry V, Henry IV's eldest son, ascended the throne at the age of 25, upon the death of his father. It was to be a fairly short reign and once again a time of war with France. Henry V claimed the throne of France and the famous battle of Agincourt took place during his reign. In both style and weight, Henry V's coinage was a continuation of his father's successful light coinage but can be differentiated from Henry IV's coinage in several ways. Firstly, a cross pattée can be found in the obverse legend of all Henry IV's pennies, at 12 o'clock. By contrast Henry V's coins bear a cross pattée with a pellet in the centre or a pierced cross instead. Secondly, it is a matter of elimination; most issues tend to have marks such as annulets and trefoils on the coin, so collectors should check all the varieties to see which type a specimen falls into. It is also important to check the reverse legend to ensure that you have the correct mint. It will either be London, York, Durham, Calais (Henry VI) or Canterbury (Henry VII). And thirdly, compare the portraits which are slightly different, particularly in the hair.

Collecting Hints

Henry V's pennies are fairly easy to obtain but tend to be found in less than Fine condition and are often slightly crude in style and manufacture. Collectors should try to obtain an example in at least Fine condition; coins in VF or better condition are rare. Heavily clipped coins in base metal, similar in style to the pennies of this era, are often found and are contemporary forgeries which may easily be distinguished by their low silver content.

London Mint

Obverse Legend (usually found) HENRIC REX ANGL — Henry King of England

Reverse Legend CIVITAS LONDON — City of London

Obverse 'Emaciated' facing bust of king, short and broad lettering in legend, with annulet and pellet usually by crown.

Reverse Large plain cross, three pellets in each quarter, annulet after LON in legend.

H51D-005 VG £175 F £350 VF —

Legends As above.

Obverse die of a Henry IV penny, but a mullet has been punched over pellet to right of crown. The reverse has ordinary lettering. This variety sometimes has a broken annulet added by crown.

H51D-010 VG £150 F £300 VF —

As above, but the king has a tall neck with a mullet to left and broken annulet to right of the crown.

H51D-015 VG £25 F £50 VF £100

As above, but with a whole instead of a broken annulet.

H51D-020 VG £25 F £50 VF £100

As above, but with a trefoil to the right of the crown; mullet still to left.

H51D-025 VG £30 F £55 VF £110

Obverse Legend HENRIC DI GRA REX ANGL — Henry by the grace of God King of England

Reverse Legend As previous.

Obverse New neat bust with no marks on coin

The obverse die for this type is sometimes used for coins of Henry VI.

H51D-030 VG £30 F £55 VF £110

Durham Mint

Obverse Legend Similar to H51D-005.

Reverse Legend CIVITAS DUNOLM — City of Durham

Obverse Facing bust of king with tall neck. Mullet to left and broken annulet to right of crown.

H51D-035 VG £45 F £90 VF £180

Similar, but complete annulet instead of broken annulet to side of crown.

H51D-040 VG £40 F £80 VF £160

New neat bust with mullet to left and annulet to right of crown; also with an annulet in one quarter of the reverse.

H51D-045 VG £40 F £80 VF £160

York Mint

Obverse Legend Similar to H51D-015.

Reverse Legend CIVITAS EBORACI — City of York

Obverse Facing bust of king with tall neck; mullet to left and broken annulet to right of crown.

Reverse Quatrefoil in centre of reverse cross.

H51D-050 VG £25 F £45 VF £90

As above, but a whole instead of a broken annulet beside the king.

H51D-055 VG £25 F £50 VF £100

As above, but with a pellet above the mullet.

H51D-060 VG £40 F £80 VF £160

Sometimes with a trefoil above the mullet or with mullet to left and trefoil to right of crown.

H51D-065 VG £25 F £45 VF £90

New neat bust with mullet to left and trefoil to right of crown.

H51D-070 VG £30 F £60 VF £120

As above, but made with local dies which make the lettering slightly crude in style. Mullet to left and lis to right of crown and an annulet in one quarter of the reverse.

H51D-075 VG £25 F £55 VF £110

Henry VI First Reign 1422–1461

Henry VI, Henry V's son, became king while still an infant and until he came of age the controlling power in the country rested with the King's Council. Henry VI favoured peace with France but Richard Duke of York, a descendant from the second son of Edward III and heir apparent to the English throne, favoured war. In 1455 this difference precipitated the War of the Roses, the conflict between the Lancastrians (Henry VI) and the Yorkists (Edward IV). The nobility attached itself to either faction but changed allegiance as the balance of power shifted. Eventually in 1461, Henry VI was defeated by Richard's son Edward, who became Edward IV.

Henry VI's long reign is interesting from a numismatic point of view. Despite the immense upheaval and even a civil war, an adequate supply of coinage was maintained throughout the period. Several mints were active, in particular Calais. Henry's coinage may be divided into various classes, distinguished by minor varieties on the coins such as annulets or trefoils. These marks, each specific to a particular moneyer and die, were used as a form of quality control so that if there was a problem with a coin, the person responsible could be identified. There are eleven different issues in total, and all can be dated accurately. Stylistically, Henry VI's coins tend to be very different from previous issues. When identifying pay particular attention to the legend, the mint (if it is Calais it is almost definitely Henry VI), and any marks in the field or legends, such as annulets. The Henry V penny is very crude, compared to the Henry VI one which is neat. It must also be remembered that some of Henry VI's issues were muled with the last issues of Henry V. For coins from the Durham mint, if the reverse legend reads CIVITAS DUNOLIN collectors should refer to Edward IV's First Reign.

Annulet Issue 1422–1427

London Mint

Obverse Legend HENRICUS REX ANGLIE — Henry King of England

Reverse Legend CIVITAS LONDON — City of London

Obverse Facing bust of king.

Reverse Large cross with three pellets in each quarter, annulet in two quarters.

H61D-005 VG £25 F £50 VF £100

Calais Mint

Obverse Legend As previous.

Reverse Legend VILLA CALISIE — Town of Calais

Obverse Facing bust of king with an annulet either side of neck.

Reverse As previous.

H61D-010 VG £22 F £45 VF £90

As previous, but only one annulet in quarter on the reverse.

H61D-015 VG £25 F £50 VF £100

York Mint

Obverse Legend As previous.

Reverse Legend CIVITAS EBORACI — City of York

Obverse Facing bust of king, a lis either side of neck.

Reverse Annulets in two quarters on reverse.

H61D-020 VG £300 F £650 VF —

Annulet Trefoil Sub-Issue

Calais Mint

Similar to H61D-010, but a trefoil of pellets to left of crown; two annulets on the reverse.

H61D-025 VG £50 F £100 VF £200

Similar to above, but only one annulet on the reverse.

H61D-030 VG £60 F £120 VF £240

Rosette Mascle Issue 1427–1430

All these issues have rosettes and mascles somewhere in the legends.

London Mint

Obverse Legend HENRICUS REX ANGLIE — Henry King of England

Reverse Legend CIVITAS LONDON — City of London

Obverse Facing bust of king, no marks by crown or neck.

Reverse Cross with three pellets in each quarter.

H61D-035 VG £40 F £80 VF £160

Calais Mint

As previous, but the reverse legend reads VILLA CALISIE — Town of Calais.

H61D-040 VG £30 F £60 VF £120

York Mint

York was an ecclesiastical mint under the control of Archbishop Kemp. Many of these issues appear to be clipped.

Obverse Legend As previous.

Reverse Legend CIVITAS EBORACI (sometimes misspelled) — City of York

Obverse Facing bust of king, crosses by hair, no rosette in legend.

Reverse Cross with quatrefoil in centre.

H61D-045 VG £25 F £50 VF £100

As previous, but saltires by hair.

H61D-050 VG £25 F £50 VF £100

As previous, but no saltires by hair, with a mullet either side of crown.

H61D-055 VG £25 F £50 VF £100

Durham Mint

At the time, Durham was an ecclesiastical mint under the control of Bishop Langley.

Obverse Legend As previous.

Reverse Legend CIVITAS DVNOLMI — City of Durham

Obverse Star to left of crown, no rosettes in legend.

Reverse Plain cross in centre, three pellets in each quarter.

H61D-060 VG £50 F £100 VF £200

Pinecone Mascle Issue 1430–1434

All the coins from this issue have a pinecone and a mascle in the legend.

London Mint

Obverse Legend HENRICUS REX ANGLIE — Henry King of England

Reverse Legend CIVITAS LONDON — City of London

Obverse Facing bust of king, no marks in field.

Reverse Plain cross, three pellets in each quarter.

H61D-065 VG £50 F £100 VF £200

Calais Mint

As previous, but the reverse legend reads VILLA CALISIE — Town of Calais.

H61D-070 VG £25 F £50 VF £100

York Ecclesiastical Mint under Archbishop Kemp

Obverse Legend As previous.

Reverse Legend CIVITAS EBORACI — City of York

Obverse Mullet by crown.

Reverse Quatrefoil in centre of cross.

H61D-075 VG £25 F £50 VF £100

Legends As previous.

Obverse Rosette on breast.

Reverse No quatrefoil in centre of the reverse cross.

H61D-080 VG £25 F £50 VF £100

As previous, but a mullet on breast instead of a rosette.

H61D-085 VG £25 F £50 VF £100

Durham Mint

Durham was an ecclesiastical mint under the control of Bishop Langley.

Obverse Legend As previous.

Reverse Legend CIVITAS DVNOLMI — City of Durham

Obverse Facing bust of king, no marks.

Reverse Cross with three pellets in each quarter.

H61D-090 VG £50 F £100 VF £200

Leaf Mascle Issue 1434–1435

London Mint

Obverse Legend HENRICUS REX ANGLIE — Henry King of England

Reverse Legend CIVITAS LONDON — City of London

Obverse Facing bust of king, leaf on breast, mascle and saltires in legend.

Reverse Plain cross with three pellets in each quarter.

H61D-095 VG £40 F £80 VF £160

Calais Mint

Obverse Legend As previous.

Reverse Legend VILLA CALISIE — Town of Calais

Obverse Facing bust of king, leaf on breast.

Reverse As previous, but mascle and saltires in legend and a leaf below SIE.

H61D-100 VG £40 F £80 VF £160

Leaf Trefoil Issue 1435–1438

London Mint

Obverse Legend HENRICUS REX ANGLIE — Henry King of England

Reverse Legend CIVITAS LONDON — City of London

Obverse Facing bust of king, leaf on breast, saltires and trefoil in legend.

Reverse Plain cross with three pellets in each quarter, leaf and trefoil in legend.

H61D-105 VG £50 F £100 VF £200

Calais Mint

As previous, except that the reverse legend reads VILLA CALISIE — Town of Calais.

H61D-110 ex. rare

Durham Mint

Obverse Legend HENRICUS REX ANGLIE — Henry King of England

Reverse Legend CIVITAS DUNOLM — City of Durham

Obverse Facing bust of king, leaf on breast, saltires and leaf in legend.

Reverse Cross on reverse with two rings in centre, no marks in legend.

H61D-115 VG £75 F £150 VF £300

No pennies were struck for the trefoil issue (1438–1454).

Leaf Pellet Issue 1445–1454

London Mint

Obverse Legend HENRICUS REX ANGLIE — Henry King of England

Reverse Legend CIVITAS LONDON — City of London

Obverse Facing bust of king with leaf on breast, a pellet either side of crown, saltires in legend.

Reverse Plain cross sometimes with an extra pellet in two quarters.

H61D-120 VG £35 F £70 VF £140

As above, but no pellets by crown.

H61D-125 VG £35 F £70 VF £140

Similar to H61D-120, but a trefoil in obverse legend.

H61D-130 VG £40 F £80 VF £160

York Mint

York was an ecclesiastical mint under the control of Archbishop Booth.

Obverse Legend HENRICUS REX ANGLIE — Henry King of England

Reverse Legend CIVITAS EBORACI — City of York

Obverse Facing bust of king sometimes with leaf on breast; a pellet either side of crown.

Reverse Quatrefoil and pellet in centre of reverse, sometimes an extra pellet in two quarters.

H61D-135 VG £25 F £50 VF £100

There is also a variety, slightly crude in style, which was struck with local dies. It is identical to the previous issue, but there is another pellet either side of the king's hair.

H61D-140 VG £25 F £50 VF £100

Durham Mint

Durham was an ecclesiastical mint under the control of Bishop Neville.

Obverse Legend As previous.

Reverse Legend CIVITAS DUNOLM — City of Durham

Obverse Facing bust of king with leaf on breast, sometimes trefoil in legend.

Reverse Cross with two rings in centre.

H61D-145 VG £75 F £150 VF £300

No pennies were struck during the unmarked issue (1453–1454).

Cross Pellet Issue 1454–1460

London Mint

Obverse Legend HENRICUS REX ANGLIE — Henry King of England

Reverse Legend CIVITAS LONDON — City of London

Obverse Facing bust of king, a saltire on neck and a pellet either side of crown.

Reverse Plain cross, three pellets in each quarter, mascle(s) or mullet and mascle in legend.

H61D-150 VG £80 F £160 VF £320

York Mint

York was an ecclesiastical mint under the control of Archbishop William Booth.

Obverse Legend As previous.

Reverse Legend CIVITAS EBORACI — City of York

Obverse Facing bust of king, leaf sometimes on breast, saltires beside neck.

Reverse Quatrefoil in centre of cross.

H61D-155 VG £50 F £100 VF £200

Durham Mint

Durham was an ecclesiastical mint under the control of Bishop Laurence Booth.

Obverse Legend HENRICUS REX ANGLIE — Henry King of England

Reverse Legend CIVITAS DUNOLM — City of Durham

Obverse Saltire and 'B' either side of neck, a pellet either side of crown.

Reverse Two rings in centre of cross, the three pellets in each quarter are sometimes linked by lines.

H61D-160 VG £100 F £200 VF £400

No pennies were struck for the lis-pellet issue (1456–1460).

Edward IV First Reign 1461–1470

In 1461, Edward Duke of York deposed Henry VI and proclaimed himself King Edward IV of England. With the Lancastrians defeated, Henry fled and was finally captured and imprisoned in the Tower of London. He was released and restored to the throne in 1470, but only for a few months. Throughout this period virtual civil war raged in England but the continuing conflict did not affect the output of coinage, not least because issuing coins in the name of a new king was a means of manifesting his authority.

Under Edward IV, the heavy and the light coinages were produced. With the rising value of silver in Europe, coins from Eng-land were again being smuggled abroad, melted down and sold at a profit. As a result, in 1464, the weight of all coins was reduced by about 20%, producing the light coinage. Heavy coinage pennies weigh about 15 grains (1.0 gram) and those from the light coinage weigh 12 grains (0.8 grams). Edward's coins are quite easy to distinguish. Above, in the section devoted to Edward III, we have listed how these coins differ from the previous issues of Edward I to Edward III. In order to identify an Edward IV penny, collectors should first check that the obverse legend bears the king's name EDWARD. Secondly look at the face, which in Edward IV's case will be fairly youthful. Compare it to Edward I, II, III, and also Edward IV's second reign, paying particular attention to the crown and hair style. The coins from Edward IV's second reign tend to be very crude in style. It is also important to remember that the coinage became progressively smaller in size.

Having identified the monarch, it is important to find the mint, which is on the reverse, preceded by the word VILLA (town) or CIVITAS (city). For Edward IV they are the following: CIVITAS LONDON — City of London; CIVITAS DVNOLIN — City of Durham; CIVITAS BRISTOLI or BRISTOW — City of Bristol; CIVITAS CANTOR — City of Canterbury; CIVITAS EBORA-CI — City of York. If a coin is not from one of the above mints, it is not Edward IV's first reign.

After finding the correct mint, look for marks of interest on the coin, usually found on the obverse near the king's head. When you have found some marks, go through the following pages until you find the exact variety. If it is not there, check Edward IV's second reign carefully.

Collecting Hints

Edward IV's pennies are reasonably available, except for the heavy coinage issue of 1461–1464. Many coins tend to be rather crude in style, with areas of weakness, due to the quality of the strike. Collectors should try to obtain an example in at least Fine condition and visually attractive. Coins from the London mint tend to be of a slightly better quality than the other mints, in particular Durham.

Heavy Coinage 1461–1464

Weighing 15 grains (1.0 gram), these coins are, in some cases, very similar to the light coinage. Collectors should check every detail carefully and, if necessary, weigh the coin; also note that several dies from this issue omitted DI GRA in the obverse legend.

London Mint

Obverse Legend EDWARD DI GRA REX ANGL — Edward by the grace of God King of England

Reverse Legend CIVITAS LONDON — City of London

Obverse Facing bust of king, lis on breast, pellet either side of crown and mascle after REX; mintmark plain cross.

Reverse Extra pellet in two quarters of the reverse cross.

E41D-005 VG £125 F £250 VF £500

Legends As previous.

Obverse Facing bust of king, quatrefoils by neck; mintmark rose.

Reverse Cross with three pellets in each quarter.

E41D-010 ex. rare

As previous, but an eye after TAS in reverse legend.

E41D-015 VG £150 F £300 VF £600

Legends As previous.

Obverse Facing bust of king, annulets by neck; mintmark rose.

Reverse Cross with three pellets in each quarter.

E41D-020 VG £160 F £350 VF £650

York Mint

York was an ecclesiastical mint under the control of Archbishop Booth.

Obverse Legend EDWARD DI GRA REX ANG — Edward by the grace of God King of England

Reverse Legend CIVITAS EBORACI — City of York

Obverse Facing bust of king, quatrefoils by bust, mintmark rose.

Reverse Voided quatrefoil in centre of reverse cross.

E41D-025 VG £125 F £250 VF £500

Durham Mint

There is uncertainty as to where to class this type. It would appear that the obverse is from a Henry VI penny. The reverse, with the spelling of Durham DUNOLIN, appears to be that of Edward IV. Both have mintmarks of plain cross and this was used during the reigns of both Henry VI and Edward IV. Sometimes this issue has one or more pellets beside the crown and, on the reverse, a rose in the centre and an extra pellet in the quarters.

Obverse Legend HENRICUS REX ANGLIE (or altered die) — Henry King of England

Reverse Legend CIVITAS DUNOLIN — City of Durham

Obverse Facing crowned bust of Henry VI.

Reverse As previous.

E41D-030 VG £125 F £250 VF £500

Light Coinage 1464–1470

These pennies weigh 12 grains (0.8 grams); sometimes DI GRA is omitted from the obverse legend. Also, some words miss out odd letters.

London Mint

Obverse Legend EDWARD DI GRA REX ANGL — Edward by the grace of God King of England

Reverse Legend CIVITAS LONDON — City of London

Obverse Facing bust of king, annulets by neck; mintmark rose.

Reverse Plain cross, three pellets in each quarter.

This coin was struck using the heavy coinage die; the weight should, therefore, be checked.

E41D-035 VG — F £150 VF £300

As previous, but quatrefoils at neck, mintmark sun or crown.

E41D-040 VG £30 F £60 VF £120

As previous, but trefoil and quatrefoil by neck; mintmark crown.

E41D-045 VG £32 F £65 VF £130

As previous, but saltires by neck; mintmark crown.

E41D-050 VG £32 F £65 VF £130

As previous, but trefoils by neck; mintmark crown or long cross fitchée.

E41D-055 VG £30 F £60 VF £120

As previous, but facing bust of king without marks; mintmark long cross fitchée.

E41D-060 ex. rare

Bristol Mint

Obverse Legend EDWARD DI GRA REX ANGL — Edward by the grace of God King of England

Reverse Legend VILLA BRISTOW — Town of Bristol

Obverse Facing bust of king, quatrefoils or saltires by neck; mintmark crown.

Reverse Plain cross, three pellets in each quarter.

E41D-065 VG £90 F £180 VF £360

Obverse Legend As previous.

Reverse Legend VILLA BRI (trefoil) STOLL — Town of Bristol

Obverse As previous, with quatrefoils by neck.

Reverse As previous, but trefoil in legend.

E41D-070 VG £100 F £200 VF £400

Obverse Legend As previous.

Reverse Legend VILLA BRISTOLL — Town of Bristol

Obverse Trefoil to right of neck.

Reverse As previous.

E41D-075 VG £110 F £225 VF £450

Canterbury Mint

Two mints were active in Canterbury during this period. The ecclesiastical mint under Archbishop Bourchier, and the royal mint under the control of the king.

Canterbury Ecclesiastical Mint

Obverse Legend EDWARD DI GRA REX ANGL — Edward by the grace of God King of England

Reverse Legend CIVITAS CANTOR — City of Canterbury

Obverse Facing bust of king, quatrefoils or saltires by neck, knot on breast; mintmark pall.

Reverse Plain cross, three pellets in each quarter.

E41D-080 VG £75 F £150 VF £300

As above, but no marks by neck.

E41D-085 VG £75 F £150 VF £300

As E41D-080, but no knot on king's breast.

E41D-090 VG £80 F £160 VF £320

As previous, but crosses by neck.

E41D-095 VG £75 F £150 VF £300

Canterbury Royal Mint

As previous, but quatrefoils by neck; mintmark crown.

E41D-100 VG £125 F £250 VF £500

Durham Mint
King's Receiver

Varieties of this type exist. The legends are often blundered for Durham and York, especially with the locally made dies issue.

Obverse Legend EDWARD DI GRA REX ANGL — Edward by the grace of God King of England

Reverse Legend CIVITAS DUNOLM, DVNOLI, DER(H)AM — City of Durham (varieties)

Obverse Facing bust of king; mintmark plain cross or rose.

Reverse Rose usually in centre.

E41D-105 VG £20 F £40 VF £80

Bishop Booth

Legends As previous.

Obverse 'B' and 'D' either side of neck; mintmark rose.

Reverse 'B' in centre.

E41D-110 VG £30 F £60 VF £120

As previous, but quatrefoil and 'B' by neck; mintmark sun.

E41D-115 VG £30 F £60 VF £120

Legends As previous.

Obverse 'D' and quatrefoil by neck; mintmark sun.

Reverse Plain cross.

E41D-120 VG £30 F £60 VF £120

Legends As previous.

Obverse Quatrefoils by neck, mintmark crown.

Reverse Plain cross.

E41D-125 VG £30 F £60 VF £120

As previous, but trefoils by neck; mintmark crown.

E41D-130 VG £30 F £60 VF £120

As previous, but lis by neck; mintmark crown.

E41D-135 VG £32 F £65 VF £130

York Mint
Sede Vacante Issue 1464–1465

Obverse Legend EDWARD DI GRA REX ANGL — Edward by the grace of God King of England

Reverse Legend CIVITAS EBORACI — City of York

Obverse Facing bust of king; quatrefoils either side of neck; mintmark sun or rose.

Reverse Plain cross.

E41D-140 VG £45 F £90 VF £180

Ecclesiastical Mint under Archbishop Neville, 1465–1470

This issue was rather crude in style, being struck from locally made dies.

Legends As previous.

Obverse Facing bust of king, a 'G' and key by neck; mintmark plain cross or rose.

Reverse Quatrefoil in centre.

E41D-145 VG £32 F £65 VF £130

As previous, but struck from better quality London-made dies and bearing different mintmarks: sun, lis, or long cross fitchée.

E41D-150 VG £22 F £45 VF £90

As previous, but no marks by neck; mintmark large lis.

E41D-155 ex. rare

As previous, but quatrefoils by neck.

E41D-160 VG £32 F £65 VF £130

As previous, but trefoils by neck.

E41D-165 VG £40 F £80 VF £160

Henry VI Restored Oct. 1470 — April 1471

During Edward IV's reign England was being torn apart by the War of the Roses and in October 1470 the king was forced to flee to the Continent, and Henry VI was released from the Tower and restored to the throne. This second reign of his however only lasted a few months as Edward, having mustered support for his own restoration, returned to England in 1471, defeated his enemies and regained the throne. Henry VI was once again imprisoned in the Tower, where he was murdered the same night.

Despite the brevity of Henry VI's second reign, three mints were active and, in the case of the London mint, three different dies were used. The coins of Henry VI's restored reign are fairly similar to those of his first reign but with a few minor differences. Firstly, the mintmark, found in the legend above the king's head, which for London is a cross pattée, Restoration Cross or a short-cross fitchée; Henry's first reign coinage did not use these mintmarks. However, Henry V did use a cross pattée, but this had a pellet in the centre. If the mintmark is not clearly visible, collectors will have to compare the styles of Henry V and Henry VI; they are very different, with the Henry V issues being very crude in style.

The minor differences between the reigns are as follows :

1. A cross pattée with pellet in centre found on issues of Henry V.

2. There is a slight difference in the obverse legend, which for Henry VI Restored is HENRIC (or HENRICU, HERICU) DI GRA REX ANGL (or ANG). The legend of Henry VI's first reign usually reads HENRICUS REX ANGLIE.

Pay particular attention to the king's name and the spelling, as in all cases it is different from the previous issue.

Collecting Hints

The short period of Henry VI's second reign explains why all issues are rare, in every grade. Collectors should try to obtain an example in at least Fine condition, so that it can be easily differentiated from previous issues.

London Mint

Obverse Legend HENRIC DI GRA REX ANGL — Henry by the grace of God King of England

Reverse Legend CIVITAS LONDON — City of London

Obverse Facing bust of king; mintmarks cross pattée, Restoration cross, short cross fitchée.

Reverse Cross with three pellets in each quarter.

H61D-165 VG £225 F £450 VF £900

Bristol Mint

This coin is of the highest rarity.
Obverse Legend As previous.
Reverse Legend CIVITAS BRISTOW — City of Bristol

Obverse As previous, with mintmark cross fitchée only.

Reverse As previous.

H61D-170 ex. rare

York Mint

Obverse Legend As previous.

Reverse Legend CIVITAS EBORACI — City of York

Obverse Facing bust of king, 'G' and a key either side of neck; mintmark lis.

Reverse A quatrefoil in centre of the reverse cross.

H61D-175 VG £150 F £300 VF £600

Edward IV Second Reign 1471–1483

Edward IV landed in England in 1471 to recover the throne from Henry VI and, after two victories at Barnet and Tewkesbury, succeeded.

The coinage of Edward's second reign continued from the first reign. All the denominations and styles remained the same.

The 'initial mark', or mintmark, was becoming increasingly more important as a form of quality control, linking coins to specific dies without the coins having to look different to the general public which in England, as elsewhere, wanted conformity in the coinage. It is important to bear in mind that a coin had to be actually worth its weight in silver or gold, it was not a token or a promissory issue but a penny's worth of silver. Before accepting it in payment, traders would inspect a coin carefully, particularly as forgeries were produced in large quantities and clipped coins and inferior European issues were in circulation. But the mintmark also served another purpose, which is especially useful to the collector, as coins can be accurately dated using the mintmark. In previous issues, such as Henry VI's and Edward IV's first reigns, many issues can be dated to within a few years. However, during Edward IV's second reign, the use of the mintmark to denote the date was firmly established.

As mentioned earlier, the issues of the second reign are very similar to those of the first and in that section we have given full details on how to differentiate Edward IV's reign from others. Then, an elimination process has to be used to differentiate between Edward IV's own two reigns. Firstly, find the mint where the coin was issued. This can be found on the reverse of the coin and should read as follows: CIVITAS LONDON (City of London), CIVITAS BRISTOW or BRISTOLL (City of Bristol), CIVITAS CANTOR (City of Canterbury), CIVITAS DERAM or DUNOLMIE (City of Durham), or CIVITAS EBORACI (City of York). Now that you know where the coin was issued, look for the mintmark in the obverse legend above the king's head. Finally, look for any unusual marks on the coin. These can often be found on either side of the king's neck. Then, using an elimination process, go through the various types until you find one which corresponds to your coin.

Should you have difficulty in classifying your coin, re-check the obverse legend making sure it is a coin of Edward. Then re-check, using the information on Edward IV's first reign, to make sure that you have the correct Edward. Do not be too concerned if your coin is not exactly like the coin in the illustration. Many different dies were used, and no two dies are exactly the same. Also bear in mind that letters, during this period, were not always written as they are today.

The mintmarks found on coins from Edward IV's second reign are as follows:

Years	Mintmark	Mint
1471–1483	rose	York or Durham
1471	short cross fitchée	
1471–1472	large annulet, trefoil	
1471–1472	rose	Bristol
1471–1473	pansy	Durham

Years	Mintmark	Mint
1472–1473	small annulet	
1472–1473	sun	Bristol
1473–1477	pellet in annulet	
	cross and four pellets	
	cross in circle	
1473–1477	cross pattée	
	pierced cross	
1477–1480	pierced cross and pellet	
	pierced cross	
	pierced cross and central pellet	
	rose	Canterbury
1480–1483	heraldic cinquefoil	
	long cross fitchée	Canterbury
	halved sun and rose?	it is uncertain whether this mintmark is for Edward IV or for Edward V

London Mint

Obverse Legend EDWARD DI GRA REX ANGL — Edward by the grace of God King of England

Reverse Legend CIVITAS LONDON — City of London

Obverse No marks by bust; mintmarks from 1471 short cross fitchée to 1480–1483 heraldic cinquefoil (refer to table).

Reverse Plain cross, three pellets in each quarter.

E41D-170 VG £30 F £60 VF £120

Bristol Mint

This issue is of the highest rarity.
Obverse Legend As previous.
Reverse Legend CIVITAS BRISTOW — City of Bristol
Obverse As previous; mintmark rose.
Reverse As previous.

E41D-175 ex. rare

Canterbury Mint

Obverse Legend As previous.
Reverse Legend CIVITAS CANTOR — City of Canterbury
Obverse As previous; mintmark rose or long cross fitchée.
Reverse As previous.

E41D-180 VG £60 F £120 VF £240

As previous, but a 'C' on the king's breast and mintmark rose only.

E41D-185 VG £65 F £130 VF £250

Durham Mint

This was an ecclesiastical mint under the control of Bishop Booth.
Obverse Legend As previous.
Reverse Legend CIVITAS DERAM or DUNOLMIE — City of Durham
Obverse No marks on coin; mintmark short cross fitchée or trefoil.

Reverse No marks in centre of cross.

E41D-190 VG £22 F £45 VF £90

Legends As previous.
Obverse 'B' and trefoil by neck; mintmark trefoil, rose or pellet in annulet.
Reverse 'D' in centre of reverse cross.

E41D-195 VG £25 F £50 VF £100

Legends As previous.
Obverse A lis either side of the neck; mintmark rose.
Reverse 'D' in centre of reverse cross.

E41D-200 VG £22 F £45 VF £90

The following issues (E41D-205–235) were struck from locally made dies.
Legends As previous.
Obverse Crosses over crown and on breast; mintmark rose.
Reverse 'D' in centre of reverse cross, extra pellet in one or four quarters.

E41D-205 VG £22 F £45 VF £90

Legends As previous.
Obverse Crosses over crown; mintmark rose or pansy.
Reverse 'D' in centre of cross, a 'V' under CIVI in legend.

E41D-210 VG £25 F £50 VF £100

As previous, but 'B' to left of crown, 'V' on breast; mintmark pansy.

E41D-215 VG £20 F £40 VF £80

As previous, but crosses by shoulders.

E41D-220 VG £20 F £40 VF £80

Sede Vacante Issue 1476

Legends As previous.
Obverse Plain bust, no marks; mintmark rose.
Reverse 'D' in centre of reverse.

E41D-225 VG £35 F £70 VF £140

Bishop Dudley Issue

Legends As previous.
Obverse 'V' to right of neck; mintmark rose.
Reverse 'D' in centre of reverse cross.

E41D-230 VG £25 F £50 VF £100

Legends As previous.
Obverse 'D' and 'V' either side of neck; mintmark heraldic cinquefoil.
Reverse In most cases a 'D' in the centre of reverse cross.

E41D-235 VG £20 F £40 VF £80

York Ecclesiastical Mint

Archbishop Neville Issue 1471–1472

Obverse Legend As previous.

Reverse Legend CIVITAS EBORACI — City of York

Obverse Facing bust of king, quatrefoils by neck; mintmark short cross fitchée over lis.

Reverse Quatrefoil in centre of reverse cross.

E41D-240 VG £100 F £200 VF £400

As previous, but 'G' and key either side of neck on obverse; mintmark short cross fitchée over lis.

E41D-245 VG £20 F £40 VF £80

Sede Vacante Issue — Archbishop Neville Suspended 1472–1475

As previous, but plain cross in centre of obverse, no quatrefoil.

E41D-250 VG £20 F £40 VF £80

Legends As previous.

Obverse No marks by neck; mintmark small annulet, cross in circle or rose. A few issues have a rose on the breast

Reverse Quatrefoil in the reverse cross in most cases.

E41D-255 VG £100 F £200 VF £400

Legends As previous.

Obverse 'E' and rose either side of neck; mintmark rose.

Reverse Quatrefoil in centre.

E41D-260 VG £22 F £45 VF £90

Archbishop Neville Restored 1475–1476

As previous, but 'G' and rose either side of king's neck; mintmark rose.

E41D-265 VG £22 F £45 VF £90

As previous, but 'G' and key either side of neck; mintmark rose over annulet.

E41D-275 VG £25 F £50 VF £100

As previous, but mintmark rose.

E41D-280 VG £22 F £45 VF £90

Sede Vacante Issue 1476

As previous but no marks by neck; mintmark rose. Rose on king's breast. Quatrefoil on reverse.

E41D-285 VG £25 F £50 VF £100

Archbishop Lawrence Booth Issue 1476–1480

As previous, but 'B' and key either side of neck; mintmark rose and cinquefoil.

E41D-290 VG £22 F £45 VF £90

Sede Vacante Issue 1480

Legends As previous.

Obverse 'B' and key either side of neck; mintmark rose.

Reverse Plain cross, no quatrefoil.

E41D-295 VG £25 F £50 VF £100

Archbishop Rotherham Issue 1480–1483

Legends As previous.

Obverse 'T' and key either side of neck; mintmark rose.

Reverse Quatrefoil in centre.

E41D-300 VG £25 F £50 VF £100

As previous, but a star on the king's breast.

E41D-305 VG £100 F £250 VF —

As previous, but a star on the king's breast and to the right of the king's crown.

E41D-310 VG £65 F £150 VF £300

Edward IV or V

As mentioned earlier, there is uncertainty regarding which reign this issue should be classed in, but most numismatists are of the opinion that, while the dies were made for Edward IV's second reign, they were used to produce coinage under Edward V. Despite the uncertainty, the issue is extremely rare. It was struck at the London mint and the only way to differentiate it is through the mintmark which is halved sun and rose.

Obverse Legend EDWARD DI GRA REX ANGL — Edward by the grace of God King of England

Reverse Legend CIVITAS LONDON — City of London

Obverse Plain bust of king, no marks, but mintmark halved sun and rose.

Reverse Plain cross, three pellets in each quarter.

E41D-315 VG — F £800 VF £1,600

Edward V 1483

Edward V was only 12 years old when, upon his fathers death, he inherited the throne. As the country could obviously not be governed by a child, rival factions tried to obtain control and Richard Duke of Gloucester, who was the younger brother of Edward IV, proclaimed himself Protector of the Realm. To consolidate power he executed his rivals and placed Edward V and his younger brother Richard in the Tower of London where they were murdered a few months later.

While evidence exists that pennies were struck, it is uncertain that any have survived. From records we believe that the London mint produced coins for this period with a boar's head as mintmark. From what we can ascertain from contemporary evidence, this issue is as follows:

Obverse Legend EDWARD DI GRA REX ANGL — Edward by the grace of God King of England

Reverse Legend CIVITAS LONDON — City of London

Obverse Facing bust of king, no marks; mintmark boar's head.

Reverse Cross, three pellets in each quarter.

E51D-005 ex. rare

Richard III 1483–1485

Richard Duke of Gloucester usurped his nephew Edward V in 1483 and reigned as Richard III. He was, however, blamed for the murder of the young king and his ruthlessness alienated many of the nobility who had previously supported him. Having survived one rebellion, Richard was killed during the Battle of Bosworth.

This short reign produced few changes in the coinage but all of Richard III's coins are rare, and fairly easy to differentiate. Firstly, the obverse legend begins with the king's name, RICARD, and only one other issue is similar, that of Richard II. Richard I's coins read HENRICUS. To distinguish between the coins of Richard II and Richard III look at the different style of hair, eyes and the size. Then look at the mintmark, in the legend above the king; Richard II only used mintmark cross pattée while Richard III's coinage did not use this but the mintmarks boar's head, sun and rose, or rose and lis instead.

Collecting Hints

All of Richard III's coins are rare. Pennies tend to be found in about Fine condition, often on small flans with weaknesses in the legend. It is fairly difficult to find a coin in Fine or better condition. Collectors who simply want a coin from this reign might well consider a groat, which is a more attractive and more readily available coin, but please note that any Richard III coin is expensive.

London Mint

Obverse Legend RICARD DEI GRA REX ANG(L) — Richard by the grace of God King of England

Reverse Legend CIVITAS LONDON — City of London

Obverse Facing bust of king; mintmark boar's head.

Reverse Plain cross, three pellets in each quarter.

R31D-005 unique

York Mint

This was an ecclesiastical mint under the control of Archbishop Rotherham.

Obverse Legend As previous.

Reverse Legend CIVITAS EBORACI — City of York

Obverse Bust of king with no marks; mintmark sun and rose.

Reverse Quatrefoil in centre.

R31D-010 VG £250 F £500 VF £1,000

As previous, but 'T' and key either side of neck; mintmark rose or boar's head.

R31D-015 VG £150 F £300 VF £600

Durham Mint

This was an ecclesiastical mint under the control of the Bishop of Sherwood.

Obverse Legend As previous.

Reverse Legend CIVITAS DURRAM — City of Durham

Obverse 'S' on king's breast; mintmark lis.

Reverse 'D' in centre of reverse cross.

R31D-020 VG £125 F £250 VF £500

Henry VII 1485–1509

In 1485, Henry Tudor sailed with his army from France and landed at Milford Haven in Wales. He confronted Richard III at the Battle of Bosworth, defeating his army and killing him, whereupon he assumed the English throne as Henry VII. Although Henry was a Tudor, he descended from Lancastrians and by his marriage to Elizabeth of York finally succeeded in ending the Wars of the Roses.

Henry VII's reign was important for the production of coinage and new denominations were introduced, such as the sovereign (20 shillings) and the testoon (one shilling). Moreover the whole style of the coinage, which had remained more or less unaltered for over two hundred years, changed; this is particularly noticeable with denominations such as the groat and though somewhat less noticeable with the penny. The king's bust became much more lifelike and the reverse shields far more detailed. Undoubtedly influenced by the European Renaissance, the quality of coins was improved. Henry VII's pennies can be divided into two main types: the old type which, at a rough glance, is similar to that of previous kings, such as Henry VI, and the so-called 'sovereign' type which depicts the king seated on the throne on the obverse and the royal shield over a cross dividing the legend on the reverse.

First Coinage

This fairly scarce issue is similar to that of Henry VI and Henry V. However, there are some important differences. Having established that a penny is a Henry by checking that the obverse legend begins with HENRIC, compare the styles using the illustrations below; Henry VII's hair and crown are very different in style. Also look at the reverse where the centre cross on Henry VII's coinage is usually thinner and the three pellets in each quarter smaller. Finally pay attention to the mintmark, found above and slightly to the right of the king's head; Henry VII used mintmarks that are not found on the previous issues.

Collecting Hints

Pennies from this issue are surprisingly difficult to obtain, especially when compared to the groats and halfgroats which tend to be readily available. Collectors should try to obtain an example in at least Fine condition. When this issue is available it tends to be in reasonable condition, unclipped and usually on full flans.

London Mint

Obverse Legend HENRIC DI GRA REX ANG (varieties) — Henry by the grace of God King of England

Reverse Legend CIVITAS LONDON — City of London

Obverse Facing bust of king; mintmark lis upon sun and rose.

Reverse Cross with three pellets in each quarter.

H71D-005 VG £225 F £450 VF £900

A very rare variety exists with crosses either side of bust.

H71D-010 ex. rare

Canterbury Mint

While the crown looks similar to that of Henry VI, this issue is the only one with the letter M in the centre of the reverse cross.
Obverse Legend As previous.

Reverse Legend CIVITAS CANTOR — City of Canterbury

Obverse The king has an open instead of an arched crown; mintmark tun.

Reverse 'M', for Archbishop Morton, in centre of cross.

H71D-015 ex. rare

Legends As previous.

Obverse The king has an arched crown; mintmark tun.

Reverse Plain cross in centre.

H71D-020 VG £40 F £80 VF £160

Durham Mint

Obverse Legend As previous.

Reverse Legend CIVITAS DERAM — City of Durham

Obverse 'S', for Bishop Sherwood, on king's breast; mintmark cross.

Reverse 'D' in centre of reverse cross.

H71D-025 VG £70 F £140 VF £280

York Mint

Obverse Legend As previous.

Reverse Legend CIVITAS EBORACI — City of York

Obverse 'T' and cross either side of king's bust. This issue sometimes has a cross on the king's breast; mintmark lis upon sun and rose.

Reverse 'H' in centre of reverse cross.

H71D-030 VG £35 F £70 VF £140

Legends As previous.

Obverse 'T' and trefoil either side of king's bust; mintmark lis over sun and rose.

Reverse Quatrefoil in centre of cross, and an extra pellet in two quarters.

H71D-035 VG £40 F £80 VF £160

Sovereign Coinage

The sovereign coinage is so called because the new style, showing the sovereign on the throne, was first used in the production of Henry VII sovereigns. That coin dramatically put an end to the two hundred year old style which had changed little since the reign of Edward I, signalling the close of medieval England and the dawn of the Renaissance period.

The weight of the coins remained the same as in the previous issues but, as you can see, the new issue was far more detailed. The mintmark system remained and the mintmark, which as mentioned earlier was a form of quality control and can also be used to date various issues, can be found just to the right of the king's crown. The mint's name can also be found on the coin and, as with earlier issues, it makes up the reverse legend. The first word is always CIVITAS (City of) followed by LONDON, EBORACI (York), DERAM or DIRHAM (Durham).

As with previous issues, many varieties exist. We have listed them all. Should a coin not fall into any of these classes, remember that Henry VIII also issued sovereign pennies and refer to that section for details on how to differentiate the two reigns.

Collecting Hints

Henry VII sovereign pennies are available, usually in VG to about Fine condition. They are often slightly clipped with legends difficult to read. Collectors should try to obtain an example in at least Fine condition. VF and EF coins sometimes become available. However, as with previous issues, these are very popular with collectors and tend to sell quickly.

London Mint

Obverse Legend HENRICUS DI GRA REX ANG (varieties) — Henry by the grace of God King of England

Reverse Legend CIVITAS LONDON — City of London

Obverse King seated on throne, no pillars to side of throne, no stops in legend; no mintmark.

Reverse The king's shield over a cross.

H71D-040 ex. rare

As previous, but single pillar to throne on king's right side; mintmark lis, cinquefoil or nothing.

H71D-045 VG £20 F £40 VF £100

As previous, but ornate lettering in obverse legend with rosette stops; mintmark lis.

H71D-050 VG £25 F £45 VF £110

As previous, but two pillars either side of king; mintmark pansy or nothing, saltire stops in obverse legend.

H71D-055 VG £20 F £40 VF £100

As previous, but small square lettering in obverse legend; no mintmark.

H71D-060 VG £20 F £40 VF £100

As previous, but two double pillars either side of king; mintmark, nothing, crosslet or pheon. The legends are slightly neater in style.

H71D-065 VG £25 F £45 VF £110

Durham Ecclesiastical Mint

Bishop Sherwood

Obverse Legend As previous.

Reverse Legend CIVITAS DERAM or DIRHAM — City of Durham

Obverse King seated on throne that has one pillar, crozier to right of king; no mintmark.

Reverse 'D' and 'S' either side of shield.

H71D-070 VG £25 F £50 VF £120

As previous, but the king's throne now has two pillars, no crozier.

H71D-075 VG £30 F £60 VF £130

Bishop Fox

Legends As previous.

Obverse King's throne with one pillar.

Reverse Bishop's mitre above shield, 'RD' or 'DR' divided by shield.

H71D-080 VG £25 F £50 VF £120

As previous, but the king's throne has two pillars.

H71D-085 VG £25 F £50 VF £120

York Ecclesiastical Mint under Archbishop Rotherham

Obverse Legend As previous.

Reverse Legend CIVITAS EBORACI — City of York

Obverse King seated on throne with no pillars; trefoil stops in legend.

Reverse A key either side of shield.

H71D-090 VG £25 F £50 VF £110

As previous, with a single pillar to throne.

H71D-095 VG £25 F £50 VF £110

As previous, but single pillar to throne, rosette or no marks in the legend; also the lettering is more ornate.

H71D-100 VG £25 F £50 VF £110

As previous, but a pillar either side of king, sometimes with crosses between legs of throne.

H71D-105 VG £25 F £50 VF £110

Henry VIII 1509–1547

Henry VIII's reign was not only historically important, but also saw several important numismatic changes. Henry VIII, who came to the throne at the age of only nineteen and has become notorious for his numerous wives, first married Katherine of Aragon and remained married to her for twenty-four years. During the first sixteen years of Henry's reign, the first coinage was issued; it was fairly similar to the last issue of his father, Henry VII. However, the second coinage of 1526–1544 changed in many respects. Not only were new gold denominations introduced but, with higher bullion prices on the Continent, the weight of the silver coins was reduced to bring their value more in line with their European equivalents. Finally the style of the coins changed, except for the penny and halfpenny. Henry VIII's first coinage bore his father's portrait but his second had his own.

When Henry decided to marry Anne Boleyn, the Pope refused to dissolve his marriage with Katherine of Aragon whereupon the king broke all ties with Rome and the Catholic Church. Proclaiming himself head of the English Church, Henry precipitated a major crisis in the country as monasteries and church property were destroyed and people executed for not recognising Henry VIII as head of the Church. During this period of uncertainty the only change numismatically was the closure of the ecclesiastical privilege mints of Canterbury, York and Durham which had been an added source of revenue for the Church of Rome. From this period onwards, all mints were royal mints under the control of the crown which received all the revenue.

Although Henry profited considerably from taking over the Church, by 1544 he was running short of money not least because of his extravagant personal lifestyle and expenditure. He decided therefore to debase the silver coinage as this would provide him with huge profits. The third coinage of 1544–1547 was duly debased and only about one third of the coins' content was actually silver, the rest being copper. This was the first time in English history since the Roman period when the intrinsic silver value of the coins did not correspond to the denominational value and the debased coinage was, understandably, extremely unpopular. The third coinage also bore a new portrait of a much older Henry while the sovereign penny was discontinued and replaced by an issue with a facing bust of the king. New gold denominations were introduced, due mainly to the fluctuating gold price on the Continent. Also, the testoon, the forerunner of the shilling, was successfully introduced into circulation in some quantity. Upon Henry's death in 1547, England was on the verge of a crisis; the coinage was in a poor state, the English Church was almost non existent and the legacy of Henry's tumultuous marital life were two daughters, Mary and Elizabeth, and a frail, sickly son Edward, who would succeed him.

On the face of it, Henry VIII sovereign pennies are fairly similar to those of Henry VII. When trying to identify them, collectors might be hampered by the fact that many of the coins only turn up in VG condition and are sometimes clipped, thus losing vital clues as to which issue they belong. Collectors should bear these few points in mind when identifying an issue:

1. The obverse legends of Henry VII and Henry VIII first issue are the same, but Henry VIII's second issue has a different legend.

2. The coin's mint is found in the reverse legend.

Having identified the mint, collectors will notice on most issues various letters beside the shield, or symbols such as keys. By going through the various issues of that mint it is possible to place the coin in its correct issue.

3. If it is clear, check the mintmark which is found, in all cases, just to the right of the king's crown, at the beginning of the legend. Then check that the mintmark falls into the correct issue.

4. Refer to the illustrations for each issue, as in some issues there are varieties, such as different styles of throne.

First Coinage 1509–1526

London Mint

Obverse Legend HENRIC DI GRA REX ANGL — Henry by the grace of God King of England

Reverse Legend CIVITAS LONDON — City of London

Obverse Seated king on throne; mintmark castle or portcullis.

Reverse The king's shield over a cross.

H81D-005 VG £35 F £75 VF £150

Canterbury Ecclesiastical Mint under Archbishop William Warham

Obverse Legend As previous.

Reverse Legend CIVITAS CANTOR — City of Canterbury

Obverse As previous; mintmark martlet.

Reverse 'WA' above shield.

H81D-010 ex. rare

Legends As previous.

Obverse As previous; mintmark pomegranate.

Reverse Shield dividing 'WA'.

H81D-015 VG £35 F £75 VF £150

Durham Ecclesiastical Mint
Bishop Thomas Ruthall 1509–1523

Obverse Legend As previous.

Reverse Legend CIVITAS DVRRAM — City of Durham

Obverse As previous; mintmark lis.

Reverse 'TD' above shield.

H81D-020 VG £30 F £60 VF £130

Legends As previous.

Obverse As previous; mintmark lis or radiant star.

Reverse Shield dividing 'TD'.

H81D-025 VG £30 F £60 VF £130

Bishop Thomas Wolsey 1523–1529

Even though this issue continued into the second coinage by some three years, the obverse legend remained the same as for all the first issues.

Legends As previous.

Obverse As previous; mintmark spur rowel.

Reverse Shield dividing 'TW', Cardinal's hat below.

H81D-030 VG £60 F £150 VF £300

Second Coinage

London Mint

Obverse Legend H.D.G. ROSA SIE SPIA — Henry by the grace of God a rose without a thorn (abbreviated)

Reverse Legend CIVITAS LONDON — City of London

Obverse Sovereign type, king on throne; mintmark rose, lis, arrow or sunburst.

Reverse King's shield over cross.

H81D-035 VG £30 F £60 VF £120

Canterbury Ecclesiastical Mint
Archbishop William Warham

Obverse Legend As previous.

Reverse Legend CIVITAS CANTOR — City of Canterbury

Obverse As previous; mintmark 'T', cross patonce, uncertain.

Reverse Shield dividing 'WA'.

H81D-040 VG £60 F £125 VF £250

Archbishop Thomas Cranmer

Legends As previous.

Obverse As previous; mintmark Catherine Wheel.

Reverse Shield dividing 'TC'.

H81D-045 VG £50 F £100 VF £200

Durham Ecclesiastical Mint
Bishop Wolsey 1529

Obverse Legend As previous.

Reverse Legend CIVITAS DVRRAM — City of Durham

Obverse As previous; mintmark trefoil, crescent, star, cross with pellet in one angle.

Reverse Shield dividing 'TW', Cardinal's hat below shield.

H81D-050 VG £20 F £40 VF £80

Sede Vacante Issue 1529–1530

Legends As previous.

Obverse As previous; mintmark star or radiant star.

Reverse Plain shield and cross; no marks on reverse.

H81D-055 VG £40 F £80 VF £160

Bishop Cuthbert Tunstall 1530

Legends & Obverse As previous.

Reverse Shield dividing 'CD'.

H81D-060 VG £20 F £40 VF £80

York Ecclesiastical Mint under Archbishop Edward Lee

Obverse Legend As previous.

Reverse Legend CIVITAS EBORACI — City of York

Obverse As previous; mintmark key.

Reverse Shield dividing 'EL'.

H81D-065 VG £60 F £120 VF £240

Third Coinage or Debased Issue 1544–1547

As mentioned earlier, by 1544 Henry VIII was running short of money and decided to drastically lower the fineness of his silver coins to about one third silver and two thirds copper. He also changed his portrait on the coinage; he now looked much older and had a beard. With Henry VIII head of the Church, there were no more ecclesiastical mints and mints such as York and Canterbury were controlled by the king. During this period two mints were active in London, the Tower mint and Southwark, which was situated just south of the River Thames. Southwark became an important mint so, instead of referring to a London mint, a differentiation is made henceforth between the Tower and the Southwark mints. In the third coinage there are three slightly different styles of bust which however are often difficult to recognise on small denominations such as the penny. As a result, a coin may not look exactly like the one that is photographed. Finally collectors should bear in mind that the third coinage is fairly similar to the posthumous issue of 1547–1551.

Tower Mint

Obverse Legend H.D.G. ROSA SINE SPINA — Henry by the grace of God a rose without a thorn (abbreviated)

Reverse Legend CIVITAS LONDON — City of London

Obverse Facing bust of king; mintmark lis or none.

Reverse King's shield over cross.

H81D-070 VG £35 F £70 VF £150

Southwark Mint

Legends As previous.

Obverse Facing bust of king; mintmark none.

Reverse 'S' or 'SE' in forks of cross.

H81D-075 ex. rare

Bristol Mint

Obverse Legend As previous.

Reverse Legend CIVITAS BRISTOLI — City of Bristol

Obverse Facing bust of king; no mintmark. Lombardic lettering in legend.

Reverse King's shield over cross.

H81D-080 VG £40 F £80 VF £160

Canterbury Mint

Obverse Legend As previous.

Reverse Legend CIVITAS CANTOR — City of Canterbury

Obverse Facing bust of king; no mintmark, sometimes saltires or trefoil in legend.

Reverse As previous, but sometimes has a spur.

H81D-085 VG £40 F £85 VF £170

York Mint

Obverse Legend As previous.

Reverse Legend CIVITAS EBORACI — City of York

Obverse Facing bust of king; no mintmark. Roman and Lombardic lettering in legend.

Reverse As H81D-070.

H81D-090 VG £40 F £85 VF £170

Posthumous Coinage

Edward VI, Henry's son from his marriage to Jane Seymour, was only nine when his father died and he inherited the throne. As he was too young to govern, the affairs of England were assumed by a Council. From 1547 to 1551 the posthumous coinage of Henry VIII was produced, still bearing Henry's name and bust. This was a period of economic unrest, generated by the inflation which was caused by the circulation of low quality coins of poor silver content. Moreover, the huge influx of South and Central American gold and silver into Spain and from there into the rest of Europe destabilised the price of bullion metals and aggravated the situation.

The posthumous issue varied little from the previous one, with the silver coins being heavily debased. The only difference with the penny was a slightly altered bust and the mintmark, which often appeared only on the reverse. The third and posthumous issues can be differentiated by the busts, as the posthumous issue has a three-quarters bust; it is also important to pay particular attention to the mintmark and ensure it matches the issue. The reverse remained the same as the third issue. During this period a new mint opened in London, the Durham House mint. Located in the Strand in what was formerly a palace of the Bishops of Durham, it became for a short period London's third mint.

Collecting Hints

The same as for the third issue.

Tower Mint

Obverse Legend H.D.G. ROSA SINE SPINA — Henry by the grace of God a rose without a thorn (abbreviated)

Reverse Legend CIVITAS LONDON — City of London

Obverse Facing or three-quarters bust of king; mintmark arrow, 'K', grapple or none.

Reverse King's arms over cross; mintmarks as obverse.

H81D-095 VG £30 F £65 VF £130

Southwark Mint

As previous, but mintmark 'E' only.

H81D-100 VG £60 F £125 VF —

Durham House Mint

Obverse Legend As previous.

Reverse Legend RED CUIQ Q S EST — Render to each that which is his own

Obverse As previous, but mintmark bow.

Reverse As previous.

H81D-105 VG £100 F £200 VF —

Bristol Mint

Obverse Legend As previous.

Reverse Legend CIVITAS BRISTOLI — City of Bristol

Obverse Facing bust of king with more body; no mintmark. Roman lettering in legend.

Reverse As previous.

H81D-110 VG £35 F £75 VF £150

Canterbury Mint

Obverse Legend As previous.

Reverse Legend CIVITAS CANTOR — City of Canterbury

Obverse Bust of king with more body; no mintmark. Lozenge stops in legend.

Reverse As previous.

H81D-115 VG £30 F £70 VF £150

York Mint

Obverse Legend As previous.

Reverse Legend CIVITAS EBORACI — City of York

Obverse Bust of king; no mintmark. Roman lettering in legend.

Reverse As previous.

H81D-120 VG £30 F £70 VF £150

Edward VI 1547–1553

Edward VI assumed the throne in 1547 at the age of nine and died in 1553, having been sickly throughout his short life and leaving no male heir. Although his reign was short, it was an important time of change for the coinage. With the English economy in a poor state, due mainly to the debasement of silver coinage, a change was necessary. Although Edward's first three issues (1547–1553) all produced base silver coinage, the fine silver issue was introduced during the third coinage. This issue was one of new denominations, the silver crown, halfcrown, shilling, sixpence and threepence, which would last until decimalization in 1971. The coins were of good silver and high quality design. The aim was to revitalise the economy with a well produced quality coinage, which would be readily acceptable both in England and in Europe. As inflation had been rising over the previous thirty years, the penny was becoming much less important. In fact, during the next few reigns, the most common coins were the shilling, sixpence and groat. Although the main reason for the growth in larger denomination coins was the huge influx of silver from South America coupled with inflation, England was also becoming wealthier.

Collecting Hints

All of Edward VI's pennies were struck in base metal, except for the extremely rare fine silber issue, and all coins from the first issue are difficult to obtain in any condition. The third issue is fairly common, but rarely turns up in better than Fine condition. Often the metal is rather flaky and brittle, as well as being dull in colour. If collectors simply want an Edward VI coin, they might prefer a fine issue shilling or sixpence, which are both extremely attractive coins.

First Period 1547–1549

Tower Mint

Obverse Legend E.D.G. ROSA SINE SPINA — Edward by the grace of God a rose without a thorn (abbreviated)

Reverse Legend CIVITAS LONDON — City of London

Obverse Side bust of crowned king; mintmark arrow.

Reverse King's arms over cross.

E61D-005 VG £150 F £300 VF £800

Southwark Mint

As previous, but mintmark 'E' on reverse.

E61D-010 VG £150 F £300 VF £800

Bristol Mint

Obverse Legend As previous.

Reverse Legend CIVITAS BRISTOLI — City of Bristol

Obverse As previous, but no mintmark.

Reverse As previous.

E61D-015 VG £150 F £300 VF £800

No pennies were struck during the second coinage from 1549–50.

Third Coinage 1550–1553

London Issue

It is uncertain at which London mint this issue was struck.

Obverse Legend E.D.G. ROSA SINE SPINA — Edward by the grace of God a rose without a thorn (abbreviated)

Reverse Legend CIVITAS LONDON — City of London

Obverse Large rose in centre; mintmark escallop.

Reverse Long cross over king's shield.

E61D-020 VG £50 F £100 VF £200

York Mint

Obverse Legend As previous.

Reverse Legend CIVITAS EBORACI — City of York

Obverse As previous, but mintmark mullet.

Reverse As previous.

E61D-025 VG £45 F £90 VF £200

Fine Silver Issue

This coin is of the highest rarity and possibly unique.

Obverse Legend E.D.G. ROSA SINE SPI — Edward by the grace of God a rose without a thorn (abbreviated)

Reverse Legend CIVITAS LONDON — City of London

Obverse Sovereign-type king enthroned holding orb and sceptre.

Reverse As previous.

E61D-030 ex. rare

Mary 1553–1554

Mary was Henry VIII's eldest child, by his first wife Katherine of Aragon and the throne would have passed to her upon Edward VI's death. Just before the young king died, however, he was persuaded by the Duke of Northumberland to exclude her from the succession because she was a staunch Catholic and Lady Jane Grey, Northumberland's daughter-in-law, was named in her stead. But, due to the Duke of Northumberland's unpopularity, the plan miscarried and Mary assumed the throne. Lady Jane Grey and her husband were put to death and Elizabeth, Mary's younger sister, imprisoned in the Tower of London. Mary proceeded with the restoration of the Roman Catholic faith to England and the punishment of those who had supported the Protestant Reformation.

Only four gold and three silver denominations were issued during Mary's reign. The groat is by far the most common, the other issues tending to be rare.

Collecting Hints

The fine silver issue is rare in any condition and very difficult to obtain, while collectors should be aware that Victorian copies exist. As an example from Mary's reign, collectors might well consider a groat instead, as these coins have an attractive portrait and are easier to find.

Obverse Legend M.D.G. ROSA SINE SPINA — Mary by the grace of God a rose without a thorn (abbreviated)

Reverse Legend VERITAS TEMP FILIA — Truth is the daughter of time

Obverse Crowned bust left of queen; mintmark pomegranate.

Reverse Long cross over royal shield.

M1D-005 VG £200 F £450 VF £900

As previous, but reverse legend reads CIVITAS LONDON — City of London (Tower mint); no mintmark.

M1D-010 VG £200 F £450 VF £900

Base Issue

Despite existing controversy, we believe that this issue is genuine and not a forgery.

Obverse Legend M.D.G. ROSA SINE SPINA — Mary by the grace of God a rose without a thorn

Reverse Legend CIVITAS LONDON — City of London

Obverse A rose; mintmark rose.

Reverse As previous.

M1D-015 VG £50 F £100 VF —

Philip and Mary 1554–1558

Although it was hoped in England that Mary would marry an Englishman, she had set her heart on her cousin Philip, the Prince of Spain, who was a devout Catholic and they married in 1554, whereupon Philip became the King Consort. In an attempt to boost his popularity, Mary had Philip's portrait placed on the coins as well as her own. This was the first time that the portrait of a joint ruler can be found on any English coin. Owing to inflation and the abundance of silver in Europe, the penny continued to be superseded in importance by the shilling and sixpence, which were re-introduced after a brief absence, and the groat. Philip and Mary pennies are classed in two distinct types, the fine silver and the base issue.

Collecting Hints

Fine silver issue pennies are rare in any condition and Victorian copies exist. The average grade of the base issue is about Fine and due to their low silver content coins often appear to have been made from lead or zinc. For an example from this reign, collectors might opt for a shilling, sixpence or groat, which are relatively common and far more attractive.

Fine Silver Issue

Obverse Legend P Z M D G ROSA SINE SPINE — Philip and Mary by the grace of God a rose without a thorn (abbreviated)

Reverse Legend CIVITAS LONDON — City of London (Tower mint)

Obverse Crowned bust of queen left; mintmark lis.

Reverse Long cross over royal shield.

PM1D-005 VG £200 F £400 VF £800

Base Issue

Obverse Legend As previous.

Reverse Legend CIVITAS LONDON — City of London (Tower mint)

Obverse Rose; mintmark halved rose and 'H' (or castle).

Reverse Long cross over royal shield.

PM1D-010 VG £50 F £100 VF £225

Elizabeth I 1558–1603

Before her death in 1558, Mary had secured the right of succession for Elizabeth, Henry VIII's second daughter. By the middle of the sixteenth century, England was impoverished and in religious turmoil; but Elizabeth's reign was a creative, adventurous and eventually very prosperous period marked by the multifarious contributions of such figures as Shakespeare, Francis Drake and Walter Raleigh. The Queen was an able monarch, strong willed but inspiring. Guided as much by political considerations and a desire to distance the country and her court from the Catholic centres of power as by religious faith, Elizabeth re-established Protestantism in England. The country prospered under Elizabeth, not least by engaging in piratical attacks on the Spanish ships returning from their colonies in South America loaded with silver and gold. The breakdown of relations with Spain culminated in the defeat of the Spanish Armada in 1588 which further enhanced England's international position. The confidence and prosperity of the country, as in previous times, was reflected in its coinage with bold, good quality coins being produced.

Henry VIII had left the coinage of England in a poor state and little had been done subsequently to improve either the quantity or the quality of the coins in circulation. The coinage system as a whole required reform, with high quality coins of good weight and high silver content, and this was a task Elizabeth boldly set about to accomplish. Throughout her reign large quantities of both gold and silver coins of many different denominations were produced thus meeting a need in England, but also on the Continent where they facilitated commerce. Much of the silver used to strike coins was captured from the Spanish, and a wide range of silver denominations was introduced, the shilling and sixpence being the most important. At the end of the period, a silver crown and halfcrown were introduced and replaced the gold denominations of these coins. Small denomination coins were also struck and were very popular with the small traders and merchants. The groat (fourpence), threepence, halfgroat (twopence), three-halfpence, penny, three-farthings and halfpenny were all introduced but no farthings were produced because they would have been too small to handle and easily lost. For the first time a milled or machine-made coinage was struck, produced by an ex-employee of the Paris mint, Eloye Mestrell. This issue was fairly successful but there was animosity in the Tower mint towards Mestrell, which ultimately led to his dismissal, as it was felt by the mint employees that his machinery would cause unemployment. Some of Elizabeth's denominations were dated and those that were not carry a mintmark, usually found on both sides of the coin, which can be used to accurately date a coin. As before, mintmarks were used as a form of quality control, so that each coin could be linked to a particular die and thus moneyer.

Unlike some rulers, Elizabeth recognised the need for small denomination coinage and the penny was produced throughout her reign although it was not one of the denominations made during the milled coinage trials. This was probably due to the difficulty in making such a small sized coin. Elizabeth's hammered coinage can be divided into six issues, distinguishable by slight differences in the features but all bearing the same legends, which read E.D.G. ROSA SINE SPINA on the obverse and CIVITAS LONDON on the reverse. All of Elizabeth's issues were struck at the Tower mint.

Collecting Hints

Most of Elizabeth I's coins are readily available and the penny is no exception; it can usually be found in VG to VF condition but is sometimes creased or bent. One problem with this denomination is that it is very small in size and collectors may want a larger coin, such as a shilling or sixpence, in order to fully appreciate the fine work and detail of these issues.

First Issue 1559–1560

There is an excessively rare variety of this coin that is dated 1558 in the obverse legend.

Obverse Legend E.D.G. ROSA SINE SPINA — Elizabeth by the grace of God a rose without a thorn

Reverse Legend CIVITAS LONDON — City of London (Tower mint)

Obverse Bust of Elizabeth facing left; mintmark lis, wire-line inner circle.

Reverse Royal shield over long cross.

EL1D-005 VG £100 F £200 VF £450

Second Issue 1560–1561

Obverse Bust of Elizabeth facing left; mintmark cross crosslet or martlet; beaded inner circles.

Reverse Royal shield in centre over long cross.

EL1D-010 VG £20 F £45 VF £90

Third Issue 1561–1577

As previous, but mintmark rose, portcullis, lion, coronet, castle, acorn, eglantine; beaded inner circles.

EL1D-015 VG £18 F £35 VF £70

Fourth Issue 1578–1582

As previous, but mintmark Greek cross, Latin cross, sword; beaded inner circles.

EL1D-020 VG £18 F £35 VF £70

Fifth Issue 1582–1600

As previous, but mintmark bell, 'A', escallop, crescent, hand, tun, woolpack, key, anchor, '0'.

N.B. Pennies of mintmarks key, anchor and '0' bear the mintmark on the obverse only.

EL1D-025 VG £16 F £30 VF £60

Sixth Issue 1601–1602

As previous, but mintmark '1' (for 1601) or '2' (for 1602).

EL1D-030 VG £22 F £45 VF £90

While many of the previous issues hardly vary in style, we have listed them by their six classes to correspond with the other denominations produced, where there is considerable differences in some of the issues.

James I 1603–1625

When Elizabeth died unmarried and childless in 1603, the English throne went to James VI of Scotland who was the son of Mary Queen of Scots and the great-grandson of Margaret Tudor, daughter of Henry VII. Unlike many previous kings, James I was used to royal duties as he had ruled Scotland since infancy and was 37 years old when he assumed the English crown. England continued to prosper due mainly to the initiative of merchants who traded goods from the newly found colonies, but this was also a time of political intrigue and there was the well known attempt on James I's life and that of the entire Parliament in 1605, the Gunpowder Plot.

James I's coinage changed little from that of Elizabeth I, except for the gold denominations, in production and in style. The most notable feature was the introduction of the copper farthing, which was issued to help with the problem of small change. Continuing a trend caused by inflation and the large quantities of silver and gold being imported into Europe, mainly by the Spanish, the penny became increasingly less important as a denomination. Two main types of penny were produced, the first bearing the king's bust on the obverse, the second just a rose. The only coin to be dated during James's reign was the sixpence but, as the mintmark system continued during this period, coins can be accurately dated accordingly. The mintmark is found on the obverse and/or reverse of the coin. Finally, another significant change to the coins was in the design of the reverse shield, which is found on most denominations. Since James was king of both England and Scotland, his heraldic emblem included the Scottish coat of arms.

First Coinage 1603–1604

Obverse Legend I.D.G. ROSA SINE SPINA — James by the grace of God a rose without a thorn

Obverse Bust of king facing right, letter I behind head to denote denomination (1 penny).

Reverse Square shield with mintmark above; mintmark thistle or lis. No legend.

J11D-005 VG £30 F £60 VF £120

Second Coinage 1604–1619

The mintmark does not always appear on both sides. There is also a very rare variety which has the same obverse and reverse legend. This variety is found with the mullet mintmark and plain cross over book.

Obverse Legend I.D.G. ROSA SINE SPINA — James by the grace of God a rose without a thorn

Reverse Legend TUETUR UNITA DEUS — May God guard these (kingdoms) united

Obverse Rose in centre of coin; mintmark lis, rose, escallop, grapes, coronet, key, bell, mullet, tower, trefoil, cinquefoil, plain cross or none.

Reverse Thistle in centre of coin.

J11D-010 VG £12 F £25 VF £50

Third Coinage

Legends As previous.

Obverse As previous, but mintmarks spur rowel, none, lis or trefoil.

Reverse As previous, but no stops in the legend.

J11D-015 VG £14 F £28 VF £55

Charles I 1625–1649

Upon the death of James I in 1625 his twenty-five year old son Charles inherited the throne. Charles I was James's second son, his elder brother Henry having died while James was still reigning. Charles later married Henrietta Maria, daughter of Henry IV of France. Unfortunately, Charles's political judgement was appalling and he soon made enemies at a period when the whole of Europe was questioning the moral basis of absolute monarchy. Charles refused to accept direction from Parliament and for eleven years ruled without convening it. England was divided between the royalists and those who supported Parliament and when Civil War eventually broke out, Charles and his supporters were defeated.

Numismatically, Charles I's reign is unarguably the most interesting and complicated reign of any English monarch. This is not only because of the many varieties produced by the Tower mint, but also due to the re-opening of a number of provincial mints during the Civil War. The quantities, style and denominations are very diverse, thus giving the collector a rich field to collect. During the early part of Charles' reign, the Tower mint in London produced huge quantities of coins to satisfy demand; the penny was no exception: the number of varieties and variations in both style and design is immense. During the 1630s Nicholas Briot, a Frenchman who had worked at the Paris mint, struck machine-made milled coins at the Tower mint. These were far superior to the hammered issues, both in quality and design; Briot's coinage is always neat and well designed. A new mint at Aberystwyth, Wales was opened during Charles reign, located so as to strike silver coinage from the newly mined silver from the Welsh mines.

During the turmoil of the Civil War there was, once again, a need for provincial mints to become active as the transportation of coins was difficult and hazardous. These mints were royalist controlled and needed to produce coinage quickly, often to pay the troops' wages. For this reason, most of the denominations produced by these provincial mints were large, usually from the shilling upwards, as it was not possible in the strained circumstances of the Civil War to provide the country with a balanced coinage. Another interesting feature of the period are the siege pieces produced in towns such as Newark and Pontefract when they were besieged by Parliamentarian forces. These emergency issues were often made by cutting up silver plates and striking them with home-made dies. All of these siege pieces are interesting and under-appreciated. In 1642, the Tower mint in London fell under control of Parliament, but coins with the bust of Charles I were still produced there until 1648. The quantity and diversity of Charles I's coinage is immense. In each denomination section we have tried to provide information linking the coins to this turbulent period of English history.

Collecting Hints

Charles I pennies are fairly common and may be considered an almost insignificant denomination in contemporary terms as the penny had little buying power and, with growing prosperity, was becoming of little importance. Pennies were also becoming very small and this hinders the collector, as often the legends and mintmarks are unclear and difficult to read. The coins are usually found in about Fine condition, but VF examples can be obtained. They are often found holed and in poor condition and it is thought that this was done officially to make the coins invalid or to lower the denomination during the later part of the 17th century, when the production of milled coins was the norm. Most pennies were issued at the Tower mint, between 1625 and 1642. However, several provincial mints also produced pennies, most of which are rare and difficult to obtain.

Tower Mint
Tower Mint under King 1625–1642

Obverse Legend C.D.G. ROSA SINE SPINA — Charles by the grace of God a rose without a thorn

Reverse Legend IUS THRONUM FIRMAT — Justice strengthens the throne

Obverse Rose in centre.

Reverse Rose in centre; mintmark lis, blackamoor's head, two pellets.

C11D-005 VG £12 F £25 VF £50

As previous, but no inner circles.

C11D-010 VG £12 F £25 VF £50

As previous, but inner circle on reverse only.

C11D-015 VG £10 F £22 VF £45

Obverse Legend CAROLUS D.G.MA.B.F.ET HI REX.-Charles by the grace of God King of Great Britain France and Ireland

Reverse Legend IUSTITIA THRONUM FIRMAT — Justice strengthens the throne

Obverse Bust of king facing left wearing a ruff and mantle, figure 'I' behind head to denote denomination; mintmark plume or rose.

Reverse Oval shield.

C11D-020 VG £10 F £22 VF £45

As previous, but no inner circles; mintmark plume or rose.

C11D-025 VG £10 F £22 VF £45

More armour visible, no inner circles; mintmark plume, rose.

C11D-030 VG £12 F £25 VF £50

As previous, but inner circle on obverse; mintmark plume, rose.

C11D-035 VG £12 F £25 VF £50

As previous, but inner circle both sides; mintmark plume over rose.

C11D-040 VG £12 F £25 VF £50

As previous, but inner circle on reverse; mintmark rose on obverse and plume on reverse.

C11D-045 VG £12 F £25 VF £50

Legends As previous.

Obverse Bust of king facing left wearing a lace collar, figure 'I' behind king's head to denote denomination, no inner circles; mintmark harp, one or two pellets.

Reverse Oval shield dividing 'C.R.' (CAROLUS REX).

C11D-050 VG £20 F £45 VF £90

As previous, but no 'C.R.' on reverse.

C11D-055 VG £10 F £22 VF £45

As previous, inner circle on obverse; mintmark harp.

C11D-060 VG £10 F £22 VF £45

As previous, inner circle on reverse; mintmark harp.

C11D-065 VG £12 F £25 VF £50

As previous, but shield round in shape on reverse, no inner circles; mintmark bell, triangle, one or two pellets.

C11D-070 VG £12 F £25 VF £50

As previous, but inner circle on obverse; mintmark triangle or two pellets.

C11D-075 VG £12 F £25 VF £50

Aberystwyth Bust Type

Legends As previous.

Obverse Bust of king facing left, wearing pointed lace collar, small flat single arched crown, inner circle sometimes on obverse; mintmark one or two pellets, or none.

Reverse Shield.

C11D-080 VG £14 F £28 VF £55

Tower Mint under Parliament 1642–1648

As previous, but the king looks considerably older; mintmark pellets, inner circle on obverse only.

C11D-085 VG £22 F £45 VF £90

Briot's Coinage 1631–1639

These coins were milled, i.e. struck by machine, at the Tower mint by Nicholas Briot and the quality of production was superb. Coins can be found in Fine or even VF condition. They are usually well struck, and with all the details clearly visible. I have often wondered why Briot did not produce more coins, and why the entire output of coins from the Tower mint was not converted to milled coinage. It was probably due to the animosity felt against the Frenchman coupled with professional jealousy. The workers used to making hammered issues were afraid of losing their jobs if the new process was accepted.

Obverse Legend CARO MAG. BRIT FR ET HI R(EX.) — Charles King of Great Britain France and Ireland

Reverse Legend IUSTITIA THRONUM FIRMAT — Justice strengthens the throne

Obverse Crowned bust of king with value behind. Legend starts at the bottom of the coin.

Reverse Square-topped shield over cross.

C11D-090 VG — F £60 VF £120

No pennies were issued during the second coinage of 1638–1639.

Provincial Mints

The penny in most of the provincial issues, apart from Aberystwyth, appears to have been more of an afterthought since the main purpose of these mints was to produce coinage for the payment and armament of the royalist troops. Moreover, money was important as a vehicle of propaganda, informing the population which areas were controlled by the king and, with messages such as the Declaration on the coins, reinforcing the royalist cause.

Collecting Hints

No collection is complete without a coin from the Civil War period. With so many types and varieties available, especially in the larger denominations, collectors should obtain an example quite easily. However, as already mentioned, most pennies are rare and are often in poor condition; you should only try to obtain an example of the penny if you are definitely interested in the denomination.

Aberystwyth Mint 1638–1642

The Aberystwyth mint, opened in 1638, used locally mined silver to produce reasonable quality hammered coins; the dies for this issue were made in London. The mint concentrated on the production of smaller denomination coins, i.e. from the halfcrown to the penny. Plumes can be found on coins from this mint, and the penny is no exception having plumes in the centre of the obverse, where a shield is usually found on the other issues. N.B. Should the reverse mintmark be different from those listed, check the coin in the Oxford listings (C11D-120 -125).

Obverse Legend CARO D.G. M B F ET H REX — Charles by the grace of God King of Great Britain France and Ireland

Reverse Legend IUSTITIA THRONUM FIRMAT — Justice strengthens the throne

Obverse Bust of king, figure 'I' behind king's head, no inner circles; mintmark book

Reverse Plumes.

C11D-095 VG £60 F £120 VF £240

As previous, but with inner circles.

C11D-100 VG £60 F £120 VF £240

As previous, but obverse legend reads CAROLUS instead of CARO.

C11D-105 VG £60 F £120 VF £240

Briot Bust

Similar, but Briot-style bust on the obverse. The king's crown touches the inner circle.

C11D-110 VG £65 F £130 VF £260

Aberystwyth Furnace Mint 1648–1649

This mint, actually situated at the silver mine itself, opened for a very short time. The castle at Aberystwyth had been damaged and there was need in the area for coinage. However, no records survive from the mint. The mintmark will easily differentiate this issue from the earlier issues, which had an open book as a mintmark. This issue uses the mintmark crown.

Legends As previous.

Obverse As previous, but mintmark crown, with inner circles.

Reverse As previous; the plumes are of different design to the regular issue of Aberystwyth mintmark crown on reverse, inner circles.

C11D-115 VG £300 F £550 VF —

Oxford Mint 1642–1646

By 1642 Civil War was imminent, Parliament had taken control of the Tower mint in London and, towards the end of the year, Charles established his permanent headquarters in Oxford and made preparations to set up a mint there. He summoned Thomas Bushell, who had set up the mint in Aberystwyth, and for metal the king borrowed gold and silver plates from the University colleges, which he promised to repay. The Oxford mint produced some spectacular coins including the triple unite and a silver pound, as well as more mundane coins such as the penny. The Oxford pennies sometimes used the obverse die from the Aberystwyth mint and collectors should compare an example with the other provincial mints in order to identify it correctly, paying particular attention to the mintmark on both sides of the coin and the style of plumes. The use of the obverse Aberystwyth die was probably due to the great urgency for coins; as a result the usual formalities of mintmarks had to be discarded.

Obverse Legend CARO D G M B F ET H REX — Charles by the grace of God King of Great Britain France and Ireland

Reverse Legend As previous.

Obverse Bust of king with large lace collar; mintmark book. This is an Aberystwyth die.

Reverse Small plume; mintmark pellet.

C11D-120 VG £75 F £150 VF £350

Legends As previous.

Obverse As previous, but narrower bust; mintmark book.

Reverse Large plume; mintmark four pellets.

C11D-125 VG £75 F £150 VF £350

Legends As previous.

Obverse Fine bust of king, not from Aberystwyth dies; mintmark lis.

Reverse Small plume; mintmark mullet or pellet.

C11D-130 VG £75 F £150 VF £350

Legends As previous.

Obverse Wider bust of king; mintmark lis.

Reverse Small plumes, mintmark lis.

C11D-135 VG £90 F £180 VF £400

Declaration Type

The obverse of this issue is very similar to all the issues from the Oxford mint. However, it is very rare in any grade.

Obverse Legend As previous, but CAROL instead of CARO

Reverse Legend As previous.

Obverse Bust of king, no mark behind his head; mintmark lis.

Reverse The declaration in centre of coin: RELIG PRO LEG ANG LIBER PAR. 1644 — The religion of the Protestants the laws of England the liberty of Parliament

C11D-140 VG £300 F £500 VF —

Bristol Mint 1643–1645

Bristol was captured by the Royalists in July 1643 and Charles I immediately asked Thomas Bushell to set up a mint there. It was an important mint producing reasonable quality silver coins and a few extremely rare gold issues but in 1645 Bristol fell to the Parliamentarians and the mint was closed. Collectors should pay particular attention to the mintmark and the style of plumes when ascertaining which mint a coin is from.

Collecting Hints

Pennies from Bristol mint are rare in any grade; large denominations, however, tend to be more available.

Obverse Legend CARO D G M BF ET H REX — Charles by the grace of God King of Great Britain France and Ireland

Reverse Legend IUSTITIA THRONUM FIRMAT — Justice strengthens the throne

Obverse Crowned bust facing left, with 'I' behind the king's head; mintmark pellet.

Reverse Large plumes.

C11D-145 VG £180 F £400 VF £800

Exeter Mint 1643–1646

Exeter was captured by Royalists in 1643. It became a fairly important mint producing mainly crowns and halfcrowns but also some pennies. The town finally surrendered to the Parliamentarians in April 1646.

Collecting Hints

Exeter pennies are rare in any grade.

Obverse Legend CARO M B F E H R — Charles by the grace of God King of Great Britain France and Ireland

Reverse Legend THRO IUS FIRMAT 1644 — Justice strengthens the throne 1644

Obverse Crowned bust of king facing left, 'I' behind king's head; mintmark rose.

Reverse Large rose in centre; mintmark rose.

C11D-150 VG £125 F £250 VF £550

Commonwealth 1649–1660

Collecting Hints

This issue is fairly common, especially in the lower grades.

These issues, which have no legends and were purposefully simple in design, were struck for the full Commonwealth period.

Obverse St George's shield within wreath.

Reverse St George's shield and Irish shield, value (I) above.

COM1D-005 VG £20 F £35 VF £90

Charles II 1660–1685

Charles II, nicknamed the Merry Monarch, returned to England from exile in 1660. Oliver Cromwell had died and his younger brother had no intention of continuing to rule. With the restoration of the monarchy there was also a move away from the strict Puritanism of the Commonwealth which had banned games, fairs and sports.

From 1660 to 1662 hammered and machine-made coins were struck in three separate issues. The penny, which was a fairly common denomination by this time, was produced in all three issues. Thomas Simon produced the dies for the three issues, so all show superb detail.

Hammered and Machine-Made Issue 1660–1662

Collecting Hints

This undated issue is fairly common and easily available in Fine condition. VF and EF examples do exist but tend to be scarce and under-appreciated. Often, due to the coin's small size, much of the legend is missing, and some coins have ragged edges. Collectors should try to obtain a coin in at least Fine condition with as round a planchet and as much legend showing as possible.

First Issue

Obverse Legend CAROLUS II D G MAG BRI F ET H REX — Charles II by the grace of God King of Great Britain France and Ireland

Reverse Legend CHRISTO AUSPICE REGNO — I reign under the auspices of Christ

Obverse Bust facing left; mintmark crown, no mark of value behind king's head and no inner circles.

Reverse The king's arms over a cross.

C21DH-005 VG £18 F £40 VF £80

As previous, but omitting mintmark.

C21DH-010 VG £18 F £40 VF £80

Machine-made Issue

There is also a variety with a single arched crown, and the obverse legend starting at 8 o'clock.

As previous, but with mark of value (I) behind king's head; mintmark on both sides. The obverse legend starts at the bottom or top of the coin.

C21DH-015 VG £16 F £35 VF £70

Third Issue

Legends As previous.

Obverse Bust of king facing left, legend starts at top of coin; mintmark crown, mark of value (I) behind king's head, inner circles.

Reverse As previous, but inner circles.

C21DH-020 VG £20 F £40 VF £80

Three Farthings

Elizabeth I 1558–1603

The three-farthings was introduced in Elizabeth I's third and fourth issues as part of a plan to produce large quantities of coins of varying denominations and high metal content. It bears a bust of the queen with a rose behind on the obverse and the royal shield with the date above on the reverse, while a mintmark can be found at the beginning of the obverse and reverse legend. The three-farthings closely resembles the three-halfpence, differing only in the diameter which for unclipped specimens is 14 mm for the three-farthings and 16 mm for the three-halfpence. Halfgroats and pennies were also produced at the time but are all undated, except for the extremely rare 1558 penny, and they also omit the rose behind the queen's head. No three-farthings were issued in 1558, so the penny can be easily identified.

Collecting Hints

This issue used to be very rare, but significant quantities have been found in the last twenty years, either with metal detectors or by beach-combers in the river Thames, mostly in Poor to VG condition. Many coins are clipped and fragmented and often holed, due to their thinness or the acidic mud in which they have been found. Moreover, the dates are often crudely engraved. Coins in VF or EF condition are very rare.

Obverse Legend E. D. G. ROSA SINE SPINA — Elizabeth by the grace of God a rose without a thorn

Reverse Legend CIVITAS LONDON — City of London

Obverse Bust of queen with rose behind; mintmark at beginning of legend.

Reverse Royal arms with date above; mintmark at beginning of legend.

Mintmark Pheon (1561–1562), coronet (1567–1568), ermine (1572–1573), acorn (1573), eglantine (1573–1577), plain cross (1578–1579), long cross (1581) or sword (1582).

EL3F-005 VG £45 F £100 VF £300

Milled Issue

Only three examples of this issue are known to exist.

Obverse Legend E. D. G. ROSA SINE SPINA — Elizabeth by the grace of God a rose without a thorn

Reverse Legend CIVITAS LONDON — City of London

Obverse Bust of queen with rose behind; mintmark star.

Reverse Square shield over cross, 1563 above; mintmark star.

EL3F-010 ex. rare

Halfpenny

The halfpenny was successfully introduced under Edward I. During previous reigns, silver pennies had been cut in half and sometimes quarters to produce halfpennies and farthings. Some examples are illustrated below.

Thanks to metal detectors, Henry I and Henry III halfpennies have been found in recent years but they are all extremely rare and very little is known about them. They circulated alongside the more common cut coinage and although it is possible that they were patterns or trials, these specimens did see circulation. No documentary evidence exists, and it is possible that there are coins and issues which are still to be discovered.

Obverse Legend HENRICUS REX — King Henry

Reverse Legend TERRI (or ELIS) ON LUND — Terry (or Elis) of London

Obverse Crowned bust of king holding sceptre.

Reverse Short cross, four pellets in each quarter.

H3HD-005 ex. rare

Henry I 1100–1135

During the last few years, Henry I silver halfpennies have been found in the London area. This issue was possibly a pattern or trial but it is obvious that several specimens entered circulation. However, it was not until Edward I's reign that the halfpenny was successfully introduced.

Obverse Legend HENRIC REX — King Henry

Reverse Legend GODWIN A ON WI — Godwin of Winchester

Obverse Uncrowned facing bust.

Reverse Cross potent with cross of pellets in each angle.

H1HD-005 ex. rare

As previous, but crowned bust.

H1HD-010 ex. rare

Henry III 1216–1272

These two issues, which were both struck at the London mint, have been discovered recently. They are of the short-cross coinage 1216–1247 and similar in style to the pennies, but only half the size. They circulated alongside the much more common cut pennies, which served as halfpennies.

Edward I 1272–1307

Edward I successfully introduced the halfpenny as part of the new coinage. It was an important and much needed denomination. Before the issue was introduced traders produced halfpennies by cutting pennies in half, which was obviously impractical in some cases and often inconvenient. The new denominations issued under Edward I allowed trade to increase and facilitated the country's prosperity.

Halfpennies from all hammered reigns tend to be difficult to identify. Most coins are small, often clipped or in poor condition. Moreover, many appear to have blundered legends due to the difficulty in making dies small enough for the denomination. The fact that Edward II, III and IV also issued halfpennies can hamper the collector when trying to identify an issue. All Edward I issues are linked to the classification system used for the penny. In general, Edward I's issues are larger than those of later kings. Throughout this chapter we will be show how to identify different reigns but many coins are often impossible to identify due to their poor condition.

As with other denominations, although London is by far the most common mint it was not the only mint to strike halfpennies, and five other mints were active during Edward I's reign. The entire legend on the reverse of the coin is the mint's name and read CIVITAS LONDON or LONDONIENSIS for London, VILLA BRISTOLLIE for Bristol, CIVITAS LINCOL for Lincoln, NOVI CASTRI for Newcastle-upon-Tyne, CIVITAS EBORACI for York, or VILLA BEREVVICI (varieties) for Berwick. Varieties exist in most cases and legends are often blundered or illegible in parts.

As with the other coins of this period, the denomination is not written on the coin, which was worth its weight in silver. Thus, a halfpenny would be half the size and weight of the penny. In all issues the king's name is found on the obverse of the coin. It is the first word in the obverse legend. It will read EDWA or EDWR (minor varieties). If it reads RICARD or HENRI it is an issue of Richard or Henry.

London Mint

As mentioned earlier, the class numbering system relates to the penny issue, as the two denominations are fairly similar.

Class 3B

Obverse Legend EDW R ANGL DNS HYB — Edward King of England Lord of Ireland

Reverse Legend LONDONIENSIS or CIVITAS LONDON — London or City of London

Obverse Facing bust of king, his drapery as a segment of a circle.

Reverse Long cross, three pellets in each quarter.

E1HD-005 VG £25 F £45 VF £90

As previous, but reversed 'N's in reverse legend.

E1HD-010 VG £30 F £50 VF £100

Class 3C

As previous, but facing bust of king, drapery as two wedges.

E1HD-015 VG £25 F £45 VF £90

Class 3G

As previous, but larger letters and wider crown.

E1HD-020 VG £25 F £45 VF £90

Class 4C

As previous, but larger face with much more hair, comma abbreviation marks and thick-waisted 'S' in obverse legend.

E1HD-025 VG £25 F £50 VF £100

Class 4E

As previous, but three pellets on king's breast on obverse and a pellet in reverse legend.

E1HD-030 VG £30 F £60 VF £120

Class 6

Legends As previous.
Obverse Facing bust of king, small lettering and double-barred 'N' in legend.
Reverse Long cross, three pellets in each quarter.

E1HD-035 VG £30 F £60 VF £120

Class 7

As previous, but larger lettering.

E1HD-040 VG £30 F £60 VF £120

Class 9

As previous, but pot-hook 'N' in obverse legend, sometimes star on the king's breast with the crown band curved at the edges.

E1HD-045 VG £25 F £45 VF £90

Class 10

Obverse Legend EDWAR R ANGL DNS HYB (varieties exist) — Edward King of England Lord of Ireland
Reverse Legend As previous.
Obverse Narrow letters in legend, the king has a long face.
Reverse As previous.

E1HD-050 VG £25 F £45 VF £90

Bristol Mint

Obverse Legend As Class 3C.
Reverse Legend VIL(L)A BRISTOLLIE — Town of Bristol. There is one die reading IIISTOLLIE, this is a die-maker's error.
Obverse Similar to Class 3C.
Reverse As previous.

E1HD-055 VG £45 F £80 VF £180

As previous, but similar to Class 3G.

E1HD-060 VG £45 F £80 VF £180

Lincoln Mint

Obverse Legend As Class 3C.
Reverse Legend CIVITAS LINCOL or LINCOC — City of Lincoln
Obverse Similar to Class 3C.
Reverse As previous.

E1HD-065 VG £50 F £100 VF £200

Newcastle Mint

Obverse Legend As previous.
Reverse Legend NOVI CASTRI — Newcastle-upon-Tyne
Obverse As Class 3C but king has a long narrow face.
Reverse Long cross with single pellet in each angle.

E1HD-070 VG £100 F £200

York Mint

Obverse Legend As previous.

Reverse Legend CIVITAS EBORACI — City of York

Obverse As Class 3B.

Reverse Long cross, three pellets in each quarter.

E1HD-075 VG £40 F £75 VF £150

Berwick Mint

The rare halfpenny issue, like the pennies, does not fall into the usual classes of Edward I's coinage. This is because the dies for this issue were not made in London but produced locally.

Obverse Legend EDW R ANGL DNS HYB — Edward King of England Lord of Ireland

Reverse Legend VILLA BEREVVICI — Town of Berwick

Obverse Facing bust of king wearing trifoliate crown, Lombardic 'E' in legend.

Reverse Long cross, three pellets in each quarter, Roman 'E' in legend.

E1HD-080 ex. rare

Obverse Legend As previous

Reverse Legend VILLA BERREWYCI (or BERREVICI) — Town of Berwick

Obverse King wearing bifoliate crown, sometimes pellets in legend.

Reverse As previous, but Lombardic 'E'.

E1HD-085 ex. rare

As previous, but EDWA instead of EDWR and Lombardic 'N' in obverse legend.

E1HD-090 VG £60 F £120 VF £220

As previous, but Roman 'N' in obverse legend.

E1HD-095 VG £60 F £120 VF £220

The later Berwick issues are listed under Edward II and Edward III respectively.

Edward II 1307–1327

Only two mints produced halfpennies during the reign of Edward II, London and Berwick, probably because there were sufficient halfpennies circulating from Edward I's new coinage. The main difference between Edward II's halfpennies and Edward I's is the obverse legend which, on Edward II's London issue reads ED-

WARDUS REX A(NG). Also, on some issues, the central fleur of the king's crown looks like a battle axe.

London Mint

Obverse Legend EDWARDUS REX A(NG) — Edward King of England

Reverse Legend CIVITAS LONDON — City of London

Obverse Facing bust of king, usually with the central fleur of the crown in the shape of a battle axe.

Reverse Long cross, three pellets in each quarter.

E2HD-005 VG £40 F £80 VF £150

Many very minor varieties of this issue exist. Some numismatists consider some of the issue could be varieties of Edward I Class 10. However, we feel coins with this obverse legend should be included in Edward II, in particular, those with the new style crown, as this corresponds with Edward II's penny issues.

Berwick Mint

As with Edward I's Berwick halfpenny issue, those of Edward II do not fall into the usual issues. This is because the dies for this issue were not made in London, but produced locally.

Obverse Legend EDWARDUS REX AN — Edward King of England

Reverse Legend VILLA BEREWICI (varieties) — Town of Berwick

Obverse Facing bust of king. Lombardic 'E' in legend

Reverse As previous issues, colon before VIL in legend.

E2HD-010 VG £60 F £120 VF £220

Edward III 1327–1377

Many different varieties of halfpennies were issued during the reign of Edward III. We will point out why a particular issue is unique. Halfpennies are difficult to identify, mainly because of their size. It is often difficult to see marks on the coins, especially those in the lower grades. It is important, when identifying your halfpenny, to check the obverse legends. Most reigns are slightly different. Look at the bust of the king. Does it look like the coin in our illustration? Also, look for any unusual marks on the coin. Many of Edward III's issues had a star in the legends. To identify an Edward halfpenny it may be necessary to refer to the chapters of Edward I, II and III. Edward IV's halfpennies are very different in style from those of the first three Edwards, and they are much smaller. It is also important to bear in mind that a coin of Edward will have his name on the obverse at the top and will read EDWARD, EDWA and the other varieties. If a coin reads RICARD or HENRI, it is an issue of Richard or Henry.

Three mints were active during the reign of Edward III. They were London, Reading and Berwick. The Reading and Berwick mints are both very rare. The mint's name can be found on the reverse of the coin. The three mints read CIVITAS LONDON for London, VILLA BERV(V)ICI for Berwick and VILLA RADINGY (the N often reversed or unbarred) for Reading.

During this period, the English coinage was the envy of much of Europe as it could be relied upon for good weight and good metal content. It is not surprising, therefore, that the English coinage was copied on the Continent where many coins look very similar to the English issues; however, there are differences. During Edward III's reign copies of halfpennies were produced on the Continent; they are very similar in style to those of Edward III, except that the obverse legend reads, in most cases, EDWARDIENSIS. These coins are an interesting addition to any collection.

First Coinage 1327–1335

Struck only at the Berwick mint, this issue is very easy to recognise as in all cases there is either one or two bear's heads in the reverse quarters.

Obverse Legend EDWARDUS ANGLIE D OR EDWARDUS DEI GRA R (varieties) — Edward by the grace of God King of England

Reverse Legend VILLA BERV(V)ICI — Town of Berwick

Obverse Facing bust of king.

Reverse Bear's head in one or two quarters.

E3HD-005 VG £40 F £80 VF £160

Second Coinage 1335–1343

Coins from this issue were struck in silver of slightly less fineness; in fact the silver content was reduced from .925 to .833. This unpopular change was reversed with the introduction of the third coinage. The London issue is again easily identifiable by a star at the end of the obverse legend.

London Mint

This issue is very similar to the previous issue of Edward II. However, the obverse legend is slightly different; also, there is a star at the end of the legend. Halfpennies were also struck for the first coinage issue using Edward II dies. This issue is indistinguishable.

Obverse Legend EDWARDUS REX A(NG) — Edward King of England

Reverse Legend CIVITAS LONDON — City of London

Obverse Facing bust of king, star at the end of legend, very neat bust with a flat crown.

Reverse Long cross, three pellets in each quarter.

E3HD-010 VG £18 F £35 VF £70

Reading Mint

Obverse Legend As previous.

Reverse Legend VILLA RADINGY — Town of Reading

Obverse Facing bust of king, star at end of legend.

Reverse Escallop in one quarter of reverse.

E3HD-015 VG £225 F £450 VF —

Third or Florin Coinage 1344–1351

Two mints were active during this issue, London and Reading. This issue has a fairly distinct type of bust. The king has much more bushy hair, and has a broad neck and shoulders, there is no star at the end of the legends. However, other marks can be found on the coin.

London Mint

Obverse Legend EDWARDUS REX (AN) — Edward King of England

Reverse Legend CIVITAS LONDON — City of London

Obverse Facing bust of king, sometimes two pellets by REX, sometimes pellet or small saltire either side of crown.

Reverse Long cross, three pellets in each quarter.

E3HD-020 VG £18 F £35 VF £70

As previous, but an extra pellet or saltire in one quarter of the reverse.

E3HD-025 VG £22 F £40 VF £75

Obverse Legend EDWARDUS REX — King Edward

Reverse Legend As previous.

Obverse Two pellets, two saltires or nothing before REX in legend, sometimes a pellet either side of crown.

Reverse Long cross, three pellets in each quarter.

E3HD-030 VG £22 F £40 VF £75

Reading Mint

Obverse Legend EDWARDUS REX (AN) — Edward King of England

Reverse Legend VILLA RADINGY — Town of Reading

Obverse Facing bust of king.

Reverse Long cross, escallop in one quarter, three pellets in the other three quarters.

E3HD-035 VG £200 F £425

As previous, but a saltire in the obverse legend.

E3HD-040 rare

Fourth Coinage 1351–1377

Pre Treaty Period 1351–1361

This very rare issue is extremely difficult to identify. The main difference is in the lettering. Many of the letters are broken or have parts missing. The mintmark, which is found on the obverse above the king's head, is cross 2(3), however, the mintmark in many issues is not clear.

Obverse Legend EDWARDUS REX AN — Edward King of England

Reverse Legend CIVITAS LONDON — City of London

Obverse Facing bust of king, broken letters in legend; mintmark cross 2(3).

Reverse Long cross, three pellets in each quarter.

E3HD-045 VG £80 F £150 VF £300

Another extremely rare variety exists which was struck in 1356

Obverse Legend EDWARDUS REX — Edward King

Reverse Legend CIVITAS LONDON — City of London

Obverse Facing bust of king; mintmark crown.

Reverse As previous, but an annulet in one quarter.

E3HD-050 ex. rare

Transitional Treaty Period

The only point which distinguishes this issue is that there are two pellets above the mintmark cross potent (5). This issue is rare.

Obverse Legend EDWARDUS REX AN — Edward King of the English

Reverse Legend CIVITAS LONDON — City of London

Obverse Facing bust of king, two pellets over mintmark cross potent (5). The lettering of both obverse and reverse legends sometimes varies in size.

Reverse Long cross, three pellets in each quarter.

E3HD-055 VG £70 F £150 VF £300

Treaty Period 1361–1369

This issue is differentiated by several minor marks, which are specific to this issue.

Obverse Legend EDWARDUS REX AN — Edward King of England

Reverse Legend CIVITAS LONDON — City of London

Obverse Facing bust of king; mintmark cross potent.

Reverse Double or single pellet stops after DON, unbarred 'A' in TAS.

E3HD-060 VG £20 F £40 VF £75

Legends As previous.

Obverse As previous, but pellet before EDWARDUS.

Reverse Two or one annulet after DON, barred 'A' in TAS.

E3HD-065 VG £20 F £40 VF £75

No halfpennies were produced during the post-treaty period (1369–1377).

Richard II 1377–1399

Richard II produced three main types of halfpennies during his reign. All were produced at the London mint and are fairly easy to identify. All obverse legends start with the king's name RICARD; should the coin read HENRI or EDWARD it is an issue of either Henry or Edward. Richard III also produced halfpennies, which are very rare. To differentiate between the two Richards' halfpennies refer to the mintmark, found above the king's head, just before the start of the obverse legend. In Richard II's coinage, in all cases, the mintmark is cross pattée whereas in Richard III's issues the mintmark is sun and rose or boar's head. Should the mintmark not be clear, refer to the various marks found on the coin. For example, the early style of Richard II had marks on the king's breast, the later style had fishtail lettering. Fishtail lettering is when the ends of most letters in the legends are broken and curved outwards, so looking like a fish tail.

First Issue

Obverse Legend RICHARD REX ANGL — Richard King of England

Reverse Legend CIVITAS LONDON — City of London

Obverse Facing bust of king, annulet or saltire on breast, reversed Roman 'N's in legend.

Reverse Long cross, three pellets in each quarter.

R2HD-005 VG £40 F £80 VF £180

Intermediate Issue

Legends As previous.

Obverse No marks on king's breast, Lombardic 'N's in legend.

Reverse Usually Lombardic 'N's in legend.

R2HD-010 VG £30 F £55 VF £100

Late Bust Issue

Fishtail Lettering

Obverse Legend RICARD REX ANGL (F or I sometimes) — Richard King of England

Reverse Legend CIVITAS LONDON — City of London

Obverse Facing bust of king but no marks on bust; the legend has fishtail lettering making all the letters look very fancy.

Reverse Fishtail lettering in the legend.

R2HD-015 VG £30 F £55 VF £100

As previous, but short stubby lettering.

R2HD-020 VG £35 F £70 VF £140

Henry IV 1399–1413

Henry IV's halfpennies are very difficult to identify. This is mainly due to the fact that they are usually clipped or in poor condition, making it very difficult to see marks which would differentiate them from more common reigns. To identify a coin, firstly check that the obverse legend reads HENRIC; if it reads EDWARD or RICARD it is an issue from the reign of Edward or Richard. Secondly, the mint, found in the reverse legend, should read CIVITAS LONDON, as London was the only mint that produced halfpennies under Henry IV. Thirdly, try to distinguish the mint-mark, which in all cases is cross pattée, with nothing in the centre. This mintmark is specific to Henry IV but might not be clear on a coin. Then pay attention to the king's bust, as Henry IV's busts are different from those of other reigns. In particular, pay close attention to the reign of Henry V. Finally, look for any marks, such as annulets, on the coin. Then see if any issue has these markings in it. When trying to identify a Henry IV halfpenny, also check the issues of Henry V, VI and VII.

Collecting Hints

All of Henry IV's coins are very rare and usually difficult to identify, and the halfpenny is no exception. Halfpennies are often found in about Fine condition, clipped and with weak legends. Collectors should try to obtain an example with as many clear distinguishing marks as possible. Also, when obtaining this coin from a dealer, ensure that the coin is guaranteed to be an issue of Henry IV.

Heavy Coinage 1399–1412

Coins from the heavy coinage weigh some 20% more than the light coinage. The weight difference is not a simple way to identify this issue due to the fact that most issues were clipped and are worn. Accurate weighing of the two issues would be most misleading.

Obverse Legend HENRIC REX ANGL — Henry King of England

Reverse Legend CIVITAS LONDON — City of London

Obverse Facing small bust of king; mintmark cross pattée.

Reverse Long cross, three pellets in each quarter.

H4HD-005 VG £100 F £200 VF £425

As previous, but larger bust with rounded shoulders and annulets by neck.

H4HD-010 VG £100 F £200 VF £425

Light Coinage 1412–1423

This issue used the same dies as the heavy coinage. An unclipped example from the heavy coinage should weigh 4.5 grains (0.29 grams) and from the light coinage 3.75 grains (0.24 grams). However, due to clipping and wear most coins from these issues can not be classed.

Legends As previous.

Obverse and Reverse As previous.

H4HD-015 VG £110 F £225 VF £450

This issue used a new set of dies which were very different from the previous one.

As previous, but whole or broken annulets usually either side of crown or neck.

H4HD-020 VG £110 F £225 VF £450

As previous, but with two pellets to right of neck.

H4HD-025 rare

Henry V 1413–1422

Henry V's coins are somewhat easier to identify than those of the previous reigns, because they bear a number of distinguishing marks. Firstly, check that the coin has the king's name at the start of the obverse legend and reads HENRIC — should it read RICARD or EDWARD the coin is an issue of Richard or Edward. Now check that the mint, on the reverse legend, reads CIVITAS LONDON, because during this reign halfpennies were only produced at the London Mint. The mintmarks on all issues are either cross pattée with pellet in centre, or pierced cross. The only certain way for collectors to identify an issue is to check through each class, paying particular attention to the various marks and the king's bust. If a coin is not found, collectors should refer to Henry IV, VI and VII.

Collecting Hints

Henry V's halfpennies are fairly common and usually obtainable in Fine condition. They are mostly unclipped with clear legends and marks. Collectors should try to obtain an example in at least Fine condition with clear legends.

Obverse Legend HENRIC REX ANGL — Henry King of England

Reverse Legend CIVITAS LONDON — City of London

Obverse Very thin emaciated bust of king, annulet either side of crown.

Reverse Long cross, three pellets in each quarter.

H5HD-005 VG £20 F £40 VF £90

As previous, but the obverse is an altered die of Henry IV's last issue (H4HD-020); a mullet over the annulet to right of crown differentiates this issue.

H5HD-010 VG £60 F £125 VF £225

As previous, but new-style bust of king of usual style, a broken annulet either side of crown.

H5HD-015 VG £20 F £40 VF £90

As previous, but broken annulet by hair.

H5HD-020 VG £20 F £40 VF £90

As previous, but one annulet broken by crown and another annulet unbroken by crown.

H5HD-025 VG £30 F £60 VF £110

As previous, but annulet to one side and trefoil to the other side of crown.

H5HD-030 VG £20 F £40 VF £90

This issue was probably struck during the reign of Henry VI. The obverse die is obviously that of Henry V, while the reverse die is that of Henry VI.

Legends As previous.

Obverse New, neat bust with hollow neck; no marks on coin.

Reverse Widely separated pellets on reverse.

H5HD-035 VG £50 F £100 VF £180

Henry VI First Reign 1422–1461

As with all other denominations, many issues of halfpenny were produced during the reign of Henry VI. Each issue is easily identifiable by specific markings which were put on the coins as a form of quality control so that, if a problem arose, a coin could be returned to the appropriate mint and checked for weight and metal fineness. Firstly, to find that you have a coin of Henry, check that the obverse legend reads HENRIC. Then check the mint, on the reverse legend. Three mints were active under Henry VI, London, York and Calais in France, which was under English rule during this period, and their reverse legends read CIVITAS LONDON, CIVITAS EBORACI, VILLA CALIS (minor varieties are known) respectively. Finally, collectors should look for any unusual marks, such as annulets, rosettes or mascles, and go through each issue to see if the coin ties in with a particular class. If unsuccessful, also check the reigns of Henry IV, V and VI second reign, as well as Henry VII.

Annulet Issue 1422–1427

This issue has annulets somewhere on the coin.

London Mint

Obverse Legend HENRIC REX ANGL — Henry King of England

Reverse Legend CIVITAS LONDON — City of London

Obverse Facing bust of king.

Reverse Annulets in two quarters.

H6HD-005 VG £15 F £30 VF £60

Calais Mint

Obverse Legend As previous.

Reverse Legend VILLA CALIS(IE) — Town of Calais

Obverse Facing bust of king, annulet by neck.

Reverse As previous.

H6HD-010 VG £15 F £30 VF £60

York Mint

Obverse Legend As previous.

Reverse Legend CIVITAS EBORACI

Obverse Facing bust of king, a lis either side of neck.

Reverse As previous.

H6HD-015 VG £200 F £400 VF £750

Rosette Mascle Issue 1427–1430

This issue has a rosette and mascles somewhere in the legend.

London Mint

Obverse Legend As previous.

Reverse Legend CIVITAS LONDON — City of London

Obverse Facing bust of king, rosettes and mascles in legend.

Reverse Long cross, three pellets in each quarter.

H6HD-020 VG £20 F £40 VF £75

Calais Mint

As previous, but reverse legend reads VILLA CALIS(IE) — Town of Calais.

H6HD-025 VG £20 F £40 VF £75

Pinecone Mascle Issue 1430–1434

This issue has pinecones and mascles in the legends.

London Mint

Obverse Legend As previous.

Reverse Legend CIVITAS LONDON — City of London

Obverse Facing bust of king, pinecones and mascles in legend.

Reverse As previous.

H6HD-030 VG £22 F £45 VF £80

Calais Mint

As previous, but reverse legend reads VILLA CALIS(IE) — Town of Calais.

H6HD-035 VG £22 F £45 VF £80

Leaf Mascle Issue 1434–1435

This issue has a leaf somewhere on the coin and a mascle usually in the obverse or reverse legend.

London Mint

Obverse Legend As previous.

Reverse Legend CIVITAS LONDON — City of London

Obverse Leaf on king's breast.

Reverse Leaf below 'N' of LON or 'S' of TAS.

H6HD-040 VG £20 F £40 VF £80

Calais Mint

Obverse Legend As previous.

Reverse Legend VILLA CALIS(IE) — Town of Calais

Obverse Facing bust of king with leaf on breast.

Reverse Leaf under SIE of legend.

H6HD-045 VG £30 F £60 VF £120

Leaf Trefoil Issue 1435–1448

This issue sometimes has a leaf on the king's breast, and has a trefoil of pellets in the legend.

London Mint

Obverse Legend As previous.

Reverse Legend CIVITAS LONDON — City of London

Obverse Facing bust of king, leaf on breast, trefoil in legend.

Reverse Long cross, three pellets in each quarter.

H6HD-050 VG £20 F £40 VF £75

As previous, but no leaf on breast.

H6HD-055 VG £25 F £50 VF £85

Calais Mint

The Calais mint also produced a piedfort, or double thickness, coin for this issue, which, however, is considered a pattern and is extremely rare.

As H6HD-050 except for reverse legend, which reads VILLA CALIS(IE).

H6HD-060 ex. rare

Trefoil Issue 1438–1443

This issue, struck at the London mint, has trefoils either side of neck and a leaf on the breast.

Obverse Legend As previous.

Reverse Legend CIVITAS LONDON — City of London

Obverse Facing bust of neck and a leaf on the king's breast, sometimes trefoils in legend.

Reverse Long cross, three pellets in each quarter. One die has an extra pellet in two quarters.

H6HD-065 VG £25 F £50 VF £90

No halfpence were struck for the trefoil pellet issue.

Leaf Pellet Issue 1445–1454

This issue, struck at the London mint, has a leaf on the king's breast and pellet either side of crown.

Obverse Legend HENRIC REX ANGLI — Henry King of the English

Reverse Legend CIVITAS LONDON — City of London

Obverse Facing bust of king, leaf on king's breast and pellet either side of crown.

Reverse As previous.

H6HD-070 VG £20 F £40 VF £80

No halfpennies were issued for the unmarked issue of 1453–1454.

Cross Pellet Issue 1454–1460

This issue, struck at the London mint, has a saltire or cross on the obverse.

As previous, but a saltire either side of king's neck.

H6HD-075 VG £40 F £80 VF £150

As previous, but a single saltire on the king's neck, a mullet can also be found after HENRIC in the obverse legend. The reverse is the same as the previous issue.

H6HD-080 VG £30 F £60 VF £120

Edward IV First Reign 1461–1470

During Edward IV's first reign halfpennies were produced at four mints, London, Bristol, Canterbury and York. The provincial mints are all rare but the London mint produced a considerable number of coins. Edward IV's first reign coinage can be divided into the heavy and the light. The heavy coinage was only produced at the London mint and, with one rare exception, can be easily identified by the mintmark rose. The light coinage, so called because of the reduced weight of the coins, is very similar to Edward IV's second reign coinage, which is not surprising, as the two reigns were only divided by a few months. Collectors should check both reigns when identifying an issue. Edward IV's halfpennies are fairly easy to identify; firstly check that the obverse legend, starting at the top, reads EDWARD — if it reads RICARD or HENRIC it is an issue of Richard or Henry. Although Edward I, II and III also produced halfpennies, the issues are very different in style and size and the coins from the earlier reigns are larger. Edward IV's coins have a varied selection of mintmarks which are not found on the earlier issues, also the busts are different in style and size.

As mentioned earlier, four mints were active during Edward IV's reign. The mint's name can be found on the reverse legend and read CIVITAS LONDON for London, CIVITAS CANTOR for Canterbury, CIVITAS EBORACI for York and VILLA BRISTOW for Bristol. It is important to remember that Edward IV had two reigns; should collectors not find a coin in the first reign, they should refer to the second reign.

Collecting Hints

Most Edward IV halfpenny issues are fairly rare, especially the provincial mints. However, some issues from the London mint are quite common. These are usually available in about Fine condition. VF examples, while rare, are available. Many issues tend to be slightly clipped. They often look oval in shape, probably due to the tall bust of the king. In most cases there is a clear mintmark.

Heavy Coinage 1461–1464

Collectors should check the mintmark, as well as all the other marks on the coin, when identifying this series. During this issue only the London mint was active.

Obverse Legend EDWARD DI GRA REX — Edward by the grace of God King

Reverse Legend CIVITAS LONDON — City of London

Obverse Facing bust of king, lis on breast and a pellet either side of crown; mintmark plain cross.

Reverse Long cross, three pellets in each quarter, but in some cases four pellets in two quarters.

E4HD-005 VG £60 F £120 VF £250

Legends As previous.

Obverse Facing bust of king, quatrefoils either side of bust; mintmark rose.

Reverse Long cross, three pellets in each quarter.

E4HD-010 VG £40 F £80 VF £160

As previous, but saltires by bust; mintmark rose.

E4HD-015 VG £50 F £100 VF £180

As previous, but no marks by bust; mintmark rose.

E4HD-020 VG £35 F £75 VF £140

As previous, but annulet by bust; mintmark rose.

E4HD-025 VG £35 F £75 VF £140

Light Coinage 1464–1470

London Mint

Obverse Legend EDWARD DI GRA REX (A) — Edward by the grace of God King

Reverse Legend CIVITAS LONDON — City of London

Obverse Facing bust of king, saltires by neck; mintmark sun, crown or rose.

Reverse Long cross, three pellets in each quarter.

E4HD-030 VG £35 F £65 VF £120

As previous, but trefoils at neck; mintmark sun, crown or long cross fitchée.

E4HD-035 VG £20 F £40 VF £80

As previous, but no marks at neck; mintmark long cross fitchée.

E4HD-040 ex. rare

Bristol Mint

Obverse Legend As previous.

Reverse Legend VILLA BRISTOW — Town of Bristol

Obverse Facing bust of king, crosses by neck; mintmark crown.

Reverse Long cross, three pellets in each quarter.

E4HD-045 VG £70 F £150 VF £300

As previous, but trefoils by neck; mintmark crown.

E4HD-050 VG £55 F £100 VF £200

Canterbury Mint

Ecclesiastical Mint under Archbishop Bourchier

Obverse Legend As previous.

Reverse Legend CIVITAS CANTOR — City of Canterbury

Obverse Facing bust of king, trefoils by neck; mintmark pall.

Reverse Long cross, three pellets in each quarter.

E4HD-055 VG £60 F £120 VF £240

As previous, but no marks by king's neck; mintmark pall.

E4HD-060 VG £60 F £120 VF £240

Royal Mint

Legends As previous.

Obverse Facing bust of king, saltires by neck; mintmark crown.

Reverse Long cross, three pellets in each quarter.

E4HD-065 VG £40 F £80 VF £160

As previous, but trefoils at neck; mintmark crown.

E4HD-070 VG £40 F £80 VF £160

York Royal Mint

Obverse Legend As previous.

Reverse Legend CIVITAS EBORACI — City of York

Obverse Facing bust of king, saltires by neck; mintmark lis or sun.

Reverse As previous.

E4HD-075 VG £40 F £80 VF £160

As previous, but trefoils at neck; mintmark lis.

E4HD-080 VG £40 F £80 VF £160

Henry VI Restored Oct. 1470 — April 1471

During this very short period two mints produced halfpennies, London and Bristol. The London issue is fairly similar to the first reign of Henry VI although there are several differences. Firstly the obverse legend reads HENRIC DI GRA REX, also the mintmark short cross fitchée, which can be found on this issue, was not used on a halfpenny by any other Henry. The Bristol halfpenny, which is extremely rare, is easily identifiable being the only halfpenny produced at this mint by a Henry.

London Mint

Obverse Legend HENRIC DI GRA REX — Henry by the grace of God King

Reverse Legend CIVITAS LONDON — City of London

Obverse Facing bust of king, no marks; mintmark short cross fitchée.

Reverse Long cross, three pellets in each quarter.

H6HD-085 VG £120 F £250 VF £500

Bristol Mint

Obverse Legend As previous.

Reverse Legend VILLA BRISTOW — Town of Bristol

Obverse Facing bust of king; mintmark cross

Reverse As previous.

H6HD-090 ex. rare

Edward IV Second Reign 1471–1483

The halfpennies for the second reign of Edward IV are very much a continuation from the first reign, which is hardly surprising as the two periods were only separated by a few months. During Edward's second reign the London and Royal Canterbury mint continued production; also, the Durham mint produced halfpennies for this reign only. We have given details in Edwards IV's first reign of how to identify the various issues; the only new detail is, of course, the Durham mint. The production of halfpennies at this mint is unique to this reign. The mint's name, as with other issues, is found on the reverse of the coin and reads CIVITAS DERAM. It is important that, should collectors not find a coin under the second coinage, they should refer to the first coinage which is in many cases very similar.

London Mint

Obverse Legend EDWARD DI GRA REX — Edward by the grace of God King

Reverse Legend CIVITAS LONDON — City of London

Obverse Facing bust of king, no marks by neck; mintmark short cross fitchée, annulet, pellet in annulet, cross and four pellets, cross in circle, pierced cross, cross and one pellet, cinquefoil.

Reverse Long cross, three pellets in each quarter.

E4HD-085 VG £60 F £100 VF £200

As previous, but pellet either side of neck; mintmark pierced cross.

E4HD-090 VG £20 F £40 VF £80

Canterbury Royal Mint

Obverse Legend As previous.

Reverse Legend CIVITAS CANTAR — City of Canterbury

Obverse Facing bust of king, 'C' on king's breast; mintmark rose.

Reverse Long cross, three pellets in each quarter, large 'C' in centre of cross.

E4HD-095 VG £40 F £80 VF £150

As previous, but no 'C' on reverse; mintmark rose.

E4HD-100 VG £35 F £70 VF £140

As previous, without 'C'; mintmark long cross fitchée.

E4HD-105 VG £40 F £80 VF £150

Durham Ecclesiastical Mint under Bishop Booth

Obverse Legend As previous.

Reverse Legend CIVITAS DERAM — City of Durham

Obverse Facing bust of king; mintmark rose.

Reverse Long cross, three pellets in each quarter with large 'D' in centre of cross.

E4HD-110 VG £60 F £130 VF £250

As previous, but 'V' to left of neck.

E4HD-115 VG £60 F £130 VF £250

Edward IV or V

As with other denominations, there is uncertainty over which reign this issue should be classed in, but most numismatists are of the opinion that, while the dies were made for Edward IV's second reign, they were used to produce coins under Edward V.

Obverse Legend EDWARD DI GRA REX — Edward by the grace of God King

Reverse Legend CIVITAS LONDON — City of London

Obverse Facing bust of king, no mark in field; mintmark halved sun and rose.

Reverse Long cross, three pellets in each quarter.

E4HD-120 VG £200 F £400 VF £800

No halfpennies were issued using dies from the reign of Edward V.

Richard III 1483–1485

During Richard III's short reign only the London mint produced halfpennies. The issues are fairly easy to identify as RICARD can be found on the obverse, at the beginning of the legend. The only other Richard to produce halfpennies was Richard II, but his issues are very different in style. Also different mintmarks were used by the two monarchs; Richard II used cross pattée and Richard III used mintmark sun and rose and boar's head.

Collecting Hints

Richard III halfpennies are extremely rare in any grade.

Obverse Legend RICARD DI GRA REX — Richard by the grace of God King

Reverse Legend CIVITAS LONDON — City of London

Obverse Facing bust of king; mintmark sun and rose.

Reverse Long cross, three pellets in each quarter.

R3HD-005 VG £200 F £350 VF £700

As previous, but mintmark boar's head.

R3HD-010 VG £225 F £400 VF £800

Henry VII 1485–1509

During Henry VII's reign quantities of halfpennies were produced at the London, Canterbury and York mints. All issues are of the facing bust variety because the coins were becoming too small for the profile style. This is unfortunate, as the quality of workmanship, in both design and style, was much better in the profile issue.

Henry VII's halfpennies are fairly easy to identify. The obverse legend, starting at the top, reads HENRIC — if it reads RICARD or EDWARD it is an issue of Richard or Edward. Henry IV, V and VI (both reigns) all issued halfpennies, but Henry VII's issues are different in many ways. The portraits are different in style, the king's crown has an arch in the more common issues and Henry VII used different mintmarks. Another feature, on the reverse of the coin, is the centre cross which is ornate at the edges in most issues whereas previously it had been a plain cross.

It is important to remember that many issues from the same reign are slightly different. Collectors might have to check through several reigns when identifying a coin, especially if it is in poor condition. Remember to check the mintmark, also look for any unusual marks on the coins.

Three mints were active producing Henry VII halfpennies. The mint name can be found on the reverse of the coin and reads CIVITAS LONDON for London, CIVITAS CANTOR for Canterbury and CIVITAS EBORACI for York.

Collecting Hints

The London issue halfpennies are fairly common; they are usually available in about Fine condition, VF examples are scarce but obtainable. Both the Canterbury and York mints are fairly scarce. Many issues are very small, sometimes missing parts of their legend. Usually this is due not to clipping, but to the way the coins were struck. With the price of silver rising over the last few centuries, coins were getting smaller. The halfpenny would, during this period, be considered a small denomination with fairly little buying power.

London Mint

Open Crown Issue

Obverse Legend HENRIC D (E) I GRA REX — Henry by the grace of God King

Reverse Legend CIVITAS LONDON — City of London

Obverse Facing bust of king with open crown; mintmark lis upon sun and rose or lis-rose dimidiated.

Reverse Long cross, three pellets in each quarter.

H7HD-005 VG £40 F £100 VF £180

As previous, but trefoil at king's neck; mintmark rose.

H7HD-010 VG £40 F £100 VF £180

As previous, but crosses by king's neck; mintmark rose or cross fitchée.

H7HD-015 VG £35 F £80 VF £160

Arched Crown Issue

As previous, but facing bust of king wearing an arched crown; mintmark none or cinquefoil.

H7HD-020 VG £18 F £35 VF £70

As previous, but saltires by neck; no mintmark.

H7HD-025 VG £18 F £35 VF £70

As H7HD-020, but crown has a lower arch, the lettering in the legends is also more ornate; no mintmark.

H7HD-030 VG £20 F £38 VF £75

As previous, but much smaller portrait; mintmark pheon or lis.

H7HD-035 VG £25 F £45 VF £85

Canterbury Mint
Ecclesiastical Issue under Archbishop Morton

Obverse Legend As previous.

Reverse Legend CIVITAS CANTOR — City of Canterbury

Obverse Facing bust of king wearing open early style crown; no mintmark.

Reverse As previous, but 'M' in centre of reverse.

H7HD-040 ex. rare

Obverse Legend As previous, except for horizontal lines before king's name.

Reverse Legend As previous.

Obverse Facing bust of king wearing double-arched crown, the four lines in the legend are probably an uncertain mintmark.

Reverse As previous.

H7HD-045 ex. rare

This issue was issued by the king and Bishop jointly.
Obverse Legend As H7HD-040.

Reverse Legend As previous.

Obverse Facing bust of king wearing arched crown; mintmark none or lis.

Reverse No 'M' in centre.

H7HD-050 VG £50 F £50 F £100 VF £200

York Mint

York was an ecclesiastical mint under the control of Archbishop Savage.

Obverse Legend As previous.

Reverse Legend CIVITAS EBORACI — City of York

Obverse Facing bust of king wearing single-arched crown, key below king's bust; mintmark uncertain.

Reverse Long cross, three pellets in each quarter.

H7HD-055 VG £50 F £100 VF £200

Henry VIII 1509–1547

Henry VIII produced a variety of halfpennies. During the first and second coinage the issues are fairly similar to those of his father, Henry VII. However, the issues, which all have an arched crown, tend to be slightly crude in style and the mintmarks used are different. The provincial mints had various marks or letters in the field specific to their class, moreover, during the second coinage the obverse legend changed radically to H.DG ROSA SIE SPIA — Henry by the grace of God a rose without a thorn.

During the third and the posthumous coinages, the king has a more life-like bust similar to the one used on larger denominations such as the groat; the reverse, however, remains the same. The third and posthumous issues were struck in base silver. A total of four mints struck halfpennies during Henry VIII's reign: London, Canterbury, York and Bristol. The London mint is henceforth referred to as Tower mint to avoid confusion with the other two mints which operated in London around this period. The mint's name can be found on the reverse of the coin in the legends and read as follows for the various issues:

London — CIVITAS LONDON (1st and 2nd coinage)

Bristol — CIVITAS BRISTOLI (3rd coinage)

Canterbury — CIVITAS CANTOR (1st, 2nd and 3rd coinage)

York — CIVITAS EBORACI (2nd and 3rd coinage)

Tower — CIVITAS LONDON (3rd coinage)

Collecting Hints

The halfpenny was becoming a less important denomination and this is clearly illustrated by the rather poor production of these issues. Many of the issues are unclear, often with legends that are difficult to read. The average condition in which all issues are available is less than Fine. Collectors should try to obtain a coin in the best possible grade, preferably with a legible mint-name and portrait.

First Coinage 1509–1526

London Mint

Obverse Legend HENRIC DI GRA REX AGL — Henry by the grace of God King of England

Reverse Legend CIVITAS LONDON — City of London

Obverse Facing bust of king; mintmark castle or portcullis crowned.

Reverse Long cross, three pellets in each quarter.

H8HD-005 VG £20 F £45 VF £80

Canterbury Mint

Obverse Legend As previous.

Reverse Legend CIVITAS CANTOR — City of Canterbury

Obverse Facing bust of king dividing 'W.A.' (for Archbishop Warham); mintmark pomegranate or cross fitchée.

Reverse As previous.

H8HD-010 VG £60 F £120 VF £220

Second Coinage 1526–1544

This issue can be easily differentiated from the first coinage by the new obverse legend, and different mintmark.

London Mint

Obverse Legend H DG ROSA SIE SPIA — Henry by the grace of God a rose without a thorn

Reverse Legend CIVITAS LONDON — City of London

Obverse Facing bust of king; mintmark rose, lis, arrow or sunburst

Reverse Long cross, three pellets in each quarter.

H8HD-015 VG £20 F £45 VF £80

Canterbury Mint

Obverse Legend As previous.

Reverse Legend CIVITAS CANTOR — City of Canterbury

Obverse Facing bust of king dividing 'W.A' (for Archbishop Warham); mintmark 'T' or cross patonce. Mainly Lombardic lettering in the legend.

Reverse As previous.

H8HD-020 VG £35 F £60 VF £120

As previous, but 'T.C.' (for Thomas Cranmer) divided by bust; mintmark Catherine Wheel.

H8HD-025 VG £30 F £55 VF £110

York Mint

Obverse Legend As previous.

Reverse Legend CIVITAS EBORACI — City of York

Obverse Facing bust of king dividing 'T.W.' (for Thomas Wolsey); mintmark voided cross.

Reverse As previous.

H8HD-030 VG £30 F £55 VF £110

Sede Vacante Issue

Legends As previous.

Obverse Facing bust of king, key below bust; mintmark cross voided.

Reverse As previous.

H8HD-035 VG £40 F £75 VF £150

As previous, but facing bust of king dividing 'E.L' or 'LE' (Archbishop Lee) on the obverse.

H8HD-040 VG £30 F £55 VF £110

Third Coinage

This issue is very different from the first and second coinages as the obverse has a more life-like bust of the ageing king; it is, however, very similar to the posthumous issue. In most cases, due to the poor condition of the coins, the issues are impossible to distinguish and class. Tiny differences have been listed in all cases but unfortunately it is often impossible to see these small marks and differences on the coins. The reverse of the coin, in all cases, remained very similar to the first and second coinages.

Tower Mint

Obverse Legend H.D.G ROSA SINE SPINA — Henry by the grace of God a rose without a thorn

Reverse Legend CIVITAS LONDON — City of London

Obverse Facing, ageing bust of king; mintmark lis or none. Lombardic lettering in the legend.

Reverse Long cross, three pellets in each quarter, pellet in annulet in centre.

H8HD-045 VG £30 F £50 VF £90

Bristol Mint

Obverse Legend As previous.

Reverse Legend CIVITAS BRISTOLI — City of Bristol

Obverse As previous, but no mintmark.

Reverse As previous, but no pellet in annulet.

H8HD-050 VG £40 F £80 VF £90

Canterbury Mint

Obverse Legend As previous, but some read H8 D.G instead of H.D.G.

Reverse Legend CIVITAS CANTOR — City of Canterbury

Obverse As previous, trefoil stops in legend; no mintmark.

Reverse As previous, trefoil stops in legend.

H8HD-055 VG £30 F £50 VF £90

York Mint

Obverse Legend As H8HD-045.

Reverse Legend CIVITAS EBORACI

Obverse As previous; no mintmark. Mixed lettering and trefoil stops in the legend.

Reverse As previous.

H8HD-060 VG £30 F £50 VF £90

Posthumous Coinage 1547–1551

As mentioned earlier, the halfpennies for the posthumous issue are virtually identical to those of the third issue. The main differences are as follows: the third coinage issues of the Tower and Canterbury mints have Lombardic lettering while the posthumous issue has Roman lettering which looks more like the lettering of today. However, the third coinage sometimes does have some Roman lettering in the legends. The main difference with the York mint is the stops which are found on the coin; in the third coinage they are trefoils and the posthumous issue has either single pellets or lozenges.

Tower Mint

Obverse Legend H. DG ROSA SINA SPINA — Henry by the grace of God a rose without a thorn

Reverse Legend CIVITAS LONDON — City of London

Obverse Facing bust of ageing king; no mintmark. Roman lettering in the legend.

Reverse Long cross, three pellets in each quarter.

H8HD-065 VG £30 F £50 VF £100

Canterbury Mint

Obverse Legend As previous, but sometimes reads H8.

Reverse Legend CIVITAS CANTOR — City of Canterbury

Obverse As previous.

Reverse As previous.

H8HD-070 VG £35 F £60 VF £120

York Mint

Obverse Legend As H8HD-065.

Reverse Legend CIVITAS EBORACI — City of York

Obverse As previous; no mintmark. Lozenge or pellet stops in the legend, mixed style of lettering.

Reverse As previous.

H8HD-075 VG £30 F £50 VF £100

Edward VI 1547–1553

During this short reign, several issues of halfpenny were produced in Edward VI's name. The first issue, produced during the first period from April 1547 to January 1549, was struck at the Tower and Bristol mints. These two issues are both extremely rare and had the crowned bust of the king on the obverse, while the reverse still had the long cross with three pellets in each quarter. During the third period (1550–1553), a halfpenny was produced which omitted the king's head on the obverse and replaced it with a rose; the royal shield is found on the reverse. This issue is very rare, but not as rare as the issues from the first period. All these coins were struck in base silver and no halfpennies were produced during Edward VI's fine silver issue.

Collecting Hints

These issues are rare in any grade. Collectors will have great difficulty obtaining a specimen.

First Period April 1547 — Jan 1549

Tower Mint

Obverse Legend EDG ROSA SIN SPIN — Edward by the grace of God a rose without a thorn

Reverse Legend CIVITAS LONDON — City of London

Obverse Crowned bust of king; mintmark uncertain.

Reverse Long cross with three pellets in each angle.

E6HD-005 VG £200 F £400 VF £800

Bristol Mint

Obverse Legend As previous, or ED6 DG instead of EDG.

Reverse Legend CIVITAS BRISTOLI — City of Bristol

Obverse As previous, but no mintmark.

Reverse As previous.

E6HD-010 VG £180 F £350 VF £700

Third Period 1550–1553

This issue was only struck at the Tower mint and often used as a farthing because of its base silver content.

Obverse Legend EDG ROSA SINE SPINA — Edward by the grace of God a rose without a thorn

Reverse Legend CIVITAS LONDON — City of London

Obverse Rose in centre; mintmark escallop.

Reverse Royal shield over cross.

E6HD-015 VG £150 F £250 VF £500

No halfpennies were struck during the reigns of Mary or Philip and Mary.

Elizabeth I 1558–1603

Although no halfpennies were struck during the first twenty years of Elizabeth's reign, they were produced in some quantity during the fifth and sixth issues (1582–1602). These halfpennies, due to their very small size, did not have either the queen's portrait or legends; there was, however, a portcullis on the obverse and the reverse had a cross with three pellets in each quarter. Most issues had mintmarks which are found on the obverse above the portcullis.

Collecting Hints

Elizabeth's halfpennies are fairly scarce but obtainable. They are usually available in the higher grades. Fine and VF examples are not uncommon. They are rarely found damaged or clipped.

Fifth Issue 1582–1600

Obverse Portcullis; mintmarks none, 'A', escallop, crescent, hand, tun, woolpack, key, anchor or '0'.

Reverse Cross with three pellets in each quarter.

ELHD-005 VG £20 F £40 VF £70

Sixth Issue 1601–1602

The mintmark denoted the date the coin was made, '1' for 1601 and '2' for 1602.

Obverse As previous, but mintmark '1' or '2'.

Reverse As previous.

ELHD-010 VG £22 F £45 VF £75

James I 1603–1625

Halfpennies were produced during all three coinages of James I. The first coinage issue is very similar to the issues of Elizabeth I; the only difference is the mintmark. James I used mintmark thistle and lis. During the second and third coinages the style was completely changed; on the obverse is a simple rose and a thistle on the reverse. The second coinage coins have a mintmark above the thistle but the third coinage coins have no mintmark.

Collecting Hints

Halfpennies from the first coinage are fairly scarce, due to the fact that they were only produced for two years; however, they are usually obtainable in Fine condition, VF examples are not rare. Halfpennies from the second and third coinages are fairly common and usually obtainable in Fine to EF condition.

First Coinage 1603–1604

Obverse Portcullis; mintmark thistle or lis.

Reverse Long cross, three pellets in each quarter.

J1HD-005 VG £20 F £30 VF £50

Second Coinage 1604–1619

Obverse Rose.

Reverse Thistle with mintmark lis, rose, escallop, grapes, coronet, key, bell, mullet and cinquefoil.

J1HD-010 VG £18 F £28 VF £50 EF £80

Third Coinage 1619–1625

Obverse Rose.

Reverse Thistle; no mintmark.

J1HD-015 VG £18 F £28 VF £50 EF £80

Charles I 1625–1649

Hardly any halfpennies were produced during Charles I's reign. This is surprising considering the diversity, and quantity, of denominations that Charles I produced. The first, and most common, issue was struck at the Tower mint. This issue is easily recognisable, simply having a rose either side of the coin; there is no legend or mintmark. The only other Charles I halfpenny was produced at the Aberystwyth mint. This issue has a rose on the obverse, plumes on the reverse. As with the Tower mint issue, it has no legend or mintmark.

Collecting Hints

The Tower mint issue is fairly common, usually obtainable in about Fine condition. VF examples exist and are obtainable. The Aberystwyth issue is rare and difficult to obtain in any grade.

Tower Mint

Obverse Rose, no mintmark.

Reverse Rose.

C1HD-005 VG £18 F £30 VF £50

Aberystwyth Mint 1638–1642

Obverse Rose, no mintmark.

Reverse Plumes.

C1HD-010 VG £80 F £150 VF £250

Commonwealth 1649–1660

The Commonwealth period was the last to produce the silver halfpenny which was replaced by a milled copper coin during Charles II's reign. The halfpennies of the Commonwealth are very plain, with no mintmark. There is the St George's cross on the obverse and the Irish harp on the reverse. Forgeries of this issue are quite common, they are usually very thick and the style is slightly different.

Collecting Hints

This issue is fairly scarce; coins are usually available in Fine or VF condition. Sometimes the coins are clipped or officially holed to devalue them.

Obverse St George's cross.

Reverse Arms of Ireland.

COMHD-005 VG £20 F £40 VF £75

No halfpennies were produced during the hammered coinage of Charles II (1660 -1662).

Farthing

Farthings, with one exception, were first produced in England during the reign of Edward I. The exception is an extremely rare specimen which was produced for Henry III. Farthings were part of Edward I's recoinage plan and were one of several new denominations introduced. Previously, the need for smaller denominations had been met by cutting pennies in half or quarters.

Any problem encountered by collectors is likely to be due to the farthing's size and value. Being the smallest denomination, it was seldom hoarded and in fact farthings, unlike pennies, have not been found in large hoards. Most issues are also extremely small, which has made it difficult to locate them with metal detectors as few can pick up a signal the size of a farthing. For these reasons, farthings tend to be rare.

Another difficulty could be identification. If the farthing is unclipped and in at least Fine condition, this problem should not arise. However, most issues are often weakly struck and sometimes clipped, making them difficult to identify. Also, halfpennies were often clipped and so resemble farthings.

Farthings were not produced in such a variety as denominations such as the penny were, but they were produced in most reigns. It is important to remember that all farthings were issued with full legends. If unsure, collectors should also refer to the halfpenny chapter when identifying an issue they think is a farthing.

Henry III 1216–1272

This issue has only recently been discovered and is extremely rare. It was struck at the London mint during the short-cross coinage. It is similar to the penny in style, but very small. It is uncertain whether this issue can be considered a pattern as no documentary evidence exists. At the time of writing, with only two specimens known, this issue cannot be considered important as a denomination, but rather a trial issue.

Obverse Legend HENRICUS REX — King Henry

Reverse Legend TERRI ON LUND — Terry of London

Obverse Bust of king holding sceptre.

Reverse Short cross, three pellets in each quarter.

H3FA-005 ex. rare

Edward I 1272–1307

Edward I farthings were produced in very large quantities; London was by far the most prolific mint although Berwick, Bristol, Lincoln, Newcastle and York all issued farthings. These mints, in most cases, are very rare. The farthing, in all cases, is fairly similar to Edward's penny issues. The obverse has a crowned facing bust of the king, the legend starts EDWARDUS or ER for Edward. The reverse has the mint's name in the legend, a long cross dividing the coin and three pellets in each quarter.

The weight and fineness of Edward's farthing issues, unlike the other denominations, varies. The first three issues from the London mint weigh 6.85 grains (0.44 grams), the rest of the issues weigh 5.5 grains (0.36 grams); the value of the coins, however, remained the same. This was because the heavier issues had a lower fineness, or silver content, than the lighter issues. It is thought that the coins were made larger in order to make them easier to strike and handle. Coins of low fineness have never been popular in England and the public preferred the inconvenience of a smaller coin with a high metal content.

As mentioned earlier, six mints were active during Edward I's reign. The mint's name can be found on the reverse of the coin. They read LONDONIENSIS or CIVITAS LONDON for London, VILLA BEREVVICI for Berwick, VILLA BRISTOLLIE for Bristol, CIVITAS LINCOL for Lincoln, NOVICASTRI for Newcastle, and CIVITAS EBORACI for York.

When identifying farthings, use the same procedure as with pennies or groats. Firstly check the obverse legend; there are varieties, which are important. These varieties are one of the main, and easiest, ways of identifying farthings from the first three reigns of Edward. However, the farthing may not fall into a class, as many issues share the same obverse legend. Collectors should then check through each issue, looking for the various marks or differences, as they will differentiate the issue.

London Mint

Heavy Weight 6.85 grains (0.44 grams)

Class 1A

Obverse Legend EDWARDUS REX — King Edward

Reverse Legend LONDONIENSIS — London

Obverse Facing bust of king wearing bifoliate crown.

Reverse Long cross, three pellets in each quarter.

E1FA-005 VG £20 F £50 VF £125

Class 1C

As previous, but the king is wearing a trifoliate crown.

E1FA-010 VG £25 F £60 VF £140

Class 2

As previous, but reversed 'N's in reverse legend.

E1FA-015 VG £20 F £45 VF £125

Class 3C

As E1FA-010, but the king has a larger face and bushier hair.

E1FA-020 VG £20 F £45 VF £125

Reduced Weight 5.5 grains (0.36 grams)
Class 3D/3E

Obverse Legend ER ANGLIE — Edward King of England

Reverse Legend LONDONIENSIS — London

Obverse Facing bust of king, no inner circle.

Reverse As previous.

E1FA-025 VG £20 F £45 VF £125

Class 4

Obverse Legend As previous

Reverse Legend CIVITAS LONDON — City of London

Obverse As previous, but king wears a tall narrow crown.

Reverse As previous.

E1FA-030 VG £35 F £60 VF £140

Class 5

As previous, but the king has a wider crown; large irregular lettering in the legends.

E1FA-035 VG £35 F £60 VF £140

Class 6/7

As previous, but king has almond shaped eyes; double-barred 'N' in legend.

E1FA-040 VG £70 F £140 VF220

Class 8

Obverse Legend ER ANGL DN — Edward King of England Lord (of Ireland)

Reverse Legend As previous.

Obverse Closed 'E' in legend.

Reverse As previous.

E1FA-045 VG £35 F £60 VF £140

Class 9

Similar to previous but pot-hook, unbarred 'N's in legend.

E1FA-050 VG £35 F £60 VF £140

Class 10 (& 11)

This issue is often struck on an oval flan, and was possibly also struck during Edward II's reign.

Obverse Legend EDWARDUS REX A(N) — Edward King of England

Reverse Legend CIVITAS LONDON — City of London

Obverse Inner circle, the king has a narrow face and narrow lettering in the legend.

Reverse As previous.

E1FA-055 VG £20 F £50 VF£ 90

Berwick Mint

Obverse Legend EDWARDUS REX — King Edward

Reverse Legend VIIIA BERVVICI — Town of Berwick

Obverse Facing bust of king.

Reverse Long cross, three pellets in each quarter.

E1FA-060 ex. rare

Bristol Mint
Class 3C

Obverse Legend EDWARDUS REX — King Edward

Reverse Legend VILLA BRISTOLLIE — Town of Bristol

Obverse Large face with bushy hair.

Reverse As previous.

E1FA-065 VG £50 F £100 F £200

Class 3G

Obverse Legend E R ANGLIE — Edward King of England

Reverse Legend As previous.

Obverse No inner circle.

Reverse As previous.

E1FA-070 VG £60 F £120 VF £220

Lincoln Mint
Class 3G

Obverse Legend E R ANGLIE — Edward King of England

Reverse Legend CIVITAS LINCOL — City of Lincoln

Obverse No inner circle.

Reverse As previous.

E1FA-075 VG £80 F £150 VF £300

Newcastle Mint
Class 3E

Obverse Legend E R ANGLIE — Edward King of England

Reverse Legend NOVI CASTRI — Newcastle

Obverse Facing bust with no inner circle.

Reverse As previous, but pellet-barred 'N's on reverse.

E1FA-080 VG £150 F £300

As previous, but only one pellet in each quarter on reverse.

E1FA-085 ex. rare

York Mint

Class 3C

Obverse Legend EDWARDUS REX — King Edward

Reverse Legend CIVITAS EBORACI — City of York

Obverse Inner circles, and the king has a large face with bushier hair.

Reverse Long cross, three pellets in each quarter.

E1FA-090 VG £125 F £200 VF £350

Class 3E

Obverse Legend E R ANGLIE — Edward King of England

Reverse Legend As previous.

Obverse No inner circle.

Reverse As previous.

E1FA-095 VG £125 F £200 VF £350

Edward II 1307–1327

Of the two mints which produced farthings during Edward II's reign, Berwick is extremely rare and London is rare. The London issue is very similar to Edward I's last London farthing, although there are a few differences. The combination of rarity and poor condition has resulted in little research being done towards classing these issues. In fact, in most cases, it appears probable that Edward I's last issue was in production during Edward II's reign. Although the obverse legend of Edward II farthings is often unclear, and varieties seem to exist, one of the main difference between the two reigns is in the lettering. In most of Edward II's issues the 'N's are unbarred and the 'E' is slightly different in style. Also, in many of Edward II's issues, the king has a more pointed face; in Edward I's issues the king has a rounder face.

London Mint

Obverse Legend EDWARDUS REX (AN) — Edward King of England

Reverse Legend CIVITAS LONDON — City of London

Obverse Facing bust of king with inner circle, crown with wedge-shaped or uneven petals to central lis, usually with unbarred 'N's in legend; mintmark plain Initial cross or Initial cross pattée.

Reverse Long cross, three pellets in each quarter.

E2FA-005 VG £40 F £80 VF £180

Berwick Mint

Obverse Legend EDWARDUS REX — King Edward

Reverse Legend VILLA BERVICCI — Town of Berwick

Obverse This issue is virtually identical to that of Edward I, except that on Edward II issues one of the spears in the crown is broken.

Reverse Long cross, three pellets in each quarter.

E2FA-010 VG £100 F £200

Edward III 1327–1377

Edward III's issues, while fairly similar to those of the two previous reigns, are fairly easy to identify, having various markings or different obverse legends. Three mints produced Edward III's farthings; London was the most prolific, while Berwick is rare and the farthing from the Reading mint is unique. In all issues the king's name appears on the obverse of the coin, starting at the top. If instead of EDWARDUS it reads RICARD or HENRI, it is an issue of Richard or Henry.

First Coinage 1327–1335

London Mint

Obverse Legend EDWARDUS REX (A) — King Edward

Reverse Legend CIVITAS LONDON — City of London

Obverse Facing bust of king, the crown is flat and there is a star at the end of the obverse legend.

Reverse Long cross, three pellets in each quarter.

E3FA-005 VG £60 F £120 VF £200

Berwick Mint

Obverse Legend EDWARDUS REX — King Edward

Reverse Legend VILLA BERVICCI — Town of Berwick

Obverse Facing bust of king.

Reverse Bear's head in two quarters of reverse.

E3FA-010 VG £100 F £200 VF —

Second Coinage 1335–1343

This issue was struck at the London mint in .833 silver although the usual silver content for coins of this period was .925.

Obverse Legend EDWARDUS REX A — Edward King of England

Reverse Legend CIVITAS LONDON — City of London

Obverse Similar to the previous London issue with a star at the end of the obverse legend; however, the issue is rougher in style and the king's crown is taller.

Reverse Long cross, three pellets in each quarter.

E3FA-015 VG £40 F £80 VF £150

Third or Florin Coinage 1344–1351

This issue was struck in .925 silver.

London Mint

Obverse Legend EDWARDUS REX — King Edward

Reverse Legend CIVITAS LONDON — City of London

Obverse Facing bust of king with bushy hair, broad neck and shoulders; the crown has neat broad fleurs or prongs.

Reverse As previous.

E3FA-020 VG £40 F £65 VF £120

Reading Mint

As previous, but escallop in one quarter of reverse and reverse legend reads VILLA RADINGY — Town of Reading.

E3FA-025 Unique

Fourth Coinage

These issues were struck in London.

Series E 1354–1355

Obverse Legend EDWARDUS REX (AN) — King Edward

Reverse Legend CIVITAS LONDON — City of London

Obverse Facing crowned bust of king, broken letters in legend; mintmark cross 2.

Reverse Long cross, three pellets in each quarter.

E3FA-030 VF £100 F £200 VF —

As previous, but annulet in one quarter of reverse.

E3FA-035 ex. rare

Treaty Period 1361–1369

Obverse Legend EDWARDUS REX — King Edward

Reverse Legend CIVITAS LONDON — City of London

Obverse Facing bust of king, pellet stop in legend.

Reverse As previous.

E3FA-040 VG £80 F £180 VF £300

Post Treaty Period 1369–1377

Obverse Legend EDWARD REX ANGL — Edward King of England

Reverse Legend CIVITAS LONDON — City of London

Obverse The king has a large head and no neck.

Reverse As previous.

E3FA-045 VG £100 F £200 VF £325

Richard II 1377–1399

Richard II was the only Richard to produce farthings and this makes identifying an issue fairly easy as the coins bear the king's name, RICARD, on the obverse. All farthings issued by Richard are rare and were only struck at the London mint.

Collecting Hints

All issues of Richard II are rare in any grade. They are usually available in about Fine condition but VF examples exist. Collectors may have great difficulty in obtaining an example.

Obverse Legend RICARD REX ANGL — Richard King of England

Reverse Legend CIVITAS LONDON — City of London

Obverse Facing small bust of king.

Reverse Long cross, three pellets in each quarter.

R2FA-005 VG £125 F £275 VF £500

As previous, but a small rose after REX.

R2FA-010 VG £140 F £300 VF £550

As R2FA-005, bust but larger bust.

R2FA-015 ex. rare

As previous, but on reverse a rose in each quarter instead of pellets.

R2FA-020 VG £250 F £550 VF £1,100

Henry IV 1399–1413

Farthings were issued during both the heavy and the light coinages of Henry IV. The heavy coinage is approximately 20% heavier than the light coinage but both issues are very rare. The two issues have variations which differentiate them from other reigns; not only is HENRIC found on the obverse, starting at the top but also the coins show a face of the king without a neck, whereas all other reigns have a proper bust. On the light coinage there is a slipped trefoil after REX in the obverse legend. Also, LONDON on the obverse legend appears to be spelled LOIDOI.

Collecting Hints

All coins from Henry IV's reign are very rare and the farthing is no exception. Collectors may have great difficulty in obtaining an example in any grade.

Heavy Coinage 1399–1412

Obverse Legend HENRIC REX ANGL — Henry King of England

Reverse Legend CIVITAS LONDON — City of London

Obverse Face of king with no neck.

Reverse Long cross, three pellets in each quarter.

H4FA-005 VG £300 F £500 VF £1,000

Light Coinage 1412–1413

Obverse Legend As previous.

Reverse Legend CIVITAS LONDON (appears LOIDOI) — City of London

Obverse Small face without neck, slipped trefoil after REX.

Reverse As previous.

H4FA-010 VG £325 F £600 VF £1,150

Henry V 1413–1422

Only one issue of farthing was produced during the reign of Henry V and it is very different from that of Henry IV as the king has a neck. However, this issue is fairly similar to those of Henry VI and the main difference is that Henry VI's issues have various marks, such as annulets, on the coin. Collectors should check both reigns when identifying farthings from this period as both reigns have the obverse legend starting with the king's name, HENRIC. During Henry V's reign the farthing was only produced at the London mint.

Obverse Legend HENRIC REX ANGL — Henry King of England

Reverse Legend CIVITAS LONDON — City of London

Obverse Facing bust of king with small face but with a neck; no marks elsewhere on coin.

Reverse Long cross, three pellets in each quarter

H5FA-005 VG £100 F £225 VF £375

Henry VI First Reign 1422–1461

Farthings were produced for most of Henry VI's issues and struck at the London and Calais mints. Each issue is easily identifiable by various marks which are found on the coin. To the untrained eye, a Henry V issue is fairly similar to Henry VI's issues and both reigns should be referred to when identifying a coin from this period. In all cases the king's name is found in the obverse legend, at the top of the coin, and should read HENRIC; if it reads RICARD or EDWARD, it is an issue of Richard or Edward. The mint's name can be found on the reverse of the coin and for the issues of Henry VI reads CIVITAS LONDON for London or VILLA CALIS for Calais (possible varieties exist).

Annulet Issue 1422–1427

London Mint

Obverse Legend HENRIC REX ANGL — Henry King of England

Reverse Legend CIVITAS LONDON — City of London

Obverse Facing bust of king; mintmark cross pommée.

Reverse Long cross, three pellets in each quarter and two annulets in two quarters.

H6FA-005 VG £100 F £225 VF £400

Calais Mint

Obverse Legend As previous.

Reverse Legend VILLA CALAIS — Town of Calais

Obverse Facing bust of king, annulet either side of neck.

Reverse As previous, but no annulets.

H6FA-010 VG £150 F £375 VF £700

Rosette Mascle Issue 1427–1430

This issue has rosettes and mascles somewhere in the legends.

London Mint

Obverse Legend As previous.

Reverse Legend CIVITAS LONDON — City of London

Obverse Facing bust of king, rosettes and mascles in legend.

Reverse Long cross, three pellets in each quarter.

H6FA-015 VG £80 F £150 VF £300

Calais Mint

Obverse Legend As previous.

Reverse Legend VILLA CALIS — Town of Calais

Obverse As previous; mintmark cross pommée.

Reverse As previous.

H6FA-020 VG £85 F £160 VF £325

Pinecone Mascle Issue 1430–1434

This issue has pinecones and mascles in the legend.

London Mint

Obverse Legend As previous.

Reverse Legend CIVITAS LONDON — City of London

Obverse Facing bust of king, pinecones and mascles in the legend.

Reverse Long cross, three pellets in each quarter.

H6FA-025 VG £80 F £150 VF £300

Calais Mint

As previous, but reverse legend reads VILLA CALIS — Town of Calais.

H6FA-030 VG £100 F £225 VF £400

Leaf Trefoil Issue 1435–1438

This issue was only struck at the London mint.

Obverse Legend As previous.

Reverse Legend CIVITAS LONDON — City of London

Obverse Facing bust of king, leaf on breast, trefoil and saltire stops in legend.

Reverse Long cross, three pellets in each quarter.

H6FA-035 VG £80 F £150 VF £300

Leaf Pellet Issue 1443–1445

This issue was only struck at the London mint.
Legends As previous.

Obverse Facing bust of king with leaf on breast, with a pellet either side of crown.

Reverse As previous, but usually extra pellet in two quarters.

H6FA-040 VG £100 F £225 VF £375

Cross Pellet Issue 1454–1460

This issue was only struck at the London mint.
As previous, but a saltire either side of the neck and a pellet either side of the crown.

H6FA-045 VG £100 F £225 VF £375

Edward IV First Reign 1461–1470

Edward IV had two issues, the light and the heavy coinage, so called because of the difference in weight but in the case of farthings weight cannot be used to help identify various issues. Farthings were struck during both coinages of Edward IV but only at the London mint. The king's name is always found on the obverse of the coin at the top and should read EDWARD.

Collecting Hints

These issues are extremely rare and difficult to obtain in any grade.

Heavy Coinage 1461–1464

Obverse Legend EDWARD REX ANGLI — Edward King of England

Reverse Legend CIVITAS LONDON — City of London

Obverse Facing bust of king; mintmark plain cross.

Reverse Long cross, three pellets in each quarter.

E4FA-005 VG £400 F £650 VF £1,400

Light Coinage 1464–1470

Obverse Legend EDWARD DI GRA REX — Edward King by the grace of God

Reverse Legend As previous.

Obverse Facing bust of king; mintmark rose.

Reverse As previous.

E4FA-010 VG £300 F £500 VF £1,100

As previous, but trefoil either side of neck; mintmark crown.

E4FA-015 VG £500 F £700 VF £1,500

No farthings were struck for Henry VI Restored, Edward IV's second reign, Edward IV/V, Edward V or Richard III.

Henry VII 1485–1509

Only one type of farthing was issued during the reign of Henry VII. It is a very rare issue and was struck at the London mint. It is easily identifiable by its unique obverse legend, while the style of bust is also very different to any other issues. Collectors should not confuse the farthing with the halfpenny issue of the same reign; pay particular attention to the size of the coins. Remember, issues of later kings tend to be smaller than the issue of earlier kings because the weights of the coins were being reduced.

Collecting Hints

This issue is very rare in any grade and difficult to obtain; the usual grade in which they are found is Fine.

Obverse Legend HENRIC DI GRA REX — Henry King by the grace of God

Reverse Legend CIVITAS LONDON — City of London

Obverse Facing crowned bust of King with arched crown; mintmark uncertain.

Reverse Long cross, three pellets in each quarter.

H7FA-005 VG £125 F £200 VF £350

Henry VIII 1509–1547

All issues of Henry VIII farthings are extremely rare and collectors will have great difficulty in obtaining an example.

First Coinage 1509–1526

Obverse Legend HENRIC DI GRA REX — Henry King by the grace of God

Reverse Legend CIVITAS LONDON — City of London

Obverse Portcullis; mintmark portcullis in legend.

Reverse Rose on long cross.

H8FA-005 VG £350 F £650 VF £1,100

Second Coinage 1526–1544

Obverse Legend RUTILANS ROSA — A dazzling rose

Reverse Legend DEO GRACIA — By the grace of God

Obverse Portcullis; mintmark probably lis in legend, or rose or sunburst.

Reverse Long cross with one pellet in each quarter; no mintmark.

H8FA-010 VG £350 F £650 VF £1,100

Obverse Legend As previous

Reverse Legend DEO GRACIS — By the grace of God

Obverse Portcullis; mintmark arrow in legend.

Reverse Rose on long cross.

H8FA-015 ex. rare

An issue exists as H8FA-015, but with mintmark Catherine wheel. This is probably from the Canterbury mint, which used this mintmark under Archbishop Thomas Cranmer.

H8FA-020 ex. rare

No farthings were struck for the third or posthumous coinages.

Edward VI 1547–1553

Edward VI's farthing was issued in base silver during the third period of coinage (1550–1553). The issue is fairly similar to that of Henry VIII, with a portcullis on the obverse, but the obverse legend is different. The reverse differs by not having a rose in the centre of the long cross.

> ## Collecting Hints
>
> This issue is extremely rare in any grade; collectors may have great difficulty in obtaining an example.

Obverse Legend E. D.G. ROSA SINE SPI — Edward by the grace of God a rose without a thorn

Reverse Legend CIVITAS LONDON — City of London

Obverse Portcullis; mintmark uncertain.

Reverse Long cross, three pellets in each quarter.

E6FA-005 ex. rare

No farthings were struck during the reign of Mary, Philip and Mary or Elizabeth I due mainly to the fact that a silver farthing was just too small to be struck and was also easily lost. And although the farthing was a useful denomination for the less affluent, the rich and powerful citizens of the land did not need it, so none were produced. During this period lead tokens were produced by small businessmen, especially in London. It is thought that these tokens represented the value of a farthing. These issues often had a simple design or the issuer's initials but very little is known about them and no law was passed making them legal tender. However, they became an acceptable part of life, particularly in London.

James I 1603–1625

During James I's reign the first copper farthings were introduced. James, who was also King of Scotland, realised that small denomination coins of base metal would be acceptable to the English especially as copper coins had been circulating successfully in Scotland and Europe for some considerable time. However, the English seemed to have had an obsession with gold and silver, trusting the real market value these precious metals had. This is illustrated in the havoc caused by Henry VIII's large denomination base silver coins. James I decided not to issue the farthings himself; instead, the production was put into the hands of John Harrington, Lord of Exton. Lord Harrington was heavily charged for this privilege but also made a large profit. Unlike larger denominations, they did not contain their value in metal. The issues produced by Lord Harrington are known as Harringtons. Lord Harrington died in 1614 and the right to produce farthings passed to his son, who died a few months later, and then back to Harrington's wife, Lady Anne Harrington. It appears that Lady Harrington either sold, or gave, the farthing patent to Lodewicke, Duke of Lennox. The issues of the Duke of Lennox were larger than Harrington's. Several varieties of each issue exist but in all cases the obverse has a crown with sceptres behind and a crowned harp is found on the reverse. These issues, especially the Lennox, are fairly similar to those of Charles I. However, they can be very easily identified by referring to the obverse legend. All coins of James I bear the king's name, IACO, while those of Charles I read CARO, CARA or CAROLUS.

> ## Collecting Hints
>
> James I farthings are fairly common, usually obtainable in Fine and VF condition; EF examples are not uncommon. In the last 20 years many coins have been found in the River Thames. Examples are often bent but can be easily straightened and, unlike silver coins, leave little damage. Forgeries of this reign exist. Collectors should refer to the information given about forgeries after Charles I.

Harrington Issues

Tin Surface Issue

These issues originally had a surface of tin which served two purposes. Firstly, to make counterfeiting more difficult; secondly, to make the coins look like silver and, therefore, more acceptable. Issues with original tin showing are more valuable than issues without and coins in VF or better condition must have a full tin surface to command the values stated here. These small Harringtons are on a 12.25 mm flan.

Obverse Legend IACO DG MAG BRIT — James by the grace of God King of Great Britain

Reverse Legend (continued from the obverse legend) FRA ET HIB REX — France and Ireland

Obverse Two sceptres through a crown.

Reverse Crowned harp.

J1FA-005 VG £15 F £30 VF £60 EF £100

As previous, but central jewel on circlet of crown.

J1FA-010 VG £20 F £40 VF £70 EF £110

Larger Size Issue

This issue is larger (15 mm flan) and the coin surface was not tin washed. From now on no other issues were washed in tin.
As previous, but crowned harp is reversed.

J1FA-015 VG £8 F £20 VF £35 EF £65

Lennox Issue

This issue can be easily differentiated by referring to the obverse legends. The Lennox obverse legend starts at the top, or bottom of the coin while the Harrington issue has the legend starting before the top of the coin. All Lennox issues are of the new larger size (15 mm flan).

Legends As previous.

Obverse Crown with sceptres in centre; no mintmark. The legend starts at the top of the coin.

Reverse Crowned harp; mintmark at start of legend.

J1FA-020 VG £6 F £18 VF £35 EF £60

As previous, but mintmark both sides.

J1FA-025 VG £6 F £18 VF £35 EF £60

As previous, but mintmark on obverse only.

J1FA-030 VG £6 F £18 VF £35 EF £60

As previous, but larger crowns on obverse and reverse.

J1FA-035 VG £6 F £18 VF £35 EF £60

This issue is oval, the legends start at the bottom of the coin and there is a mintmark on both sides.

Obverse Legend As previous.

Reverse Legend As previous.

Obverse As previous, with long sceptres.

Reverse As previous.

J1FA-040 VG £20 F £45 VF £80

Charles I 1625–1649

All of Charles I's farthings were made under the king's licence, as with the previous issues of James I; neither the Tower nor any provincial mints produced farthings. In 1623, during James I's reign, the Duke of Lennox had also become Duke of Richmond but died a few months later. The farthing patent passed jointly to his widow Frances, Duchess of Richmond, and Sir Francis Crane. The first issues of Charles I are known as Richmond issues, after the patent holder. In 1634 another farthing patent was issued, to Lord Maltravers, Henry Howard and Sir Francis Crane; these issues are known as Maltravers. During this period huge quantities of forged farthings were in circulation and the situation became unacceptable as the poor felt conned and un-

fairly treated by the authorities. As a result Lord Maltravers was asked to introduce a new style denomination. This was called the Rose farthing, it was much smaller and also thicker. However, the main difference was the metal and the way in which it was made. Most of the coin was made of copper, but a small brass 'plug' was inserted into part of the coin. This made the issue almost impossible to forge and the production of forgeries swiftly ended.

Richmond or Royal Issues

This issue is an altered die from James I's Lennox issue (J1FA-030).

Obverse Legend CARO OVER IACO D.G. MAG BRI — Charles by the grace of God King of Great Britain

Reverse Legend FRA ET HIB REX — France and Ireland

Obverse Crown with two sceptres; mintmark above crown.

Reverse Crown over harp; no mintmark.

C1FA-005 VG £5 F £18 VF £30 EF £50

As previous, but new die with king's name spelt CARA; mintmark on obverse.

C1FA-010 VG £40 F £70 VF £125 EF £200

As previous, with new die with king's name spelt CARO.

C1FA-015 VG £5 F £18 VF £30 EF £50

The next four issues, instead of having single stops in the legend, have apostrophe stops.

Obverse Legend As previous.

Reverse Legend As previous.

Obverse As previous.

Reverse As previous, but the harp has an eagle's head.

C1FA-020 VG £5 F £18 VF £30 EF £50

As previous, but the harp is beaded.

C1FA-025 VG £5 F £18 VF £30 EF £50

As previous, but the harp is scroll fronted with five jewels.

C1FA-030 VG £10 F £25 VF £40 EF £60

As previous, but with seven jewels.

C1FA-035 VG £5 F £18 VF £30 EF £50

Transitional Issue

This issue is fairly similar to the previous one, however, it has a double arched crown on both sides as used for the Maltravers issue.

C1FA-040 VG £25 F £30 VF £60 EF £100

Maltravers Issues

This issue is easily identified because it has inner circles on the obverse and reverse.

Obverse Legend CAROLUS D.G. MAG BR — Charles by the grace of God King of Great Britain

Reverse Legend FRAN ET HIB REX — France and Ireland

Obverse Crown with two sceptres in inner circles; mintmark at start of legend.

Reverse Harp with crown above; no mintmark.

C1FA-045 VG £8 F £25 VF £40 EF £60

As previous, but mintmark both sides.

C1FA-050 VG £5 F £18 VF £30 EF £50

As previous, but different mintmark either side (i.e. muled).

C1FA-055 VG £5 F £18 VF £30 EF £50

Oval Issues

These reasonably scarce issues are fairly similar to the last issues of James I. In fact Charles I's first issue actually uses the James I die. However, the king's name has been altered to CARO from IACO. These issues are oval and, in all cases, the legend starts at the bottom of the coin.

Obverse Legend CARO (over IACO) DG MAG BRI — Charles by the grace of God King of Great Britain

Reverse Legend FRA ET HIB REX — France and Ireland

Obverse Crown with two long sceptres; mintmark on both sides. The king's name is over that of James I, this is just an altered die from the previous reign.

Reverse Crown and harp.

C1FA-060 VG £15 F £30 VF £50 EF £100

As previous, but mintmark on obverse only.

C1FA-065 VG £12 F £25 VF £45 EF £90

Maltravers Issue

Maltravers oval type, with king's full name but no inner circles. Note the double-arched crown which makes this a Maltravers issue.

Obverse Legend CAROLUS DG MAG BRIT — Charles by the grace of God King of Great Britain

Reverse Legend FRAN ET HIB REX — France and Ireland

Obverse Crown and sceptre; mintmark both sides.

Reverse Harp and crown.

C1FA-070 VG £15 F £30 VF £60 EF £100

It is important to note that, for all the previous issues, varieties exist in the legends. When identifying an issue it is most important that collectors should refer to the number of arches on the crown, to the point where the legend starts and to any inner circles and stops in the legend.

Rose Farthing

These issues are smaller and thicker than the previous ones. They are made of copper, with a brass plug in the coin to deter forgers. On many coins of poorer condition the plug has fallen out and this leaves a rather unsightly gap. The obverse of the coin has a crown with two sceptres. The reverse a crowned rose, hence the name Rose farthing.

Obverse Legend CAROLUS D G MAG BRIT — Charles by the grace of God King [of] Great Britain

Reverse Legend FRAN ET HIB REX — France and Ireland

Obverse Double-arched crown with small sceptres in inner circle.

Reverse Double rose within inner circle.

C1FA-75 VG £10 F £20 VF £30 EF £40

As previous, but sceptres on obverse just break inner circle.

C1FA-80 VG £8 F £16 VF £24 EF £34

As previous, but sceptres almost reach outer circle.

C1FA-85 VG £6 F £14 VF £22 EF £32

As previous, but obverse legend reads CAROLUS DG. MAG BRI.

C1FA-90 VG £15 F £30 VF £42 EF £55

As previous, but muled with the next issue: the obverse has a double-arched crown, the reverse a single-arched crown.

C1FA-95 VG £8 F £16 VF £24 EF £34

Obverse Legend CAROLUS D G. MAG BRI — Charles by the grace of God King of Great Britain

Reverse Legend FRA ET HIB REX — France and Ireland

Obverse Single-arched crown over two sceptres.

Reverse Single plain rose with crown above.

C1FA-100 VG £6 F £14 VF £22 EF £32

As previous, but sceptres below crown and the king's name in the obverse legend shortened to CAROLU.

C1FA-105 VG £20 F £50 VF £100 EF —

Forgeries
of James I and Charles I Farthings

There are large numbers of forged James I, and particularly, Charles I farthings and although no small Harrington farthings appear to have been forged, many Lennox, Richmond and Maltravers have been. The following information will explain the differences between the genuine coins and the forgeries: Forgeries tend to have erratic lettering and spelling; the whole layout of the coin can look a mess. Many forgeries are irregular in shape, often with excess metal outside the legends. The harp and the crown often lack detail and are erratic in style. Many forgeries tend to be thin and bent although some forgeries are too thick; a genuine coin should feel very springy with a flat, even surface. Genuine coins tend to be of correct shape and are usually not clipped.

Commonwealth and Cromwell
1649–1660

No farthings were issued for circulation during this period. However, a fairly large number of patterns were struck. There is no doubt that these issues circulated, many as tokens or patterns. This reflected the need for small change. During the period from 1648 to 1670 huge quantities of tokens were issued. These were mainly farthings and halfpennies. The tokens were issued by small traders or the towns themselves. The government seemed unable, or unwilling, to produce small denomination coins. There was, undoubtedly, an enormous need for small denomination coins and it was finally met by Charles II who, in 1672, introduced huge quantities of halfpennies and farthings into circulation.

Elizabeth I

Countermarked Coins

During the beginning of Elizabeth I's long reign there was a considerable number of base issue coins in circulation from the reigns of Henry VIII and Edward VI. But, recognising the importance of having good quality coins of high fineness in circulation, Elizabeth I decided to withdraw the base issues in 1559 and replace them with good quality silver coins of high fineness. Among the many denominations thus returned to the mint were base issue shillings from Edward VI's second and third period coinages. Probably due to the urgent need for low denomination coins, it was decided to counterstamp some of these shillings; the second period shillings were counterstamped with a portcullis, the third period issues with a greyhound. They were then returned to circulation with a value of fourpence-halfpenny and twopence-farthing respectively, in accordance with their true silver content. Nevertheless, this short-term solution was unpopular and the large quantities of good quality silver coins being produced in the 1560s also made it unnecessary. The replacement of the base coinage was a considerable expense to Elizabeth I. It shows Elizabeth's determination to bring good quality coins of high fineness into circulation. No records exist of how many coins were counterstamped, however, very few examples exist.

Fourpence Halfpenny

Obverse Edward VI second period base shilling counterstamped with a portcullis.

Reverse Edward VI base shilling.

ELCTM-005 ex. rare

Twopence Farthing

Obverse Edward VI third period base shilling counterstamped with a seated greyhound.

Reverse Edward VI base shilling.

ELCTM-010 ex. rare

Portcullis Coinage

These coins, which were struck by the Tower mint for the Company of merchants, were bullion coins for world-wide trading. They were struck for trading in the East Indies and were produced from 1600–1601. They were struck to weigh the same as the Spanish silver 8, 4, 2, 1 *reale* respectively.

N.B. Varieties in the legends exist.

Eight Testern

Obverse Legend ELIZABETH D.G. ANG FR ET HIB REGINA — Elizabeth by the grace of God Queen of England, France and Ireland

Reverse Legend POSUI DEUM ADIVTOREM MEUM — I have made God my helper

Obverse Crown over royal shield, crowned E.R. either side of shield; mintmark '0'.

Reverse Crowned portcullis, chain either side; mintmark '0'.

ELPOR-005 F £1,000 VF £2,000

Four Testern

As previous, but FRA ET HIBER instead of FR ET HIB in obverse legend.

ELPOR-010 F £600 VF £1,200

Two Testern

As previous, but FR ET HIBER REGIN in obverse legend.

ELPOR-015 F £600 VF £1,200

One Testern

As previous, but FR ET HI REGINA in obverse legend.

ELPOR-020 F £400 VF £800

Charles I

Siege Issues

Unusual and irregular denominations were struck in besieged towns, due to the urgency and lack of facilities. Regular siege issue denominations such as shillings and halfcrowns are listed under their relative denominations but unusual denominations are listed in this chapter. In some cases, the reverse legends bear the name of the town and OBS for OBSESSA, siege.

Carlisle Three Shillings

> ## Collecting Hints
>
> These issues are extremely rare and when available usually found in Fine to VF condition.

Obverse Crowned CR with rosette on each side and IIIS (3 shillings) below.

Reverse OBS CARL 1645 in three or two lines.

C1SG-005 VG £1,200 F £2,500 VF £5,000

Newark Ninepence

> ## Collecting Hints
>
> This is one of the most common siege issues. Specimens are available in most grades and often show original gilding from the host plates from which they were made.

Obverse Large crown between CR, IX below.

Reverse OBS NEWARKE or NEWARK 1645 or 1646 in three lines.

C1SG-010 VG £150 F £300 VF £600

Pontefract Two Shillings

> ## Collecting Hints
>
> This issue is extremely rare.

Obverse Legend DUM SPIRO SPERO — Whilst I live I hope

Reverse Legend None.

Obverse Large crown over CR.

Reverse Castle gateway with P.C at sides and vertically to the left of the tower.

C1SG-015 ex. rare

Scarborough Besieged

Because of the way the coins were produced, a very large number of denominations exist for this siege town. Silver plates were literally cut into squares, weighed and the value was then punched below. A castle, either with a gateway or two turrets, was then struck above the denomination. The following denominations exist:

Five shillings and eightpence; crown; three shillings and fourpence; three shillings; two shillings and tenpence; halfcrown; two shillings and fourpence; two shillings and twopence; two shillings (varieties exist); one shilling and ninepence; one shilling and sixpence; one shilling and fourpence; one shilling and threepence; one shilling and twopence; one shilling and a penny; one shilling; eleven pence; tenpence; ninepence; seven pence; sixpence; fourpence.

> ## Collecting Hints
>
> All these denominations are extremely rare. Nineteenth century forgeries exist for many issues. These forgeries can be very good and collectors should exercise extreme caution when purchasing an example.

Several fantasy issues also exist for other towns. They were struck in the nineteenth century, when there was a revival of interest in the history of this period.

Unofficial Coins and Tokens circulating in England

This book is solely devoted to English coins. However, during the hammered coinage, coins from other countries, as well as tokens and jetons, circulated alongside English coins. As these issues are often found by metal detectors we have decided to list the most common. These coins circulated because many of them were silver and had a similar value to the English coins. After all, all coins during this period were simply worth their weight in gold or silver. As a result of there often being a shortage of small denominations, these foreign issues became a useful source of small change.

Richard I denier of Aquitaine

This province of France was controlled by England during this period.

Irish Henry III Penny

Low Countries' Sterlings

These coins were copies of Edward I's pennies. All legends are different from the Edward issues. Most of continental issues have an uncrowned bust of the king.

Venetian Silver Coins

These coins from the 13th/14th century have been found in large quantities in the river Thames.

Irish Philip and Mary Groat

The obverse is similar to the English sixpence; however, the reverses show a large harp.

Jetons

English Jetons

Jetons were used from Edward I's reign to the early part of the 20th century. They were first used as reckoning counters in mathematics and finance, in a similar way as an abacus is used. The later issues were used as gaming counters. The early English is-

sues, which were made of brass, are nearly always holed. These usually show the bust of the king on the obverse.

Foreign Jetons

Most jetons were produced in France and Germany. Many of these were exported to England. The most common were the Nuremberg jetons produced by the Krauvinkle family. These jetons were produced in huge quantities and are very common.

Ecclesiastical Tokens

Boy Bishop Tokens

Boy Bishop tokens are ecclesiastical issues or tokens; they were only used in Medieval times in the Suffolk area. It is thought that they were given to the poor on religious holidays and could perhaps have been redeemed for food. These issues usually show a Bishop's head on the obverse while the reverse bears a long cross with three pellets in each quarter. There are many varieties of these issues.

Ecclesiastical Issues

Very little is known about the following tokens. They were used over a considerable period of time and are often found in farmland.

Trade Tokens

The other main lead issue was thought to have been produced by local traders, mainly in large towns. Most have been found in London and often have a variety of designs. There are virtually no records relating to these tokens and this, combined with the fact that the issuer's name or town rarely appears on these issues, explains why very little has been discovered about them.

The lead tokens are often known as 'wine tavern' tokens, and probably had a value of a fraction of a penny. These tokens were the forerunners to the popular brass and copper 17th century issues, which were produced in large quantities by most traders, in most towns.

Tokens were produced to compensate for the lack of small denominations. They illustrate the failure of certain monarchs to be aware of the needs of the poor by providing adequate small denominations. However, Charles II recognised the problem and in the 1670s introduced large quantities of copper farthings and halfpennies. As a result, the tokens in circulation became unnecessary and obsolete; their production was finally forbidden by law in the late 1670s.

Lead tokens

Brass and copper tokens

Coin Weights

Merchants and traders needed to confirm that the coinage they received in payment for goods was of the full correct weight. As a result, it became necessary to introduce coin weights for most large gold and silver denominations. These weights were made of brass. They often had a portrait of the reigning monarch on the obverse, the weight on the reverse. Most European gold coins of this period had coin weights produced for them and many merchants carried weights for both English and foreign issues. The Low Countries produced large quantities of coin weights, often for export. These issues can usually be identified by a 'hand' counterstamped on the weight.

James I gold unite   James I half unite   Charles I gold crown
(after 1612)   (after 1612)

Milled Coins
1658 to date

Introduction to the milled coinage section

A Guide to using the Tables

Following the descriptive information, history and collecting hints relating to the denomination, the tables for each reign generally comprise three sections. Certain conventions have been used in the layout, and these are detailed below.

SECTION 1: The Broad Definition (5 columns)

Column 1: The name of the denomination.
Column 2: The metal from which the coin is made. If described as 'gold' the coin is, unless otherwise stated, of 22 carat gold, i.e. 22/24 (0.917) pure. If 'silver' it is of sterling silver (0.925 fine) unless another fineness is given.

Column 3: The weight of the coin in grams. If found specimens vary markedly from the official weight, a weight range of most commonly found specimens is given.

Column 4: The diameter, usually to the nearest millimetre (mm).

Column 5: The reverse alignment. This means the alignment of the reverse seen if the coin is firstly held at the rim between two fingers, top and bottom, with the obverse facing and upright, and then rotated 180 degrees between the fingers.

Further information relating to the points above may be given as a footnote to the 5-column broad definition table.

SECTION 2: The Description

Each different obverse used during the reign is listed in sequence as Obverse 1, 2, etc. and briefly described. The different portrayals of the monarch are listed as Head 1, 2, etc. and the placement of the head facing left or right is stated. The legend on the obverse then follows in block capitals, without punctuation. There are often so many different variations of punctuation within a given reign that it is more appropriate to refer to the relevant photograph and correlate it with punctuation varieties given in Section 3.

Any bracketed wording in italics following the legend description does not form part of the legend on the coin but is intended to provide information on the relevant issue, usually in the case of the commemorative issues. If this information is obvious from the legend then this bracketed information is omitted.

The reverses are similarly listed as Reverse 1, 2, etc. following the obverse list. Provenance marks (e.g. roses and plumes) or their absence are not considered to constitute a different obverse or reverse but are listed in Section 3 as variations within a single obverse or reverse.

The edge is then described (e.g. 'milled') or in the case of a lettered edge, the edge legend is given. The term 'milled' denotes straight-across milling or graining. If diagonal, chevron or other pattern milling exists, then it is described as such.

With all legends, bracketed information not italicized indicates information not as written but a variable which is listed in Section 3, e.g. (date). The terms 'regnal date' and 'edge date' are interchangeable.

SECTION 3: The Main Table

The table columns usually (but not invariably) are in the following sequence for each variety:
1. The reference number of the variety.
2. The date as depicted on the coin.
3. (optional) The mintmark as it appears on the coin. The name of the mint and the position of the mintmark will usually appear immediately above Section 3.

4. Features of the coin. These are the characteristics which qualify the coin as a distinct variety of the series, e.g. 'proof' or 'edge plain'. If no entry appears, it is usually the date which forms the characteristic feature. An entry reading, e.g., '9 over 8' refers to an overdate, where '9' occurs in the corrected date. Where the corrected date contains two or more identical digits, the entry will read, e.g. 'first 3 over 2', 'latter 7 over 6'.

5. (optional) The edge date or regnal date which forms part of the legend in Section 2.

6. The obverse number as in Section 2.

7. The reverse number as in Section 2.

8. The retail price in the various grades in which the coin is usually found. Prior to 1816 the highest grade given is usually EF, and the price for an FDC specimen of a proof coin is given in this column. The prices are in Pounds Sterling and are those which one would expect to pay from a reputable dealer, including handling fees, tax, etc. For very low priced items these ancillary charges form a disproportionate, and therefore substantial, fraction of the price quoted.

Many price boxes are left blank. This is because a price is considered inappropriate; for example, the coin may not exist in the grade stated, or it may be impossible to distinguish it (e.g. a proof in fine condition). Alternatively, it may be of negligible value in the grade stipulated.

The term 'BV' in the prices column denotes that the price one should expect to pay will bear a relationship to the bullion value of the metal in the piece. It must be stressed that this does not mean that the coin can be acquired for simply its bullion value. To this figure must be added any applicable local taxes (e.g. value added tax, sales tax), together with any handling fees and a reasonable profit margin to be charged by the dealer. Demand may also render the market value above the bullion value even though the one value may bear a relationship to the other.

Footnotes to the table are cross-referenced to notes in the table itself, usually in the Features column.

Translation of Foreign Legends

Below are listed most of the foreign legends on the milled coinage, together with English translations. Abbreviations are translated directly rather than the reader being referred to the unabbreviated word. Some duplication has been used to allow for easy location of the translation; if any difficulty is encountered it may help to break the foreign legend into sections and to look these up separately. Latin regnal years (after the term 'Anno Regni') should be split into separate words and the resulting translated numbers added together. Error legends are included and translated directly; the corrected foreign legend is given after the English version.

All legends are in Latin unless stated otherwise before the English version.

ANG	England
ANNA	(Queen) Anne
ANNA DEI GRATIA	(Queen) Anne, by the Grace of God.
ANNO	Year (In the year of)
ANNO EGNI	In the year of the reign..... *(error: should be ANNO REGNI)*
ANNO REGNI	In the year of the reign.....
BBITANNIAR	Of the British territories *(error: should be BRITANNIAR)*
BRITANNIA REX FID DEF	King of Britain, Defender of the Faith.
BRITANNIAB	Of the British territories *(error: should be BRITANNIAR)*
BRITANNIAE EEGINA	Queen of the British territories *(error: should be BRITANNIAR REGINA)*

BRITANNIAR — Of the British territories

BRITANNIAR REG FID DEF — Queen of the British territories, Defender of the Faith.

BRITANNIAR REGINA — Queen of the British territories.

BRITANNIAR REX FID DEF — King of the British territories, Defender of the Faith.

BRITANNIARUM REGINA FID DEF — Queen of the British territories, Defender of the Faith.

BRITANNIARUM REX FID DEF — King of the British territories, Defender of the Faith.

BRITANNIARUM REX FIDEI DEFENSOR — King of the British territories, Defender of the Faith.

BRITT OMN REGINA — Queen of all the British territories,

BRITT REGINA — Queen of the British territories.

BRIVANNIA — Britain (or Britannia) (error: should be BRITANNIA)

BRVN ET L DVX S R I A TH ET EL — Duke of Brunswick and Lueneburg, Arch-Treasurer and Elector of the Holy Roman Empire.

BRVN ET L DVX S R I A TH ET PR EL — Duke of Brunswick and Lueneburg, Arch-Treasurer and Prince Elector of the Holy Roman Empire.

BRVN ET LVN DVX S R I A TH ET PR EL — Duke of Brunswick and Lueneburg, Arch-Treasurer and Prince Elector of the Holy Roman Empire.

CAROLVS — Charles

CAROLVS A CAROLO — Charles, son of Charles

CAROLVS II — Charles II

CAROLVS II D G M B F H REX — Charles II, by the Grace of God, King of Great Britain, France and Ireland.

CHRISTO AVSPICE REGNO — I reign under the auspice of Christ

CRAOLVS — Charles (error: should be CAROLVS)

D G — By the Grace of God

D G BR OMN REX F D IND IMP — By the Grace of God, King of all the British territories, Defender of the Faith, Emperor of India.

DECIMO — Ten

DECUS ET TUTAMEN ANNO REGNI — An ornament and a safeguard; in the year of the reign.

DECUS ET TUTAMEN — An ornament and a safeguard.

DECVS ANNO REGNI ET TVTAMEN — An ornament and a safeguard; in the year of the reign. (error: transposed word order)

DECVS ET TVTAMEN AN REG — An ornament and a safeguard; in the year of the reign......

DECVS ET TVTAMEN ANNO REGNI — An ornament and a safeguard; in the year of the reign......

DECVS ET TVTAMEN — An ornament and a safeguard.

DEI GARTIA — By the Grace of God. (error: should be DEI GRATIA)

DEI GRA BRITT OMN REGINA F D — By the Grace of God, Queen of all the British territories, Defender of the Faith.

DEI GRA BRITT OMN REX FID DEF IND IMP — By the Grace of God, King of all the British territories, Defender of the Faith, Emperor of India.

DEI GRATIA REGINA F D — By the Grace of God, Queen, Defender of the Faith.

DEI GRATIA — By the Grace of God

DIEU ET MON DROIT (French) — God and my right.

DIRIGE DEUS GRESSUS MEOS — May the Lord direct my steps.

DIRIGIT DEUS GRESSUS MEOS — The Lord directs my steps.

DRITANNIAR — Of the British territories. (error: should be BRITANNIAR)

DVODECIMO — Twelve

EDWARDVS VII — Edward VII

EDWARDVS VIII D G BR OMN REX F D IND IMP — Edward VIII, by the Grace of God, King of all the British territories, Defender of the Faith, Emperor of India.

EDWARDVS VIII — Edward VIII

ELIZABETH II DEI GRA BRITT OMN REGINA F D — Elizabeth II, by the Grace of God, Queen of all the British territories, Defender of the Faith.

ELIZABETH II DEI GRA REG F D — Elizabeth II, by the Grace of God, Queen, Defender of the Faith.

ELIZABETH II DEI GRATIA BRITT OMN REGINA FIDEI DEFENSOR — Elizabeth II, by the Grace of God, Queen of all the British territories, Defender of the Faith.

ELIZABETH II DEI GRATIA BRITT OMN REGINA — Elizabeth II, by the Grace of God, Queen of all the British territories.

ELIZABETH II DEI GRATIA REGINA F D — Elizabeth II, by the Grace of God, Queen, Defender of the Faith.

ELIZABETH II DEI GRATIA REGINA — Elizabeth II, Queen by the Grace of God,.

ERA — France (error: should be FRA)

F D — Defender of the Faith.

FID DEF BRITT REG — Queen of the British territories, Defender of the Faith.

FID DEF — Defender of the Faith.

FIDEI DEFENSOR BRITANNIARUM REX — King of the British territories, Defender of the Faith.

FRA — France

GEI GRA — By the Grace of God. (error: should be DEI GRA)

GEOE III — George III (error: should be GEOR III)

GEOGIVS — George (error: should be GEORGIVS)

GEOR III D G BRITT REX F D — George III, by the Grace of God, King of the British territories, Defender of the Faith.

GEORGIUS II REX — King George II

GEORGIUS III — George III.

GEORGIUS III D G BRITANNIARUM REX F D — George III, by the Grace of God, King of the British territories, Defender of the Faith.

GEORGIUS III DEI GRATIA REX — George III, King, by the Grace of God.

GEORGIUS IIII — George IV.

GEORGIUS IIII D G BRITANNIAR REX F D — George IV, by the Grace of God, King of the British territories, Defender of the Faith.

GEORGIUS IV — George IV

GEORGIVS — George I (or George)

GEORGIVS D G M BR ET HIB REX F D — George I, by the Grace of God, King of Great Britain and Ireland, Defender of the Faith.

GEORGIVS D G M BR FR ET HIB REX F D — George I, by the Grace of God, King of Great Britain, France and Ireland, Defender of the Faith.

GEORGIVS DEI GRA — George I, by the Grace of God.

GEORGIVS II — George II

GEORGIVS II REX — King George II

GEORGIVS III — George III

GEORGIVS III DEI GRATIA — George III, by the Grace of God.

GEORGIVS REX — King George I

GEORGIVS V — George V

GEORGIVS V D G BRITT OMN REX F D IND IMP — George V, by the Grace of God, King of all the British territories, Defender of the Faith, Emperor of India.

GEORGIVS V DEI GRA BRITT OMN REX FID DEF IND IMP — George V, by the Grace of God, King of all the British territories, Defender of the Faith, Emperor of India.

GEORGIVS VI — George VI.

GEORGIVS VI D G BR OMN REX F D IND IMP — George VI, by the Grace of God, King of all the British territories, Defender of the Faith, Emperor of India.

GEORGIVS VI D G BR OMN REX FIDEI DEF — George VI, by the Grace of God, King of all the British territories, Defender of the Faith.

GEORIVS — George (error: should be GEORGIVS)

GRACIA — By the Grace (error: should be GRATIA)

GRI — George (VI), King and Emperor.

GULIELMUS IIII — William IV.

GULIELMUS IIII D G BRITANNIAR REX F D — William IV, by the Grace of God, King of all the British territories, Defender of the Faith.

GULIELMUS IIII DEI GRATIA — William IV, by the Grace of God.

GVIELMVS — William (error: should be GVLIELMVS)

GVILELMVS — William (error: should be GVLIELMVS)

GVIR — King George VI.

GVLEELMVS — William (error: should be GVLIELMVS)

GVLELMVS — William (error: should be GVLIELMVS)

GVLIEEMVS — William (error: should be GVLIELMVS)

GVLIEIMVS — William (error: should be GVLIELMVS)

GVLIELMS — William (error: should be GVLIELMVS)

GVLIELMVS ET MARIA — William and Mary.

GVLIELMVS ET MARIA D G — William and Mary, by the Grace of God.

GVLIELMVS III — William III.

GVLIELMVS TERTIVS — William III.

GVLIEMVS — William (error: should be GVLIELMVS)

GVLILMVS — William (error: should be GVLIELMVS)

HAS NISI PERITVRVS MIHI ADIMAT NEMO — Let nobody remove these (letters) from me on pain of death

HI — Ireland

HIB — Ireland

HIB REX ET REGINA — King and Queen of Ireland

HIPEX — King of Ireland (error: should be HIB REX)

HIPREX — King of Ireland (error: should be HIB REX)

HONI SOIT QUI MAL Y PENSE (French) — Evil to him who evil thinks.

IACOBVS II — James II.

IACOBVS II DEI GRATIA — James II, by the Grace of God.

IACOBVS SECVNDVS — James II

ICH DIEN (German) — I serve.

IIIB — Ireland (error: should be HIB)

IND IMP — Emperor (or Empress) of India.

M B F ET H REX F D B ET L D S R I A T ET E — King of Great Britain, France and Ireland, Defender of the Faith, Duke of Brunswick and Lueneburg, Arch-Treasurer and Elector of the Holy Roman Empire.

MAB BR — Great Britain. (error: should be MAG BR)

MAG BR(I) FR(A) ET HI(B) REX ET REGINA — King and Queen of Great Britain, France and Ireland.

MAG BR(I) FR(A) ET HIB REG	Queen of Great Britain, France and Ireland.
MARIA	Mary
MDCCCLI CIVIUM INDUSTRIA FLORET CIVITAS MCMLI	1851 By the Industry of its people the State flourishes 1951.
MRG BR	Great Britain. *(error: should be MAG BR)*
MVRIA	Mary *(error: should be MARIA)*
NEMO ME IMPUNE LACESSIT	Nobody provokes me with impunity.
NONO	Nine
NVMMORVM FAMVLVS	The servant of the coinage (i.e. a minor coinage)
OCTAVO	Eight
OLIVAR D G R P ANG SCO HIB &c PRO	Oliver, by the Grace of God, Protector of the Republic of England, Scotland, Ireland, etc.
PAX QVAERITVR BELLO	Peace is sought through war.
PLEIDOIL WYF I'M GWLAD (Welsh)	I am true to my country.
PRIMO	One
PROTECTOR LITERIS LITERAE NVMMIS CORONA ET SALVS	A protector of the letters, the letters are a garland and a safeguard to the coinage.
QVARTO	Four
QVATTVOR MARIA VINDICO	I conquer the four seas.
QVINTO	Five
REGINA	Queen
REX	King
RRITANNIAR	Of the British territories *(error: should be BRITANNIAR)*
SECVNDO	Two
SEPTIMO	Seven
SEXTO	Six
SIC VOC NON VOBIS	We labour thus, but not for ourselves.
TERTIO	Three
TERTIVS	Third
TIRTIO	Three *(error: should be TERTIO)*
TRICESIMO	Thirty
UNDECIMO	Eleven
VICESIMO	Twenty
VICTORIA D G BRIT REG F D	Victoria, by the Grace of God, Queen of Britain (or British Territories), Defender of the Faith.
VICTORIA D G BRITANNIAR REGINA F D	Victoria, by the Grace of God, Queen of the British territories, Defender of the Faith.
VICTORIA D G BRITANNIARUM REGINA F D	Victoria, by the Grace of God, Queen of the British territories, Defender of the Faith.
VICTORIA D G BRITT REG F D	Victoria, by the Grace of God, Queen of the British territories, Defender of the Faith.
VICTORIA DEI GRA BRITT REGINA FID DEF IND IMP	Victoria, by the Grace of God, Queen of the British territories, Defender of the Faith, Empress of India.
VICTORIA DEI GRATIA BRITANNIAR REG F D	Victoria, by the Grace of God, Queen of the British territories, Defender of the Faith.
VICTORIA DEI GRATIA BRITT REGINA F D	Victoria, by the Grace of God, Queen of the British territories, Defender of the Faith.
VICTORIA REGINA	Queen Victoria.

Five Guineas

Charles II 1660–1685

The British five guinea piece is one of the most spectacular and impressive series of machine struck currency ever produced. The Charles II coin, minted each year from 1668 until the last of the king's reign in 1684, comprises a formidable series.

The coin, although now invariably referred to as the five guinea piece, was in the 17th and 18th centuries also known as the five pound piece. It must be remembered that the guinea was not always valued at twenty-one shillings as it was in later times. During the reign of Charles II it had a value of twenty shillings, and thereafter until fixed by Proclamation in 1717 it fluctuated, rather like the value of bullion gold does today.

The obverse and reverse of the Charles II five guinea piece were designed by John Roettier (1631–c.1700). The coin is similar in size to the crown, and is the only gold coin to bear an inscription on the edge. Like that on the crown and halfcrown, the inscription includes a regnal year, that is, a date counting from the inception of the king's reign. However, in the case of Charles II, the regnal year counts from the death of Charles I (by execution) rather than from 1660. The obverse and reverse of the five guinea piece are somewhat similar to those of the crown, but the portrait is different, especially at the truncation. The angles between the reverse shields are bisected by sceptres instead of interlinked 'C's. The latter do appear, however, as a group of four in the centre of the reverse.

The edge inscription was not, as is commonly thought, applied to the finished struck coinage. However, in later years the striking of the two sides and the edge may have been effected simultaneously. In the earlier years the blanks were first cut out from metal which had been rolled into strips using horse power. These blanks were then sent to have the edges impressed by a secret process devised by one Pierre Blondeau, an ex-engineer from the Paris mint, who jealously guarded his methods. The blanks were then returned to the mint to have their obverses and reverses struck in a hand-operated press. A long and detailed description of rolling, cutting and striking of blanks is contained in Pepys's Diary for 19 May 1663.

The wording of the edge inscription DECUS ET TUTAMEN was said by Leake, writing in 1726, to have been suggested by Mr Evelyn, based on a vignette of Cardinal de Richelieu's Greek Testament, printed at the Louvre in Paris.

The elephant (with or without castle) occurs more frequently on the five guinea piece than on the crown. This symbol indicates that the gold has been imported from the Africa Company.

Denomination	Metal	Weight (grams)	Diameter (mm)	Rev. alignment
Five Guineas 1668-1669	Gold	41.0–42.0	37	↓
Five Guineas 1670-1684	Gold	41.0–41.8	37	↓

Obverse 1 Head 1, right; pointed truncation; lock of hair to right of truncation; CAROLVS II DEI GRATIA

Obverse 2 Head 2, right; larger, rounded truncation, without lock of hair to right; same legend

Reverse 1 Four crowned cruciform shields between which are four sceptres, with four interlinked 'C's at the centre; MAG BR FRA ET HIB REX (date)

Edge DECVS ET TVTAMEN ANNO REGNI (regnal date)

Obv. 1   Obv. 2

Rev. 1

No.	Date	Features	Edge date	Obv.	Rev.	F	VF	EF
C25GM-005	1668		VICESIMO	1	1	900	1700	4500
C25GM-010	1668	elephant below head	VICESIMO	1	1	900	1700	4500
C25GM-015	1669		VICESIMO PRIMO	1	1	950	1800	4500
C25GM-020	1669	elephant below head	VICESIMO PRIMO	1	1	1100	2000	5000
C25GM-025	1670		VICESIMO SECVNDO	1	1	950	1800	4500
C25GM-030	1671		VICESIMO TERTIO	1	1	950	1800	4500
C25GM-035	1672		VICESIMO QVARTO	1	1	950	1800	4500
C25GM-040	1673		VICESIMO QVINTO	1	1	950	1800	4500
C25GM-045	1674	[1]	VICESIMO SEXTO	1	1	950	1800	4500
C25GM-050	1675	[2]	VICESIMO SEPTIMO	1	1	950	1800	4500
C25GM-055	1675	elephant below head [2]	VICESIMO SEPTIMO	1	1	950	1800	4500
C25GM-060	1675	elephant and castle below head [2]	VICESIMO SEPTIMO	1	1	1200	2500	7000
C25GM-065	1676	[3]	VICESIMO SEPTIMO	1	1	950	1800	4500
C25GM-070	1676		VICESIMO OCTAVO	1	1	950	1800	4500
C25GM-075	1676	elephant and castle below head	VICESIMO OCTAVO	1	1	950	1800	4500
C25GM-080	1677		VICESIMO NONO	1	1	950	1800	4500
C25GM-085	1677	elephant and castle below head	VICESIMO NONO	1	1	950	1800	4500
C25GM-090	1678		TRICESIMO	1	1	950	1800	4500
C25GM-095	1678	8 over 7	TRICESIMO	1	1	950	1800	4500
C25GM-100	1678	elephant and castle below head; 8 over 7	TRICESIMO	1	1	950	1800	4500
C25GM-105	1678	8 over 7	TRICESIMO	2	1	950	1800	4500
C25GM-110	1679		TRICESIMO PRIMO	2	1	950	1800	4500
C25GM-115	1680		TRICESIMO SECVNDO	2	1	950	1800	4500
C25GM-120	1680	elephant and castle below head	TRICESIMO SECVNDO	2	1	1200	2500	7000
C25GM-125	1681		TRICESIMO TERTIO	2	1	950	1800	4500
C25GM-130	1681	elephant and castle below head	TRICESIMO TERTIO	2	1	950	1800	4500
C25GM-135	1682		TRICESIMO QVARTO	2	1	950	1800	4500
C25GM-140	1682	elephant and castle below head	TRICESIMO QVARTO	2	1	950	1800	4500
C25GM-145	1683		TRICESIMO QVINTO	2	1	950	1800	4500
C25GM-150	1683	elephant and castle below head	TRICESIMO QVINTO	2	1	950	1800	4500
C25GM-155	1684		TRICESIMO SEXTO	2	1	950	1800	4500
C25GM-160	1684	elephant and castle below head	TRICESIMO SEXTO	2	1	950	1800	4500

1. Minor alterations to head from 1674.
2. Edge date shared with 1676.
3. Edge date shared with 1675.

James II 1685–1688

John Roettier continued to design the dies for the five guinea piece. Although the facial features are very similar to the portrait he produced for the silver coins, there are marked differences in the area of the truncation.

The 1686 five guinea piece is frequently described as having misplaced or transposed sceptres, although very few catalogues explain what this means. On a correctly oriented coin, if the date is placed at 'North', the sceptre ending in a harp is pointing in a 'North-West' direction, while the one ending in a lis is pointing

'South-West'. On the 1686 coin, these two sceptres have changed places. A similar variety exists on the 1700 guinea, which it is believed appears in this book for the first time in any catalogue.

Denomination	Metal	Weight (grams)	Diameter (mm)	Rev. alignment
Five Guineas	Gold	41.5–42.0	37	↓

Obverse 1 Head 1, left; IACOBVS II DEI GRATIA

Obverse 2 Head 2, left, hair arrangement slightly different and further forward; same legend

Reverse 1 Four crowned cruciform shields between which are four sceptres wrongly arranged (see above); MAG BR FRA ET HIB REX (date)

Reverse 2 Similar but sceptres are correctly arranged; the four crowns are slightly larger; same legend

Edge DECVS ET TVTAMEN ANNO REGNI (regnal date)

Obv. 1   Obv. 2

Rev. 1

Normal Sceptres (Rev. 2)   Transposed Sceptres (Rev. 1)

No.	Date	Features	Edge date	Obv.	Rev.	F	VF	EF
J25G-005	1686	[1]	SECVNDO	1	1	1300	2100	5000
J25G-010	1687		TERTIO	1	2	1200	1900	5000
J25G-015	1687	elephant and castle below head	TERTIO	1	2	1300	2100	5000
J25G-020	1687		TERTIO	2	2	1200	1900	5000
J25G-025	1688		QVARTO	1	2	1200	1900	5000
J25G-030	1688	elephant and castle below head	QVARTO	1	2	1300	2100	5000
J25G-035	1688		QVARTO	2	2	1200	1900	5000

1. So-called 'sceptres misplaced' variety.

William and Mary 1688–1694

Following the removal of James II, his daughter Mary and her husband Prince William of Orange ruled jointly by agreement. Their heads were placed in conjoined fashion on the coinage, with William's head uppermost. This classical style owed much to Greek and Roman coinage, as coins of later periods with joint rulers were normally designed showing them face to face.

The reign of William and Mary saw a departure from previous designs for the reverse of the five guinea piece. Although the cruciform shields design was retained on the crown piece, the shilling and the sixpence, the five guinea piece and other gold coins followed the halfcrown in introducing a crowned shield on the reverse. Curiously, however, by the time the first five guinea pieces were struck in 1691, the halfcrown had reverted to the cruciform shield design.

There is some doubt about the attribution of William and Mary coinage, but the five guinea piece was probably the work of James and Norbert Roettier.

The elephant and castle symbol continued to be placed on some of the coins to indicate gold from the Africa Company. Such coins were struck in each of the four years of minting, and are slightly scarcer than those struck without the symbol.

Edge DECVS ET TVTAMEN ANNO REGNI (regnal date)

Obv. 1

Rev. 1   Rev. 2

No.	Date	Features	Edge date	Obv.	Rev.	F	VF	EF
WM5G-005	1691		TERTIO	1	1	1000	1900	4200
WM5G-010	1691	elephant and castle below head	TERTIO	1	1	1100	2100	4800
WM5G-015	1692		QVARTO	1	2	1000	1900	4200
WM5G-020	1692	elephant and castle below head	QVARTO	1	2	1100	2100	4800
WM5G-025	1693		QVINTO	1	2	1000	1900	4200
WM5G-030	1693	elephant and castle below head	QVINTO	1	2	1100	2100	4800
WM5G-035	1694		SEXTO	1	2	1000	1900	4200
WM5G-040	1694	4 over indeterminate figure	SEXTO	1	2	1300	2200	4800
WM5G-045	1694	elephant and castle below head	SEXTO	1	2	1100	2100	4800
WM5G-050	1694	elephant and castle below head; 4 over indeterminate figure	SEXTO	1	2	1400	2400	5500

William III 1695–1701

The William III five guinea piece was minted only in the final three years of the reign of the king. There are thus no specimens corresponding to the early head seen on the silver coinage, and no gold was struck at the five provincial mints.

The design of this series was probably Johann Crocker (aka John Croker), James Roettier having died in 1698 and his brother Norbert having moved to France in 1695 under a cloud. The series is probably best known for the so-called 'fine work' piece of 1701, an engraving of intricate detail, especially in the hair, and sharply struck, almost to proof standard. The reverse of the series reverted to the cruciform shields of Charles II and James II. The shield reverse of William and Mary had not proved successful.

Denomination	Metal	Weight (grams)	Diameter (mm)	Rev. alignment
Five Guineas	Gold	41.5–41.8	36	↓

Obverse 1 Heads 1, right; GVLIELMVS ET MARIA DEI GRATIA

Reverse 1 Crowned shield; MAG BR FR ET HIB REX ET REGINA (date)

Reverse 2 Similar but central lion on shield is smaller

Denomination	Metal	Weight (grams)	Diameter (mm)	Rev. alignment
Five Guineas	Gold	41.6–41.7	37	↓

Obverse 1 Head 1, right; GVLIELMVS III DEI GRA

Obverse 2 Head 2, right, larger, more detailed and sharply struck; same legend

Reverse 1 Four crowned cruciform shields between which are four sceptres, with central lion of Nassau; MAG BR FRA ET HIB REX (date)

Reverse 2 Similar but details slightly redesigned. The harp is much larger, the crowns slightly smaller;

Reverse 3 Similar but sceptres are more ornamented

Edge DECVS ET TVTAMEN ANNO REGNI (regnal date)

Obv. 1   Obv. 2

Rev. 1   Rev. 2

Plain Sceptre (Rev. 2)   Ornamental Sceptre (Rev. 3)

No.	Date	Features	Edge date	Obv.	Rev.	F	VF	EF
W35G-005	1699		UNDECIMO	1	1	900	1700	3800
W35G-010	1699	elephant and castle below head	UNDECIMO	1	1	1000	1800	4000
W35G-015	1700		DVODECIMO	1	1	900	1700	3800
W35G-020	1701	¹	DECIMO TERTIO	2	2	900	1600	3200
W35G-025	1701	¹	DECIMO TERTIO	2	3	900	1600	3200

1. 'Fine work' type; each '1' in date now resembles a 'J'.

Anne 1702–1714

The series began with one of the most exotic and valuable of all British coins, the Vigo piece of 1703. Only a very few remain in existence. The provenance mark VIGO indicates that the gold from which the coins were struck was captured from Spanish galleons at the battle at Vigo Bay in October 1702.

The Glendining's catalogue for the sale of the 'Vigo Bay' Collection in October 1992 states that three different obverse dies were used for the striking of the Vigo five guinea piece, and that 'certainly less (*sic*) than twenty pieces survive'. If one compares the illustration in this catalogue with that in *The Milled Coinage of England* (Spink), it is clear that there is a marked difference in the positioning of the VIGO mark; moreover, the MCE specimen appears to have no stops on the obverse, whereas on the Glendining pieces they are clearly evident.

After the Vigo coin, the five guinea piece was struck again in 1705 and 1706 before the Union of England and Scotland necessitated a redesign in the reverse shields to indicate the Union. It is worthy of note that the five guinea piece is the only British coin to be struck with a post-Union reverse dated 1706, even though the Union occurred on 1 May 1707 (just over a month after the calendar year changeover from 1706 to 1707, which in those days occurred in March).

A further apparent date anomaly has a simple explanation. If one compares the regnal edge year on five guinea pieces with those on crowns and halfcrowns, in some cases they are the same, and in others the regnal year is one year earlier on the five guinea piece, e.g. QVARTO (4th year) on the 1705 five guinea piece, but QVINTO (5th year) on the silver. The explanation is that the five guinea pieces were being struck early enough in the year to take the monarch's preceding regnal year. The edge date was changed on the anniversary of the accession, not at the beginning of the calendar year.

Post-Union type five guinea pieces were struck in five years up to 1714, the year of Anne's death.

The first head of Anne was engraved by John Croker from a portrait by Sir Godfrey Kneller. The later head, introduced in 1711, was engraved either by Croker or his assistant Samuel Bull. The reverses were probably by Croker and/or Bull. The first reverse is considered to be by Croker.

Denomination	Metal	Weight (grams)	Diameter (mm)	Rev. alignment
Five Guineas	Gold	41.6–41.8	37–38	↓

Obverse 1 Head 1, left; ANNA DEI GRATIA

Obverse 2 Head 2, left, older portrait, hair arrangement different; same legend

Reverse 1 Four crowned cruciform shields (of England, Scotland, France, Ireland) between which are four sceptres; central rose; MAG BR FRA ET HIB REG (date)

Reverse 2 Similar but two shields separately show conjoined English/Scottish arms; central Star of the Order of the Garter instead of rose; shields are broader; crowns redesigned; MAG BRI FR ET HIB REG (date). Lettering and date are smaller.

Reverse 3 Similar but shields are narrower and taller; lettering and date as large as on Reverse 1 harp is different; other minor modifications; same legend

Reverse 4 Similar to Reverse 2 but lettering as large as on Reverse 1

Edge DECVS ET TVTAMEN ANNO REGNI (regnal date)

Obv. 1   Obv. 2

Rev. 1   Rev. 2

Rev. 3   Rev. 4

No.	Date	Features	Edge date	Obv.	Rev.	F	VF	EF
A5G-005	1703	VIGO below head; stops on obverse [1]	SECVNDO	1	1	20000	30000	50000
A5G-010	1703	VIGO below head; no stops on obverse	SECVNDO	1	1	20000	30000	50000
A5G-015	1705		QVARTO	1	1	1100	2500	7000
A5G-020	1706		QVINTO	1	1	1100	2500	7000
A5G-025	1706		QVINTO	1	2	1100	2500	7000
A5G-030	1709		OCTAVO	1	3	1100	2500	7000
A5G-035	1711		DECIMO	2	4	1100	2500	7000
A5G-040	1713		DVODECIMO	2	4	1100	2500	7000
A5G-045	1714		DECIMO TERTIO	2	4	1100	2500	7000
A5G-050	1714	4 over 1 or 3	DECIMO TERTIO	2	4	1100	2500	7000

1. Three slightly different obverses; position of VIGO differs markedly.

George I 1714–1727

The series is a standard type, using an obverse by Croker and a reverse by J.R. Ochs, senior. The general overall design of the previous reign is followed, but both sides of the coin bear the long abbreviated Hanoverian titles of the king. The portrait is similar to that on the crown but the neck is bare.

The value of the guinea had fluctuated over the years from twenty shillings to about thirty shillings and back to a level of twenty-one shillings and sixpence at the beginning of the reign. A Proclamation in December 1717 reduced the value to twenty-one shillings.

Collecting Hints

The series is scarce, especially in the higher grades, only four dates being struck. A fine condition coin should be adequate.

Denomination	Metal	Weight (grams)	Diameter (mm)	Rev. alignment
Five Guineas	Gold	41.7–41.8	37	↓

Obverse 1 Head 1, right; GEORGIVS D G M BR FR ET HIB REX F D

Reverse 1 Four crowned cruciform shields between which are four sceptres; central Star of the Order of the Garter; BRVN ET L DVX S R I A TH ET EL (date)

Edge DECVS ET TVTAMEN ANNO REGNI (regnal date) (but note 1720 footnote 2 below)

Obv. 1   Rev. 1

No.	Date	Features	Edge date	Obv.	Rev.	F	VF	EF
G15G-005	1716	[1]	SECVNDO	1	1	1000	2500	6000
G15G-010	1717	[1]	TERTIO	1	1	1000	2500	6000
G15G-015	1717	D of DECVS inverted (edge) [1]	TERTIO	1	1	1000	2500	6000
G15G-020	1720	[2]	SEXTO	1	1	1000	2500	6000
G15G-025	1726		DECIMO TERTIO	1	1	1000	2500	6000
G15G-030	1726	each N on edge inverted (top left of N has no serif) [3]	DECIMO TERTIO	1	1	1000	2500	6000

1. Cross before DECVS and after TVTAMEN (edge) on 1716 and 1717 only.
2. Edge reads DECUS ET TUTAMEN not DECVS ET TVTAMEN.
3. A similar variety occurs on the 1726 crown.

George II 1727–1760

The five guinea pieces of George II were the last of this denomination struck as regular coinage. The series began in 1729, the obverse again the work of John Croker, who by this time was approaching retirement. Some of the coins of 1729 bear the provenance mark 'E.I.C' below the head, denoting gold obtained from the East India Company. At least some of the work on the reverses was done by Tanner, who was Croker's apprentice from January 1728 (old style Calendar).

A change to an older head was made in 1746. The 1741 coin bearing the young head was the last gold coin struck before the changeover. As with the silver coins, the five guinea piece of 1746 had the provenance mark LIMA below the head, denoting that the gold had been obtained during Admiral Anson's circumnavigation of the world. The use of the word LIMA is something of a mystery, as there appears to be no direct connection with the Peruvian port of that name.

The older portrait was the work of John Croker and Tanner. The last five guinea piece for general circulation was issued in 1753.

Collecting Hints

The young head coinage was struck in relatively high relief, and coins need to be in about very fine condition to retain most of the detail. One specimen of each reign is all that most collectors will aim for, and it is probably advisable to select the somewhat more flatly struck old head type, where a fine condition specimen is still an attractive coin.
Edges of five guinea pieces of George II should always be carefully examined for mount marks and pinholes.

Edge DECVS ET TVTAMEN ANNO REGNI (regnal date)

Obv. 1 Obv. 2

Rev. 1 Rev. 2

No.	Date	Features	Edge date	Obv.	Rev.	F	VF	EF
G25G-005	1729		TERTIO	1	1	850	1700	4000
G25G-010	1729	PROOF; edge plain [1]		1	1			25000
G25G-015	1729	EIC below head	TERTIO	1	1	850	1700	4000
G25G-020	1731		QVARTO	1	2	850	1700	4000
G25G-025	1731	PROOF [2]	QVARTO	1	2			30000
G25G-030	1735		OCTAVO	1	2	850	1700	4000
G25G-035	1738	[3]	DVODECIMO	1	2	850	1700	4000
G25G-040	1741		DECIMO QVARTO	1	2	850	1700	4000
G25G-045	1741	41 over 35	DECIMO QVARTO	1	2	850	1700	4000
G25G-050	1746	LIMA below head	DECIMO NONO	2	2	850	1700	4000
G25G-055	1748		VICESIMO SECVNDO	2	2	850	1700	4000
G25G-060	1753		VICESIMO SEXTO	2	2	850	1700	4000

1. May weigh below 40 grams.
2. The portrait is very slightly different from the regular piece (hair slightly forward); minor reverse differences also exist.
3. Obverse lettering is smaller than on previous dates.

Minor reverse variations occur, especially to the harp and shield border.

Denomination	Metal	Weight (grams)	Diameter (mm)	Rev. alignment
Five Guineas	Gold	41.8–42.0	37	↓

Obverse 1 Head 1, left; GEORGIVS II DEI GRATIA

Obverse 2 Head 2, left, older portrait; same legend

Reverse 1 Crowned shield; M B F ET H REX F D B ET L D S R I A T ET E (date)

Reverse 2 Similar but shield slightly redesigned

Five Pounds

George IV 1820–1830

The so-called five guinea piece was known at its inception as a five pound piece. The guinea had a variable value, usually between about twenty or thirty shillings, and only later was its value fixed at the 21 shilling level recognised and used until comparatively recent times. There is thus some case for viewing the modern five pound piece as a continuation of the five guinea piece. However, the series is separate from its predecessor, and it will be treated thus in this catalogue. The value of the pieces struck from 1826 onwards was fixed at five pounds rather than five pounds five shillings. Moreover, coins struck after the 'Great Recoinage' of 1816 have a more modern 'feel' than those struck earlier.

The only five pound pieces struck for George IV were those of 1826 issued in the cased proof set of that year, and the unique 1829 coin. The obverse was by William Wyon from a bust of the monarch by Sir Francis Chantrey. The reverses were by Johann Baptiste Merlen.

Collecting Hints

This coin will normally be found in the cased proof set, although isolated examples sometimes come up for sale. Occasionally, specimens exhibit signs of repair in the obverse field.

Denomination	Metal	Weight (grams)	Diameter (mm)	Rev. alignment
Five Pounds	Gold	39.8–40.0	38	↓

Obverse 1 Head 1, left; GEORGIUS IV DEI GRATIA 1826

Obverse 2 Head 2, left; same legend but date 1829

Reverse 1 Shield within mantle, crown above; BRITANNIARUM REX FID DEF

Edge DECUS ET TUTAMEN ANNO REGNI SEPTIMO

Obv. 1

Rev. 1

No.	Date	Features	Obv.	Rev.	EF	FDC
G45P-005	1826	PROOF [1]	1	1	7000	10000
G45P-010	1826	PROOF; edge plain [2]	1	1	35000	50000
G45P-015	1826	PROOF on thick flan; edge plain [3]	1	1	45000	60000
G45P-020	1829	PROOF or pattern; edge plain [4]	2	1		90000

1. Issued in cased proof sets.
2. Possibly a pattern.
3. Possibly a pattern; weight 46.5 grams.
4. Unique; weight 38.7 grams.

William IV 1830–1837

Unusually, no five pound pieces were struck for this reign, even though a proof set was issued in 1831 containing a two pound piece. Note, however, the existence of the crown piece of 1831 struck in gold. This weighs about 40 grams, possibly intentionally corresponding to the usual weight of a five pound piece.

Victoria 1837–1901

The first five pound piece issued for this reign is one of the most famous and attractive of all British coins. Known colloquially as the 'Una and the Lion' piece, it was issued in 1839 in the cased proof sets of that year. The coin was designed by William Wyon, and it depicts on the reverse Queen Victoria, representing Una, leading the British Lion.

The Una and the Lion five pound piece has acquired a cult status in numismatics, similar to that of the Gothic crown. The coin comes up for sale only rarely, and probably most remain within the cased proof sets. There are a number of varieties, as well as pieces of a similar nature struck in various metals. These are properly regarded as patterns. Indeed, some might be equally regarded as pattern crowns, since the coin bears no mark of value and indeed is almost medallic in appearance. A few even bear an obverse similar to the 1839 proof crown. For these reasons most of these pieces are considered as being outside the scope of this book.

The next five pound piece to be struck has come to be regarded almost as the definitive example of this coin. This was the piece struck for the 1887 Golden Jubilee. At first sight, this coin resembles a crown piece struck in gold, but there are distinct differences. The principal designs on both the obverse (by Boehm) and the reverse (by Pistrucci) are smaller than on the crown. Although not rare, the 1887 five pound piece is universally popular. Proofs were struck for inclusion in the proof sets of that year.

In 1893 a similar issue of proof and non-proof five pound pieces marked the introduction of the new veiled head obverse on the gold and silver coinage. This obverse was by Thomas Brock. The issue retained the Pistrucci reverse.

Obv. 3   Rev. 1

Rev. 2   Rev. 3

Collecting Hints

Although the 'Una' coin needs to be in mint condition for the quality of this piece to be fully appreciated, this coin would probably take pride of place in a collection whatever its condition.

Care needs to be taken with the 1887 and 1893 five pound pieces because of the widespread existence of forgeries, known euphemistically as restrikes or as being 'wrong'. Many of these are of high quality and of correct weight, and they often mislead experienced dealers. For the average collector or investor, the 1887 and 1893 five pound pieces are amongst the few coins where it is probably advisable to aim for a specimen in no higher than about very fine condition. A genuine coin will often have an 'old' look, frequently with numerous minor surface marks while a forgery often has a 'clean' look and a somewhat weak strike.

Many coins of the 1887 issue are early strikings, and these are easily confused with proofs. Familiarisation with genuine proofs will enable one to distinguish them with relative ease. The proofs have wide, clearly defined rims, and the milling on the edge has a cutting feel to the fingers.

Denomination	Metal	Weight (grams)	Diameter (mm)	Rev. alignment
Five Pounds 1839	Gold	38.7–39.3	38	↑
Five Pounds 1887–1893	Gold	40.0	37	↑

Obverse 1 Head 1, left; VICTORIA D G BRITANNIARUM REGINA F D

Obverse 2 Head 2, left; VICTORIA D G BRITT REG F D

Obverse 3 Head 3, left; VICTORIA DEI GRA BRITT REGINA FID DEF IND IMP

Reverse 1 Victoria as Una, standing, leading a lion left; DIRIGE DEUS GRESSUS MEOS; MDCCCXXXIX (=1839) in exergue

Reverse 2 Similar but DIRIGIT instead of DIRIGE, and Garter Star missing from robes

Reverse 3 St George and Dragon; (date) and initials B.P. in exergue

Edge 1 DECUS ET TUTAMEN ANNO REGNI TERTIO in large letters

Edge 2 Similar but small lettering

Edge 3 plain

Edge 4 milled

Obv. 1

Obv. 2

No.	Date	Features	Obv.	Rev.	Edge	VF	EF	UNC
VY5P-005	1839	[1]	1	1	2			18000
VY5P-010	1839		1	1	3			20000
VY5P-015	1839	[1]	1	2	1			18000
VY5P-020	1839		1	2	3			30000
VJ5P-025	1887		2	3	4	450	600	850
VJ5P-030	1887	PROOF	2	3	4			3500
VJ5P-035	1887	PROOF; no initials B.P. in exergue	2	3	4			4000
VO5P-040	1893		3	3	4	500	900	1200
VO5P-045	1893	PROOF	3	3	4			3800

1. Fillet decorations vary (obv.).

Patterns exist of the 1839 issue in several metals, some of which are identical in design to the above.

Commonwealth Mint

Mintmark: S: Sydney, Australia
Position of mintmark: On ground line above centre of date (reverse)

No.	Date	Mintmark	Features	Obv.	Rev.	FDC
VJ5P-050	1887	S	PROOF	1	1	75000

Edward VII 1902-1910

A five pound piece was struck in 1902 to mark the coronation of Edward VII. Matt proof specimens were included in the cased proof set, and a very small number of proof pieces bearing an 'S' (Sydney) mintmark exist. This mark is at the centre of the ground line above the date.

The issue used the portrait of Edward VII by George William de Saulles (1862-1903), while the reverse retained the Pistrucci depiction of St George and the dragon.

Collecting Hints

Very competent forgeries exist. Matt proofs usually exhibit faint hairlines which may be a product of mint finishing.

Denomination	Metal	Weight (grams)	Diameter (mm)	Rev. alignment
Five Pounds	Gold	39.9–40.0	37	↑

Obverse 1 Head 1, right; EDWARDVS VII DEI GRA BRITT OMN REX FID DEF IND IMP

Reverse 1 St George and dragon, 1902 in exergue

Edge milled

Obv. 1   Rev. 1

No.	Date	Features	Obv.	Rev.	VF	EF	UNC
E75P-005	1902		1	1	500	650	800
E75P-010	1902	matt PROOF [1]	1	1			700

1. Issued in cased proof sets.

Commonwealth Mint

Mintmark: S: Sydney, Australia
Position of Mintmark: On ground line above centre of date (reverse)

No.	Date	Mintmark	Features	Obv.	Rev.	FDC
E75P-015	1902	S	matt PROOF	1	1	75000

George V 1910–1936

As with the previous reign, a five pound piece was struck in 1911 to mark the coronation. However, for some reason no ordinary (non-proof) specimens were struck, and only proof examples from the sets exist.

The portrait of the king was designed by Sir Bertram MacKennal (1863-1931), while the Pistrucci reverse was again retained.

Collecting Hints

Despite the fact that this is a proof-only issue, forgeries exist. One also frequently comes across specimens which have been extensively scuffed, and some doubt has been cast on the genuineness of some of these. If a coin appears weakly struck it should be avoided.
The 1911 coin is difficult to find as a single coin. This is because there is no non-proof issue, and most of the proofs are still in the sets.
The apparent 'dig' on the king's head above the ear is part of the design.

Denomination	Metal	Weight (grams)	Diameter (mm)	Rev. alignment
Five Pounds	Gold	39.9–40.0	37	↑

Obverse 1 Head 1, left; GEORGIVS V DEI GRA BRITT OMN REX FID DEF IND IMP

Reverse 1 St George and dragon; 1911 in exergue

Edge milled

Obv. 1   Rev. 1

No.	Date	Features	Obv.	Rev.	EF	FDC
G55P-005	1911	PROOF [1]	1	1	900	1400

1. Issued in cased proof sets.

Edward VIII 1936

The Edward VIII five pounds is strictly speaking a pattern, as probable royal approval was about to be granted at the time of the abdication. However, because its official status rests only on this technicality, and to provide continuity, it is included in this catalogue.
The portrait of Edward VIII is by Thomas Humphrey Paget, and faces left at the insistence of the king, who considered this placement more flattering and wished to discontinue the tradition of opposite facings for successive monarchs. The reverse is the St George and dragon design of Pistrucci.

Denomination	Metal	Weight (grams)	Diameter (mm)	Rev. alignment
Five Pounds	Gold	40.0	37	↑

Obverse 1 Head 1, left; EDWARDVS VIII D G BR OMN REX F D IND IMP

Reverse 1 St George and dragon; 1937 in exergue

Edge milled

Obv. 1   Rev. 1

No.	Date	Obv.	Rev.	FDC
E85P-005	1937	1	1	175000

George VI 1937–1952

Coronation issue five pound pieces of 1937 were again issued only in cased proof sets. These sets contained four coins, each of which comprised the only British coin of that denomination for the reign.
The obverse portrait was by Thomas Humphrey Paget, the reverse again being the Pistrucci St George and dragon.

Denomination	Metal	Weight (grams)	Diameter (mm)	Rev. alignment
Five Pounds	Gold	39.9–40.0	37	↑

Obverse 1 Head 1, left; GEORGIVS VI D G BR OMN REX F D IND IMP

Reverse 1 St George and dragon, 1937 in exergue

Edge plain

Obv. 1   Rev. 1

No.	Date	Features	Obv.	Rev.	EF	FDC
G65P-005	1937	PROOF [1]	1	1	600	750

1. Issued in cased proof sets.

Elizabeth II 1952 —

With the accession of Elizabeth II there was a departure from normal practice in the issuing of gold coinage. No gold coins were included in the proof sets of 1953 issued for the coronation, and the only British gold coins struck in that year were a small number struck in order to provide continuity of the series. These were not released, nor were similar coins dated 1957. The coins bore the obverse portrait of Elizabeth II by Mary Gillick, and the Pistrucci St George and dragon reverse.

No further five pound pieces were struck until 1980, nine years after decimalization. They then continued to be issued in a somewhat irregular fashion, both as individual cased coins and in cased sets. The coins from 1980 to 1984 bore a portrait of the queen by Arnold Machin, and those from 1985 used later portraits by Raphael David Maklouf. The 1989 issue commemorating the 500th anniversary of the gold sovereign differed markedly from the regular issue.

Denomination	Metal	Weight (grams)	Diameter (mm)	Rev. alignment
Five Pounds	Gold	40.0	37	↑

Obverse 1 Head 1, right; ELIZABETH II DEI GRA BRITT OMN REGINA F D

Obverse 2 Head 1, right; ELIZABETH II DEI GRATIA REGINA F D

Obverse 3 Head 2, right; same legend

Obverse 4 Head 3, right; ELIZABETH II DEI GRA REG F D

Obverse 5 Head 4, right; same legend

Obverse 6 Queen facing on throne, holding orb and sceptre; ELIZABETH II DEI GRA REG FID DEF *(for the 500th anniversary of the gold sovereign)*

Obverse 7 Similar but 'U' in circle below throne

Reverse 1 St George and dragon, (date) in exergue

Reverse 2 Similar but 'U' in circle to left of date

Reverse 3 Crowned shield within double rose; ANNIVERSARY OF THE GOLD SOVEREIGN 1489–1989

Edge milled

Obv. 1   Obv. 3

Obv. 4   Obv. 6

Rev. 1   Rev. 3

No.	Date	Features	Obv.	Rev.	Unc
EL25P-005	1953	PROOF or pattern	1	1	200000
EL25P-010	1957	PROOF	2	1	150000
EL25P-015	1980	PROOF [1]	3	1	500
EL25P-020	1981	PROOF [1]	3	1	500
EL25P-025	1982	PROOF [1]	3	1	500
EL25P-030	1984	[2]	3	2	400
EL25P-035	1984	PROOF [1]	3	1	500
EL25P-040	1985	[2]	4	2	400
EL25P-045	1985	PROOF [3]	4	1	500
EL25P-050	1986	[2]	4	2	400
EL25P-055	1987	[2]	5	2	400
EL25P-060	1988	[2]	5	2	400
EL25P-065	1989	[2]	7	3	500
EL25P-070	1989	PROOF [1]	6	3	600
EL25P-075	1990	[2]	4	2	450
EL25P-080	1990	PROOF [1]	4	1	500
EL25P-085	1991	[2]	4	2	480
EL25P-090	1991	PROOF [1]	4	1	550
EL25P-095	1992	[2]	4	2	480
EL25P-100	1992	PROOF [1]	4	1	550
EL25P-105	1993	[2]	4	2	500
EL25P-110	1993	PROOF [1]	4	1	550
EL25P-115	1994	[2]	4	2	500
EL25P-120	1994	PROOF [1]	4	1	550
EL25P-125	1995	[2]	4	2	500
EL25P-130	1995	PROOF [1]	4	1	550

1. Issued cased and in cased proof sets.
2. Issued cased.
3. Issued in cased proof sets.

The gold strikings of the 1990 and 1993 cupronickel five pounds are listed in the relevant section and do not appear in the table above.

Fifty Shillings

Oliver Cromwell (Commonwealth 1649–1660)

The gold 50 shillings of Oliver Cromwell was, together with the broad, the first gold coin styled similarly to modern coinage. It was designed by Thomas Simon (also called Symonds) and depicts Cromwell as a Roman Emperor.

This coin seldom comes up for sale, and only eleven specimens are thought to exist. Snelling considered the fifty shillings to be no more than the proof version of the broad.

Denomination	Metal	Weight (grams)	Diameter (mm)	Rev. alignment
Fifty Shillings	Gold	22.7	30	↓

Obverse 1 Head 1, left; OLIVAR D G R P ANG SCO HIB &c PRO

Reverse 1 Crowned shield; PAX QVAERITVR BELLO 1656

Edge (in relief): PROTECTOR LITERIS LITERAE NVMMIS CORONA ET SALVS

Obv. 1   Rev. 1

No.	Date	Obv.	Rev.	VF	EF
CR50S-005	1656	1	1	15000	20000

Two Guineas

Charles II 1660–1685

The coin nowadays known as the two guinea piece was first minted in 1664. The nominal value of the piece was forty shillings, and it was known initially as a forty-shilling piece, then later as a double-guinea or a two guinea piece. The term 'guinea' was a colloquial name referring to the place of origin of much of the gold used to produce the coins. However, although the two guinea piece began at a value of forty shillings, its value fluctuated over the years until set at forty-two shillings by Proclamation early in the 18th century.

The obverse and reverse of the new coin were designed by John Roettier (1631-c.1700). The designs are similar to those used on the five guinea piece, with significant modifications compared with the halfcrown design being made. These modifications were made to prevent gilding and passing off halfcrowns as the gold coin. The two guinea piece was considered too thin to allow an edge inscription to be used, as on the five guinea piece. This was a further distinguishing mark from the halfcrown, which bore a lettered edge. From 1664 to 1669 a perpendicular graining was used on the two guinea piece to deter filing or clipping. It was then decided that diagonal graining would afford greater security, and this was used from 1671 onwards.

The elephant (with or without castle) denotes gold obtained from the African Company in Guinea. The charter granted to the company included a clause allowing the insertion of this symbol on the coins.

Edge (1664–1669) milled (vertically); (1671–1684) milled (diagonally)

Obv. 1

Obv. 2

Rev. 1

No.	Date	Features	Obv.	Rev.	F	VF	EF
C22GM-005	1664		1	1	400	1000	4000
C22GM-010	1664	elephant below head	1	1	350	800	3500
C22GM-015	1665	[1]	2	1			
C22GM-020	1669	[2]	1	1	3000		
C22GM-025	1671	[3]	1	1	400	1000	4000
C22GM-030	1675		2	1	350	800	3000
C22GM-035	1676		2	1	350	800	3000
C22GM-040	1676	elephant and castle below head	2	1	350	800	3000
C22GM-045	1677		2	1	350	800	3000
C22GM-050	1678	usually or always 8 over 7	2	1	350	800	3000
C22GM-055	1678	elephant below head	2	1	4000		
C22GM-060	1678	elephant and castle below head	2	1	350	800	3000
C22GM-065	1679		2	1	350	800	3000
C22GM-070	1680		2	1	350	800	3000
C22GM-075	1681	[4]	2	1	350	800	3000
C22GM-080	1682		2	1	350	800	3000
C22GM-085	1682	elephant and castle below head	2	1	350	800	3000
C22GM-090	1683		2	1	350	800	3000
C22GM-095	1683	elephant and castle below head	2	1	350	800	3000
C22GM-100	1684		2	1	350	800	3000
C22GM-105	1684	elephant and castle below head	2	1	350	800	3000

1. Possibly unique.
2. Extremely rare.
3. Last 1 of date is reversed from usual orientation.
4. Lettering slightly larger.

Denomination	Metal	Weight (grams)	Diameter (mm)	Rev. alignment
Two Guineas 1664-1669	Gold	16.6-16.8	30–32	↓
Two Guineas 1671-1684	Gold	16.5-16.7	30–32	↓

Obverse 1 Head 1, right; pointed truncation; lock of hair to right of truncation; CAROLVS II DEI GRATIA

Obverse 2 Head 2, right; larger, rounded truncation, without lock of hair to right; same legend

Reverse 1 Four crowned cruciform shields between which are four sceptres, with four interlinked 'C's at the centre; MAG BR FRA ET HIB REX (date)

James II 1685–1688

This series consists of only two dates, 1687 and 1688, and is a one-type issue. The design is by John Roettier. There are again marked differences between the obverse and reverse of this coin and those of the silver halfcrown, to prevent unscrupulous conversions from being attempted.

There are no elephant or elephant and castle provenance marks on this series. However, it should be mentioned that Ruding reported a 1686 coin with elephant and castle below the head. This coin appears to be unknown today.

Collecting Hints

A good fine specimen should be acceptable to most collectors.

Denomination	Metal	Weight (grams)	Diameter (mm)	Rev. alignment
Two Guineas	Gold	16.7	31–32	↓

Obverse 1 Head 1, left; IACOBVS II DEI GRATIA

Reverse 1 Four crowned cruciform shields between which are four sceptres; MAG BR FRA ET HIB REX (date)

Edge milled (diagonally)

Obv. 1   Rev. 1

No.	Date	Features	Obv.	Rev.	F	VF	EF
J22G-005	1687		1	1	600	1500	4000
J22G-010	1688	usually or always 8 over 7	1	1	650	1500	4000

William and Mary 1688–1694

Apart from a very rare 1691 piece, the first two guinea piece of this reign struck for regular use was minted in 1693. This was well after the other gold coinage had entered circulation. By this time, the value of the guinea had risen to almost 30 shillings, from the 20 shillings which had been its value at the beginning of the reign of Charles II.

The reverse of the two guinea piece of William and Mary was radically redesigned from that of previous reigns. At first sight, this seems a curious decision. Deliberate design alterations had always been incorporated to differentiate it from the halfcrown, which was of a similar size. The new shield reverse was, however, very similar to the redesigned reverse of the William and Mary halfcrown of 1689-1690. However, it must be remembered that by 1693 the halfcrown had again reverted to the cruciform shield reverse.

Although there is doubt about the exact attribution of much of the William and Mary coinage, it appears likely that the two guinea piece was the work of James and Norbert Roettier. The reverse is not the happiest of designs. It is a confusion of intricate detail, and is usually encountered weakly or flatly struck.

The elephant and castle symbol was reintroduced on all dates to denote gold obtained from the African Company.

Collecting Hints

In order to appreciate the detail of the design of this coin, especially on the reverse, specimens need to be in at least Very fine condition.
Coins bearing the elephant and castle symbol are significantly scarcer than those without, unlike the Charles II series.

Denomination	Metal	Weight (grams)	Diameter (mm)	Rev. alignment
Two Guineas	Gold	16.7-16.8	31–32	↓

Obverse 1 Heads 1, right; GVLIELMVS ET MARIA DEI GRATIA

Reverse 1 Crowned shield; MAG BR FR ET HIB REX ET REGINA (date)

Edge milled (diagonally)

Obv. 1   Rev. 1

No.	Date	Features	Obv.	Rev.	F	VF	EF
WM2G-005	1691	elephant and castle below head	1	1	2000		
WM2G-010	1693		1	1	500	1000	3500
WM2G-015	1693	elephant and castle below head	1	1	650	1300	4000
WM2G-020	1694	usually or always 4 over 3	1	1	500	1000	3500
WM2G-025	1694	elephant and castle below head usually or always 4 over 3	1	1	650	1300	4000

William III 1695–1701

There were no two guinea pieces minted depicting the early head of William III as on the other gold coins, and the only date minted was the 1701 'fine work' specimen corresponding to the five guinea piece with an almost identical portrait.

The reverse again depicted the cruciform shields of the Charles II and James II era, as the shield reverse of the William and Mary series had proved unsuccessful. Although the reverse appears at first glance to be identical to that of the five guinea piece, there are marked differences. The crowns and the harp are in particular very different.

The 1701 two guinea piece was probably designed by Johann Crocker, aka John Croker. James Roettier died in 1698 and his brother Norbert had moved to France in 1695.

Collecting Hints

This is a scarce coin of excellent workmanship, although the head seems somewhat gross and rather too large in proportion to the flan. A fine condition specimen should be adequate for most collectors.

Denomination	Metal	Weight (grams)	Diameter (mm)	Rev. alignment
Two Guineas	Gold	16.7	31–32	↓

Obverse 1 Head 1, right; GVLIELMVS III DEI GRA

Reverse 1 Four crowned cruciform shields between which are four sceptres, with central lion of Nassau; MAG BR FRA ET HIB REX (date)

Edge milled (diagonally)

Obv. 1

Rev. 1

No.	Date	Obv.	Rev.	F	VF	EF
W32G-005	1701	1	1	800	1500	4000

Anne 1702–1714

The only two guinea pieces of Anne were struck as a one-type issue after the Union of England and Scotland. There is no transition to a slightly more mature head, as with the five guinea piece.

The portrait of Anne was engraved by Croker from a design by Sir Godfrey Kneller. The reverse is considered to be by either Croker or Bull, or possibly both.

The 1714 coin is usually catalogued as being with the 4 of the date over a 3. However, careful examination reveals that the faint overdate may be a 4 over a 1 instead of a 3. It must be remembered that the 'J-type' 1 has several of the characteristics of a 3.

Collecting Hints

A specimen in fine to Very fine condition will be adequate. This series frequently occurs mounted and gilt.

Denomination	Metal	Weight (grams)	Diameter (mm)	Rev. alignment
Two Guineas	Gold	16.7-16.8	31–32	↓

Obverse 1 Head 1, left; ANNA DEI GRATIA

Reverse 1 Four crowned cruciform shields between which are four sceptres; central Star of the Order of the Garter; MAG BRI FR ET HIB REG (date)

Edge milled (diagonally)

Obv. 1

Rev. 1

No.	Date	Features	Obv.	Rev.	F	VF	EF
A2G-005	1709		1	1	450	1000	3000
A2G-010	1711		1	1	450	1000	3000
A2G-015	1713		1	1	450	1000	3000
A2G-020	1714		1	1	450	1000	3000
A2G-025	1714	4 over 1 or 3 [1]	1	1	450	1000	3000

1. See notes above.

George I 1714–1727

The series is a one-type issue, struck only in 1717, 1720 and 1726. The obverse was by Croker and the reverse by J. R. Ochs, senior. The general design is a scaled-down version of the five guinea piece.

The value of the guinea had fluctuated over the years from twenty shillings to about thirty shillings and back to a level of twenty-one shillings and sixpence at the beginning of the reign. A Proclamation in December 1717 reduced the value to twenty-one shillings.

Collecting Hints

A fine condition coin should be acceptable to most collectors.

Denomination	Metal	Weight (grams)	Diameter (mm)	Rev. alignment
Two Guineas	Gold	16.8	31–32	↓

Obverse 1 Head 1, right; GEORGIVS D G M BR FR ET HIB REX F D

Reverse 1 Four crowned cruciform shields between which are four sceptres; central Star of the Order of the Garter; BRVN ET L DVX S R I A TH ET EL (date)

Edge milled (diagonally)

Obv. 1

Rev. 1

No.	Date	Features	Obv.	Rev.	F	VF	EF
G12G-005	1717		1	1	500	1200	3500
G12G-010	1720	[1]	1	1	600	1400	5000
G12G-015	1726	[2]	1	1	500	1200	3500

1. Rarity usually somewhat underrated.
2. Date numerals larger and formed differently from previous dates.

George II 1727–1760

Although in previous reigns the two guinea piece has in general mirrored the issue of five guinea pieces, during the reign of George II there were marked differences. No coins bearing the provenance marks E.I.C. or LIMA were issued. The main difference between the two issues was that three different portraits were used on the two guinea piece instead of two. The second head, used in 1739 and 1740, has become known as the 'intermediate head', as the other two are in common parlance termed the 'young' and 'old' heads. However, these terms derive mainly from the silver coinage. Since the heads on the gold are in any case different in many ways from those on the silver, the terms 'young', 'intermediate' and 'old' are something of a misnomer when applied to the gold, but nevertheless they persist. The intermediate and old heads are in fact very similar to each other. The chief difference on the obverses is the reversion of the 'U' in the king's name back to a 'V'.

The first two guinea piece was issued relatively late into the reign, in 1734 (following a 1733 pattern). This was some years after the silver denominations had begun. The series seems to have been widely circulated, and is often found in only fine condition. Hammered gold had been demonetized in 1732 and 1733. The last two guinea piece was struck in 1753, and the denomination terminated.

A change was made to the graining (milling) during the reign of George II. Leake, writing in the 18th century, noted that 'in 1739 ... the graining which had hitherto been diagonal strokes was now made angular, upon occasion of a gang of guinea filers, who had taken more liberty than usual with the guineas, and for the discovery of whom a reward was publicly advertised. This alteration in the graining is certainly an improvement.' The 'angular' graining referred to is the shape of a chevron, or arrow-head.

The first head of George II was by Croker. The second and third heads were generally by Tanner, with some assistance from Croker on the earlier type. The reverses may have been by Tanner and/or Ochs, junior.

Collecting Hints

A fine condition coin will normally be acceptable to most collectors.
Modern forgeries exist for some dates, notably 1738, 1739 and 1748. A genuine 1739 'intermediate head' (Head 2) coin will normally have a very tiny raised flaw in the field behind the king's head. A genuine 1738 coin frequently has a scratch-like flaw resembling an arc of a circle under the head.

Denomination	Metal	Weight (grams)	Diameter (mm)	Rev. alignment
Two Guineas	Gold	16.8	31–32	↓

Obverse 1 Head 1, left; GEORGIVS II DEI GRATIA

Obverse 2 Head 2, left, older portrait; GEORGIUS II DEI GRATIA

Obverse 3 Head 3, left, very similar but hair slightly more profuse; GEORGIVS II DEI GRATIA

(note the difference in spelling on Obverse 2)

Reverse 1 Crowned shield; M B F ET H REX F D B ET L D S R I A T ET E 1734

Reverse 2 Similar but crown and shield are somewhat different; same legend (date)

Edge (1734-1738) milled (diagonally); (1739-1753) milled (with chevrons)

Obv. 1   Obv. 2

Obv. 3

Rev. 1   Rev. 2

No.	Date	Features	Obv.	Rev.	F	VF	EF
G22G-005	1734	4 over 3	1	1	1300	3000	
G22G-010	1735		1	2	300	700	1500
G22G-015	1738	1	1	2	280	550	1100
G22G-020	1739	2	1	2	280	550	1100
G22G-025	1739	2	2	2	280	550	1100
G22G-030	1740		2	2	300	600	1200
G22G-035	1748	2	3	2	320	700	1400
G22G-040	1753	3	3	2	350	900	2000

1. DEI can occur widely spaced (obv.).
2. Lettering size varies.
3. Reverse has small lettering; graining is coarse.

Two Pounds

George IV 1820–1830

As the five pound piece replaced the five guinea piece, so after the Great Recoinage the two guinea piece gave way to the gold two pound coin. However, unlike its larger counterpart, the first two pounds struck was a currency piece, the well known and much admired 1823 coin, known at the time as the 'double sovereign'.

The obverse portrait of the king was designed by Johann Baptiste Merlen. This designer was known primarily for his reverses, and the portrait for the 1823 two pound piece was the only obverse he engraved, using as a basis a model by Sir Francis Chantrey. The elegance of this portrait compared with Pistrucci's portrait for the sovereign reveals that the choice of designer and engraver was a wise one. Apparently, Pistrucci was unwilling to work from the model of another artist. The quality of the strike was exceptional, producing what some consider to be the most beautiful two pound piece ever produced. The reverse of this coin (by Pistrucci) has been the basis for the design of this denomination up to the present day.

In 1826, a proof two pounds was struck for inclusion in the proof set. The obverse was by William Wyon from a bust of the monarch by Chantrey, and the reverse was by Johann Baptiste Merlen. This coin was very similar to the proof five pound piece struck for the same set.

Edge DECUS ET TUTAMEN ANNO REGNI (regnal date)

Obv. 1   Obv. 2

Rev. 1   Rev. 2

No.	Date	Features	Edge date	Obv.	Rev.	F	VF	EF	UNC
G42P-005	1823		IV	1	1	260	320	600	850
G42P-010	1823	PROOF	IV	1	1				4000
G42P-015	1825	PROOF or pattern; edge plain		2	2				5000
G42P-020	1826	PROOF [1]	SEPTIMO	2	2				3500

1. Issued in cased proof sets.

William IV 1830–1837

A proof two pound piece designed by William Wyon was struck in 1831 for inclusion in the cased proof set. This was the largest gold coin struck during this reign. The obverse was engraved by William Wyon after a bust designed by Sir Francis Chantrey. The reverse was designed and engraved by Johann Baptiste Merlen.

Denomination	Metal	Weight (grams)	Diameter (mm)	Rev. alignment
Two Pounds	Gold	16.0	28	↓

Obverse 1 Head 1, left; GEORGIUS IIII D G BRITANNIAR REX F D

Obverse 2 Head 2, left; GEORGIUS IV DEI GRATIA 1826

Reverse 1 St George and dragon; 1823 in exergue

Reverse 2 Shield within mantle, crown above; BRITANNIARUM REX FID DEF

Denomination	Metal	Weight (grams)	Diameter (mm)	Rev. alignment
Two Pounds	Gold	15.9	28	↓

Obverse 1 Head 1, right; GULIELMUS IIII D G BRITANNIAR REX F D. WW on truncation of head

Reverse 1 Crowned shield on mantle; ANNO 1831

Edge plain

Obv. 1

Rev. 1

No.	Date	Features	Obv.	Rev.	EF	FDC
W42P-005	1831	PROOF [1]	1	1	3000	5000

1. Issued in cased proof sets.

Edge milled

Obv. 1

Obv. 2

Rev. 1

No.	Date	Features	Obv.	Rev.	VF	EF	UNC
VJ2P-005	1887		1	1	250	350	450
VJ2P-010	1887	PROOF	1	1		500	1000
VJ2P-015	1887	PROOF no initials B.P. in exergue	1	1		600	1200
VO2P-020	1893		2	1	260	380	500
VO2P-025	1893	PROOF	2	1		550	1200

Victoria 1837-1901

The omission of a two pound piece from the proof set of 1839 was curious when one considers the coverage of this set from the five pounds to the farthing. The 1853 set also did not include this denomination, and it was not struck during this reign until 1887. This piece, minted for the Golden Jubilee, resembles a smaller version of the five pounds, with an obverse by Boehm and using the Pistrucci St George and dragon reverse. This is probably the best known and most popular example of this denomination, and proofs were struck for inclusion in the proof sets.

In 1893 a two pound piece was struck in both ordinary and proof versions to mark the introduction of the new veiled head obverse by Thomas Brock. The Pistrucci reverse was retained.

Commonwealth Mint

Mintmark: S: Sydney, Australia

Position of mintmark: On ground line above centre of date (reverse)

No.	Date	mm	Features	Obv.	Rev.	EF	UNC
VJ2P-030	1887	S	PROOF	1	1		30000

Edward VII 1902-1910

A two pound piece was struck in 1902 to mark the coronation of Edward VII. Matt proof specimens were included in the cased proof set, and a very small number of proof pieces bearing an 'S' (Sydney) mintmark exist. This mark is at the centre of the ground line above the date.

The issue used the portrait of Edward VII by George William de Saulles (1862-1903), while the reverse retained the Pistrucci depiction of St George and the dragon.

Collecting Hints

A large number of forgeries exist, especially of the 1887 coin. Many of these are of poor quality and 'wear' differently from genuine coins, especially around the head and breast of St George. However, many of the fakes are very difficult to detect. Because of the prevalence of these 'restrikes', as some dealers like to call them, it is probably advisable to look for coins in about very fine condition with a genuinely old appearance.

As with five pound pieces, care must be taken not to confuse proofs with early strikings. The rims and milling of genuine proofs should be examined whenever so that one becomes familiar with their appearance.

Denomination	Metal	Weight (grams)	Diameter (mm)	Rev. alignment
Two Pounds	Gold	16.0	28	↑

Obverse 1 Head 1, left; VICTORIA D G BRITT REG F D

Obverse 2 Head 2, left; VICTORIA DEI GRA BRITT REGINA FID DEF IND IMP

Reverse 1 St George and dragon; (date) and initials B.P. in exergue

Collecting Hints

Very competent forgeries exist.

Denomination	Metal	Weight (grams)	Diameter (mm)	Rev. alignment
Two Pounds	Gold	16.0	28	↑

Obverse 1 Head 1, right; EDWARDVS VII DEI GRA BRITT OMN REX FID DEF IND IMP

Reverse 1 St George and dragon; 1902 in exergue

Edge milled

Obv. 1

Rev. 1

No.	Date	Features	Obv.	Rev.	VF	EF	UNC
E72P-005	1902		1	1	240	320	380
E72P-010	1902	matt PROOF [1]	1	1		320	380

1. Issued in cased proof sets.

Commonwealth Mint

Mintmark: S: Sydney, Australia
Position of mintmark: On ground line above centre of date (reverse)

No.	Date	mm	Features	Obv.	Rev.	UNC
E72P-015	1902	S	matt PROOF	1	1	30000

George V 1910–1936

As with the previous reign, a two pound piece was struck in 1911 to mark the coronation. However, for some reason no ordinary (non-proof) specimens were struck, and only proof examples from the sets exist.
The portrait of the king was designed by Sir Bertram MacKennal (1863-1931), while the Pistrucci reverse was again retained.

Collecting Hints

Despite the fact that this is a proof-only issue, forgeries exist. One also frequently comes across specimens which have been extensively scuffed, and some doubt has been cast on the genuineness of some of these. Genuine single pieces are somewhat difficult to find, as most of the proofs are still in the sets.
The apparent 'dig' on the king's head above the ear is part of the design.

Denomination	Metal	Weight (grams)	Diameter (mm)	Rev. alignment
Two Pounds	Gold	16.0	28	↑

Obverse 1 Head 1, left; GEORGIVS V DEI GRA BRITT OMN REX FID DEF IND IMP

Reverse 1 St George and dragon, 1911 in exergue

Edge milled

Obv. 1

Rev. 1

No.	Date	Features	Obv.	Rev.	EF	FDC
G52P-005	1911	PROOF [1]	1	1	450	800

1. Issued in cased proof sets.

Edward VIII 1936

The Edward VIII two pounds is strictly speaking a pattern, as probable royal approval was about to be granted at the time of the abdication. However, because its official status rests only on this technicality, and to provide continuity, it is included in this catalogue.
The portrait of Edward VIII is by Thomas Humphrey Paget, and faces left at the insistence of the king, who considered this placement more flattering and wished to discontinue the tradition of opposite facings for successive monarchs. The reverse is the St George and dragon design by Pistrucci.

Denomination	Metal	Weight (grams)	Diameter (mm)	Rev. alignment
Two Pounds	Gold	16.0	28	↑

Obverse 1 Head 1, left; EDWARDVS VIII D G BR OMN REX F D IND IMP

Reverse 1 St George and dragon, 1937 in exergue

Edge milled

Obv. 1

Rev. 1

No.	Date	Obv.	Rev.	FDC
E82P-005	1937	1	1	70000

George VI 1937–1952

Coronation issue two pound pieces of 1937 were again issued only in cased proof sets. These sets contained four coins, each of which comprised the only British coin of that denomination for the reign.
The obverse portrait was by Thomas Humphrey Paget, the reverse again being the Pistrucci St George and dragon.

Collecting Hints

Gold coins of 1937 must always be examined carefully for edge damage. The tight fitting inserts in the case often meant that the coins were prised out, and the plain edge was very susceptible to marks.

Denomination	Metal	Weight (grams)	Diameter (mm)	Rev. alignment
Two Pounds	Gold	16.0	28	↑

Obverse 1 Head 1, left; GEORGIVS VI D G BR OMN REX F D IND IMP

Reverse 1 St George and dragon, 1937 in exergue

Edge plain

Obv. 1

Rev. 1

No.	Date	Features	Obv.	Rev.	EF	FDC
G62P-005	1937	PROOF [1]	1	1	320	420

1. Issued in cased proof sets.

Elizabeth II 1952 —

With the accession of Elizabeth II there was a departure from normal practice in the issuing of gold coinage. No gold coins were included in the proof sets of 1953 issued for the coronation, and the only British gold coins struck in that year were a small number struck in order to provide continuity of the series. These were not released. The coins bore the obverse portrait of Elizabeth II by Mary Gillick, and the Pistrucci St George and dragon reverse. No further two pound pieces were struck until 1980, nine years after decimalization. They then continued to be issued in a somewhat irregular fashion, both as individual cased coins and in cased sets. The coins from 1980 to 1983 bear a portrait of the queen by Arnold Machin, and those from 1985 use later portraits by Raphael David Maklouf.

The proof gold two pounds of 1986, 1994 and 1995 are unusual in that they may be regarded either as gold versions of the nickel-brass two pounds or as true gold issues. Gold versions of base metal coins are not unusual (e.g. the 1990 and 1993 five pounds) but the incorporation of the coins into proof sets of gold coinage is a somewhat unusual step. The gold versions are, therefore, listed in this catalogue primarily as true gold issues, with entries in the base metal section bearing the same reference number as in the gold section.

Denomination	Metal	Weight (grams)	Diameter (mm)	Rev. alignment
Two Pounds	Gold	16.0	28	↑

Obverse 1 Head 1, right; ELIZABETH II DEI GRA BRITT OMN REGINA F D

Obverse 2 Head 2, right; ELIZABETH II DEI GRATIA REGINA F D

Obverse 3 Head 3, right; ELIZABETH II DEI GRA REG F D

Obverse 4 Head 3, right; ELIZABETH II DEI GRATIA REGINA F D TWO POUNDS

Obverse 5 Queen facing on throne, holding orb and sceptre; ELIZABETH II DEI GRA REG FID DEF *(for the 500th anniversary of the gold sovereign)*

Reverse 1 St George and dragon, (date) in exergue

Reverse 2 Thistle on St Andrew's Cross; 1986

Reverse 3 Crowned shield within double rose; ANNIVERSARY OF THE GOLD SOVEREIGN 1489–1989

Reverse 4 Bank of England's Corporate Seal with Crown and Cyphers of William and Mary; BANK OF ENGLAND 1694 1994

Reverse 5 Dove carrying olive branch *(for 50th anniversary of end of World War II)*

Reverse 6 Array of flags rising from UN 50 logo; NATIONS UNITED FOR PEACE 1945-1995 *(for 50th anniversary of United Nations)*

Edge milled

Obv. 1

Obv. 2   Obv. 3

Obv. 4   Obv. 5

Rev. 1   Rev. 2

Rev. 3

Rev. 4   Rev. 5

Rev. 6

No.	Date	Features	Obv.	Rev.	FDC
EL22P-005	1953	PROOF or pattern	1	1	75000
EL22P-010	1980	PROOF [1]	2	1	220
EL22P-015	1982	PROOF [1]	2	1	220
EL22P-020	1983	PROOF [1]	2	1	220

No.	Date	Features	Obv.	Rev.	FDC
EL22P-025	1985	PROOF [2]	3	1	220
EL22P-030	1986	PROOF [1]	4	2	220
EL22P-035	1987	PROOF [1]	3	1	220
EL22P-040	1988	PROOF [1]	3	1	220
EL22P-045	1989	PROOF [1]	5	3	280
EL22P-050	1990	PROOF [1]	3	1	220
EL22P-055	1991	PROOF [1]	3	1	240
EL22P-060	1992	PROOF [1]	3	1	240
EL22P-065	1993	PROOF [1]	3	1	240
EL22P-070	1994	PROOF [1]	4	4	350
EL22P-075	1994	PROOF [3]	3	4	450
EL22P-080	1995	PROOF [4]	4	5	350
EL22P-085	1995	PROOF [4]	4	6	350

1. Issued cased and in cased proof sets.
2. Issued in cased proof sets.
3. Error obverse; Royal Mint will exchange for correct obverse coin; issued cased.
4. Issued cased.

Broad

Oliver Cromwell (Commonwealth 1649–1660)

The Cromwell broad of twenty shillings was the forerunner of the guinea and the sovereign. Designed by Thomas Simon (also called Symonds), it was struck by Blondeau prior to his return to France in 1656. It is of similar size to the 50 shilling piece.

Denomination	Metal	Weight (grams)	Diameter (mm)	Rev. alignment
Broad	Gold	9.0–9.1	29–30	↓

Obverse 1 Head 1, left; OLIVAR D G R P ANG SCO HIB &c PRO

Reverse 1 Crowned shield; PAX QVAERITVR BELLO 1656

Edge milled

Obv. 1   Rev. 1

No.	Date	Obv.	Rev.	VF	EF
CRBR-005	1656	1	1	4000	7000

Guinea

Charles II 1660–1685

The guinea of 1663 was the first machine-struck gold coin to be struck. The coin was first struck on 6 February 1663 (1662 old style), and made current by a Proclamation of 27 March 1663. Relatively few of this date were issued, and the king's portrait was redesigned twice during the following year. The denomination was originally equivalent to one pound, or twenty shillings, but during the reign the rise in the price of gold led to its changing hands at a premium. In 1670 the weight of the coin was reduced, but the price of gold continued to rise, and the guinea traded at 22 shillings in the 1680s.

The term 'guinea' was not an official name. Much of the gold used to produce the early coins came from Guinea in Africa. The African Company was granted a Charter which allowed them to place their symbol (an elephant, or later an elephant and castle) on the coins, and the colloquial term 'guinea' originated thus. The placement of this symbol may have been responsible for the re-design of the early guineas. It is noticeable that the first head had an almost straight truncation, and the elephant symbol appeared uncomfortably squashed beneath it. The head was hastily redesigned in 1664, one of the new features being an incuse indentation cut into the centre of the truncation. The elephant symbol was now larger, and fitted neatly into the indentation. The symbol fell into disuse in 1668, but was revived in 1674, redesigned as an elephant and castle. Curiously, however, there are two very rare pieces of 1677 and 1678 bearing the elephant only symbol.

In 1672 the head was again redesigned to accommodate the older features of the king, and the truncation was rounded as on the larger gold.

The guinea coinage was designed by John Roettier. With its various revisions in design, it is a more complex series than either the two guinea piece or the five guinea piece. Like the larger gold coins, deliberate design differences vis-a-vis the silver designs were introduced. This was intended to prevent fraud and confusion with a silver coin, in this case the shilling, although occasionally one comes across a gilded shilling which has had sceptres engraved on the reverse.

Denomination	Metal	Weight (grams)	Diameter (mm)	Rev. alignment
Guinea 1663-69	Gold	8.4-8.5	25	↓
Guinea 1670-1684	Gold	8.3-8.4	25	↓

Average gold content 0.9100 (from assays carried out in 1773, figures corrected).

Obverse 1 Head 1, right; truncation almost straight and is pointed at the front; lock of hair to right of truncation; CAROLVS II DEI GRATIA

Obverse 2 Head 2, right, truncation indented, otherwise slightly redesigned; same legend

Obverse 3 Head 3, right; tie higher; hair slightly different; same legend

Obverse 4 Head 4, right; older portrait, rounded truncation, without lock of hair to right; same legend

Reverse 1 Four crowned cruciform shields between which are four sceptres, with four interlinked 'C's at the centre; MAG BR FRA ET HIB REX (date)

Reverse 2 Similar but sceptres are longer

Edge (1663-1669) milled (vertically); (1670–1684) milled (diagonally)

Obv. 1   Obv. 2

Obv. 3   Obv. 4

Rev. 1   Rev. 2

No.	Date	Features	Obv.	Rev.	F	VF	EF
C2GNM-005	1663		1	1	500	1700	4000
C2GNM-010	1663	elephant below head	1	1	450	1500	3500
C2GNM-015	1664		2	2	400	1100	2500
C2GNM-020	1664	elephant below head	2	2	1000		
C2GNM-025	1664		3	2	240	750	2000
C2GNM-030	1664	elephant below head	3	2	250	900	2400
C2GNM-035	1665		3	2	250	850	2400
C2GNM-040	1665	elephant below head	3	2	250	900	2400
C2GNM-045	1666		3	2	240	750	2000
C2GNM-050	1667		3	2	240	750	2000
C2GNM-055	1668		3	2	240	750	2000
C2GNM-060	1668	elephant below head	3	2	900	2500	
C2GNM-065	1669		3	2	240	750	2000

No.	Date	Features	Obv.	Rev.	F	VF	EF
C2GNM-070	1670		3	2	240	750	2000
C2GNM-075	1671		3	2	240	750	2000
C2GNM-080	1672		3	2	240	750	2000
C2GNM-085	1672		4	2	200	650	1600
C2GNM-090	1673		3	2	240	750	2000
C2GNM-095	1673		4	2	200	650	1600
C2GNM-100	1673	CRAOLVS instead of CAROLVS (obv.)	4	2	300	1200	4000
C2GNM-105	1674		4	2	280	850	2200
C2GNM-110	1674	elephant and castle below head	4	2	700	1800	6000
C2GNM-115	1675		4	2	220	700	1800
C2GNM-120	1675	CRAOLVS instead of CAROLVS (obv.)	4	2	300	1200	4000
C2GNM-125	1675	elephant and castle below head	4	2	220	700	2000
C2GNM-130	1676		4	2	200	650	1600
C2GNM-135	1676	elephant and castle below head	4	2	220	700	2000
C2GNM-140	1677		4	2	200	650	1600
C2GNM-145	1677	elephant below head latter 7 over 5	4	2	700	1800	
C2GNM-150	1677	elephant and castle below head	4	2	220	700	2000
C2GNM-155	1678		4	2	200	650	1600
C2GNM-160	1678	elephant below head	4	2	700	1800	
C2GNM-165	1678	elephant and castle below head	4	2	300	800	2500
C2GNM-170	1679		4	2	200	650	1600
C2GNM-175	1679	elephant and castle below head	4	2	220	700	2000
C2GNM-180	1680		4	2	200	650	1600
C2GNM-185	1680	elephant and castle below head	4	2	300	800	2500
C2GNM-190	1681		4	2	200	650	1600
C2GNM-195	1681	elephant and castle below head	4	2	220	700	2000
C2GNM-200	1682		4	2	200	650	1600
C2GNM-205	1682	rev. → [1]	4	2	220	700	2000
C2GNM-210	1682	elephant and castle below head	4	2	250	800	2200
C2GNM-215	1683		4	2	200	650	1600
C2GNM-220	1683	elephant and castle below head	4	2	300	800	2500
C2GNM-225	1684		4	2	200	650	1600
C2GNM-230	1684	elephant and castle below head	4	2	250	800	2200

1. cf. halfcrown 1682 variety.

James II 1685–1688

The guinea was struck in each of the four years of this reign, and exists both with and without the elephant and castle mark for each year. There are two very similar portraits, with a changeover during 1686. The difference between the two heads is not as significant as on the halfcrown, the only other denomination to undergo a portrait change.

The James II coinage was the work of John Roettier.

Denomination	Metal	Weight (grams)	Diameter (mm)	Rev. alignment
Guinea	Gold	8.5	25–26	↓

Average gold content 0.9094 (from assays carried out in 1773, figures corrected)

Obverse 1 Head 1, left; IACOBVS II DEI GRATIA

Obverse 2 Head 2, left, slightly redesigned; same legend

Reverse 1 Four crowned cruciform shields between which are four sceptres; MAG BR FRA ET HIB REX (date)

Edge milled (diagonally)

Obv. 1   Obv. 2   Rev. 1

No.	Date	Features	Obv.	Rev.	F	VF	EF
J2GN-005	1685	[1]	1	1	250	750	2200
J2GN-010	1685	elephant and castle below head	1	1	300	850	2800
J2GN-015	1686		1	1	250	750	2200
J2GN-020	1686	elephant and castle below head	1	1	500	1500	
J2GN-025	1686		2	1	250	750	2200
J2GN-030	1686	elephant and castle below head	2	1	350	1100	3500
J2GN-035	1687		2	1	250	750	2200
J2GN-040	1687	7 over 6	2	1	280	750	2400
J2GN-045	1687	elephant and castle below head	2	1	300	850	2800
J2GN-050	1688		2	1	250	750	2200
J2GN-055	1688	elephant and castle below head	2	1	300	850	2800

1. Some struck on broad flan.

The harp varies somewhat in shape through this series.

William and Mary 1688–1694

By the end of the reign of William and Mary the guinea had risen in value to nearly 30 shillings. The exchanges between gold and silver were accompanied by much haggling, the cause of which was invariably the prevalence of clipped silver coinage and the extent of the clipping. The exchange rate for full weight silver coins was nearer the original 20 shillings rate.

In common with the other gold coinage, the reverse of the William and Mary guinea broke with tradition. The depiction of a shield was similar to the new reverses on the larger gold coins, but it was of irregular shape rather than being straight sided with ornamentations.

The guinea was the work of James and Norbert Roettier. Unlike the half guinea, there was only one basic obverse design, although the elephant and castle symbol can be found on all of the dates struck. The reappearance of the elephant only symbol on some coins of 1692 and 1693, both rare, is curious after so many years. However, these coins usually (always?) occur with the symbol placed so tightly against the truncation that there is room for doubt as to whether it is really an elephant and castle after all, with the castle obliterated by the busts. Kenyon (*Gold Coins of England*, 1884) lists no William and Mary coinage exhibiting the elephant alone. This is a field requiring further research.

Denomination	Metal	Weight (grams)	Diameter (mm)	Rev. alignment
Guinea	Gold	8.5	25	↓

Obverse 1 Heads 1, right; GVLIELMVS ET MARIA DEI GRATIA

Reverse 1 Crowned shield; MAG BR FR ET HIB REX ET REGINA (date)

Edge milled (diagonally)

Obv. 1 Rev. 1

No.	Date	Features	Obv.	Rev.	F	VF	EF
WMGN-005	1689		1	1	220	600	1800
WMGN-010	1689	elephant and castle below head	1	1	250	800	2000
WMGN-015	1690		1	1	220	600	1800
WMGN-020	1690	elephant and castle below head	1	1	250	800	2000
WMGN-025	1691		1	1	220	600	1800
WMGN-030	1691	elephant and castle below head	1	1	250	800	2000
WMGN-035	1692		1	1	220	600	1800
WMGN-040	1692	elephant below head [1]	1	1	300	900	2400
WMGN-045	1692	elephant and castle below head	1	1	250	800	2000
WMGN-050	1693		1	1	220	600	1800
WMGN-055	1693	elephant below head [1]	1	1	800		
WMGN-060	1693	elephant and castle below head	1	1	800		
WMGN-065	1694		1	1	220	600	1800
WMGN-070	1694	4 over 3	1	1	220	600	1800
WMGN-075	1694	elephant and castle below head	1	1	250	800	2000
WMGN-080	1694	elephant and castle below head 4 over 3	1	1	250	800	2000

1. See under main heading above.

The harp on the reverse shield varies considerably in shape and orientation.

William III 1695–1701

The shield reverse of the William and Mary gold coinage was apparently considered unsatisfactory, and the William III guinea reverted to the cruciform shields reverse of Charles II and James II. At the centre was depicted the lion of Orange-Nassau.

The series was probably designed by John Croker. In common with the half guinea, the first guinea was issued in 1695, some years before the two guinea and five guinea pieces were issued.

The situation with regard to the exchange of gold and silver coins was becoming chaotic at the beginning of the reign. Exchanges between the guinea and clipped and unclipped hammered and milled silver coins produced a variety of rates of exchange. A decision was taken in Parliament to limit the exchange rate of the guinea to 25 shillings, and to prohibit the minting or import of guineas from 2nd March 1695 to 1st January 1696. Later, the rate was reduced to 22 shillings and the importation rule cancelled.

The William III guinea is not a well documented series. Catalogues exist in which the descriptions are confusing or wanting, with the die allocations incorrect. There are probably a number of varieties which are unrecorded. The 1700 misplaced sceptres guinea listed below appears to be hitherto unknown. The silver coinage of William III is notorious for errors and varieties, and it is probably only because the gold is not so widely collected and available that similar varieties have not been documented. However, the use of provincial mints was no doubt responsible for many of the errors encountered in the silver series. No gold was struck at provincial mints.

Denomination	Metal	Weight (grams)	Diameter (mm)	Rev. alignment
Guinea 1695-1700	Gold	8.4	25–26	↓
Guinea 1701	Gold	8.4	26–27	↓

Average gold content 0.9123 (from assays carried out in 1773, figures corrected).

Obverse 1 Head 1, right; GVLIELMVS III DEI GRA

Obverse 2 Head 2, slightly different, right; same legend

Obverse 3 Head 3, very different, more detailed and sharply struck, right; same legend

Reverse 1 Four crowned cruciform shields between which are four sceptres, with central lion of Nassau; MAG BR FRA ET HIB REX (date)

Reverse 2 Similar but slightly redesigned; a different harp

Reverse 3 Slightly redesigned; another harp; the English lions are much narrower; the 7 in 1700 is much thinner

Reverse 4 As Reverse 3 but two of the sceptres are misplaced as on the 1686 Five Guineas

Reverse 5 Redesigned; the English lions are as wide as on Reverses 1 and 2; the crowns are narrower compared with the shields

Reverse 6 As Reverse 5 but the sceptres are slightly more ornamented

Reverse 7 As Reverse 6 but the sceptres are less ornamented than on Reverse 5

Edge milled (diagonally)

Obv. 1   Obv. 2   Obv. 3

Rev. 1   Rev. 2   Rev. 4

Rev. 5   Rev. 6 Enlarged   Rev. 7

No.	Date	Features	Obv.	Rev.	F	VF	EF
W3GN-005	1695		1	1	200	500	1200
W3GN-010	1695	5 over indeterminate digit	1	1	250	600	1400
W3GN-015	1695	elephant and castle below head	1	1	250	700	1500
W3GN-020	1696		1	1	200	500	1200
W3GN-025	1696	elephant and castle below head	1	1	800		
W3GN-030	1697		1	2	200	500	1200
W3GN-035	1697		2	2	200	500	1200
W3GN-040	1697	elephant and castle below head	2	2	400	1200	3000
W3GN-045	1698	[1]	2	2	200	400	1000
W3GN-050	1698	large date and lettering (rev.)	2	2	200	400	1000
W3GN-055	1698	elephant and castle below head	2	2	250	600	1600
W3GN-060	1699		2	2	200	500	1200
W3GN-065	1699	elephant and castle below head	2	2	800		
W3GN-070	1700		2	2	200	450	1000
W3GN-075	1700	elephant and castle below head	2	2	300	750	1500
W3GN-080	1700		2	3	250	500	1200
W3GN-085	1700	[2]	2	4	450	900	2000
W3GN-090	1701		2	5	200	450	1000

No.	Date	Features	Obv.	Rev.	F	VF	EF
W3GN-095	1701	elephant and castle below head	2	5	1000		
W3GN-100	1701		2	6	200	450	1000
W3GN-105	1701		2	7	300	800	2500
W3GN-110	1701	[3]	3	5	450	1200	4000

1. Size of lions varies.
2. See James II 5 Guineas for description of misplaced sceptres.
3. 'Fine work' type.

1695-1700: '1' in date is reversed-Z type
1701: '1' in date is J-type

Almost all of the 1701 issue was coined from withdrawn foreign gold coinage in circulation.

Anne 1702–1714

The guinea was minted from the first year of Anne's accession with the basic design virtually unchanged. The portrait of Anne differed very little from that used on the shilling; the customary 'undraped bust' for gold was undoubtedly considered unsuitable. The reverse continued the cruciform shields theme, but the lion of Nassau was replaced by a rose, and subsequently by a Star of the Order of the Garter following the Union of Scotland and England.

Some guineas were struck in 1703 bearing the VIGO provenance mark, but all VIGO gold is rare. Phillips's 'State of the Nation', 1726, records that only 34 lb. weight of gold was struck in 1703, compared with 3642 lb. in 1702. No pre-Union guineas were struck with the elephant and castle mark, but post-Union specimens exist dated 1707, 1708, 1709. These are significantly scarcer than the 'plain' type.

The series was probably engraved by John Croker, assisted by Samuel Bull. The first head of Anne was designed by Sir Godfrey Kneller.

Collecting Hints

While a fine to very fine condition specimen will be satisfactory for most purposes, coins in very fine to extremely fine are most attractive and are often sharply struck with a prooflike appearance. The series is under-documented and careful study may well yield new varieties. The elephant and castle specimens are possibly scarcer than sometimes thought.

Denomination	Metal	Weight (grams)	Diameter (mm)	Rev. alignment
Guinea	Gold	8.3	25	↓

Average gold content 0.9134 (from assays carried out in 1773, figures corrected)

Obverse 1 Head 1, left; ANNA DEI GRATIA

Obverse 2 Head 2, left; hair arrangement at top different; same legend

Obverse 3 Head 3, slightly different, left; same legend

Reverse 1 Four crowned cruciform shields between which are four sceptres; central rose; MAG BR FRA ET HIB REG (date)

Reverse 2 Similar but two shields separately show conjoined English/Scottish Arms; central Star of the Order of the Garter instead of rose; shields are broader; MAG BRI FR ET HIB REG (date).

Edge milled (diagonally)

Obv. 1   Obv. 2   Obv. 3

Rev. 1   Rev. 2

Before Union of England and Scotland

No.	Date	Features	Obv.	Rev.	F	VF	EF
AGN-005	1702	¹	1	1	220	600	1800
AGN-010	1702	PROOF; edge plain	1	1		2500	5000
AGN-015	1703	VIGO below head	1	1	3000	6000	12000
AGN-020	1705		1	1	250	700	2000
AGN-025	1706		1	1	250	700	2000
AGN-030	1707		1	1	250	700	2000

1. Almost all coined from withdrawn foreign gold in circulation.

After Union of England and Scotland

No.	Date	Features	Obv.	Rev.	F	VF	EF
AGN-035	1707		1	2	220	600	1800
AGN-040	1707	elephant and castle below head	1	2	500	1000	3000
AGN-045	1707		2	2	500	1000	3500
AGN-050	1708		1	2	500	1000	3500
AGN-055	1708		2	2	220	500	1500
AGN-060	1708	elephant and castle below head	2	2	450	1000	3000
AGN-065	1709		2	2	220	500	1500
AGN-070	1709	elephant and castle below head	2	2	450	1000	3000
AGN-075	1710		3	2	200	400	900
AGN-080	1711		3	2	200	400	900
AGN-085	1712		3	2	200	400	900
AGN-090	1713		3	2	200	400	900
AGN-095	1713	3 over 1	3	2	200	400	900
AGN-100	1714		3	2	200	400	900
AGN-105	1714	both 'A's in GRATIA unbarred (obv.)	3	2	200	400	900

Minor reverse variations occur.

George I 1714–1727

The guinea series of George I is notable for the five different obverse portraits of the king. The first of these was on the guinea of 1714, itself a remarkable piece for a number of reasons. It was the only denomination in any metal struck in 1714, the first year of the reign, and a date shared with many coins of Anne. In addition, the reverse legend is unlike any other of this reign, as it includes the term PR (princeps), using smaller lettering overall to allow its inclusion. The head of George I on the obverse is also unique to this date. This coin has become known as the 'Prince Elector' guinea, and is much sought after.

The second head of George I was introduced in 1715, but changed during that year to one with less profusion of hair. Further changes in design were introduced in 1716 and 1723. Curiously, Leake, writing in the 18th century, noted that 'the Guinea of 1722 is supposed to have His Majesty's face the most resembling him of any'. Leake further notes the 1724 guinea being 'remarkable for a very broad margin between the legend and the edge of the coin'.

The obverse dies were largely the work of John Croker, but the low relief third type has been attributed to Croker and/or James Bull. The reverses were by Croker and/or J. R. Ochs, senior.

Kenyon, writing in *Gold Coins of England* refers to a 1727 guinea with a somewhat different head, which 'cannot have been engraved by Croker'. It is probable that this coin is a pattern.

The elephant and castle provenance mark made its last appearance during this reign, bowing out on the 1726 coin.

The value of the guinea had fluctuated over the years from twenty shillings to about thirty shillings and back to a level of twenty-one shillings and sixpence at the beginning of the reign. A Proclamation in December 1717 reduced the value to twenty-one shillings.

Collecting Hints

Unless one is aiming to collect one of each type, a single specimen of this reign in fine to very fine condition should be acceptable. The last head on a somewhat broader flan than usual is arguably the most attractive, and the date 1726 is the best value for money.

Denomination	Metal	Weight (grams)	Diameter (mm)	Rev. alignment
Guinea	Gold	8.3–8.4	25–26	↓

Average gold content 0.9135 (from assays carried out in 1773, figures corrected).

Obverse 1 Head 1, right; GEORGIVS D G MAG BR FR ET HIB REX F D

Obverse 2 Head 2, right, less profuse hair; GEORGIVS D G M BR FR ET HIB REX F D

Obverse 3 Head 3, right, lower relief, still less hair; same legend

Obverse 4 Head 4, right, different tie and hair; same legend

Obverse 5 Head 5, right, smaller and older; same legend

Reverse 1 Four crowned cruciform shields between which are four sceptres; central Star of the Order of the Garter; BRVN ET LVN DVX S R I A TH ET PR EL 1714

Reverse 2 Similar but larger lettering reading BRVN ET L DVX S R I A TH ET EL (date)

Edge milled (diagonally)

Obv. 1 Prince Elector   Obv. 3

Obv. 4   Obv. 5

Rev. 1 Prince Elector   Rev. 2

No.	Date	Features	Obv.	Rev.	F	VF	EF
G1GN-005	1714	¹	1	1	350	800	2500
G1GN-010	1715		2	2	240	550	1400
G1GN-015	1715		3	2	200	450	1200
G1GN-020	1716		3	2	200	450	1200
G1GN-025	1716		4	2	200	450	1200
G1GN-030	1717		4	2	200	450	1200
G1GN-035	1718		4	2	800		
G1GN-040	1718	8 over 7	4	2	1000		
G1GN-045	1719		4	2	200	450	1200
G1GN-050	1720		4	2	200	450	1200
G1GN-055	1721		4	2	200	450	1200
G1GN-060	1721	elephant and castle below head	4	2	1400		
G1GN-065	1722		4	2	200	450	1200
G1GN-070	1722	elephant and castle below head	4	2	1400		
G1GN-075	1723		4	2	200	450	1200
G1GN-080	1723		5	2	200	450	1200
G1GN-085	1724		5	2	200	450	1200
G1GN-090	1725		5	2	200	450	1200
G1GN-095	1726		5	2	200	450	1200
G1GN-100	1726	elephant and castle below head ²	5	2	500		
G1GN-105	1727		5	2	200	450	1200

1. 'Prince Elector' type.
2. Tie (obv.) slightly different from above coin.

George II 1727–1760

The guinea series of George II is a complex one. The coin was struck for almost every year of this relatively long reign, and the designs underwent a number of subtle changes, especially with regard to lettering size. The so-called 'intermediate head' also makes an appearance. Provenance marks E.I.C. (East India Company) and LIMA (gold obtained during Anson's voyage around the world) also occur. In 1732 the old hammered gold pieces were demonetized, and some of the gold from these may have been recoined into the current issues.

The reverse of the guinea reverted to the shield design last seen under William and Mary. This seems at first a curious decision, as this reverse had not been a success. However, it was considered unwise to retain a design so near that of the shilling reverse. A proclamation of 1741 stated that gilt shillings of Anne had been particularly susceptible to being passed off as guineas, as the heads on the two coins were virtually identical.

Gilding of shillings was not the only problem. In 1739, the diagonal milling had to be changed to a more sophisticated chevron design 'upon occasion of a gang of Guinea-filers, who had taken more liberty than usual with the Guineas' (Martin-Leake, writing at the time). These filers had found it easy to restore diagonal milling to clipped coins. A clergyman, Peter Vallavine, received a reward of 100 pounds for inventing the chevron design.

The guinea and the shilling were the only coins struck in 1727, the first year of the reign. J.R. Ochs, senior was responsible for both of these early coins, and they were the only coins of George II designed by him. Later work was by Croker, Tanner and Ochs, junior.

Denomination	Metal	Weight (grams)	Diameter (mm)	Rev. alignment
Guinea 1727 Obv.2: Rev. 2	Gold	8.3–8.4	24–25	↓
Guinea all others 1727-60	Gold	8.3–8.4	25–26	↓

Average gold content 0.9140 (from assays carried out in 1773, figures corrected).

Obverse 1 Head 1, left; GEORGIVS II DEI GRATIA in small lettering

Obverse 2 Head 1, left; same legend but larger

Obverse 3 Head 2, narrower, left; same legend

Obverse 4 Head 2, left; same legend, even larger

Obverse 5 Head 3, left; same legend but GEORGIUS (lettering slightly smaller)

Obverse 6 Head 3, left; same legend but larger

Obverse 7 Head 4, older, left; same legend but GEORGIVS

Obverse 8 Head 4, left; same legend but even larger

Reverse 1 Crowned shield; M B F ET H REX F D B ET L D S R I A T ET E (date) in small lettering and numerals

Reverse 2 Similar but shield smaller; lettering and numerals slightly larger

Reverse 3 Similar but shield squarer

Reverse 4 Similar but lettering and numerals slightly larger

Reverse 5 Similar but lettering and numerals larger

Edge (1727–38) milled (diagonally); (1739–60) milled (with chevrons)

Obv. 1   Obv. 2   Obv. 3

Obv. 4   Obv. 5   Obv. 6

Obv. 7   Obv. 8

Rev. 1   Rev. 2   Rev. 3

Rev. 4   Rev. 5

No.	Date	Features	Obv.	Rev.	F	VF	EF
G2GN-005	1727		1	1	400	1000	2000
G2GN-010	1727	[1]	2	2	250	700	1400
G2GN-015	1728		2	2	250	700	1400
G2GN-020	1729	PROOF; edge plain	3	3			4000
G2GN-025	1729	PROOF; edge plain; rev. ↑ [2]	3	3			4500
G2GN-030	1729	E.I.C. below head	3	3	300	800	1600
G2GN-035	1730		3	3	250	700	1400
G2GN-040	1731		3	3	250	700	1400
G2GN-045	1731	E.I.C. below head	3	3	300	800	1600
G2GN-050	1732		3	3	250	700	1400
G2GN-055	1732	E.I.C. below head	3	3	300	800	1600
G2GN-060	1732		4	3	200	500	1200
G2GN-065	1732	E.I.C. below head	4	3	350	900	1800
G2GN-070	1733		4	3	200	500	1200
G2GN-075	1734		4	3	200	500	1200
G2GN-080	1735		4	3	200	500	1200
G2GN-085	1736		4	3	200	500	1200
G2GN-090	1737		4	3	200	500	1200
G2GN-095	1738		4	3	200	500	1200

No.	Date	Features	Obv.	Rev.	F	VF	EF
G2GN-100	1739	[3]	5	4	200	450	1000
G2GN-105	1739	E.I.C. below head	5	4	350	900	1800
G2GN-110	1740		5	4	200	450	1000
G2GN-115	1741	41 over 39	5	4	1000		
G2GN-120	1743		5	4	2000	4500	
G2GN-125	1745		6	4	250	600	1400
G2GN-130	1745	LIMA below head	6	4	500	1200	2200
G2GN-135	1746		7	4	220	500	1100
G2GN-140	1747		8	5	170	350	750
G2GN-145	1748		8	5	170	350	750
G2GN-150	1749		8	5	170	350	750
G2GN-155	1750		8	5	170	350	750
G2GN-160	1751		7	5	160	320	700
G2GN-165	1752		7	5	160	320	700
G2GN-170	1753		7	5	160	320	700
G2GN-175	1755		7	5	160	320	700
G2GN-180	1756		7	5	160	320	700
G2GN-185	1758		7	5	160	320	700
G2GN-190	1759		7	5	160	320	700
G2GN-195	1760		7	5	160	320	700

1. Flan slightly smaller than usual.
2. Weight can be c. 8.0 grams.
3. 'Intermediate head'.

George III 1760–1820

When one considers the extensive gaps between issues of silver coinage during this long reign, the regularity with which the guinea was struck appears remarkable. The coin was issued almost every year for the first forty years of the reign. However, the relatively high price of silver compared with face value of silver coins prevented the use of this metal for coinage until later in the reign.

George III reigned for sixty years, and during this time the guinea underwent a number of changes. No fewer than six different portraits of the monarch were used. In 1774 almost 20 million worn guineas of William III and Anne were melted and recoined as guineas and half guineas.

The issue of guineas from 1787 to 1799 has become known in common parlance as the 'spade guinea' because of the spade-shaped shield on the reverse. In Victorian times the coin was popular as a fob piece attached to gold watch chains. The overall popularity of the coin has arguably been undeserved; the coin has a somewhat mechanical design, and the shield looks as if it is drawn with a ruler and a pair of compasses. The bust is flat and lacking in detail. The coin does not even have rarity to commend it; it is the most frequently encountered type of guinea.

Towards the end of the century, gold began to become scarce and to rise in value. Revolution and war in Europe had drained resources, and many people were hoarding the metal. Parliament passed a Bill making banknotes legal tender to any amount, and by 1799 the issue of spade guineas was at an end. Half-and third-guineas continued to be struck, however.

In 1813, a one-year type guinea was struck to pay Wellington's army on the Pyrenees, as the local populace would accept only gold for purchases. The issue was 80,000 pieces, and the gold for the issue was imported from India in the form of gold mohur and pagoda coins. The coin has become known as the 'military guinea'. Gold was still scarce, and the guinea was trading on the fee market at about 27 shillings in paper money. The coining of this piece for the special requirement of supplying the army was therefore a poor deal for the British government, and the 1813 guinea was the last guinea to be struck.

The guineas from 1761 to 1773 were engraved by Richard Yeo. The reverses were from a design by Tanner. The guinea of 1774–1786 was the work of Thomas Pingo. His son Lewis was appointed Chief Engraver in 1780 and designed the spade guinea and the military guinea. The head for the latter was based on a design by Nathaniel Marchant.

Collecting Hints

Specimens in very fine condition will usually be adequate. The spade guinea of 1787-1799 is one of the few coins which possibly are more attractive in very fine than in extremely fine condition. In higher grades there is very little more detail visible, and a very fine coin seems to have more character.

Care must be taken with guineas dated 1798, as modern forgeries exist, another reason why fine to very fine condition coins may be considered preferable. In particular, beware any coin on which the central vertical line on the shield continues above the top of the shield to touch the base of the crown. It does seem, however, that a few genuine pieces have this characteristic.

Denomination	Metal	Weight (grams)	Diameter (mm)	Rev. alignment
Guinea 1761-1786	Gold	8.4	24	↓
Guinea 1787-1813	Gold	8.4	24	↑

Average gold content 0.9146 at beginning of reign (from assays carried out in 1773, figures corrected).

Obverse 1 Head 1, right; GEORGIVS III DEI GRATIA

Obverse 2 Head 2, right, hair more profuse; same legend

Obverse 3 Head 3, right, slightly different; same legend

Obverse 4 Head 4, larger, right; hair extends below truncation; same legend

Obverse 5 Head 5, smaller, right; truncation more pointed; same legend

Obverse 6 Head 6, smaller, very different, right; same legend

Obverse 7 Head 7, right; the truncation is more rounded than on Obverse 6

Reverse 1 Crowned shield; M B F ET H REX F D B ET L D S R I A T ET E ; (date) divided by crown

Reverse 2 Crowned spade-shaped shield; same legend but in opposite position around rim; (date) at bottom

Reverse 3 Crowned shield in Garter; BRITANNIARUM REX FIDEI DEFENSOR; HONI SOIT QUI MAL Y PENSE on Garter; Date 1813 between Garter and edge legend

Edge milled (with chevrons)

Obv. 1 Obv. 2 Obv. 3

Obv. 4 Obv. 5 Obv. 6 Military Type

Rev. 1 Rev. 2 Rev. 3 Military Type

No.	Date	Features	Obv.	Rev.	F	VF	EF
G3GN-005	1761		1	1	500	1000	2500
G3GN-010	1761	PROOF; edge plain	1	1			3500
G3GN-015	1763		2	1	300	600	1500
G3GN-020	1764		2	1	300	600	1500
G3GN-025	1765		3	1	110	250	500
G3GN-030	1766		3	1	110	220	450
G3GN-035	1767		3	1	110	250	500
G3GN-040	1768		3	1	110	250	500
G3GN-045	1769		3	1	110	250	500
G3GN-050	1770		3	1	110	250	500
G3GN-055	1771		3	1	110	250	500
G3GN-060	1772		3	1	110	250	500
G3GN-065	1773	[1]	3	1	110	250	500
G3GN-070	1774	[2]	4	1	110	200	400
G3GN-075	1774	PROOF; edge plain; rev. ↑ [3]	4	1			1800
G3GN-080	1775		4	1	110	200	400
G3GN-085	1776		4	1	110	200	400
G3GN-090	1777		4	1	110	200	400
G3GN-095	1778		4	1	110	200	400
G3GN-100	1779		4	1	110	200	400
G3GN-105	1781	[4]	4	1	110	200	400
G3GN-110	1782		4	1	110	200	400
G3GN-115	1783		4	1	120	240	500
G3GN-120	1784		4	1	110	200	400
G3GN-125	1785		4	1	110	170	350
G3GN-130	1786		4	1	110	170	350
G3GN-135	1787		5	2	100	160	320
G3GN-140	1787	PROOF; edge plain [5]	5	2			2000
G3GN-145	1788		5	2	100	160	320
G3GN-150	1789		5	2	100	160	320
G3GN-155	1790		5	2	100	160	320
G3GN-160	1791		5	2	100	160	320
G3GN-165	1792		5	2	100	160	320
G3GN-170	1793		5	2	100	160	320
G3GN-175	1794		5	2	100	160	320
G3GN-180	1795		5	2	110	200	400
G3GN-185	1796		5	2	110	200	400
G3GN-190	1797		5	2	100	160	320
G3GN-195	1798	[6]	5	2	95	150	280
G3GN-200	1798	8 over 7	5	2	130	200	400
G3GN-205	1799		5	2	120	200	400
G3GN-210	1813	[7]	6	3	150	350	600
G3GN-215	1813	PROOF [7]	7	3			2500

1. Differences in laurel berries occur (obv.).
2. Many struck from reclaimed gold from William III and Anne guineas.
3. Usually has die flaw in reverse field.
4. Date change; see below.
5. Can occur with weight as low as 7 grams.
6. Several counterfeits exist.
7. 'Military' guinea.

Reverse 1: from 1761 to 1779 the '1' in the date is a 'J' type; from 1781 to 1786 it is a Roman I.

Sovereign

George III 1760–1820

The proclamation of 1 July 1817 giving legal tender to the sovereign introduced a coin which was to become of major importance. The guinea of twenty-one shillings had last been minted in 1813, and the sovereign, valued at twenty shillings, took its place in the new order after the Great Recoinage. It was obviously not realised at the time how important the sovereign would become as a unit in transactions of gold bullion.

As with the other new coinage, the quality of striking of the sovereign was very high. In practice, it was not invariably so, and extremely fine or better specimens can vary slightly in the sharpness of strike. Nevertheless, the workmanship and strike are consistently better than on the sovereigns produced today.

The public did not immediately take to the sovereign, preferring paper money. In addition, many of the coins were hoarded as curiosities. This explains why the 1817 coin often turns up in higher grades. Because of lack of demand, fewer coins were minted in subsequent years.

The obverse and reverse were designed by Benedetto Pistrucci. The reverse of the 1817 sovereign was the first use of the St George and dragon design.

Collecting Hints

The George III sovereign is a popular coin in all grades from fine upwards. If looking for specimens in extremely fine condition, one should try to obtain one with a sharp strike and prooflike fields.

Denomination	Metal	Weight (grams)	Diameter (mm)	Rev. alignment
Sovereign	Gold	8.0	22	↓

Obverse 1 Head 1, right; GEORGIUS III D G BRITANNIAR REX F D (date)

Reverse 1 St George and dragon; HONI SOIT QUI MAL Y PENSE on Garter

Edge milled

Obv. 1

Rev. 1

No.	Date	Features	Obv.	Rev.	F	VF	EF	UNC
G3SV-005	1817		1	1	120	190	400	600
G3SV-010	1817	PROOF	1	1				5000
G3SV-015	1818	[1]	1	1	130	240	800	1200
G3SV-020	1818	PROOF	1	1				6500
G3SV-025	1819	[2]	1	1	10000	20000		
G3SV-030	1820	[3]	1	1	120	190	400	600

1. Minor alterations in lettering occur.
2. Unknown in higher grades.
3. Date numerals vary in size.

George IV 1820–1830

Pistrucci continued as the designer, and sovereigns were struck for each year of the reign. The reverse was modified, discarding the Garter with its legend, but retaining the St George and dragon theme. This design is very similar to that used in modern times. The early obverse portrait of the king by Pistrucci compared unfavourably with those on the five and two pound pieces by William Wyon and Johann Baptiste Merlen respectively. It was disliked by the king and replaced in 1825 with a bare head design by William Wyon. The reverse was altered to a crowned shield design by Merlen.

Proofs were struck in 1826 for inclusion in the cased proof sets.

Collecting Hints

This series should be collected in very fine or better condition. Counterfeits exist for a number of dates, and coins with a pitted surface or poor definition should be avoided.

Denomination	Metal	Weight (grams)	Diameter (mm)	Rev. alignment
Sovereign	Gold	8.0	22	↓

Obverse 1 Head 1, left; GEORGIUS IIII D G BRITANNIAR REX F D

Obverse 2 Head 2, left; GEORGIUS IV DEI GRATIA (date)

Reverse 1 St George and dragon; (date) in exergue

Reverse 2 Crowned shield; BRITANNIARUM REX FID DEF

Edge milled

Obv. 1   Obv. 2

Rev. 1   Rev. 2

No.	Date	Features	Obv.	Rev.	F	VF	EF	UNC
G4SV-005	1821		1	1	110	170	350	500
G4SV-010	1821	PROOF	1	1				3500
G4SV-015	1822		1	1	110	170	350	500
G4SV-020	1823		1	1	200	500	1000	1750
G4SV-025	1824		1	1	110	170	350	500
G4SV-030	1825		1	1	140	280	750	1100
G4SV-035	1825		2	2	110	170	350	500
G4SV-040	1825	PROOF; edge plain	2	2				4000
G4SV-045	1826		2	2	110	170	350	500
G4SV-050	1826	PROOF [1]	2	2				2500
G4SV-055	1827		2	2	110	170	350	500
G4SV-060	1828		2	2	1500	3000	4500	

No.	Date	Features	Obv.	Rev.	F	VF	EF	UNC
G4SV-065	1829		2	2	110	170	350	500
G4SV-070	1830		2	2	110	170	350	500

1. Issued in cased proof sets.

William IV 1830-1837

The general overall design continued during this reign. The obverse portrait was by William Wyon from a bust by Sir Francis Chantrey, and the reverse was a slightly modified shield design by Johann Baptiste Merlen. Proofs were struck in 1831 for inclusion in the cased proof sets, and these differ from the ordinary coin in having a plain edge.

Collecting Hints

Fine to very fine condition specimens should be adequate. There is little increase in visible detail in the higher grades, especially on the reverse.

Denomination	Metal	Weight (grams)	Diameter (mm)	Rev. alignment
Sovereign	Gold	8.0	22	↓

Obverse 1 Head 1; GULIELMUS IIII D G BRITANNIAR REX F D W.W. (with stops) on truncation of head

Reverse 1 Crowned shield on mantle; below: ANNO (date)

Edge milled

Obv. 1   Rev. 1

No.	Date	Features	Obv.	Rev.	F	VF	EF	UNC
W4SV-005	1831		1	1	120	200	500	750
W4SV-010	1831	PROOF edge plain [1]	1	1				2700
W4SV-015	1831	WW without stops (obv.) [2]	1	1	120	200	500	750
W4SV-020	1832		1	1	110	180	450	700
W4SV-025	1832	PROOF	1	1				5500
W4SV-030	1832	WW without stops (obv.) [2]	1	1	110	180	450	700
W4SV-035	1833		1	1	110	180	450	700
W4SV-040	1835		1	1	110	180	450	700
W4SV-045	1836		1	1	110	180	450	700
W4SV-050	1837		1	1	110	180	450	700

1. Issued in cased proof sets.
2. Slightly different head introduced during this year.

Occasionally, one comes across specimens of this series which have a raised 'N' as if randomly dropped on the reverse shield. These letters are of the same size and shape as the 'N's in 'ANNO', and it is possible that specimens exist with 'A' and 'O' similarly placed

Victoria 1837-1901

The Victorian sovereign is one of the most important and popular series in the world, and yet it is curiously under-researched. Because few people collect the sovereign by date, the varieties within the series are largely unknown to the average collector. Others have no doubt yet to be discovered.

Sovereigns were minted for almost every year of the queen's reign, and the series is further complicated on two counts: firstly, the production of the coins at three mints in Australia, and secondly, the adoption of the St George and dragon reverse from 1871 while the shield reverse continued to be in use until 1874 in London and until 1887 in Australia. The result, coupled with the longevity of Victoria, was one of the longest and complex series of a denomination within one reign. No London sovereigns were struck from 1881 to 1883 because of extensive renovations at the Royal Mint.

The sovereign is nowadays one of the main coins used in trading of gold bullion throughout the world. Although sovereigns of the earlier reigns are occasionally dealt with in bulk quantities between dealers, the Victorian and later sovereigns are given daily buy-sell quotations on bullion markets around the world.

It is not generally realised that the dies for the sovereigns up to 1859 were the same as those used for the copper farthings. From comparison of the two series, it appears that a given die was used firstly to strike sovereigns, and then, when it became a little worn, it was transferred to strike farthings, which were not considered so important. The use of die numbers may have been to help in providing information on how many coins could be struck from one die. Normally, a die could be relied upon to produce about 100,000 pieces.

The 1859 sovereign listed below with obverse 4 is usually known as the 'Ansell' sovereign. Mr. G. F. Ansell of the Royal Mint experimented with a sample of Australian gold containing antimony, arsenic and lead, from which these sovereigns were produced. Before treatment of the metal by Ansell it had proved too brittle for use in coinage.

The young head of Victoria was designed by William Wyon. This continued to be used until 1887, even though Wyon had died in 1851. The jubilee head was engraved by Leonard Charles Wyon from a design by Sir Joseph Edgar Boehm. The veiled head was designed by Sir Thomas Brock. The reverses are in some doubt, but the shield reverse was possibly the work of Johann Baptiste Merlen, while the St George and dragon reverse was originally by Pistrucci but engraved by other hands.

Collecting Hints

One example of each type in extremely fine or better condition will be adequate for most collectors. Specimens of the veiled head type in top grades are surprisingly scarce.

Many forgeries exist of Victorian sovereigns. These are not too difficult to spot when one has handled genuine specimens on a regular basis, but to a novice they can be deceptive. Often the date numerals appear not quite 'right'; the lettering may be unevenly spaced or the surface may be somewhat rough. A forgery's 'ring' when dropped on to a hard surface is often duller than that of a genuine coin. Another characteristic, which needs to be learnt by experience, is that the coin does not reflect light in the same way as a genuine coin, and the way in which the coin has worn appears strange. Some forgeries have the edge milling at a slight diagonal instead of 'straight across'.

Denomination	Metal	Weight (grams)	Diameter (mm)	Rev. alignment
Sovereign 1838-1887 obv.7	Gold	8.0	22	↓
Sovereign 1887 obv.8-1901	Gold	8.0	22	↑

Obverse 1 Head 1, left; WW in relief on truncation; VICTORIA DEI GRATIA (date)

Obverse 2 Head 2, left, slightly larger, WW in relief, neck and hair slightly different, rim slightly thicker; same legend (date)

Obverse 3 Head 2, left; WW incuse; same legend (date)

Obverse 4 Head 3, left; WW incuse, raised line along lower edge of rear ribbon; same legend (date) (= 1859)

Obverse 5 Head 4, left; WW in relief, truncation more rounded; same legend (date)

Obverse 6 Head 5, left; WW in relief, only partially visible; VICTORIA D G BRITANNIAR REG F D (no date)

Obverse 7 Head 6, left; WW in relief bolder and fully visible, hair at neck slightly different; same legend

Obverse 8 Head 7, 'Jubilee' type, left; VICTORIA D G BRITT REG F D

Obverse 9 Head 8, veiled, left; VICTORIA DEI GRA BRITT REGINA FID DEF IND IMP

Reverse 1 Crowned shield within wreath; BRITANNIARUM REGINA FID DEF

Reverse 2 Similar but shield narrower; harp, crown, orb and ornamentation below shield slightly different; same legend

Reverse 3 Similar but legend orientation slightly different; rim slightly thicker. Some coins have die number below wreath (see listings)

Reverse 4 St. George and Dragon; horse's tail is short; large BP and (date) in exergue

Edge milled

Obv. 1   Obv. 2   Obv. 3

Normal rear ribbon   Obv. 4: rear ribbon   Obv. 5

Obv. 7   Obv. 8   Obv. 9

Rev. 1   Rev. 2

Rev. 3   Rev. 4

No.	Date	Features	Obv.	Rev.	F	VF	EF	UNC
VYSV-005	1838	[1]	1	1	100	140	280	500
VYSV-010	1838	PROOF; edge plain [2]	1	1				3500
VYSV-015	1838	PROOF; edge plain; rev. ↑	1	1				3500
VYSV-020	1839		1	1	150	250	800	1200
VYSV-025	1839	PROOF	1	1				4500
VYSV-030	1839	PROOF; edge plain [3]	1	1				2500
VYSV-035	1839	PROOF; edge plain; rev. ↑	1	1				3500
VYSV-040	1839	PROOF [4]	1	3				5000
VYSV-045	1841		1	1	450	850	2000	4000
VYSV-050	1842		1	1	80	90	180	240
VYSV-055	1843		1	1	80	90	180	240
VYSV-060	1843	3 over 2	1	1	120	160	240	300
VYSV-065	1843		1	2	1500	2500	3500	5000
VYSV-070	1844		1	1	80	90	180	300
VYSV-075	1844	first 4 over inverted 4	1	1	120	160	250	320
VYSV-080	1845		1	1	80	90	180	300
VYSV-085	1846		1	1	80	90	180	300
VYSV-090	1847		1	1	80	90	180	300
VYSV-095	1848		1	1	200	280	400	600
VYSV-100	1848		2	3	80	90	180	300
VYSV-105	1849		2	3	80	90	180	300
VYSV-110	1850		2	3	80	90	180	300
VYSV-115	1851		2	3	80	90	180	300
VYSV-120	1852		2	3	80	90	180	300
VYSV-125	1853		2	3	80	90	180	300
VYSV-130	1853		3	3	80	90	180	300
VYSV-135	1853	PROOF [3]	3	3				5500
VYSV-140	1853	PROOF; rev. ↑	3	3				5500
VYSV-145	1854		2	3	80	90	180	300
VYSV-150	1854		3	3	80	90	180	300
VYSV-155	1855		2	3	80	90	180	300
VYSV-160	1855		3	3	80	90	180	300
VYSV-165	1856		3	3	80	90	180	300
VYSV-170	1857		3	3	80	90	180	300
VYSV-175	1858		3	3	80	90	180	300
VYSV-180	1859		3	3	80	90	180	300
VYSV-185	1859	[5]	4	3	250	600	2500	
VYSV-190	1860		3	3	80	90	160	300
VYSV-195	1861		3	3	80	90	160	300
VYSV-200	1862		3	3	80	90	160	300
VYSV-205	1863	no die number below wreath (rev.)	3	3	80	90	160	300
VYSV-210	1863	no die number below wreath (rev.) '827' in raised numerals on truncation instead of 'WW' (obv.) [6]	3	3	1500	2500		
VYSV-215	1863	die number below wreath (rev.)	3	3	80	90	160	300
VYSV-220	1863	die number 22 below wreath (rev.) '827' in raised numerals on truncation instead of 'WW' (obv.) [6]	3	3	1200	2000		
VYSV-225	1864	die number below wreath (rev.)	3	3	80	90	160	300
VYSV-230	1864	PROOF raised 'I' to left of incuse 'WW' (obv.) [7]	3	3				5000
VYSV-235	1865	die number below wreath (rev.)	3	3	80	90	160	240
VYSV-240	1866	die number below wreath (rev.)	3	3	80	90	160	240
VYSV-245	1868	die number below wreath (rev.)	3	3	80	90	160	240
VYSV-250	1869	die number below wreath (rev.)	3	3	80	90	160	240
VYSV-255	1870	die number below wreath (rev.)	3	3	80	90	160	240

No.	Date	Features	Obv.	Rev.	F	VF	EF	UNC
VYSV-260	1870	die number below wreath (rev.)	5	3	80	90	150	230
VYSV-265	1871	die number below wreath (rev.)	5	3	80	90	150	230
VYSV-270	1871		6	4	BV	80	120	160
VYSV-275	1871	PROOF	6	4				3000
VYSV-280	1871	PROOF; rev. ↑	6	4				3000
VYSV-285	1871	PROOF; edge plain; rev. ↑ [8]	6	4				2000
VYSV-290	1872	no die number below wreath (rev.)	2	3	80	90	150	230
VYSV-295	1872	die number below wreath (rev.)	5	3	80	90	150	230
VYSV-300	1872		6	4	BV	80	120	160
VYSV-305	1873	die number below wreath (rev.)	5	3	80	90	150	230
VYSV-310	1873		6	4	BV	80	120	160
VYSV-315	1874	die number below wreath (rev.)	5	3	600	1500		
VYSV-320	1874		6	4	80	90	130	160
VYSV-325	1876		6	4	80	90	130	160
VYSV-330	1878		6	4	80	90	130	160
VYSV-335	1879		6	4	120	280	700	1200
VYSV-340	1880	PROOF; edge plain	5	3				6000
VYSV-345	1880		6	4	80	90	130	160
VYSV-350	1880	[9]	7	4	90	100	150	180
VYSV-355	1880	PROOF	7	4				4500
VYSV-360	1884		6	4	80	90	130	160
VYSV-365	1884		7	4	80	90	130	160
VYSV-370	1885		6	4	85	95	140	170
VYSV-375	1885		7	4	85	95	140	170
VYSV-380	1887	PROOF	5	3				5000
VYSV-385	1887	PROOF; edge plain	5	3				6000
VJSV-390	1887		8	4	BV	75	110	140
VJSV-395	1887	PROOF [10]	8	4				700
VJSV-400	1888		8	4	BV	BV	90	120
VJSV-405	1889		8	4	BV	BV	90	120
VJSV-410	1890		8	4	BV	BV	90	120
VJSV-415	1891		8	4	BV	BV	90	120
VJSV-420	1891	PROOF in lead [11]	8	4				5000
VJSV-425	1892		8	4	BV	BV	90	120
VOSV-430	1893		9	4	BV	BV	90	120
VOSV-435	1893	PROOF [3]	9	4				900
VOSV-440	1894		9	4	BV	BV	90	110
VOSV-445	1895		9	4	BV	BV	90	110
VOSV-450	1896		9	4	BV	BV	90	110
VOSV-455	1898		9	4	BV	BV	90	110
VOSV-460	1899		9	4	BV	BV	90	110
VOSV-465	1900		9	4	BV	BV	90	110
VOSV-470	1901		9	4	BV	BV	90	110

1. Variety exists with minor reverse differences.
2. Minor design differences from usual; possibly a pattern.
3. Issued in cased proof sets.
4. With this reverse, presumably struck in 1848 or later.
5. The 'Ansell' sovereign; see above.
6. Possibly a trial piece to test new position for die number.
7. Possibly a trial piece to test new position for die number; a similar farthing exists (q.v.).
8. Varieties exist: small or large BP in exergue (rev.).
9. No BP in exergue (rev.).
10. Position of JEB on truncation varies (obv.).
11. Weight c. 5.4 grams.

Minor design variations occur to Reverse 4, especially to the horse's tail and initials BP.

Commonwealth Mints

Mintmarks

M: Melbourne, Australia (opened June 1872)
P: Perth, Australia (opened June 1899)
S: Sydney, Australia (opened May 1855)

Position of Mintmarks

Obverses 6 and 7 Below head

Reverse 3 Below shield

Reverse 4 On ground line above centre of date

No.	Date	mm	Features	Obv.	Rev.	F	VF	EF	UNC
VYSV-475	1871	S		3	3	100	130	220	300
VYSV-480	1871	S		5	3	85	100	160	220
VYSV-485	1871	S	PROOF	3/5?	3				3500
VYSV-490	1871	S		6	4	80	90	130	180
VYSV-495	1871	S	PROOF	6	4				3000
VYSV-500	1872	M		5	3	85	100	160	220
VYSV-505	1872	M	rev. ↑	5	3	400	600	1000	1500
VYSV-510	1872	M	2 over 1 [1]	5	3	300	500	800	1200
VYSV-515	1872	M		6	4	100	140	300	420
VYSV-520	1872	S		5	3	85	100	160	220
VYSV-525	1872	S		6	4	80	90	130	180
VYSV-530	1873	M		6	4	80	90	130	180
VYSV-535	1873	S		5	3	85	100	160	220
VYSV-540	1873	S		6	4	80	90	130	180
VYSV-545	1874	M		5	3	90	110	180	240
VYSV-550	1874	M		6	4	80	90	130	180
VYSV-555	1874	S		6	4	80	90	130	180
VYSV-560	1875	M		6	4	80	90	130	180
VYSV-565	1875	S		5	3	85	95	150	220
VYSV-570	1875	S	PROOF	5	3				3500
VYSV-575	1875	S		6	4	80	90	130	180
VYSV-580	1876	M		6	4	80	90	130	180
VYSV-585	1876	S		6	4	80	90	130	180
VYSV-590	1877	M		6	4	80	90	130	180
VYSV-595	1877	S		5	3	85	95	150	220
VYSV-600	1878	M		6	4	80	90	130	180
VYSV-605	1878	S		5	3	85	95	150	220
VYSV-610	1879	M		6	4	80	90	130	180
VYSV-615	1879	S		5	3	85	95	150	220
VYSV-620	1879	S		6	4	80	90	130	180
VYSV-625	1880	M	[2]	5	3	400	800	1500	
VYSV-630	1880	M		6	4	80	90	130	180
VYSV-635	1880	S		5	3	85	95	150	220
VYSV-640	1880	S	PROOF	5	3				3500
VYSV-645	1880	S		6	4	80	90	130	180
VYSV-650	1880	S		7	4	80	90	130	180
VYSV-655	1880	S	PROOF	6/7?	4				3000
VYSV-660	1881	M		5	3	100	130	250	350
VYSV-665	1881	M		6	4	80	90	130	180
VYSV-670	1881	S		5	3	85	95	150	220
VYSV-675	1881	S		6	4	80	90	130	180
VYSV-680	1881	S		7	4	80	90	130	180
VYSV-685	1881	S	PROOF	6/7?	4				3000
VYSV-690	1882	M		5	3	85	100	180	250
VYSV-695	1882	M	PROOF	5	3				3500
VYSV-700	1882	M		6	4	80	90	130	180
VYSV-705	1882	M		7	4	80	90	130	180
VYSV-710	1882	S	[3]	5	3	85	95	150	220
VYSV-715	1882	S		7	4	80	90	130	180
VYSV-720	1883	M		5	3	150	300	900	
VYSV-725	1883	M		6	4	80	90	130	180
VYSV-730	1883	M		7	4	80	90	130	180
VYSV-735	1883	S		5	3	85	95	150	220
VYSV-740	1883	S	PROOF	5	3				3500
VYSV-745	1883	S		7	4	80	90	130	180
VYSV-750	1884	M		5	3	85	100	180	240
VYSV-755	1884	M		6	4	80	90	130	180
VYSV-760	1884	M		7	4	80	90	130	180
VYSV-765	1884	M	PROOF	6/7?	4				3000
VYSV-770	1884	S		5	3	85	95	150	220
VYSV-775	1884	S		7	4	80	90	130	180
VYSV-780	1885	M		5	3	85	100	180	240
VYSV-785	1885	M	PROOF	5	3				3500
VYSV-790	1885	M		7	4	80	90	130	180
VYSV-795	1885	M	PROOF	7	4				3000
VYSV-800	1885	S		5	3	85	95	150	220
VYSV-805	1885	S		7	4	80	90	130	180
VYSV-810	1886	M		5	3	1200	2000	3000	
VYSV-815	1886	M	PROOF	5	3				7000
VYSV-820	1886	M		7	4	80	90	130	180
VYSV-825	1886	S		5	3	85	95	150	220
VYSV-830	1886	S	PROOF	5	3				3500
VYSV-835	1886	S		7	4	80	90	130	180
VYSV-840	1887	M		5	3	500	1000	2200	
VYSV-845	1887	M		7	4	80	90	130	180
VYSV-850	1887	M	PROOF	7	4				3000
VJSV-855	1887	M		8	4	BV	BV	100	130
VJSV-860	1887	M	PROOF	8	4				3000
VYSV-865	1887	S		5	3	85	95	150	220
VYSV-870	1887	S	PROOF	5	3				3500
VYSV-875	1887	S		7	4	80	90	130	170
VJSV-880	1887	S		8	4	100	150	300	400
VJSV-885	1887	S	PROOF	8	4				3000
VJSV-890	1888	M		8	4	BV	BV	90	120
VJSV-895	1888	M	PROOF	8	4				3000
VJSV-900	1888	S		8	4	80	100	140	180
VJSV-905	1889	M		8	4	BV	BV	90	120
VJSV-910	1889	M	PROOF	8	4				3000
VJSV-915	1889	S		8	4	BV	BV	90	120

No.	Date	mm	Features	Obv.	Rev.	F	VF	EF	UNC
VJSV-920	1890	M		8	4	BV	BV	90	120
VJSV-925	1890	M	PROOF	8	4				3000
VJSV-930	1890	S		8	4	BV	BV	90	120
VJSV-935	1891	M		8	4	BV	BV	90	120
VJSV-940	1891	S		8	4	BV	BV	90	120
VJSV-945	1892	M		8	4	BV	BV	90	120
VJSV-950	1892	S		8	4	BV	BV	90	120
VJSV-955	1893	M		8	4	BV	BV	90	120
VJSV-960	1893	M	PROOF	8	4				3000
VOSV-965	1893	M		9	4	BV	BV	90	110
VOSV-970	1893	M	PROOF	9	4				3000
VJSV-975	1893	S		8	4	BV	BV	90	120
VJSV-980	1893	S	PROOF	8	4				3000
VOSV-985	1893	S		9	4	BV	BV	90	110
VOSV-990	1893	S	PROOF	9	4				3000
VOSV-995	1894	M		9	4	BV	BV	90	110
VOSV-1000	1894	M	PROOF	9	4				3000
VOSV-1005	1894	S		9	4	BV	BV	90	110
VOSV-1010	1894	S	PROOF	9	4				3000
VOSV-1015	1895	M		9	4	BV	BV	90	110
VOSV-1020	1895	M	PROOF	9	4				3000
VOSV-1025	1895	S		9	4	BV	BV	90	110
VOSV-1030	1896	M		9	4	BV	BV	90	110
VOSV-1035	1896	M	PROOF	9	4				3000
VOSV-1040	1896	S		9	4	BV	BV	90	110
VOSV-1045	1897	M		9	4	BV	BV	90	110
VOSV-1050	1897	M	PROOF	9	4				3000
VOSV-1055	1897	S		9	4	BV	BV	90	110
VOSV-1060	1898	M		9	4	BV	BV	90	110
VOSV-1065	1898	M	PROOF	9	4				3000
VOSV-1070	1898	S		9	4	BV	BV	90	110
VOSV-1075	1899	M		9	4	BV	BV	90	110
VOSV-1080	1899	M	PROOF	9	4				3000
VOSV-1085	1899	P		9	4	BV	BV	90	110
VOSV-1090	1899	P	PROOF	9	4				3000
VOSV-1095	1899	S		9	4	BV	BV	90	110
VOSV-1100	1900	M		9	4	BV	BV	90	110
VOSV-1105	1900	M	PROOF	9	4				3000
VOSV-1110	1900	P		9	4	BV	BV	90	110
VOSV-1115	1900	S		9	4	BV	BV	90	110
VOSV-1120	1901	M		9	4	BV	BV	90	110
VOSV-1125	1901	M	PROOF	9	4				3000
VOSV-1130	1901	P		9	4	BV	BV	90	110
VOSV-1135	1901	P	PROOF	9	4				3000
VOSV-1140	1901	S		9	4	BV	BV	90	110

1. Opening of Melbourne mint delayed from 1871.
2. Obverse slightly modified during 1880.
3. Two slightly different obverses exist.

Edward VII 1902–1910

Matt proof sovereigns were struck in 1902 for the cased matt proof set of that year, and ordinary specimens were minted for each year of the reign at the London, Melbourne, Perth and Sydney mints. Coins were struck for the first time at the Ottawa mint during 1908, 1909, and 1910. These bear the mintmark 'C', unusual in denoting the name of the country instead of the city. The sovereign uses the portrait of Edward VII by George William de Saulles (1862-1903) and the reverse St George and dragon by Pistrucci.

Collecting Hints

The obverses are not always well struck, and extremely fine or better specimens may appear to be only in very fine condition. Forgeries exist; see under 'Victoria'.

Denomination	Metal	Weight (grams)	Diameter (mm)	Rev. alignment
Sovereign	Gold	8.0	22	↑

Obverse 1 Head 1, right; EDWARDVS VII D G BRITT OMN REX F D IND IMP

Reverse 1 St George and dragon, (date) in exergue

Edge milled

Obv. 1   Rev. 1

No.	Date	Features	Obv.	Rev.	F	VF	EF	UNC
E7SV-005	1902		1	1	BV	BV	BV	90
E7SV-010	1902	matt PROOF [1]	1	1	BV	BV	90	120
E7SV-015	1903		1	1	BV	BV	BV	90
E7SV-020	1904		1	1	BV	BV	BV	90
E7SV-025	1905		1	1	BV	BV	BV	90
E7SV-030	1906		1	1	BV	BV	BV	90
E7SV-035	1906	matt PROOF	1	1				10000
E7SV-040	1907		1	1		BV	BV	90
E7SV-045	1908		1	1	BV	BV	BV	90
E7SV-050	1909		1	1	BV	BV	BV	90
E7SV-055	1910		1	1	BV	BV	BV	90

1. Issued in cased proof sets.

Commonwealth Mints

Mintmarks

C: Ottawa, Canada (opened January 1908)

M: Melbourne, Australia

P: Perth, Australia

S: Sydney, Australia

No.	Date	mm	Features	Obv.	Rev.	F	VF	EF	UNC
E7SV-060	1902	M		1	1	BV	BV	BV	90
E7SV-065	1902	P		1	1	BV	BV	BV	90
E7SV-070	1902	P	matt PROOF [1]	1	1				
E7SV-075	1902	S		1	1	BV	BV	BV	90
E7SV-080	1902	S	matt PROOF	1	1				3500
E7SV-085	1903	M		1	1	BV	BV	BV	90
E7SV-090	1903	P		1	1	BV	BV	BV	90
E7SV-095	1903	S		1	1	BV	BV	BV	90
E7SV-100	1904	M		1	1	BV	BV	BV	90
E7SV-105	1904	M	PROOF	1	1				2500
E7SV-110	1904	P		1	1	BV	BV	BV	90
E7SV-115	1904	S		1	1	BV	BV	BV	90
E7SV-120	1905	M		1	1	BV	BV	BV	90
E7SV-125	1905	P		1	1	BV	BV	BV	90
E7SV-130	1905	S		1	1	BV	BV	BV	90
E7SV-135	1906	M		1	1	BV	BV	BV	90
E7SV-140	1906	P		1	1	BV	BV	BV	90
E7SV-145	1906	S		1	1	BV	BV	BV	90
E7SV-150	1907	M		1	1	BV	BV	BV	90
E7SV-155	1907	P		1	1	BV	BV	BV	90
E7SV-160	1907	S		1	1	BV	BV	BV	90
E7SV-165	1908	C	satin PROOF	1	1	1500	3000	4500	
E7SV-170	1908	M		1	1	BV	BV	BV	90
E7SV-175	1908	P		1	1	BV	BV	BV	90
E7SV-180	1908	S		1	1	BV	BV	BV	90
E7SV-185	1909	C		1	1	180	250	400	
E7SV-190	1909	M		1	1	BV	BV	BV	90
E7SV-195	1909	P		1	1	BV	BV	BV	90
E7SV-200	1909	S		1	1	BV	BV	BV	90
E7SV-205	1910	C		1	1	180	250	400	
E7SV-210	1910	M		1	1	BV	BV	BV	90
E7SV-215	1910	M	PROOF	1	1				2500
E7SV-220	1910	P		1	1	BV	BV	BV	90
E7SV-225	1910	S		1	1	BV	BV	BV	90

1. Exists?

George V 1910–1936

Proof sovereigns were struck at the London mint for inclusion in some of the proof sets of 1911. These coins are of high quality and, unlike those struck for the 1902 sets, have a polished field. Sovereigns were struck for every year from 1911 to 1932 at one or more of the British or Commonwealth mints, but notable gaps occur at some of the mints, and some of the date/mintmark combinations are very rare. Sovereigns were struck for the first and only time at the Bombay mint, in 1918. These coins have an 'I' (India) mintmark. Coins were also struck at Pretoria, South Africa, from 1923 to 1928 ('SA' mintmark), including the 1923 proof, which was included in a cased set of proof coins of South Africa.

In 1935, the State of Victoria in Australia sought to strike a sovereign to commemorate the centenary of the foundation of Melbourne in 1835. Permission from London was not forthcoming, and a commemorative florin was issued instead.

Many sovereigns were exported to the United States for redemption of debts. Because the holding of gold in the form of foreign coins was illegal in that country at the time, the coins were melted down into ingots. Consequently, some dates such as 1917 (London mint) are now virtually unobtainable.

The series divides into two main types. Sir Bertram MacKennal (1863-1931) designed the two portraits of George V, while the reverse continued the Pistrucci St George and dragon design. The latter also appears in two different designs, which can be distinguished at a glance by an experienced eye, but which on close examination appear surprisingly similar. The sword and broken lance have slight differences, but the chief distinction lies in the different way in which the two designs strike into the metal. All of the London mint coins are of the first type.

Collecting Hints

The series is an interesting one because of the degrees of rarity of some of the date/mintmark combinations. Some of these have proved to be considerably rarer, and some less rare, than at one time thought.
Forgeries exist, some of which are crude and even grotesque. See under 'Victoria'.

Denomination	Metal	Weight (grams)	Diameter (mm)	Rev. alignment
Sovereign	Gold	8.0	22	↑

Obverse 1 Head 1, left; GEORGIVS V D G BRITT OMN REX F D IND IMP

Obverse 2 Head 2, left, smaller; same legend

Reverse 1 St George and dragon, (date) in exergue

Reverse 2 Similar but slightly redesigned

Edge milled

Obv. 1

Obv. 2

Rev. 1

Rev. 2

No.	Date	Features	Obv.	Rev.	VF	EF	UNC
G5SV-005	1911		1	1	BV	BV	BV
G5SV-010	1911	PROOF [1]	1	1	BV	100	300
G5SV-015	1912		1	1	BV	BV	BV
G5SV-020	1913		1	1	BV	BV	BV
G5SV-025	1914		1	1	BV	BV	BV
G5SV-030	1915		1	1	BV	BV	BV
G5SV-035	1916	[2]	1	1	80	95	130
G5SV-040	1917	[3]	1	1	2000	3000	4000
G5SV-045	1925	[4]	1	1	BV	BV	BV

1. Issued in cased proof sets.
2. Many were melted down.
3. Almost all were melted down; crude forgeries exist.
4. Many were struck as late as 1952.

Commonwealth Mints

Mintmarks

I: Bombay, India (opened August 1918)

M: Melbourne, Australia

P: Perth, Australia

S: Sydney, Australia

SA: Pretoria, South Africa (opened December 1922)

No.	Date	mm	Features	Obv.	Rev.	VF	EF	UNC
G5SV-050	1911	C		1	1	75	100	130
G5SV-055	1911	M		1	1	BV	BV	BV
G5SV-060	1911	M	PROOF	1	1			3000
G5SV-065	1911	P		1	1	BV	BV	BV
G5SV-070	1911	S		1	1	BV	BV	BV
G5SV-075	1912	M		1	1	BV	BV	BV
G5SV-080	1912	P		1	1	BV	BV	BV
G5SV-085	1912	S		1	1	BV	BV	BV
G5SV-090	1913	C		1	1	400	550	750
G5SV-095	1913	M		1	1	BV	BV	BV
G5SV-100	1913	P		1	1	BV	BV	BV
G5SV-105	1913	S		1	1	BV	BV	BV
G5SV-110	1914	C		1	1	250	400	550
G5SV-115	1914	M		1	1	BV	BV	BV
G5SV-120	1914	P		1	1	BV	BV	BV
G5SV-125	1914	S		1	1	BV	BV	BV
G5SV-130	1914	S	PROOF	1	1			2500
G5SV-135	1915	M		1	1	BV	BV	BV
G5SV-140	1915	P		1	1	BV	BV	BV
G5SV-145	1915	S		1	1	BV	BV	BV
G5SV-150	1916	C		1	1	10000	15000	25000
G5SV-155	1916	M		1	1	BV	BV	BV
G5SV-160	1916	P		1	1	BV	BV	BV
G5SV-165	1916	S		1	1	BV	BV	BV
G5SV-170	1917	C		1	1	75	100	130
G5SV-175	1917	M		1	1	BV	BV	BV
G5SV-180	1917	P		1	1	BV	BV	BV
G5SV-185	1917	S		1	1	BV	BV	BV
G5SV-190	1918	C		1	1	75	100	130
G5SV-195	1918	I		1	1	BV	BV	80
G5SV-200	1918	M		1	1	BV	BV	BV
G5SV-205	1918	P		1	1	BV	BV	BV
G5SV-210	1918	S		1	1	BV	BV	BV
G5SV-215	1919	C		1	1	75	100	130
G5SV-220	1919	M		1	1	BV	75	100
G5SV-225	1919	P		1	1	BV	BV	BV
G5SV-230	1919	S		1	1	BV	BV	BV
G5SV-235	1920	M		1	1	800	1400	1800
G5SV-240	1920	P		1	1	BV	BV	BV
G5SV-245	1920	S		1	1	30000	60000	80000
G5SV-250	1921	M		1	1	3000	5000	7000
G5SV-255	1921	P		1	1	BV	75	90
G5SV-260	1921	S		1	1	800	1200	1600
G5SV-265	1922	M		1	1	1800	3500	5000
G5SV-270	1922	P		1	1	BV	75	90
G5SV-275	1922	S		1	1	3000	5000	9000
G5SV-280	1923	M		1	1	BV	80	100
G5SV-285	1923	P		1	1	BV	75	85
G5SV-290	1923	S		1	1	1500	3000	5000
G5SV-295	1923	SA	[1]	1	1	1000	3000	6000
G5SV-300	1923	SA	PROOF [2]	1	1			700
G5SV-305	1924	M		1	1	BV	90	110
G5SV-310	1924	P		1	1	BV	75	85
G5SV-315	1924	S		1	1	400	600	900
G5SV-320	1924	SA		1	1	1500	2500	4000
G5SV-325	1925	M		1	1	BV	BV	BV
G5SV-330	1925	P		1	1	BV	75	85
G5SV-335	1925	S		1	1	BV	BV	80
G5SV-340	1925	SA		1	1	BV	BV	BV
G5SV-345	1926	M	[3]	1	1	BV	BV	BV
G5SV-350	1926	P		1	1	BV	BV	BV

No.	Date	mm	Features	Obv.	Rev.	VF	EF	UNC
G5SV-355	1926	S		1	1	8000	12000	18000
G5SV-360	1926	S	PROOF	1	1			25000
G5SV-365	1926	SA		1	1	BV	BV	BV
G5SV-370	1927	P		1	1	BV	BV	BV
G5SV-375	1927	SA		1	1	BV	BV	BV
G5SV-380	1928	M		1	1	1200	1800	2500
G5SV-385	1928	P		1	1	BV	BV	BV
G5SV-390	1928	SA		1	1	BV	BV	BV
G5SV-395	1929	M		2	2	1000	1600	2200
G5SV-400	1929	P		2	2	BV	BV	BV
G5SV-405	1929	SA		2	2	BV	BV	BV
G5SV-410	1930	M		2	2	100	140	220
G5SV-415	1930	P		2	2	BV	BV	BV
G5SV-420	1930	SA		2	2	BV	BV	BV
G5SV-425	1931	M		2	2	180	300	450
G5SV-430	1931	P		2	2	BV	BV	BV
G5SV-435	1931	SA		2	2	BV	BV	BV
G5SV-440	1932	SA		2	2	BV	80	120

1. VF specimens may be worn proofs.
2. Issued in cased proof sets of South Africa.
3. Edge milling varies in fineness.

Edward VIII 1936

The Edward VIII sovereign is strictly speaking a pattern, as probable royal approval was about to be granted at the time of the abdication. However, because its official status rests only on this technicality, and to provide continuity, it is included in this catalogue.

The portrait of Edward VIII is by Thomas Humphrey Paget, and faces left at the insistence of the king, who considered this placement more flattering and wished to discontinue the tradition of opposite facings for successive monarchs. The reverse is the St George and dragon design originally by Pistrucci. The edge is milled, unlike that of the George VI proof.

Denomination	Metal	Weight (grams)	Diameter (mm)	Rev. alignment
Sovereign	Gold	8.0	22	↑

Obverse 1 Head 1, left; EDWARDVS VIII D G BR OMN REX F D IND IMP

Reverse 1 St George and dragon, 1937 in exergue

Edge milled

Obv. 1   Rev. 1

No.	Date	Obv.	Rev.	UNC
E8SV-005	1937	1	1	50000

George VI 1937–1952

The only George VI sovereigns struck were the proofs included in the cased proof sets of 1937. These sets contained four coins, each of which comprised the only British coin of that denomination for the reign. Curiously, through an oversight, the sovereign was not legal tender because the Proclamation of March 1937 happened to specify that legal tender sovereigns have a milled edge.

The obverse portrait was by Thomas Humphrey Paget, the reverse again being the Pistrucci St George and dragon.

Collecting Hints

Collecting Hints

Gold coins of 1937 must always be examined carefully for edge damage. The tight fitting inserts in the case often meant that the coins were prised out, and the plain edge was very susceptible to marks.

Denomination	Metal	Weight (grams)	Diameter (mm)	Rev. alignment
Sovereign	Gold	8.0	22	↑

Obverse 1 Head 1, left; GEORGIVS VI D G BR OMN REX F D IND IMP

Reverse 1 St George and dragon, 1937 in exergue

Edge plain

Obv. 1   Rev. 1

No.	Date	Features	Obv.	Rev.	EF	FDC
G6SV-005	1937	PROOF [1]	1	1	280	400

1. Issued in cased proof sets.

Elizabeth II 1952 —

No gold coins were included in the proof sets of 1953 issued for the coronation, and the only British sovereigns struck in that year were a small number struck in order to provide continuity of the series. These were not released. The coins bore the obverse portrait of Elizabeth II by Mary Gillick, and the Pistrucci St George and dragon reverse.

The production of sovereigns was resumed in 1957. The portrait was similar to the 1953 piece but the obverse legend was revised. The coin was struck for most of the years up to 1968, then resumed in 1974 (post-decimalization) using an older portrait by Arnold Machin. From 1979 many proofs were struck for inclusion in proof sets and as individually cased proofs. In 1985 a new portrait by Raphael David Maklouf was introduced.

The reverse uses the Pistrucci St George and dragon design throughout, except for 1989 when a proof sovereign was struck for the 500th anniversary of the sovereign. This had a completely new obverse and reverse.

Collecting Hints

This series normally occurs in extremely fine or mint state. Forgeries exist of the non-proof coins.

Denomination	Metal	Weight (grams)	Diameter (mm)	Rev. alignment
Sovereign	Gold	8.0	22	↑

Obverse 1 Head 1, right; ELIZABETH II DEI GRA BRITT OMN REGINA F D

Obverse 2 Head 1, right; ELIZABETH II DEI GRATIA REGINA F D

Obverse 3 Head 2, right; same legend

Obverse 4 Head 3, right; ELIZABETH II DEI GRA REG F D

Obverse 5 Queen facing on throne, holding orb and sceptre; ELIZABETH II DEI GRA REG FID DEF *(for the 500th anniversary of the gold sovereign)*

Reverse 1 St George and dragon, (date) in exergue

Reverse 2 Crowned shield within double rose; ANNIVERSARY OF THE GOLD SOVEREIGN 1489–1989

Edge milled

Obv. 1   Obv. 2

Obv. 3   Obv. 4   Obv. 5

Rev. 1   Rev. 2

No.	Date	Features	Obv.	Rev.	UNC
EL2SV-005	1953	PROOF or pattern [1]	1	1	30000
EL2SV-010	1957	[2]	2	1	BV
EL2SV-015	1957	PROOF	2	1	3000
EL2SV-020	1958		2	1	BV
EL2SV-025	1958	PROOF	2	1	3000
EL2SV-030	1959		2	1	BV
EL2SV-035	1962		2	1	BV
EL2SV-040	1963		2	1	BV
EL2SV-045	1964		2	1	BV
EL2SV-050	1965		2	1	BV
EL2SV-055	1966		2	1	BV
EL2SV-060	1967		2	1	BV
EL2SV-065	1968		2	1	BV
EL2SV-070	1974		3	1	BV
EL2SV-075	1976		3	1	BV
EL2SV-080	1978		3	1	BV
EL2SV-085	1979		3	1	BV
EL2SV-090	1979	PROOF [3]	3	1	110
EL2SV-095	1980		3	1	BV
EL2SV-100	1980	PROOF [4]	3	1	110
EL2SV-105	1981		3	1	BV
EL2SV-110	1981	PROOF [4]	3	1	110
EL2SV-115	1982		3	1	BV
EL2SV-120	1982	PROOF [4]	3	1	110
EL2SV-125	1983	PROOF [4]	3	1	110
EL2SV-130	1984	PROOF [4]	3	1	110
EL2SV-135	1985	PROOF [4]	4	1	110
EL2SV-140	1986	PROOF [4]	4	1	110
EL2SV-145	1987	PROOF [4]	4	1	120
EL2SV-150	1988	PROOF [4]	4	1	125
EL2SV-155	1989	PROOF [4]	5	2	180
EL2SV-160	1990	PROOF [4]	4	1	150
EL2SV-165	1991	PROOF [4]	4	1	150
EL2SV-170	1992	PROOF [4]	4	1	150
EL2SV-175	1993	PROOF [4]	4	1	150
EL2SV-180	1994	PROOF [4]	4	1	150
EL2SV-185	1995	PROOF [4]	4	1	150

1. Possibly about 10 exist.
2. Milling finer than on subsequent years.
3. Issued cased.
4. Issued cased and in cased proof sets.

Half Guinea

Charles II 1660–1685

The first milled half guinea was struck in 1669. This was some years after the guinea had entered circulation, and the various alterations made to the portrait to accommodate the elephant and castle symbol had already occurred by 1669. The result was that the half guinea series has only two main obverse types instead of four. Although the portrait with the indentation to accommodate the symbol was used until 1672, no coins with the elephant and castle are known before the 1676 coin, by which time the larger head was in use. Unlike the guinea, no half guineas display the elephant only symbol.

The half guinea was designed by John Roettier.

> ## Collecting Hints
>
> This is a scarce series, and Charles II half guineas in high grades command high prices. In general, prices are higher than for guineas in similar grades. Because the half guinea is an expensive series to collect, and because pieces are seen so seldom, documentation of varieties has not been as thorough as on silver coinage, and no doubt a number of unrecorded varieties exist.

Denomination	Metal	Weight (grams)	Diameter (mm)	Rev. alignment
Half guinea	Gold	4.2	20	↓

Obverse 1 Head 1, right; pointed truncation with lock of hair to right of truncation; CAROLVS II DEI GRATIA

Obverse 2 Head 2, right; older portrait, rounded truncation, without lock of hair to right; same legend

Reverse 1 Four crowned cruciform shields between which are four sceptres, with four interlinked 'C's at the centre; MAG BR FRA ET HIB REX (date)

Edge (1669) milled (vertically); (1670–1684) milled (diagonally)

Obv. 1	Obv. 2	Rev. 1

No.	Date	Features	Obv.	Rev.	F	VF	EF
C2HGM-005	1669		1	1	250	700	2500
C2HGM-010	1670		1	1	220	500	2000
C2HGM-015	1671		1	1	250	700	2500
C2HGM-020	1672		1	1	250	700	2500
C2HGM-025	1672		2	1	220	500	2000
C2HGM-030	1673		2	1	250	700	2500
C2HGM-035	1674		2	1	250	700	2500
C2HGM-040	1675		2	1	500	1800	
C2HGM-045	1676		2	1	220	500	2000
C2HGM-050	1676	latter 6 over 4 or 5	2	1	240	550	2200
C2HGM-055	1676	elephant and castle below head	2	1	350	1000	5000
C2HGM-060	1677		2	1	220	500	2000

No.	Date	Features	Obv.	Rev.	F	VF	EF
C2HGM-065	1677	elephant and castle below head	2	1	350	1000	3500
C2HGM-070	1678		2	1	220	500	2000
C2HGM-075	1678	8 over 7	2	1	240	550	2200
C2HGM-080	1678	elephant and castle below head	2	1	300	700	2500
C2HGM-085	1678	8 over 7 elephant and castle below head	2	1	300	700	2500
C2HGM-090	1679		2	1	180	450	1500
C2HGM-095	1680		2	1	220	550	2200
C2HGM-100	1680	elephant and castle below head	2	1	500		
C2HGM-105	1681		2	1	220	550	2200
C2HGM-110	1682		2	1	220	550	2200
C2HGM-115	1682	elephant and castle below head	2	1	300	700	2500
C2HGM-120	1683		2	1	220	550	2200
C2HGM-125	1683	elephant and castle below head	2	1	500		
C2HGM-130	1684		2	1	200	500	1800
C2HGM-135	1684	elephant and castle below head	2	1	240	550	2000

James II 1685–1688

John Roettier designed the head of James II for this series, which uses the basic design layout of the previous reign. There is, however, no motif of interlinked initials at the centre of the reverse. Unlike the guinea, there is only one obverse type. The elephant and castle symbol was used only during 1686, and this variety is particularly scarce. All James II half guineas are rare in extremely fine condition.

> ## Collecting Hints
>
> This is an attractive coin, but for most collectors a specimen in fine condition will be acceptable. However, much more obverse detail is visible on a very fine coin.

Denomination	Metal	Weight (grams)	Diameter (mm)	Rev. alignment
Half guinea	Gold	4.2	20	↓

Obverse 1 Head 1, left; IACOBVS II DEI GRATIA

Reverse 1 Four crowned cruciform shields between which are four sceptres; MAG BR FRA ET HIB REX (date)

Edge milled (diagonally)

Obv. 1	Rev. 1

417

No.	Date	Features	Obv.	Rev.	F	VF	EF
J2HG-005	1686		1	1	240	600	2000
J2HG-010	1686	elephant and castle below head	1	1	600	1700	4500
J2HG-015	1687		1	1	240	600	2000
J2HG-020	1688		1	1	240	600	2000

William and Mary 1688–1694

The credit for the design of the heads of William and Mary for the gold coinage is generally given to James and Norbert Roettier. However, the first type of half guinea in 1689 deserves careful study. The somewhat caricatured heads appear to be very much in the style of George Bower (? — 1689/90), who, for example, designed the first type of halfpenny and farthing in 1689, and who produced a number of medals having somewhat grotesque and cartoon-like busts. The heads of the king and queen on the half-penny, farthing and the first type of half guinea also do not possess the mutual harmony and statesmanlike appearance of the later Roettier work.

The half guinea was minted each year of the reign until Mary's death in 1694. The elephant and castle symbol appeared on some coins of 1691 and 1692, and there is a rare variety of 1692 apparently bearing the elephant only symbol. However, see the 'Guinea' section of this catalogue for comments on the status of similar guineas of William and Mary.

Denomination	Metal	Weight (grams)	Diameter (mm)	Rev. alignment
Half guinea	Gold	4.2	20	↓

Obverse 1 Heads 1, right; GVLIELMVS ET MARIA DEI GRATIA

Obverse 2 Heads 2, right; same legend

Reverse 1 Crowned shield; MAG BR FR ET HIB REX ET REGINA (date)

Reverse 2 Similar but shield is differently shaped; crown and harp are very different

Edge milled (diagonally)

Obv. 1

Obv. 2

Rev. 1

Rev. 2

No.	Date	Features	Obv.	Rev.	F	VF	EF
WMHG-005	1689		1	1	300	700	2000
WMHG-010	1690		2	2	220	600	1800
WMHG-015	1691		2	2	220	600	1800
WMHG-020	1691	elephant and castle below head	2	2	220	600	1800
WMHG-025	1692		2	2	220	600	1800
WMHG-030	1692	elephant and castle below head	2	2	220	600	1800
WMHG-035	1692	elephant below head [1]	2	2	400		
WMHG-040	1693		2	2	700	1800	
WMHG-045	1693	3 over 2	2	2	800	2000	
WMHG-050	1694		2	2	220	600	1800
WMHG-055	1694	4 over 3	2	2	250	650	2000

1. See comments under Guinea section — William and Mary.

William III 1695–1701

On the death of Mary from smallpox in 1694, the obverse of the half guinea was redesigned to depict the undraped bust of William alone. The shield reverse of William and Mary had not been a success. It was a poorly proportioned effort, and the intricate design on the shield within such a small area had only led to a confusion of detail. The reverse was therefore recut using the cruciform shields design of earlier reigns, but with the lion of Orange-Nassau at the centre.

One detail which the reverses share with the silver coinage but not with the other gold denominations is the variation in the shape of the harp usually known as 'early harp' and 'late harp' on the silver. As far as is known, there are no harp variations within any particular date, the 'late harp' being introduced in 1697.

The elephant and castle symbol appears on three dates, 1695, 1696 and 1698. The 1696 coin is unusual in that no half guineas were struck in this year without the symbol.

The half guinea was probably the work of James Roettier and/or John Croker. The reverse of the 'late harp' type is considered to be by Croker alone.

Denomination	Metal	Weight (grams)	Diameter (mm)	Rev. alignment
Half guinea	Gold	4.2	20	↓

Obverse 1 Head 1, right; GVLIELMVS III DEI GRA

Reverse 1 Four crowned cruciform shields between which are four sceptres, with central lion of Nassau; MAG BR FRA ET HIB REX (date)

Reverse 2 Similar but harp larger and of different design

Edge milled (diagonally)

Obv. 1

Rev. 1

Rev. 2

No.	Date	Features	Obv.	Rev.	F	VF	EF
W3HG-005	1695		1	1	130	350	750
W3HG-010	1695	elephant and castle below head	1	1	180	500	1300
W3HG-015	1696	elephant and castle below head	1	1	150	400	950
W3HG-020	1697		1	2	150	400	950
W3HG-025	1698		1	2	130	350	750
W3HG-030	1698	elephant and castle below head	1	2	180	500	1300
W3HG-035	1700		1	2	130	350	750
W3HG-040	1701		1	2	130	350	750

No.	Date	Features	Obv.	Rev.	F	VF	EF
AHG-005	1702		1	1	250	700	1800
AHG-010	1703	VIGO below head	1	1	3000	7000	
AHG-015	1705		1	1	250	700	1800
AHG-020	1707		1	2	180	450	1200
AHG-025	1708		1	2	180	450	1200
AHG-030	1709		1	2	180	450	1200
AHG-035	1710		1	2	180	450	1200
AHG-040	1711		1	2	180	450	1200
AHG-045	1712		1	2	180	450	1200
AHG-050	1713		1	2	180	450	1200
AHG-055	1714		1	2	180	450	1200

Anne 1702–1714

Pre-Union half guineas were struck in 1702, 1703 and 1705. The coin of 1703 includes the provenance mark VIGO below the head and is very rare. Gold to produce this coin was captured from Spanish galleons at the battle at Vigo Bay in October 1702. Half guineas with the post-Union reverse were minted in 1707 and each year thereafter until Anne's death in 1714. Pre-Union coins depict a rose in the centre of the reverse, and post-Union coins a Star of the Order of the Garter.

Gold of previous reigns had used an undraped bust of the monarch to prevent fraudulent conversion of silver coins, which had depicted an undraped bust. However, the use of an undraped bust was not considered appropriate for Anne, with the result that many sixpences were gilded, engraved with sceptres, and passed off as half guineas. Subsequent coins of the Georges again used differing types of busts.

Unlike the guinea, the half guinea has only one type of obverse. This runs across the change from pre-Union to post-Union and is a characteristic shared with the sixpence. The obverse was the work of John Croker, from an original design by Sir Godfrey Kneller. The first reverse was by Croker and the second by Croker and/or Bull.

George I 1714–1727

Although at first sight the half guinea appears to continue the design used during the reign of Anne, there are important differences. The long and greatly abbreviated German titles of the king were incorporated into the legends, and the arms of Brunswick, Lüneburg, Saxony and the crown of Charlemagne were all crammed into one of the reverse shields. Clearly, the half guinea was too small a coin to depict such minutiae, but the overall impression is not unpleasing. The convention of the undraped bust on the gold to distinguish it from the silver was resumed.

There was no half guinea equivalent to the 'Prince Elector' guinea of 1714. The denomination ran from 1715 to 1727, with two different obverses rather than the five known on the guinea. The elephant and castle symbol made its last appearance on a half guinea in 1721. This piece is very rare.

The half guinea was the work of John Croker and/or J. R. Ochs, senior. The work of Ochs was probably restricted to the reverses.

The value of the guinea had fluctuated over the years from twenty shillings to about thirty shillings and back to a level of twenty-one shillings and sixpence at the beginning of the reign. A Proclamation in December 1717 reduced the value to twenty-one shillings.

Collecting Hints

Coins in fine condition will probably be adequate for most collectors, but very fine specimens are considerably more attractive.

Collecting Hints

Fine condition coins are often considerably lacking in detail on the obverse. A very fine coin should be looked for if possible. The elephant and castle coin of 1721 is greatly valued in any condition.

Denomination	Metal	Weight (grams)	Diameter (mm)	Rev. alignment
Half guinea	Gold	4.2	20	↓

Obverse 1 Head 1, left; ANNA DEI GRATIA

Reverse 1 Four crowned cruciform shields between which are four sceptres; central rose; MAG BR FRA ET HIB REG (date)

Reverse 2 Similar but two shields separately show conjoined English/Scottish arms; central Star of the Order of the Garter instead of rose; shields are broader; MAG BRI FR ET HIB REG (date).

Edge milled (diagonally)

Denomination	Metal	Weight (grams)	Diameter (mm)	Rev. alignment
Half guinea	Gold	4.2	20	↓

Obverse 1 Head 1, right; GEORGIVS D G M BR FR ET HIB REX F D

Obverse 2 Head 2, right, smaller and older; same legend

Reverse 1 Four crowned cruciform shields between which are four sceptres; central Star of the Order of the Garter; BRVN ET L DVX S R I A TH ET EL (date)

Edge milled (diagonally)

Obv. 1   Rev. 1: Before Union Rev. 2: After Union

Obv. 1   Obv. 2   Rev. 1

No.	Date	Features	Obv.	Rev.	F	VF	EF
G1HG-005	1715		1	1	160	320	800
G1HG-010	1717		1	1	160	320	800
G1HG-015	1718		1	1	150	300	700
G1HG-020	1718	8 over 7	1	1	160	320	800
G1HG-025	1719		1	1	150	300	700
G1HG-030	1720		1	1	160	320	800
G1HG-035	1721		1	1	350	800	
G1HG-040	1721	elephant and castle below head	1	1	1500		
G1HG-045	1722		1	1	160	320	800
G1HG-050	1722	latter 2 over 0 [1]	1	1	170	350	850
G1HG-055	1723		1	1	220	450	1200
G1HG-060	1724		1	1	160	320	800
G1HG-065	1725		2	1	140	280	700
G1HG-070	1726		2	1	140	280	700
G1HG-075	1727	[2]	2	1	140	280	700

1. Overdate often remarkably clear.
2. Date resembles 1721.

Some specimens of 1725 and 1726 have a line running down the king's forehead parallel to the profile line (cf. quarter guinea 1718, obverse 2).

George II 1727–1760

The half guinea series of George II approximately parallels the guinea, with several differences. There was no issue corresponding to the first two types of guinea of 1727, bearing the obverse by J. R. Ochs, and no half guineas were struck at all that year. The variations in size of lettering are also less prevalent on the half guinea.

Fraudulent conversion of sixpences by gilding and passing them off as half guineas had become an epidemic. Because of this, with this issue the reverse was given a crowned shield design. This was a more pleasing effort than that used on the William and Mary coinage, and it proved successful in stopping the counterfeiters. While the milling on the guinea was in 1739 changed to a chevron design to thwart 'guinea-filers', the half guinea was too thin to permit this conversion.

John Croker initially prepared the dies for the George II half guinea. Subsequent work was by Tanner (who succeeded as Chief Engraver in 1791) and Ochs, junior.

Collecting Hints

A fine to very fine condition specimen will be adequate for most purposes.

Denomination	Metal	Weight (grams)	Diameter (mm)	Rev. alignment
Half guinea	Gold	4.2	20	↓

Obverse 1 Head 1, left; GEORGIVS II DEI GRATIA

Obverse 2 Head 2, left; same legend but GEORGIUS

Obverse 3 Head 2, left; same legend but GEORGIVS

Obverse 4 Head 3, left, older; same legend but larger lettering

Reverse 1 Crowned shield; M B F ET H REX F D B ET L D S R I A T ET E (date) in small lettering and numerals

Reverse 2 Similar but shield slightly different

Edge milled (diagonally)

Obv. 1   Obv. 2   Obv. 4   Rev. 1

No.	Date	Features	Obv.	Rev.	F	VF	EF
G2HG-005	1728		1	1	200	500	1400
G2HG-010	1728	PROOF; edge plain [1]	1	1			4000
G2HG-015	1728	PROOF; edge plain; rev. ↑	1	1			4500
G2HG-020	1729		1	1	200	500	1400
G2HG-025	1729	E.I.C. below head	1	1	350	800	2000
G2HG-030	1730		1	1	700	1500	
G2HG-035	1730	E.I.C. below head	1	1	350	900	2500
G2HG-040	1731		1	1	240	700	1700
G2HG-045	1731	E.I.C. below head	1	1	900	2000	
G2HG-050	1732		1	1	200	500	1400
G2HG-055	1732	E.I.C. below head	1	1	900	2000	
G2HG-060	1734		1	1	180	450	1100
G2HG-065	1736		1	1	200	500	1400
G2HG-070	1737		1	1	800	2000	
G2HG-075	1738		1	1	170	420	1000
G2HG-080	1739		1	1	170	420	1000
G2HG-085	1739	E.I.C. below head	1	1	900	2000	
G2HG-090	1740	[2]	2	1	240	700	1700
G2HG-095	1743	[3]	2	1	2000		
G2HG-100	1745		2	1	240	700	1700
G2HG-105	1745	LIMA below head	2	1	650	1800	3500
G2HG-110	1746		3	1	180	450	1100
G2HG-115	1747		4	2	200	550	1500
G2HG-120	1748		4	2	180	450	1000
G2HG-125	1749		4	2	500	1400	
G2HG-130	1750		4	2	170	400	850
G2HG-135	1751		4	2	170	420	900
G2HG-140	1751	latter 1 over 0	4	2	200	480	1000
G2HG-145	1752		4	2	170	420	900
G2HG-150	1753	[4]	4	2	160	380	750
G2HG-155	1755		4	2	160	380	750
G2HG-160	1756		4	2	140	320	650
G2HG-165	1758		4	2	140	320	650
G2HG-170	1759		4	2	130	280	550
G2HG-175	1759	9 over 8	4	2	200	400	800
G2HG-180	1760		4	2	130	280	550

1. Reverse ↓ as ordinary issue.
2. 'Intermediate head'.
3. Possibly only one exists.
4. 3 in date has a straight top.

George III 1760–1820

The half guinea was minted for almost every year of this long reign. Seven different heads of the monarch by four different designers span the series. Beginning in 1762, the first two heads were by Thomas Yeo, the last of this type being struck in 1775. In 1774 and 1775 there also appeared a new type bearing a head designed by Thomas Pingo. This was of inferior workmanship and struck up so poorly that it is surprising that any were issued. This type is rarely encountered, and it was replaced during 1775 by a coin having a much improved portrait by the same designer. Thus, in 1775 there were issued three completely different versions of the half guinea. Many of these would have been from recalled gold coins of William III and Anne, 20 million of which were remelted at this time.

Thomas Pingo's son Lewis was appointed Chief Engraver in January 1780. Lewis Pingo produced a very different head for the 'spade' half guinea of 1787-1800. This was slightly modified for the issue of 1801-1803, on which the 'spade' shield was replaced by a shield in garter design. From 1800 to 1811 only half guineas and third guineas were issued. In 1801, the king relinquished his claim to the French throne, and the reverse legend was altered to reflect this. The Hanoverian quartering was also moved from the royal arms on the reverse on to an escutcheon at the centre of the shield. This reverse then continued until 1813 using another very different head (1804-1813) engraved by Lewis Pingo from a design by Nathaniel Marchant.

The reverses initially carried over the Tanner design from the previous reign. However, Tanner's eyesight was now failing, and the engraving was possibly done by Richard Yeo.

Collecting Hints

Generally speaking, the half guinea is attractive enough in fine condition for most purposes. Certainly the somewhat flatly struck 'spade' type does not exhibit much greater detail in higher grades. Thus, one of each main type in fine condition should be adequate.

One does not have to be so vigilant about forgeries as in the guinea series, but possibly one should be cautious of 'hype' regarding the 1813 coin. The guinea of this date, a one-year type, commands a good premium. The half guinea of 1813 is somewhat scarce, but that is all. The fact that most collectors of half guinea do not collect by date is also a factor to be taken into account when pricing this coin.

Denomination	Metal	Weight (grams)	Diameter (mm)	Rev. alignment
Half guinea 1762–86	Gold	4.2	20	↓
Half guinea 1787–1813	Gold	4.2	20–21	↑

Obverse 1 Head 1, right; GEORGIVS III DEI GRATIA

Obverse 2 Head 2, right, slightly different; same legend

Obverse 3 Head 3, right, poorly executed and struck; same legend

Obverse 4 Head 4, right, similar but better crafted; same legend

Obverse 5 Head 5, right, somewhat similar; same legend

Obverse 6 Head 6, right, similar but slightly broader; same legend

Obverse 7 Head 7, very different, right; same legend

Reverse 1 Crowned shield; M B F ET H REX F D B ET L D S R I A T ET E; (date) divided by crown

Reverse 2 Crowned spade-shaped shield; same legend but in opposite position around rim; (date) at bottom

Reverse 3 Crowned shield in Garter; BRITANNIARUM REX FIDEI DEFENSOR; HONI SOIT QUI MAL Y PENSE on Garter; (date) between Garter and edge legend

Edge milled (diagonally)

Obv. 1

Obv. 2

Obv. 3

Obv. 4

Obv. 5

Obv. 7

Rev. 1

Rev. 2

Rev. 3

No.	Date	Features	Obv.	Rev.	F	VF	EF
G3HG-005	1762		1	1	250	800	1800
G3HG-010	1763		1	1	280	820	1900
G3HG-015	1764		2	1	140	380	900
G3HG-020	1765		2	1	220	650	1800
G3HG-025	1765	5 over 4	2	1	220	650	1800
G3HG-030	1766		2	1	140	380	900
G3HG-035	1768		2	1	140	380	900
G3HG-040	1769		2	1	140	380	900
G3HG-045	1772		2	1	400	1200	3000
G3HG-050	1773		2	1	140	380	900
G3HG-055	1774		2	1	200	550	1500
G3HG-060	1774		3	1	700	1900	
G3HG-065	1775		2	1	200	550	1500
G3HG-070	1775		3	1	250	700	1800
G3HG-075	1775	PROOF; edge plain [1]	3	1			5000
G3HG-080	1775		4	1	110	200	420
G3HG-085	1776		4	1	110	200	420
G3HG-090	1777		4	1	110	200	420
G3HG-095	1778		4	1	110	200	420
G3HG-100	1779		4	1	120	230	480
G3HG-105	1781	[2]	4	1	110	200	420
G3HG-110	1783		4	1	250	700	
G3HG-115	1784		4	1	110	200	400
G3HG-120	1785		4	1	110	200	400
G3HG-125	1786		4	1	110	200	400
G3HG-130	1787		5	2	100	170	350
G3HG-135	1787	PROOF; edge plain	5	2			1000
G3HG-140	1787	PROOF in silver; edge plain	5	2			750
G3HG-145	1788		5	2	100	170	350
G3HG-150	1789		5	2	100	170	350
G3HG-155	1790		5	2	100	170	350
G3HG-160	1791		5	2	100	170	350
G3HG-165	1792		5	2	400	900	
G3HG-170	1793		5	2	100	170	350
G3HG-175	1794		5	2	100	170	350
G3HG-180	1795		5	2	110	190	400
G3HG-185	1796		5	2	100	170	350
G3HG-190	1797		5	2	100	170	350
G3HG-195	1798		5	2	95	160	320
G3HG-200	1798	8 over 7	5	2	140	220	450
G3HG-205	1800		5	2	150	300	550
G3HG-210	1801		6	3	80	120	200
G3HG-215	1802		6	3	80	120	200
G3HG-220	1803		6	3	80	120	200
G3HG-225	1804		7	3	80	120	200
G3HG-230	1805		7	3	500		
G3HG-235	1806		7	3	80	120	200
G3HG-240	1808		7	3	80	120	200
G3HG-245	1809		7	3	80	120	200
G3HG-250	1810		7	3	80	120	200
G3HG-255	1811		7	3	110	180	320
G3HG-260	1813		7	3	100	170	290

1. May weigh more than current coin; usually has die flaws on reverse.
2. Date change; reverse 1: from 1762 to 1779 the '1' in the date is a 'J' type; from 1781 to 1786 it is a Roman I.

Half Sovereign

George III 1760–1820

With the Great Recoinage, the half sovereign was struck as the companion piece to the sovereign, and became the smallest gold coin in regular use. The workmanship and striking of the half sovereign was not quite up to the standard of the sovereign. However, the coin received more extensive use and turns up in worn condition more often than the sovereign.

The obverse was designed by Benedetto Pistrucci, and the reverse was engraved by William Wyon, possibly from a design by Pistrucci.

Denomination	Metal	Weight (grams)	Diameter (mm)	Rev. alignment
Half Sovereign	Gold	4.0	19	↓

Obverse 1 Head 1, right; GEORGIUS III DEI GRATIA (date)

Reverse 1 Crowned shield; BRITANNIARUM REX FID DEF

Edge milled

Obv. 1   Rev. 1

No.	Date	Features	Obv.	Rev.	F	VF	EF	UNC
G3HS-005	1817		1	1	75	120	200	300
G3HS-010	1817	PROOF	1	1				2000
G3HS-015	1818		1	1	80	130	220	350
G3HS-020	1818	latter 8 over 7	1	1	120	200	300	500
G3HS-025	1818	PROOF	1	1				5000
G3HS-030	1820		1	1	75	120	200	320

George IV 1820–1830

The George IV half sovereign occurs with two different obverse portraits and three different reverses. The first reverse was struck only in 1821, and depicts an ornate garnished shield. This coin is seldom found in any condition, and was withdrawn because of its similarity to the sixpence. The laureate head on the obverse of this coin was retained when the new reverse was introduced in 1823. In 1826 both the obverse and reverse were redesigned following the king's displeasure with his portrait, and proof specimens of the new type of half sovereign were included in the 1826 proof sets.

The first obverse was designed by Pistrucci and the second by William Wyon. The reverses were by Johann Baptiste Merlen. The reverse of the 1821 coin includes the initials WWP (for William Wellesley Pole, the Master of the Mint) hidden in the centres of the three shamrock leaves.

Denomination	Metal	Weight (grams)	Diameter (mm)	Rev. alignment
Half Sovereign	Gold	4.0	19	↓

Obverse 1 Head 1, left; GEORGIUS IIII D G BRITANNIAR REX F D

Obverse 2 Head 2, left; GEORGIUS IV DEI GRATIA (date)

Reverse 1 Crowned shield garnished with rose, shamrock, thistle; ANNO 1821

Reverse 2 A square topped shield, ungarnished except at foot; ANNO (date)

Reverse 3 Somewhat different shield, lightly garnished; BRITANNIARUM REX FID DEF

Edge milled

Obv. 1   Obv. 2

Rev. 1   Rev. 2   Rev. 3

No.	Date	Features	Obv.	Rev.	F	VF	EF	UNC
G4HS-005	1821		1	1	200	450	1200	1700
G4HS-010	1821	PROOF	1	1				2500
G4HS-015	1823		1	2	100	250	500	750
G4HS-020	1823	PROOF	1	2				3500
G4HS-025	1824		1	2	100	250	500	700
G4HS-030	1825		1	2	90	220	450	650
G4HS-035	1825	PROOF [1]	1	2				2000
G4HS-040	1825	PROOF; edge plain	1	2				2000
G4HS-045	1826		2	3	100	240	480	650
G4HS-050	1826	PROOF [2]	2	3				1100
G4HS-055	1827		2	3	110	200	350	550
G4HS-060	1828	[3]	2	3	110	200	350	550

1. Head very slightly different; possibly a pattern.
2. Issued in cased proof sets.
3. Some possibly struck in 1829.

William IV 1830–1837

The half sovereign is arguably the most interesting of the denominations of this short reign. It begins with a plain edge proof issue of 1831 on a flan somewhat smaller than used hitherto. It is possible that the diameter of 18mm was chosen so that the obverse dies could be prepared from the same master tools used for the Maundy fourpence. After a regular issue in 1834 on a similar flan, the diameter of the flan is increased from 1835 onwards to the 19mm used in previous reigns. Varieties of the last two dates, 1836 and 1837, are known which have different obverses, apparently taken from the dies for the sixpence. This may have been the result of an error.

The obverse of the series was engraved by William Wyon from a design by Sir Francis Chantrey. The reverses were designed and engraved by Johann Baptiste Merlen.

Collecting Hints

Isolated examples of the 1831 proof issue are difficult to obtain, although they occasionally turn up, sometimes heavily scuffed. The ordinary issue coins should be sought in at least fine to very fine condition. The reverse is very slightly convex and tends to wear in the centre even when the obverse is still fine or better.

Denomination	Metal	Weight (grams)	Diameter (mm)	Rev. alignment
Half Sovereign 1831-1834	Gold	4.0	18	↓
Half Sovereign 1835-1837	Gold	4.0	19	↓

Obverse 1 Head 1; GULIELMUS IIII D G BRITANNIAR REX F D

Obverse 2 Similar but struck on larger flan. The Head is the same size as on Obverse 1

Obverse 3 Similar but head slightly larger and lettering orientation slightly different (from a sixpence die)

Reverse 1 Crowned and garnished shield; below: ANNO (date)

Reverse 2 Similar but struck on larger flan. Very slightly different design from Reverse 1

Edge milled

| Obv. 1 | Obv. 3 | Rev. 1 |

No.	Date	Features	Obv.	Rev.	F	VF	EF	UNC
W4HS-005	1831	PROOF edge plain [1]	1	1				1400
W4HS-010	1834		1	1	100	150	450	650
W4HS-015	1835		2	2	90	150	450	650
W4HS-020	1836		2	2	100	200	500	750
W4HS-025	1836		3	2	700	1400	2500	4000
W4HS-030	1837		2	2	100	175	450	700
W4HS-035	1837		3	2	700	1400	2500	4000

1. Issued in cased proof sets.

Victoria 1837-1901

The Victorian half sovereign was a much-used coin, and in general received even more circulation wear than the sovereign. It was minted almost every year of the reign, but specimens in extremely fine condition are difficult to find. This applies especially in the case of the young head coins bearing the Australian mintmarks. As with the sovereign, the series is not extensively collected by date, and no doubt unrecorded varieties occur. The young head of Victoria was designed by William Wyon, the jubilee head by Sir Joseph Edgar Boehm and the old head by Sir Thomas Brock. The shield reverse was slightly modified from the design for William IV by Johann Baptiste Merlen. The later St George and dragon reverses were based on the old Pistrucci design, but the initials BP do not appear. How the egotistical Italian, who spelt his name in full on the 1818 crown, would have hated that!

Collecting Hints

A specimen of each type in very fine or extremely fine condition will be acceptable to most collectors. Forgeries are not so much of a problem as they are with sovereigns.

Denomination	Metal	Weight (grams)	Diameter (mm)	Rev. alignment
Half Sovereign Obv.1-3	Gold	4.0	19	↓
Half Sovereign Obv.4-6	Gold	4.0	19	↑

Obverse 1 Head 1, left;. VICTORIA DEI GRATIA (date)

Obverse 2 Head 2, left, left-hand fillet is narrower; same legend (date)

Obverse 3 Head 3, left in slightly lower relief; truncation slightly different; same legend (date)

Obverse 4 Head 4, left, 'Jubilee' type; VICTORIA DEI GRATIA; initials JEB on truncation

Obverse 5 Similar but no JEB on truncation

Obverse 6 Head 5, left, veiled; VICTORIA DEI GRA BRITT REGINA FID DEF IND IMP

Reverse 1 Crowned and garnished shield; BRITANNIARUM REGINA FID DEF. Some coins have die number below wreath (see listings)

Reverse 2 Similar but redesigned; the crown is very different (Imperial); same legend (date)

Reverse 3 St George and dragon; (date) in exergue

Edge milled

| Obv. 1 | Obv. 4 | Obv. 6 |

| Rev. 1 | Rev. 2 | Rev. 3 |

No.	Date	Features	Obv.	Rev.	F	VF	EF	UNC
VYHS-005	1838		1	1	80	120	250	350
VYHS-010	1839	PROOF; edge plain [1]	1	1				1400
VYHS-015	1839	PROOF; edge plain; rev.↑	1	1				1400
VYHS-020	1839	PROOF in silver; edge plain	1	1				1500
VYHS-025	1841		1	1	85	130	270	380
VYHS-030	1842		1	1	70	90	180	250
VYHS-035	1843		1	1	85	130	270	380
VYHS-040	1844		1	1	75	100	200	280
VYHS-045	1845		1	1	120	200	500	800
VYHS-050	1846		1	1	75	100	200	280
VYHS-055	1847		1	1	80	120	250	350
VYHS-060	1848		1	1	75	100	200	350
VYHS-065	1848	latter 8 over 7	1	1	100	140	270	400
VYHS-070	1849		1	1	70	90	170	250
VYHS-075	1850		1	1	85	125	450	1000
VYHS-080	1851		1	1	65	80	140	200
VYHS-085	1852		1	1	75	100	200	280
VYHS-090	1853		1	1	75	100	200	280
VYHS-095	1853	PROOF [1]	1	1				2500
VYHS-100	1854		1	1	500			
VYHS-105	1855		1	1	70	90	170	240
VYHS-110	1856		1	1	70	90	170	240

No.	Date	Features	Obv.	Rev.	F	VF	EF	UNC
VYHS-115	1857		1	1	75	95	180	260
VYHS-120	1858	2	1	1	70	90	170	240
VYHS-125	1859	3	1	1	70	90	170	240
VYHS-130	1860		1	1	70	90	170	240
VYHS-135	1861		1	1	70	90	170	240
VYHS-140	1862		1	1	200	500	1750	3500
VYHS-145	1863	no die number below wreath (rev.)	1	1	70	90	170	240
VYHS-150	1863	die number below wreath (rev.)	1	1	80	110	190	280
VYHS-155	1864	die number below wreath (rev.)	1	1	65	85	150	200
VYHS-160	1865	die number below wreath (rev.)	1	1	65	85	150	200
VYHS-165	1866	die number below wreath (rev.)	1	1	65	85	150	200
VYHS-170	1867	die number below wreath (rev.)	1	1	65	85	150	200
VYHS-175	1869	die number below wreath (rev.)	1	1	65	85	150	200
VYHS-180	1870	die number below wreath (rev.)	1	1	65	85	150	200
VYHS-185	1871	die number below wreath (rev.) 4	1	1	65	85	150	200
VYHS-190	1871	PROOF; die number below wreath (rev.) 5	1	1				3000
VYHS-195	1871	PROOF; edge plain die number below wreath (rev.) 5	1	1				3500
VYHS-200	1872	die number below wreath (rev.) 6	1	1	65	80	140	180
VYHS-205	1873	die number below wreath (rev.)	1	1	65	80	140	180
VYHS-210	1874	die number below wreath (rev.)	1	1	65	80	140	180
VYHS-215	1875	die number below wreath (rev.)	1	1	65	80	140	180
VYHS-220	1876	die number below wreath (rev.)	1	1	65	80	140	180
VYHS-225	1876	die number below wreath (rev.)	2	1	65	80	140	180
VYHS-230	1877	die number below wreath (rev.)	1	1	65	80	130	170
VYHS-235	1877	die number below wreath (rev.)	2	1	65	80	130	170
VYHS-240	1878	die number below wreath (rev.)	2	1	65	80	130	170
VYHS-245	1878	PROOF; die number below wreath (rev.)	2	1				4500
VYHS-250	1879	die number below wreath (rev.)	2	1	65	80	150	200
VYHS-255	1880	die number below wreath (rev.)	2	1	65	80	130	170
VYHS-260	1880	die number below wreath (rev.)	3	1	65	80	130	170
VYHS-265	1880	no die number below wreath (rev.) 7	3	1	65	80	130	170
VYHS-270	1880	PROOF; no die number below wreath (rev.)	3	1				2500
VYHS-275	1883		3	1	65	75	120	160
VYHS-280	1884		3	1	65	75	120	160
VYHS-285	1885		3	1	65	75	120	160
VYHS-290	1886	PROOF	3	1				2500

No.	Date	Features	Obv.	Rev.	F	VF	EF	UNC
VJHS-295	1887		4	2	50	60	75	90
VJHS-300	1887	PROOF 1	4	2				400
VJHS-305	1887		5	2	120	300	800	
VJHS-310	1888	8	5	2				
VJHS-315	1890		4	2	250			
VJHS-320	1890		5	2	50	60	80	100
VJHS-325	1891		5	2	50	60	85	110
VJHS-330	1892		5	2	50	60	85	110
VJHS-335	1893		5	2	50	60	85	110
VOHS-340	1893		6	3	50	60	80	100
VOHS-345	1893	PROOF 1	6	3				450
VOHS-350	1894		6	3	50	60	80	100
VOHS-355	1895		6	3	50	60	80	100
VOHS-360	1896		6	3	50	60	80	100
VOHS-365	1897		6	3	50	60	80	100
VOHS-370	1898		6	3	50	60	80	100
VOHS-375	1899		6	3	50	60	80	100
VOHS-380	1900		6	3	50	60	80	100
VOHS-385	1901		6	3	50	60	80	100

1. Issued in cased proof sets.
2. Minor obv lettering orientation differences introduced during this year.
3. Date slightly larger than previous years.
4. Minor obv orientation differences occur.
5. Usually die number 1?
6. Minor obverse and reverse differences introduced.
7. Minor reverse differences introduced.
8. Possibly all forgeries.

Commonwealth Mints

Mintmarks

M: Melbourne, Australia (opened June 1872)
P: Perth, Australia (opened June 1899)
S: Sydney, Australia (opened May 1855)

Position of Mintmarks

Reverse 1 Below shield
Reverse 2 Below shield

Reverse 3 On ground line above centre of date

No.	Date	mm	Features	Obv.	Rev.	F	VF	EF	UNC
VYHS-390	1871	S		1	1	75	130	500	800
VYHS-395	1871	S	PROOF	1	1				3000
VYHS-400	1872	S	1	1	1	85	180	650	950
VYHS-405	1873	M		1	1	85	150	500	750
VYHS-410	1875	S		1	1	85	170	600	900
VYHS-415	1877	M		2	1	85	170	600	900
VYHS-420	1879	S		2	1	85	180	650	950
VYHS-425	1880	S		3	1	85	180	650	950
VYHS-430	1880	S	PROOF	3	1				3500
VYHS-435	1881	M		3	1	120	280	1100	1600
VYHS-440	1881	M	PROOF	3	1				4000
VYHS-445	1881	S		3	1	120	250	1000	1600
VYHS-450	1882	M		2	1	85	170	600	900
VYHS-455	1882	M		3	1	85	170	600	900
VYHS-460	1882	S		3	1	120	280	1200	1800
VYHS-465	1883	S		3	1	85	170	600	850
VYHS-470	1883	S	PROOF	3	1				3000
VYHS-475	1884	M		3	1	120	320	1200	1800
VYHS-480	1884	M	PROOF	3	1				4000
VYHS-485	1885	M		3	1	140	400	1500	2200
VYHS-490	1886	M		3	1	80	150	500	750
VYHS-495	1886	M	PROOF	3	1				3000
VYHS-500	1886	S		3	1	85	170	600	850
VYHS-505	1887	M		3	1	130	350	1300	2000
VYHS-510	1887	S		3	1	80	130	250	400
VYHS-515	1887	S	PROOF	3	1				2500
VJHS-520	1887	M		4	2	100	180	400	700
VJHS-525	1887	M	PROOF	4	2				3000
VJHS-530	1887	S		4	2	100	180	400	700
VJHS-535	1887	S	PROOF	4	2				3000
VJHS-540	1889	S		5	2	120	220	500	850
VJHS-545	1891	S		5	2	100	180	400	700
VJHS-550	1891	S	PROOF	5	2				3000
VJHS-555	1893	M		5	2	110	200	550	800
VJHS-560	1893	M	PROOF	5	2				3000
VOHS-565	1893	M		6	3	500			
VOHS-570	1893	M	PROOF	6	3				5000
VOHS-575	1893	S		6	3	60	90	180	250
VOHS-580	1893	S	PROOF	6	3				2500
VOHS-585	1896	M		6	3	65	100	220	350
VOHS-590	1896	M	PROOF	6	3				2500
VOHS-595	1897	S		6	3	60	90	180	250
VOHS-600	1899	M		6	3	60	90	180	250
VOHS-605	1899	M	PROOF	6	3				2500

No.	Date	mm	Features	Obv.	Rev.	F	VF	EF	UNC
VOHS-610	1899	P	PROOF	6	3				2500
VOHS-615	1900	M		6	3	60	90	180	250
VOHS-620	1900	M	PROOF	6	3				2500
VOHS-625	1900	P		6	3	70	120	280	450
VOHS-630	1900	S		6	3	60	85	170	220

1. Minor differences obverse and reverse.

Edward VII 1902–1910

Half sovereigns were struck at the London mint for each year of the reign, and at the three Australian mints for some of the years. Unlike the sovereign, the half sovereign was not struck at the Ottawa mint. Matt proof half sovereigns were struck in 1902 at the London mint for inclusion in the proof sets.

The portrait of Edward VII was by George William de Saulles (1862-1903); the reverse retains the Pistrucci St George and dragon.

Collecting Hints

Choice extremely fine or better specimens are scarce.

Denomination	Metal	Weight (grams)	Diameter (mm)	Rev. alignment
Half Sovereign	Gold	4.0	19	↑

Obverse 1 Head 1, right; EDWARDVS VII D G BRITT OMN REX F D IND IMP

Reverse 1 St George and dragon; (date) in exergue; no BP in exergue

Reverse 2 Similar but with BP (initials of designer) in exergue and other minor differences

Edge milled

Obv. 1

Rev. 1

No.	Date	Features	Obv.	Rev.	VF	EF	UNC
E7HS-005	1902		1	1	50	65	80
E7HS-010	1902	matt PROOF [1]	1	1			95
E7HS-015	1903		1	1	50	65	80
E7HS-020	1904		1	1	50	65	80
E7HS-025	1904		1	2	50	65	80
E7HS-030	1905		1	2	50	65	80
E7HS-035	1906		1	2	50	65	80
E7HS-040	1906	matt PROOF	1	2			2500
E7HS-045	1907		1	2	50	65	80
E7HS-050	1908		1	2	50	65	80
E7HS-055	1909		1	2	50	65	80
E7HS-060	1910		1	2	50	65	80

1. Issued in cased proof sets.

Commonwealth Mints

Mintmarks

M: Melbourne, Australia
P: Perth, Australia
S: Sydney, Australia

Position of Mintmarks:

On ground line above centre of date

No.	Date	mm	Features	Obv.	Rev.	VF	EF	UNC
E7HS-065	1902	S		1	1	70	150	250
E7HS-070	1902	S	matt PROOF	1	1			2500
E7HS-075	1903	S		1	1	70	140	230

No.	Date	mm	Features	Obv.	Rev.	VF	EF	UNC
E7HS-080	1904	P		1	1	250	600	1200
E7HS-085	1904	P		1	2	250	600	1200
E7HS-090	1906	M		1	2	70	150	240
E7HS-095	1906	S		1	2	70	140	220
E7HS-100	1907	M		1	2	70	150	250
E7HS-105	1908	M		1	2	70	150	250
E7HS-110	1908	P		1	2	250	600	1200
E7HS-115	1908	S		1	2	70	140	220
E7HS-120	1909	M		1	2	70	150	240
E7HS-125	1909	P		1	2	200	500	900
E7HS-130	1910	S		1	2	70	130	200

George V 1910–1936

The half sovereign series of George V is not as extensive as the sovereign series. Proofs were struck in 1911 for the cased set, and ordinary coins for each year up to 1915, but no further London mint half sovereigns were minted during this reign.

Commonwealth mint sovereigns were struck during a number of years. These included the 1923 Pretoria mint proof pieces which formed part of the cased proof set of that year.

The obverse portrait of George V was designed by Sir Bertram MacKennal (1863-1931). The reverse continued to use the Pistrucci St George and dragon design.

Collecting Hints

The George V half sovereign is easier to find in extremely fine or better condition than those of previous reigns. In particular the Australian mint coins occur in quantities in top condition.

Denomination	Metal	Weight (grams)	Diameter (mm)	Rev. alignment
Half Sovereign	Gold	4.0	19	↑

Obverse 1 Head 1, left; GEORGIVS V D G BRITT OMN REX F D IND IMP

Reverse 1 St George and dragon, (date) in exergue

Edge milled

Obv. 1

Rev. 1

No.	Date	Features	Obv.	Rev.	VF	EF	UNC
G5HS-005	1911		1	1	50	55	65
G5HS-010	1911	PROOF [1]	1	1			180
G5HS-015	1912		1	1	50	55	65
G5HS-020	1913		1	1	50	55	65
G5HS-025	1914		1	1	50	55	65
G5HS-030	1915		1	1	50	55	65

1. Issued in cased proof sets.

Commonwealth Mints

Mintmarks

M: Melbourne, Australia
P: Perth, Australia
S: Sydney, Australia
SA: Pretoria, South Africa

Position of Mintmarks:

On ground line above centre of date

No.	Date	mm	Features	Obv.	Rev.	VF	EF	UNC
G5HS-035	1911	P		1	1	55	70	80
G5HS-040	1911	S		1	1	55	70	80
G5HS-045	1911	S	PROOF	1	1			2500
G5HS-050	1912	S		1	1	55	70	80
G5HS-055	1914	S		1	1	55	70	80
G5HS-060	1915	M		1	1	55	75	90
G5HS-065	1915	P		1	1	55	70	80
G5HS-070	1915	S		1	1	50	55	65
G5HS-075	1916	S		1	1	50	55	65
G5HS-080	1918	P		1	1	350	600	850
G5HS-085	1919	P	[1]	1	1			
G5HS-090	1920	P	[1]	1	1			
G5HS-095	1923	SA	PROOF [2]	1	1			500
G5HS-100	1925	SA		1	1	50	60	70
G5HS-105	1926	SA		1	1	50	60	70

1. Struck but not circulated.
2. Issued in cased proof sets of South Africa.

George VI 1937–1952

The only George VI half sovereigns struck were the proofs included in the cased proof sets of 1937. These sets contained four coins, each of which comprised the only British coin of that denomination for the reign.

The obverse portrait was by Thomas Humphrey Paget, the reverse again being the Pistrucci St George and dragon.

Denomination	Metal	Weight (grams)	Diameter (mm)	Rev. alignment
Half Sovereign	Gold	4.0	19	↑

Obverse 1 Head 1, left; GEORGIVS VI D G BR OMN REX F D IND IMP

Reverse 1 St George and dragon, 1937 in exergue

Edge plain

Obv. 1

Rev. 1

No.	Date	Features	Obv.	Rev.	VF	EF	FDC
G6HS-005	1937	PROOF [1]	1	1	100	150	200

1. Issued in cased proof sets.

Elizabeth II 1952 —

No gold coins were included in the proof sets of 1953 issued for the coronation, and the only British half sovereigns struck in that year were a small number struck in order to provide continuity of the series. These were not released. The coins bore the obverse portrait of Elizabeth II by Mary Gillick, and the Pistrucci St George and dragon reverse.

There was no issue of half sovereigns corresponding to the pre-decimal sovereign issue of 1957-1968. After decimalization, the denomination was struck for most years from 1980 onwards as a cased proof, and in 1982 as a non-proof coin.

The first head of the monarch was designed by Arnold Machin and the second head by Raphael David Maklouf. The reverse continues the Pistrucci St George and dragon design.

Denomination	Metal	Weight (grams)	Diameter (mm)	Rev. alignment
Half Sovereign	Gold	4.0	19	↑

Obverse 1 Head 1, right; ELIZABETH II DEI GRA BRITT OMN REGINA F D

Obverse 2 Head 2, right; ELIZABETH II DEI GRATIA REGINA F D

Obverse 3 Head 3, right; ELIZABETH II DEI GRA REG F D

Obverse 4 Queen facing on throne, holding orb and sceptre; ELIZABETH II DEI GRA REG FID DEF *(for the 500th anniversary of the gold sovereign)*

Reverse 1 St George and dragon, (date) in exergue

Reverse 2 Crowned shield within double rose; ANNIVERSARY OF THE GOLD SOVEREIGN 1489–1989

Edge milled

Obv. 1   Obv. 2

Obv. 3   Obv. 4

Rev. 1   Rev. 2

No.	Date	Features	Obv.	Rev.	UNC
EL2HS-005	1953	PROOF or pattern	1	1	20000
EL2HS-010	1980	PROOF [1]	2	1	60
EL2HS-015	1982		2	1	BV
EL2HS-020	1982	PROOF [1]	2	1	60
EL2HS-025	1983	PROOF [1]	2	1	60
EL2HS-030	1984	PROOF [1]	2	1	60
EL2HS-035	1985	PROOF [1]	3	1	70
EL2HS-040	1986	PROOF [1]	3	1	70
EL2HS-045	1987	PROOF [1]	3	1	70
EL2HS-050	1988	PROOF [1]	3	1	70
EL2HS-055	1989	PROOF [1]	4	2	100
EL2HS-060	1990	PROOF [1]	3	1	75
EL2HS-065	1991	PROOF [1]	3	1	75
EL2HS-070	1992	PROOF [1]	3	1	75
EL2HS-075	1993	PROOF [1]	3	1	75
EL2HS-080	1994	PROOF [1]	3	1	80
EL2HS-085	1995	PROOF [1]	3	1	80

1. Issued cased and in cased proof sets.

Third Guinea

George III 1760–1820

The third guinea is unique amongst the gold coinage in being the only denomination struck entirely within a single reign. At its inception in 1797, the financial situation at the Bank of England was precarious. The stocks of gold were very low, and banknotes were given legal tender status. In order to help pay its dividends, an issue of what were at that time known as 'seven shilling pieces' was made, with the odd amounts of each dividend being made up in silver. The issue was authorised in October, 1797, with an initial order of £315,000 face value.

The denomination was struck almost every year until 1813. From 1800 to 1811 only half guineas and third guineas were issued. In 1801, the king relinquished his claim to the French throne, and the reverse legend was altered to reflect this.

The first type of third guinea was designed and engraved by Lewis Pingo. The portrait of the king is somewhat curious and is by no means the designer's best work. In 1804, Lewis Pingo engraved a very different bust after a design by Nathaniel Marchant. This is similar to that seen on the Military Guinea of 1813, and is Nathaniel Marchant's first work on the coinage. Both reverses were the work of Lewis Pingo.

Collecting Hints

Specimens in very fine to extremely fine condition are needed to show this coin to its full advantage. Always check for mount marks on the edge.

Denomination	Metal	Weight (grams)	Diameter (mm)	Rev. alignment
Third Guinea	Gold	2.8	17	↑

Obverse 1 Head 1, right; GEORGIVS III DEI GRATIA

Obverse 2 Head 2, right; same legend

Reverse 1 Crown; MAG BRI FR ET HIB REX (date)

Reverse 2 Crown (slightly different), with date immediately below; FIDEI DEFENSOR BRITANNIARUM REX with cross at top of legend

Reverse 3 Similar but a mullet at top of legend

Edge milled

Obv. 1	Obv. 2	Rev. 1	Rev. 3

No.	Date	Features	Obv.	Rev.	F	VF	EF
G3TG-005	1797		1	1	55	85	150
G3TG-010	1798		1	1	55	85	150
G3TG-015	1799		1	1	65	100	200
G3TG-020	1800		1	1	55	85	150
G3TG-025	1801		1	2	55	85	150
G3TG-030	1802		1	2	55	85	150
G3TG-035	1803		1	2	55	85	150
G3TG-040	1804		2	3	55	85	150
G3TG-045	1806		2	3	55	85	150
G3TG-050	1808		2	3	55	85	150
G3TG-055	1809		2	3	55	85	150
G3TG-060	1810		2	3	55	85	150
G3TG-065	1811		2	3	150	350	800
G3TG-070	1813		2	3	100	190	350
G3TG-075	1813	PROOF	2	3			1500

Quarter Guinea

George I 1714–1727

At the beginning of the reign of George I the price of silver had risen considerably, resulting in much of the silver coinage being melted down. Consequently, relatively few silver coins were struck. In 1717, the value of the guinea was reduced by Proclamation to 21 shillings, and in 1718 it was thought appropriate to strike a new gold denomination equal to a quarter of a guinea to provide a useful coin approximating in value to the crown piece. The coin had to be proportionate in weight to the other gold coins. What was not realised at the time was that a coin of such small size would prove unpopular and impractical in use. Many were put aside as keepsakes, and of those which entered circulation a considerable number were lost. Leake, writing at the time, complained that the coins were 'too diminutive for use'. The coin was discontinued after the 1718 issue, and in the following few years there was a slightly increased output of guineas and half guineas.

Despite the small size of the quarter guinea, the coin took the form of a scaled-down version of the guinea and half guinea, with all of the intricate detail on the shields and with the long German titles of the king being retained. The coin is an attractive piece nevertheless, even though some magnification is needed to examine it properly. It was the work of Croker and/or J. R. Ochs, senior.

Collecting Hints

Because many of the coins were kept as keepsakes when first issued, the quarter guinea is not difficult to find in the higher grades. A specimen in very fine to extremely fine condition is adequate for most purposes.

It is not generally known that there are two slightly different busts on this series. On one, there is a line running down the forehead of the king, and this coin is often catalogued as having a scratch on the bust. Consequently, it may be possible to pick up such a piece at auction or elsewhere at a reduced price. Specimens in fine condition or thereabouts must be examined carefully for mount marks on the edge. Crimped specimens are not uncommon.

Denomination	Metal	Weight (grams)	Diameter (mm)	Rev. alignment
Quarter guinea	Gold	2.1	16	↓

Obverse 1 Head 1, right; GEORGIVS D G M BR FR ET HIB REX F D

Obverse 2 Head 2, right, similar but with line running down forehead parallel to profile line

Reverse 1 Four crowned cruciform shields between which are four sceptres; central Star of the Order of the Garter; BRVN ET L DVX S R I A TH ET PR EL 1718

Edge milled diagonally

Obv. 1

Rev. 1

No.	Date	Obv.	Rev.	F	VF	EF
G1QG-005	1718	1	1	55	120	200
G1QG-010	1718	2	1	55	120	200

George III 1760–1820

When George III came to the throne, the price of silver had again risen dramatically. No silver coins were minted for several years, with the exception of the few 'Northumberland' shillings struck, and crown pieces had become very scarce. Despite the unpopularity of the gold quarter guinea during the reign of George I, it was again considered necessary to produce this denomination to fill the gap between the low denomination silver and the larger gold coins. Unfortunately, the coin met the same fate as its predecessor, and was struck for only one year, 1762.

The quarter guinea was mainly the work of Richard Yeo, who designed and engraved the obverse. The reverse was engraved by him based on the Tanner designs for the George II gold coinage.

Collecting Hints

As with the George I coin, this piece is not difficult to find in high grade. Low grade specimens often have mount marks, and creased specimens are even more prevalent than with the George I coin.

Denomination	Metal	Weight (grams)	Diameter (mm)	Rev. alignment
Quarter Guinea	Gold	2.1	16	↓

Obverse 1 Head 1, right; GEORGIVS III DEI GRATIA

Reverse 1 Crowned shield; M B F ET H REX F D B ET L D S R I A T ET E; 1762 divided by crown

Edge milled diagonally

Obv. 1

Rev. 1

No.	Date	Obv.	Rev.	F	VF	EF
G3QG-005	1762	1	1	55	110	180

Crown

Oliver Cromwell (Commonwealth 1649–1660)

The 1658 crown of Oliver Cromwell was the first of the struck portrait crowns. Although sometimes considered to be technically a pattern, it deserves a place in any catalogue of regular coinage as the coins obviously entered circulation. It must be remembered that this was at a time when it was estimated that the united weekly earnings of a man, his wife and two children was ten shillings (two crowns).

The crown was designed by Thomas Simon (also called Symonds) and portrays Cromwell as a Roman Emperor, draped and laureate.

Collecting Hints

The most noticeable feature of the Cromwell crown is often the die flaw across the lower half of the obverse. The flaw is always present to some degree, but coins with only a trace of flaw command somewhat higher prices. Some collectors like to acquire an example with the flaw markedly formed.

The 'Tanner's Copy' was struck in the 18th century, and is outside the scope of this book.

Denomination	Metal	Weight (grams)	Diameter (mm)	Rev. alignment
Crown	Silver	30.0	40–41	↓

Obverse 1 Head 1, left; OLIVAR D G R P ANG SCO HIB &c PRO

Reverse 1 Crowned shield; PAX QVAERITVR BELLO 1658

Edge (in relief): HAS NISI PERITVRVS MIHI ADIMAT NEMO

Obv. 1	Rev. 1

No.	Date	Features	Obv.	Rev.	F	VF	EF
CRCR-005	1658	8 over 7	1	1	650	1100	2000
CRCR-010	1658	struck in gold; 8 over 7 [1]	1	1			75000

1. Die flaw prominent; weight 46 or 50 grams; 2 known.

Charles II 1660–1685

An issue of Charles II hammered crowns was authorised, but never produced. The crowns of 1662 thus became the first coins struck for circulation of the new milled, or machine struck, coinage. This took its place alongside the earlier hammered coinage still in circulation, although a Proclamation in September 1661 had demonetised the Commonwealth coinage from November 1661, later postponed to March 1662 (new style Calendar). The contract for Chief Engraver was won by John (aka Jan) Roettier (1631-c.1703) in a hard-fought contest against Thomas Simon (c.1623-1665).

Crowns of Charles II are relatively plentiful in very good and even in fine condition, but considerably scarcer in very fine or better. The earlier dates are particularly attractive in the higher grades. It is possible that the reason why so many crowns were struck was the payment by Louis XIV to the British in 1662 to purchase the town of Dunkirk. This payment was in the form of 1.5 million silver ecus, which may have been recoined into crowns.

The crowns of 1662 and 1663 are slightly larger in diameter than those of 1664 and later. The weight, however, remained constant, and the post-1663 coins must, therefore, have been struck on a slightly thicker flan. The rose below the head on many of the 1662 coins indicates silver from the West of England mines. It is considered that 1662 crowns were struck in February and March 1663 (new style Calendar), which under the old style was still 1662.

The scarcity of the issues of 1665 and, to a lesser extent, 1666 is due probably to the ravages of the Great Plague and the Fire of London. The elephant occasionally encountered below the head of the 1666 coin (and the elephant and castle below some issues of 1680 and 1681) denote silver from the Africa Company in Guinea. The most commonly found Charles II crown is the third head type, with its somewhat unattractive flat appearance, giving the illusion that the coin is more worn than it actually is.

With the advent of the milled coinage, the practice arose of marking the edge of the larger denominations with an inscription in raised lettering which included the year of the reign, referred to in this catalogue as the 'regnal date'. Thus, for example, the first year of the reign is regnal date 1, the second is regnal date 2, and so on. It is interesting to note that the monarch's regnal date in the case of Charles II is calculated from the death of Charles I in 1649 rather than from the beginning of the reign of Charles II.

The reason for and the method of application of the edge inscription is of interest. Filing and clipping of coinage to acquire silver had become endemic in the years of hammered coins. It was considered that an edge inscription (or milling on the smaller coins) would render these activities more detectable and also serve as a deterrent. The wording of the edge inscription 'Decus et Tutamen' was said by Leake, writing in 1726, to have been suggested by Mr. Evelyn, based on a vignette of Cardinal de Richelieu's Greek Testament, printed at the Louvre, Paris. The French began to mark their ecus with edge lettering shortly after the first British issue of lettered crowns.

The edge inscription was not, as is commonly thought, applied to the finished struck coinage. However, in later years the striking of the two sides and the edge may have been effected simultaneously. In the earlier years the blanks were first cut out from metal which had been rolled into strips using horse power. These blanks were then sent to have the edges impressed by a secret process devised by one Pierre Blondeau, an ex-engineer from the Paris mint, who jealously guarded his methods. The blanks were then returned to the Mint to have their obverses and reverses struck in a hand-operated press.

A long and detailed description of rolling, cutting and striking of blanks is contained in Pepys's Diary for 19 May 1663.

Very large numbers of Charles II crowns were minted, and collectors will recognise the relative scarcity of other denominations in comparison. It seems strange that such a large quantity of high denomination coins should be minted until one remembers that much low denomination hammered coinage was still in circulation. In addition, the gold crown was now discontinued, and the crown had to bridge the gap between the halfcrown and the guinea until the first half guineas were minted in 1669.

is in Roman numerals; from 1667 onwards it is in words, except for the rare 1667 numeral edge variety C2CR-120

Obv. 1   Obv. 2

Obv. 3   Obv. 3 Elephant below

Obv. 4   Obv. 5

Rev. 1   Rev. 2

Collecting Hints

A collection of one specimen of each date in fine condition will produce an attractive set of this underpriced series.

For the more sophisticated collector, an upgrading to very fine and/or inclusion of several varieties will give an outstanding and enviable collection.

For the truly serious numismatist, a collection in extremely fine or of a grade as close as possible to extremely fine as possible (one for each major type) is probably all that can be hoped for; lack of buying opportunity and funds will normally prohibit the inclusion of many different dates or minor varieties from a collection in these grades. As with almost all Charles II coinage, the price of specimens rises steeply with each increase in grade.

Denomination	Metal	Weight (grams)	Diameter (mm)	Rev. alignment
Crown 1662-1663	Silver	29.8–30.1	40	↓
Crown 1664-1669	Silver	29.8–30.1	38	↓
Crown 1670-1684	Silver	29.8–30.1	39	↓

But note exceptions below.

Obverse 1 Head 1, right, rose below; CAROLVS II DEI GRA.

Obverse 2 Head 1 with minor alterations, right, no rose; CAROLVS II DEI GRATIA

Obverse 3 Head 2, smaller than Head 1, right; same legend

Obverse 4 Head 3, right; larger, with flat appearance in higher grades; same legend

Obverse 5 Head 4, right; largest head with longer tie; same legend

Reverse 1 Four cruciform shields, top and bottom two quartered (England/France), interlinked pairs of 'C's in angles. MAG BR FRA ET HIB REX (date)

Reverse 2 Similar but shields of England and France separated and not quartered; crowns and harp slightly different

Edge (in relief): Usually DECVS ET TVTAMEN ANNO REGNI (regnal date) but may vary as in tables below. From 1663 to 1666 the regnal date

No.	Date	Features	Edge date	Obv.	Rev.	F	VF	EF
C2CRM-005	1662	[1]		1	1	55	250	1200
C2CRM-010	1662	PROOF [2]		1	1			6000
C2CRM-015	1662	rev. ↑ [2]		1	1	60	300	1400
C2CRM-020	1662	[3]	1662	1	1	65	350	1500
C2CRM-025	1662	[1]		2	1	65	350	1500
C2CRM-030	1662	rev. ↑ [2]		2	1	70	380	1500
C2CRM-035	1662	PROOF; edge plain		2	1			8000
C2CRM-040	1662	[4]	1662	2	1	70	380	1600
C2CRM-045	1663	[5]	XV	2	2	55	250	1200
C2CRM-050	1663	no stops rev.	XV	2	2	70	300	1500
C2CRM-055	1663	[6]		2	2	500		
C2CRM-060	1663	PROOF [7]	XV	2	2			7000
C2CRM-065	1663	PROOF in gold [8]	XV	2	2			40000
C2CRM-070	1664	[9]	XVI	3	2	55	250	1300
C2CRM-075	1664	PROOF	XVI	3	2			7000
C2CRM-080	1665		XVI	3	2	500		

No.	Date	Features	Edge date	Obv.	Rev.	F	VF	EF
C2CRM-085	1665		XVII	3	2	250	1500	
C2CRM-090	1665	5 over 4	XVII	3	2	250	1500	
C2CRM-095	1666		XVIII	3	2	120	900	
C2CRM-100	1666	ANN instead of ANNO (edge)	XVIII	3	2	150	1200	
C2CRM-105	1666	RE.X instead of REX (rev.)	XVIII	3	2	200	1500	
C2CRM-110	1666	elephant below head	XVIII	3	2	300	1500	
C2CRM-115	1666	elephant below head reads RE.X on rev.	XVIII	3	2	400	1200	
C2CRM-120	1667		XVIII	3	2	1500		
C2CRM-125	1667	[10]	DECIMO NONO	3	2	70	350	1700
C2CRM-130	1668		VICESIMO	3	2	60	300	1500
C2CRM-135	1668	DECVS ET TVTAMEN inverted relative to rest of inscription (edge)	VICESIMO	3	2	350	1500	
C2CRM-140	1668	8 over 7	VICESIMO	3	2	70	350	1700
C2CRM-145	1669		VICESIMO PRIMO	3	2	300	1700	
C2CRM-150	1669	9 over 8	VICESIMO PRIMO	3	2	300	1700	
C2CRM-155	1670		VICESIMO SECVNDO	3	2	70	350	1700
C2CRM-160	1670	70 over 69	VICESIMO SECVNDO	3	2	100	600	
C2CRM-165	1671	[11]	VICESIMO TERTIO	3	2	60	250	1500
C2CRM-170	1671	T of ET over R (rev.)	VICESIMO TERTIO	3	2	100	500	
C2CRM-175	1671	ET over FR (rev.)	VICESIMO TERTIO	3	2	140	700	
C2CRM-180	1671		VICESIMO TERTIO	4	2	60	250	1500
C2CRM-185	1671		VICESIMO QVARTO	4	2	700	2000	
C2CRM-190	1672	[9]	VICESIMO QVARTO	4	2	60	250	1500
C2CRM-195	1673		VICESIMO QVARTO	4	2	700	2000	
C2CRM-200	1673	[12]	VICESIMO QVINTO	4	2	60	250	1500
C2CRM-205	1673	3 over 2 [12]	VICESIMO QVINTO	4	2	70	350	1700
C2CRM-210	1674	[13]	VICESIMO SEXTO	4	2	4000		
C2CRM-215	1675		VICESIMO SEPTIMO	4	2	400		
C2CRM-220	1675	EGNI instead of REGNI (edge)	VICESIMO SEPTIMO	4	2	500		
C2CRM-225	1675	5 over 3 [14]	VICESIMO SEPTIMO	4	2	300		
C2CRM-230	1676		VICESIMO OCTAVO	4	2	60	220	1300
C2CRM-235	1676	EGNI instead of REGNI (edge)	VICESIMO OCTAVO	4	2	70	300	1600
C2CRM-240	1677	[15]	VICESIMO NONO	4	2	60	250	1500
C2CRM-245	1677	7 over 6 [16]	VICESIMO NONO	4	2	80	350	1800
C2CRM-250	1678	8 over 7 [17]	TRICESIMO	4	2	160	900	
C2CRM-255	1679		TRICESIMO PRIMO	4	2	60	220	1300
C2CRM-260	1679		TRICESIMO PRIMO	5	2	70	350	1700
C2CRM-265	1679	reads HIBR.EX (rev.)	TRICESIMO PRIMO	5	2	80	400	1800
C2CRM-270	1680		TRICESIMO SECVNDO	4	2	80	350	1700
C2CRM-275	1680	80 over 79	TRICESIMO SECVNDO	4	2	70	300	1500
C2CRM-280	1680		TRICESIMO SECVNDO	5	2	60	250	1500
C2CRM-285	1680	80 over 79	TRICESIMO SECVNDO	5	2	70	300	1600
C2CRM-290	1681		TRICESIMO TERTIO	5	2	70	300	1600
C2CRM-295	1681	elephant and castle below head	TRICESIMO TERTIO	5	2	1200	5000	
C2CRM-300	1682	[18]	TRICESIMO QVARTO	5	2	120	600	2200

No.	Date	Features	Edge date	Obv.	Rev.	F	VF	EF
C2CRM-305	1682	2 over 1	TRICESIMO QVARTO	5	2	80	400	1800
C2CRM-310	1682	QVARTO appears to read QVRRTO (edge) [19]	TRICESIMO QVRRTO	5	2	90	500	2000
C2CRM-315	1682	2 over 1; QVARTO appears to read QVRRTO (edge) [19]	TRICESIMO QVRRTO	5	2	100	600	2400
C2CRM-320	1683	[20]	TRICESIMO QVINTO	5	2	140	1000	
C2CRM-325	1684		TRICESIMO SEXTO	5	2	90	500	

1. Edge reads DECVS ET TVTAMEN; minor varieties exist.
2. Edge reads DECVS ET TVTAMEN.
3. Edge reads DECVS ET TVTAMEN 1662.
4. Edge reads DECVS ET TVTAMEN 1662; minor varieties exist.
5. Some have the crowns and harp of Reverse 1.
6. No edge date.
7. Some or all have the crowns and harp of Reverse 1.
8. Has the crowns and harp of Reverse 1; weight c. 60 grams.
9. Minor obverse varieties exist.
10. Edge stop varieties exist.
11. Occurs with and without stop after HIB (rev.).
12. Minor stop varieties exist.
13. Possibly only one or two exist.
14. Harp alignment varies (rev.).
15. Alignment of latter 7 in date varies.
16. Some have die flaw above head.
17. 8 probably always over 7.
18. Coin without overdate rarer.
19. Edge probably QVARTO over TERTIO.
20. Rarer than denoted in some catalogues.

The number of harp strings varies through this series. It is possible that the variation constituted a form of internal code denoting the die number.

James II 1685–1688

John Roettier continued as chief engraver during the reign of James II. The short and eventful reign of James II was marked by a brief series of coinage spanning just three dates, with no rare varieties and no proofs or patterns.

Collecting Hints

Assembling a set of James II crowns in fine condition, either by date and variety or by type, should present only moderate difficulty; however, some of the varieties are quite rare in very fine or better. Many of the crowns of this series are weakly struck, especially at the top of the wreath on the obverse and at the date. Consequently, very fine specimens may appear to be in a lower grade than they actually are. Adjustment marks are often seen on James II crowns. These marks appear similar to scratches, and were caused by filing the coins before issue to ensure that the weight was correct.

Denomination	Metal	Weight (grams)	Diameter (mm)	Rev. alignment
Crown	Silver	29.8-30.2	38-39	↓

Obverse 1 Head 1, left; IACOBVS II DEI GRATIA

Obverse 2 Head 2, left; smaller, with shorter tie; same legend

Reverse 1 Four cruciform shields; MAG BR FRA ET HIB REX (date)

435

Edge (in relief): DECVS ET TVTAMEN ANNO REGNI (regnal date)

Obv. 1   Obv. 2

Rev. 1

No.	Date	Features	Edge date	Obv.	Rev.	F	VF	EF
J2CR-005	1686		SECVNDO	1	1	80	400	2000
J2CR-010	1686	no stops on obv [1]	SECVNDO	1	1	100	700	5000
J2CR-015	1687	[2]	TERTIO	2	1	70	300	800
J2CR-020	1687	struck on 41mm diameter flan	TERTIO	2	1	100	450	1100
J2CR-025	1688		QVARTO	2	1	80	400	1000
J2CR-030	1688	A in IACOBVS and last A in GRATIA unbarred	QVARTO	2	1	90	500	1200
J2CR-035	1688	8 over 7	QVARTO	2	1	90	500	1200

1. Rare in very fine or better.
2. Edge lettering size varieties exist.

The number of harp strings varies through this series. It is possible that the variation constituted a form of internal code denoting the die number.

William and Mary 1688–1694

Following the removal of James II, his daughter Mary and her husband Prince William of Orange ruled jointly by agreement. Their heads were placed in conjoined fashion on the coinage, with William's head uppermost. This classical style owed much to Greek and Roman coinage, as previous hammered coinage depicting joint rulers was normally designed showing them face to face.

Crowns were not struck until the latter part of the brief reign of William and Mary. Only one type of crown was issued, with no patterns or proofs. The design was unusual in a number of respects: the conjoined heads of a dual monarchy; the central lion of Orange-Nassau on the reverse, and the placement of the date around its four quarters. The happy coincidence of 'W' and 'M' resembling each other when inverted gave rise to the attractive lattice design in the angles of the reverse, and the letters fit so neatly that it is quite possible to collect the coins for years without realising the significance of the lattices.

The William and Mary crown was probably designed by James Roettier aided by his brother Norbert.

Collecting Hints

The crowns of William and Mary are somewhat weakly struck, and a strictly fine condition coin can appear flat and lacking in detail; for this reason it is advisable to acquire specimens nearer very fine if possible. Extremely fine specimens are rare and command high prices. Adjustment marks (see James II) are again often noted on this issue.

Denomination	Metal	Weight (grams)	Diameter (mm)	Rev. alignment
Crown	Silver	29.6–30.0	38–39	↓

Obverse 1 Heads 1, right; GVLIELMVS ET MARIA DEI GRATIA

Reverse 1 Four cruciform shields around lion of Orange-Nassau. MAG BR FR ET HI REX ET REGINA. Monogrammed 'WM' and one digit of date in each angle.

Edge (in relief): DECVS ET TVTAMEN ANNO REGNI (regnal date)

Obv. 1   Rev. 1

No.	Date	Features	Edge date	Obv.	Rev.	F	VF	EF
WMCR-005	1691		TERTIO	1	1	200	500	1500
WMCR-010	1691	TERTTIO instead of TERTIO (edge)	TERTTIO	1	1	250	600	1800
WMCR-015	1692		QVARTO	1	1	200	500	1500
WMCR-020	1692	2 over inverted 2 [1]	QVARTO	1	1	500	1200	3500
WMCR-025	1692	2 over inverted 2	QVINTO	1	1	250	600	1600

1. Rarer than denoted in most catalogues.

The number of harp strings varies through this series. It is possible that the variation constituted a form of internal code denoting the die number.

William III 1695–1701

The short reign of William III, following Mary's death from smallpox in 1694, produced one of the most interesting series of crowns to be minted. The early dies were engraved by James Roettier and, following Roettier's dismissal for smuggling, by John Croker (1670-1740 old style). They include probably the most frequently encountered 17th century crown and also some of the rarest dates and varieties.

Unlike the minor silver coinage, the crowns of William III were not minted at the provincial mints, and thus did not suffer the many spelling and orientation errors which were prolific on the provincial mint coins. The only major spelling error encountered on the crown is the 1696 issue with GEI instead of DEI on the obverse.

Collecting Hints

Whether collecting by date or by type, this series presents a formidable challenge. The stumbling block is the 1697, which is needed whether collecting by date or by type, and which is notoriously difficult to obtain in nice condition. There are a number of minor edge errors which are worth looking out for, and the obverse of any 1696 crown should always be checked for the GEI error.

An attempt should be made to acquire all of the major varieties in fine or better condition. Curiously, one of the scarcer dates, 1700, is possibly more plentiful in very fine condition than in fine. Anyone able to assemble a set including all of the major dates and varieties in very fine grade can be justifiably proud of such an achievement.

Denomination	Metal	Weight (grams)	Diameter (mm)	Rev. alignment
Crown	Silver	29.4-30.0	38-39	↓

Obverse 1 Head 1, curved breastplate, right; GVLIELMVS III DEI GRA

Obverse 2 Head 2, right; straight breastplate, hair at top more profuse. Same legend.

Obverse 3 Head 3, right; die re-engraved, tie of finer design.

Reverse 1 Four cruciform shields, the top of each of which is convex, i.e. points outwards in the centre. Harp with top of left side higher than right. MAG BR FRA ET HIB REX (date)

Reverse 2 Similar but redesigned harp with left and right sides of similar height; shields larger, with centre of top concave, i.e. pointing inwards; central cartouche and lion smaller

Reverse 3 Similar but a different harp

Edge (in relief): DECVS ET TVTAMEN ANNO REGNI (regnal date)

Obv. 1

Obv. 2

Obv. 3

Rev. 1

Rev. 2

Rev. 3

No.	Date	Features	Edge date	Obv.	Rev.	F	VF	EF
W3CR-005	1695		SEPTIMO	1	1	60	180	700
W3CR-010	1695		OCTAVO	1	1	50	150	600
W3CR-015	1695	[1]	OCAVO	1	1	70	250	1000
W3CR-020	1695	PROOF; edge plain [2]		1	1			3500
W3CR-025	1696		OCTAVO	1	1	60	170	600
W3CR-030	1696	NNO instead of ANNO (edge)	OCTAVO	1	1	70	200	750
W3CR-035	1696	[1]	OCAVO	1	1	70	200	750
W3CR-040	1696	PROOF; edge plain [3]		1	1			6000
W3CR-045	1696	PROOF; edge plain; rev. ↑ [3]		1	1			6000
W3CR-050	1696	6 over 5	OCTAVO	1	1	100	300	1200
W3CR-055	1696	6 over 9 or inverted 6	OCTAVO	1	1	100	300	1200
W3CR-060	1696	no stops in obv legend	OCTAVO	1	1	90	250	1000
W3CR-065	1696	G of GRA over D (obv.)	OCTAVO	1	1	70	200	750
W3CR-070	1696	GEI instead of DEI (obv.) [4]	OCTAVO	1	1	120	1500	
W3CR-075	1696		OCTAVO	2	1	90	300	1000
W3CR-080	1696	no stops in rev. legend	OCTAVO	2	1	120	350	1400
W3CR-085	1696	edge lettering blundered	OCTOCTAVO OCTAVTAVO or similar	2	1	120	500	2000
W3CR-090	1696		TRICESIMO	2	1	1000		
W3CR-095	1697	[5]	NONO	2	2	400	2000	
W3CR-100	1700	[6]	DVODECIMO	3	3	90	150	500
W3CR-105	1700		DECIMO TERTIO	3	3	150	250	1000
W3CR-110	1700	D over reversed D in DECIMO (edge)	DECIMO TERTIO	3	3	180	300	1200

1. Edge date misspelt.
2. Border teeth wider; reverse ↓ as ordinary issue; may have die flaws.
3. Rev differs slightly from usual Reverse 1.
4. Extremely rare above fine condition.
5. May not exist in EF+.
6. Possibly most plentiful date in VF+ grade.

The number of harp strings varies through this series. It is possible that the variation constituted a form of internal code denoting the die number.

Anne 1702–1714

For the coinage of Anne, John Croker, together with his assistant Samuel Bull (d. 1726), produced a portrait of the queen based on a painting by Sir Godfrey Kneller.

This series includes a number of notable 'firsts'. Provenance marks (marks showing the origin of the metal) used for the first time are: VIGO for silver obtained from Spanish galleons at Vigo Bay in 1702; plumes (in the angles on the reverse) for silver from Wales; roses and plumes (also in the reverse angles) for silver from the 'Company for smelting down lead with Pitcoale and Seacoale'. Stephen Martin Leake, writing at the time, comments that roses and plumes coins were referred to as 'Quaker's Money', because Quakers were considered prominent amongst the owners of the mines. E below the head of Anne indicates that the coins were struck at Edinburgh.

After the Union of England and Scotland in 1707, the top and bottom shields on the reverse were each divided into the arms of England and Scotland. Before the Union the arms of England and Scotland had been allocated separate shields.

Collecting Hints

With the possible exception of 1705, a serious collector will attempt to obtain a specimen of each main date or type in very fine or better condition. The 1703 and 1713 are actually easier to find in very fine than are the otherwise more plentiful dates such as 1707 and 1708. However, the overall date scarcity of 1703 and 1713 still makes them more expensive than 1707 and 1708. All dates are rare in UNC condition.

Adjustment marks continue to be a problem with crowns of this period. Further care must also be taken because Anne crowns are sometimes found with traces of brooch mounting on the reverse. The marks often coincide with the position of the crowns above the shields, and can be easily missed if one is not careful. Care must also be taken that hairlines have not been re-engraved.

Denomination	Metal	Weight (grams)	Diameter (mm)	Rev. alignment
Crown	Silver	29.9-30.3	38–40	↓

Obverse 1 Head 1, left; ANNA DEI GRATIA

Obverse 2 Head 2, slightly larger, left; same legend

Obverse 3 Head 3, left; hair re-engraved and more detailed; same legend

Reverse 1 Four undivided cruciform shields around central lion of the Garter; MAG BR FRA ET HIB REG (date). Usually known as the 'Before Union' reverse

Reverse 2 Similar but shields are wider and the top and bottom are each divided into the arms of England and Scotland. BR FRA of legend now becomes BRI FR. Known as 'After Union' reverse.

Reverse 3 As Reverse 2 but BR FRA in legend as on Reverse 1.

Edge (in relief): DECVS ET TVTAMEN ANNO REGNI (regnal date)

Obv. 1   Obv. 2

Obv. 3

Rev. 1   Rev. 2

Before Union of England and Scotland

No.	Date	Features	Edge date	Obv.	Rev.	F	VF	EF
ACR-005	1703	VIGO below head [1]	TERTIO	1	1	130	400	1200
ACR-010	1705	plumes on rev.	QVINTO	1	1	180	500	1600
ACR-015	1706	roses and plumes on rev. [2]	QVINTO	1	1	120	400	1200
ACR-020	1707	roses and plumes on rev.	SEXTO	1	1	110	350	1000

1. Reverse is struck in lower relief than later pieces; flan sometimes slightly larger than most other dates.
2. Flan often slightly larger than most other dates.

After Union of England and Scotland

No.	Date	Features	Edge date	Obv.	Rev.	F	VF	EF
ACR-025	1707	E below head	SEXTO	2	2	90	270	750
ACR-030	1707	E below head	SEPTIMO	2	2	1500		
ACR-035	1707		SEPTIMO	2	2	100	300	850
ACR-040	1708		SEPTIMO	2	2	150	450	1200
ACR-045	1708	plumes on rev.	SEPTIMO	2	2	110	350	1000
ACR-050	1708	plumes on rev. [1]	SEPTIMO	2	3	1500		
ACR-055	1708	E below head	SEPTIMO	2	2	100	300	800
ACR-060	1708	8 over 7 E below head	SEPTIMO	2	2	110	350	1000
ACR-065	1713	roses and plumes on rev.	DVODECIMO	3	2	110	270	700
ACR-070	1713	roses and plumes on rev.	DVODECIM (error)	3	2	120	350	900

1. Exists?

The number of harp strings varies through this series. It is possible that the variation constituted a form of internal code denoting the die number.

George I 1714–1727

John Croker and a Swiss engraver, Johann Rudolf Ochs (b. 1673), appear to have been responsible for engraving the dies for this series, which continues the general overall design of earlier series, with some modifications.

With the accession of George Louis, Elector of Hanover, as King George I, the crown was redesigned to include the Hanoverian line. The German titles of the king appear in the reverse legend, while one of the reverse shields now contain the arms of Brunswick-Lüneburg.

The title of FIDEI DEFENSOR (Defender of the Faith), often shortened to FID DEF, or in this case F.D., appears for the first time.

Provenance marks of this series are: roses and plumes (in the angles on the reverse) for silver from the 'Company for smelting down lead with Pitcoale and Seacoale', and SSC in the reverse angles, denoting silver from the South Sea Company.

There are no pattern or proof crowns of George I.

Denomination	Metal	Weight (grams)	Diameter (mm)	Rev. alignment
Crown	Silver	30.0	38–39	↓

Obverse 1 Head 1, GEORGIVS D G M BR FR ET HIB REX F D

Reverse 1 Four cruciform shields. BRVN ET L DVX S R I A TH ET EL (date)

Edge (in relief): (1716 & 1726) DECVS ET TVTAMEN ANNO REGNI (regnal date)

(1718-23) DECUS ET TUTAMEN ANNO REGNI (regnal date)

Obv. 1   Rev. 1

No.	Date	Features	Edge date	Obv.	Rev.	F	VF	EF
G1CR-005	1716	roses and plumes on rev.	SECVNDO	1	1	200	400	1200
G1CR-010	1718	roses and plumes on rev. [1]	QUINTO	1	1	260	650	1800
G1CR-015	1718	8 over 6 roses and plumes on rev. [1]	QUINTO	1	1	230	500	1400
G1CR-020	1720	roses and plumes on rev.	SEXTO	1	1	260	650	1800
G1CR-025	1720	20 over 18 roses and plumes on rev.	SEXTO	1	1	230	500	1400
G1CR-030	1723	SSC on rev.	DECIMO	1	1	200	420	1300
G1CR-035	1726	roses and plumes on rev. [2]	DECIMO TERTIO	1	1	220	500	1400
G1CR-040	1726	roses and plumes on rev.; each N on edge inverted (top left of N has no serif) [3]	DECIMO TERTIO	1	1	250	550	1500

1. Edge reads QUINTO, not QVINTO as in some catalogues.
2. Roses and plumes are slightly smaller than on previous dates.
3. A similar variety occurs on the 1726 five guineas.

The number of harp strings varies through this series. It is possible that the variation constituted a form of internal code denoting the die number.

George II 1727–1760

The crowns of George II are of two distinct types, those bearing the young head designed by Croker and those depicting the old head designed by Tanner (d. 1775), who had come to England from Germany in 1728, and who succeeded Croker as Chief Engraver after the latter's death in 1740. Although there are ten different dates, all crowns of George II are scarce, and particularly so in the high grades.

Provenance marks seen for the first time are: roses (without plumes), denoting silver from mines in the West of England; and LIMA below the head, for coins struck from silver captured by Admiral Anson during his voyages around the world. The use of the term LIMA has not been satisfactorily explained, but presumably it is possible that the mark was meant to duplicate the mint-mark on some of the captured silver coinage. It may, however, be wrong to call it a provenance mark.

It was noted towards the end of the 18th century that George II crowns 'disappeared as soon as coined, and, indeed, are too burdensome for common use, two halfcrowns better answering the purpose'.

Denomination	Metal	Weight (grams)	Diameter (mm)	Rev. alignment
Crown	Silver	29.5-30.0	38–39	↓

Obverse 1 Head 1, GEORGIVS II DEI GRATIA

Obverse 2 Head 2, older; same legend but GEORGIUS instead of GEORGIVS

Obverse 3 Head 2; same legend but GEORGIVS

Reverse 1 Four crowned cruciform shields. M B F ET H REX F D B ET L D S R I A T ET E (date)

Reverse 2 Similar but a different harp

Edge (in relief): DECVS ET TVTAMEN ANNO REGNI (regnal date)

Obv. 1   Obv. 3

439

Rev. 1   Rev. 2

No.	Date	Features	Edge date	Obv.	Rev.	F	VF	EF
G2CR-005	1731	[1]	(unknown)	1	1			
G2CR-010	1732	roses and plumes on rev. [2]	SEXTO	1	1	200	350	750
G2CR-015	1732	roses and plumes on rev. PROOF; edge plain		1	1			3000
G2CR-020	1734	roses and plumes on rev. [2]	SEPTIMO	1	2	220	380	850
G2CR-025	1734	roses and plumes on rev.; edge reads DEC... AME...NNO REGNI [2]	SEPTIMO	1	2	350	600	
G2CR-030	1735	roses and plumes on rev. [2]	OCTAVO	1	2	210	360	800
G2CR-035	1735	roses and plumes on rev.; each 'E' on edge is over a 'B' [2]	OCTAVO	1	2	280	500	1000
G2CR-040	1735	T of OCTAVO over V (edge) [2]	OCTAVO	1	2	280	500	1000
G2CR-045	1736	roses and plumes on rev.	NONO	1	2	200	350	750
G2CR-050	1739	roses on rev.	DVO-DECIMO	1	2	180	320	650
G2CR-055	1741	roses on rev.	DECIMO QVARTO	1	2	180	320	650
G2CR-060	1743	roses on rev.	DECIMO SEPTIMO	2	2	180	320	650
G2CR-065	1746	LIMA below head	DECIMO NONO	3	2	200	320	600
G2CR-070	1746	PROOF [3]	VICESIMO	3	2			1800
G2CR-075	1750		VICESIMO QVARTO	3	2	250	400	800
G2CR-080	1751	[4]	VICESIMO QVARTO	3	2	260	420	900

1. Plain in reverse angles; reported by Folkes in 1763 to weigh 30.0 grams; possibly a pattern; existence unknown today.
2. Often struck on slightly ovoid flan.
3. No LIMA below head; wider beading than on currency crowns.
4. Same regnal edge year as 1750 coin.

The number of harp strings varies through this series. It is possible that the variation constituted a form of internal code denoting the die number.

The reverse legend and date on the 1750 and 1751 coins are more finely formed than on previous dates.

George III 1760–1820

The crown series of George III, using the term in its broadest sense, is extraordinary! For many years, hardly any silver coinage was produced, owing to an acute shortage of the metal. Although a profusion of shillings and sixpences was issued in 1787, it became apparent towards the end of the century that a new issue of crowns and halfcrowns was needed. A large number of captured Spanish American silver dollars (8 reales) was available, and, in fact, were being unofficially used as currency. It was therefore decided to countermark the obverse of each Spanish 8 reales with an oval stamp bearing the head of George III. The punch was the official one used at Goldsmith's Hall for marking silver, but the counterstamping itself was done at the mint. These coun-

termarked dollars were issued in 1797 with a nominal value of 4 shillings and 9 pence. A few silver ecus of France and American dollars also appear to have been counterstamped at that time. A good deal of satirical comment was passed about the counterstamping of the Spanish coins, including the saying that the product depicted 'the head of a fool on the head of an ass', and 'two Kings' heads are not worth a crown', this last being a comment on the nominal value of 4 shillings and 9 pence.

It soon became apparent that a large quantity of coins bearing forged countermarks were in circulation. An alteration was therefore made to the shape and size of the counterstamp. This was changed to an octagonal form with a larger head of the king. Taken from a Maundy penny die, this too proved a target for forgers, and often the striking was too shallow. In 1804 it was decided that the Spanish dollars should be completely overstruck with new dies. These were made by Küchler at Matthew Boulton's Soho mint in Birmingham. It was to create a new issue, to be called 'Bank of England Dollars'. This issue includes a large number of die varieties and proofs, and carried the first depiction of Britannia on a silver coin. A further issue was made in 1810 and 1811, all of the coins still bearing the date 1804.

Curiously, the only issue of true crowns was struck during just the last three years of the long reign of George III, beginning in October 1818. This marked the beginning of the 'Great Recoinage of 1816' using new equipment in new premises at Tower Hill, London. The striking is of unusually fine quality. Although struck in fairly low relief, it is not uncommon for high grade specimens to be mistaken for proofs because of their mirror fields. The design by Benedetto Pistrucci (1784-1855) includes the first representation of St George and the dragon on a silver coin, a tradition that has continued on coinage to the present day. At the time, Pistrucci was living at Brunet's Hotel, Leicester Square, London, and St George is said to have been modelled on a waiter at the hotel.

Benedetto Pistrucci was a temperamental Italian gem-engraver who had found favour with William Wellesley Pole, the Master of the Mint. Some measure of his egotism can be determined by the placement of his name in full on both obverse and reverse of the crown. Although he was considered by many to be a slow worker, he was very defensive about this reputation.

Collecting Hints

Almost all collectors of countermarked Spanish American dollars will collect one of each type of counterstamp combined with one of each mintmark of the original coin, i.e. Mexico City, Lima, etc. However, there is no reason at all why one should not collect also by date of the original coin, although it would be a formidable, yet fascinating task, not least because of its educational value.

It should be remembered that the grade of a counter-marked coin is normally taken as the grade of the countermark, but obviously if the original coin is in superior condition the piece will be that much more desirable. Since the octagonal counterstamp was taken from the Maundy penny die, comparison with the penny provides a useful way of detecting the many coins bearing false octagonal counterstamps.

The most interesting characteristics of the series of Bank Dollars are the diverse die varieties of both obverse and reverse. The various combination of these produce a wide array of collectable material. The copper proofs are an integral part of the series and should not be ignored. This series was overstruck on Spanish American dollars, and sometimes one comes across a piece on which the original date on the underlying coin is visible. Even more interestingly, one can also occasionally encounter specimens on which the date on the underlying coin is after 1804. This clearly shows that the dollars were overstruck with the 1804 date for some years after that date.

Only in extremely fine or better condition can the quality of the excellent striking of the series of crowns of 1818 to 1820 be appreciated. The novice collector may understandably sometimes believe he has acquired a proof, owing to the high quality of the finish, but the true proofs are sharper, often with a steely blue hue around the main design.

Obverse 13 Similar but on Spain 8 reales

Obverse 14 Similar but on France ecu

Obverse 15 Similar but on American dollar

Reverse As of the appropriate host coin, partially flattened where stamped

Edge As of the appropriate host coin

Obv. oval counterstamp

Obv. octagonal counterstamp

Rev.

Denomination	Metal	Weight (grams)	Diameter (mm)	Rev. alignment
Counterstamped Spanish/Sp American dollar	Silver	c.27	38–40	↑

Denomination	Metal	Weight (grams)	Diameter (mm)	Rev. alignment
Counterstamped French ecu or US dollar	Silver	27-30	c.40	as host coin

Oval Counterstamp

Obverse 1 George III head, right, in oval counterstamped on Mexico 8 reales obverse

Obverse 2 Similar but on Peru 8 reales

Obverse 3 Similar but on Bolivia 8 reales

Obverse 4 Similar but on Guatemala 8 reales

Obverse 5 Similar but on Chile 8 reales

Obverse 6 Similar but on Spain 8 reales

Obverse 7 Similar but on France ecu

Obverse 8 Similar but on American dollar

Octagonal Counterstamp

Obverse 9 George III head in octagon counterstamped on Mexico 8 reales obverse

Obverse 10 Similar but on Peru 8 reales

Obverse 11 Similar but on Bolivia 8 reales

Obverse 12 Similar but on Guatemala 8 reales

No.	Date	Obv.	Rev.	F	VF	EF
G3CR-005	none	1	1	90	160	300
G3CR-010	none	2	2	120	210	400
G3CR-015	none	3	3	150	250	550
G3CR-020	none	4	4	200	400	700
G3CR-025	none	5	5	300	600	1000
G3CR-030	none	6	6	300	600	1000
G3CR-035	none	7	7	500		
G3CR-040	none	8	8	3000		
G3CR-045	none	9	9	120	260	450
G3CR-050	none	10	10	350	700	
G3CR-055	none	11	11	180	400	700
G3CR-060	none	12	12	600	1200	
G3CR-065	none	13	13	450	900	
G3CR-070	none	14	14	2500		
G3CR-075	none	15	15	2000		

Denomination	Metal	Weight (grams)	Diameter (mm)	Rev. alignment
Bank of England Dollar	Silver	25–28	41	↑

Obverse 1 Head 1, right; C.H.K.(with stops) on truncation. GEORGIUS III DEI GRATIA REX (stop after REX); top leaf points to left hand side of 'E'

Obverse 2 As obverse 1 but C.H.K reads CHK (no stops)

Obverse 3 As obverse 1 but leaf points to centre of 'E'

Obverse 4 As obverse 3 but no stop after REX

Obverse 5 As obverse 1 but leaf points to right hand side of 'E'

Reverse 1 Britannia seated, with shield, in oval garter, this inscribed FIVE SHILLINGS DOLLAR; BANK OF ENGLAND 1804 around rim. Small 'K' in relief below shield

Reverse 2 As Reverse 1 but 'K' is inverted (in relief)

Reverse 3 As Reverse 1 but 'K' is inverted and incuse

Edge plain or with faint patterning of squares

Obv. 1

Obv. 1 details

Obv. 3   Obv. 4   Obv. 5

Rev. 1

No.	Date	Features	Obv.	Rev.	F	VF	EF
G3CR-080	1804		1	1	75	130	300
G3CR-085	1804	PROOF	1	1			600
G3CR-090	1804	PROOF in copper	1	1			400
G3CR-095	1804		1	3	120	240	600
G3CR-100	1804		2	1	100	200	500
G3CR-105	1804	PROOF	2	1			750
G3CR-110	1804		3	1	100	200	500
G3CR-115	1804	PROOF	3	1			500
G3CR-120	1804	PROOF in silver gilt	3	1			1000
G3CR-125	1804	PROOF in copper	3	1			350
G3CR-130	1804		3	2	100	200	500
G3CR-135	1804	PROOF	3	2			600

No.	Date	Features	Obv.	Rev.	F	VF	EF
G3CR-140	1804	PROOF in copper	3	2			400
G3CR-145	1804		3	3	100	200	500
G3CR-150	1804	PROOF in copper	3	3			750
G3CR-155	1804		4	1	85	150	350
G3CR-160	1804	PROOF	4	1			600
G3CR-165	1804	PROOF in copper [1]	4	1			400
G3CR-170	1804		5	1	150	300	700
G3CR-175	1804		5	2	120	240	600
G3CR-180	1804	PROOF	5	2			600
G3CR-185	1804	PROOF in copper	5	2			600
G3CR-190	1804		5	3	120	240	600
G3CR-195	1804	PROOF in copper	5	3			600

1. Flan thickness varies.

Denomination	Metal	Weight (grams)	Diameter (mm)	Rev. alignment
Crown	Silver	28.3	39	↓

Obverse 1 Head 1, right; GEORGIUS III D G BRITANNIARUM REX F D (date)

Reverse 1 St George and dragon within Garter. HONI SOIT QUI MAL Y PENSE

Edge (in relief): DECUS ET TUTAMEN ANNO REGNI (regnal date)

Obv. 1   Rev. 1

No.	Date	Features	Edge date	Obv.	Rev.	F	VF	EF	UNC
G3CR-200	1818		LVIII	1	1	20	60	250	450
G3CR-205	1818	PROOF	LVIII	1	1				1200
G3CR-210	1818	edge DECVS ANNO REGNI ET TVTAMEN [1]	LVIII	1	1	800	2000	4500	
G3CR-215	1818		LIX	1	1	20	60	250	450
G3CR-220	1819	[2]	LIX	1	1	20	60	250	450
G3CR-225	1819	9 over 8	LIX	1	1	25	90	400	700
G3CR-230	1819	no edge stops	LIX	1	1	25	90	400	700
G3CR-235	1819	[3]	LX	1	1	20	70	280	500
G3CR-240	1819	PROOF	LX	1	1				1200
G3CR-245	1819	PROOF; edge plain		1	1				5000
G3CR-250	1820	[4]	LX	1	1	20	60	250	450
G3CR-255	1820	20 over 19	LX	1	1	25	90	400	700
G3CR-260	1820	S of SOIT over T (rev.)	LX	1	1	25	80	300	500
G3CR-265	1820	PROOF	LX	1	1				1200

1. Error edge; wording transposed.
2. Variety occurs with garter slightly wider.
3. Occurs with and without stop after TVTAMEN (edge).
4. Occurs with and without stop after TVTAMEN (edge); this date continued to be minted after death of George III.

Currency coins of this series were struck almost to proof standard.

George IV 1820–1830

Benedetto Pistrucci, the designer of the George III head, executed a laureate head of George IV for the crown, while on the reverse the St George and dragon were enlarged and the surrounding

Garter and legend omitted. Although now considered by many a handsome piece, the king considered the portrait unflattering, and the 1826 proof coinage exhibited a new and younger portrait by William Wyon (1795-1851), based on a bust by Sir Francis Legatt Chantrey (1781-1842). The St George and dragon reverse was also discontinued in favour of an elaborate crowned shield design, although the use of Pistrucci's St George and dragon design was far from over.

The initials W.W.P. appear in tiny letters in the ground line to the left of the dragon on the reverse, and are those of William Wellesley Pole, Master of the Mint.

Collecting Hints

As with the crowns of George III, fine condition specimens do not allow one to appreciate the characteristic high quality of production of this series; an 'as struck' specimen of an 1821 or 1822 crown is a delight to the eye, especially if with an original tone. Look for signs of wear on St George reverses in the form of a whiteness on St George's head and breast, on the dragon's body, and down the central line of the sword. Proof 1826 crowns will normally be in high grade, and most collectors will require only perfect or near-perfect specimens.

Denomination	Metal	Weight (grams)	Diameter (mm)	Rev. alignment
Crown	Silver	28.3	39	↓

Obverse 1 Head 1, laureate, left; GEORGIUS IIII D G BRITANNIAR REX F D

Obverse 2 Head 2, so-called 'bare head', left; GEORGIUS IV DEI GRATIA 1826

Reverse 1 St George and dragon, date in exergue below. WWP (see above) in groundline

Reverse 2 Crowned garnished shield; BRITANNIARUM REX FID DEF; scroll below inscribed DIEU ET MON DROIT

Edge (in relief): DECUS ET TVTAMEN ANNO REGNI (regnal date). The edge lettering is smaller on the 1826 issue

Obv. 1   Obv. 2

Rev. 1   Rev. 2

No.	Date	Features	Edge date	Obv.	Rev.	F	VF	EF	UNC
G4CR-005	1821		SECUNDO	1	1	20	70	350	800
G4CR-010	1821	WWP initials inverted (rev.)	SECUNDO	1	1	30	90	500	950
G4CR-015	1821	PROOF	SECUNDO	1	1				2500
G4CR-020	1821	PROOF in copper	SECUNDO	1	1				900
G4CR-025	1821	PROOF in copper; edge plain		1	1				900
G4CR-030	1821	PROOF [1]	TERTIO	1	1				4000
G4CR-035	1822		SECUNDO	1	1	25	100	550	1100
G4CR-040	1822	PROOF	SECUNDO	1	1				3500
G4CR-045	1822		TERTIO	1	1	22	80	450	950
G4CR-050	1822	PROOF	TERTIO	1	1				2500
G4CR-055	1823	PROOF; edge plain		1	1				
G4CR-060	1823	PROOF in white metal; edge plain		1	1				15000
G4CR-065	1825	PROOF or pattern; edge plain		2	2				5000
G4CR-070	1825	PROOF or pattern in Barton's metal; edge plain		2	2				3500
G4CR-075	1826	PROOF [2]	SEPTIMO	2	2				3000
G4CR-080	1826	PROOF; edge plain [3]		2	2				5000
G4CR-085	1826	PROOF (?) [4]	LVIII	2	2			7000	

1. Error edge; see note below.
2. Issued in cased proof sets.
3. Some may weigh below 28 grams.
4. Incuse edge lettering; possibly unique; see note below.

The fact that the 1821 error edge crowns are all proofs possibly indicates that this coin is more in the nature of a pattern than a genuine error coin.

Barton's metal is a laminated product consisting of thin sheets of gold bonded to a copper base.

James Morton has pointed out that, although the 1826 proof crown with regnal year LVIII is usually described as having an error date of the previous reign, the edge closely resembles in style that of the young head Victorian crown. He suggests that the coin may have been struck as a trial piece for the Victorian edge collar (around 1840?) and that the use of George IV dies may have been fortuitous.

William IV 1830–1837

One of the rarest issues, the series has an obverse by William Wyon and a reverse by Jean Baptiste Merlen and is highly prized by collectors. The crowns can perhaps be properly described either as patterns or proofs. Certainly the inclusion of the 1831 in the proof set of that year merits its inclusion in this catalogue.

Collecting Hints

Most collectors will lack the opportunity to acquire anything other than a specimen of the standard 1831 proof crown; the acquisition of this piece is in itself a considerable achievement owing to its rarity.

A number of electrotype copies of the 1831 piece exist. These were initially fashioned in two halves, and an edge examination of any specimen, especially if in about very fine condition, is essential; if there is a line down the middle, or if the coin does not 'ring' clearly on striking when placed horizontally on one finger, it is almost certainly not genuine. However, electrotypes do have a significant value as collectors' pieces.

Denomination	Metal	Weight (grams)	Diameter (mm)	Rev. alignment
Crown	Silver	27.0-28.0	39	↓

Obverse 1 Head 1, right; GULIELMUS IIII D G BRITANNIAR REX F D.

W W incuse on truncation of head

Obverse 2 Head 1, right; same legend; W WYON in relief on truncation

Reverse 1 Crowned shield on mantle; below: ANNO (date)

Edge (on 1832 only) DECUS ET TUTAMEN ANNO REGNI TERTIO (in raised lettering) between two ornate raised borders

Obv. 1   Rev. 1

No.	Date	Features	Edge date	Obv.	Rev.	EF	FDC
W4CR-005	1831	PROOF; edge plain [1]		1	1		4000
W4CR-010	1831	PROOF in gold; edge plain [2]		1	1		60000
W4CR-015	1831	PROOF; edge plain [3]		2	1		5000
W4CR-020	1831	PROOF; edge plain; rev. ↑		2	1		7000
W4CR-025	1832	PROOF in lead [4]	TERTIO	1	1	4000	
W4CR-030	1834	PROOF; edge plain		1	1	9000	11000

1. Issued in cased proof sets.
2. Weight 40 to 41 grams, possibly made to correspond to 5 pound piece weight.
3. Reverse ↓ as stated above; see also subsequent coin.
4. Weight 28.3 grams; minor reverse differences from usual Reverse 1; possibly only two exist.

Victoria 1837–1901

The first crowns of Victoria were the plain edge proofs struck in 1839 for incorporation in the cased proof sets of that year. No currency crowns were struck at that time, but a slightly modified design was used to strike currency pieces in 1844, 1845 and 1847. In 1847 there was issued one of the most famous and elegant coins ever struck, the Victorian 'Gothic' crown. Its design was a bold and daring departure from previous issues, and Victoria is reported to have been delighted with it. The reason for its issue remains a mystery, but possibly it was connected with the tenth anniversary of the accession. The lettering on both sides and on the edge is in superbly crafted Gothic script, with the date in Roman numerals. The queen is wearing a crown, not nowadays considered unusual on a coin, but at that time not seen on a British coin since the 17th century.

The Gothic crown was reissued in 1853 for inclusion in the cased proof set, and, apart from patterns, occurs only with these two dates. There is, however, something of a mystery resulting from Victorian numismatic literature. Many books refer to a crown dated 1851, usually of the young head type, whereas no such coin appears to exist. It seems that plagiarism without checking facts was rife in Victorian numismatic circles. Possibly the story emanated from a source who was unable to read Gothic numerals correctly! Another mystery is that several books of 1850-70 fail to mention the Gothic crown in the listings. Possibly the Gothic crown was considered a pseudo-medal? It certainly resembles a medal in some ways, although it must be remembered that it appears in the 1853 proof sets, presumably as a crown piece.

The 1879 crown is a curious piece. According to the Royal Mint, it appears to have been struck for exhibition and presentation purposes, with some being supplied to 'certain well-placed indi-

viduals'. Note also the existence of somewhat curious proofs of other denominations dated 1879.

The crowns of 1887 to 1892 were the first to be issued with a milled edge, and circulated widely. However, they were disliked because of the portrait of the Queen wearing a ridiculously small crown. The 1893 to 1900 issue was better received.

H. W. Henfrey wrote, puzzlingly, of the denomination in 1885: 'They were driven out of circulation by the bankers, who sent to the Mint for silver, and the employers who sent to their banks for silver, both of whom so constantly stipulated against taking five-shilling pieces that they remained in the hands of the Mint. Yet about £2000 worth of these coins are made every year to go to the Falkland Islands. There, the whalers, English, German, Swedes and Americans assemble to pass the winter in harbour, and amongst them the only accepted currency is the English five-shilling piece; for them, therefore, it is manufactured, and to the Falkland Islands it is sent. This noble coin, by far the handsomest in our country, is now no longer issued in this country, and will soon become as much a thing of the past as guineas'.

The young head and Gothic crown obverses were designed by William Wyon. The young head reverse was probably by Johann Baptiste Merlen, and the Gothic reverse was by William Dyce. With regard to the 1887 to 1900 issue, the reverses used the old Pistrucci St George and dragon design from the crowns of 1821 and 1822. The jubilee head obverse was by Sir Joseph Edgar Boehm (1834-1890) and the veiled head by Sir Thomas Brock (b.1847).

Collecting Hints

Although the young head crown is a frequently encountered coin in fine condition, it is notoriously difficult to obtain in a grade of extremely fine or better, and the value accordingly rises steeply, one's aspirations competing with one's wallet. A set of the three dates in mint condition or near would certainly be a difficult goal to achieve.

The 'Gothic' crown is often considered to be the most beautiful crown minted. It is not a rare coin but high international demand maintains its high price and ensures that it will in turn always be resaleable. Many forgeries exist; a genuine 1847 lettered edge coin will usually 'look' old and have sharp edge lettering in the higher grades. The 'V' of 'Victoria' will align approximately with 'et' on the edge and with 'tur' of 'tueatur' on the reverse. However, note that the alignment of the plain edge type is exactly opposite to this, i.e. at 180 degrees. In this case, of course, the 'et' on the edge will not be evident. This alignment check is also useful in determining whether a lettered edge type has had its edge lettering removed. Always carefully check the date and the edge in case the dealer or auction house has been careless — you may pick up a bargain, even an 1846 pattern!

The Jubilee and Old Head series should be collected in at least extremely fine condition, preferably with each regnal date variety. When grading, attention should be paid to the sharpness of the edge lettering as well as that of the design.

Care must be taken in distinguishing the 1887 proof crown from the many early strikings of the ordinary coin. On the proof, the 'knife edge' of the milling is of the same width straight across, and is so sharp that it almost cuts the fingers; on an ordinary coin the indentations forming the milling have a slightly convex appearance.

Denomination	Metal	Weight (grams)	Diameter (mm)	Rev. alignment
Crown 1839	Silver	28.1-28.3	39	↑
Crown 1844-1853	Silver	28.3	39	↓
Crown 1887-1900	Silver	28.3	39	↑

Obverse 1 Head 1, left; VICTORIA DEI GRATIA with 'T' of Victoria level with tip of nose. Date below head

Obverse 2 Head 1, left; VICTORIA DEI GRATIA in larger lettering with 'O' of VICTORIA level with tip of nose. Date below head

Obverse 3 Head 2, 'Gothic' type, left; VICTORIA DEI GRATIA BRITANNIAR REG F D in Gothic script

Obverse 4 Head 3, 'Jubilee' type with small crown on head, left; VICTORIA D G BRITT REG F D

Obverse 5 Head 4, 'Old Head' type, left; VICTORIA DEI GRA BRITT REGINA FID DEF IND IMP

Reverse 1 Crowned shield within branches. BRITANNIARUM REGINA FID DEF

Reverse 2 'Gothic' type. Cruciform shields, TUEATUR UNITA DEUS ANNO DOM (date in numerals) in Gothic script

Reverse 3 St George and dragon, date in exergue below

Edge 1844-1847, head 1: (incuse) DECUS ET TUTAMEN ANNO REGNI (regnal date). 1847-1853, head 2, Gothic issue: (in relief): DECUS ET TUTAMEN ANNO REGNI (regnal date). 1887-1892: milled. 1893-1900: (in relief): DECUS ET TUTAMEN ANNO REGNI (regnal date)

Obv. 5   Rev. 1

Rev. 2   Rev. 3

Obv. 1   Obv. 2

Obv. 3   Obv. 4

No.	Date	Features	Edge date	Obv.	Rev.	F	VF	EF	UNC
VYCR-005	1839	PROOF; edge plain [1]		1	1				3500
VYCR-010	1844	[2]	VIII	2	1	22	70	800	2500
VYCR-015	1844	edge inscription struck twice in different positions	VIII	2	1	100	400		
VYCR-020	1844	PROOF	VIII	2	1				8000
VYCR-025	1845	[2]	VIII	2	1	22	70	800	2500
VYCR-030	1845	AANNO instead of ANNO (edge)	VIII	2	1	40	120		
VYCR-035	1845	PROOF	VIII	2	1				8000
VYCR-040	1845	PROOF; edge plain [3]		2	1				10000
VYCR-045	1845	PROOF; edge plain; rev. ↑ [3]		2	1				10000
VYCR-050	1847		XI	2	1	25	90	1000	3000
VYCR-055	1847	edge milled [4]		2	1				15000
VGCR-060	1847	PROOF	UNDECIMO	3	2	240	350	600	900
VGCR-065	1847	PROOF in fine silver; heavily frosted; rev. ↑ [5]	UNDECIMO	3	2				1500
VGCR-070	1847	PROOF; edge plain; rev. ↑ [6]		3	2	280	450	800	1200
VGCR-075	1847	PROOF, frosted [7]	UNDECIMO	3	2				1800
VGCR-080	1847	PROOF; edges chamfered; lettering weak; rev. ↑	UNDECIMO	3	2				1800
VGCR-085	1847	PROOF in gold; edge plain		3	2				60000
VGCR-090	1847	PROOF in white metal; edge plain		3	2				2500
VGCR-095	1847	PROOF; rev. ↑ [8]	DECIMO SEPTIMO	3	2				8000
VGCR-100	1853	PROOF [1]	DECIMO SEPTIMO	3	2				3500
VGCR-105	1853	PROOF; edge plain		3	2				5000
VYCR-110	1879	PROOF; edge plain [9]		2	1				50000
VJCR-115	1887			4	3	12	20	40	70
VJCR-120	1887	PROOF [10]		4	3				500
VJCR-125	1888			4	3	24	50	120	200
VJCR-130	1888	narrow date [11]		4	3	16	35	80	140
VJCR-135	1889			4	3	10	20	50	90
VJCR-140	1890			4	3	12	30	70	120
VJCR-145	1891			4	3	12	35	80	130
VJCR-150	1892			4	3	12	40	90	140

445

No.	Date	Features	Edge date	Obv.	Rev.	F	VF	EF	UNC
VOCR-155	1893		LVI	5	3	12	35	120	180
VOCR-160	1893	PROOF[1]	LVI	5	3				550
VOCR-165	1893		LVII	5	3	14	50	150	220
VOCR-170	1894	[12]	LVII	5	3	14	50	150	220
VOCR-175	1894	[12]	LVIII	5	3	14	50	150	220
VOCR-180	1895		LVIII	5	3	14	50	150	220
VOCR-185	1895		LIX	5	3	14	50	150	220
VOCR-190	1896		LIX	5	3	14	55	170	240
VOCR-195	1896		LX	5	3	14	50	150	220
VOCR-200	1897		LX	5	3	14	50	150	220
VOCR-205	1897		LXI	5	3	14	50	150	220
VOCR-210	1898	[13]	LXI	5	3	15	60	180	250
VOCR-215	1898	[13]	LXII	5	3	14	50	150	220
VOCR-220	1899		LXII	5	3	14	50	150	220
VOCR-225	1899		LXIII	5	3	14	50	150	220
VOCR-230	1900		LXIII	5	3	14	50	150	220
VOCR-235	1900		LXIV	5	3	14	50	150	220

1. Issued in cased proof sets.
2. Type of edge stops vary.
3. Obverse lettering slightly smaller.
4. Possibly struck around 1887.
5. Struck at a much later date as Mint visit presentation pieces.
6. May weigh below 28 grams; some or all may be struck in fine silver.
7. Sealed in glass for 1851 Exhibition; inscription is on outer silver surround
8. Minted in 1853 or later with error date; weight 27.6 grams; probably unique; see note below.
9. Probably reverse ↑ as other 1879 proofs
10. Issued in proof sets.
11. Minor reverse differences from previous coin; streamer thicker.
12. A reverse slightly different from other dates.
13. Minor reverse differences exist.

The 1847 Gothic crown bearing the regnal edge date DECIMO SEPTIMO (not SEPTIMO as sometimes recorded) is usually referred to as an error edge coin, This is a misdescription, barring the unlikely event that it was known in 1847 that the next issue was to be minted in 1853, the date corresponding to DECIMO SEPTIMO. It is thus listed as an error date, and was presumably struck in 1853, or possibly later. It might be more correctly termed an error reverse coin than an error edge.

Edward VII 1901–1910

The king's portrait on the one-year type crowns of Edward VII was designed by George William de Saulles (1862-1903), while the reverse retained the Pistrucci St George and dragon. An interesting comment on the engraver appears in *The Times* of 26 January 1902: 'Contrary to some unauthorised rumours, Mr. de Saulles is not a foreigner. He is an Englishman, born of English parents in Birmingham.'

Collecting Hints

Mint state or near for the ordinary issue, and FDC for the matt proof are the minimum criteria to aim for. Condition is critical in the case of the proof, as the original matt surface is impaired with even a trace of wear. To the untrained eye, a slightly impaired coin can appear perfect, and a beginner should take any opportunity of inspecting a set of FDC matt proofs, if the occasion arises.

Denomination	Metal	Weight (grams)	Diameter (mm)	Rev. alignment
Crown	Silver	28.3	39	↑

Obverse 1 Head 1, right; EDWARDVS VII DEI GRA BRITT OMN REX FID DEF IND IMP

Reverse 1 St George and dragon, date in exergue below

Edge (in relief): DECUS ET TUTAMEN ANNO REGNI II

Obv. 1   Rev. 1

No.	Date	Features	Obv.	Rev.	F	VF	EF	UNC
E7CR-005	1902		1	1	30	50	90	130
E7CR-010	1902	matt PROOF [1]	1	1			90	120

1. Issued in cased proof sets.

George V 1910–1936

Although George V reigned for over a quarter of a century, the issue of crowns spans only ten years. The absence of a crown in 1911 is somewhat curious, and is a major omission in the numismatic scene, especially as three different types of official proof sets were struck. The series of George V crowns is dominated by one of the most famous and sought after types, the 'wreath' crown, which can be regarded as the last series of circulating crowns as a true denomination, bearing the same design in consecutive years. Today we have a succession of isolated commemorative issues. Next to the rarest date, the 1934, stands the ubiquitous 1935, without which crowns of George V would have been scarce as a single type. Although the 1935 crown is plentiful, the so-called 'raised edge' proof variety, issued in a red box, is scarce and much sought after. The unusual 'specimen' issue with incuse edge, also issued in a red box, is equally popular, though not as scarce. It is worthy of note that the raised edge type is not legal tender, as the proclamation conferring legality on 1935 crowns specified that the edge was to be incusely marked.

The issue of the wreath crown in 1927 coincided with a redesign of the whole series (apart from Maundy), and a cased proof set was issued to commemorate this. For the first time, the mark of denomination 'CROWN' appeared, and each of the other five pieces in the new set now bore a mark of denomination in words.

The obverse of both types of crown was designed by Sir Bertram MacKennal (1863-1931). The reverse of the wreath crown was by George Kruger Gray (1880-1943), and that of the 1935 crown by Percy Metcalfe.

Collecting Hints

The wreath crown is a scarce series and is collectable in any grade, but it will generally be encountered in about very fine condition. Extremely fine specimens can be found without great difficulty, although the 1934 can present a real problem.

The 1935 crown, at first sight a common and somewhat bland coin, is in fact probably the most interesting coin of all. There are a number of varieties, and fascinatingly some of these are at times overlooked by one or more parties to a transaction; certainly a number of error edge raised lettering issues have passed through major London salerooms without being spotted by the cataloguers, and the order of words on the edge must always be checked (not too obviously!) when one is offered a 'raised edge' crown. Similarly, raised lettering crowns in about fine condition occasionally appear in bulk dealer lots of standard 1935 crowns.

Denomination	Metal	Weight (grams)	Diameter (mm)	Rev. alignment
Crown	0.500 Silver	28.3	39	↑

Obverse 1 Head 1, left; GEORGIVS V DEI GRA BRITT OMN REX

Obverse 2 Head 2, left; GEORGIVS V DG BRITT OMN REX FD IND IMP *(for the Silver Jubilee)*

Reverse 1 Crown, date above, these within wreath; FID DEF IND IMP CROWN

Reverse 2 St George and dragon in 'art deco' style; CROWN 1935 *(for the Silver Jubilee)*

Edge (Obv. 1/Rev. 1) milled. (Obv. 2/Rev. 2) (incuse): DECUS ET TUTAMEN ANNO REGNI XXV

Obv. 1   Obv. 2

Rev. 1   Rev. 2

No.	Date	Features	Obv.	Rev.	F	VF	EF	UNC
G5CR-005	1927	PROOF [1]	1	1	70	90	110	130
G5CR-010	1927	PROOF from sandblasted dies [2]	1	1				1000
G5CR-015	1928		1	1	75	95	130	160
G5CR-020	1928	PROOF	1	1				600
G5CR-025	1929		1	1	75	100	140	170

No.	Date	Features	Obv.	Rev.	F	VF	EF	UNC
G5CR-030	1929	PROOF	1	1				600
G5CR-035	1930		1	1	75	100	140	170
G5CR-040	1930	PROOF	1	1				600
G5CR-045	1931		1	1	75	110	140	180
G5CR-050	1931	PROOF	1	1				650
G5CR-055	1932		1	1	90	125	160	220
G5CR-060	1932	PROOF	1	1				1000
G5CR-065	1933		1	1	75	95	130	150
G5CR-070	1933	PROOF	1	1				600
G5CR-075	1934		1	1	250	450	800	1200
G5CR-080	1934	PROOF	1	1				4000
G5CR-085	1935		2	2	6	8	11	15
G5CR-090	1935	edge error [3]	2	2	100	150	250	350
G5CR-095	1935	SPECIMEN [4]	2	2			30	45
G5CR-100	1935	PROOF in sterling silver	2	2				2000
G5CR-105	1935	PROOF; raised edge lettering [5]	2	2			200	240
G5CR-110	1935	PROOF; raised error edge lettering reads DECUS ANNO REGNI ET TVTAMEN. XXV [5]	2	2			600	900
G5CR-115	1935	PROOF or pattern with edge inscription in finer lettering	2	2				2000
G5CR-120	1935	PROOF in gold; raised edge lettering [6]	2	2				12000
G5CR-125	1936		1	1	90	130	170	220
G5CR-130	1936	PROOF	1	1				1500

1. Issued in cased proof sets.
2. Struck to facilitate photography of coin.
3. DECUS ET TVTA section of edge legend missing.
4. Prooflike field; issued in red box.
5. Issued in red box.
6. Issued in red box; 25 to 30 issued to recipients chosen by ballot; weight c.48 grams.

Edward VIII 1936

The Edward VIII crown is strictly speaking a pattern, as probable royal approval was about to be granted at the time of the abdication. However, because its official status rests only on this technicality, and to provide continuity, it is included in this catalogue. The portrait of Edward VIII is by Thomas Humphrey Paget (1893–1974), and faces left at the insistence of the king, who considered this placement more flattering and wished to discontinue the tradition of opposite facings for successive monarchs. The reverse is by George Kruger Gray.

Denomination	Metal	Weight (grams)	Diameter (mm)	Rev. alignment
Crown	Silver	28.2	39	↑

Obverse 1 Head 1, left; EDWARDVS VIII D G BR OMN REX

Reverse 1 Royal arms supported and crowned; FID DEF IND IMP CROWN 1937

Edge milled

Obv. 1   Rev. 1

447

No.	Date	Obv.	Rev.	Unc
E8CR-005	1937	1	1	100000

George VI 1937–1952

The only two crowns of George VI were issued for the Coronation in 1937 and for the Festival of Britain in 1951. Both used obverses by Paget, with reverses by Kruger Gray in 1937 and of the Pistrucci St George and dragon in 1951. The latter was the first British crown struck in cupronickel, 400 years after the first was struck in silver, and it was struck only as a proof. Besides marking the Festival of 1951, it also commemorates the 100 years anniversary of the Great Exhibition held in London's Hyde Park in 1851. It was said that the reverse of this crown was made from a punch originally manufactured for an 1899 crown. The 1951 crown was issued to the public at a price of 5 shillings and 6 pence, and some were struck at the Festival site on London's South Bank. Unfortunately, no special mintmark was incorporated into the design.

Collecting Hints

None of the George VI crowns is difficult to obtain, unless one is seeking the more exotic frosted varieties. Indeed, perhaps the most difficult items are original 1951 cardboard boxes (maroon and green) in pristine state with official leaflet. The boxes occur both with slide-off and pull-off lids, the latter being scarcer. Contrary to what one is sometimes told, the 1951 proof crowns in boxes and those in proof sets are identical.

Denomination	Metal	Weight (grams)	Diameter (mm)	Rev. alignment
Crown 1937	0.500 Silver	28.3	39	↑
Crown 1951	Cupronickel	28.3	39	↑

Obverse 1 Head 1, left; GEORGIVS VI D G BR OMN REX *(for the Coronation)*

Obverse 2 Head 2, left; GEORGIVS VI D G BR OMN REX F D FIVE SHILLINGS *(for the Festival of Britain)*

Reverse 1 Royal arms supported and crowned; FID DEF IND IMP CROWN 1937 *(for the Coronation)*

Reverse 2 St George and dragon, 1951 in exergue below *(for the Festival of Britain)*

Edge (1937) milled; (1951) incusely inscribed MDCCCLI CIVIUM INDUSTRIA FLORET CIVITAS MCMLI

Obv. 1   Obv. 2

Rev. 1   Rev. 2

No.	Date	Features	Obv.	Rev.	F	VF	EF	UNC
G6CR-005	1937	[1]	1	1	6	9	12	18
G6CR-010	1937	PROOF [2]	1	1			15	40
G6CR-015	1937	PROOF heavily frosted [3]	1	1				120
G6CR-020	1937	PROOF from sandblasted dies [4]	1	1				800
G6CR-025	1951	PROOF [5]	2	2			6	8
G6CR-030	1951	PROOF, heavily frosted with brilliant field [6]	2	2				250
G6CR-035	1951	PROOF from sandblasted dies [4]	2	2				800
G6CR-040	1951	PROOF; edge plain	2	2				150

1. Issued for several years.
2. Issued in cased proof sets.
3. Possibly in sterling silver.
4. Struck to facilitate photography of coin.
5. Issued in card box and in cased proof sets.
6. Edge lettering finer than on previous coin.

Elizabeth II 1952-

Crowns of Elizabeth II are characterised by high mintage issues struck not for circulation but to commemorate events or anniversaries. They are generally collected for the sake of completeness rather than for their artistic merit, although the proofs in original cases are attractive.

Collecting Hints

Elizabeth II crowns are encountered in extremely fine or mint state more frequently than in any other grade, and the perverse collector may wish to acquire a specimen of each in the worst possible grade. It is surprising how many of these crowns exist in fair to fine condition. There are no doubt many who would say that the beauty of the Churchill increases in direct proportion to the amount of wear it has sustained.

Denomination	Metal	Weight (grams)	Diameter (mm)	Rev. alignment
Crown	Cupronickel	28.3	39	↑

Obverse 1 Queen on horseback; ELIZABETH II DEI GRATIA BRITT OMN REGINA FIDEI DEFENSOR FIVE SHILLINGS

Obverse 2 Head 1, right; ELIZABETH II DEI GRATIA REGINA F D; below head: FIVE SHILLINGS *(for the British Trade Fair in New York)*

Obverse 3 Head 1, right; ELIZABETH II DEI GRATIA REGINA F D with wider spacing than above; below head: 1965

Reverse 1 Cruciform shields and emblems around crown, date below

Reverse 2 Head of Churchill; CHURCHILL

Edges (1953) FAITH AND TRUST I WILL BEAR UNTO YOU (incuse). (1960-65) milled

Obv. 1

Obv. 2

Obv. 3

Rev. 1

Rev. 2

No.	Date	Features	Obv.	Rev.	VF	EF	UNC
EL2CR-005	1953		1	1	4	6	8
EL2CR-010	1953	YO instead of YOU (edge)	1	1	30	40	50
EL2CR-015	1953	PROOF [1]	1	1		20	35
EL2CR-020	1953	PROOF from sandblasted dies [2]	1	1			800
EL2CR-025	1960		2	1	3	5	8
EL2CR-030	1960	polished die specimen	2	1		7	14
EL2CR-035	1960	PROOF frosted bust	2	1			300
EL2CR-040	1965	[3]	3	2		2	3

1. Issued in cased proof sets.
2. Struck to facilitate photography of coin.
3. R in CHURCHILL varies (rev.).

Double Florin

Victoria 1837–1901

The double florin is one of the shortest denominations on record, yet it includes a number of interesting varieties. Like the florin of 1887 it uses a reverse design based on that originally used by John Roettier on the gold of Charles II. This comprised four cruciform shields with sceptres laid out in the angles between them. The obverse of the double florin used the controversial Boehm portrait of the queen, engraved by Leonard Charles Wyon.

The 1887 coin with Arabic style '1' in the date was included in the proof sets of 1887, and proofs also exist of the type with Roman 'I' in the date. This denomination, unpopular at the time of issue, lasted until 1890, when it had outlived its usefulness. The use of the Boehm portrait no doubt accelerated its demise.

Denomination	Metal	Weight (grams)	Diameter (mm)	Rev. alignment
Double Florin	Silver	22.6	36	↑

Obverse 1 Head 1, left; VICTORIA DEI GRATIA. The field is flat.

Obverse 2 Similar but many minor differences. The field is slightly concave.

Reverse 1 Four crowned cruciform shields with sceptres in angles; FID DEF BRITT REG (date). Roman I instead of 1 in 1887

Reverse 2 Similar but many minor differences. Arabic 1 in date. The field is very slightly concave

Edge milled

Obv. 1   Rev. 1

No.	Date	Features	Obv.	Rev.	F	VF	EF	UNC
VJDFL-005	1887	Roman I in date	1	1	7	14	30	45
VJDFL-010	1887	PROOF Roman I in date	1	1				300
VJDFL-015	1887	Arabic 1 in date	1	2	7	12	28	40
VJDFL-020	1887	Arabic 1 in date	2	2	7	12	28	40
VJDFL-025	1887	PROOF Arabic 1 in date [1]	2	2				250
VJDFL-030	1888		2	2	8	18	35	50
VJDFL-035	1888	second I in VICTORIA is inverted '1'	2	2	14	30	60	100
VJDFL-040	1889		2	2	7	14	30	45
VJDFL-045	1889	second I in VICTORIA is inverted '1'	2	2	16	35	70	110
VJDFL-050	1890	[2]	2	2	8	15	30	55

1. Issued in cased proof sets.
2. Reverse design is very slightly larger than on previous years.

Three Shillings

George III 1760–1820

In 1811 there was a shortage of silver coinage for circulation. Although the countermarked dollars and five shilling bank tokens had been useful in this respect, no halfcrowns had been minted since 1751, and the last issue of shillings and sixpences for general use had been in 1787. In many parts of the country tradesmen issued private silver tokens during 1811, but these were not accepted outside the immediate area where they were issued.

To alleviate the situation, the Bank of England issued its own tokens for three shillings and for eighteen pence. Silver was at a high price, and the weights of these denominations were proportionately lower than normal. The fact that these issues were tokens rather than true coins rendered this shortfall acceptable.

The issue of three shilling tokens was a short one, from 1811 to 1816, and comprises two distinct types. The 1811 issue includes a number of minor varieties on both obverse and reverse. The tokens were withdrawn from issue in March 1820, thereafter being accepted only as bullion by weight.

The first type of three shillings token (1811-12) was probably designed by Lewis Pingo. The second type (1812-16) used the Marchant design employed on the gold coinage. This was engraved by Thomas Wyon, who designed and engraved the reverse.

Obv. 1   Obv. 2

Rev. 1   Rev. 2

Denomination	Metal	Weight (grams)	Diameter (mm)	Rev. alignment
Three Shillings	Silver	15.0	35	↑

Obverse 1 Head 1, right; GEORGIUS III DEI GRATIA REX

Obverse 2 Head 2, right; same legend

Reverse 1 BANK TOKEN 3 SHILL (date) within wreath of oak leaves

Reverse 2 Similar but less profuse wreath of oak and olive

Edge plain

No.	Date	Features	Obv.	Rev.	F	VF	EF	UNC
G33S-005	1811	[1]	1	1	12	30	70	110
G33S-010	1811	PROOF [1]	1	1				600
G33S-015	1812		1	1	12	32	75	120
G33S-020	1812	[2]	2	2	12	32	75	120
G33S-025	1812	PROOF	2	2				600
G33S-030	1812	PROOF in gold	2	2				10000
G33S-035	1812	PROOF in platinum	2	2				7000
G33S-040	1813		2	2	12	32	75	120
G33S-045	1814		2	2	12	32	75	120
G33S-050	1815		2	2	12	32	75	120
G33S-055	1816		2	2	150	300		

1. Wreath and lettering orientation varies (obv.); number of acorns varies (rev.).
2. Lettering orientation varies (obv.).

Halfcrown

Oliver Cromwell (Commonwealth 1649–1660)

The halfcrown is unique in the short Cromwell series in that it occurs not only with two dates but as two types. The 1656 halfcrown is therefore the earliest milled coin having what became for the milled coinage a conventional layout, with an obverse bust and a heraldic reverse, both with lettering around the rim of each face.

The coin was designed by Thomas Simon (also called Symonds) and portrays Cromwell as a Roman Emperor, draped and laureate.

The 'Tanner's Copy' was struck in the 18th century, and is outside the scope of this book.

Denomination	Metal	Weight (grams)	Diameter (mm)	Rev. alignment
Halfcrown	Silver	14.6-15.1	32–34	↓

Obverse 1 Head 1, left; OLIVAR D G R P ANG SCO HI &c PRO

Obverse 2 Similar but HIB instead of HI

Reverse 1 Crowned shield; PAX QVAERITVR BELLO (date)

Edge (in relief) HAS NISI PERITVRVS MIHI ADIMAT NEMO

Obv. 2   Rev. 1

No.	Date	Features	Obv.	Rev.	F	VF	EF
CRHC-005	1656		1	1	600	1500	3000
CRHC-010	1658		2	1	300	600	1100
CRHC-015	1658	PROOF in gold 1	2	1			30000

1. Weight c. 27 grams; about 6 known.

Charles II 1660–1685

The first machine-struck halfcrown was issued in 1663, the year after the issue of the first crown, on whose design by Roettier it is based. The new minor silver coinage was not universally popular. Pepys records in his diary for 23 November 1663 that the financier Blackwell found it 'deadly inconvenient for telling, it is so thick and the edges are made to turn up'. The issue of halfcrowns continued for over twenty years, broken only in 1665 during the Great Plague, and used a design which continued throughout the reign with only minor modifications. It is believed that the ravages of the plague were also responsible for the low issue of halfcrowns up to 1669, almost all of which used over-strikings of 1664 and possibly other dates.

Provenance marks used in this series are: elephant and castle (or elephant) denoting silver from the Africa Company; plume for silver from Welsh mines.

Denomination	Metal	Weight (grams)	Diameter (mm)	Rev. alignment
Halfcrown 1663	Silver	15.0–15.5	33–34	↓
Halfcrown 1664-1684	Silver	14.8–15.3	32–34	↓

Obverse 1 Head 1, right; CAROLVS II DEI GRATIA

Obverse 2 Head 2, right; same legend

Obverse 3 Head 3, smaller, right; same legend

Obverse 4 Head 4, very similar to 3, right; same legend

Obverse 5 Head 5, much larger, right; same legend

Reverse 1 Four cruciform shields with pair of interlinked 'C's in angles. MAG BR FRA ET HIB REX. Date at top

Edge (in relief) (all dates except 1667) DECVS ET TVTAMEN ANNO REGNI (regnal date); (1667 only) DECVS ET TVTAMEN AN REG (regnal date). From 1662 to 1666 the regnal year is in Roman numerals; from 1667 onwards it is in words.

Obv. 1   Obv. 2

Obv. 3   Obv. 4

Obv. 5   Rev. 1

No.	Date	Features	Edge date	Obv.	Rev.	VG	F	VF	EF
C2HCM-005	1663		XV	1	1	30	50	250	1200
C2HCM-010	1663	rev. ↑	XV	1	1	35	60	350	1500
C2HCM-015	1663	rev. 90 degrees anticlockwise	XV	1	1	35	60	350	1500
C2HCM-020	1663	no stops on obv	XV	1	1	35	60	350	1500
C2HCM-025	1663	no stops on obv; R of FRA over B (rev.)	XV	1	1	60	100	600	2500
C2HCM-030	1663	V of CAROLVS over S (obv.)	XV	1	1	35	60	350	1500
C2HCM-035	1663	no stops on obv and V of CAROLVS over S (obv.)	XV	1	1	40	70	400	1700
C2HCM-040	1663	PROOF	XV	1	1				8000
C2HCM-045	1664		XVI	2	1	50	80	450	2000
C2HCM-050	1666	last 6 over indeterminate digit [1]	XVIII	3	1	500	800		
C2HCM-055	1666	last 6 over 4 elephant below head [1]	XVIII	3	1	250	350	1200	6000
C2HCM-060	1666	last 6 over indeterminate digit elephant below head [1]	XVIII	3	1	250	350	1200	6000
C2HCM-065	1667	7 over 4 [1]	DECIMO NONO	3	1	1100			
C2HCM-070	1668	8 over 4 [1]	VICESIMO	3	1	60	100	600	2500
C2HCM-075	1669		VICESIMO PRIMO	3	1	140	250	1200	
C2HCM-080	1669	R of PRIMO over I (edge)	VICESIMO PRIMO	3	1	140	250	1200	
C2HCM-085	1669	9 over 4	VICESIMO PRIMO	3	1	70	130	700	
C2HCM-090	1670		VICESIMO SECVNDO	3	1	25	40	170	1000
C2HCM-095	1670	MRG instead of MAG (rev.)	VICESIMO SECVNDO	3	1	50	90	600	

No.	Date	Features	Edge date	Obv.	Rev.	VG	F	VF	EF
C2HCM-100	1670	A of MAG over R (rev.)	VICESIMO SECVNDO	3	1	35	60	250	
C2HCM-105	1671	[2]	VICESIMO TERTIO	4	1	25	40	140	900
C2HCM-110	1671	A of MAG over R (rev.)	VICESIMO TERTIO	4	1	40	60	220	
C2HCM-115	1671	1 over 0	VICESIMO TERTIO	4	1	30	50	160	950
C2HCM-120	1672		VICESIMO TERTIO	4	1	150	300		
C2HCM-125	1672		VICESIMO QVARTO	4	1	25	40	140	900
C2HCM-130	1672		VICESIMO QVARTO	5	1	50	80	250	1500
C2HCM-135	1673		VICESIMO QVINTO	5	1	25	40	130	900
C2HCM-140	1673	B of BR over R (rev.)	VICESIMO QVINTO	5	1	30	50	150	1000
C2HCM-145	1673	A of FRA over R (rev.)	VICESIMO QVINTO	5	1	30	50	150	1000
C2HCM-150	1673	EGNI instead of REGNI (edge)	VICESIMO QVINTO	5	1	40	60	160	1000
C2HCM-155	1673	plume below head [3]	VICESIMO QVINTO	5	1	1000	1500		
C2HCM-160	1673	plume below head and in centre of rev.	VICESIMO QVINTO	5	1	2000	3000		
C2HCM-165	1674		VICESIMO SEXTO	5	1	60	100	400	1500
C2HCM-170	1674	4 over 3	VICESIMO SEXTO	5	1	70	120	500	2000
C2HCM-175	1675		VICESIMO SEPTIMO	5	1	40	70	300	1200
C2HCM-180	1675	EGNI instead of REGNI (edge)	VICESIMO SEPTIMO	5	1	50	80	400	1300
C2HCM-185	1675	reversed 1 in date	VICESIMO SEPTIMO	5	1	70	120	500	
C2HCM-190	1676		VICESIMO OCTAVO	5	1	25	40	110	750
C2HCM-195	1676	EGNI instead of REGNI (edge)	VICESIMO OCTAVO	5	1	35	60	130	950
C2HCM-200	1676	reversed 1 in date [4]	VICESIMO OCTAVO	5	1	30	45	120	800
C2HCM-205	1677		VICESIMO NONO	5	1	25	40	120	800
C2HCM-210	1678		TRICESIMO	5	1	60	100	500	
C2HCM-215	1679		TRICESIMO PRIMO	5	1	25	40	90	600
C2HCM-220	1679	GRATTA instead of GRATIA (obv.)	TRICESIMO PRIMO	5	1	30	50	110	700
C2HCM-225	1679	DECNS instead of DECVS (edge)	TRICESIMO PRIMO	5	1	30	50	110	700
C2HCM-230	1679	DNCVS instead of DECVS (edge)	TRICESIMO PRIMO	5	1	30	50	110	700
C2HCM-235	1679	both 'V's on edge are inverted 'A's	TRICESIMO PRIMO	5	1	25	40	100	600
C2HCM-240	1679	N in REGNI is inverted R (edge)	TRICESIMO PRIMO	5	1	40	60	120	750
C2HCM-245	1679	PRICESIMO instead of TRICESIMO (edge)	PRICESIMO PRIMO	5	1	30	50	110	650
C2HCM-250	1680		TRICESIMO SECVNDO	5	1	60	100	500	
C2HCM-255	1680	RGNI instead of REGNI (edge)	TRICESIMO SECVNDO	5	1	70	120	700	
C2HCM-260	1680	D in SECVNDO inverted (edge)	TRICESIMO SECVN(D)O	5	1	60	110	600	
C2HCM-265	1681		TRICESIMO TERTIO	5	1	30	50	160	800
C2HCM-270	1681	1 over 0	TRICESIMO TERTIO	5	1	35	60	180	1000
C2HCM-275	1681	elephant and castle below head	TRICESIMO TERTIO	5	1	800	1200		
C2HCM-280	1682		TRICESIMO QVARTO	5	1	40	70	250	1200
C2HCM-285	1682	PROOF (?) rev. ↑ [5]	TRICESIMO QVARTO	5	1	50	80	350	1500

No.	Date	Features	Edge date	Obv.	Rev.	VG	F	VF	EF
C2HCM-290	1682	2 over 1	TRICESIMO QVARTO	5	1	50	80	350	1500
C2HCM-295	1682	82 over 79	TRICESIMO QVARTO	5	1	50	80	350	1500
C2HCM-300	1683		TRICESIMO QVINTO	5	1	25	40	120	700
C2HCM-305	1683	plume below head [6]	TRICESIMO QVINTO	5	1				
C2HCM-310	1684	4 over 3 [1]	TRICESIMO SEXTO	5	1	40	70	400	

1. This date always overstruck.
2. Some struck on 34-35 mm flans.
3. Broken 3 in date exists.
4. See note below.
5. see note below; cf. 1682 guinea variety.
6. only recorded specimen in poor to fair condition realised £3200 at auction (Spink June 1980).

The 1676 variety sometimes known as 'inverted 1' is the same as that recorded here as 'reversed 1'; the digit is not inverted, nor is the coin rare as some reference books imply.

The 1682 with reverse ↑ has been noted in VF condition with an unusually sharp strike, and may have been struck as a proof. See the entry for the 1682 guinea.

The number of harp strings varies through this series. It is possible that the variation constituted a form of internal code denoting the die number.

James II 1685–1688

John Roettier, continuing as Chief Engraver, produced this short series of only four dates, which nevertheless includes a number of varieties of interest.

Obv. 1   Obv. 2

Edge (in relief) DECVS ET TVTAMEN ANNO REGNI (regnal date)

Rev. 1

No.	Date	Features	Edge date	Obv.	Rev.	F	VF	EF
J2HC-005	1685		PRIMO	1	1	60	190	900
J2HC-010	1686		SECVNDO	1	1	60	190	900
J2HC-015	1686	6 over 5	SECVNDO	1	1	80	300	1200
J2HC-020	1686		TERTIO	1	1	70	220	1000
J2HC-025	1686	V of IACOBVS over B (obv.)	TERTIO	1	1	70	220	1000
J2HC-030	1686	V of IACOBVS over S (obv.)	TERTIO	1	1	70	220	1000
J2HC-035	1687		TERTIO	1	1	60	190	900
J2HC-040	1687	7 over 6	TERTIO	1	1	70	220	1100
J2HC-045	1687	6 over 8	TERTIO	1	1	100	300	1200
J2HC-050	1687		TERTIO	2	1	70	220	1100
J2HC-055	1687	PROOF	TERTIO	2	1			6000
J2HC-060	1688		QVARTO	2	1	70	220	1100

The number of harp strings varies through this series. It is possible that the variation constituted a form of internal code denoting the die number.

William and Mary 1688–1694

The halfcrowns were, apart from the so-called 'Maundy Money', the first silver coins issued in the reign of William and Mary. The depiction of a single crowned shield on the reverse was a radical departure from the design used during the previous two reigns. During 1689 the first and fourth quarters of the shield were themselves quartered, displaying the arms of France and England. In 1691 this design reverted to the old four-shield motif, while at the same time a very different design of busts was introduced on the obverse.

It is interesting to note that, while on the crowns and the 1691 and 1693 halfcrowns the date is placed to be read from one position, on the 1692 halfcrown it rotates around the central lion. This anomaly may have been responsible for the (later recut) error inverting of some of the last date digits on a few of the halfcrowns and crowns.

The attribution of William and Mary coinage is not always clear. John Roettier was ill, and probably delegated work to his sons James and Norbert. The two main types of halfcrown are so different, not only in the concept of the reverse but also in the style of the busts, that it is difficult to believe that they are by the same designer. The first resembles the work of Norbert Roettier, and the second that of James.

No provenance marks or proofs exist in this series.

Denomination	Metal	Weight (grams)	Diameter (mm)	Rev. alignment
Halfcrown	Silver	14.9-15.1	33	↓

Obverse 1 Head 1, left; tie turns down at end; IACOBVS II DEI GRATIA

Obverse 2 Head 2, slightly larger, left; tie turns up at end; same legend

Reverse 1 Four cruciform shields with surmounting crowns; MAG BR FRA ET HIB REX (date)

Collecting Hints

Only the most avid collector of varieties will attempt to assemble a set of the minor variations of the crown on the reverse of the 1689 halfcrown, but this coin should always be checked for the very striking L over M type and for the 'FRA' reverse, both scarce. Similarly, the 1690, in itself a particularly scarce date, must always be examined for the major 'GRETIA' variety. The later type of 1691-93 is struck in very low relief and a very fine or extremely fine specimen may appear as fine or very fine to the untrained eye. In addition, these pieces are frequently found with haymarking.

Interesting contemporary forgeries exist which command unusually high prices. Some exhibit non-existent die/date/edge combinations.

Denomination	Metal	Weight (grams)	Diameter (mm)	Rev. alignment
Halfcrown	Silver	14.7-15.0	33-34	↓

Obverse 1 Heads 1, right; GVLIELMVS ET MARIA DEI GRATIA

Obverse 2 Heads 2, closer together and in low relief, right; same legend

Reverse 1 Crown above quartered shield, each quarter undivided; MAG BR FR ET HIB REX ET REGINA. Date divided by crown.

Reverse 2 Similar but first and fourth quarters themselves divided into arms of England and France.

Reverse 3 Four crowned cruciform shields around lion of Orange-Nassau, with monogrammed 'WM' and one digit of date in each angle; MAG BR FR ET HI REX ET REGINA

Edge (in relief) DECVS ET TVTAMEN ANNO REGNI (regnal date)

Obv. 1   Obv. 2

Rev. 1   Rev. 2

Rev. 3

No.	Date	Features	Edge date	Obv.	Rev.	F	VF	EF
WMHC-005	1689	¹	PRIMO	1	1	40	100	400
WMHC-010	1689	FRA instead of FR (rev.)	PRIMO	1	1	50	130	550
WMHC-015	1689	second L of GVLIELMVS over M (obv.)	PRIMO	1	1	45	110	450
WMHC-020	1689	first V of GVLIELMVS over A (obv.)	PRIMO	1	1	45	110	450
WMHC-025	1689	no stops on obv.	PRIMO	1	1	50	130	550
WMHC-030	1689	¹	PRIMO	1	2	50	130	550
WMHC-035	1690		SECVNDO	1	2	70	170	700
WMHC-040	1690	GRETIA instead of GRATIA; second V of GVLIELMVS over S (obv.)	SECVNDO	1	2	90	220	900
WMHC-045	1690		TERTIO	1	2	90	220	900
WMHC-050	1691		TERTIO	2	3	50	130	550
WMHC-055	1692		QVARTO	2	3	50	130	550
WMHC-060	1692		QVINTO	2	3	100	250	1200
WMHC-065	1693		QVINTO	2	3	50	130	550
WMHC-070	1693	3 over inverted 3	QVINTO	2	3	60	150	600

1. Design variations on reverse crown exist.

Reverse 3: variations occur in the monogrammed 'WM'.
The 1691 to 1693 dates are read in two lines, left to right, with the English shield at the top of the coin

William III 1695–1701

Because of the large quantity of halfcrowns minted during the reign of William and Mary, the halfcrown was the only major silver denomination not to be issued in 1695. When it resumed in 1696, there began a series of halfcrowns which was to become unrivalled in the complexity of its varieties, oddities and errors. With the withdrawal of hammered coinage, it was necessary to use provincial mints at Bristol, Chester, Exeter, Norwich and York using local labour which was responsible for a plethora of mistakes, all of which render the series of absorbing interest. A proposed mint at Hereford never opened. There are so many minor variations in the design and size of, for example, the shields, the harp and the central lion that the noted scholar and numismatist Jackson Kent proffered the opinion that it would be 'an impossible task' to produce a complete list. For this reason we have selected those varieties which can be regarded as noteworthy, while making annotations on the minor ones. It should be mentioned that, for the sake of expediency, some varieties (such as the harp variations of 1699-1701) are referred to only in annotated form when they would probably have been noted as separate varieties if they had occurred, say, in the reign of James II. For these reasons, there is an inconsistency for which we offer no apology; otherwise the listing, after permutating each variety with each other and with the mintmark, could have covered scores of pages and been of very little interest to the majority of collectors, and even then would probably be incomplete.

In view of the above, it is remarkable that the obverse head of the monarch remained virtually identical throughout the series. The oddly designed head of one excessively rare 1696 coin is almost certainly a pattern and is therefore outside the scope of this catalogue.

In several reference works the 1696 halfcrown with large shields and so-called 'early harp' is referred to as type 1, while the small shield coinage is called type 3. Mr. Jackson Kent disputed this notation, and the cataloguer, on examining the evidence, is inclined to agree. For this reason, the usual notation of types 1, 2 and 3 become in this catalogue reverses 2, 3 and 1 respectively. The reasoning is as follows:

1. The small shields with convex tops closely resemble those of the last issue of William and Mary, and the central lion and escutcheon are also very similar. It would be unusual for a radical change of design to be made which then reverts almost exactly to that of the previous reign.

2. The large shields with concave tops continue into 1697 and through to 1701. We are thus asked to believe not only that the design reverts during 1696 to that of William and Mary but that at the beginning of 1697 it switches back to the design used in the first half of 1696.

3. The reason for the notation used in E.S.C. and other works appears to be due solely to the fact that the so-called 'early harp' resembles that used on the 1695 crowns. However, there is no other factor in support of the usual notation; even the 1695 shields are convex, as are those on the reverse denoted in this catalogue as 'Reverse 1'.

Provenance marks (on 1701 halfcrowns only) are: plumes (silver from Welsh mines); elephant and castle below head (silver from the Africa Company).

Collecting Hints

If, as Jackson Kent said, it is an impossible task to list all of the varieties of the William III halfcrown, the difficulty of assembling a collection of varieties can be imagined. A comprehensive collection by date and variety would be a life's work and a source of endless fascination, and it would probably yield several new discoveries. In more practicable terms, one should attempt to acquire any piece which differs from anything in one's collection to any marked degree. Certainly most collectors will require specimens of each provincial mintmark; such pieces are particularly difficult to find in very fine or better.

Denomination	Metal	Weight (grams)	Diameter (mm)	Rev. alignment
Halfcrown	Silver	14.6-15.1	33	↓

Obverse 1 Head 1, right; GVLIELMVS III DEI GRA

Reverse 1 Four cruciform shields, each convex at the top and similar in width to each surmounting crown, all around central lion of Nassau; the harp with Irish shield has top left and top right roughly level; MAG BR FRA ET HIB REX (date) (with or without stops)

Reverse 2 Similar but the shields are wider than the crowns and are concave at the top; the lion is smaller; the harp has top left well above top right; same legend

Reverse 3 Similar but the harp is somewhat similar to that on Reverse 1, with both tops of sides level; the harp and the lion can vary in shape and size

Edge (in relief) DECVS ET TVTAMEN ANNO REGNI (regnal date)

Obv. 1

Rev. 1

Rev. 2   Rev. 3

No.	Date	mm	Features	Edge date	Obv.	Rev.	F	VF	EF
W3HC-005	1696			OCTAVO	1	1	35	100	350
W3HC-010	1696	B	[1]	OCTAVO	1	1	40	130	500
W3HC-015	1696	B	PROOF	OCTAVO	1	1			8000
W3HC-020	1696	C		OCTAVO	1	1	55	190	700
W3HC-025	1696	E		OCTAVO	1	1	75	280	950
W3HC-030	1696	E	DECVS AMEN AMEN instead of DECVS ET TVTAMEN (edge)	OCTAVO	1	1	90	350	1200
W3HC-035	1696	N	[1]	OCTAVO	1	1	40	140	500
W3HC-040	1696	y		OCTAVO	1	1	55	190	700
W3HC-045	1696			OCTAVO	1	2	40	110	400
W3HC-050	1696		PROOF on thick flan; edge plain [2]		1	2			3500
W3HC-055	1696	B		OCTAVO	1	2	45	130	450
W3HC-060	1696	B	struck on thick flan [3]	OCTAVO	1	2	1200		
W3HC-065	1696	C		OCTAVO	1	2	50	150	550
W3HC-070	1696	E		OCTAVO	1	2	60	180	650
W3HC-075	1696	E	E over B (mintmark)	OCTAVO	1	2	70	210	700
W3HC-080	1696	N		OCTAVO	1	2	90	300	1100
W3HC-085	1696	y		OCTAVO	1	2	50	150	500
W3HC-090	1696	y	y over E (mintmark)	OCTAVO	1	2	60	170	600
W3HC-095	1696	y	arms of Scotland at date	OCTAVO	1	2	800		
W3HC-100	1696			OCTAVO	1	3	70	250	1000
W3HC-105	1696	C		OCTAVO	1	3	70	250	1000
W3HC-110	1696	E		OCTAVO	1	3	70	250	1000
W3HC-115	1696	E		NONO	1	3	200	800	3000
W3HC-120	1696	N		OCTAVO	1	3	90	400	1500
W3HC-125	1697			NONO	1	3	35	100	350
W3HC-130	1697		7 over 6	NONO	1	3	50	140	550
W3HC-135	1697		GRR instead of GRA (obv.)	NONO	1	3	120	400	1000
W3HC-140	1697		GVLIEIMVS instead of GVLIELMVS (obv.)	NONO	1	3	60	180	600
W3HC-145	1697		PROOF; edge plain		1	3			8000
W3HC-150	1697	B		NONO	1	3	40	130	500
W3HC-155	1697	B	no stops on rev.	NONO	1	3	50	160	650
W3HC-160	1697	B	no harp strings	NONO	1	3	50	160	650
W3HC-165	1697	B	PROOF on thick flan [4]	NONO	1	3			10000
W3HC-170	1697	C		NONO	1	3	45	140	550
W3HC-175	1697	C	no harp strings	NONO	1	3	55	170	700
W3HC-180	1697	E		NONO	1	3	40	130	500
W3HC-185	1697	E	TVTAMEN instead of TVTAMEN (edge)	NONO	1	3	60	160	650
W3HC-190	1697	E	E over C (mintmark) [5]	NONO	1	3	70	180	800
W3HC-195	1697	E	E over B (mintmark) [5]	NONO	1	3	70	180	800
W3HC-200	1697	E	[6]	OCTAVO	1	3	400	1500	
W3HC-205	1697	N		NONO	1	3	40	130	500
W3HC-210	1697	N	arms of Scotland at date	NONO	1	3	600	2500	
W3HC-215	1697	N	[6]	OCTAVO	1	3	200	800	3000
W3HC-220	1697	y	[7]	NONO	1	3	40	120	450
W3HC-225	1697	y	no harp strings	NONO	1	3	50	140	550

No.	Date	mm	Features	Edge date	Obv.	Rev.	F	VF	EF
W3HC-230	1697	y	6	OCTAVO	1	3	200	800	3000
W3HC-235	1698			DECIMO	1	3	30	85	300
W3HC-240	1698		8 over 7	DECIMO	1	3	80	200	800
W3HC-245	1698		GRΛ instead of GRA (obv.)	DECIMO	1	3	40	100	400
W3HC-250	1698		GVLIEIMVS instead of GVLIELMVS (obv.)	DECIMO	1	3	70	170	650
W3HC-255	1698			UNDECIMO	1	3	250	850	
W3HC-260	1698		6	OCTAVO	1	3	1000		
W3HC-265	1699		8	UNDECIMO	1	3	50	130	500
W3HC-270	1699		TΛTAMEN instead of TVTAMEN (edge)	UNDECIMO	1	3	60	150	650
W3HC-275	1699		DECΛS ET TΛTAMEN instead of DECVS ET TVTAMEN	UNDECIMO	1	3	80	190	850
W3HC-280	1699		arms of Scotland at date 9	UNDECIMO	1	3	700		
W3HC-285	1699		central lion inverted (rev.)	UNDECIMO	1	3	90	250	1000
W3HC-290	1700			DVODECIMO	1	3	40	100	350
W3HC-295	1700		10	DECIMO TERTIO	1	3	40	100	350
W3HC-300	1700		DECΛS instead of DECVS (edge)	DECIMO TERTIO	1	3	50	120	450
W3HC-305	1701		11	DECIMO TERTIO	1	3	50	120	400
W3HC-310	1701		no stops on rev. 12	DECIMO TERTIO	1	3	60	140	500
W3HC-315	1701		elephant and castle below head 13	DECIMO TERTIO	1	3	1000		
W3HC-320	1701		plumes on rev. 14	DECIMO TERTIO	1	3	60	180	650

1. Shield width varies.
2. At least some are reverse ↑.
3. Weight. 21.3 grams.
4. Wt c.21 grams; mintmark partially removed from coin (not die); edge lettering larger than regular issue.
5. May read TΛTAMEN (edge).
6. Error edge.
7. Variety exists with badly cut 'y'.
8. Harp varies; variety reads GRΛ (obv.).
9. Variety reads GRΛ (obv.).
10. Lettering and harp vary.
11. Lettering and harp vary; see note below.
12. See note below.
13. Has large reverse lettering; see note below.
14. Has small reverse lettering; see note below.

The number of harp strings varies through this series. It is possible that the variation constituted a form of internal code denoting the die number.

Halfcrowns of 1701 have each L in GVLIELMVS with a much more prominent lower serif than those of other dates

Marks and Operating Periods of Provincial Mints

B: BRISTOL: September 1696 to September 1698
C: CHESTER: October 1696 to June 1698
E: EXETER: August 1696 to July 1698
N: NORWICH: September 1696 to April 1698
y: YORK: September 1696 to April 1698

Anne 1702–1714

John Croker continued as Chief Engraver, assisted by James Bull. Croker produced a portrait based on a painting of Anne by Sir Godfrey Kneller. After the complexities of the William III coinage, the Anne series appears at first sight fairly simple, but collectors will find that it is not without challenge; it also straddles the union of England and Scotland, and thus has interesting historical significance. Provenance marks used are: VIGO for silver

gleaned from Spanish galleons at Vigo Bay in 1702; plumes (in the reverse angles) for silver from Wales; roses and plumes (alternately in the angles of the reverse) for silver from the 'Company for smelting down lead with Pitcoale and Seacoale'. The mintmark E below the head of Anne represents coins struck at Edinburgh.

After the Union in 1707, the top and bottom shields on the reverse were each divided into the arms of England and Scotland.

Collecting Hints

Fine condition specimens are relatively plentiful and most collectors will require very fine or extremely fine coins. Some of the rarities are, however, difficult to find in the higher grades. This is particularly true of the 1709E, a piece which exhibits inferior workmanship and which is rarely encountered in above fine condition. Curiously, the 1703 VIGO is probably more easily found in very fine condition than in fine, probably the result of hoarding of the first date struck. Any coin offered as 1703 without VIGO must be examined closely for signs of artificial removal of the provenance mark.

Some dates, notably 1709 (plain), often occur with a slightly concave reverse. These coins suffer less wear on the reverse than on the obverse.

Denomination	Metal	Weight (grams)	Diameter (mm)	Rev. alignment
Halfcrown	Silver	14.8–15.0	33–34	↓

Obverse 1 Head 1, left; ANNA DEI GRATIA

Reverse 1 Four undivided cruciform shields with surmounting crowns; MAG BR FRA ET HIB REG (date); usually known as 'Before Union' reverse.

Reverse 2 Similar but top and bottom shields are each divided into the arms of England and Scotland; crowns are thinner; MAG BRI FR ET HIB REG (date); known as 'After Union' reverse.

Edge (in relief) DECVS ET TVTAMEN ANNO REGNI (regnal date)

Obv. 1

Rev. 1   Rev. 2

Before Union of England and Scotland

No.	Date	Features	Edge date	Obv.	Rev.	F	VF	EF
AHC-005	1703	VIGO below head	TERTIO	1	1	40	110	400
AHC-010	1703		TERTIO	1	1	400	1200	
AHC-015	1704	plumes on rev.	TERTIO	1	1	50	160	600
AHC-020	1705	plumes on rev.	QVINTO	1	1	45	120	400
AHC-025	1706	roses and plumes on rev.	QVINTO	1	1	35	100	300
AHC-030	1707	roses and plumes on rev.	SEXTO	1	1	30	85	250

After Union of England and Scotland

No.	Date	Features	Edge date	Obv.	Rev.	F	VF	EF
AHC-035	1707	E below head	SEXTO	1	2	26	65	150
AHC-040	1707	E below head; ET*T*TAMEN instead of ET TVTAMEN	SEXTO	1	2	70	170	400
AHC-045	1707	E below head [1]	SEPTIMO	1	2	800	2000	5000
AHC-050	1707		SEPTIMO	1	2	30	75	180
AHC-055	1707	ET.T.TVTAMEN instead of ET TVTAMEN (edge)	SEPTIMO	1	2	70	170	400
AHC-060	1707	struck on thick flan [2]	SEPTIMO	1	2	1000		
AHC-065	1708	E below head [3]	SEPTIMO	1	2	30	75	180
AHC-070	1708		SEPTIMO	1	2	30	65	160
AHC-075	1708	plumes on rev.	SEPTIMO	1	2	35	90	220
AHC-080	1709		OCTAVO	1	2	30	75	180
AHC-085	1709	E below head; rev. ↑ [4]	OCTAVO	1	2	75	400	2000
AHC-090	1710	roses and plumes on rev.	NONO	1	2	35	110	300
AHC-095	1712	roses and plumes on rev.	UNDECIMO	1	2	35	100	250
AHC-100	1713		DVODECIMO	1	2	35	80	200
AHC-105	1713	roses and plumes on rev.	DVODECIMO	1	2	35	90	250
AHC-110	1714	roses and plumes on rev.	DECIMO TERTIO	1	2	35	90	250
AHC-115	1714	roses and plumes on rev.; ANN instead of ANNO (edge)	DECIMO TERTIO	1	2	70	200	500
AHC-120	1714	4 over 3 roses and plumes on rev.	DECIMO TERTIO	1	2	35	90	250

1. At least one specimen exists in EF condition.
2. Weight 20–21 grams.
3. 1 in date varies.
4. Inferior workmanship; numerals different from those on London 1709 coin. The '1' is a reversed-Z instead of the J-type.

Minor obverse varieties occur. The number of harp strings varies through this series. It is possible that the variation constituted a form of internal code denoting the die number.

George I 1714–1727

The halfcrown series was redesigned to accommodate the Hanoverian accession and the reverse legend includes a greatly abbreviated form of the German titles of the new king. The reverse translates from the Latin as: 'Duke of Brunswick and Lüneburg, Arch-Treasurer of the Holy Roman Empire, and Elector'. The Brunswick-Lüneburg arms are incorporated in one of the reverse shields.

The design was the work of John Croker, aided by J. R. Ochs, senior.

Provenance marks are: roses and plumes (see Anne); SSC (silver from The South Sea Company).

Denomination	Metal	Weight (grams)	Diameter (mm)	Rev. alignment
Halfcrown	Silver	15.0-15.1	33–34	↓

Obverse 1 Head 1, right; GEORGIVS D G M BR FR ET HIB REX F D

Reverse 1 Four crowned cruciform shields; BRVN ET L DVX S R I A TH ET EL (date)

Edge (in relief) DECVS ET TVTAMEN ANNO REGNI (regnal date) (but see 1723 note 4)

Obv. 1   Rev. 1

No.	Date	Features	Edge date	Obv.	Rev.	F	VF	EF
G1HC-005	1715	PROOF or PATTERN; edge plain [1]		1	1			6000
G1HC-010	1715	roses and plumes on rev.	SECVNDO	1	1	75	200	600
G1HC-015	1715	roses and plumes on rev.; edge lettering transposed	SECVNDO	1	1	300		
G1HC-020	1715	roses and plumes on rev.; edge plain		1	1	500	1800	
G1HC-025	1717	roses and plumes on rev. [2]	TIRTIO	1	1	75	200	600
G1HC-030	1720	roses and plumes on rev. [3]	SEXTO	1	1	100	280	800
G1HC-035	1720	20 over 17 roses and plumes on rev.	SEXTO	1	1	75	200	600
G1HC-040	1723	SSC on rev. [4]	DECIMO	1	1	75	200	600
G1HC-045	1726	roses and plumes on rev. [5]	DECIMO TERTIO	1	1	800	1800	

1. Plain in angles; usually has die flaw by GEORGIVS (obv.).
2. Regnal edge date always misspelt.
3. Unaltered date.
4. Edge reads DECUS ET TUTAMEN not DECVS ET TVTAMEN.
5. Roses and plumes smaller than on earlier dates.

Each '1' in the date on the 1715 coin is a 'J' type. Subsequent dates have a 'Z' type '1'.

George II 1727–1760

As with the crowns, the early head of the king by Croker contrasts with the later head by Tanner, as do the relative scarcities of the two types. The first type is struck in relatively high relief and consequently can be difficult to find in top grades, and commands high prices thus. The LIMA halfcrown with the older head is one of the most popular and frequently encountered coins of this denomination.

Provenance marks are: roses (or roses and plumes) as on earlier issues; LIMA below the head for coins struck in silver captured by Admiral Anson. The reason for the use of the word LIMA has never been satisfactorily established, and it may therefore be wrong to call it a provenance mark.

Compared with the George I coinage, some of the German titles of the king are transferred from the obverse to the reverse. The reverse translation now reads: 'King of Great Britain, France and Ireland, Defender of the Faith, Duke of Brunswick and Lüneburg, Arch-Treasurer of the Holy Roman Empire and Elector'.

Collecting Hints

The young head halfcrowns (1731-1741) are moderately scarce and a minimum grade of fine should be sought. The older head type is fairly easily found and most collectors will look for a very fine or better coin. The last two dates minted (1750 and 1751) are both scarce but a higher proportion of them have survived in very fine or extremely fine condition, possibly as a result of their being collected after the death of the king.

The 1745 and 1746 halfcrowns frequently occur with edge pinholes, no doubt the result of a short-lived fashion for mounting the pieces for personal adornment; consequently, the edges of coins from this period must always be carefully examined.

Denomination	Metal	Weight (grams)	Diameter (mm)	Rev. alignment
Halfcrown	Silver	14.8-15.1	34	↓

Obverse 1 Head 1, left; GEORGIVS II (Head) DEI GRATIA

Obverse 2 Head 2, left; GEORGIUS II (Head) DEI GRATIA

Obverse 3 Head 2, left; same legend but GEORGIVS instead of GEORGIUS

Reverse 1 Four crowned cruciform shields; M B F ET H REX F D B ET L D S R I A T ET E (date)

Edge (in relief) DECVS ET TVTAMEN ANNO REGNI (regnal date)

Obv. 1   Obv. 3

Rev. 1

No.	Date	Features	Edge date	Obv.	Rev.	F	VF	EF
G2HC-005	1731	PROOF or PATTERN; edge plain		1	1			2500
G2HC-010	1731	roses and plumes on rev. [1]	QVINTO	1	1	40	120	600
G2HC-015	1732	roses and plumes on rev.	SEXTO	1	1	40	120	600
G2HC-020	1734	roses and plumes on rev.	SEPTIMO	1	1	40	120	600
G2HC-025	1735	roses and plumes on rev.	OCTAVO	1	1	40	120	600
G2HC-030	1736	roses and plumes on rev.	NONO	1	1	45	130	650
G2HC-035	1739	roses on rev.	DVODECIMO	1	1	35	110	350
G2HC-040	1741	roses on rev. [2]	DECIMO QVARTO	1	1	35	110	350
G2HC-045	1741	41 over 39 roses on rev.	DECIMO QVARTO	1	1	45	130	400
G2HC-050	1743	roses on rev.	DECIMO SEPTIMO	2	1	35	100	280
G2HC-055	1745	roses on rev.	DECIMO NONO	2	1	35	100	280
G2HC-060	1745	5 over 3 roses on rev.	DECIMO NONO	2	1	40	120	350
G2HC-065	1745	LIMA below head [3]	DECIMO NONO	2	1	30	60	180
G2HC-070	1746	LIMA below head [3]	DECIMO NONO	3	1	30	60	180
G2HC-075	1746	6 over 5 LIMA below head	DECIMO NONO	3	1	40	75	240
G2HC-080	1746	PROOF [4]	VICESIMO	3	1			900
G2HC-085	1750		VICESIMO QVARTO	3	1	45	130	380
G2HC-090	1751		VICESIMO QVARTO	3	1	50	150	450

1. Q of QVINTO appears to be on its side on some or all specimens (edge).
2. A variety has slightly larger obv lettering.
3. Scottish arms vary.
4. The head is very slightly different from that on the ordinary issue.

The number of harp strings varies through this series. It is possible that the variation constituted a form of internal code denoting the die number.

George III 1760–1820

The scarce countermarked Spanish or Spanish-American 4 reales was a by-product of the much larger issue of countermarked 8 reales, the result of the silver shortage of the period. The true halfcrown was issued only during the last five years of the reign, using the new equipment at Tower Hill, and yet it yielded two quite different designs for the portrait.

Thomas Wyon engraved the portrait of the king for the first halfcrown, from a design by Benedetto Pistrucci. Wyon designed and engraved the reverse. The first type of halfcrown has become known as the 'Bull Head' type, and it was replaced during 1817. The replacement bore a smaller and more attractive head, also by Wyon after Pistrucci, with a reverse by Pistrucci himself. Thomas Wyon died of consumption in September 1817, and it fell to Pistrucci to engrave the dies subsequently.

The new designs for the halfcrown after the 'Great Recoinage' incorporated a number of innovations. Indeed, the designs owed more to those of the Spanish coinage which had been counterstamped and used as currency. The date was placed under the head as on the 4 reales rather than, as previously, on the reverse. The reverse design of the halfcrown is similar to that of the 4 reales, and for the first time the reverse is not inverted relative to the obverse. This, too, is characteristic of the Spanish coinage.

No.	Date	Obv.	Rev.	F	VF	EF
G3HC-005	none	1	1	100	200	400
G3HC-010	none	2	2	150	300	700
G3HC-015	none	3	3	300	500	900
G3HC-020	none	4	4	150	300	600
G3HC-025	none	5	5	200	400	750
G3HC-030	none	6	6	400	650	1100

Occasionally one meets a piece with the reverse counterstamped, or with the counterstamp inverted.

Denomination	Metal	Weight (grams)	Diameter (mm)	Rev. alignment
Halfcrown	Silver	14.1	32	↑

Obverse 1 Head 1, right; GEORGIUS III (Head) DEI GRATIA (date)

Obverse 2 Head 2, smaller, right; GEORGIUS III DEI GRATIA (date)

Reverse 1 Shield with Garter, crown above; BRITANNIARUM REX FID DEF; on Garter HONI SOIT QUI MAL Y PENSE

Reverse 2 Similar but differently designed; same legends

Edge milled

Obv. 1   Obv. 2

Rev. 1   Rev. 2

No.	Date	Features	Obv.	Rev.	F	VF	EF	UNC
G3HC-035	1816	[1]	1	1	10	35	120	180
G3HC-040	1816	PROOF	1	1				1000
G3HC-045	1816	PROOF; edge plain	1	1				1200
G3HC-050	1817		1	1	9	30	110	170
G3HC-055	1817	D of DEI over T (obv.)	1	1	14	55	200	300
G3HC-060	1817	PROOF	1	1				1000
G3HC-065	1817	PROOF; edge plain	1	1				1500
G3HC-070	1817	PROOF in copper	1	1				700
G3HC-075	1817		2	2	9	30	110	170
G3HC-080	1817	each 'S' in Garter motto reversed (rev.)	2	2	20	70	200	300
G3HC-085	1817	PROOF	2	2				1000
G3HC-090	1817	PROOF; edge plain	2	2				900
G3HC-095	1818		2	2	12	40	130	200
G3HC-100	1818	PROOF	2	2				1600
G3HC-105	1819		2	2	9	30	110	170
G3HC-110	1819	9 over 8	2	2	50	100	400	600
G3HC-115	1819	PROOF	2	2				1400
G3HC-120	1820	[2]	2	2	10	35	120	180
G3HC-125	1820	PROOF	2	2				1600
G3HC-130	1820	PROOF; edge plain	2	2				1500

1. Issued in 1817.
2. Reverse orientation slightly different from previous dates.

Collecting Hints

While most collectors will be content with one specimen of the countermarked 4 reales, the connoisseur or historian will probably try to acquire as many different types of host coin as he can find; certainly there is scope for original research here. The host coin is usually in about fine condition, but it should be noted that the grade of the coin is usually taken as the grade of the countermark. One must beware of 4 reales with octagonal countermarks. Some authorities believe that all of these are forgeries, but opinions differ. For example, Baldwins paid £320 for an octagonally counterstamped Potosi 4 reales at Glendining's in March 1990.

The halfcrowns of 1816-1820 are reasonably plentiful in higher grades, and the best possible specimens should be acquired. The quality of striking is excellent, and uncirculated specimens frequently exhibit proof-like characteristics. Check the edges, even of very fine specimens, as circulated plain edge proofs are sometimes encountered.

Denomination	Metal	Weight (grams)	Diameter (mm)	Rev. alignment
Counterstamped Spanish Silver 4 reales or Spanish-American 4 reales		13- 14	32- 34	↑
Counterstamped other foreign coins (halfcrown size)	Silver	as host coin	as host coin	as host coin

Oval Counterstamp

Obverse 1 George III head, right, in oval counterstamped on Spanish 4 reales obverse

Obverse 2 Similar but on Spanish-American 4 reales obverse

Obverse 3 Similar but on other foreign coins (halfcrown size)

Octagonal Counterstamp

Obverse 4 George III head in octagon counterstamped on Spanish 4 reales obverse

Obverse 5 Similar but on Spanish-American 4 reales obverse

Obverse 6 Similar but on other foreign coins (halfcrown size)

Reverse As of the appropriate host coin, partially flattened where stamped

Edge As of the appropriate host coin

Obv. Oval Counterstamp   Obv. Octagonal Counterstamp

Rev.

George IV 1820–1830

The first issue of halfcrowns used the laureate head of the monarch by Benedetto Pistrucci as on the crowns, which was changed in 1824/25 to the Wyon portrait owing to the king's disapproval of his portrayal. The reverse underwent two major changes of design, resulting in 1825 in an obverse and reverse both very similar to those on the 1826 proof crown. The axis alignment reverted to that used on pre-George III coinage. It is not generally appreciated that the reverses include the carefully hidden initials both of William Wellesley Pole, Master of the Mint, in the centres of the shamrocks, and those of Johann Baptiste Merlen, designer of the reverse, in the beading around the rim.

Collecting Hints

Most of the dates are not too difficult to find in extremely fine or near, but the 1823 with the early reverse is a real rarity, seldom offered in the major salerooms, and even then usually only in fair or fine condition.

Denomination	Metal	Weight (grams)	Diameter (mm)	Rev. alignment
Halfcrown	Silver	14.1	32	↓

Obverse 1 Head 1, laureate, left; GEORGIUS IIII D G BRITANNIAR REX F D

Obverse 2 Head 2, so-called 'bare head', left; GEORGIUS IV DEI GRATIA (date)

Reverse 1 Garnished shield with surmounting large crown; ANNO (date)

Reverse 2 Similar but many minor differences (thistle leaves, harp strings, shamrock stalks, crown, etc.)

Reverse 3 Crowned shield within Garter and collar; ANNO (date); on Garter HONI SOIT QUI MAL Y PENSE

Reverse 4 Garnished flat-top shield with surmounting helmet and small crown; BRITANNIARUM REX FID DEF;

on scroll DIEU ET MON DROIT

Edge milled

Obv. 1   Obv. 2

Rev. 1   Rev. 2

Rev. 3   Rev. 4

No.	Date	Features	Obv.	Rev.	F	VF	EF	UNC
G4HC-005	1820		1	1	10	35	120	180
G4HC-010	1820	PROOF	1	1				600
G4HC-015	1820	PROOF; edge plain	1	1				1200
G4HC-020	1820	PROOF	1	2				800
G4HC-025	1821		1	1	10	35	120	180
G4HC-030	1821		1	2	25	60	300	450
G4HC-035	1821	PROOF	1	2				1200
G4HC-040	1823	[1]	1	2	250	800		
G4HC-045	1823		1	3	12	50	150	220
G4HC-050	1823	PROOF	1	3				1200
G4HC-055	1824		1	3	14	60	180	260
G4HC-060	1824	PROOF	1	3				1200
G4HC-065	1824	PROOF in copper; edge plain	1	3				500
G4HC-070	1824	[1]	2	4	500			
G4HC-075	1825		2	4	12	40	130	200
G4HC-080	1825	PROOF	2	4				250
G4HC-085	1825	PROOF; edge plain	2	4				600
G4HC-090	1825	PROOF in Barton's metal; edge plain [2]	2	4				1500
G4HC-095	1826		2	4	10	35	120	180
G4HC-100	1826	PROOF [3]	2	4				700
G4HC-105	1828		2	4	12	50	180	260
G4HC-110	1829		2	4	12	50	180	260

1. Patterns exist.
2. Barton's metal is a laminated product consisting of thin sheets of gold bonded to a copper base.
3. Issued in cased proof sets.

William IV 1830–1837

The design of the halfcrown by William Wyon (obv.) and Johann Baptiste Merlen (rev.) was very similar to that of the proof crown, and remained identical throughout the reign except for the variation of Wyon's initials on the obverse.

Collecting Hints

The coins should be collected in extremely fine or better condition. This is not a scarce series, with the possible exception of the 1835; however, very fine pieces do retain most of the detail of the design, especially on the reverse, and may be satisfactory to collectors wishing to concentrate on acquiring better pieces of more interesting series.

Denomination	Metal	Weight (grams)	Diameter (mm)	Rev. alignment
Halfcrown	Silver	14.1	32	↓

Obverse 1 Head 1, right; W.W. incuse on truncation in small block capitals; GULIELMUS IIII D G (Head) BRITANNIAR REX F D

Obverse 2 Similar but W.W. incuse in script, somewhat larger; hair slightly differently arranged

Reverse 1 Crowned shield on mantle; below ANNO (date)

Edge milled

Obv. 1   Rev. 1

In particular, the lettering is irregular and poorly formed, and the background lines are not parallel to the axis of the shield. The view has been expressed that they may have been copies made in about 1870, but this seems unlikely, given that the portrait resembles the later 1874 type, indicating that they were fabricated after that date.

No.	Date	Features	Obv.	Rev.	F	VF	EF	UNC
W4HC-005	1831		1	1	600			
W4HC-010	1831	PROOF; edge plain [1]	1	1				500
W4HC-015	1831	PROOF	2	1				3000
W4HC-020	1831	PROOF; edge plain [2]	2	1				800
W4HC-025	1831	PROOF; edge plain; rev. ↑ [3]	2	1				1200
W4HC-030	1834		1	1	20	90	300	450
W4HC-035	1834	PROOF	1	1				1800
W4HC-040	1834		2	1	10	40	140	200
W4HC-045	1834	PROOF	2	1				1200
W4HC-050	1834	PROOF; edge plain	2	1				3000
W4HC-055	1835		2	1	15	70	300	450
W4HC-060	1836		2	1	10	40	140	200
W4HC-065	1836	6 over 5	2	1	15	60	200	250
W4HC-070	1836	PROOF; edge plain	2	1				3000
W4HC-075	1837		2	1	15	70	300	450

1. Issued in cased proof sets; hair arrangement slightly different from that on usual obverse 1; obverse border teeth finer.
2. A few were issued in cased proof sets; may weigh only c. 13 grams.
3. Rim may be shallower than on other plain edge proofs of this date; possibly struck at a later date.

Victoria 1837–1901

Although the halfcrown series of Victoria began with an interesting and complex set of varieties for the first date, 1839, it continued in a lower key with only the change of date, and occasionally of type, providing interest. After 1850, a long gap in the series was occasioned by an attempt to promote the florin as a precursor of decimal currency, but in 1874 the halfcrown was reintroduced, and the elegant high relief portrait of the first decade gave way to a low relief and less attractive example. It had unfortunately been found that the high relief coinage wore too quickly for practical purposes. The unpopular Boehm portrait of 1887 and the Brock 1893 design were similar to those on the other silver denominations. The 1893 coin is the first bearing the denomination mark 'HALF CROWN'.

Collecting Hints

The serious collector will look only for extremely fine or better specimens throughout this series. The quality of the early high relief pieces up to 1850 can only be appreciated properly in these grades, and the later halfcrowns are so prolific in fine or very fine that their appeal will be mainly directed towards making up date sets rather than serious study of the workmanship.

The note in the crown section on distinguishing the 1887 proof crown applies equally to the 1887 and 1893 halfcrowns.

Occasionally one comes across halfcrowns dated between about 1866 and 1871, usually in fair or fine condition. These exhibit marked differences from the regular coins, and are probably contemporary forgeries, even though at least one is reported to have been authenticated by the Royal Mint.

Denomination	Metal	Weight (grams)	Diameter (mm)	Rev. alignment
Halfcrown 1839–87 rev. 1	Silver	14.1	32	↓
Halfcrown 1887–1901 revs 2,3	Silver	14.1	32	↑

Obverse 1 Head 1, left; one plain and one ornate fillet in the hair, W.W. in relief on the truncation. VICTORIA DEI GRATIA (date)

Obverse 2 Head 2, left; similar but both fillets are ornate. W.W. in relief; same legend

Obverse 3 Head 3, left; similar but both fillets are plain. W.W. in relief; same legend

Obverse 4 Head 4, left; both fillets are plain. W.W. incuse; same legend

Obverse 5 Head 5, left; both fillets are plain. No initials on truncation; same legend

Obverse 6 Head 6, in lower relief, left; both fillets plain. No initials on truncation; same legend but slight spacing variations

Obverse 7 Head 7, 'Jubilee' type with small crown on head, left. VICTORIA (Head) DEI GRATIA

Obverse 8 Head 8, 'Old Head' type, left. VICTORIA DEI (Head) GRA BRITT REG

Reverse 1 Crowned shield within branches. BRITANNIARUM REGINA FID DEF. Slight variations from 1879

Reverse 2 Crowned shield within Garter and collar. BRITANNIARUM REGINA FID DEF (date)

Reverse 3 Crowned 'spade' shield in collar of the Garter. FID DEF IND IMP HALF (date) CROWN

Edge milled

Obv. 1   Obv. 4

Obv. 5   Obv. 6

Obv. 7

Obv. 8

Rev. 1

Rev. 2

Rev. 3

No.	Date	Features	Obv.	Rev.	F	VF	EF	UNC
VYHC-005	1839		1	1	500	1100	4000	
VYHC-010	1839	PROOF	1	1				3000
VYHC-015	1839	PROOF; edge plain; rev. ↑ [1]	1	1				600
VYHC-020	1839	PROOF; edge plain [1]	1	1				600
VYHC-025	1839	PROOF; edge plain	2	1				2000
VYHC-030	1839	PROOF; edge plain; rev. ↑	3	1				5000
VYHC-035	1839		4	1	500	1100	4000	
VYHC-040	1839	PROOF	4	1				3500
VYHC-045	1839	PROOF; edge plain	4	1				3000
VYHC-050	1840		4	1	18	70	200	350
VYHC-055	1841		5	1	60	200	700	1200
VYHC-060	1842		5	1	14	50	160	250
VYHC-065	1843		5	1	25	80	250	400
VYHC-070	1844		5	1	12	45	140	220
VYHC-075	1844	struck on large flan; edge plain	5	1	100	400		
VYHC-080	1845		5	1	12	45	140	220
VYHC-085	1846		5	1	15	55	170	270
VYHC-090	1848	[2]	5	1	50	160	700	1000
VYHC-095	1848	latter 8 over 6	5	1	40	140	600	900
VYHC-100	1848	latter 8 over 7	5	1	50	160	700	1000
VYHC-105	1849	large date	5	1	20	70	200	350
VYHC-110	1849	small date	5	1	50	160	500	1000
VYHC-115	1850		5	1	20	75	250	450
VYHC-120	1850	PROOF	5	1				2500
VYHC-125	1853	PROOF [1]	5	1				1500
VYHC-130	1862	PROOF	1	1				1500
VYHC-135	1862	PROOF; edge plain; rev. ↑	1	1				3000
VYHC-140	1864	PROOF; rev. ↑ [3]	1	1				2500
VYHC-145	1864	PROOF; edge plain; rev. ↑ [3]	1	1				2500
VYHC-150	1874		6	1	10	30	100	140
VYHC-155	1874	PROOF	6	1				800
VYHC-160	1874	PROOF; edge plain	6	1				1500

No.	Date	Features	Obv.	Rev.	F	VF	EF	UNC
VYHC-165	1874	PROOF in gold; edge plain	6	1				15000
VYHC-170	1875		6	1	10	35	110	150
VYHC-175	1875	PROOF	6	1				1200
VYHC-180	1875	PROOF; edge plain	6	1				5000
VYHC-185	1876		6	1	12	35	120	160
VYHC-190	1876	6 over 5	6	1	18	50	150	200
VYHC-195	1877		6	1	12	35	120	160
VYHC-200	1878		6	1	12	35	120	160
VYHC-205	1878	PROOF	6	1				1500
VYHC-210	1879	[4]	6	1	12	35	120	160
VYHC-215	1879	PROOF; rev. ↑	6	1				1000
VYHC-220	1879	PROOF; edge plain; rev. ↑ [5]	6	1				1500
VYHC-225	1880		6	1	12	35	120	160
VYHC-230	1880	PROOF	6	1				1500
VYHC-235	1881	[6]	6	1	10	30	100	140
VYHC-240	1881	PROOF	6	1				1200
VYHC-245	1881	PROOF; edge plain	6	1				4000
VYHC-250	1882		6	1	12	35	120	160
VYHC-255	1883		6	1	10	30	100	140
VYHC-260	1884		6	1	10	30	100	140
VYHC-265	1885		6	1	10	30	100	140
VYHC-270	1885	PROOF	6	1				1500
VYHC-275	1886		6	1	10	30	100	140
VYHC-280	1886	PROOF	6	1				3000
VYHC-285	1887		6	1	10	28	90	120
VYHC-290	1887	PROOF	6	1				3000
VJHC-295	1887	[7]	7	2	5	8	12	15
VJHC-300	1887	PROOF [1]	7	2				130
VJHC-305	1888		7	2	6	10	45	70
VJHC-310	1889	[8]	7	2	6	9	40	60
VJHC-315	1890		7	2	6	14	60	90
VJHC-320	1891		7	2	6	14	60	90
VJHC-325	1892		7	2	6	14	60	90
VOHC-330	1893	[8]	8	3	6	12	50	75
VOHC-335	1893	PROOF [1]	8	3				160
VOHC-340	1894		8	3	6	14	60	90
VOHC-345	1895		8	3	6	12	55	80
VOHC-350	1896		8	3	6	14	60	90
VOHC-355	1897		8	3	6	12	50	75
VOHC-360	1898		8	3	6	15	65	95
VOHC-365	1899		8	3	6	14	60	90
VOHC-370	1900		8	3	6	12	50	75
VOHC-375	1901		8	3	6	12	50	70

1. Issued in cased proof sets.
2. Obverse lettering irregularly spaced.
3. Struck for Albert Memorial opening.
4. Minor obverse differences occur.
5. Number of border teeth vary on reverse.
6. Minor obverse orientation differences occur.
7. Minor differences occur in crown (obv.).
8. Reverse border teeth vary in size.

Edward VII 1902–1910

The obverse portrait of Edward by George William de Saulles (1862-1903) was produced by a mechanical reduction process from the original master. The series was a one-type issue. It was the first which included a dated coin for every year of a monarch's reign.

Collecting Hints

Although, with the exception of the 1905, Edward VII halfcrowns are easily found in fine condition, in top grades they can be surprisingly elusive. Moreover, the nature of the striking, and the manner in which they wear, can deceive the inexperienced eye as to how much wear a coin has sustained. Careful comparison with both the obverse and reverse of, say, a 1902 matt proof halfcrown will often show that one's optimism has not been justified. In the lower grades the 'P' of 'PENSE' is usually the first letter of the reverse to become worn off.

Clever forgeries of the 1905 halfcrown exist, and any coins with concave or 'blistered' fields should be suspect.

Denomination	Metal	Weight (grams)	Diameter (mm)	Rev. alignment
Halfcrown	Silver	14.1	32	↑

Obverse 1 Head 1, right; EDWARDVS VII DEI GRA BRITT OMN REX

Reverse 1 Crowned shield within Garter; FID DEF IND IMP HALF (date) CROWN

On Garter HONI SOIT QUI MAL Y PENSE

Edge milled

Obv. 1

Rev. 1

No.	Date	Features	Obv.	Rev.	F	VF	EF	UNC
E7HC-005	1902		1	1	6	14	40	60
E7HC-010	1902	matt PROOF [1]	1	1			35	50
E7HC-015	1903		1	1	30	100	350	600
E7HC-020	1904		1	1	12	50	300	500
E7HC-025	1905		1	1	80	250	700	1000
E7HC-030	1906		1	1	6	18	80	120
E7HC-035	1907		1	1	6	18	80	120
E7HC-040	1908		1	1	7	20	100	150
E7HC-045	1909		1	1	6	18	80	130
E7HC-050	1910		1	1	6	18	70	100

1. Issued in cased proof sets.

George V 1910–1936

As with Edward VII, the halfcrown was struck for each year of the reign, and used the well-known portrait of the monarch by Sir Bertram MacKennal, whose initials B.M. appear on the truncation. The first reverse, although similar to that of the Edward VII coinage, is struck and wears so differently from its predecessor that many collectors would be forgiven for believing it to be a different reverse, and most would be baffled if asked to differentiate between the two. In fact, apart from minor differences in lettering, the main alteration is the omission of the beaded circle around the shield. The George V coins also have a slightly concave or 'dished' appearance contrasting with the rather 'flat' look of the Edward VII halfcrowns.

Because of the increase in the price of silver, in 1920 the alloy was changed to include 50% of silver instead of 92.5%. Coins up to 1922 tarnished very unattractively, and a change in the base metal (non-silver) constituents after then rendered the alloy more

acceptable in this respect. The striking of the 50% silver coinage appears in lower relief relative to that of the 1911-19 coinage due possibly either to the different metal resistance to pressure or to a change in the method of striking to accommodate the new alloy. The belief held by some that the design changed in 1920 is not borne out by inspection.

The reverse of the halfcrown was altered in 1927 as part of a radical redesigning of the silver currency by George Kruger Gray (1880-1943). The 1927 halfcrown bearing the new design was issued only as a proof as part of the cased proof set of that year, the first currency issue being in 1928. The reverse again sported a shield, but of a very different design. One of its more unusual features was a large slot at the top left corner, intended to represent the hole through which the lance was meant to pass.

The new design of halfcrown was minted until the death of the king in 1936.

Collecting Hints

This series should be collected in extremely fine or better condition. Those looking for a sequence of dates in fine or very fine should not find the task of assembling them too difficult. A few of the dates are surprisingly difficult to find in top condition.

Care should be taken in grading; it is, for example, easy to overestimate the grade of the reverses of the halfcrowns of 1928-36 and particular attention should be paid to the amount of detail present in the hair of the obverse portrait. Conversely, many collectors undergrade extremely fine coins between 1920 and 1927. What sometimes appears as a 'dig' on the portrait of the early dates, especially the 1911 proof, is in fact part of the design, as can be seen clearly if one inspects a 1911 proof set. Single 1911 proof coins are occasionally catalogued as being 'with nick on the portrait' in auctions. It may be worth bidding on these!

The use of 'silver dip' is not normally recommended, but there is no doubt that chemical removal of the ugly yellow tarnish often seen on very fine to extremely fine pieces in the period 1920-22 does enhance their appearance.

Denomination	Metal	Weight (grams)	Diameter (mm)	Rev alignment
Halfcrown 1911-19	0.925 Silver	14.1	32	↑
Halfcrown 1920-22	Silver 50% Copper 40% Nickel 10%	14.1	32	↑
Halfcrown 1922-27	Silver 50% Copper 50%	14.1	32	↑
Halfcrown 1927-36	Silver 50% Copper 40% Nickel 5% Zinc 5%	14.1	32	↑

Obverse 1 Head 1; B.M. on truncation, left; GEORGIVS DEI GRA BRITT OMN REX

Obverse 2 Head 2, so-called 'modified effigy', left; BM (no stops) further to right; same legend. beading recut; beads are wider than previously, and fewer in number

Reverse 1 Crowned shield within Garter; FID DEF IND IMP HALF (date) CROWN

On Garter HONI SOIT QUI MAL Y PENSE

Reverse 2 Shield with flanking interlinked and crowned 'G's. FID DEF IND IMP HALF CROWN (date)

Edge milled

Obv. 1   Obv. 2

Rev. 1   Rev. 2

No.	Date	Features	Obv.	Rev.	F	VF	EF	UNC
G5HC-005	1911		1	1	4	10	35	70
G5HC-010	1911	PROOF [1]	1	1			50	75
G5HC-015	1912		1	1	5	12	40	60
G5HC-020	1913		1	1	5	14	50	90
G5HC-025	1914		1	1	4	8	16	30
G5HC-030	1915		1	1	4	8	16	30
G5HC-035	1916		1	1	4	8	16	30
G5HC-040	1917		1	1	4	8	16	30
G5HC-045	1918		1	1	4	8	16	30
G5HC-050	1919		1	1	4	10	20	40
G5HC-055	1920	[2]	1	1	4	10	25	40
G5HC-060	1921		1	1	4	12	30	50
G5HC-065	1922	[3]	1	1	4	10	25	40
G5HC-070	1923		1	1	4	8	16	25
G5HC-075	1924		1	1	4	14	35	55
G5HC-080	1925		1	1	5	20	130	200
G5HC-085	1926	[4]	1	1	4	10	30	50
G5HC-090	1926	[5]	2	1	4	10	30	50
G5HC-095	1927	[5]	2	1	3	7	25	40
G5HC-100	1927	PROOF in nickel	2	1				2000
G5HC-105	1927	PROOF [1]	2	2	10	15	20	30
G5HC-110	1927	PROOF from sandblasted dies [6]	2	2				500
G5HC-115	1928		2	2	3	6	10	15
G5HC-120	1928	PROOF	2	2				450
G5HC-125	1929		2	2	3	6	10	15
G5HC-130	1929	PROOF	2	2				450
G5HC-135	1930		2	2	5	15	70	120
G5HC-140	1930	PROOF	2	2				600
G5HC-145	1931		2	2	3	6	10	15
G5HC-150	1931	PROOF	2	2				450
G5HC-155	1932		2	2	3	7	12	25
G5HC-160	1932	PROOF	2	2				500
G5HC-165	1933		2	2	3	6	10	15
G5HC-170	1933	PROOF	2	2				450
G5HC-175	1934		2	2	3	8	20	30
G5HC-180	1934	PROOF	2	2				450
G5HC-185	1935		2	2	3	6	10	15
G5HC-190	1935	PROOF	2	2				450
G5HC-195	1936		2	2	3	6	10	15
G5HC-200	1936	PROOF	2	2				450

1. Issued in cased proof sets.
2. Metal composition change; see table above; a few may exist in sterling silver.
3. Minor reverse differences occur; metal composition changes during year; see table above.
4. Defective obverse legend stops exist.
5. Reverse beading recut.
6. Struck to facilitate photography of coin.

Edward VIII 1936

The Edward VIII halfcrown is strictly speaking a pattern, as probable Royal approval was about to be granted at the time of the abdication. However, because its official status rests only on this technicality, and to provide continuity, it is included in this catalogue.

The portrait of Edward VIII is by Thomas Humphrey Paget, and faces left at the insistence of the king, who considered this placement more flattering and wished to discontinue the tradition of opposite facings for successive monarchs. The reverse is by George Kruger Gray (1880-1943)

Denomination	Metal	Weight (grams)	Diameter (mm)	Rev. alignment
Halfcrown	Silver	14.1	32	↑

Obverse 1 Head 1, left; EDWARDVS VIII D G BR OMN REX

Reverse 1 Standard Flag bearing Royal arms flanked by interlinked 'E's on each side forming an internal figure '8'; FID DEF IND IMP HALF CROWN 1937

Edge milled

Obv. 1   Rev. 1

No.	Date	Obv.	Rev.	UNC
E8HC-005	1937	1	1	20000

George VI 1937–1952

Thomas Humphrey Paget designed the portrait of George VI facing left, as on the George V coinage. The reverse was by George Kruger Gray, and was a redesigned version of the George V reverse. However, curiously, the shield hangs from a nail; a touch of humour, or surrealism, perhaps?

Proofs were struck in 1937 for the proof set, and in small quantities each year, possibly for testing purposes. The next official release of proofs was for the proof sets of 1950 and 1951. By this time, the coins were being struck in cupronickel.

Collecting Hints

Collect only in mint state, unless one is investing in silver, or enjoying the fun of assembling a date set. Always examine the edges of 1950 and 1951 proofs for corrosion. The 1950 is particularly susceptible, being in the corner of the cardboard box and liable to attack from a damp atmosphere. Resist the temptation to silver dip streaky cupronickel proofs, or indeed any coins in this metal. The marks will disappear, but will come back within days.

Denomination	Metal	Weight (grams)	Diameter (mm)	Rev. alignment
Halfcrown 1937-46	0.5 Silver	14.1	32	↑
Halfcrown 1947-52	Cupronickel	14.1	32	↑

Obverse 1 Head 1, left; GEORGIVS VI D G BR OMN REX

Reverse 1 Shield, flanked by crowned interlinked 'G's. FID DEF IND IMP HALF CROWN (date)

Reverse 2 Similar but IND IMP missing

Edge milled. The milling is finer from 1947-1952

Obv. 1

Rev. 1

Rev. 2

No.	Date	Features	Obv.	Rev.	F	VF	EF	UNC
G6HC-005	1937		1	1	2	3	5	7
G6HC-010	1937	PROOF [1]	1	1				15
G6HC-015	1937	PROOF from sandblasted dies [2]	1	1				300
G6HC-020	1938		1	1	2	3	6	8
G6HC-025	1938	PROOF	1	1				450
G6HC-030	1939		1	1	2	3	5	7
G6HC-035	1939	PROOF	1	1				450
G6HC-040	1940		1	1	2	3	5	7
G6HC-045	1940	PROOF	1	1				450
G6HC-050	1941		1	1	2	3	5	7
G6HC-055	1941	PROOF	1	1				450
G6HC-060	1942		1	1	2	3	5	7
G6HC-065	1943		1	1	2	3	5	7
G6HC-070	1943	PROOF	1	1				450
G6HC-075	1944		1	1	2	3	5	7
G6HC-080	1945		1	1	2	3	5	7
G6HC-085	1945	PROOF	1	1				450
G6HC-090	1946		1	1	2	3	5	7
G6HC-095	1946	PROOF	1	1				450
G6HC-100	1946	PROOF in cupronickel [3]	1	1				1500
G6HC-105	1947		1	1	2	2	3	4
G6HC-110	1947	PROOF	1	1				500
G6HC-115	1948		1	1	2	2	3	4
G6HC-120	1948	PROOF	1	1				500
G6HC-125	1949		1	2	2	2	3	4
G6HC-130	1949	PROOF	1	2				500
G6HC-135	1950		1	2	2	2	3	4
G6HC-140	1950	PROOF [1]	1	2				8
G6HC-145	1950	PROOF from sandblasted dies [2]	1	2				300
G6HC-150	1951		1	2	2	2	3	4
G6HC-155	1951	PROOF [1]	1	2				8
G6HC-160	1951	PROOF from sandblasted dies [2]	1	2				300
G6HC-165	1952	[4]	1	2	12000			

1. Issued in cased proof sets.
2. Struck to facilitate photography of coin.
3. Metal composition change; see table above.
4. Possibly unique.

Elizabeth II 1952 —

The original design by Mary Gillick for the Queen's portrait resulted in a weak striking lacking in detail, and the dies were soon recut to provide a sharper image. The first year (1953) is the only coin bearing the obverse 'BRITT OMN' (transl: of all the British possessions).

The beginning of the modern practice of collecting by date in the early sixties came too late to preserve in mint state many of the otherwise common pieces of the fifties, with the consequence that some of the dates are difficult to find thus.

Denomination	Metal	Weight (grams)	Diameter (mm)	Rev. alignment
Halfcrown	Cupronickel	14.1	32	↑

Obverse 1 Head 1, right; ELIZABETH II DEI GRATIA BRITT OMN REGINA

Obverse 2 Head 1 (recut), right; ELIZABETH II DEI GRATIA REGINA

Reverse 1 Crowned shield flanked by E and R; FID DEF HALF CROWN (date)

Edge milled

Obv. 1

Obv. 2

Rev. 1

No.	Date	Features	Obv.	Rev.	EF	UNC
EL2HC-005	1953	[1]	1	1	2	5
EL2HC-010	1953	PROOF [2]	1	1		8
EL2HC-015	1953	PROOF from sandblasted dies [3]	1	1		300
EL2HC-020	1954	[4]	2	1	3	15
EL2HC-025	1954	PROOF	2	1		300
EL2HC-030	1955		2	1	2	5
EL2HC-035	1955	PROOF	2	1		300
EL2HC-040	1956		2	1	2	5
EL2HC-045	1956	PROOF	2	1		300
EL2HC-050	1957		2	1	2	4
EL2HC-055	1957	PROOF	2	1		300
EL2HC-060	1958		2	1	3	14
EL2HC-065	1958	PROOF	2	1		300
EL2HC-070	1959		2	1	3	15
EL2HC-075	1959	PROOF	2	1		300
EL2HC-080	1960		2	1	2	4
EL2HC-085	1960	PROOF	2	1		300
EL2HC-090	1961	[5]	2	1	2	4
EL2HC-095	1961	struck from polished blanks [6]	2	1	2	6
EL2HC-100	1961	PROOF	2	1		300
EL2HC-105	1962	[7]	2	1	2	3
EL2HC-110	1962	PROOF	2	1		300
EL2HC-115	1963		2	1	2	3

No.	Date	Features	Obv.	Rev.	EF	UNC
EL2HC-120	1963	PROOF	2	1		300
EL2HC-125	1964		2	1	2	3
EL2HC-130	1964	PROOF	2	1		300
EL2HC-135	1965		2	1	2	3
EL2HC-140	1965	PROOF	2	1		300
EL2HC-145	1966		2	1	2	3
EL2HC-150	1966	PROOF	2	1		300
EL2HC-155	1967	[8]	2	1	2	3
EL2HC-160	1967	PROOF	2	1		300
EL2HC-165	1970	PROOF [9]	2	1	2	3

1. Some have recut head.
2. Issued in cased proof sets.
3. Struck to facilitate photography of coin.
4. Reverse border teeth slightly larger than on other years.
5. May have no 'E.F.' initials below shield (filled die).
6. Often wrongly termed 'polished die' variety; see below.
7. Minor varieties on portrait occur.
8. Issued for some years.
9. Issued in sealed cased proof sets; no ordinary issue coins of this date.

It has been surmised that the 1961 halfcrowns struck on polished blanks may have used blanks remaining from the issue of 1953 proof halfcrowns.

The halfcrown was demonetised on 1 January 1970.

Florin

Victoria 1837–1901

In 1847 Sir John Bowring proposed a motion in the House of Commons for the introduction of a decimal currency, and the striking of coins to the value of one-tenth and one-hundredth of a pound. The motion was subsequently withdrawn on the understanding that a one-tenth pound coin would be struck to test public opinion. Much discussion ensued as to the name of the proposed coin. Pattern coins of 1848 exist with the names Centum, Decade and Dime, but eventually the term 'florin' was adopted. This was an old English coinage term, but the name probably found favour because coins of similar size and value in some European countries had become known as florins.

The first adopted design for the florin was rather unusual. We are now used to seeing a crowned monarch on coinage, but the portrait of Victoria wearing a crown must have been a shock to the public when one considers that such a device had not been seen on coinage for nearly 200 years. Even more of a shock, including allegedly to the queen herself, was the omission of the term D.G. (=DEI GRATIA = by the grace of God). This omission caused the coin to be known popularly as the 'Godless Florin'.

The Godless florin was minted for one year only, 1849, although it may have been issued also during 1850 and 1851, but bearing the 1849 date. In 1851 a more elegant design was introduced which was similar in many respects to the Gothic crown of 1847. By now, the halfcrown had been discontinued as a further step to establishing the florin as a decimal coin. The Gothic florin was struck until 1887, when it was superseded by the jubilee and later the veiled head issues with obverses similar to the other silver coinage of the period.

One particular issue of Gothic florin deserves special mention. Salzman has suggested that the 1867 coin with the 42 arcs obverse may have been an error date, but examination of the details establishes this fact beyond all reasonable doubt. The minting of a 42-arc florin as the only piece in a 48-arc series is highly unlikely ten years before the 42-arc design was introduced. The highest die number recorded in ESC for 1867 is 9, with the exception of the 42-arc 1867 coin, which is die 32! Furthermore, the variety has no WW on the obverse, unlike all others of 1851 to 1876. The coin was undoubtedly struck in 1877 with the date wrongly 'spelt', that is, if it exists at all, about which there are doubts!

The alteration of the term BRIT to BRITT in 1867 may have been to denote a Latin abbreviation plural, representing 'Britains', i.e. Britain and its Colonies.

The Godless and Gothic florins had obverses designed by William Wyon and reverses by William Dyce. The jubilee florin had an obverse designed by Sir Joseph Edgar Boehm and engraved by Leonard Charles Wyon. Wyon is credited with designing the reverse, but this is obviously heavily influenced by the John Roettier design of the Charles II gold coinage. The veiled head florin had its obverse designed by Brock and the reverse by Sir Edward Poynter.

Denomination	Metal	Weight (grams)	Diameter (mm)	Rev. alignment
Florin 1849	Silver	11.3	28	↓
Florin 1851-1887 (Gothic type)	Silver	11.3	30	↓
Florin 1887-1892 (Jubilee type)	Silver	11.3	29.5	↑
Florin 1893-1901	Silver	11.3	28.5	↑

Obverse 1 Head 1, left; VICTORIA REGINA 1849

Obverse 2 Head 2, left; VICTORIA D G BRIT REG F D (date); WW below head; 48 ornamental arcs between legend and rim

Obverse 3 Head 3, left, slightly older; legend and date as Obverse 2 but BRITT instead of BRIT; WW; 48 arcs

Obverse 4 Similar but no WW; 48 arcs

Obverse 5 Similar but 42 arcs

Obverse 6 Head 4, left, slightly older; legend and date as Obverse 3 no WW; 39 arcs

Obverse 7 Head 3, no WW, left; 34 arcs

Obverse 8 Head 4, no WW, left; 34 arcs

Obverse 9 Head 3, no WW, left; 46 arcs

Obverse 10 Head 5, left; VICTORIA DEI GRATIA

Obverse 11 Head 6, left, slightly redesigned; same legend

Obverse 12 Head 7, left; VICTORIA DEI GRA BRITT REGINA FID DEF IND IMP

Note that on obverses 2 to 9 the date is in Roman numerals. The legend and date are in Gothic script

The 34 arc obverses are also known as 33 arc obverses in some catalogues

Reverse 1 Four crowned cruciform shields with rose at centre; rose, thistle, rose and shamrock in angles; ONE FLORIN ONE TENTH OF A POUND

Reverse 2 Similar but redesigned; cross in centre; same legend but in Gothic script

Reverse 3 Four crowned cruciform shields with Star of Garter in centre and sceptres in angles; FID DEF BRITT REG (date)

Reverse 4 Three shields separated by rose, shamrock and thistle; Garter; crown above; ONE FLORIN TWO SHILLINGS (date)

Edge milled

Obv. 1   Obv. 2

Obv. 3   Obv. 5

Obv. 6   Obv. 8

Obv. 9   Obv. 10

Obv. 12

Rev. 1   Rev. 2

Rev. 3

Rev. 4

No.	Date	Features	Obv.	Rev.	F	VF	EF	UNC
VGL-005	1849	WW next to date	1	1	10	30	80	110
VGL-010	1849	WW next to date partially erased	1	1	10	30	85	120

No.	Date	Date on coin incl. following punctuation	Features	Obv.	Rev.	F	VF	EF	UNC
VGFL-015	1851	mdcccli.	[1]	2	2	2000			
VGFL-020	1851	mdcccli.	PROOF; edge plain	2	2				6000
VGFL-025	1851	mdcccli.	PROOF	2	2				5000
VGFL-030	1852	mdccclii.		2	2	12	40	110	140
VGFL-035	1852	mdccclii.	2 over 1 [2]	2	2	20	70	180	260
VGFL-040	1852	mdccclii.	PROOF	2	2				1000
VGFL-045	1853	mdcccliii		2	2	12	40	110	150
VGFL-050	1853	mdcccliii	PROOF	2	2				1200
VGFL-055	1854	mdcccliv		2	2	300	1200		
VGFL-060	1855	mdccclv		2	2	12	45	120	160
VGFL-065	1856	mdccclvi		2	2	12	45	130	180
VGFL-070	1857	mdccclvii		2	2	12	45	130	180
VGFL-075	1858	mdccclviii		2	2	16	60	170	250
VGFL-080	1859	mdccclix		2	2	24	90	250	400
VGFL-085	1859	mdccclix.		2	2	16	60	170	250
VGFL-090	1859	mdccclix.	m in date is double struck inverted m [3]	2	2	50	180	600	1000
VGFL-095	1860	mdccclx.		2	2	12	45	130	180
VGFL-100	1862	mdccclxii	[4]	2	2	25	100	300	450
VGFL-105	1862	mdccclxii	PROOF; edge plain [4]	2	2				3000
VGFL-110	1863	mdccclxiii		2	2	60	200	600	1300
VGFL-115	1863	mdccclxiii	PROOF; edge plain	2	2				3000
VGFL-120	1864	mdccclxiv	with die number	2	2	12	45	120	160
VGFL-125	1864	mdccclxiv	struck on thick flan; with die number [5]	2	2	400	550	700	900
VGFL-130	1864	mdccclxiv	PROOF; struck on thick flan; with die number	2	2				2500
VGFL-135	1865	mdccclxv	with die number	2	2	12	50	130	170
VGFL-140	1865	mdccclxv:	with die number [6]	2	2	15	70	180	240
VGFL-145	1865	mdccclxv:	with die number; rev. →	2	2	18	85	220	300
VGFL-150	1866	mdccclxvi	with die number	2	2	16	80	200	270
VGFL-155	1866	mdccclxvi:	with die number	2	2	28	140	350	500
VGFL-160	1867	mdccclxvii	with die number	2	2	24	120	320	450
VGFL-165	1867	mdccclxvii	PROOF	3	2				2500
VGFL-170	1867	mdccclxvii	PROOF; edge plain; rev. ↑	3	2				2500
VGFL-175	1867 (1877)	mdccclxvii	with die number [7]	5	2	1200			
VGFL-180	1868	mdccclxviii	with die number	3	2	12	45	130	180
VGFL-185	1869	mdccclxix	with die number	3	2	12	40	120	160
VGFL-190	1869	mdccclxix	PROOF; with die number	3	2				2000

No.	Date	Date on coin incl. following punctuation	Features	Obv.	Rev.	F	VF	EF	UNC
VGFL-195	1870	mdccclxx	with die number	3	2	12	40	120	160
VGFL-200	1870	mdccclxx	PROOF; with die number [8]	3	2				3000
VGFL-205	1871	mdccclxxi	with die number	3	2	12	40	120	160
VGFL-210	1871	mdccclxxi	PROOF; with die number; rev. ↑	3	2				2500
VGFL-215	1871	mdccclxxi	PROOF; with die number; edge plain; rev. ↑	3	2				2500
VGFL-220	1872	mdccclxxii	with die number	3	2	10	35	110	150
VGFL-225	1873	mdccclxxiii	with die number	3	2	10	35	100	150
VGFL-230	1873	mdccclxxiii	PROOF; with die number	3	2				2500
VGFL-235	1874	mdccclxxiv	with die number	3	2	12	40	120	180
VGFL-240	1874	mdccclxxiv	4 over 3; with die number [9]	3	2	25	80	200	350
VGFL-245	1875	mdccclxxv	with die number	3	2	12	40	120	180
VGFL-250	1876	mdccclxxvi	with die number	3	2	12	45	130	190
VGFL-255	1877	mdccclxxvii	with die number [10]	3	2	12	45	130	190
VGFL-260	1877	mdccclxxvii.	with die number	4	2	12	45	130	190
VGFL-265	1877	mdccclxxvii.	with die number [10]	5	2	12	45	130	190
VGFL-270	1877	mdccclxxvii.		5	2	100	400		
VGFL-175 duplicated entry	1877 (1867)	mdcccclxvii (.)	with die number [11]	5	2	1200			
VGFL-275	1878	mdccclxxviii	with die number	5	2	12	40	120	160
VGFL-280	1878	mdccclxxviii	PROOF; with die number	5	2				2500
VGFL-285	1879	mdccclxxix	with die number	3	2	50	200		
VGFL-290	1879	mdccclxxix		3	2	50	200		
VGFL-295	1879	mdccclxxix		5	2	12	40	120	180
VGFL-300	1879	mdccclxxix		6	2	12	40	120	180
VGFL-305	1879	mdccclxxix	PROOF	6	2				1500
VGFL-310	1879	mdccclxxix	PROOF; edge plain; rev. ↑	6	2				1500
VGFL-315	1880	mdccclxxx		7	2	14	45	130	190
VGFL-320	1880	mdccclxxx		8	2	12	40	120	180
VGFL-325	1880	mdccclxxx	PROOF	8	2				2500
VGFL-330	1881	mdccclxxxi		8	2	10	35	100	130
VGFL-335	1881	mdccclxxxri [12]		8	2	12	45	120	160
VGFL-340	1881	mdccclxxxi	PROOF	8	2				2500
VGFL-345	1881	mdccclxxxi	PROOF; edge plain; rev. ↑	8	2				3000
VGFL-350	1883	mdccclxxxiii		8	2	10	35	100	130
VGFL-355	1884	mdccclxxxiv		8	2	10	35	100	130
VGFL-360	1885	mdccclxxxv		8	2	10	35	100	130
VGFL-365	1885	mdccclxxxv	PROOF	8	2				3000
VGFL-370	1886	mdccclxxxvi		8	2	10	35	100	130
VGFL-375	1886	mdccclxxxvi	PROOF	8	2				3000
VGFL-380	1887	mdccclxxxvii		9	2	10	35	100	130
VGFL-385	1887	mdccclxxxvii	PROOF	9	2				3000

1. Any extant are possibly all worn proofs; florin not legal tender until March 1852.
2. Last i of date is over stop.
3. Most have larger pellet shaped stops on obverse.
4. Stop after 'brit' (see below).
5. Specimens recorded with die nos. 32, 40, 47; weight 14.5–14.8 grams.
6. Usually die numbers 44 to 51.
7. Error date possibly struck in 1877. Catalogued also under date 1877; not known whether with stop after date; may not exist.
8. Recorded by Dickinson.
9. Overdate: last v of date appears over ii; usually die nos. 29 and 30.
10. Die number position varies (see below).
11. Error date reads 1867. Catalogued also under date 1867; not known whether with stop after date; may not exist.
12. Last x of date appears as r (broken punch).

No.	Date	Features	Obv.	Rev.	F	VF	EF	UNC
VJFL-390	1887	[1]	10	3	5	8	14	18
VJFL-395	1887	PROOF [2]	10	3				120
VJFL-400	1888		11	3	6	10	30	40
VJFL-405	1889	[3]	11	3	6	10	30	40
VJFL-410	1890		11	3	8	20	60	80
VJFL-415	1891		11	3	12	50	120	160
VJFL-420	1892		11	3	12	50	120	160
VJFL-425	1892	PROOF [4]	11	3				2500
VOFL-430	1893		12	4	5	10	40	65
VOFL-435	1893	PROOF [2]	12	4				150
VOFL-440	1894		12	4	6	14	60	110
VOFL-445	1895		12	4	6	14	60	80
VOFL-450	1896		12	4	6	15	70	90
VOFL-455	1897		12	4	6	12	50	75
VOFL-460	1898		12	4	6	15	70	90
VOFL-465	1899		12	4	6	15	70	90
VOFL-470	1900		12	4	6	12	50	75
VOFL-475	1901		12	4	6	12	50	70

1. Initials JEB on truncation vary in size and position (obv.).
2. Issued in cased proof sets.
3. Minor rev. Differences exist.
4. Possibly 5 struck.

Florins of 1862 appear to have stops after 'brit' instead of a colon. However, examples exist with a colon having its upper stop faintly visible, so the stop is probably a colon resulting from using a deficient punch.

Florins have no die numbers except for coins of 1864 to 1879 when stated. Die numbers are on obverse under Victoria's bust to the right of her brooch. Some examples of 1877 have the die number to the left of the brooch.

Edward VII 1902–1910

The florin of Edward VII, designed by George William de Saulles (1862-1903), displayed a most unusual and original reverse. The low-relief finely detailed standing Britannia design was a complete departure from anything seen previously. Coin design is generally highly derivative from previous reigns, and it was a bold move to introduce such a variation of the Britannia theme.

Matt proofs were struck in 1902 for inclusion in the cased sets, and the florin was subsequently struck for each year of the reign.

Collecting Hints

The last numeral of the date frequently wears off before any of the legends, and this can lead to confusion as to the date on coins bordering on fine condition. '3' and '5' are particularly liable to be confused. However, it should be remembered that the 1905 florin is not as scarce as the halfcrown of that date.

The obverse of the Edward VII florin is often weakly struck.

Denomination	Metal	Weight (grams)	Diameter (mm)	Rev. alignment
Florin	Silver	11.3	28.5	↑

Obverse 1 Head 1, right; EDWARDVS VII DEI GRA BRITT OMN REX FD IND IMP

Reverse 1 Britannia standing with shield and spear; ONE FLORIN TWO SHILLINGS (date)

Edge milled

Obv. 1

Rev. 1

No.	Date	Features	Obv.	Rev.	F	VF	EF	UNC
E7FL-005	1902		1	1	6	12	40	60
E7FL-010	1902	matt PROOF [1]	1	1			35	50
E7FL-015	1903		1	1	8	16	80	120
E7FL-020	1904		1	1	10	20	90	140
E7FL-025	1905		1	1	20	50	200	350
E7FL-030	1906		1	1	6	15	60	90
E7FL-035	1907		1	1	7	18	90	180
E7FL-040	1908		1	1	8	18	100	240
E7FL-045	1909		1	1	8	22	100	160
E7FL-050	1910		1	1	6	15	55	80

1. Issued in cased proof sets.

Minor differences of orientation and lettering size in word 'FLORIN' (rev.) occur from 1902 to 1904.

George V 1910–1936

The florin was minted for every year of this reign except 1934. Throughout the series the reverse used the cruciform shields and sceptres motif last seen on the Victoria jubilee head florin. From 1911 to 1926 the design of this was very similar to the jubilee design, but from 1927 the motif was radically redesigned with much larger sceptres in the angles.

The obverse portrait of George V was from a design by Sir Bertram MacKennal (1863-1931). Curiously, the (re-)designer of the 1911-1926 reverse was not recorded, but the 1927-1936 reverse was by George Kruger Gray (1880-1943). It is interesting to note the evolution of the cruciform shields and sceptres design from the John Roettier guinea of 1663 to the florin of 1936.

Because of the increase in the price of silver, in 1920 the alloy was changed to include 50% of silver instead of 92.5%. Coins up to 1922 tarnished very unattractively, and a change in the base metal (non-silver) constituents after then rendered the alloy more acceptable in this respect. The striking of the 50% silver coinage appears in lower relief relative to that of the 1911-19 coinage due possibly either to the different metal resistance to pressure or to a change in the method of striking to accommodate the new alloy.

Collecting Hints

This series should be collected in extremely fine or better condition. Those looking for a sequence of dates in fine or very fine should not find the task of assembling them too difficult. A few of the dates are surprisingly difficult to find in top condition.

Care should be taken in grading; it is, for example, easy to overestimate the grade of the reverses of the florins of 1928-36 and particular attention should be paid to the amount of detail present in the hair of the obverse portrait.

What sometimes appears as a 'dig' on the portrait of the early dates, especially the 1911 proof, is in fact part of the design, as can be seen clearly if one inspects a 1911 proof set. Single 1911 proof coins are sometimes knocked down cheaply in salerooms because they have been catalogued as 'with nick on the portrait'.

The use of 'silver dip' is not normally recommended, but there is no doubt that chemical removal of the ugly yellow tarnish often seen on very fine to extremely fine pieces in the period 1920-22 does enhance their appearance.

Denomination	Metal	Weight (grams)	Diameter (mm)	Rev. alignment
Florin 1911-19	0.925 fine Silver	11.3	28.5	↑
Florin 1920-22	Silver 50% — Copper 40% — Nickel 10%	11.3	28.5	↑
Florin 1922-26	Silver 50% — Copper 50%	11.3	28.5	↑
Florin 1927-36	Silver 50% — Copper 40% — Nickel 5% — Zinc 5%	11.3	28.5	↑

Obverse 1 Head 1, left; B.M. on truncation; depression on neck above BM; GEORGIVS V D G BRITT OMN REX F D IND IMP

Obverse 2 Head 2, left, no depression

Obverse 3 Head 3, so-called 'modified effigy', left; BM (no stops) further to right; beading recut; beads are wider than previously, and fewer in number; GEORGIVS V DEI GRA BRITT OMN REX

Reverse 1 Four crowned cruciform shields with sceptres in angles; ONE FLORIN (date)

Reverse 2 Similar but redesigned; FID DEF IND IMP (date) ONE FLORIN

Edge milled

Obv. 1

Obv. 3

Rev. 1

Rev. 2

No.	Date	Features	Obv.	Rev.	F	VF	EF	UNC
G5FL-005	1911		1	1	4	10	32	45
G5FL-010	1911	PROOF [1]	1	1			45	75
G5FL-015	1911		2	1	4	10	32	45
G5FL-020	1912		2	1	4	12	40	70
G5FL-025	1913		2	1	5	15	55	90
G5FL-030	1914	[2]	2	1	4	8	16	24
G5FL-035	1915		2	1	4	8	16	24
G5FL-040	1916		2	1	4	8	16	24
G5FL-045	1917		2	1	4	8	18	28
G5FL-050	1918		2	1	4	8	16	24
G5FL-055	1919		2	1	4	8	18	26
G5FL-060	1920	[3]	2	1	3	10	25	35
G5FL-065	1921		2	1	3	10	25	35
G5FL-070	1922	[4]	2	1	3	10	25	35
G5FL-075	1922	PROOF in gold	2	1				8000
G5FL-080	1923		2	1	3	8	18	25
G5FL-085	1924		2	1	3	12	35	50
G5FL-090	1925		2	1	4	15	90	140
G5FL-095	1926		2	1	3	12	35	50
G5FL-100	1927	PROOF [1]	3	2	25	30	35	40
G5FL-105	1927	PROOF from sandblasted dies [5]	3	2				350
G5FL-110	1928		3	2	3	6	10	15
G5FL-115	1928	PROOF	3	2				500
G5FL-120	1929		3	2	3	6	10	15
G5FL-125	1929	PROOF	3	2				500
G5FL-130	1930		3	2	3	7	12	18
G5FL-135	1930	PROOF	3	2				500
G5FL-140	1931		3	2	3	6	10	15
G5FL-145	1931	PROOF	3	2				500
G5FL-150	1932		3	2	5	10	75	120
G5FL-155	1932	PROOF	3	2				700
G5FL-160	1933		3	2	3	6	10	15
G5FL-165	1933	PROOF	3	2				400
G5FL-170	1935		3	2	3	6	10	15
G5FL-175	1935	PROOF	3	2				400
G5FL-180	1936		3	2	3	5	8	12
G5FL-185	1936	PROOF	3	2				400

1. Issued in cased proof sets.
2. Rim teeth size vary.
3. Metal composition change; see first table.
4. Metal composition changes during year; see first table.
5. Struck to facilitate photography of coin.

Coins struck in 0.925 silver appear to be struck in higher relief than those on 0.500 silver. This may be due to the purer metal being softer and thereby having a lower resistance to pressure.

Edward VIII 1936

The Edward VIII florin is strictly speaking a pattern, as probable royal approval was about to be granted at the time of the abdication. However, because its official status rests only on this technicality, and to provide continuity, it is included in this catalogue. The portrait of Edward VIII is by Thomas Humphrey Paget, and faces left at the insistence of the king, who considered this placement more flattering and wished to discontinue the tradition of opposite facings for successive monarchs. The reverse is by George Kruger Gray (1880-1943)

Denomination	Metal	Weight (grams)	Diameter (mm)	Rev. alignment
Florin	0.5 Silver	11.3	28.5	↑

Obverse 1 Head 1, left; EDWARDVS VIII D G BR OMN REX

Reverse 1 Crowned rose flanked by thistle and shamrock, E and R below last two; FID DEF IND IMP TWO SHILLINGS 1937

Edge milled

Obv. 1

Rev. 1

No.	Date	Obv.	Rev.	Unc
E8FL-005	1937	1	1	15000

George VI 1937–1952

Thomas Humphrey Paget designed the portrait of George VI facing left, as on the George V coinage. The reverse was by George Kruger Gray, and depicted a crowned rose between a thistle and a shamrock.

Proofs were struck in 1937 for the proof set, and in small quantities each year, possibly for testing purposes. The next official release of proofs was for the proof sets of 1950 and 1951. By this time, the coins were being struck in cupronickel.

Collecting Hints

Collect only in mint state, unless one is investing in silver, or enjoying the fun of assembling a date set. Always examine the edges of 1950 and 1951 proofs for corrosion. Resist the temptation to silver dip streaky cupronickel proofs, or indeed any coins in this metal. The marks will disappear, but will come back within days.

Denomination	Metal	Weight (grams)	Diameter (mm)	Rev. alignment
Florin 1937-46	0.5 Silver	11.3	28.5	↑
Florin 1947-51	Copper 75%; Nickel 25%	11.3	28.5	↑

Obverse 1 Head 1, left; GEORGIVS VI D G BR OMN REX

Reverse 1 Crowned rose flanked by thistle and shamrock, G and R below last two; FID DEF IND IMP TWO SHILLINGS (date)

Reverse 2 Similar but IND IMP missing

Edge milled. The milling is finer from 1947-1951

Obv. 1   Rev. 1   Rev. 2

No.	Date	Features	Obv.	Rev.	F	VF	EF	UNC
G6FL-005	1937		1	1	2	3	5	7
G6FL-010	1937	PROOF [1]	1	1			8	12
G6FL-015	1937	PROOF from sandblasted dies [2]	1	1				250
G6FL-020	1938		1	1	2	3	7	10
G6FL-025	1938	PROOF	1	1				300
G6FL-030	1939		1	1	2	3	5	8
G6FL-035	1939	PROOF	1	1				300
G6FL-040	1940		1	1	2	3	5	8
G6FL-045	1940	PROOF	1	1				300
G6FL-050	1941		1	1	2	3	5	7
G6FL-055	1941	PROOF	1	1				300
G6FL-060	1942		1	1	2	3	5	7
G6FL-065	1942	PROOF	1	1				300
G6FL-070	1943		1	1	2	3	5	7
G6FL-075	1944		1	1	2	3	5	7
G6FL-080	1944	PROOF	1	1				300
G6FL-085	1945		1	1	2	3	5	7
G6FL-090	1945	PROOF	1	1				300
G6FL-095	1946		1	1	2	3	5	7
G6FL-100	1946	PROOF	1	1				300
G6FL-105	1946	PROOF in cupronickel [3]	1	1				1200
G6FL-110	1947	[4]	1	1			2	5
G6FL-115	1947	PROOF	1	1				380

No.	Date	Features	Obv.	Rev.	F	VF	EF	UNC
G6FL-120	1948		1	1			2	5
G6FL-125	1948	PROOF	1	1				380
G6FL-130	1949		1	2			2	5
G6FL-135	1949	PROOF	1	2				380
G6FL-140	1950		1	2			2	5
G6FL-145	1950	PROOF [1]	1	2				7
G6FL-150	1950	PROOF from sandblasted dies [2]	1	2				250
G6FL-155	1951		1	2			2	5
G6FL-160	1951	PROOF [1]	1	2				7
G6FL-165	1951	PROOF from sandblasted dies [2]	1	2				250

1. Issued in cased proof sets.
2. Struck to facilitate photography of coin.
3. Trial piece for cupronickel coinage.
4. Metal composition change; see table above.

Obv. 1

Obv. 2

Rev. 1

Elizabeth II 1952 -

The original design by Mary Gillick for the queen's portrait resulted in a weak striking lacking in detail, and the dies were soon recut to provide a sharper image. The first year (1953) is the only coin bearing the obverse 'BRITT OMN' (transl: of all the British possessions).

The beginning of the modern practice of collecting by date in the early sixties came too late to preserve in mint state many of the otherwise common pieces of the fifties, with the consequence that some of the dates are difficult to find thus.

Collecting Hints

Collect in mint state. Acquiring examples of the unofficially struck proofs is an interesting challenge.

Denomination	Metal	Weight (grams)	Diameter (mm)	Rev. alignment
Florin 1953-70	Copper 75% Nickel 25%	11.3	28.5	↑

Obverse 1 Head 1, right; ELIZABETH II DEI GRATIA BRITT OMN REGINA

Obverse 2 Head 1 (recut), right; ELIZABETH II DEI GRATIA REGINA

Reverse 1 Concentric roses in centre surrounded by thistles, shamrocks, leeks; FID DEF TWO SHILLINGS (date)

Edge milled

No.	Date	Features	Obv.	Rev.	EF	UNC
EL2FL-005	1953	[1]	1	1	3	5
EL2FL-010	1953	PROOF [2]	1	1		9
EL2FL-015	1953	PROOF from sandblasted dies [3]	1	1		250
EL2FL-020	1954		2	1	6	25
EL2FL-025	1954	PROOF	2	1		250
EL2FL-030	1955		2	1	3	5
EL2FL-035	1955	PROOF	2	1		250
EL2FL-040	1956		2	1	3	5
EL2FL-045	1956	PROOF	2	1		250
EL2FL-050	1957		2	1	5	20
EL2FL-055	1957	PROOF	2	1		250
EL2FL-060	1958		2	1	4	12
EL2FL-065	1958	PROOF	2	1		250
EL2FL-070	1959		2	1	5	20
EL2FL-075	1959	PROOF	2	1		250
EL2FL-080	1960		2	1	2	4
EL2FL-085	1960	PROOF	2	1		250
EL2FL-090	1961		2	1	2	4
EL2FL-095	1961	PROOF	2	1		250
EL2FL-100	1962	[4]	2	1	1	3
EL2FL-105	1962	PROOF	2	1		250
EL2FL-110	1963		2	1	1	3
EL2FL-115	1963	PROOF	2	1		250
EL2FL-120	1964		2	1	1	2
EL2FL-125	1964	PROOF	2	1		250
EL2FL-130	1965		2	1	1	2
EL2FL-135	1965	struck in brass or nickel-brass [5]	2	1		300
EL2FL-140	1965	PROOF	2	1		250
EL2FL-145	1966		2	1	1	2
EL2FL-150	1966	PROOF	2	1		250
EL2FL-155	1967	[6]	2	1	1	2
EL2FL-160	1967	struck on both sides with rev. design	rev. 1	1	90	120
EL2FL-165	1967	PROOF	2	1		250
EL2FL-170	1970	PROOF [7]	2	1	2	4

1. Some have recut head.
2. Issued in cased proof sets.
3. Struck to facilitate photography of coin.
4. Several very minor varieties exist.
5. Weight 9.5 grams.
6. Issued for some years.
7. Issued in sealed cased proof sets; no ordinary issue coins of this date.

The florin continued as legal tender for several years after decimalization as an equivalent to the 10 pence coin.

Eighteen Pence Bank Token

George III 1760–1820

In 1811 there was a shortage of silver coinage for circulation. Although the countermarked dollars and five shilling bank tokens had been useful in this respect, no halfcrowns had been minted since 1751, and the last issue of shillings and sixpences for general use had been in 1787. In many parts of the country tradesmen issued private silver tokens during 1811, but these were not accepted outside the immediate area where they were issued.

To alleviate the situation, the Bank of England issued its own tokens for three shillings and for eighteen pence. Silver was trading on the free market at a high price, and the weights of these denominations were proportionately lower than normal. The fact that these issues were tokens rather than true coins rendered this shortfall acceptable.

As with the three shilling tokens, the issue of eighteen pence tokens was a short one, from 1811 to 1816, and comprised two distinct types. They were withdrawn from issue in March 1820, and were accepted after this date only as bullion by weight.

The first type (1811-12) was probably designed by Lewis Pingo. The second type (1812-16) used the Marchant design employed on the gold coinage. The actual engraving of the die is usually attributed to Thomas Wyon, who designed and engraved the reverse, but some doubt exists as to whether he engraved the obverse.

An unusual feature of the reverse is the use of the abbreviations 's' and 'd' for shilling and pence.

Denomination	Metal	Weight (grams)	Diameter (mm)	Rev. alignment
Eighteen Pence	Silver	7.4	27	↑

Obverse 1 Head 1, right; GEORGIUS III DEI GRATIA REX

Obverse 2 Head 2, right; same legend

Reverse 1 BANK TOKEN 1s 6d (date) within wreath of oak leaves

Reverse 2 Similar but lettering different and less profuse wreath of oak and olive

Edge: plain

Obv. 1   Obv. 2

Rev. 1   Rev. 2

No.	Date	Features	Obv.	Rev.	F	VF	EF	UNC
G318D-005	1811		1	1	10	20	45	60
G318D-010	1811	PROOF	1	1				350
G318D-015	1812		1	1	10	20	45	60
G318D-020	1812		2	2	10	18	40	55
G318D-025	1812	PROOF	2	2				350
G318D-030	1812	PROOF; small lettering on rev.	2	2				1500
G318D-035	1812	PROOF in platinum [1]	2	2				3000
G318D-040	1813		2	2	10	18	40	55
G318D-045	1813	PROOF in platinum	2	2				3000
G318D-050	1814		2	2	10	18	40	55
G318D-055	1815		2	2	10	18	40	55
G318D-060	1816		2	2	10	18	40	55

1. Two specimens weigh 15.7 and 16.6 grams.

Shilling

Oliver Cromwell (Commonwealth 1649–1660)

Unlike the halfcrown, the Cromwell shilling occurs only with the date 1658. It was designed by Thomas Simon (also called Symonds) and portrays Cromwell as a Roman Emperor, draped and laureate. The 'Tanner's Copy', struck in the 18th Century, is outside the scope of this book.

Collecting Hints

Forgeries exist. On genuine specimens there is usually a die flaw near the top laurel wreath. The coin should be collected in fine condition or better.

Denomination	Metal	Weight (grams)	Diameter (mm)	Rev. alignment
Shilling	Silver	6.0	25–26	↓

Obverse 1 Head 1, left; OLIVAR D G R P ANG SCO HIB &c PRO

Reverse 1 Crowned shield; PAX QVAERITVR BELLO 1658

Edge milled

Obv. 1   Rev. 1

No.	Date	Features	Obv.	Rev.	F	VF	EF
CRSH-005	1658	1	1	1	280	500	850

1. Usually a die flaw near top laurel leaf (obv.).

Charles II 1660–1685

The new machine-struck shilling was designed by John Roettier (1631-c.1703). It was first struck in 1663, but, without any struck the following year, the ravages of the Plague and Great Fire had taken their toll before the issue resumed in 1666. It is possible that at least one original die was lost in the fire, and certainly the curious use of the guinea dies during 1666 lends credence to the theory that an emergency issue was necessary.

The subsequent issues up to 1684 are of much interest, the various combinations of date, head and provenance marks producing many pieces of considerable rarity.

Provenance marks are: plumes (below head and/or in centre of reverse) for silver from Welsh mines; elephant and castle or elephant alone (below head) for silver from the Africa Company.

Collecting Hints

The series is a very difficult one to collect exhaustively, many of the date/head/silver-provenance combinations being very rare in any condition; in addition, the rarity of even common pieces of Charles II coinage in very fine or better condition renders the acquisition of a comprehensive collection a very difficult task. One should be perhaps thankful that the edges were milled rather than bearing regnal years with their attendant errors and varieties.

For a series of such complexity, one should attempt to acquire varieties in any condition; rejection of a rare piece purely on grounds of condition may result in a gap in one's collection which proves permanent. Indeed, there is a mystique about a very worn coin of such age, bearing a smudge clearly identifiable as, say, a plume, and acquired after much searching.

Denomination	Metal	Weight (grams)	Diameter (mm)	Rev. alignment
Shilling 1663	Silver	6.0	25–26	↓
Shilling 1666-1684	Silver	5.7-5.9	25–26	↓

Obverse 1 Head 1, right; CAROLVS II DEI GRATIA

Obverse 2 Head 2, right; minor differences in hair arrangement; same legend

Obverse 3 Head 3, right; very different and without drapery, identical to head on guinea (always with elephant below); same legend

Obverse 4 Head 4, right; similar to Heads 1 and 2 but laurel wreath and tie slightly different; same legend

Obverse 5 Head 5, much larger, right; ties point slightly downwards; same legend

Obverse 6 Head 6, slightly redesigned, right; ties almost straight; same legend

Reverse 1 Central star enclosed by four cruciform shields with surmounting crowns; MAG BR FRA ET HIB REX (date). On examples with plume on reverse, the plume *replaces* the star.

Edge 1663-68: milled (vertically); 1669-84: milled (diagonally)

Obv. 1   Obv. 2   Obv. 3

Obv. 4   Obv. 5   Obv. 6

Rev. 1   Rev. 1 Shields transposed

No.	Date	Features	Obv.	Rev.	F	VF	EF
C2SHM-005	1663		1	1	50	200	750
C2SHM-010	1663	rev. ↑	1	1	80	320	1000
C2SHM-015	1663	GARTIA instead of GRATIA (obv.)	1	1	120	800	
C2SHM-020	1663	Scotland/ Ireland shields transposed	1	1	100	600	
C2SHM-025	1663	A of FRA over G (rev.)	1	1	80	300	950
C2SHM-030	1663	PROOF in copper; edge plain	1	1			1500
C2SHM-035	1663		2	1	50	200	750
C2SHM-040	1666	[1]	2	1	400	1200	2500
C2SHM-045	1666	elephant below head	2	1	240	900	2500
C2SHM-050	1666	elephant below head	3	1	850	2200	
C2SHM-055	1666		4	1	500	1500	
C2SHM-060	1668		2	1	240	800	2200
C2SHM-065	1668		4	1	40	160	550
C2SHM-070	1668	8 over 3 (?)	4	1	60	240	750
C2SHM-075	1669	9 over 6 (?) [2]	2	1	400	1200	
C2SHM-080	1669		4	1	1000		
W3SHM-035	1669	head of William III [3]			750		
C2SHM-085	1670		4	1	70	260	950
C2SHM-090	1671		4	1	80	450	1300
C2SHM-095	1671	plume both sides	4	1	150	600	1500
C2SHM-100	1672		4	1	50	180	650
C2SHM-105	1672	2 over 1	4	1	60	200	800
C2SHM-110	1673		4	1	70	260	950
C2SHM-115	1673	3 over 2	4	1	80	300	1100
C2SHM-120	1673	plume both sides	4	1	150	600	
C2SHM-125	1674		4	1	70	260	950
C2SHM-130	1674	4 over 3	4	1	70	270	1000
C2SHM-135	1674	plume both sides	4	1	200	700	1400
C2SHM-140	1674	plume on rev.	4	1	250	1000	
C2SHM-145	1674		5	1	200	800	
C2SHM-150	1675		5	1	100	450	1300
C2SHM-155	1675	5 over 3	5	1	100	450	1400
C2SHM-160	1675		4	1	120	550	2000
C2SHM-165	1675	5 over 4	4	1	120	550	2000
C2SHM-170	1675	plume both sides	4	1	150	600	3000
C2SHM-175	1676		4	1	50	140	500

No.	Date	Features	Obv.	Rev.	F	VF	EF
C2SHM-180	1676	6 over 5	4	1	60	160	600
C2SHM-185	1676	plume both sides	4	1	200	750	
C2SHM-190	1677		4	1	60	160	600
C2SHM-195	1677	plume below head	4	1	250	1200	
C2SHM-200	1678		4	1	120	300	1100
C2SHM-205	1678	8 over 7	4	1	120	300	1100
C2SHM-210	1679		4	1	50	140	500
C2SHM-215	1679	9 over 7	4	1	70	180	700
C2SHM-220	1679	plume both sides	4	1	150	600	
C2SHM-225	1679	plume below head	4	1	150	800	
C2SHM-230	1680		4	1	500	1200	2500
C2SHM-235	1680	80 over 79	4	1	400	1000	2200
C2SHM-240	1680	plume both sides	4	1	500	1400	3000
C2SHM-245	1681		4	1	100	400	1000
C2SHM-250	1681	1 over 0	4	1	100	400	1000
C2SHM-255	1681	1 over 0 elephant and castle	4	1	3000		
C2SHM-260	1682	2 over 1	4	1	400	1000	2500
C2SHM-265	1683		4	1	700	2000	
C2SHM-270	1683		6	1	100	350	950
C2SHM-275	1684	[4]	6	1	130	450	1200

1. At least one exists in EF condition.
2. A few with straight milling.
3. Error date (1696); see William III; reference number cross-indexed.
4. Rarer than indicated in some catalogues.

James II 1685–1688

The cruciform shields design of John Roettier was continued during the reign of James II. The brief series includes a number of interesting varieties, but no patterns or proofs. The only provenance mark noted is the plume on the reverse of the very rare variety of 1685. There is doubt whether the intention was to denote Welsh silver, and it is thought probable that confusion occurred with a punch from a Charles II coin. Unusually, here a provenance mark replaces part of the design, i.e. the central star.

Collecting Hints

This series should be collected in at least fine condition. As with Charles II, the scarcity, and consequently the price, rises steeply as the grade increases. It is not uncommon to find very fine or better pieces which have the higher points, particularly the hair, not properly struck up, and flecking or haymarking is also commonly seen. A well struck piece in very fine condition or better, without blemishes, will always command a premium.

Denomination	Metal	Weight (grams)	Diameter (mm)	Rev alignment
Shilling	Silver	5.7-6.0	25–26	↓

Obverse 1 Head 1, left; IACOBVS II (head) DEI GRATIA

Reverse 1 Central star enclosed by four cruciform shields with surmounting crowns; MAG BR FRA ET HIB REX (date). On the 1685 plume variety, the plume *replaces* the star

Edge milled (diagonally)

Obv. 1

Rev. 1

No.	Date	Features	Obv.	Rev.	F	VF	EF
J2SH-005	1685	[1]	1	1	70	220	650
J2SH-010	1685	no stops on rev.	1	1	100	320	900
J2SH-015	1685	plume on rev. [2]	1	1	7500		
J2SH-020	1686	[1]	1	1	70	220	650
J2SH-025	1686	latter 6 over 5	1	1	120	400	1000
J2SH-030	1686	V of IACOBVS over S (obv.) [1]	1	1	75	280	700
J2SH-035	1686	G of MAG over A (rev.)	1	1	90	350	950
J2SH-040	1687	[3]	1	1	80	270	800
J2SH-045	1687	7 over 6	1	1	70	220	650
J2SH-050	1687	7 over 6 G of MAG over A (rev.) [4]	1	1	75	240	700
J2SH-055	1688	[5]	1	1	80	270	750
J2SH-060	1688	latter 8 over 7 [6]	1	1	90	340	900

1. Minor varieties of reverse stops exist.
2. Plume replaces central star.
3. 7 not over 6.
4. G over A variety possibly occurs without overdate.
5. Latter 8 not over 7.
6. Most or all have no stop after HIB (rev.).

The number of harp strings varies through this series. It is possible that the variation constituted a form of internal code denoting the die number.

William and Mary 1688–1694

John Roettier, the Chief Engraver, developed an affliction of the hands at the beginning of this reign, and he delegated work to his two sons, James (1663-98) and Norbert (1665-?). A design of shilling very similar to those of preceding reigns was continued. The practice of placing a motif of interlinked initials in the angles, discontinued during the reign of James II, was revived, with a clever lattice design formed of a linked 'W' and 'M'. The series comprises two dates, with no patterns, proofs or provenance marks.

Collecting Hints

Fine condition specimens, although attractive, should be improved upon whenever possible because much delicate portrait detail is lost in this grade. The coinage is quite difficult to find in top condition.

Denomination	Metal	Weight (grams)	Diameter (mm)	Rev. alignment
Shilling	Silver	5.9-6.0	25–26	↓

Obverse 1 Heads 1, right; GVLIELMVS ET MARIA DEI GRATIA

Reverse 1 Four cruciform shields around lion of Orange-Nassau, with monogrammed 'WM' and one digit of date in each angle; MAG BR FR ET HI REX ET REGINA

Edge milled (diagonally)

Obv. 1

Rev. 1

No.	Date	Features	Obv.	Rev.	F	VF	EF
WMSH-005	1692	[1]	1	1	55	220	750
WMSH-010	1692	inverted 1 in date [1]	1	1	70	300	950
WMSH-015	1693	[2]	1	1	50	200	600
WMSH-020	1693	9 over 0 or 6 or inverted 9	1	1	80	350	1000
WMSH-025	1693	3 over inverted 2	1	1	80	350	1000

1. Minor stop varieties exist.
2. Minor stop varieties exist; orientation of head against legend differs.

William III 1695–1701

As with the sixpence, the first issue of the shilling coinage in 1695 was of a single type without varieties, but in 1696, with the withdrawal of the hammered coinage, the London and five provincial mints embarked upon a series of considerable complexity and interest. Included were a large number of errors, several of which are remarkable in nature. These were no doubt due to the use of new and inexperienced workers in the local mints.

The early coinage was probably engraved by James Roettier before his conviction at a mint enquiry in 1697 for smuggling dies to France; later work was by John Croker, but some doubt remains about the exact attribution of several pieces of 1696-97.

As with the halfcrowns, the variegation of the series, especially with reference to such details as harp design, is so complex that expediency requires some abbreviation. Therefore, some minor varieties are omitted or referred to only in note form.

Jackson Kent has pointed out that the conventionally accepted title of 'Third Bust Variety' is unfortunate, since the so-called 'First' and 'Third' busts resemble each other more closely than do the 'Third' and 'Third Variety' busts. Moreover, the so-called 'Second Bust' is almost certainly a pattern, and therefore outside the scope of this book. We have therefore renumbered the remaining five heads 1 to 5 in this catalogue.

Provenance marks are: plumes (either in angles on reverse or singly below head) for silver from Welsh mines; roses (in angles) for silver from West of England mines.

Collecting Hints

Because of the number of varieties and errors in this series, many of which are quite rare, collectors will find that if they insist on a minimum grade, say fine, they will end up with many gaps in their collection. Consequently, one should acquire any example offered of the rarer varieties, provided that it bears sufficient detail to identify the piece. The fact that there is only one reverse for this series makes the task of completing the set somewhat easier.

Although the 1696 and 1697 are probably overall the commonest dates, the 1700 is arguably the most frequently encountered in extremely fine or better condition. This is because a large quantity in mint state was discovered in a bank vault towards the end of the 19th century.

All of the shield positional varieties involve the Irish shield, directly or indirectly, and one should therefore always examine all reverses with the date at the top, and check that the harp is on the left. This is advisable also for other denominations of this period, but particularly so with this series.

Shillings of William III are frequently marked by the twin curses of weak striking and adjustment marks, and it is up to the individual collector to decide whether these afflictions detract from the coin or simply form part of its mintage history. A very weakly struck extremely fine coin of this series can sometimes appear to the uninitiated as about fine to very fine, while a heavily adjusted piece will seem to be badly scratched. In fact, the filing adjustment was carried out before issue to correct the weight to that officially authorised.

The first head shilling lacking the tie at the back of the head is not a true variety, nor is that reading GVLIEIMVS; these apparent varieties are caused by die wear in various degrees.

Denomination	Metal	Weight (grams)	Diameter (mm)	Rev. alignment
Shilling	Silver	5.8-6.2	25–26	↓

Obverse 1 Head 1, right; GVLIELMVS (head) III DEI GRA

Obverse 2 Head 2, right; same legend

Obverse 3 Head 3, right; same legend

Obverse 4 Head 4, right; same legend

Obverse 5 Head 5, very different, right; known as 'flaming hair' type; same legend but different lettering style

Obverse 6 Head 6, right; known as 'high hair' type; same legend

Heads 1, 3, 4 are all very similar; note especially the arrangement of the hair at the back of the head, and the tie

Reverse 1 Four cruciform shields around lion of Nassau; MAG BR FRA ET HIB REX (date)

Edge milled (diagonally)

Obv. 1   Obv. 2   Obv. 3

Obv. 5   Obv. 6   Rev. 1

No.	Date	mm	Features	Obv.	Rev.	F	VF	EF
W3SH-005	1695			1	1	30	100	300
W3SH-010	1696		[1]	1	1	20	60	150
W3SH-015	1696		no rev. stops	1	1	25	75	190
W3SH-020	1696		MAB instead of MAG (rev.)	1	1	150	500	

No.	Date	mm	Features	Obv.	Rev.	F	VF	EF
W3SH-025	1696		GVLIEMVS instead of GVLIELMVS (obv.)	1	1	60	180	
W3SH-030	1696		GVLIELM∀S instead of GVLIELMVS (obv.)	1	1	40	120	400
W3SH-035	1669		1669 instead of 1696 [2]	1	1	750		
W3SH-040	1696		PROOF on thick flan	1	1		1000	3500
W3SH-045	1696	B		1	1	30	110	350
W3SH-050	1696	B	struck over hammered shilling	1	1	50	150	500
W3SH-055	1696	C		1	1	30	110	350
W3SH-060	1696	C	PROOF on thick flan	1	1		1200	4000
W3SH-065	1696	E		1	1	30	110	350
W3SH-070	1696	N	[3]	1	1	30	130	600
W3SH-075	1696	y		1	1	30	100	300
W3SH-080	1696	Y		1	1	35	110	350
W3SH-085	1696	Y	Y over inverted Y (mintmark)	1	1	45	140	500
W3SH-090	1696		[4]	2	1			
W3SH-095	1696	C		3	1	60	200	800
W3SH-100	1696	E		3	1	800		
W3SH-105	1696	y		3	1	600		
W3SH-110	1697		[5]	1	1	20	60	150
W3SH-115	1697		Scotland/ Ireland shields transposed (rev.)	1	1	250	1000	
W3SH-120	1697		shields rotated clockwise 90 degrees (rev.)	1	1	250	1000	
W3SH-125	1697		no rev. stops	1	1	25	70	180
W3SH-130	1697		GVLELMVS instead of GVLIELMVS (obv.)	1	1	70	200	500
W3SH-135	1697		GRI instead of GRA (obv.)	1	1	90	300	800
W3SH-140	1697		DE(over A)I instead of DEI (obv.)	1	1	50	140	500
W3SH-145	1697	B		1	1	30	110	350
W3SH-150	1697	C		1	1	30	110	350
W3SH-155	1697	C	Scotland/ Ireland shields transposed (rev.)	1	1	250	1000	
W3SH-160	1697	E		1	1	30	110	400
W3SH-165	1697	N		1	1	30	120	450
W3SH-170	1697	y		1	1	30	100	300
W3SH-175	1697	y	France/ Ireland shields transposed (rev.)	1	1	600		
W3SH-180	1697	y	Scotland/ Ireland shields transposed (rev.)	1	1	600		
W3SH-185	1697	Y		1	1	35	110	350
W3SH-190	1697		[6]	3	1	20	65	170
W3SH-195	1697	B	[6]	3	1	35	110	350
W3SH-200	1697	C	[7]	3	1	35	110	350
W3SH-205	1697	C	no rev. stops	3	1	40	120	380
W3SH-210	1697	C	Scotland shield at date	3	1	250	1000	
W3SH-215	1697	E		3	1	35	110	350
W3SH-220	1697	N	[6]	3	1	35	110	350
W3SH-225	1697	y		3	1	35	110	350
W3SH-230	1697			4	1	20	65	170

No.	Date	mm	Features	Obv.	Rev.	F	VF	EF
W3SH-235	1697		GVLIELMⱯS instead of GVLIELMVS (obv.)	4	1	40	120	400
W3SH-240	1697	B		4	1	35	110	350
W3SH-245	1697	C		4	1	70	200	650
W3SH-250	1697	C	struck on thick flan [8]	4	1	200	600	
W3SH-255	1698			4	1	30	90	250
W3SH-260	1698		PROOF; edge plain	4	1			1500
W3SH-265	1698		plumes on rev.	4	1	80	250	800
W3SH-270	1698		[9]	5	1	50	140	450
W3SH-275	1698		PROOF; edge plain	5	1			2000
W3SH-280	1699			5	1	35	100	300
W3SH-285	1699		struck on thick flan [10]	5	1	300		
W3SH-290	1699			6	1	35	100	300
W3SH-295	1699		PROOF; edge plain	6	1			1600
W3SH-300	1699		plumes on rev.	6	1	70	200	500
W3SH-305	1699		roses on rev.	6	1	80	280	700
W3SH-310	1700		[11]	6	1	30	60	140
W3SH-315	1700		plume below head [12]	6	1	1400		
W3SH-320	1701		[9]	6	1	35	100	300
W3SH-325	1701		plumes on rev.	6	1	70	200	500

1. Flan diameter varies.
2. Error date.
3. Very rare in EF plus.
4. Probably unique (VF); sold at Spink auction no.3, February 1979 for £13000.
5. Lions, harps, stops vary.
6. Lettering size varies.
7. Sometimes reads FR.A instead of FRA (rev.).
8. Weight c. 9.0–10.2 grams.
9. Lions vary (rev.).
10. Weight 8.3 grams.
11. 'O's in date vary; reverse stops vary.
12. About 5 known.

The number of harp strings varies through this series. It is possible that the variation constituted a form of internal code denoting the die number. Other minor reverse variations occur, notably to the harp.

Marks and Operating Periods of Provincial Mints

B: BRISTOL: September 1696 to September 1698

C: CHESTER: October 1696 to June 1698

E: EXETER: August 1696 to July 1698

N: NORWICH: September 1696 to April 1698

y or Y: YORK: September 1696 to April 1698

Anne 1702–1714

The shilling series is the most complex denomination of Anne in its diversity of varieties. Straddling the Union of England and Scotland, it also exhibits a number of new provenance marks and mintmarks.

At the beginning of the reign, the Chief Engraver John Croker and his assistant James Bull produced a portrait based on a painting of Anne by Sir Godfrey Kneller. After the Union of England and Scotland, the Scottish engraver James Clerk worked on the shilling and smaller denominations, but there is doubt about the exact attribution of some of the dies.

Provenance marks are: VIGO (below head) for silver obtained from Spanish galleons at Vigo Bay in 1702; plumes (in angles on reverse) for silver from Wales; roses and plumes (alternately in angles on reverse) for silver from the 'Company for smelting down lead with Pitcoale and Seacoale'. The mintmarks E and E* represent coins struck at Edinburgh. The shilling is the only denomination bearing the VIGO mark on coins struck in 1702, the same year as the capture of the silver bullion at Vigo Bay. All other VIGO coins are dated 1703.

It is interesting to surmise the reason for the star mark placed next to the E on some Edinburgh coinage between 1707 and 1709, since no positive reason for this mark appears to be known. For example, moneyers from London had been sent to Edinburgh in 1707 to supervise the coining of the new post-Union coinage, and had remained until March, 1709.

After the Union, two of the shields on the reverse were each divided into the arms of England and Scotland; previously the arms had been placed separately on two shields.

Collecting Hints

This series should be collected in at least very fine condition with the exception of the rarer varieties. The intricacies of the numerous varieties of 1707 and 1708 are such that one needs not only to have a good memory but also some expertise in identification unless one is prepared to carry an illustrated catalogue when buying. We trust that you will find the present catalogue an improvement on previous attempts to illustrate this series!

The 1711 is a coin which should always be examined carefully, since this date is shared by the common Head 5 and the rare Head 3. Luckily, the identification is easy, even with worn pieces. The rare Head 3 has what looks like an indentation or cut at the top, caused by the hair arrangement, whereas the common Head 5 is somewhat uneven but relatively smooth in comparison, rather as if the queen were wearing a hairnet. The 1703, although much scarcer overall than, say, the 1711 Head 5, appears to have been preserved in quantities in higher grades, so that in very fine or extremely fine the 1703 is not all that much scarcer. It is, incidentally, more likely to be flecked or haymarked than the 1711. The 1707 plain variety is also frequently found in top condition.

Denomination	Metal	Weight (grams)	Diameter (mm)	Rev. alignment
Shilling	Silver	5.9–6.0	25–26	↓

Obverse 1 Head 1, left; two curls at top, relatively long tie; ANNA DEI GRATIA

Obverse 2 Head 2, left; curls different, tie shorter; same legend

Obverse 3 Head 3, left; curls flatter; same legend

Obverse 4 Head 4, so-called 'Edinburgh bust' (Edinburgh mint), left; very similar to Obverse 3 but the tie is noticeably shorter; same legend.

Obverse 5 Head 5, left; deeply engraved 'hairnet' effect; same legend

Reverse 1 'Before Union reverse'; thin shields convex at top; English and Scottish arms on separate shields; MAG BR FRA ET HIB REG (date)

Reverse 2 'After Union reverse'; broader shields concave at top; English and Scottish arms impaled together on two identical divided shields; MAG BRI FR ET HIB REG (date); London and Edinburgh Reverse 2 differ slightly

Edge milled (diagonally)

Obv. 1   Obv. 2   Obv. 3

Obv. 4   Obv. 5

Rev. 1   Rev. 2

Before Union of England and Scotland

No.	Date	Features	Obv.	Rev.	F	VF	EF
ASH-005	1702	[1]	1	1	50	140	350
ASH-010	1702	plumes on rev.	1	1	60	170	420
ASH-015	1702	VIGO below head [1]	1	1	50	130	320
ASH-020	1703	VIGO below head [1]	2	1	35	90	150
ASH-025	1704		2	1	300	800	1800
ASH-030	1704	plumes on rev.	2	1	70	180	450
ASH-035	1705		2	1	70	180	450
ASH-040	1705	plumes on rev.	2	1	50	140	350
ASH-045	1705	roses and plumes on rev.	2	1	45	130	320
ASH-050	1707	roses and plumes on rev.	2	1	50	140	350

1. Obverse punctuation varies.

After Union of England and Scotland

No.	Date	mm	Features	Obv.	Rev.	F	VF	EF
ASH-055	1707	E		2	2	25	70	180
ASH-060	1707	E	PROOF; edge plain [1]	2	2			2000
ASH-065	1707	E*	[2]	2	2	50	150	400
ASH-070	1707			3	2	20	55	140
ASH-075	1707		plumes on rev.	3	2	30	80	220
ASH-080	1707	E		3	2	22	60	160
ASH-085	1707	E*		4	2	200		
ASH-090	1708	E		2	2	50	140	380
ASH-095	1708	E*		2	2	30	80	220
ASH-100	1708	E*	8 over 7	2	2	80	180	500
ASH-105	1708		roses and plumes on rev.	2	2	75	180	600
ASH-110	1708			3	2	15	40	100
ASH-115	1708		plumes on rev.	3	2	22	65	170
ASH-120	1708		roses and plumes on rev.	3	2	25	70	180
ASH-125	1708	E		3	2	35	95	280

No.	Date	mm	Features	Obv.	Rev.	F	VF	EF
ASH-130	1708	E	8 over 7	3	2	45	120	380
ASH-135	1708	E*		4	2	40	110	320
ASH-140	1709			3	2	18	50	120
ASH-145	1709		ANNA over DEI (obv.)	3	2	50	150	400
ASH-150	1709		IIIB instead of HIB (rev.) [3]	3	2	30	80	180
ASH-155	1709	E*		4	2	60	180	500
ASH-160	1709	E*	rev. ↑ [3]	4	2	65	200	550
ASH-165	1710		roses and plumes on rev.	3	2	18	50	120
ASH-170	1710		PROOF; edge plain	5	2			5000
ASH-175	1710		roses and plumes on rev.	5	2	35	100	350
ASH-180	1710		PROOF; edge plain roses and plumes on rev.	5	2			3000
ASH-185	1711		[4]	3	2	60	250	900
ASH-190	1711			5	2	15	35	100
ASH-195	1712		roses and plumes on rev.	5	2	18	50	140
ASH-200	1713		3 over 2 roses and plumes on rev. [5]	5	2	22	70	180
ASH-205	1714		roses and plumes on rev.	5	2	18	50	140
ASH-210	1714		roses and plumes on rev. inverted 'L' instead of 'I' (both) in obv. legend	5	2	25	80	220
ASH-215	1714		4 over 3	5	2	50	150	400

1. Reverse shields are slightly narrower than on usual Reverse 2
2. Minor die differences exist
3. Some have star filled in on die; some are underweight
4. Virtually unknown above VF grade
5. 3 not over 2 unknown

The number of harp strings varies through this series. It is possible that the variation constituted a form of internal code denoting the die number.

George I 1714–1727

The general design of cruciform shields continued with the accession of George Louis, Elector of Hanover, as George I, but one of the duplicated England/Scotland shields was replaced by one containing the arms of Brunswick-Lüneburg, with a central depiction of the crown of Charlemagne. The long German titles of the king also appear on both obverse and reverse in a greatly abbreviated form.

It is probable that John Croker was responsible for at least some of the work of the obverse design of this series, and there is evidence that a Swiss engraver, Johan Ochs (1673-?), designed some of the reverse dies.

Provenance marks of this series are: roses and plumes (in reverse angles) for silver from the 'Company for smelting down lead with Pitcoale and Seacoale'; SS and C (in alternate angles on reverse) for silver from The South Sea Company; WCC (below head) for silver from the Welsh Copper Company, which coins also bear on the reverse as provenance marks two interlinked 'C's placed in the reverse angles alternately with a plume (i.e. totalling four 'C's and two plumes). It is an interesting possibility that this configuration may have been meant to denote Welsh Copper Company (i.e. plume, C and C). It is also worthy of note that the interlinked 'C's on the reverse are identical to those used on the coinage of Charles II, but, while those on the Charles coinage were an integral part of the design, being the initial of the king's name, in this case they are true provenance marks. For this reason it is felt correct to place the WCC coinage under 'Reverse 1' rather than allocate a new reverse design.

Provenance marks in this and the following reign were now so prolific that their existence on a coin was the rule rather than the exception.

There are no pattern or proof shillings of George I, except for a piece ascribed to Norbert Roettier dated 1716, which may have been a pattern guinea or shilling. This was produced while Roettier was working in France, and has no official status.

Collecting Hints

This series should be collected in very fine or better condition except for the very rare pieces, but the WCC pieces do turn up in very fine or extremely fine from time to time. Possibly they were hoarded as curiosities.

The 1723 variety with arms of France at date is often missed through carelessness, but there is an easy way to check it, even with below-average eyesight, and this should always be done: with the date at the top, the rare type reads SS C across the date; the common one reads C SS.

For 1723 coins, the difference between heads can be easily remembered; two loose ends to tie is Head 1; one loose end is Head 2.

The 1721 shilling with reversed roses and plumes is not a well-known coin, and therefore it is well worth checking any shilling of this date. The coin has even appeared, unnoticed and yet photographed, in the catalogue of a major London auctioneer! It should be remembered that, for a correctly orientated coin (i.e. the common variety), with the date at the top, the sequence is plume-rose from left to right across the top of the coin.

Denomination	Metal	Weight (grams)	Diameter (mm)	Rev. alignment
Shilling	Silver	5.9-6.1	25–26	↓

Obverse 1 Head 1, right; two loose ends to tie, legend undivided by head; GEORGIVS D G M BR FR ET HIB REX F D

Obverse 2 Head 2, right; one loose end and one bow to tie; minor differences to portrait; same undivided legend

Reverse 1 Four crowned cruciform shields around central star; BRVN ET L DVX S R I A TH ET EL

Edge milled (diagonally)

Obv. 1	Obv. 2	Rev. 1

No.	Date	Features	Obv.	Rev.	F	VF	EF
G1SH-005	1715	roses and plumes on rev. [1]	1	1	20	70	200
G1SH-010	1716	roses and plumes on rev.	1	1	50	200	550
G1SH-015	1717	roses and plumes on rev.	1	1	20	70	200
G1SH-020	1718	roses and plumes on rev. [2]	1	1	20	55	150
G1SH-025	1719	roses and plumes on rev.	1	1	45	160	450
G1SH-030	1720	roses and plumes on rev.	1	1	20	70	200
G1SH-035	1720	roses and plumes on rev.; edge plain [3]	1	1	100	400	
G1SH-040	1720	(plain in angles) [4]	1	1	18	60	170
G1SH-045	1721	(plain in angles)	1	1	80	400	
G1SH-050	1721	roses and plumes on rev. [5]	1	1	30	100	300
G1SH-055	1721	plumes and roses on rev. (i.e. reversed positions)	1	1	120	300	900
G1SH-060	1721	latter 1 over 0; roses and plumes on rev.	1	1	25	85	250
G1SH-065	1721	21 over 19 or 18 roses and plumes on rev.	1	1	35	120	350
G1SH-070	1722	roses and plumes on rev. [6]	1	1	20	70	200
G1SH-075	1723	roses and plumes on rev.	1	1	20	70	200
G1SH-080	1723	SS C in angles [7]	1	1	15	50	120
G1SH-085	1723	SS C in angles with one C over SS	1	1	30	90	200
G1SH-090	1723	SS C in angles arms of France at date [8]	1	1	60	400	
G1SH-095	1723	SS C in angles [9]	2	1	20	65	170
G1SH-100	1723	roses and plumes on rev.	2	1	22	75	240
G1SH-105	1723	WCC below head; plumes and interlinked 'C's on rev.	2	1	130	500	1100
G1SH-110	1724	roses and plumes on rev.	2	1	22	80	300
G1SH-115	1724	WCC below head; plumes and interlinked 'C's on rev.	2	1	130	500	1100
G1SH-120	1725	roses and plumes on rev.	2	1	22	80	300
G1SH-125	1725	roses and plumes on rev.; no stops on obv.	2	1	25	85	350
G1SH-130	1725	WCC below head; plumes and interlinked 'C's on rev.	2	1	150	600	1300
G1SH-135	1726	roses and plumes on rev.	2	1	450		

No.	Date	Features	Obv.	Rev.	F	VF	EF
G1SH-140	1726	WCC below head; plumes and interlinked 'C's on rev.	2	1	130	500	1100
G1SH-145	1727	roses and plumes on rev.	2	1	350		
G1SH-150	1727	roses and plumes on rev.; no stops on obv.	2	1	350		

1. Stops varieties exist.
2. Often found in VF+ grade.
3. An error coin.
4. Date and letters vary in size.
5. Latter 1 not over 0.
6. Obv stops vary.
7. Reads C SS across date (rev.); stops vary.
8. Reads SS C across date (rev.).
9. Harp varies.

The number of harp strings varies through this series. It is possible that the variation constituted a form of internal code denoting the die number.

George II 1727–1760

Although Croker was responsible for designing most of the new coinage, the first type of shilling has been attributed to J. R. Ochs, senior. The older portrait of the king, introduced in 1743, was largely the work of John Sigismund Tanner, who had become Chief Engraver in 1741. Croker had also worked on the dies before his death in 1741.

Provenance marks are: plumes (silver from The Welsh Copper Company); roses (silver from mines in the West of England); roses and plumes (silver from the 'Company for smelting down lead with Pitcoale and Seacoale'), all of these in the reverse angles; LIMA below the head for coins struck in silver captured by Admiral Anson during his voyage around the world, possibly in the form of coinage with the LIMA mintmark.

Collecting Hints

The young head is in relatively high relief and much detail is worn off on a fine condition coin. This series should be sought in at least very fine to extremely fine condition if an attractive specimen retaining much original detail is required. The older head by Tanner is in lower relief, but in general is more easily found (especially the 1758), and therefore most collectors will be satisfied only with extremely fine condition, except for the rarities such as 1746.

Because the 1746 Lima halfcrown and sixpence are relatively plentiful, it is easy to forget that the shilling is a fairly rare piece, and to overlook it when it does turn up. This coin is genuinely difficult to find in any grade.

Denomination	Metal	Weight (grams)	Diameter (mm)	Rev. alignment
Shilling	Silver	6.0	25–26	↓

Obverse 1 Head 1, left; GEORGIVS II (head) DEI GRATIA

Obverse 2 Head 2, left; GEORGIUS II (head) DEI GRATIA

Obverse 3 Head 2, left; GEORGIVS II (head) DEI GRATIA

Reverse 1 Four crowned cruciform shields; M B F ET H REX F D B ET L D S R I A T ET E (date)

Edge milled (diagonally)

Obv. 1   Obv. 3   Rev. 1

No.	Date	Features	Obv.	Rev.	F	VF	EF
G2SH-005	1727	plumes on rev.	1	1	50	130	500
G2SH-010	1727	roses and plumes on rev.	1	1	30	80	250
G2SH-015	1728		1	1	50	140	550
G2SH-020	1728	roses and plumes on rev.	1	1	40	100	350
G2SH-025	1728	roses and plumes on rev.; E of GEOR over R (obv.)	1	1	60	140	500
G2SH-030	1729	roses and plumes on rev.	1	1	40	100	260
G2SH-035	1731	roses and plumes on rev.	1	1	30	80	200
G2SH-040	1731	plumes on rev.	1	1	70	200	500
G2SH-045	1732	roses and plumes on rev.	1	1	40	100	260
G2SH-050	1734	roses and plumes on rev. [1]	1	1	25	70	170
G2SH-055	1735	roses and plumes on rev.	1	1	25	70	170
G2SH-060	1736	roses and plumes on rev. [2]	1	1	25	70	170
G2SH-065	1736	6 over 5 roses and plumes on rev.	1	1	35	90	250
G2SH-070	1737	roses and plumes on rev.	1	1	25	70	170
G2SH-075	1739	roses on rev.	1	1	20	55	130
G2SH-080	1739	9 over 7; roses on rev.	1	1	40	95	200
G2SH-085	1739	unusually small Garter star (rev.); roses on rev.	1	1	150		
G2SH-090	1741	roses on rev.	1	1	20	55	130
G2SH-095	1743	roses on rev.	2	1	20	50	100
G2SH-100	1743	3 over 1 roses on rev.	2	1	35	80	150
G2SH-105	1745	roses on rev.	2	1	25	65	130
G2SH-110	1745	5 over 3 roses on rev.	2	1	30	75	150
G2SH-115	1745	LIMA below head	2	1	20	50	100
G2SH-120	1746	LIMA below head	3	1	50	150	600
G2SH-125	1746	6 over 5 LIMA below head	3	1	50	150	600
G2SH-130	1746	PROOF [3]	3	1			700
G2SH-135	1747	roses on rev.	3	1	25	70	170

No.	Date	Features	Obv.	Rev.	F	VF	EF
G2SH-140	1747	latter 7 over 6; roses on rev.	3	1	30	80	190
G2SH-145	1750	oval '0' in date	3	1	30	75	160
G2SH-150	1750	oval '0' over 6	3	1	35	85	180
G2SH-155	1750	5 over 4; round '0' in date	3	1	35	85	180
G2SH-160	1750	50 over 46; oval '0' in date	3	1	60	130	300
G2SH-165	1751		3	1	40	90	180
G2SH-170	1758	4	3	1	15	25	60

1. See note below.
2. Reverse stops vary.
3. No LIMA; may have raised die flaw in reverse field; weight variations exist.
4. Possibly struck for some years.

The number of harp strings varies through this series. It is possible that the variation constituted a form of internal code denoting the die number.

Although there was a change to slightly larger lettering in 1734, this is not considered significant enough to assign new obverse and reverse numbers.

George III 1760–1820

The George III shilling series is, like the Curate's egg, an oddball, but it certainly contains some gems. Two classic rarities sandwich the ubiquitous 1787, which itself contains a multiplicity of interesting varieties. A long gap is then followed by the 'Great Recoinage' series of 1816 to 1820 with a smattering of proofs (including one in gold) to whet the appetite.

At the beginning of the reign, many of the shillings in circulation had been worn to complete blanks. Indeed, such blanks were produced in profusion by 'counterfeiters', if such a word can be used in this context. Much foreign coinage of similar size was imported and worn smooth to produce pieces similar to worn shillings.

The 'Northumberland' shilling of 1763 was distributed by the Earl of Northumberland on his appointment as Lord Lieutenant of Ireland, but the story that the issue was limited to £100 in face value is probably untrue. The portrait was designed by Richard Yeo (d. 1779), who also engraved the reverses based on the current standard design. These coins were undoubtedly hoarded, as they are probably more plentiful in very fine or extremely fine than in fair or fine condition.

The very large issue of 1787 may have been hoarded, possibly because the denomination had become so unusual that there was a reluctance to spend the coins, rather in the same way that crowns and £2 coins are hoarded today or used as gifts. The issue of 1787 is certainly as likely to be encountered in very fine or extremely fine condition as in fine. However, a curious comment is made by Stephen Martin Leake, writing in 1793, lamenting that 'we are at a loss to account for the reason of no coinage of shillings being issued, after so many dies had been engraved'. He further says that the coinage, 'made for the use of The Bank of England' is 'not in common currency'.

The series of 1787 includes a number of interesting and scarce varieties, as well as proofs and patterns. It is also divided into two main types, with and without the semee of hearts on the arms of Brunswick, although it is not generally realised that the issue without hearts was issued in error, corrected only after a large number had been minted.

The very rare issue of 1798 was struck from silver supplied by Mr. Magens Dorrien Magens (1761-1849) of the City of London. Apparently some £30,000 worth of coins were struck, but in May of that year a Privy Council Committee ruled that the issue was illegal and the coins were almost all melted down. They are so rare that even a photograph is missing from several reference works. Some years ago a club was in existence whose condition of entry was ownership of one of these coins.

After the Great Recoinage of 1816, the short series up to 1820 was made using the new machinery at Tower Hill. Initially, the design and engraving were carried out by Thomas Wyon, Junior, the obverse being based on a model by Benedetto Pistrucci. On the death of Wyon in 1817, Pistrucci himself took over the engraving of the dies. The quality of striking of this series was excellent, and again many pieces were hoarded; consequently, it is not too difficult to find specimens in the higher grades.

The shilling coinage of 1816 onwards remained legal tender until the end of 1990, when the size of the decimal 5 pence coin was reduced.

No provenance marks exist for the George III shilling coinage; the crowns in the angles of the 1787 coins resemble provenance marks but are an integral part of the design.

Collecting Hints

All of the shillings of George III should be collected in extremely fine condition, but the 1798 Dorrien Magens issue is so rare that one will be lucky if one even hears of it for sale in any condition.

The unusual GEOE error of 1817 and the plain edge 1816 and 1817 proofs are sometimes obtainable cheaply because not all dealers and auctioneers check their stock as thoroughly as they might.

The 1787 shilling should always be checked for the stop omissions, obverse and reverse. The very rare obverse without any stops at all is occasionally catalogued as the 'no stop over head' type (or even missed altogether!) because a dealer is unused to seeing the coin and does not trouble to check properly.

Shillings of the period 1816-20 sometimes occur with initials unofficially stamped on them, usually on the obverse.

Denomination	Metal	Weight (grams)	Diameter (mm)	Rev. alignment
Shilling 1763	Silver	6.0	26	↓
Shilling 1787 & 1798	Silver	6.0	25	↑
Shilling 1816-1820	Silver	5.7	24	↑

Obverse 1 Head 1, right; GEORGIVS III DEI GRATIA

Obverse 2 Head 2, right; same legend

Obverse 3 Head 3, similar to 2, right; same legend, larger lettering; no stop over head

Obverse 4 Head 4, right; GEOR III D G BRITT REX F D (date)

Reverse 1 Cruciform shields around star, plain in angles; M B F ET H REX F D B ET L D S R I A T ET E 1763

Reverse 2 Cruciform pentagonal shields around star, with crowns in angles; no hearts behind lion in Hanoverian shield. M B F ET H REX F D B ET L D S R I A T ET E 1787

Reverse 3 As Reverse 2 but with hearts

Reverse 4 As Reverse 3 but with larger lettering and dated 1798

Reverse 5 Crowned shield within Garter; HONI SOIT Q(UI) MAL Y PENSE on Garter

Edge milled

Obv. 1   Obv. 2

Obv. 3   Obv. 4

Rev. 1   Rev. 3

Rev. 4   Rev. 5

No.	Date	Features	Obv.	Rev.	F	VF	EF	UNC
G3SH-005	1763	[1]	1	1	180	300	500	650
G3SH-010	1787		2	2	10	15	25	35
G3SH-015	1787	1 over reversed 1	2	2	60	90	150	250
G3SH-020	1787	PROOF on thick flan; edge plain [2]	2	2				700
G3SH-025	1787	no stop over head	2	2	14	20	35	50
G3SH-030	1787	no stop over head PROOF	2	2				400
G3SH-035	1787	no stop over head PROOF; edge plain	2	2				600
G3SH-040	1787	no stop over head PROOF on thick flan; edge plain	2	2				700
G3SH-045	1787	no stops on obv	2	2	40	100	200	300
G3SH-050	1787	no stops on obv PROOF; edge plain	2	2				800
G3SH-055	1787	no stops at date	2	2	18	30	45	60
G3SH-060	1787	latter 7 over 6; no stops at date	2	2	35	60	90	120
G3SH-065	1787		2	3	10	15	25	35
G3SH-070	1787	1 over reversed 1	2	3	60	90	150	250
G3SH-075	1787	PROOF	2	3				400
G3SH-080	1787	PROOF on thick flan; edge plain	2	3				700
G3SH-085	1798	[3]	3	4			4500	6000

No.	Date	Features	Obv.	Rev.	F	VF	EF	UNC
G3SH-090	1816	[4]	4	5	7	12	30	45
G3SH-095	1816	PROOF	4	5				750
G3SH-100	1816	PROOF; edge plain	4	5				750
G3SH-105	1816	PROOF in gold	4	5				10000
G3SH-110	1817		4	5	7	12	30	45
G3SH-115	1817	PROOF; edge plain	4	5			450	650
G3SH-120	1817	GEOE instead of GEOR (obv.)	4	5	40	75	200	
G3SH-125	1818	[5]	4	5	12	25	90	140
G3SH-130	1819	[6]	4	5	7	12	30	45
G3SH-135	1819	9 over 8 [7]	4	5	12	20	55	80
G3SH-140	1820	[8]	4	5	8	14	35	50
G3SH-145	1820	I of HONI over S (rev.)	4	5	12	20	55	80
G3SH-150	1820	H of HONI over horizontal H	4	5	18	30	75	120
G3SH-155	1820	PROOF	4	5				600

1. 'Northumberland' shilling.
2. Weight 7.6 grams.
3. 'Dorrien Magens' shilling.
4. Issued in 1817.
5. Recut date exists.
6. 9 varies in size.
7. Do not confuse overdate with double struck 8.
8. Continued to be minted after death of George III.

George IV 1820–1830

The shillings initially used the Benedetto Pistrucci laureate head of the monarch, but this was changed during 1825 after the king's disapproval of the design, giving way to a more youthful portrait by William Wyon. The reverses, by Johann Baptiste Merlen, underwent two major changes in design, the second coinciding with the introduction of the new portrait in 1825. As with the half-crowns, the initials of William Wellesley Pole, Master of the Mint, are hidden in the centres of the shamrocks on the reverse.

Collecting Hints

The delicate design of the Pistrucci laureate head shillings and the relatively higher relief of the later bare head type make it advisable to collect the series in extremely fine or better condition if one wants to appreciate the craftsmanship put into their manufacture. Several dates, notably 1821, 1823 and 1827 are very difficult to find in mint state or near.

Denomination	Metal	Weight (grams)	Diameter (mm)	Rev. alignment
Shilling	Silver	5.7	24	↓

Obverse 1 Head 1, laureate, left; GEORGIUS IIII D G BRITANNIAR REX F D

Obverse 2 Head 2, 'bare head', left; GEORGIUS IV DEI GRATIA (date)

Reverse 1 Garnished shield with surmounting large crown; ANNO (date)

Reverse 2 Crowned shield within Garter; ANNO (date); HONI SOIT QUI MAL Y PENSE (on Garter)

Reverse 3 Lion on crown, ornament below; BRITANNIARUM REX FIDEI DEFENSOR

Edge milled

Obv. 1   Obv. 2

Rev. 1   Rev. 2   Rev. 3

No.	Date	Features	Obv.	Rev.	F	VF	EF	UNC
G4SH-005	1821		1	1	10	22	80	140
G4SH-010	1821	PROOF	1	1				600
G4SH-015	1823		1	2	25	70	200	300
G4SH-020	1823	PROOF	1	2				500
G4SH-025	1824		1	2	10	25	90	130
G4SH-030	1824	PROOF	1	2				500
G4SH-035	1825		1	2	10	25	90	130
G4SH-040	1825	5 over 3	1	2	15	35	130	200
G4SH-045	1825	PROOF	1	2				500
G4SH-050	1825		2	3	8	18	60	90
G4SH-055	1825	I instead of 1 in date	2	3	150	700		
G4SH-060	1825	PROOF	2	3				500
G4SH-065	1825	PROOF in Barton's metal; edge plain	2	3				1000
G4SH-070	1826		2	3	7	15	50	80
G4SH-075	1826	Roman I in date	2	3	20	50	150	250
G4SH-080	1826	PROOF [1]	2	3				200
G4SH-085	1826	6 over 2	2	3	12	25	70	110
G4SH-090	1827		2	3	12	45	130	170
G4SH-095	1829		2	3	10	35	110	150
G4SH-100	1829	PROOF	2	3				450

1. Issued in cased proof sets.

Barton's metal is a laminated product consisting of thin sheets of gold bonded to a copper base.

William IV 1830–1837

The shillings of William IV were of one type only, using an obverse by William Wyon and a reverse by Johann Baptiste Merlen, which latter included the denomination 'ONE SHILLING' for the first time. William Wyon had by now shown himself to be an engraver of talent, while the antics of the temperamental Pistrucci had resulted in his being moved sideways to a new post of Chief Medallist.

Proofs exist for each of the five dates, with the unusual feature on three of them of a round-top '3' in the date.

Collecting Hints

This series is of a simple and elegant design which is best appreciated in very fine or extremely fine condition.

Denomination	Metal	Weight (grams)	Diameter (mm)	Rev. alignment
Shilling	Silver	5.7	24	↓

Obverse 1 Head 1, right; GULIELMUS IIII D G BRITANNIAR REX F D

Reverse 1 'ONE SHILLING' within wreath, crown above, date below

Edge milled

Obv. 1   Rev. 1

No.	Date	Features	Obv.	Rev.	F	VF	EF	UNC
W4SH-005	1831	PROOF; edge plain [1]	1	1				450
W4SH-010	1831	PROOF	1	1				800
W4SH-015	1834		1	1	10	25	90	130
W4SH-020	1834	PROOF	1	1				600
W4SH-025	1834	PROOF round-top '3' in date	1	1				1200
W4SH-030	1835		1	1	15	40	130	170
W4SH-035	1835	PROOF round-top '3' in date	1	1				1500
W4SH-040	1836		1	1	10	25	90	130
W4SH-045	1836	PROOF round-top '3' in date	1	1				1500
W4SH-050	1836	PROOF in copper; edge plain	1	1				600
W4SH-055	1837		1	1	16	45	140	180
W4SH-060	1837	PROOF	1	1				800

1. Issued in cased proof sets.

All coins have flat-top 3 in date unless otherwise stated.

Victoria 1837–1901

The Johann Baptiste Merlen 'ONE SHILLING' reverse was continued with the accession of Victoria, while the obverse used a portrait of the young queen by William Wyon, whose initials appear on the truncation for about the first year. Later coins up to 1887, while of similar design, exhibit progressively inferior workmanship and become somewhat more crude in style.

As with the florins, the placement on the reverse of die numbers between the years 1864 and 1879 add greatly to the numismatic interest of these pieces, as well as giving some indication of their respective scarcities.

The shilling was radically redesigned in 1887 for the Silver Jubilee, and again in 1893, when the unpopular Boehm Jubilee portrait was replaced by the veiled head design by Brock. The practice of including the words 'ONE SHILLING', discarded in 1887, was reintroduced in 1893.

Collecting Hints

The series should be collected in extremely fine or better condition unless the rarity of a piece prevents its acquisition in such a grade. Anyone brave enough to attempt the fascinating task of collecting by die number and date will probably be satisfied with any piece on which the die number is readable.

Care should be taken in distinguishing 1887 Jubilee issue early strikings from the proofs; the milling on the edge of the latter almost cuts the fingers, and is 'straight across' rather than displaying a concave/convex cross-section.

Denomination	Metal	Weight (grams)	Diameter (mm)	Rev. alignment
Shilling 1838-87 obvs 1-5	Silver	5.7	24	↓
Shilling 1887-1901 obvs 6-9	Silver	5.7	24	↑

Obverse 1 Head 1, left; W.W. on truncation; VICTORIA DEI GRATIA BRITANNIAR REG F D

Obverse 2 Head 2, very slightly larger, left; W.W. on truncation; same legend

Obverse 3 Head 2, left; no W.W. on truncation; same legend

Obverse 4 Head 3, left; lower relief, slightly different design; same legend

Obverse 5 Head 4, left; slightly older features; same legend

Obverse 6 Head 5, 'Jubilee' head, left; VICTORIA DEI GRATIA BRITT REGINA F D

Obverse 7 Head 6, similar but much larger, left; same legend

Obverse 8 Head 7, veiled and draped, left; VICTORIA DEI GRA BRITT REGINA FID DEF IND IMP

Obverse 9 Head 7, left; same legend but lettering slightly larger

Reverse 1 ONE SHILLING within wreath, crown above, date below, with or without die number above date (in listings, no die number unless stated)

Reverse 2 Similar but larger lettering. Slight alterations in design

Reverse 3 Crowned shield within Garter; HONI SOIT QUI MAL Y PENSE on Garter (date)

Reverse 4 Similar but slightly different design: row of jewels on crown on Reverse 3 replaced by lines; no loop inside QUI (on Garter) unlike on Reverse 3

Reverse 5 Three shields within Garter; HONI SOIT QUI MAL Y PENSE on Garter, partially hidden by shields ONE SHILLING (date)

Reverse 6 Similar but the rose is larger

Edge milled

Obv. 1   Obv. 3

Obv. 4   Obv. 5

Obv. 6   Obv. 7   Obv. 9

Rev. 1   Rev. 2

Rev. 3

Rev. 5

No.	Date	Features	Obv.	Rev.	F	VF	EF	UNC
VYSH-005	1838		1	1	10	24	80	110
VYSH-010	1838	PROOF	1	1				700
VYSH-015	1839		1	1	12	28	90	120
VYSH-020	1839	PROOF; edge plain	1	1				700
VYSH-025	1839	PROOF; edge plain [1]	2	1				350
VYSH-030	1839		3	1	10	24	75	100
VYSH-035	1839	PROOF	3	1				1400
VYSH-040	1839	PROOF; edge plain	3	1				400
VYSH-045	1839	PROOF; edge plain; rev. ↑	3	1				400
VYSH-050	1840		3	1	14	40	120	150
VYSH-055	1840	PROOF	3	1				1200
VYSH-060	1841		3	1	14	45	130	160
VYSH-065	1842		3	1	12	30	90	120
VYSH-070	1842	PROOF	3	1				900
VYSH-075	1843		3	1	12	35	110	140
VYSH-080	1844		3	1	10	30	90	120
VYSH-085	1845		3	1	10	30	90	120
VYSH-090	1846		3	1	10	30	90	120
VYSH-095	1848	latter 8 over 6	3	1	30	90	300	500
VYSH-100	1849		3	1	10	30	90	120
VYSH-105	1850		3	1	120	400	1000	
VYSH-110	1850	50 over 46 or 49	3	1	120	400	1000	
VYSH-115	1851		3	1	30	80	300	500
VYSH-120	1851	PROOF	3	1				1500
VYSH-125	1852		3	1	10	30	90	120
VYSH-130	1853		3	1	10	30	90	120
VYSH-135	1853	PROOF [1]	3	1				500
VYSH-140	1854		3	1	50	130	500	
VYSH-145	1854	4 over 1	3	1	80	200	800	
VYSH-150	1855		3	1	10	30	90	120
VYSH-155	1856		3	1	10	30	90	120
VYSH-160	1857	[2]	3	1	10	30	90	120
VYSH-165	1857	inverted G or broken D at end of obv legend	3	1	25	90	200	
VYSH-170	1857	7 over 5	3	1	40	120	300	500
VYSH-175	1858		3	1	9	25	75	100
VYSH-180	1858	PROOF	3	1				1500
VYSH-185	1859		3	1	9	25	75	100
VYSH-190	1860		3	1	12	30	90	120
VYSH-195	1861		3	1	12	30	90	120
VYSH-200	1862		3	1	20	45	120	170
VYSH-205	1863		3	1	24	50	130	180
VYSH-210	1863	3 over 1	3	1	30	70	160	220
VYSH-215	1863	3 over 2	3	1	28	65	150	210
VYSH-220	1864	die number above date	3	1	10	30	90	120
VYSH-225	1865	die number above date	3	1	10	25	80	110
VYSH-230	1866	die number above date	3	1	10	25	80	110
VYSH-235	1866	die number above date BBITANNIAR instead of BRITANNIAR (obv.)	3	1	30	100		
VYSH-240	1867	die number above date	3	1	10	25	80	110
VYSH-245	1867	PROOF [3]	4	1				700
VYSH-250	1867	PROOF; edge plain [3]	4	1				1200
VYSH-255	1867	die number above date	4	1	25	70	200	
VYSH-260	1868	die number above date	4	1	10	25	80	110
VYSH-265	1869	die number above date	4	1	12	30	90	120
VYSH-270	1870	die number above date	4	1	12	30	90	120

No.	Date	Features	Obv.	Rev.	F	VF	EF	UNC
VYSH-275	1871	die number above date	4	1	9	20	60	80
VYSH-280	1871	PROOF die number above date	4	1				800
VYSH-285	1871	PROOF; edge plain; rev. ↑ die number above date	4	1				1500
VYSH-290	1872	die number above date	4	1	8	18	50	70
VYSH-295	1873	die number above date	4	1	8	18	50	70
VYSH-300	1874	die number above date 4	4	1	9	20	60	80
VYSH-305	1875	die number above date	4	1	9	20	60	80
VYSH-310	1876	die number above date	4	1	10	25	70	100
VYSH-315	1877	die number above date	4	1	9	20	60	80
VYSH-320	1878	die number above date	4	1	9	20	60	80
VYSH-325	1878	PROOF; die number above date	4	1				1000
VYSH-330	1879	die number above date	4	1	12	30	100	140
VYSH-335	1879	PROOF die number above date	4	1				700
VYSH-340	1879	5	5	1	9	20	60	80
VYSH-345	1879	PROOF; edge plain; rev. ↑ 6	5	1				1500
VYSH-350	1880	7	5	2	9	16	45	65
VYSH-355	1880	PROOF	5	2				600
VYSH-360	1880	PROOF; edge plain	5	2				1200
VYSH-365	1881	7	5	2	9	16	45	65
VYSH-370	1881	PROOF	5	2				600
VYSH-375	1881	PROOF; edge plain	5	2				1500
VYSH-380	1882		5	2	12	25	80	110
VYSH-385	1883		5	2	9	16	45	65
VYSH-390	1884	8	5	2	9	16	45	65
VYSH-395	1884	PROOF	5	2				700
VYSH-400	1885		5	2	8	14	35	50
VYSH-405	1885	PROOF	5	2				700
VYSH-410	1886		5	2	8	14	35	50
VYSH-415	1886	PROOF	5	2				900
VYSH-420	1887		5	2	8	14	35	50
VYSH-425	1887	PROOF	5	2				600
VJSH-430	1887	9	6	3	5	7	10	14
VJSH-435	1887	PROOF 10	6	3				80
VJSH-440	1888		6	3	6	8	22	28
VJSH-445	1888	last 8 over 7	6	3	6	8	22	28
VJSH-450	1889		6	3	15	80	400	700
VJSH-455	1889		6	4	18	90	500	850
VJSH-460	1889		7	4	6	9	24	30
VJSH-465	1889	PROOF	7	4				1000
VJSH-470	1890		7	4	7	10	26	32
VJSH-475	1891		7	4	7	10	26	32
VJSH-480	1891	PROOF	7	4				800
VJSH-485	1892		7	4	7	10	26	32
VOSH-490	1893		8	5	6	9	18	28
VOSH-495	1893		9	5	4	7	15	22
VOSH-500	1893	PROOF 1	9	5				120
VOSH-505	1894		8	5	6	9	20	30
VOSH-510	1894		9	5	6	9	20	30
VOSH-515	1895		9	5	8	12	28	45
VOSH-520	1895		9	6	5	8	17	27
VOSH-525	1896		9	5	10	15	35	60
VOSH-530	1896		9	6	5	8	17	27
VOSH-535	1897		9	6	4	8	16	25
VOSH-540	1898		9	6	5	8	17	27
VOSH-545	1899		9	6	5	8	17	28
VOSH-550	1900		9	6	5	8	15	23
VOSH-555	1901		9	6	4	8	15	22

1. Issued in cased proof sets.
2. Date size varies.
3. No die number.
4. 4 of date varies.
5. No die number above date from now on.
6. Some may exist with obverse 1 (sic).
7. Lettering and length of line below SHILLING varies (rev.).
8. Length of line below SHILLING varies (rev.).
9. Garter letters vary in size (rev.).
10. Issued in proof sets.

Edward VII 1902–1910

As with the other denominations, the shilling was a one-type issue depicting the de Saulles portrait of Edward using a mechanical reduction process. The reverse of a lion on a crown was also by de Saulles and used the same motif as the reverse of the later type of George IV shilling.

After the death of de Saulles early in the reign, W.H.J. Blakemore became responsible for hand-finishing and re-engraving dies produced by the mechanical reducer.

Collecting Hints

In common with the halfcrown and florin, 1905 is the rarest date of the Edward VII shilling. However, most of the dates are difficult to find in top condition, although in fine or very fine they present less of a problem. Collectors should look for at least extremely fine specimens, with the 1905 possibly in very fine.
The Edward VII shilling is often found somewhat weakly struck, and care should be taken in differentiating between wear and weak striking.

Denomination	Metal	Weight (grams)	Diameter (mm)	Rev. alignment
Shilling	Silver	5.7	24	↑

Obverse 1 Head 1, right; EDWARDVS VII DEI GRA BRITT OMN REX

Reverse 1 Lion on crown, with separated date, all within inner circle; FID DEF IND IMP ONE SHILLING

Edge milled

Obv. 1

Rev. 1

No.	Date	Features	Obv.	Rev.	F	VF	EF	UNC
E7SH-005	1902		1	1	5	9	20	30
E7SH-010	1902	matt PROOF 1	1	1			20	30
E7SH-015	1903		1	1	7	12	50	80
E7SH-020	1904		1	1	7	11	45	70
E7SH-025	1905		1	1	30	80	300	500
E7SH-030	1906		1	1	6	10	25	35
E7SH-035	1907		1	1	6	12	30	45
E7SH-040	1908		1	1	7	14	60	90
E7SH-045	1909		1	1	7	14	60	90
E7SH-050	1910		1	1	5	10	24	36

1. Issued in cased proof sets.

George V 1910–1936

The overall design of the shilling changed very little with the transition to a new monarch. The obverse used the portrait of the king by Sir Bertram MacKennal (1863-1931); the reverse retains the lion on crown design which was used on the Edward VII coinage and which originated on the George IV shilling.

As with the other silver denominations, the metal constituency underwent a number of changes during the reign. In 1920, the silver content was reduced to 50%, the remaining constituents being a nickel-containing copper-based alloy. This proved unsatisfactory in that it tarnished with yellow streaks. In 1922 a straight 1:1 silver-copper mix proved much more satisfactory. In 1923 and 1924, a few experimental pieces were struck in pure nickel. The silver-copper composition was changed again in 1927 to a silver-copper-nickel-zinc alloy when the new designs were introduced, and these later coins are considerably less prone to tarnishing.

Unusually for a reign of this length, the shilling was struck for every year of the reign.

Collecting Hints

Collect in extremely fine condition or better, unless one is assembling merely a date sequence in the lower 'grades. Try to acquire at least one nice condition 'yellow streak tarnish' specimen of 1920-22 to demonstrate the problem with the metal constituency of the period.

Take care not to overgrade coins of the 1927-36 period, and always examine the high points of both sides carefully before grading.

Denomination	Metal	Weight (gms)	Diameter (mm)	Rev. alignment
Shilling 1911-1919	0.925 Silver	5.7	24	↑
Shilling 1920-1922	Silver 50%; Copper 40%; Nickel 10%	5.7	24	↑
Shilling 1922-1927	Silver 50%; Copper 50%	5.7	24	↑
Shilling 1927-1936	Silver 50%; Copper 40%; Nickel 5%; Zinc 5%	5.7	24	↑

Obverse 1 Head 1, left; B.M. on truncation; GEORGIVS V DEI GRA BRITT OMN REX

Obverse 2 Head 2, so-called 'modified effigy', left; BM (no stops) further to right; same legend. Beading recut

Reverse 1 Lion on crown with separated date, all within inner circle; FID DEF IND IMP ONE SHILLING

Reverse 2 Lion on crown, different design; no circle; FID DEF IND IMP ONE SHILLING (date)

Edge milled

Obv. 1   Obv. 2

Rev. 1   Rev. 2

No.	Date	Features	Obv.	Rev.	VF	EF	UNC
G5SH-005	1911	[1]	1	1	5	12	20
G5SH-010	1911	PROOF [2]	1	1		20	40
G5SH-015	1912		1	1	6	18	35
G5SH-020	1913		1	1	9	28	55
G5SH-025	1914		1	1	5	12	20
G5SH-030	1915		1	1	5	12	20
G5SH-035	1916		1	1	5	12	20
G5SH-040	1917		1	1	6	15	25
G5SH-045	1918		1	1	5	12	20
G5SH-050	1919		1	1	5	15	25
G5SH-055	1920		1	1	5	20	35
G5SH-060	1921		1	1	5	25	45
G5SH-065	1922		1	1	5	20	35

No.	Date	Features	Obv.	Rev.	VF	EF	UNC
G5SH-070	1923		1	1	5	18	30
G5SH-075	1923	struck in nickel [3]	1	1			700
G5SH-080	1924		1	1	6	25	50
G5SH-085	1924	struck in nickel [3]	1	1			700
G5SH-090	1925		1	1	10	60	90
G5SH-095	1926		1	1	6	15	30
G5SH-100	1926		2	1	6	15	25
G5SH-105	1927		2	1	6	18	32
G5SH-110	1927		2	2	5	15	25
G5SH-115	1927	PROOF [2]	2	2			40
G5SH-120	1927	PROOF from sandblasted dies [4]	2	2			250
G5SH-125	1928		2	2	4	10	16
G5SH-130	1928	PROOF	2	2			250
G5SH-135	1929		2	2	4	10	16
G5SH-140	1929	PROOF	2	2			250
G5SH-145	1930		2	2	10	30	50
G5SH-150	1930	PROOF	2	2			400
G5SH-155	1931		2	2	4	11	18
G5SH-160	1931	PROOF	2	2			250
G5SH-165	1932		2	2	4	14	25
G5SH-170	1932	PROOF	2	2			250
G5SH-175	1933		2	2	4	11	18
G5SH-180	1933	PROOF	2	2			250
G5SH-185	1934		2	2	5	16	25
G5SH-190	1934	PROOF	2	2			250
G5SH-195	1935		2	2	4	11	18
G5SH-200	1935	PROOF	2	2			250
G5SH-205	1936		2	2	3	10	16
G5SH-210	1936	PROOF	2	2			250

1. Obverse portrait varies.
2. Issued in cased proof sets.
3. Nickel is slightly magnetic.
4. Struck to facilitate photography of coin.

Edward VIII 1936

The Edward VIII shilling is strictly speaking a pattern, as probable Royal approval was about to be granted at the time of the abdication. However, because its official status rests only on this technicality, and to provide continuity, it is included in this catalogue.

The portrait of Edward VIII is by Thomas Humphrey Paget, and faces left at the insistence of the king, who considered this placement more flattering and wished to discontinue the tradition of opposite facings for successive monarchs. The reverse is by George Kruger Gray (1880-1943). The Scottish Crest was used on the shilling after protests from Scotland that the English Crest had been used on the shillings of Edward VII and George V. Although it was intended in addition to strike shillings with an English Crest, only Scottish type coins were in fact struck.

Denomination	Metal	Weight (grams)	Diameter (mm)	Rev. alignment
Shilling	Silver	5.6	24	↑

Obverse 1 Head 1, left; EDWARDVS VIII D G BR OMN REX

Reverse 1 Facing lion on crown dividing date (1937) and flanked by St Andrew's Cross and Thistle; FID DEF IND IMP ONE SHILLING

Edge milled

Obv. 1   Rev. 1

No.	Date	Obv.	Rev.	UNC
E8SH-005	1937	1	1	15000

George VI 1937–1952

The George VI shilling saw the introduction of the unique concept of two different reverse designs for each year (apart from the very rare 1952). These were the 'English' and the 'Scottish' reverses. The design of the English reverses was influenced by the lion on crown designs of earlier reigns; the Scottish reverse had a more symmetrically posed lion holding a sword and sceptre, and seated on a smaller crown, at the sides of which lie the St Andrew's Cross and the Scottish Thistle. Both reverses were designed by George Kruger Gray (1880-1943). The obverse uses the design of the monarch by Thomas Humphrey Paget (1893-1974). There is no difference in obverse design between the English and Scottish types.

As with the other silver coinage, there was a transition in 1947 to cupronickel.

Collecting Hints

An attempt should be made to collect this series in as near mint state as possible, and the existence of two types for each date renders the task doubly challenging. Some of the pieces are quite difficult to find in this grade.

The edges of 1950 and 1951 proofs should always be examined carefully for corrosion; the 1950 may also have ribbon stains on either side from the proof set case. This cannot be removed chemically.

Denomination	Metal	Weight (grams)	Diameter (mm)	Rev. alignment
Shilling 1937-1946	Silver 50%; other 50%	5.7	24	↑
Shilling 1947-1952	Copper 75%; Nickel 25%	5.7	24	↑

Obverse 1 Head 1, left; GEORGIVS VI D G BR OMN REX

Reverse 1E (English reverse): Lion on crown dividing date; (rose) FID DEF IND IMP (rose) ONE SHILLING

Reverse 1S (Scottish reverse): Facing lion on crown dividing date and flanked by St Andrew's Cross and Thistle; same legend

Reverse 2E Similar to 1E but IND IMP missing

Reverse 2S Similar to 1S but IND IMP missing

Edge milled. The milling is finer from 1947 onwards

| Obv. 1 | Rev. 1E | Rev. 1S |

| Rev. 2E | Rev. 2S |

No.	Date	Features	Obv.	Rev.	EF	UNC
G6SH-005	1937		1	1E	4	8
G6SH-010	1937	PROOF [1]	1	1E		12
G6SH-015	1937	PROOF from sandblasted dies [2]	1	1E		200
G6SH-020	1937		1	1S	4	8
G6SH-025	1937	PROOF [1]	1	1S		12
G6SH-030	1937	PROOF from sandblasted dies [2]	1	1S		200

No.	Date	Features	Obv.	Rev.	EF	UNC
G6SH-035	1938		1	1E	6	18
G6SH-040	1938	PROOF	1	1E		250
G6SH-045	1938		1	1S	6	18
G6SH-050	1938	PROOF	1	1S		250
G6SH-055	1939		1	1E	4	12
G6SH-060	1939	PROOF	1	1E		250
G6SH-065	1939		1	1S	4	12
G6SH-070	1939	PROOF	1	1S		250
G6SH-075	1940		1	1E	4	12
G6SH-080	1940	PROOF	1	1E		250
G6SH-085	1940		1	1S	4	12
G6SH-090	1940	PROOF	1	1S		250
G6SH-095	1941		1	1E	4	8
G6SH-100	1941	PROOF	1	1E		250
G6SH-105	1941		1	1S	4	8
G6SH-110	1941	PROOF	1	1S		250
G6SH-115	1942		1	1E	4	8
G6SH-120	1942		1	1S	4	8
G6SH-125	1943		1	1E	4	8
G6SH-130	1943		1	1S	4	8
G6SH-135	1944		1	1E	4	8
G6SH-140	1944	PROOF	1	1E		400
G6SH-145	1944		1	1S	4	8
G6SH-150	1944	PROOF	1	1S		400
G6SH-155	1945		1	1E	4	8
G6SH-160	1945	PROOF	1	1E		250
G6SH-165	1945		1	1S	4	8
G6SH-170	1945	PROOF	1	1S		250
G6SH-175	1946		1	1E	4	8
G6SH-180	1946	PROOF	1	1E		250
G6SH-185	1946	PROOF in cupronickel [3]	1	1E		800
G6SH-190	1946		1	1S	4	8
G6SH-195	1946	PROOF	1	1S		250
G6SH-200	1947	[4]	1	1E	3	7
G6SH-205	1947	struck in 0.5 silver	1	1E		750
G6SH-210	1947	PROOF	1	1E		300
G6SH-215	1947		1	1S	3	7
G6SH-220	1947	PROOF	1	1S		300
G6SH-225	1948		1	1E	3	7
G6SH-230	1948	PROOF	1	1E		300
G6SH-235	1948		1	1S	3	7
G6SH-240	1948	PROOF	1	1S		300
G6SH-245	1949		1	2E	3	7
G6SH-250	1949	PROOF	1	2E		300
G6SH-255	1949		1	2S	3	7
G6SH-260	1949	PROOF	1	2S		300
G6SH-265	1950		1	2E	3	7
G6SH-270	1950	PROOF [1]	1	2E		10
G6SH-275	1950	PROOF from sandblasted dies [2]	1	2E		200
G6SH-280	1950		1	2S	3	7
G6SH-285	1950	PROOF [1]	1	2S		10
G6SH-290	1950	PROOF from sandblasted dies [2]	1	2S		200
G6SH-295	1951		1	2E	3	7
G6SH-300	1951	PROOF [1]	1	2E		12
G6SH-305	1951	PROOF from sandblasted dies [2]	1	2E		200
G6SH-310	1951		1	2S	3	7
G6SH-315	1951	PROOF [1]	1	2S		12
G6SH-320	1951	PROOF from sandblasted dies [2]	1	2S		200
G6SH-325	1952	PROOF	1	2E		8000
G6SH-330	1952	PROOF in nickel [5]	1	2E		5000

1. Issued in cased proof sets.
2. Struck to facilitate photography of coin.
3. Trial piece for cupronickel coinage.
4. Metal composition change; see table above.
5. Weight 5.6 grams; nickel is slightly magnetic.

Elizabeth II 1952 —

The original design by Mary Gillick for the queen's portrait resulted in a weak striking lacking in detail, and the dies were soon recut to provide a sharper image. The first year (1953) is the only coin bearing the obverse 'BRITT OMN' (trans: of all the British possessions).

No.	Date	Features	Obv.	Rev.	UNC
EL2SH-035	1953	PROOF from sandblasted dies [3]	1	1S	200
EL2SH-040	1954		2	1E	5
EL2SH-045	1954	PROOF	2	1E	200
EL2SH-050	1954		2	1S	5
EL2SH-055	1954	PROOF	2	1S	200
EL2SH-060	1955		2	1E	5
EL2SH-065	1955	PROOF	2	1E	200
EL2SH-070	1955		2	1S	5
EL2SH-075	1955	PROOF	2	1S	200
EL2SH-080	1956		2	1E	7
EL2SH-085	1956	PROOF	2	1E	200
EL2SH-090	1956		2	1S	7
EL2SH-095	1956	PROOF	2	1S	200
EL2SH-100	1957		2	1E	3
EL2SH-105	1957	PROOF	2	1E	200
EL2SH-110	1957		2	1S	15
EL2SH-115	1957	PROOF	2	1S	200
EL2SH-120	1958		2	1E	15
EL2SH-125	1958	PROOF	2	1E	200
EL2SH-130	1958		2	1S	3
EL2SH-135	1958	PROOF	2	1S	200
EL2SH-140	1959		2	1E	3
EL2SH-145	1959	PROOF	2	1E	200
EL2SH-150	1959		2	1S	20
EL2SH-155	1959	PROOF	2	1S	200
EL2SH-160	1960		2	1E	3
EL2SH-165	1960	PROOF	2	1E	200
EL2SH-170	1960		2	1S	4
EL2SH-175	1960	PROOF	2	1S	200
EL2SH-180	1961		2	1E	3
EL2SH-185	1961	PROOF	2	1E	200
EL2SH-190	1961		2	1S	10
EL2SH-195	1961	PROOF	2	1S	200
EL2SH-100	1962		2	1E	3
EL2SH-105	1962	PROOF	2	1E	200
EL2SH-110	1962		2	1S	3
EL2SH-115	1962	PROOF	2	1S	200
EL2SH-120	1963		2	1E	3
EL2SH-125	1963	PROOF	2	1E	200
EL2SH-130	1963		2	1S	3
EL2SH-135	1963	PROOF	2	1S	200
EL2SH-140	1964		2	1E	3
EL2SH-145	1964	PROOF	2	1E	200
EL2SH-150	1964		2	1S	3
EL2SH-155	1964	PROOF	2	1S	200
EL2SH-160	1965		2	1E	3
EL2SH-165	1965	PROOF	2	1E	200
EL2SH-170	1965		2	1S	3
EL2SH-175	1965	PROOF	2	1S	200
EL2SH-180	1966		2	1E	3
EL2SH-185	1966	PROOF	2	1E	200
EL2SH-190	1966		2	1S	3
EL2SH-195	1966	rev. ↓	2	1S	50
EL2SH-200	1966	PROOF	2	1S	200
EL2SH-205	1970	PROOF [4]	2	1E	4
EL2SH-210	1970	PROOF [4]	2	1S	4

1. Can be dated from being obverse 1.
2. Issued in cased proof sets.
3. Struck to facilitate photography of coin.
4. Issued in sealed cased proof sets; no ordinary issue coins of this date.

Collecting Hints

Collect in mint state. Acquiring examples of the un-officially struck proofs is an interesting challenge.

Denomination	Metal	Weight (grams)	Diameter (mm)	Rev. alignment
Shilling 1953-70	Copper 75%; Nickel 25%	5.7	24	↑

Obverse 1 Head 1, right; ELIZABETH II DEI GRATIA BRITT OMN REGINA

Obverse 2 Head 1 (recut), right; ELIZABETH II DEI GRATIA REGINA

Reverse 1E (English reverse): Three leopards within crowned shield; FID DEF ONE SHILLING (date)

Reverse 1S (Scottish reverse): Rampant lion within crowned shield; same legend (date)

Edge milled

Obv. 1

Obv. 2

Rev. 1E

Rev. 1S

No.	Date	Features	Obv.	Rev.	UNC
EL2SH-005	1953		1	1E	3
EL2SH-010	1953	'double headed' [1]	1	obv 1	300
EL2SH-015	1953	PROOF [2]	1	1E	8
EL2SH-020	1953	PROOF from sandblasted dies [3]	1	1E	200
EL2SH-025	1953		1	1S	3
EL2SH-030	1953	PROOF [2]	1	1S	8

Sixpence

Oliver Cromwell (Commonwealth 1649–1660)

Only a handful of Cromwell sixpences exist, possibly as few as four. All are dated 1658. The sixpence bears the same basic design as the other Cromwell coinage, being designed by Thomas Simon (also called Symonds) and portraying Cromwell as a Roman Emperor, draped and laureate.

Denomination	Metal	Weight (grams)	Diameter (mm)	Rev. alignment
Sixpence	Silver	3.0	21	↓

Obverse 1 Head 1, left; OLIVAR D G R P ANG SCO HIB &c PRO

Reverse 1 Crowned shield; PAX QVAERITVR BELLO 1658

Edge milled

No.	Date	Obv.	Rev.	F	VF
CR6D-005	1658	1	1	15000	25000

Charles II 1660–1685

The milled sixpence, designed by John Roettier (1631 — c.1703), was first struck in 1674. This was considerably later than the other silver denominations, and it was thus untouched by the problems of the Great Plague and Great Fire of London. As well as having a short span (only eleven years), it is also a much less complicated series, with only one basic design without provenance marks. Having a milled edge, it does not have the added complications of edge lettering varieties such as are encountered on the crowns and halfcrowns. As the first date of issue was 1674, there are no specimens displaying the 'straight across' milling which was used on the shilling and smaller gold coins until 1669.

Denomination	Metal	Weight (grams)	Diameter (mm)	Rev. alignment
Sixpence	Silver	2.9-3.0	21	↓

Obverse 1 Head 1, right; CAROLVS II DEI GRATIA

Reverse 1 Central star enclosed by four cruciform shields with surmounting crowns; interlinked 'C's in angles;

MAG BR FRA ET HIB REX (date)

Edge milled (diagonally)

Obv. 1   Rev. 1

No.	Date	Features	Obv.	Rev.	F	VF	EF
C26DM-005	1674		1	1	40	120	350
C26DM-010	1675		1	1	40	120	350
C26DM-015	1675	5 over 4	1	1	50	130	400
C26DM-020	1676	6 usually over 5 [1]	1	1	50	140	500
C26DM-025	1677		1	1	40	120	350
C26DM-030	1678	8 always over 7	1	1	45	130	400
C26DM-035	1679		1	1	45	130	400
C26DM-040	1680		1	1	60	180	600
C26DM-045	1681		1	1	40	120	350
C26DM-050	1682		1	1	55	160	550
C26DM-055	1682	2 over 1	1	1	50	140	450
C26DM-060	1683		1	1	40	110	320
C26DM-065	1684		1	1	45	130	400

1. 6 not over 5 may not exist.

James II 1685–1688

John Roettier continued as designer and engraver during the reign of James II, and the overall appearance of the sixpence owes much to that of its predecessor. The practice of placing interlinked initials of the monarch in the reverse angles was discontinued, although it was reinstated during the following reign.

As with the Charles II sixpence, the series is simpler than that of the larger denominations, but there are two distinct reverses, distinguished by the shape of the shields. The date 1687 straddles both of these types. Again, there are no provenance marks, and there are no proofs or patterns.

Denomination	Metal	Weight (grams)	Diameter (mm)	Rev. alignment
Sixpence	Silver	2.8-3.0	21–22	↓

Obverse 1 Head 1, left; IACOBVS II DEI GRATIA

Reverse 1 Central star enclosed by four cruciform shields with surmounting crowns, the top of each shield being concave; plain in angles; MAG BR FRA ET HIB REX (date)

Reverse 2 Similar but top of each shield is convex

Reverse 3 Similar but each shield has superimposed convex/concave tops

Edge milled (diagonally)

Obv. 1

Rev. 1

Rev. 2

Rev. 3

No.	Date	Features	Obv.	Rev.	F	VF	EF
J26D-005	1686		1	1	60	160	500
J26D-010	1686	8 over 6	1	1	80	200	650
J26D-015	1687		1	1	65	170	550
J26D-020	1687	7 over 6	1	1	65	170	550
J26D-025	1687		1	2	60	160	500
J26D-030	1687		1	3	75	190	650
J26D-035	1687	7 over 6	1	3	70	180	600
J26D-040	1688		1	3	70	180	600

The number of harp strings varies through this series. It is possible that the variation constituted a form of internal code denoting the die number.

William and Mary 1688–1694

The fact that the first sixpences were issued so late in the reign was probably responsible for the continuance of the cruciform shield reverse on this issue. It is interesting to note that the half-crowns and the gold, radically redesigned earlier in the reign, reverted to the cruciform shield design either later in the reign of William and Mary or during the period when William ruled alone. By 1693, when the first sixpence was issued, the halfcrown had already undergone this metamorphosis.

By the time the sixpences were issued, John Roettier, the Chief Engraver, had developed an affliction in his hands, and almost all of the work was carried out by his sons James (1663-98) and Norbert (b.1665), assisted by Henry Harris. There is some doubt as to the attribution of the sixpence. The style is similar to that of the later halfcrowns, which are probably by James Roettier, but are in the high relief style favoured by Norbert Roettier.

The brief series consists of only two dates, 1693 and 1694. It is worthy of note that the larger silver denominations were not struck in this final year.

There are again no provenance marks, patterns or proofs.

Collecting Hints

As there are only two dates, one should attempt to acquire both in about extremely fine condition. The William and Mary sixpence is a superbly crafted coin, and is much more attractive in this grade than in fine condition. It is frequently found with delightful toning in the higher grades. The 1694 coin is much more difficult to find than the 1693, and one may have to be satisfied with the best available.

Denomination	Metal	Weight (grams)	Diameter (mm)	Rev. alignment
Sixpence	Silver	2.9-3.0	21	↓

Obverse 1 Heads 1, right; GVLIELMVS ET MARIA DEI GRATIA

Reverse 1 Four crowned cruciform shields around lion of Orange-Nassau, with monogrammed 'WM' and one digit of date in each angle; MAG BR FR ET HI REX ET REGINA

Edge milled (diagonally)

Obv. 1   Rev. 1

No.	Date	Features	Obv.	Rev.	F	VF	EF
WM6D-005	1693		1	1	50	150	450
WM6D-010	1693	3 of date inverted (see footnote)	1	1	150	500	1500
WM6D-015	1694		1	1	90	250	800

The date is read in two lines, left to right, with the English shield at the top of the coin.

William III 1695–1701

The simplicity of the sixpence series of the previous three reigns disappeared with a vengeance on the death of Mary from small-pox in 1694. Not only are the listings of London and provincial coins complex, with many errors and varieties, but the majority of the examples exist with either large or small crowns surmounting the shields.

The early sixpences were probably the work of James Roettier, who died during the reign in 1698. Some later coins were produced by the German Johann Crocker, who took an Anglicised form for his name, John Croker. Attribution doubt exists in the intermediate period, and it is thought that some of the coins may have been the work of Henry Harris, who was Chief Engraver at the Mint during at least part of the reign.

As with the halfcrowns and shillings, the complexity of the work was due largely to the 'Great Recoinage', and the decision to withdraw the hammered coinage. The work done at the five provincial mints was often of doubtful quality. This was the result of using a new and inexperienced work-force, and the speed with which the work was expected to be done.

There exists a 1696 sixpence with what has usually been termed the 'second bust'. This provides a companion to the 1696 half-crown and shilling of this type. As stated elsewhere, the halfcrown and shilling are probably patterns and are therefore outside the scope of this book, and this may well be true of the sixpence also. However, in view of the fact that a number of these coins exist in well circulated state, and because of the use of this head in the 1697 circulating sixpence coinage, we have included it in the listings below for the sake of completion.

The very large number of varieties has again necessitated the use of expediency and selection in producing a listing of the various types existing. It is not to be taken, therefore, that the listing is exhaustive. However, it should be found to include all varieties of note which any collector should reasonably require. Some varieties are referred to in note form instead of being given a separate line.

Provenance marks are: plumes (either in angles on reverse or singly below head) for silver from Welsh mines; roses (in angles) for silver from West of England mines.

Collecting Hints

Because of the large number of varieties and errors issued during this reign, the safest course of action is to acquire the best example available bearing enough detail to identify the coin, rather than insisting upon a minimum grade such as fine.

Like the shilling, the sixpence is often found weakly struck. Some collectors do not object to this characteristic, while others prefer, say, a sharply struck very fine coin (i.e. bearing genuine wear) to a weak extremely fine specimen.

Specimens of the 1700 sixpence occur in quantities in about mint condition because a sack of the coins was found around 1950 in a bank vault.

Denomination	Metal	Weight (grams)	Diameter (mm)	Rev. alignment
Sixpence	Silver	2.8–3.1	21	↓

Obverse 1 Head 1, right; GVLIELMVS III DEI GRA

Obverse 2 Head 2, right; hair more profuse and facial expression very different, with hooked nose. same legend

Obverse 3 Head 3, right; much more like Head 1, but tie longer and hair at back of head differently arranged

Reverse 1 four cruciform shields around lion of Nassau; MAG BR FRA ET HIB REX (date). Irish harp has top left corner higher than top right; shield are surmounted by crowns of similar width

Reverse 2 Similar but a different harp, with top left and right corners at roughly equal height

Reverse 3 Similar to Reverse 2 but the surmounting crowns are narrower than the shields

Edge milled (diagonally)

Obv. 1   Obv. 2   Obv. 3

Rev. 1   Rev. 2   Rev. 3

No.	Date	mm	Features	Obv.	Rev.	F	VF	EF
W36D-005	1695			1	1	35	90	240
W36D-010	1696			1	1	15	45	110
W36D-015	1696		last 6 over 5	1	1	30	80	180
W36D-020	1696		no stops on obv.	1	1	20	60	140
W36D-025	1696		shield of Scotland at date	1	1	250	1500	
W36D-030	1696		shield of France at date	1	1	500		
W36D-035	1696		struck on thick flan	1	1	300	1000	
W36D-040	1696	B		1	1	20	55	130
W36D-045	1696	C		1	1	25	70	170
W36D-050	1696	E		1	1	30	80	200
W36D-055	1696	N		1	1	25	70	170
W36D-060	1696	y		1	1	20	50	120
W36D-065	1696	Y		1	1	30	80	200

No.	Date	mm	Features	Obv.	Rev.	F	VF	EF
W36D-070	1696	Y	no stops on obv.	1	1	40	110	250
W36D-075	1696			1	2	35	100	250
W36D-080	1696		no stops on rev.	1	2	45	120	280
W36D-085	1696			1	3	35	100	250
W36D-090	1696	B		1	2	35	110	280
W36D-095	1696	B	no stops on obv.	1	2	35	110	280
W36D-100	1696	B		1	3	35	110	280
W36D-105	1696	B	no stops on obv.	1	3	35	110	280
W36D-110	1696	C		1	3	60	180	500
W36D-115	1696	E		1	3	50	140	350
W36D-120	1696	N		1	3	45	120	300
W36D-125	1696			2	3	250	1000	
W36D-130	1696		GVLIELMVS instead of GVLIELMVS (obv.)	2	3	400	1500	
W36D-135	1696	Y	[1]	3	2	250	600	
W36D-140	1696	E	[1]	3	2	300	700	
W36D-145	1697			1	3	15	55	130
W36D-150	1697		Arms of France and Ireland transposed	1	3	400		
W36D-155	1697		GVLIELMⱯS instead of GVLIELMVS (obv.)	1	3	25	75	180
W36D-160	1697		struck on shilling blank	1	3	250		
W36D-165	1697	B		1	2	30	90	220
W36D-170	1697	B		1	3	20	70	160
W36D-175	1697	B	reads M.AG on rev.; extra stops after FRA & HIB	1	3	25	80	190
W36D-180	1697	C		1	2	35	100	240
W36D-185	1697	C		1	3	20	70	160
W36D-190	1697	C	shield of Ireland at date	1	3	400		
W36D-195	1697	E		1	2	25	80	190
W36D-200	1697	E		1	3	20	70	160
W36D-205	1697	E	E over B (mintmark)	1	3	50	150	400
W36D-210	1697	N		1	3	18	60	140
W36D-215	1697	N	rev. ↑	1	3	30	110	220
W36D-220	1697	N	GVLIEMVS instead of GVLIELMVS (obv.)	1	3	150	500	
W36D-225	1697	y		1	3	30	90	240
W36D-230	1697	y	tiny 7 in date [2]	1	3	60	250	800
W36D-235	1697	y	shield of Ireland at date	1	3	400		
W36D-240	1697		[3]	2	3	60	400	
W36D-245	1697		GVLIEMVS instead of GVLIELMVS (obv.)	2	3	120	1200	
W36D-250	1697			3	2	15	45	110
W36D-255	1697		GVLIEIMVS instead of GVLIELMVS (obv.)	3	2	30	90	200
W36D-260	1697		GⱯLIELMVS instead of GVLIELMVS (obv.)	3	2	25	75	170
W36D-265	1697		[4]	3	3	22	60	130
W36D-270	1697	B		3	2	25	75	170
W36D-275	1697	B	IRA instead of FRA (obv.)	3	2	50	130	300
W36D-280	1697	C		3	2	45	120	270
W36D-285	1697	C		3	3	45	120	270
W36D-290	1697	E		3	2	50	140	320
W36D-295	1697	E		3	3	25	75	170
W36D-300	1697	Y		3	3	40	110	260
W36D-305	1698			3	2	20	55	120
W36D-310	1698		plumes on rev.	3	2	25	70	140

No.	Date	mm	Features	Obv.	Rev.	F	VF	EF
W36D-315	1699			3	2	40	100	280
W36D-320	1699		plumes on rev.	3	2	25	70	140
W36D-325	1699		roses on rev.	3	2	30	90	250
W36D-330	1699		roses on rev. GⱯLIELMVS instead of GVLIELMVS (obv.)	3	2	50	130	320
W36D-335	1700			3	2	20	50	80
W36D-340	1700		plume below head	3	2	1800	3000	5000
W36D-345	1701			3	2	25	70	140

1. A mule, possibly struck in 1697.
2. Punch for 7 same as for the unique 1697 fourpence.
3. Various overstruck letters exist in obv legend.
4. Some have no central bar in F of FRA (obv.).

Variations in the shape of the harp occur.

Anne 1702–1714

John Croker produced a portrait based on a painting of Anne by Sir Godfrey Kneller, while his assistant James Bull is thought to have worked on some of the reverses. A very considerable number of sixpences was struck, resulting in erosion of the dies, and the 'Edinburgh' bust on some of the 1708 coins was possibly the work of the Scottish engraver James Clerk or his assistant Cave.

The shields on the reverse of the sixpence underwent a number of changes. During 1705 they were redesigned, and, two years later, in common with those on the other denominations, they were altered to accommodate the combined Arms of England and Scotland following the union of the two countries.

Provenance marks denoting the origin of the silver were: VIGO (below head) for silver obtained from Spanish galleons at Vigo Bay in 1702; plumes (in reverse angles) for silver from Wales; roses and plumes (alternately in the reverse angles) for silver from the 'Company for smelting down lead with Pitcoale and Seacoale'. The mintmark E (with or without a star) below the head of Anne represents coins struck at Edinburgh.

Collecting Hints

The Anne sixpence was in general a well-circulated coin, and, with the exception of the 1703 and 1711 dates, can be difficult to find in extremely fine condition or near. Some of the dates and varieties are scarcer than is sometimes realised, and it is well worth making some study of how frequently one encounters the individual dates and varieties. It is all too easy to assume that a piece dated 1707 or 1708 is fairly common without realising that one is thinking back to the easy availability of, say, the crowns and halfcrowns of those dates. Although few will make the error of assuming that the 1710 sixpence is common, it is perhaps not generally realised how difficult this coin is to obtain in very fine grade or above. In addition, this date is normally encountered weakly struck.

Denomination	Metal	Weight (grams)	Diameter (mm)	Rev. alignment
Sixpence	Silver	2.9–3.0	21	↓

Obverse 1 Head 1, left; ANNA DEI GRATIA

Obverse 2 Head 2, so-called 'Edinburgh Bust', left; less well defined, more pointed nose

Reverse 1 Four undivided cruciform shields (each having a concave top) with surmounting crowns; MAG BR FRA ET HIB REG (date); usually known as the 'Before Union' reverse

Reverse 2 Similar but each shield has a convex top

Reverse 3 Similar but top and bottom shields are each divided into the Arms of England and Scotland. Shields are again concave at the top; MAG BRI FR ET HIB REG (date); known as 'After Union' reverse

Reverse 4 Similar but MAG BR FRA ET HIB REG (date) (i.e. After Union type with legend as Revs 1/2)

Reverse 5 Similar to Reverse 3 but larger lis in Arms

Edge milled (diagonally)

Obv. 1   Obv. 2   Rev. 1

Rev. 2   Rev. 3   Rev. 5

Before Union of England and Scotland

No.	Date	Features	Obv.	Rev.	F	VF	EF
A6D-005	1703	VIGO below head	1	1	20	60	130
A6D-010	1705		1	1	30	90	240
A6D-015	1705	plumes on rev.	1	1	25	75	180
A6D-020	1705	plumes on rev.	1	2	30	90	230
A6D-025	1705	roses and plumes on rev.	1	2	25	80	210
A6D-030	1707	roses and plumes on rev.	1	2	25	75	180

After Union of England and Scotland

No.	Date	Features	Obv.	Rev.	F	VF	EF
A6D-035	1707		1	3	16	40	100
A6D-040	1707		1	4	1000		
A6D-045	1707	E below head	1	3	18	50	130
A6D-050	1707	PROOF; edge plain E below head	1	3			2000
A6D-055	1707	plumes on rev.	1	3	20	55	140
A6D-060	1708		1	3	16	50	120
A6D-065	1708	E below head	1	3	18	55	140
A6D-070	1708	8 over 7 E below head	1	3	30	80	200
A6D-075	1708	E* below head	1	3	18	55	140
A6D-080	1708	8 over 7 E* below head	1	3	25	65	170
A6D-085	1708	E* below head	2	3	20	65	200
A6D-090	1708	plumes on rev.	1	3	20	55	140
A6D-095	1710	roses and plumes on rev.	1	3	30	140	550
A6D-100	1711		1	3	12	30	70
A6D-105	1711		1	5	12	30	70

George I 1714–1727

With the accession of George Louis, Elector of Hanover, as George I, one of the duplicated England/Scotland shields was replaced by one containing the Arms of Brunswick-Lüneburg surrounding the crown of Charlemagne. The design also incorporates the abbreviated titles of the king. The obverses were probably the work of John Croker, while the reverses were designed by Johan Ochs, senior (b.1673).

This series has the unusual feature that every coin bears a provenance mark denoting the origin of the silver. Roses and plumes (alternately in the reverse angles) were for silver from the 'Company for smelting down lead with Pitcoale and Seacoale'; SS and C (in alternate angles on the reverse) for silver from the South Sea Company.

Denomination	Metal	Weight (grams)	Diameter (mm)	Rev. alignment
Sixpence	Silver	2.9-3.0	21	↓

Obverse 1 Head 1, right; GEORGIVS D G M BR ET HIB REX F D

Reverse 1 Four crowned cruciform shields around central star; BRVN ET L DVX S R I A TH ET EL (date)

Edge milled (diagonally)

Obv. 1   Rev. 1

No.	Date	Features	Obv.	Rev.	F	VF	EF
G16D-005	1717	roses and plumes on rev.	1	1	50	130	400
G16D-010	1717	edge plain; roses and plumes on rev. [1]	1	1	200	500	1200
G16D-015	1720	20 always over 17 roses and plumes on rev.	1	1	50	130	400
G16D-020	1723	SSC in angles on rev. [2]	1	1	25	55	130
G16D-025	1726	roses and plumes on rev. [3]	1	1	55	140	420

1. Not proofs; some currency coins were not given a milled edge in error.
2. Lettering size may vary.
3. Roses and plumes smaller than on 1717 coin.

George II 1727–1760

As with the larger silver denominations, the sixpence series incorporates the two very different portraits of the monarch. The young head was designed by John Croker, while the old head was probably produced by John Sigismund Tanner, who had joined the Mint as an apprentice around 1728. It is likely that this work on the old head was supervised by the aged Croker, in his last years of work before his death in 1741. The reverses were, as always, regarded as somewhat less important, and Tanner was

possibly allowed to work on these with less supervision. It may be that this work was aided by Johan Ochs, junior (1704-88), who had by this time begun to work at the Mint.

Provenance marks are: plumes (silver from the Welsh Copper Company); roses (silver from mines in the West of England); roses and plumes (silver from the 'Company for smelting down lead with Pitcoale and Seacoale'), all of these in the reverse angles; LIMA below the head for coins struck in silver captured by Admiral Anson in Peru during his world voyage.

Denomination	Metal	Weight (grams)	Diameter (mm)	Rev. alignment
Sixpence	Silver	3.0–3.2	21	↓

Obverse 1 Head 1, left; GEORGIVS II DEI GRATIA

Obverse 2 Head 2, left; same legend but GEORGIUS instead of GEORGIVS

Obverse 3 Head 2, left; same legend but GEORGIVS

Reverse 1 Four crowned cruciform shields; M B F ET H REX F D B ET L D S R I A T ET E (date)

Edge milled (diagonally)

Obv. 1   Obv. 3   Rev. 1

No.	Date	Features	Obv.	Rev.	F	VF	EF
G26D-005	1728		1	1	50	120	400
G26D-010	1728	PROOF; edge plain	1	1			1500
G26D-015	1728	plumes on rev.	1	1	40	100	350
G26D-020	1728	roses and plumes on rev.	1	1	25	60	160
G26D-025	1731	roses and plumes on rev.	1	1	25	60	160
G26D-030	1732	roses and plumes on rev.	1	1	25	60	160
G26D-035	1734	roses and plumes on rev.	1	1	50	110	300
G26D-040	1735	roses and plumes on rev.	1	1	50	110	300
G26D-045	1735	5 over 4; roses and plumes on rev.	1	1	65	130	400
G26D-050	1736	roses and plumes on rev.	1	1	40	85	250
G26D-055	1739	roses on rev.	1	1	25	60	160
G26D-060	1739	O in GEORGIVS over R (obv.)	1	1	40	90	240
G26D-065	1741	roses on rev.	1	1	22	55	150
G26D-070	1743	roses on rev.	2	1	22	55	150
G26D-075	1745	roses on rev.	2	1	28	70	190

No.	Date	Features	Obv.	Rev.	F	VF	EF
G26D-080	1745	5 over 3 roses on rev.	2	1	35	85	220
G26D-085	1745	LIMA below head	2	1	18	45	110
G26D-090	1746	LIMA below head	3	1	15	35	85
G26D-095	1746	PROOF [1]	3	1			250
G26D-100	1750		3	1	40	90	250
G26D-105	1751		3	1	50	110	280
G26D-110	1757		3	1	10	18	30
G26D-115	1758		3	1	10	18	30
G26D-120	1758	8 over 7	3	1	14	25	45

1. No LIMA under head.

George III 1760–1820

Compared with the complexities of the larger George III silver coins, the sixpence series is fairly simple. It is not, however, without interest. The popular 1787 coin provides a companion to the shilling, and is just as easily found in the higher grades. No doubt it was hoarded when first minted, being the first issue for 29 years. Oman reports that in 1786 it was found that sixpences in circulation were almost worn flat, and on average 36% underweight. Like the 1787 shilling, the sixpence was initially struck in large quantities without the hearts on the arms of Brunswick, until the error was spotted. The theory that the coin was hoarded is lent credence by the report by Leake in 1793 that the 1787 sixpence was 'not in common currency', and by a Mint Report of 1798 that sixpences were by now on average 38% underweight.

The 1787 sixpence, like the shilling, was designed by Lewis Pingo, who had been appointed as Chief Engraver in 1780. A number of similarities in technique can be seen if one compares Pingo's design for the sixpence with the half guinea, another of his products.

With the Great Recoinage of 1816, the series was resumed, co-incidentally again after 29 years, and the new design was very similar to that of the shilling. The initial design for the obverse was by Benedetto Pistrucci and engraved by Thomas Wyon, junior (1792-1817). The reverse was both designed and engraved by Thomas Wyon, junior. After the latter's untimely death in 1817, engraving work was carried out by Pistrucci himself, but under the prevailing legislation foreigners were debarred from holding the position of Chief Engraver. The craftsmanship and quality of striking of this series was extremely good, and specimens in the higher grades frequently exhibit a prooflike appearance.

The sixpences of 1816 and later remained legal tender even after decimalization in 1971. The coin was later demonetized despite some degree of public opinion which wanted to retain a denomination of 2-1/2 (decimal) pence.

No provenance marks exist on these coins. The crowns in the angles of the 1787 sixpence, while being positioned similarly to other provenance marks, are instead an integral part of the design.

Collecting Hints

The sixpences of George III should be collected in extremely fine or better condition. In these grades the excellent quality of the workmanship will be best appreciated.

There are a number of interesting varieties in the sixpences dated between 1817 and 1820. This is a series in which the coins are not always inspected thoroughly by dealers and auctioneers, all the more so because a good eyeglass and/or good eyesight is often needed on so small a coin. Also, these varieties are not as well known as they might be. Even the plain edge proof 1787 and 1817 sixpences can be found occasionally, sometimes in very fine!

Denomination	Metal	Weight (grams)	Diameter (mm)	Rev. alignment
Sixpence 1787	Silver	3.0	21	↑
Sixpence 1816-1820	Silver	2.8	19	↑

Obverse 1 Head 1, right; GEORGIVS III DEI GRATIA

Obverse 2 Head 2, right; GEOR III D G BRITT REX F D (date)

Reverse 1 Cruciform pentagonal shields around star, with crowns in angles; no hearts behind lion in Hanoverian shield. M B F ET H REX F D B ET L D S R I A T ET E (date)

Reverse 2 As Reverse 1 but with hearts

Reverse 3 Crowned shield within Garter; HONI SOIT QUI MAL Y PENSE on Garter

Edge milled (diagonally on 1787)

| Obv. 1 | Obv. 2 | Rev. 1 | Rev. 3 |

No.	Date	Features	Obv.	Rev.	F	VF	EF	UNC
G36D-005	1787		1	1	10	15	25	35
G36D-010	1787	PROOF; edge plain	1	1				200
G36D-015	1787	PROOF on thick flan; edge plain	1	1				500
G36D-020	1787		1	2	10	15	25	35
G36D-025	1816		2	3	10	16	30	45
G36D-030	1816	PROOF in gold	2	3				7500
G36D-035	1817		2	3	10	16	30	45
G36D-040	1817	PROOF	2	3				600
G36D-045	1817	PROOF; edge plain	2	3		80	250	400
G36D-050	1818		2	3	14	22	45	60
G36D-055	1818	PROOF	2	3				800
G36D-060	1819		2	3	12	18	35	50
G36D-065	1819	8 in date very small	2	3	16	24	50	75
G36D-070	1819	PROOF; 9 not over 8	2	3				500
G36D-075	1819	PROOF; 9 over 8	2	3				400
G36D-080	1820	[1]	2	3	15	22	45	70
G36D-085	1820	1 in date inverted; [1]	2	3	25	35	60	100
G36D-090	1820	PROOF	2	3				400

1. This date continued to be minted after death of George III.

George IV 1820–1830

The first issue of George IV sixpences used the obverse by Benedetto Pistrucci, similar to that used on the larger denominations. This depicted the laureate head of the king, an unflattering portrait much disapproved of by the monarch. In 1826 the laureate king's head was replaced by a bare head design by William Wyon. The sixpence was thus the last of the main silver coins to have the laureate head discarded.

The reverses, by Johann Baptiste Merlen, were of three very different designs. These were similar to those used on the shillings, the last design introducing the lion on crown motif which was to be reintroduced on George V sixpences about a century later.

The 1821 sixpence with the BBITANNIAR error in the obverse legend came about when the word was originally engraved as BITANNIAR in error; the beginning of the word was then re-engraved as effectively as could be done.

Collecting Hints

This series should be collected in extremely fine or better condition to allow the fineness of the engraving of this small denomination to be appreciated. Some of the dates are quite difficult to obtain in this condition.

The 1821 sixpence should always be checked carefully for the BBITANNIAR error. This coin sometimes turns up in about fine condition in mixed auction lots.

Denomination	Metal	Weight (grams)	Diameter (mm)	Rev. alignment
Sixpence	Silver	2.8	19	↓

Obverse 1 Head 1, laureate, left; GEORGIUS IIII D G BRITANNIAR REX F D

Obverse 2 Head 2, 'bare head', left; GEORGIUS IV DEI GRATIA (date)

Reverse 1 Garnished shield with surmounting large crown; ANNO (date)

Reverse 2 Crowned shield within Garter; ANNO (date); HONI SOIT QUI MAL Y PENSE (on Garter)

Reverse 3 Lion on crown, ornament below; BRITANNIARUM REX FIDEI DEFENSOR

Edge milled

Obv. 1   Obv. 2

Rev. 1   Rev. 2   Rev. 3

No.	Date	Features	Obv.	Rev.	F	VF	EF	UNC
G46D-005	1821		1	1	12	20	70	100
G46D-010	1821	BBITANNIAR instead of BRITANNIAR (obv.)	1	1	50	150	600	1000
G46D-015	1821	PROOF	1	1				250
G46D-020	1824		1	2	14	24	85	120
G46D-025	1824	PROOF	1	2				400
G46D-030	1825		1	2	12	22	75	110
G46D-035	1825	PROOF	1	2				500
G46D-040	1826		1	2	30	55	160	240
G46D-045	1826	rev. ↑	1	2	90	150	500	800
G46D-050	1826	PROOF	1	2				600
G46D-055	1826		2	3	10	18	55	80
G46D-060	1826	PROOF [1]	2	3				200
G46D-065	1826	PROOF in pewter; struck on thick flan	2	3				800
G46D-070	1827		2	3	20	40	120	180
G46D-075	1828		2	3	16	30	90	140
G46D-080	1829		2	3	14	22	75	110
G46D-085	1829	PROOF	2	3				500

1. Issued in cased proof sets.

William IV 1830–1837

The design of the William IV sixpence reflects that of the shilling. This is a one-type issue, with obverses by William Wyon and reverses by Johann Baptiste Merlen, and the words 'SIX PENCE' are used for the first time.

Collecting Hints

The series should be collected in at least very fine condition. It should be remembered that the 1836 sixpence is somewhat scarce, unlike the shilling of the same date.

Denomination	Metal	Weight (grams)	Diameter (mm)	Rev. alignment
Sixpence	Silver	2.8	19	↓

Obverse 1 Head 1, right; GULIELMUS IIII D G BRITANNIAR REX F D

Reverse 1 SIX PENCE within wreath, crown above, date below

Edge milled

Obv. 1   Rev. 1

No.	Date	Features	Obv.	Rev.	F	VF	EF	UNC
W46D-005	1831		1	1	10	20	65	90
W46D-010	1831	PROOF	1	1				400
W46D-015	1831	PROOF on thin flan; edge plain [1]	1	1				1500
W46D-020	1831	PROOF; edge plain [2]	1	1				220
W46D-025	1831	PROOF in palladium [3]	1	1				2000
W46D-030	1834		1	1	11	22	70	100
W46D-035	1834	PROOF	1	1				700
W46D-040	1834	PROOF round-top 3 in date	1	1				900
W46D-045	1835		1	1	10	20	65	90
W46D-050	1835	PROOF round-top 3 in date	1	1				1000
W46D-055	1836		1	1	16	30	100	140
W46D-060	1836	PROOF round-top 3 in date	1	1				1200
W46D-065	1837		1	1	12	25	90	120
W46D-070	1837	PROOF	1	1				800

1. Weight 1.9 grams.
2. Issued in cased proof sets.
3. Date size varies.

All coins have flat-top 3 in date unless otherwise stated.

Victoria 1837–1901

The first Victorian sixpences were struck in 1838. These retained the 'SIX PENCE' within wreath reverse by Johann Baptiste Merlen as used on the William IV coinage. The obverse portrait was by William Wyon as on the larger coins, but the engraver's initials on the truncation were absent. Presumably Wyon considered that the coin was too small to allow his initials to be read clearly, and he did not have the arrogance of his predecessor to allow him to spell his name in full, as Pistrucci did on the George III crown. The sixpence was struck, usually with a mintage of a million or more in each year, but no pieces are confirmed dated 1847 or 1849, and the 1848 coin is quite rare. It is likely that this was connected with the interest in the possible advent of decimal currency around 1848. No doubt the future of a coin valued at one-fortieth of a pound was considered in some doubt.

As with the shilling, the reverse dies for the coins between 1864 and 1879 were generally marked with the die number, in order to determine the life of each die.

To mark the Golden Jubilee of Victoria's reign in 1887, the obverse and reverse of the sixpence were redesigned, incorporating a new portrait of Victoria by Sir Joseph Edgar Boehm (1834-90) and a shield reverse. The choice of design, however, proved unfortunate. Both sides of the coin resembled the half sovereign, which was of similar size, to such an extent that many pieces were gilded and passed off as the gold coin. The redesigned shilling did not lend itself to this trickery as the similarly sized sovereign bore a St George design on the reverse. The design of the reverse of the sixpence was therefore hastily changed back during 1887 to the discarded 'SIX PENCE within wreath' type, while the shilling was allowed to retain its shield reverse. In 1893 the unpopular Boehm Jubilee portrait was replaced by a veiled head design by Sir Thomas Brock (1847-1922).

There exists a rare but distinct variety of 1887 shield sixpence hitherto unrecorded in almost all reference works. This has the engraver's initials J.E.B. on the obverse much higher, on the truncation instead of below it.

Edge milled

Obv. 1 Obv. 2 Obv. 3

Obv. 5 Obv. 6 Rev. 1

Rev. 2 Rev. 3 Rev. 4

Collecting Hints

At least some of the early Victorian sixpences should be collected in extremely fine condition. Only in this grade is it possible to appreciate fully the high standard of the work of William Wyon and the beauty of his Victoria portrait. The later coins are not so finely executed but are more plentiful and for this reason the extremely fine standard should be maintained.

To collect the 1864-1879 series by die number is to enter virtually uncharted waters, and specimens in any grade will be acceptable.

1887 Jubilee issue early strikings exist with prooflike surfaces and are sometimes sold as proofs. The striking of the milled edges should be carefully examined. The edges of true proofs almost cut the fingers when handled.

Denomination	Metal	Weight (grams)	Diameter (mm)	Rev. alignment
Sixpence 1838-87 Obverses 1-3	Silver	3.0	19	↓
Sixpence 1887-1901 Obverses 4-6	Silver	3.0	19	↑

Obverse 1 Head 1, left; VICTORIA DEI GRATIA BRITANNIAR REG F D

Obverse 2 Head 2, in lower relief, left; same legend

Obverse 3 Head 3, slightly different design, left

Obverse 4 Head 4, 'Jubilee Head', left, initials JEB on truncation; VICTORIA DEI GRATIA BRITT REGINA F D

Obverse 5 Head 4, similar, left, initials JEB below truncation; same legend

Obverse 6 Head 5, veiled and draped, left; VICTORIA DEI GRA BRITT REGINA FID DEF IND IMP

Reverse 1 SIX PENCE within wreath, crown above, date below, with or without die number above date (in listings, no die number unless stated)

Reverse 2 Similar but SIX PENCE larger. No die number

Reverse 3 Crowned shield within Garter; HONI SOIT QUI MAL Y PENSE on Garter

Reverse 4 Similar to reverses 1,2 but redesigned; crown is very different (date)

No.	Date	Features	Obv.	Rev.	F	VF	EF	UNC
VY6D-005	1838		1	1	7	18	60	85
VY6D-010	1838	PROOF	1	1				700
VY6D-015	1839		1	1	7	20	70	100
VY6D-020	1839	PROOF; edge plain [1]	1	1				180
VY6D-025	1839	PROOF; edge plain; rev. ↑	1	1				250
VY6D-030	1839	PROOF; rev. ↑ [2]	3	1				1500
VY6D-035	1840		1	1	8	24	80	110
VY6D-040	1841		1	1	8	25	85	120
VY6D-045	1842		1	1	8	24	80	110
VY6D-050	1842	each 'l' in VICTORIA is a numeral '1' (obv.)	1	1	30	90	200	
VY6D-055	1843		1	1	8	24	80	110
VY6D-060	1844		1	1	7	18	60	80
VY6D-065	1844	large 44 in date	1	1	8	22	75	95
VY6D-070	1845		1	1	8	24	80	110
VY6D-075	1846		1	1	7	18	60	80
VY6D-080	1848		1	1	40	120	400	650
VY6D-085	1848	8 over 6	1	1	40	120	400	650
VY6D-090	1848	8 over 7	1	1	40	120	400	650
VY6D-095	1850		1	1	8	22	80	100
VY6D-100	1851		1	1	8	22	80	100
VY6D-105	1852		1	1	8	22	80	100
VY6D-110	1853		1	1	7	18	60	80
VY6D-115	1853	PROOF [1]	1	1				350
VY6D-120	1854		1	1	75	300	900	1400
VY6D-125	1855		1	1	7	18	60	80
VY6D-130	1855	PROOF	1	1				500
VY6D-135	1856	[3]	1	1	8	20	75	95
VY6D-140	1857	[3]	1	1	8	20	80	100
VY6D-145	1858		1	1	8	22	90	120
VY6D-150	1858	PROOF	1	1				600
VY6D-155	1859	[4]	1	1	7	17	55	75
VY6D-160	1859	9 over 8 [4]	1	1	8	24	95	130
VY6D-165	1860		1	1	9	18	60	80
VY6D-170	1860	6 over indeterminate figure	1	1	8	20	70	95
VY6D-175	1862		1	1	30	110	400	600
VY6D-180	1863		1	1	20	80	250	400
VY6D-185	1864	die number above date	1	1	8	18	65	85
VY6D-190	1865	die number above date	1	1	9	20	75	100
VY6D-195	1866	die number above date	1	1	8	18	65	85
VY6D-200	1866		1	1	40	150	700	
VY6D-205	1867	die number above date	2	1	10	25	90	120

No.	Date	Features	Obv.	Rev.	F	VF	EF	UNC
VY6D-210	1867	die number above date PROOF	2	1				600
VY6D-215	1868	die number above date	2	1	10	28	100	150
VY6D-220	1869	die number above date	2	1	10	30	110	170
VY6D-225	1869	die number above date PROOF	2	1				700
VY6D-230	1870	die number above date	2	1	10	32	115	180
VY6D-235	1870	die number above date PROOF; edge plain	2	1				900
VY6D-240	1871	die number above date	2	1	8	22	75	110
VY6D-245	1871		2	1	0	30	100	140
VY6D-250	1871	die number above date PROOF; rev. ↑	2	1				900
VY6D-255	1871	die number above date PROOF; edge plain	2	1				700
VY6D-260	1871	PROOF	2	1				500
VY6D-265	1872	die number above date	2	1	9	22	65	95
VY6D-270	1873	die number above date	2	1	8	20	60	85
VY6D-275	1874	die number above date [5]	2	1	8	20	60	85
VY6D-280	1875	die number above date	2	1	8	20	60	85
VY6D-285	1876	die number above date	2	1	10	26	80	120
VY6D-290	1877	die number above date	2	1	9	22	65	95
VY6D-295	1877		2	1	10	26	80	120
VY6D-300	1878	die number above date	2	1	8	20	60	85
VY6D-305	1878	die number above date PROOF	2	1				600
VY6D-310	1878	8 over 7 die number above date	2	1	16	45	130	180
VY6D-315	1878	DRITANNIAR instead of BRITANNIAR (obv.) die number 6 above date [6]	2	1	50	90	350	600
VY6D-320	1879	die number above date	2	1	9	24	70	100
VY6D-325	1879		2	1	9	24	70	100
VY6D-330	1879	PROOF	2	1				500
VY6D-335	1879	PROOF; edge plain; rev. ↑ [7]	2	1				600
VY6D-340	1879	larger border beads [8]	2	1	10	26	75	110
VY6D-345	1880	larger border beads [8]	2	1	10	26	75	110
VY6D-350	1880		3	1	8	20	55	75
VY6D-355	1880	PROOF	3	1				300
VY6D-360	1881	[9]	3	1	8	20	55	75
VY6D-365	1881	PROOF	3	1				250
VY6D-370	1881	PROOF; edge plain	3	1				350
VY6D-375	1882		3	1	10	26	75	110
VY6D-380	1883		3	1	8	20	55	75
VY6D-385	1884		3	2	8	20	55	75
VY6D-390	1885		3	2	8	20	55	75
VY6D-395	1885	PROOF	3	2				300
VY6D-400	1886		3	2	7	18	45	65
VY6D-405	1886	PROOF	3	2				300
VY6D-410	1887		3	2	7	16	40	55
VY6D-415	1887	PROOF	3	2				200
VJ6D-420	1887		4	3	25	45	75	110
VJ6D-425	1887	[10]	5	3	4	7	11	15
VJ6D-430	1887	PROOF [1]	5	3				60
VJ6D-435	1887		5	4	4	8	12	16
VJ6D-440	1887	PROOF	5	4				150
VJ6D-445	1888		5	4	5	9	18	24
VJ6D-450	1888	PROOF	5	4				300
VJ6D-455	1889		5	4	5	10	20	26
VJ6D-460	1890		5	4	6	11	22	28
VJ6D-465	1890	PROOF	5	4				250

No.	Date	Features	Obv.	Rev.	F	VF	EF	UNC
VJ6D-470	1891		5	4	6	11	22	28
VJ6D-475	1892		5	4	6	11	22	28
VJ6D-480	1893		5	4	140	500	1500	
VO6D-485	1893		6	4	5	8	17	22
VO6D-490	1893	PROOF [1]	6	4				70
VO6D-495	1894		6	4	6	10	25	40
VO6D-500	1895		6	4	6	10	22	32
VO6D-505	1896		6	4	6	10	22	32
VO6D-510	1897		6	4	5	9	20	28
VO6D-515	1898		6	4	6	10	22	32
VO6D-520	1899		6	4	6	10	22	32
VO6D-525	1900		6	4	5	9	20	28
VO6D-530	1901		6	4	5	8	18	24

1. Issued in cased proof sets.
2. An unexplained piece obviously struck at a much later date (cf. 1879 proofs).
3. Variety has longer line below PENCE.
4. A clear overdate is visible at the top of the digit; plain 9 coin resembles 9 over 8.
5. 4 in date varies.
6. Always die number 6.
7. Some may have obverse 1 (sic).
8. 118 beads.
9. Date size may vary.
10. R in VICTORIA may show traces of other letter (obv.).

Edward VII 1902–1910

The sixpence series of Edward VII is a one-type issue struck for each year of the reign. The obverse depicts the portrait of the king by George William de Saulles (1862-1903) which was engraved using a mechanical reducing machine. Unlike the half-crown, florin and shilling, the reverse of the sixpence was not by de Saulles but continued the value in wreath design of the late Victorian pieces. This was itself a re-engraved version of the Merlen design first used on William IV sixpences.

After the death of de Saulles early in the reign, W.H.J. Blakemore became responsible for hand-finishing and re-engraving dies produced by the mechanical reducer.

Collecting Hints

This series should be collected in extremely fine or better condition. It must be remembered that the 1905 sixpence is not as rare as its larger companion coins.

Denomination	Metal	Weight (grams)	Diameter (mm)	Rev. alignment
Sixpence	Silver	3.0	19	↑

Obverse 1 Head 1, right; EDWARDVS VII DEI GRA BRITT OMN REX

Reverse 1 SIX PENCE within wreath, crown above, date below

Edge milled

Obv. 1

Rev. 1

No.	Date	Features	Obv.	Rev.	F	VF	EF	UNC
E76D-005	1902		1	1	4	8	20	28
E76D-010	1902	matt PROOF [1]	1	1				28
E76D-015	1903		1	1	5	10	26	36
E76D-020	1904		1	1	6	12	35	55
E76D-025	1905		1	1	5	11	30	45
E76D-030	1906		1	1	5	10	26	36
E76D-035	1907		1	1	5	10	26	36
E76D-040	1908		1	1	6	12	35	55
E76D-045	1909		1	1	5	10	26	36
E76D-050	1910		1	1	4	9	22	30

1. Issued in cased proof sets.

George V 1910–1936

The obverse of the George V sixpence used the portrait of George V by Sir Bertram MacKennal (1863-1931) engraved using the mechanical reduction machine to the appropriate size. The reverse finally discarded the Merlen reverse first used in 1831. Ironically, however, the lion on crown design which replaced it was last used on sixpences in 1829! This modified version was almost identical to that designed by de Saulles for the Edward VII shilling, and carried forward to the George V shilling.

In line with the other silver denominations, the silver content of the metal was reduced to 50% in 1920, and further modified in 1922 after it was found that streaking occurred. Another modification to the metal content was made in 1927 when the new acorn reverse was introduced. This design, depicting six acorns (presumably indicating six pence) amongst oak leaves, was one of a number of new designs for coinage by George Kruger Gray (1880-1943) and was sometimes referred to somewhat unkindly as 'the garden of weeds'. The new designs were introduced to the public in 1927 by way of a proof set of six silver coins, and were all abandoned in 1937 on the advent of the George VI coinage.

Collecting Hints

This series should be collected in extremely fine to mint state, although some of the dates are quite difficult to obtain in this condition. The acorn reverse type sixpence of 1928-36 often turns up cleaned or polished, sometimes to such an extent that it appears lacquered. Care should be taken in grading this coin, with special attention being paid to the detail on the base of each of the six acorns.

Denomination	Metal	Weight (grams)	Diameter (mm)	Rev. alignment
Sixpence 1911-20	0.925 Silver	3.0	19	↑
Sixpence 1920-22	Silver 50%; Copper 40%; Nickel 10%	3.0	19	↑
Sixpence 1922-27	Silver 50%; Copper 50%	3.0	19	↑
Sixpence 1927-36	Silver 50%; Copper 40%; Nickel 5%; Zinc 5%	3.0	19	↑

Obverse 1 Head 1, left, B.M. on truncation; GEORGIVS V DEI GRA BRITT OMN REX

Obverse 2 Head 2, so-called 'modified effigy', left; BM (no stops) further to right; beading recut; GEORGIVS V D G BRITT OMN F D IND IMP

Reverse 1 Lion on crown with separated date, all within inner circle; FID DEF IND IMP SIXPENCE

Reverse 2 Oak sprigs with six acorns; SIXPENCE A (date) D

Edge milled (finer milling 1931-36 than for previous years)

Obv. 1   Obv. 2   Rev. 1   Rev. 2

No.	Date	Features	Obv.	Rev.	VF	EF	UNC
G56D-005	1911		1	1	4	12	18
G56D-010	1911	PROOF [1]	1	1			45
G56D-015	1912		1	1	5	18	28
G56D-020	1913		1	1	7	22	35
G56D-025	1914		1	1	4	12	18
G56D-030	1915		1	1	4	12	18
G56D-035	1916		1	1	4	12	18
G56D-040	1917		1	1	5	16	28
G56D-045	1918		1	1	4	12	18
G56D-050	1919		1	1	4	14	20
G56D-055	1920	silver content 0.925	1	1	4	14	24
G56D-060	1920	silver content 0.5	1	1	4	12	20
G56D-065	1921		1	1	4	12	20
G56D-070	1922	[2]	1	1	4	14	24
G56D-075	1923		1	1	5	18	30
G56D-080	1924		1	1	5	16	27
G56D-085	1925	[3]	1	1	5	16	27
G56D-090	1926	[4]	1	1	5	16	27
G56D-095	1926		2	1	4	12	20
G56D-100	1927		2	1	4	14	24
G56D-105	1927	struck in nickel [5]	2	1			500
G56D-110	1927	PROOF [1]	2	2			28
G56D-115	1927	PROOF from sandblasted dies [6]	2	2			200
G56D-120	1928		2	2	3	8	12
G56D-125	1928	PROOF	2	2			300
G56D-130	1929		2	2	3	8	12
G56D-135	1929	PROOF	2	2			300
G56D-140	1930		2	2	3	8	12
G56D-145	1930	PROOF	2	2			400
G56D-150	1931		2	2	3	10	14
G56D-155	1931	PROOF	2	2			300
G56D-160	1932		2	2	4	14	20
G56D-165	1932	PROOF	2	2			400
G56D-170	1933		2	2	3	8	12
G56D-175	1933	PROOF	2	2			300
G56D-180	1934		2	2	3	8	12
G56D-185	1934	PROOF	2	2			400
G56D-190	1935		2	2	3	8	12
G56D-195	1935	PROOF	2	2			250
G56D-200	1936		2	2	3	7	10
G56D-205	1936	PROOF	2	2			200

1. Issued in cased proof sets.
2. Alloy occurs with and without nickel content; see table above.
3. Some have redesigned beads/rim on obverse.
4. Obverse beads/rim redesigned from 1924 issue.
5. Weight 2.9 grams; nickel is slightly magnetic.
6. Struck to facilitate photography of coin.

Edward VIII 1936

The Edward VIII sixpence is strictly speaking a pattern, as probable Royal approval was about to be granted at the time of the abdication. However, because its official status rests only on this technicality, and to provide continuity, it is included in this catalogue.

The portrait of Edward VIII is by Thomas Humphrey Paget, and faces left at the insistence of the king, who considered this placement more flattering and wished to discontinue the tradition of opposite facings for successive monarchs. The reverse is by George Kruger Gray (1880-1943)

Denomination	Metal	Weight (grams)	Diameter (mm)	Rev. alignment
Sixpence	Silver	2.8	19	↑

Obverse 1 Head 1, left; EDWARDVS VIII D G BR OMN REX

Reverse 1 Six interlinked rings of St Edmund; FID DEF IND IMP 1937 SIXPENCE

Edge milled

Obv. 1

Rev. 1

No.	Date	Obv.	Rev.	UNC
E86D-005	1937	1	1	12000

George VI 1937–1952

The obverse of the sixpence depicts the portrait of George VI designed by Thomas Humphrey Paget (1893-1974). The first reverse, by George Kruger Gray, depicts the crowned interlinked initials GRI (Georgius Rex Imperator = King George, Emperor). This was redesigned in 1949 to read GVIR (Georgius (6) Rex) after the title Emperor of India had been relinquished.

In 1947, the metal of the sixpence and other coins previously struck in silver was changed to cupronickel. At this time, Britain had to repay silver borrowed from the United States for the war effort.

Collecting Hints

This series should be collected in mint state or near. The 1950 and 1951 proofs must be examined for green edge corrosion and ribbon staining. The 1950 proof sixpence appears especially to be the coin most prone to edge corrosion in the proof set. This is because it was placed at the corner of a poorly insulated cardboard case and suffered attack from the elements.

Denomination	Metal	Weight (grams)	Diameter (mm)	Rev. alignment
Sixpence 1937-46	0.500 Silver	3.0	19	↑
Sixpence 1947-52	Copper 75%; Nickel 25%	3.0	19	↑

Obverse 1 Head 1, left; GEORGIVS VI D G BR OMN REX

Reverse 1 Crowned 'GRI' with divided date; FID DEF IND IMP SIXPENCE

Reverse 2 Crowned 'GVIR' with divided date; FID DEF SIXPENCE

Edge milled

Obv. 1

Rev. 1

Rev. 2

No.	Date	Features	Obv.	Rev.	EF	UNC
G66D-005	1937		1	1	3	6
G66D-010	1937	PROOF [1]	1	1		10
G66D-015	1937	PROOF from sandblasted dies [2]	1	1		150
G66D-020	1938		1	1	4	8
G66D-025	1938	PROOF	1	1		150
G66D-030	1939		1	1	4	8
G66D-035	1939	PROOF	1	1		150
G66D-040	1940		1	1	3	7
G66D-045	1940	PROOF	1	1		200
G66D-050	1941		1	1	3	7
G66D-055	1941	PROOF	1	1		200
G66D-060	1942		1	1	3	6
G66D-065	1943		1	1	3	6

No.	Date	Features	Obv.	Rev.	EF	UNC
G66D-070	1943	PROOF	1	1		200
G66D-075	1944		1	1	3	6
G66D-080	1944	PROOF	1	1		200
G66D-085	1945		1	1	3	6
G66D-090	1945	PROOF	1	1		200
G66D-095	1946		1	1	3	6
G66D-100	1946	PROOF	1	1		200
G66D-105	1946	PROOF in cupronickel	1	1		500
G66D-110	1947		1	1	2	6
G66D-115	1947	PROOF	1	1		220
G66D-120	1948		1	1	2	6
G66D-125	1948	PROOF	1	1		220
G66D-130	1949		1	2	2	6
G66D-135	1949	PROOF	1	2		220
G66D-140	1950		1	2	2	6
G66D-145	1950	PROOF [1]	1	2		8
G66D-150	1950	PROOF from sandblasted dies [2]	1	2		150
G66D-155	1951		1	2	2	6
G66D-160	1951	PROOF [1]	1	2		9
G66D-165	1951	PROOF from sandblasted dies [2]	1	2		150
G66D-170	1952		1	2	15	60
G66D-175	1952	PROOF [3]	1	2		1000

1. Issued in cased proof sets.
2. Struck to facilitate photography of coin.
3. Struck from polished dies.

Elizabeth II 1952 —

The original design by Mary Gillick for the queen's portrait resulted in a weak striking lacking in detail, and the dies were soon recut to provide a sharper image. The first year (1953) is the only coin bearing the obverse 'BRITT OMN' (trans.: of all the British possessions).

Collecting Hints

Collect in mint state. Acquiring examples of the unofficially struck proofs is an interesting challenge.

Denomination	Metal	Weight (grams)	Diameter (mm)	Rev. alignment
Sixpence 1953-70	Cupronickel	3.0	19	↑

Obverse 1 Head 1, right; ELIZABETH II DEI GRATIA BRITT OMN REGINA

Obverse 2 Head 1 (recut), right; ELIZABETH II DEI GRATIA REGINA

Obverse M Head as designed by Cecil Thomas for Mauritius quarter rupee 1960-1978

Reverse 1 Garland of rose, thistle, shamrock, leek; FID DEF SIX PENCE (date)

Edge milled

Obv. 1

Obv. 2

Rev. 1

No.	Date	Features	Obv.	Rev.	UNC
EL26D-005	1953	[1]	1	1	2
EL26D-010	1953	PROOF [2]	1	1	7
EL26D-015	1953	PROOF from sandblasted dies [3]	1	1	150
EL26D-020	1954		2	1	9
EL26D-025	1954	PROOF	2	1	150

No.	Date	Features	Obv.	Rev.	UNC
EL26D-030	1955		2	1	3
EL26D-035	1955	PROOF	2	1	150
EL26D-040	1956		2	1	3
EL26D-045	1956	PROOF	2	1	150
EL26D-050	1957		2	1	2
EL26D-055	1957	PROOF	2	1	150
EL26D-060	1958		2	1	9
EL26D-065	1958	PROOF	2	1	150
EL26D-070	1959		2	1	2
EL26D-075	1959	PROOF	2	1	150
EL26D-080	1960		2	1	9
EL26D-085	1960	PROOF	2	1	150
EL26D-090	1961		2	1	5
EL26D-095	1961	PROOF	2	1	150
EL26D-100	1962		2	1	2
EL26D-105	1962	PROOF	2	1	150
EL26D-110	1963		2	1	2
EL26D-115	1963	PROOF	2	1	150
EL26D-120	1964		2	1	2
EL26D-125	1964	PROOF	2	1	150
EL26D-130	1965		2	1	2
EL26D-135	1965	PROOF	2	1	150
EL26D-140	1966	[4]	2	1	2
EL26D-145	1966	struck in bronze [5]	2	1	180
EL26D-150	1966	PROOF	2	1	150
EL26D-155	1966	Error obverse	M	1	300
EL26D-160	1967	[6]	2	1	2
EL26D-165	1967	PROOF [7]	2	1	150
EL26D-170	1970	PROOF [8]	2	1	3

1. At least 2 minor varieties.
2. Issued in cased proof sets.
3. Struck to facilitate photography of coin.
4. Border teeth now become finer than on previous years.
5. Weight 3.1 grams.
6. Issued for some years.
7. At least one issued sealed in error in 1970 proof set.
8. Issued in sealed cased proof sets; no ordinary issue coins of this date.

Maundy Fourpence

Charles II 1660–1685

The early silver fourpences were used exclusively as currency, even though they are now commonly referred to as Maundy coins. The first machine struck small silver coins are often termed the 'undated Maundy' despite the fact that for well over a century only the silver pennies (and occasionally the silver twopence) were distributed as Maundy Money. The dies for this undated coinage were probably prepared by Thomas Simon (c.1623-1665) in 1664 or 1665. This was almost the only work he did following the appointment of John Roettier.

The first dated fourpence was struck in 1670, this first year of issue being shared with the threepence and the silver penny. The twopence had first been issued in 1668. The motif of interlinked 'C's (the king's initial) as used on the larger silver was here employed to represent the denomination, a cross formed from four 'C's representing four pence. This new dated small coinage was designed by John Roettier.

There are a relatively large number of overdates in this series, and on some dates an overdate is the more usually encountered variety. The date most usually seen is 1679.

Denomination	Metal	Weight (grams)	Diameter (mm)	Rev. alignment
Fourpence undated	Silver	2.0	19	varies
Fourpence 1670-1684	Silver	2.0	19	↓

Obverse 1 Head 1, left; IIII behind head; CAROLVS II D G M B F & H REX

Obverse 2 Head 2, right; CAROLVS II DEI GRATIA

Reverse 1 Shield enclosing Arms of England, Scotland, Ireland, coinjoined England/France; CHRISTO AVSPICE REGNO

Reverse 2 Four crowned interlinked 'C's with rose, thistle, fleur-de-lis, harp; MAG BR FRA ET HIB REX (date)

Edge plain

Obv. 1	Obv. 2	Rev. 1	Rev. 2

No.	Date	Features	Obv.	Rev.	F	VF	EF
C24MM-005	none	[1]	1	1	18	35	70
C24MM-010	1670		2	2	22	40	85
C24MM-015	1671		2	2	16	28	60
C24MM-020	1672	2 over 1	2	2	16	28	60
C24MM-025	1673		2	2	16	28	60
C24MM-030	1674		2	2	16	28	60
C24MM-035	1674	7 over 6	2	2	18	35	70
C24MM-040	1674	4 over horizontal 4	2	2	30	70	120
C24MM-045	1675		2	2	16	28	60
C24MM-050	1675	5 over 4	2	2	30	70	120
C24MM-055	1676		2	2	18	35	70
C24MM-060	1676	7 over 6	2	2	18	35	70
C24MM-065	1676	latter 6 over 5	2	2	18	35	70
C24MM-070	1677	[2]	2	2	16	28	60
C24MM-075	1678		2	2	16	28	60
C24MM-080	1678	8 over 6	2	2	16	28	60
C24MM-085	1678	8 over 7	2	2	16	28	60
C24MM-090	1679	[3]	2	2	14	24	50
C24MM-095	1680		2	2	15	25	55
C24MM-100	1681		2	2	15	25	55
C24MM-105	1681	B of HIB over R (rev.)	2	2	20	35	80
C24MM-110	1681	1 over 0	2	2	16	28	60
C24MM-115	1682		2	2	16	28	60
C24MM-120	1682	2 over 1	2	2	16	28	60

No.	Date	Features	Obv.	Rev.	F	VF	EF
C24MM-125	1683		2	2	16	28	60
C24MM-130	1684		2	2	18	35	70
C24MM-135	1684	4 over 3	2	2	16	28	60

1. Minor varieties exist.
2. Variety reads CAROLVS I.I.
3. Lettering and punctuation vary.

James II 1685–1688

John Roettier redesigned the silver fourpence on the accession of James II. The obverse depicts the monarch with shorter hair than on the larger silver pieces, while on the reverse the denomination appears as IIII. What is often not realised is that this representation not only denotes '4' as a Roman numeral but also continues the tradition of signifying the fourfold initials of the monarch (IACOBVS).

Denomination	Metal	Weight (grams)	Diameter (mm)	Rev. alignment
Fourpence	Silver	2.0	19	↓

Obverse 1 Head 1, left; IACOBVS II DEI GRATIA

Reverse 1 Large IIII, crowned; MAG BR FRA ET HIB REX (date)

Edge plain

Obv. 1	Rev. 1

No.	Date	Features	Obv.	Rev.	F	VF	EF
J24M-005	1686		1	1	16	28	60
J24M-010	1686	date nearer top of crown	1	1	16	28	60
J24M-015	1687	7 over 6	1	1	16	28	60
J24M-020	1687	7 over 6; 8 over 7	1	1	16	28	60
J24M-025	1688	[1]	1	1	16	28	60
J24M-030	1688	1 over 8	1	1	25	50	120
J24M-035	1688	latter 8 over 7	1	1	16	28	60

1. A slightly different obverse lettering alignment introduced for this year.

William and Mary 1688–1694

There is uncertainty about the identity of the designer of the small silver coins of William and Mary. The portraits of the king and queen are certainly very different from those on the larger coinage, and in some ways resemble caricatures. Although the designer has never been positively identified, if the medals of George Bower are studied, one often comes across very similar caricatured portraits. Bower was an engraver at the Royal Mint, a post he still held at his death on 1 March 1689 (old style calendar). He must remain a strong candidate for the designer of the early small silver. The striking of the obverse is usually sharp and in high relief, while the reverse is flatter. Whoever he was, this craftsman gave to the coinage a basic reverse design of a crowned '4' which lasted for over three hundred years.

The William and Mary obverse is unusual in that there are two distinct types, with and without a tie to the wreath on the portrait. In addition, there are a number of lettering and numeral varieties.

Small silver of William and Mary is fairly rare in extremely fine or better condition.

Denomination	Metal	Weight (grams)	Diameter (mm)	Rev. alignment
Fourpence	Silver	2.0	19	↓

Obverse 1 Heads 1, right; no tie at back of king's head; GVLIELMVS ET MARIA D G

Obverse 2 Heads 2, with tie, right; same legend

Reverse 1 Crowned '4'; MAG BR FR ET HIB REX ET REGINA

Edge plain

Obv. 1   Obv. 2   Rev. 1

No.	Date	Features	Obv.	Rev.	F	VF	EF
WM4M-005	1689	[1]	1	1	16	28	60
WM4M-010	1690	[2]	1	1	18	32	70
WM4M-015	1690	6 over 5	1	1	18	32	70
WM4M-020	1691	[3]	1	1	20	35	75
WM4M-025	1691	1 over 0	1	1	20	35	75
WM4M-030	1692	[4]	2	1	18	35	75
WM4M-035	1692	2 over 1	2	1	18	40	85
WM4M-040	1693		2	1	24	45	95
WM4M-045	1693	3 over 2	2	1	22	40	85
WM4M-050	1694	[4]	1	1	22	40	85
WM4M-055	1694		2	1	22	45	95

1. Many minor lettering, stop and head varieties exist.
2. Punctuation varieties exist.
3. Minor stop varieties exist.
4. Lettering size variations exist.

William III 1695–1701

After the death of Mary from smallpox in 1694, the obverse of the new fourpence was designed by Johann Crocker, aka John Croker (1670–1741). The reverse may have been the work of Croker or an assistant. The style of earlier reigns is continued and, being struck relatively late in the reign, none was struck at the provincial mints.

The 1702 coin is an oddity. William III died on 8th March 1701, and no coins of William III should thus bear the date 1702, even though under the old calendar 1702 began on 25th March. The fourpence is the only known William III coin to bear this date.

Denomination	Metal	Weight (grams)	Diameter (mm)	Rev. alignment
Fourpence	Silver	2.0	19	↓

Obverse 1 Head 1, right; GVLIELMVS III DEI GRA

Reverse 1 Crowned '4'; MAG BR FRA ET HIB REX (date)

Edge plain

Obv. 1   Rev. 1

No.	Date	Features	Obv.	Rev.	F	VF	EF
W34M-005	1697	[1]	1	1			
W34M-010	1698		1	1	20	35	75
W34M-015	1699		1	1	20	35	75
W34M-020	1700	[2]	1	1	20	35	75
W34M-025	1701		1	1	20	50	100
W34M-030	1702	[3]	1	1	15	25	60

1. Only one known; see BNJ 1948, p.352 re exhibition by Albert Baldwin at BNJ.
2. Punctuation varies.
3. Dated posthumously.

Anne 1702–1714

The Anne fourpence was probably the work of John Croker and/or his assistant Samuel Bull, although some doubt attaches to the identity of the engravers of the reverse. The coin appears at first glance to be of one type, but there are some major differences to the lettering and some minor varieties of the portrait and crown.

Denomination	Metal	Weight (grams)	Diameter (mm)	Rev. alignment
Fourpence	Silver	2.0	19	↓

Obverse 1 Head 1, left; ANNA DEI GRATIA

Obverse 2 Head 2, slightly different, left; same legend

Reverse 1 Crowned '4'; MAG BR FR ET HIB REG (date)

Reverse 2 Similar but MAG BR FRA ET HIB REG

Reverse 3 Similar but MAG BRI FR ET HIB REG

Reverse 4 As reverse 3 but crown is larger; serifs on '4' are larger

Edge plain

Obv. 1   Obv. 2   Rev. 1   Rev. 4

No.	Date	Features	Obv.	Rev.	F	VF	EF
A4M-005	1703		1	1	20	45	90
A4M-010	1704		1	1	15	30	60
A4M-015	1705		2	1	20	45	90
A4M-020	1706		2	2	15	30	60
A4M-025	1708		2	3	15	30	60
A4M-030	1709		2	3	15	30	60
A4M-035	1710		2	4	10	20	45
A4M-040	1713	[1]	2	4	15	30	60

1. Hair varies (obv.); variety exists with very close date.

George I 1714–1727

John Croker continued, with some assistance from Samuel Bull, to engrave the small silver coinage. The reverses may have been the work of Johann Rudolph Ochs, senior. Unlike the silver series from crown to sixpence, the small silver omitted the Hanoverian titles of the king. It was probably thought that the lengthy abbreviated titles would be too difficult to read on such a small scale. The series continues with the general overall design of earlier reigns.

Denomination	Metal	Weight (grams)	Diameter (mm)	Rev. alignment
Fourpence	Silver	2.0	19	↓

Obverse 1 Head 1, right; GEORGIVS DEI GRA

Reverse 1 Crowned '4'; MAG BRI FR ET HIB REX (date)

Edge plain

Obv. 1   Rev. 1

No.	Date	Obv.	Rev.	F	VF	EF
G14M-005	1717	1	1	20	35	75
G14M-010	1721	1	1	20	35	75
G14M-015	1723	1	1	25	45	90
G14M-020	1727	1	1	30	50	100

George II 1727–1760

The elderly John Croker engraved the obverse dies for the silver fourpence. However, unlike on the larger silver coinage, there was no transition in 1743 to the older portrait by Tanner. The isolated issue of the coin in 1760, the year of the king's death, meant that the Croker young head design was still being issued two years after the last old head Tanner design was seen on the shilling and sixpence.

Denomination	Metal	Weight (grams)	Diameter (mm)	Rev. alignment
Fourpence	Silver	2.0	19	↓

Obverse 1 Head 1, left; GEORGIVS II DEI GRATIA

Obverse 2 Similar but a threepence obverse die (used in error)

Reverse 1 Crowned '4'; MAG BRI FR ET HIB REX (date)

Reverse 2 Similar but crown slightly different; '4' is larger; same legend

Edge plain

Obv. 1

Rev. 1

Rev. 2

No.	Date	Features	Obv.	Rev.	F	VF	EF
G24M-005	1729		1	1	15	25	45
G24M-010	1731		1	1	15	25	45
G24M-015	1732		1	2	15	25	45
G24M-020	1735		1	2	15	25	45
G24M-025	1737		1	2	18	30	50
G24M-030	1739		1	2	15	25	45
G24M-035	1740		2	2	15	25	45
G24M-040	1743		1	2	20	35	60
G24M-045	1743	3 over 0	1	2	30	60	120
G24M-050	1746		1	2	15	25	45
G24M-055	1760		1	2	18	30	50

George III 1760–1820

The reign of George III probably saw the last of the 'crowned 4' silver fourpences struck for circulation. Late George III issues and those of subsequent reigns are usually encountered in higher grades, indicating that their source was probably a set of Maundy money.

The first fourpences bear a portrait very similar to that on the Northumberland shilling and the early guineas. Although uncertain, this possibly means that Richard Yeo was the designer. An intermediate type (1792-1800) depicts a very different head, the 1792 coin also incorporating a stylised reverse numeral which has caused this date of small coinage to become known as 'Wire Money'. The George III fourpences produced after the Great Recoinage incorporate the Benedetto Pistrucci head of the king. These are the only fourpences with the date on the obverse.

In 1784 the silver fourpence was redesigned with a much flatter '4' on the reverse; other minor changes were also made. The next issue, in 1786, also featured this new design, the silver penny having been similarly redesigned in lower relief in 1781. However, the twopence and threepence retained the high relief reverse. The 1784 and 1786 small silver coinage was the last struck before an even more radical redesign in 1792.

Fourpences apparently dated 1775 are dated 1776 with a broken '6'.

Denomination	Metal	Weight (grams)	Diameter (mm)	Rev. alignment
Fourpence 1762-1786	Silver	2.0	19	↓
Fourpence 1792-1800	Silver	2.0	19	↑
Fourpence 1817-1820	Silver	1.9	18	↑

Obverse 1 Head 1, right; GEORGIVS III DEI GRATIA

Obverse 2 Head 2, right; same legend

Obverse 3 Head 3, laureate, right; GEORGIUS III DEI GRATIA (date)

Reverse 1 Crowned '4' in high relief; MAG BRI FR ET HIB REX (date, across crown)

Reverse 2 Similar but in lower relief; the '4' is much flatter

Reverse 3 Completely redesigned; stylised '4' under small crown; date below '4'; same legend

Reverse 4 Redesigned; more similar to Reverse 2 but crown very different; same legend; date is below '4'

Reverse 5 Crowned '4'; BRITANNIARUM REX FID DEF (no date)

Edge plain

Obv. 1   Obv. 2   Obv. 3

Rev. 1   Rev. 3

Rev. 4   Rev. 5

No.	Date	Features	Obv.	Rev.	F	VF	EF
G34M-005	1763		1	1	5	10	25
G34M-010	1763	PROOF; rev. ↑	1	1			1200
G34M-015	1765		1	1	200	400	900
G34M-020	1765	E in GEORGIVS over R (obv.)	1	1	250	500	1000
G34M-025	1766		1	1	14	24	50
G34M-030	1770		1	1	14	24	50
G34M-035	1772		1	1	14	24	50
G34M-040	1772	2 over 0	1	1	14	24	50
G34M-045	1776	[1]	1	1	14	24	50
G34M-050	1780		1	1	14	24	50
G34M-055	1784		1	2	15	30	70
G34M-060	1786	[2]	1	2	15	26	50
G34M-065	1792	[3]	2	3	20	32	70
G34M-070	1795		2	4	14	24	50
G34M-075	1800		2	4	10	18	30
G34M-080	1817		3	5	12	16	30
G34M-085	1818		3	5	12	16	30
G34M-090	1820		3	5	12	16	30

1. Occurs with broken 6 in date resembling 5.
2. Larger lettering on obverse than previous dates.
3. 'Wire Money' issue.

George IV 1820–1830

By the reign of George IV, the small silver coins bearing a crowned numeral reverse may be considered almost exclusively as Maundy coinage. From 1822 this coinage has been minted with a similar design in each of the four denominations (1, 2, 3, 4 pence) for every year up to the present. Because of this, and the fact that few design varieties occur from now on, the individual pieces from 1822 will be tabulated in abbreviated form. Major varieties such as proofs will be noted. Few people collect, say, Maundy fourpences only, and so the expanded and detailed tables showing each year separately will appear under the heading of Maundy sets. Under this heading will also appear again full details of varieties of any individual pieces.

Denomination	Metal	Weight (grams)	Diameter (mm)	Rev. alignment
Maundy Fourpence	Silver	1.9	18	↓

Obverse 1 Head 1, left; GEORGIUS IIII D G BRITANNIAR REX F D

Reverse 1 Crowned '4' and divided date, all within wreath

Edge plain

No.	Date	Features	Obv.	Rev.	VF	EF	FDC
G44M-005	1822-1830 [1]		1	1	12	20	30

1. Proofs were struck in 1822, 1828.

William IV 1830–1837

Denomination	Metal	Weight (grams)	Diameter (mm)	Rev. alignment
Maundy Fourpence	Silver	1.9	18	↓

Obverse 1 Head 1, right; GULIELMUS IIII D G BRITANNIAR REX F D

Reverse 1 Crowned '4' and divided date, all within wreath

Edge plain

No.	Date	Features	Obv.	Rev.	VF	EF	FDC
W44M-005	1831-1837 [1]		1	1	15	25	35

1. Proofs in gold and silver were struck in 1831; proofs may exist for 1834.

Victoria 1837–1901

Denomination	Metal	Weight (grams)	Diameter (mm)	Rev. alignment
Maundy Fourpence 1838-1887	Silver	1.9	18	↓
Maundy Fourpence 1888-1901	Silver	1.9	18	↑

Obverse 1 Head 1, left; VICTORIA D G BRITANNIAR REGINA F D

Obverse 2 Head 2, left; same legend

Obverse 3 Head 3, left; VICTORIA DEI GRA BRITT REGINA FID DEF IND IMP

Reverse 1 Crowned '4' and divided date, all within wreath

Reverse 2 Similar but crown very different

Edge plain

No.	Date	Features	Obv.	Rev.	VF	EF	FDC
VY4M-005	1838-1887 [1]		1	1	10	14	18
VJ4M-010	1888-1892 [2]		2	2	12	15	18
VO4M-015	1893-1901		3	2	6	10	14

1. Proofs were struck in 1838 (silver and gold) 1839 1853 1867 1871 1878 1881 (silver).
2. Proofs were struck in 1888.

For details of proofs see Maundy listings.

Edward VII 1902–1910

Denomination	Metal	Weight (grams)	Diameter (mm)	Rev. alignment
Maundy Fourpence	Silver	1.9	18	↑

Obverse 1 Head 1, right; EDWARDVS VII D G BRITT OMN REX F D IND IMP

Reverse 1 Crowned '4' and divided date, all within wreath

Edge plain

No.	Date	Features	Obv.	Rev.	VF	EF	FDC
E74M-005	1902-1910 [1]		1	1	6	10	14

1. Matt proofs were struck in 1902.

George V 1910–1936

Denomination	Metal	Weight (grams)	Diameter (mm)	Rev. alignment
Maundy Fourpence 1911-1920	0.925 Silver	1.9	18	↑
Maundy Fourpence 1921-1936	0.5 Silver	1.9	18	↑

Obverse 1 Head 1, left; GEORGIVS V D G BRITT OMN REX F D IND IMP

Obverse 2 Head 2, so-called 'modified effigy', left; same legend

Obverse 3 Head 2, re-engraved, left; same legend

Reverse 1 Crowned '4' and divided date, all within wreath

Edge plain

No.	Date	Features	Obv.	Rev.	VF	EF	FDC
G54M-005	1911-1927 [1]		1	1	8	11	16
G54M-010	1928-1929		2	1	8	11	16
G54M-015	1930-1936		3	1	8	11	16

1. See note on 1911 issue under Maundy sets.

George VI 1937–1952

Denomination	Metal	Weight (grams)	Diameter (mm)	Rev. alignment
Maundy Fourpence 1937-1946	0.5 Silver	1.9	18	↑
Maundy Fourpence 1947-1952	0.925 Silver	1.9	18	↑

Obverse 1 Head 1, left; GEORGIVS VI D G BR OMN REX F D IND IMP

Obverse 2 Head 1, left; GEORGIVS VI D G BR OMN REX FIDEI DEF

Reverse 1 Crowned '4' and divided date, all within wreath

Edge plain

No.	Date	Features	Obv.	Rev.	VF	EF	FDC
G64M-005	1937-1948 [1]		1	1	8	10	14
G64M-010	1949-1952 [2]		2	1	8	11	15

1. See note on 1937 issue under Maundy sets.
2. 1952 sets struck in copper also exist.

Elizabeth II 1952 -

Denomination	Metal	Weight (grams)	Diameter (mm)	Rev. alignment
Maundy Fourpence	0.925 Silver	1.9	18	↑

Obverse 1 Head 1, right; ELIZABETH II DEI GRA BRITT OMN REGINA F D

Obverse 2 Head 2, recut; ELIZABETH II DEI GRATIA REGINA F D

Reverse 1 Crowned '4' and divided date, all within wreath

Edge plain

No.	Date	Features	Obv.	Rev.	VF	EF	FDC
EL24M-005	1953 [1]		1	1	55	65	70
EL24M-010	1954-1995		2	1	14	17	20

1. Varieties: see under Maundy sets.

Groat

William IV 1830–1837 & Victoria 1837–1901

The Britannia groat is characteristically so different from its Maundy counterpart that it is here treated in a separate section. The Maundy-type small silver coinage had generally ceased to be used in circulation at the time of the inception of the Britannia groat. The latter was, therefore, together with the silver three-pence, the only silver coinage denominated below the sixpence; some pieces, however, notably the silver one and a half-pence series and the 1838 twopence, circulated in the colonies.

Because the William IV groat was struck for only two years, and the transition to Victoria involved no change of reverse, the listing covers the entire series across the change of monarch.

The groat appears to have been coined following a recommendation of the philanthropist Joseph Hume, M.P. It was thus the original coin to bear the nickname 'silver Joey', a term later used for the threepence. It was initially popular for the payment of London hackney (taxi) fares, being the exact fare for half a mile, but the popularity did not extend to the hackney driver, as prior to its inception the client had often paid for his fare using a six-pence, without asking for change!

The Britannia groat was introduced simultaneously into the currency of British Guiana as the equivalent of a quarter guilder. When, however, in 1845 the silver threepence became legal tender in Britain, confusion arose. It is not generally realised that the Britannia groat is exactly the same size as the threepence (although it is thicker and heavier). Despite the fact that the edges are different, the two could not live happily together, and no currency groats were struck after 1855 apart from the 1888 issue struck for British Guiana. Apparently the groat was more popular in Scotland, and circulated there for many years after its demise in England and Wales.

The dies for the Britannia groat were designed by William Wyon, although the obverse of the isolated 1888 issue uses the Boehm jubilee portrait of Victoria.

Denomination	Metal	Weight (grams)	Diameter (mm)	Rev. alignment
Groat	Silver	1.9	16	↑

Obverse 1 Head 1 (William IV), right; GULIELMUS IIII D G BRITANNIAR REX F D

Obverse 2 Head 2 (Victoria), left; VICTORIA D G BRITANNIAR REGINA F D

Obverse 3 Head 3 (Victoria), left; same legend

Reverse 1 Britannia, seated, with shield; FOUR PENCE; date in exergue

Edge milled

Obv. 1   Obv. 2   Obv. 3   Rev. 1

William IV

No.	Date	Features	Obv.	Rev.	F	VF	EF	UNC
W44D-005	1836		1	1	6	9	20	30
W44D-010	1836	PROOF	1	1				250
W44D-015	1836	PROOF; edge plain	1	1				200
W44D-020	1836	PROOF in gold	1	1				4000
W44D-025	1836	PROOF on thin flan [1]	1	1				700
W44D-030	1837	[2]	1	1	7	10	22	35
W44D-035	1837	PROOF	1	1				500
W44D-040	1837	PROOF; edge plain	1	1				600

1. Weight 1.3 grams.
2. Minor differences occur to head (obv.).

Victoria

No.	Date	Features	Obv.	Rev.	F	VF	EF	UNC
VY4D-005	1837	PROOF or pattern; rev. ↓	2	1				1500
VY4D-010	1837	PROOF or pattern; edge plain [1]	2	1				1500
VY4D-015	1838		2	1	7	10	24	40
VY4D-020	1838	PROOF; edge plain	2	1				350
VY4D-025	1838	latter 8 over horizontal 8	2	1	15	22	50	100
VY4D-030	1839	[2]	2	1	7	11	26	42
VY4D-035	1839	PROOF; edge plain [3]	2	1				160
VY4D-040	1839	PROOF; edge plain; rev. ↓[3]	2	1				180
VY4D-045	1840	[4]	2	1	7	10	24	40
VY4D-050	1841	latter 1 over inverted 1	2	1	8	12	28	48
VY4D-055	1842		2	1	7	11	26	42
VY4D-060	1842	PROOF; edge plain	2	1				300
VY4D-065	1842	2 over 1	2	1	9	15	35	50
VY4D-070	1843		2	1	9	15	35	50
VY4D-075	1843	4 over 5	2	1	15	25	50	100
VY4D-080	1844		2	1	10	16	38	55
VY4D-085	1845		2	1	9	15	35	50
VY4D-090	1846		2	1	9	15	35	50
VY4D-095	1847	7 over 6	2	1	30	100	300	
VY4D-100	1848		2	1	10	16	38	50
VY4D-105	1848	latter 8 over 6	2	1	12	20	50	80
VY4D-110	1848	latter 8 over 7	2	1	15	25	60	100
VY4D-115	1849		2	1	10	16	38	50
VY4D-120	1849	9 over 8	2	1	12	20	50	70
VY4D-125	1851		2	1	25	90	300	
VY4D-130	1852	[5]	2	1	40	130	450	
VY4D-135	1853		2	1	50	160	500	
VY4D-140	1853	PROOF [6]	2	1				350
VY4D-145	1853	PROOF; edge plain	2	1				500
VY4D-150	1854		2	1	6	9	20	30
VY4D-155	1855		2	1	6	9	20	30
VY4D-160	1857	PROOF [7]	2	1				750
VY4D-165	1862	PROOF	2	1				700
VY4D-170	1862	PROOF; edge plain [7]	2	1				700

No.	Date	Features	Obv.	Rev.	F	VF	EF	UNC
VJ4D-175	1888	8	3	1	8	14	35	50
VJ4D-180	1888	PROOF	3	1				500

1. Obverse differs slightly (from a threepence die).
2. 9 of date varies in size; can be larger or smaller than 3.
3. Some or all issued in cased proof sets.
4. 0 in date varies.
5. 2 in date is unusually large.
6. Issued in cased proof sets; minor obverse differences exist.
7. Minor obverse differences exist (truncation).
8. Issued for Colonial use.

Silver Threepence

Charles II 1660–1685

Although the earlier threepence is often wrongly termed a Maundy coin, it is easier to appreciate it as a currency coin because it continued as such well into the 20th century. The so-called 'undated Maundy' coins were probably designed by Thomas Simon in 1664 or 1665, shortly before he died. The first dated issue, by John Roettier, appeared in 1670, together with most of the other small silver, although the twopence had first appeared in 1668. Like the other small silver, the dated threepence made use of a reverse motif of 'C's (the initial letter of Charles), the three 'C's indicating three pence. As with the fourpence and twopence, the date most usually encountered is 1679.

Denomination	Metal	Weight (grams)	Diameter (mm)	Rev. alignment
Threepence undated	Silver	1.5	17	varies
Threepence 1670–1684	Silver	1.5	17	↓

Obverse 1 Head 1, left; III behind head; CAROLVS II D G M B F & H REX

Obverse 2 Head 2, right; CAROLVS II DEI GRATIA

Reverse 1 Shield enclosing arms of England, Scotland, Ireland, France; CHRISTO AVSPICE REGNO

Reverse 2 Three crowned interlinked 'C's; MAG BR FRA ET HIB REX (date)

Edge plain

Obv. 1   Obv. 2   Rev. 1   Rev. 2

No.	Date	Features	Obv.	Rev.	F	VF	EF
C23MM-005	none		1	1	18	35	70
C23MM-010	1670		2	2	16	25	55
C23MM-015	1671		2	2	16	25	55
C23MM-020	1671	first A in GRATIA inverted	2	2	18	30	65
C23MM-025	1671	first A in GRATIA unbarred	2	2	18	30	65
C23MM-030	1672	2 over 1	2	2	16	25	55
C23MM-035	1673		2	2	16	25	55
C23MM-040	1674		2	2	18	30	65
C23MM-045	1675		2	2	18	30	65
C23MM-050	1676		2	2	16	25	55
C23MM-055	1676	latter 6 over 5	2	2	18	30	65
C23MM-060	1676	ERA instead of FRA (rev.)	2	2	18	30	65
C23MM-065	1677		2	2	18	30	65
C23MM-070	1678	[1]	2	2	16	25	55
C23MM-075	1679		2	2	15	22	45
C23MM-080	1679	0 of CAROLVS over A (obv.)	2	2	18	30	65
C23MM-085	1680	[2]	2	2	16	25	55
C23MM-090	1681		2	2	16	25	55
C23MM-095	1681	latter 1 over 0	2	2	16	25	55
C23MM-100	1682		2	2	16	25	55
C23MM-105	1682	2 over 1	2	2	16	25	55
C23MM-110	1683		2	2	16	25	55
C23MM-115	1684		2	2	16	25	55
C23MM-120	1684	4 over 3	2	2	16	25	55

1. Lettering size varies.
2. Some are struck from a badly cracked die.

James II 1685–1688

John Roettier continued as designer, producing a threepence similar in style to the Charles II coin. The interlinked 'C's are replaced by the symbol III, continuing the motif of three regnal initials (IACOBVS) as well as denoting the denomination '3'.

The James threepence in particular suffers from metal transfer during striking, as a result of the somewhat high relief portrait to which metal flowed during the process from the reverse. This resulted in the coin appearing to have a worn or weakly struck reverse in the centre. This phenomenon should be taken into account when grading this particular coin.

Denomination	Metal	Weight (grams)	Diameter (mm)	Rev. alignment
Threepence	Silver	1.5	17	↓

Obverse 1 Head 1, left; IACOBVS II DEI GRATIA

Reverse 1 Large III, crowned; MAG BR FRA ET HIB REX (date)

Edge plain

Obv. 1   Rev. 1

No.	Date	Features	Obv.	Rev.	F	VF	EF
J23M-005	1685		1	1	16	25	50
J23M-010	1685	die axes at 90 degrees	1	1	50	80	150
J23M-015	1685	struck on fourpence flan	1	1	100	180	350
J23M-020	1686		1	1	16	25	50
J23M-025	1687		1	1	16	25	50
J23M-030	1687	7 over 6	1	1	16	25	50
J23M-035	1688		1	1	16	25	50
J23M-040	1688	latter 8 over 7	1	1	16	25	50

William and Mary 1688–1694

The unknown designer of the first type of William and Mary small silver coinage produced a somewhat caricatured portrait of the two monarchs. As postulated under the fourpence entry for this reign, the design may have been the work of George Bower. A rather more staid double portrait was introduced during 1691. The reverse, representing a crowned Arabic numeral has lasted, with modifications, up to the present day.

This series is fairly rare in extremely fine or better condition.

Denomination	Metal	Weight (grams)	Diameter (mm)	Rev. alignment
Threepence	Silver	1.5	17	↓

Obverse 1 Heads 1, right; little or no tie at back of king's head; GVLIELMVS ET MARIA D G

Obverse 2 Heads 2, with tie, right; same legend

Reverse 1 Crowned '3'; MAG BR FR ET HIB REX ET REGINA (date)

Edge plain

Obv. 1   Obv. 2   Rev. 1

No.	Date	Features	Obv.	Rev.	F	VF	EF
WM3M-005	1689	[1]	1	1	15	24	50
WM3M-010	1689	rev.stops are hyphens	1	1	15	24	50
WM3M-015	1689	GVLIE(LMV over MVS)S (obv.)	1	1	16	25	50
WM3M-020	1689	no stops on rev.	1	1	16	25	50
WM3M-025	1690		1	1	16	25	50
WM3M-030	1690	6 over 5	1	1	18	30	60
WM3M-035	1690	9 over 6 or inverted 9	1	1	18	30	60
WM3M-040	1690	9 over 6 or inverted 9; BR FR over BB FB (rev.)	1	1	24	38	75
WM3M-045	1691		1	1	25	45	100
WM3M-050	1691	[2]	2	1	18	30	60
WM3M-055	1692	[2]	2	1	18	30	60
WM3M-060	1693	[2]	2	1	18	30	60
WM3M-065	1693	3 over 2 [2]	2	1	18	30	60
WM3M-070	1694	[2]	2	1	18	30	60
WM3M-075	1694	MΛRIΛ instead of MARIA (obv.) [2]	2	1	18	30	60

1. Date and stop varieties exist.
2. Date and lettering positioning varies.

Variations in the shape of the crown occur on the reverse.

William III 1695–1701

The threepence obverse was the work of Johann Crocker (John Croker). The reverse may have been by him and/or an assistant. The design concept continues from that of William and Mary. As the coins were produced after the closure of the provincial mints, none bears a mintmark. Why no small silver was produced at the provincial mints or before 1698 (apart from the unique 1697 fourpence) is open to question. It has been conjectured that this was because the Maundy ceremony was always held in London, but in fact probably only silver pennies were used during the ceremony.

Denomination	Metal	Weight (grams)	Diameter (mm)	Rev. alignment
Threepence	Silver	1.5	17	↓

Obverse 1 Head 1, right; GVLIELMVS III DEI GRA

Reverse 1 Crowned '3'; MAG BR FRA ET HIB REX (date)

Edge plain

Obv. 1   Rev. 1

No.	Date	Features	Obv.	Rev.	F	VF	EF
W33M-005	1698		1	1	18	30	60
W33M-010	1699		1	1	18	30	60
W33M-015	1700		1	1	18	30	60
W33M-020	1701	Z-type '1's in date	1	1	18	30	60
W33M-025	1701	Z-type '1's in date; GBA instead of GRA (obv.)	1	1	18	30	60
W33M-030	1701	J-type '1's in date [1]	1	1	18	30	60

1. Larger lettering than Z-type variety.

Anne 1702–1714

There is doubt about the attribution of the threepences of Anne, especially for the reverse. However, it appears that John Croker and/or his assistant Samuel Bull may have been responsible for the obverses.

Denomination	Metal	Weight (grams)	Diameter (mm)	Rev. alignment
Threepence	Silver	1.5	17	↓

Obverse 1 Head 1, left; ANNA DEI GRATIA

Obverse 2 Similar but head is larger; hair and brooch are different

Reverse 1 Crowned '3'; MAG BR FR ET HIB REG (date)

Reverse 2 Similar but MAG BR FRA ET HIB REG

Reverse 3 Similar but MAG BRI FR ET HIB REG

Edge plain

Obv. 1   Obv. 2   Rev. 3

No.	Date	Features	Obv.	Rev.	F	VF	EF
A3M-005	1703	[1]	1	1	18	35	65
A3M-010	1704		1	1	15	30	60
A3M-015	1705		1	1	15	30	60
A3M-020	1706		1	2	15	30	60
A3M-025	1707		1	1	15	30	60
A3M-030	1708		1	3	15	30	60
A3M-035	1709		1	3	15	30	60
A3M-040	1710		1	3	15	30	60
A3M-045	1713		1	3	15	30	60
A3M-050	1713		2	3	15	30	60

1. Position of date varies.

Minor head varieties may exist for some of these dates.

George I 1714–1727

The basic design of earlier reigns is continued through the reign of George I. Designed by John Croker, assisted by Samuel Bull, the obverse omits the lengthy German titles of the king which are included on the larger silver denominations. The reverse may have been the work of Johann Rudolf Ochs, senior.

Denomination	Metal	Weight (grams)	Diameter (mm)	Rev. alignment
Threepence	Silver	1.5	17	↓

Obverse 1 Head 1, right; GEORGIVS DEI GRA

Reverse 1 Crowned '3'; MAG BRI FR ET HIB REX (date)

Edge plain

Obv. 1   Rev. 1

No.	Date	Obv.	Rev.	F	VF	EF
G13M-005	1717	1	1	20	35	70
G13M-010	1721	1	1	20	35	70
G13M-015	1723	1	1	20	40	80
G13M-020	1727	1	1	20	35	70

George II 1727–1760

The young portrait of the king by John Croker was used throughout the series. This is remarkable, given that on the larger silver the portrait was superseded by an older portrait as early as 1743. The last striking of the threepence in 1760 occurred 19 years after Croker's death and two years after the issue of the last of the large silver. The reverses of this series may have been the work of the Assistant Engraver, Johann Sigismund Tanner.

Denomination	Metal	Weight (grams)	Diameter (mm)	Rev. alignment
Threepence	Silver	1.5	17	↓

Obverse 1 Head 1, left; GEORGIVS II DEI GRATIA

Reverse 1 Crowned '3'; MAG BRI FR ET HIB REX (date);

Reverse 2 Similar but a slightly different crown

Reverse 3 Similar but a different crown

Edge plain

Obv. 1   Rev. 3

No.	Date	Features	Obv.	Rev.	F	VF	EF
G23M-005	1729		1	1	15	25	45
G23M-010	1731		1	2	18	30	55
G23M-015	1731	small obverse lettering	1	2	18	30	55
G23M-020	1732	no stop over head	1	3	18	30	55
G23M-025	1732	stop over head	1	3	18	30	55
G23M-030	1735		1	3	18	30	55
G23M-035	1737		1	3	15	25	45
G23M-040	1739	[1]	1	3	15	25	45
G23M-045	1740		1	3	15	25	45
G23M-050	1743	large obv. and rev. lettering	1	3	15	25	45
G23M-055	1743	small lettering no stop over head	1	3	15	25	45
G23M-060	1743	small lettering stop over head	1	3	15	25	45
G23M-065	1746	[2]	1	3	15	25	45
G23M-070	1746	6 over 3 or 5	1	3	15	25	45
G23M-075	1760		1	3	15	25	50

1. Several stops usually missing on reverse.
2. Exists without overdate?

George III 1760–1820

Although the silver threepence was minted as a currency coin until well into the twentieth century, an alteration in the purpose of this coin undoubtedly occurred during the long reign of George III. The first two years of minting, 1762 and 1763, saw a prolific issue which was obviously intended for general circulation, as these coins normally turn up in fine or very fine condition. On the other hand, the threepences of the last type (1817-20) are usually found in very fine or extremely fine condition, indicating that their primary use was probably as a Maundy issue.

The first issue of 1762 and 1763 bears a portrait similar to that on the Northumberland shilling and the early guineas, which were the work of Richard Yeo. However, the obverse of this issue was designed and engraved by Ochs, junior. These dates, amongst the most easily found of all threepences, are followed by one of the rarest, 1765, and careful date checking is therefore essential!

The very different head of 1792 coincided with the new 'Wire Money' numerals on the reverse, thereafter abandoned. This issue was designed by Lewis Pingo. The obverse head was retained for the issue of 1795 and 1800, when the series was discontinued until after the 'Great Recoinage' in 1817.

Denomination	Metal	Weight (grams)	Diameter (mm)	Rev. alignment
Threepence 1762-1786	Silver	1.5	17	↓
Threepence 1792-1800	Silver	1.5	17	↑
Threepence 1817-1820	Silver	1.4	16	↑

Obverse 1 Head 1, right; GEORGIVS III DEI GRATIA

Obverse 2 Head 2, right; same legend

Obverse 3 Head 3, laureate, right; GEORGIUS III DEI GRATIA (date)

Reverse 1 Crowned '3' in high relief; MAG BRI FR ET HIB REX (date, across crown)

Reverse 2 Completely redesigned; stylised '3' under small crown; date below '3'; same legend

Reverse 3 Redesigned; more similar to Reverse 1 but crown very different; same legend; date is below '3'

Reverse 4 Crowned '3'; BRITANNIARUM REX FID DEF (no date)

Edge plain

Obv. 1   Obv. 2   Obv. 3

Rev. 1   Rev. 3   Rev. 4

No.	Date	Features	Obv.	Rev.	F	VF	EF
G33M-005	1762	[1]	1	1	8	15	25
G33M-010	1763	[2]	1	1	8	15	25
G33M-015	1763	PROOF; rev.↑	1	1			1000
G33M-020	1765		1	1	150	350	800
G33M-025	1766		1	1	12	20	30
G33M-030	1770		1	1	12	20	30
G33M-035	1772	small lettering	1	1	12	20	30
G33M-040	1772	large lettering; large III	1	1	12	20	30
G33M-045	1772	large lettering; small III	1	1	12	20	30
G33M-050	1780		1	1	12	20	30
G33M-055	1784	[3]	1	1	14	22	35
G33M-060	1786		1	1	12	20	30
G33M-065	1792	[4]	2	2	20	32	70
G33M-070	1795		2	3	12	20	30
G33M-075	1800		2	3	10	18	30
G33M-080	1817		3	4	12	18	30
G33M-085	1818		3	4	12	18	30
G33M-090	1820		3	4	12	18	30

1. Minor design variations; possibly over 40 different dies.
2. Minor design variations.
3. Obverse legend larger than usual.
4. 'Wire Money' issue.

George IV 1820–1830

By now the silver threepence was being struck primarily as a Maundy coin, although some were sent to the Colonies for use as currency. However, the George IV threepence is frequently found in well-circulated state, no doubt due to its being taken from Maundy sets and spent during the reign of Victoria when the circulation coin was reintroduced.

Because the Maundy coinage is dealt with separately, including details of varieties, Maundy issue threepences from George IV onwards appear in an abbreviated form.

It is worth mentioning, however, the odd case of the 1822 threepence. This bears an unusually small head, from a twopence punch. Hawkins (1887) states that the correct punch broke and the smaller one was substituted. The error was apparently rectified in time for coining the 1823 threepence.

Denomination	Metal	Weight (grams)	Diameter (mm)	Rev. alignment
Maundy Threepence	Silver	1.4	16	↓

Obverse 1 Head 1, left (small, from a twopence punch); GEORGIUS IIII D G BRITANNIAR REX F D

Obverse 2 Head 2, left (normal size); same legend

Reverse 1 Crowned '3' and divided date, all within wreath

Edge plain

| Obv. 2 | Rev. 1 |

No.	Date	Feature	Obv.	Rev.	VF	EF	FDC
G43M-005	1822 [1]		1	1	20	35	50
G43M-010	1823-1830 [2]		2	1	12	20	30

1. Proofs were struck.
2. Proofs were struck in 1828.

William IV 1830–1837

Denomination	Metal	Weight (grams)	Diameter (mm)	Rev. alignment
Maundy Threepence	Silver	1.4	16	↓

Obverse 1 Head 1, right; GULIELMUS IIII D G BRITANNIAR REX F D

Reverse 1 Crowned '3' and divided date, all within wreath

Edge plain

No.	Date	Features	Obv.	Rev.	VF	EF	FDC
W43M-005	1831-1837 [1]		1	1	20	35	50

1. Proofs in gold and silver were struck in 1831; proofs may exist for 1834.

Currency threepences of identical design were struck for Colonial use as below; these differ from the Maundy threepence in not having a prooflike surface.

Denomination	Metal	Weight (grams)	Diameter (mm)	Rev. alignment
Non-Maundy Threepence	Silver	1.4	16	↓

Obverse 1 Head 1, right; GULIELMUS IIII D G BRITANNIAR REX F D

Reverse 1 Crowned '3' and divided date, all within wreath

Edge plain

| Obv. 1 | Rev. 1 |

No.	Date	Features	Obv.	Rev.	F	VF	EF	UNC
W43D-005	1834		1	1	5	20	55	90
W43D-010	1835		1	1	5	18	50	80
W43D-015	1836		1	1	5	20	55	90
W43D-020	1837		1	1	7	22	60	100

Victoria 1837–1901

Denomination	Metal	Weight (grams)	Diameter (mm)	Rev. alignment
Maundy Threepence 1838-1887	Silver	1.4	16	↓
Maundy Threepence 1888-1901	Silver	1.4	16	↑

Obverse 1 Head 1, left; VICTORIA D G BRITANNIAR REGINA F D

Obverse 2 Head 2, left; same legend

Obverse 3 Head 3, left; VICTORIA DEI GRA BRITT REGINA FID DEF IND IMP

Reverse 1 Crowned '3' and divided date, all within wreath

Reverse 2 Similar but crown very different

Edge plain

No.	Date	Features	Obv.	Rev.	EF	FDC
VY3M-005	1838-1887 [1]		1	1	25	35
VJ3M-010	1888-1892 [2]		2	2	25	35
VO3M-015	1893-1901		3	2	20	25

1. Proofs were struck in 1838 (silver and gold); 1839 1853 1867 1871 1878 1881 (silver).
2. Proofs were struck in 1888.

For details of proofs see Maundy listings.

One of the oddities of the British series is the fact that the currency silver threepence from 1838 to 1926 was of identical design to that of the Maundy threepence, except for some of the 1887 and 1893 coins. In the higher grades, they can usually be distinguished from one another because the Maundy pieces are more sharply struck and usually have a more prooflike field. This difference is more apparent from 1888 onwards.

For the young head series of Victoria, the difference most usually cited, the prooflike field or lack of it, is by no means a certain indication as to whether a coin is a currency or Maundy issue. It is relatively easy to find mint state Maundy fourpences without any trace of a prooflike field, and presumably the same applies for the threepences. The better guideline is the sharpness of the strike, especially of the wreath on the reverse, and a trained eye will distinguish between the fineness of the detail on a Maundy piece as against a currency coin, especially on the reverse.

A curious legal anomaly has arisen because of the impossibility of distinguishing worn currency threepences from their Maundy counterparts. When decimalization was introduced in 1971, the Maundy coins maintained their legal tender status, and of course this had to be in new pence. Because of the indistinguishability of the two threepences, the currency and the Maundy threepences from 1870 were both decreed to be legal tender for 3 new pence, i.e. the old currency coins were revalued at 2.4 times their original value!

The first Victorian currency threepences used the young head portrait by William Wyon and a reverse by Johann Baptiste Merlen. They were initially struck for colonial use, but in 1845 entered general circulation in the British Isles. However, because of their close relationship to British coinage, all of the dates from 1838 are included in this book. No threepences are recorded as having been struck in 1847, 1848 and 1852 and the probable explanation for this is that at this time there was much interest in the possible advent of decimal currency; the threepence, at one-eightieth of a pound, would not easily have fit into any decimal scheme.

Collecting Hints

The Victorian silver threepence series is one of the most difficult to collect in top condition. A popular and much-used coin, it circulated extensively, and its small size did not at the time make it an obvious candidate for collecting. Now, however, it is recognised as a fascinating series and its rarity in higher grades increases its appeal. The rarity of some of the dates in extremely fine or better condition is probably much underrated. However, care must be taken that one does not buy a Maundy threepence sold as a currency piece.

Denomination	Metal	Weight (grams)	Diameter (mm)	Rev. alignment
Non-Maundy Threepence 1838–87 obv. 1	Silver	1.4	16	↓
Non-Maundy Threepence 1887–1901 obv. 2–3	Silver	1.4	16	↑

Obverse 1 Head 1, left; VICTORIA D G BRITANNIAR REGINA F D

Obverse 2 Head 2, left; same legend

Obverse 3 Head 3, left; VICTORIA DEI GRA BRITT REGINA FID DEF IND IMP

Reverse 1 Crowned '3' and divided date, all within wreath

Reverse 2 Similar but crown very different

Edge plain

Obv. 1   Obv. 2   Obv. 3

Rev. 1   Rev. 2

No.	Date	Features	Obv.	Rev.	F	VF	EF	UNC
VY3D-005	1838	1	1	1	6	12	50	80
VY3D-010	1839	2	1	1	6	14	60	100
VY3D-015	1840		1	1	6	14	60	100
VY3D-020	1841		1	1	7	16	65	110
VY3D-025	1842		1	1	7	16	65	110
VY3D-030	1843		1	1	5	12	50	80
VY3D-035	1844		1	1	7	16	65	110
VY3D-040	1845	3	1	1	6	14	55	90
VY3D-045	1846		1	1	30	70	150	
VY3D-050	1849		1	1	8	20	80	130
VY3D-055	1850		1	1	5	12	50	80
VY3D-060	1851		1	1	5	12	50	80
VY3D-065	1852		1	1	50	100	250	
VY3D-070	1853	2	1	1	30	70	150	
VY3D-075	1854		1	1	5	12	50	80
VY3D-080	1855		1	1	6	14	55	90
VY3D-085	1856		1	1	6	14	55	90
VY3D-090	1857		1	1	6	14	55	90
VY3D-095	1858		1	1	5	12	50	80
VY3D-100	1858	BRITANNIAB instead of BRITANNIAR (obv.)	1	1	50	150		
VY3D-105	1859	4	1	1	5	10	40	65
VY3D-110	1860		1	1	7	16	65	110
VY3D-115	1861		1	1	5	10	40	65
VY3D-120	1862		1	1	5	12	50	80
VY3D-125	1863		1	1	5	12	50	80
VY3D-130	1864		1	1	5	10	40	65
VY3D-135	1865		1	1	5	12	50	80
VY3D-140	1866		1	1	5	10	40	65
VY3D-145	1867	2	1	1	5	10	40	65
VY3D-150	1868		1	1	5	9	35	60
VY3D-155	1868	RRITANNIAR instead of BRITANNIAR (obv.)	1	1	30	100		
VY3D-160	1869		1	1	6	14	55	90
VY3D-165	1870		1	1	5	9	35	60
VY3D-170	1871	2	1	1	5	10	40	65
VY3D-175	1872		1	1	5	10	40	65
VY3D-180	1873		1	1	5	9	35	55
VY3D-185	1874		1	1	5	9	35	55
VY3D-190	1875		1	1	5	9	35	55
VY3D-195	1876		1	1	5	9	35	55
VY3D-200	1877		1	1	5	9	35	55
VY3D-205	1878	2	1	1	5	9	35	55
VY3D-210	1879		1	1	5	9	35	55
VY3D-215	1879	PROOF; rev. ↑	1	1				600
VY3D-220	1880		1	1	5	9	35	55

No.	Date	Features	Obv.	Rev.	F	VF	EF	UNC
VY3D-225	1881	2	1	1	5	9	35	55
VY3D-230	1882		1	1	5	9	35	55
VY3D-235	1883		1	1	5	8	30	45
VY3D-240	1884		1	1	5	8	30	45
VY3D-245	1885		1	1	5	8	30	45
VY3D-250	1886		1	1	5	8	30	45
VY3D-255	1887		1	1	5	8	30	45
VY3D-260	1887	PROOF	1	1				200
VJ3D-265	1887	5	2	2	5	7	9	12
VJ3D-270	1887	PROOF 6	2	2				50
VJ3D-275	1888	2	2	2	5	8	14	20
VJ3D-280	1889	5	2	2	5	8	12	18
VJ3D-285	1890		2	2	5	8	14	20
VJ3D-290	1891		2	2	5	8	15	22
VJ3D-295	1892		2	2	5	8	16	24
VJ3D-300	1893		2	2	7	25	120	200
VO3D-305	1893		3	2	4	7	10	15
VO3D-310	1893	PROOF 6	3	2				60
VO3D-315	1894		3	2	5	8	14	20
VO3D-320	1895		3	2	5	8	14	20
VO3D-325	1896		3	2	4	7	10	15
VO3D-330	1897		3	2	4	7	10	15
VO3D-335	1898		3	2	4	7	10	15
VO3D-340	1899		3	2	4	7	10	15
VO3D-345	1900		3	2	4	7	10	15
VO3D-350	1901		3	2	4	7	10	15

1. Proofs in gold/silver included in Maundy set listings.
2. Proofs included in Maundy set listings.
3. Date numerals vary in size; coin introduced into British Isles this year.
4. Date numerals vary.
5. Minor variations in crown occur (obv.).
6. Issued in cased proof sets.

Small progressive modifications are made to Head 1 from time to time.

Edward VII 1902–1910

Denomination	Metal	Weight (grams)	Diameter (mm)	Rev. alignment
Maundy Threepence	Silver	1.4	16	↑

Obverse 1 Head 1, right; EDWARDVS VII D G BRITT OMN REX F D IND IMP

Reverse 1 Crowned '3' and divided date, all within wreath

Edge plain

No.	Date	Features	Obv.	Rev.	EF	FDC
E73M-005	1902-1910 1		1	1	12	18

1. Matt proofs were struck in 1902.

The currency threepence, like the other denominations, was issued for each of the nine years of the reign. The obverse used the mechanically reduced portrait of Edward by de Saulles, while the reverse continued the design of earlier reigns.

Denomination	Metal	Weight (grams)	Diameter (mm)	Rev. alignment
Non-Maundy Threepence	Silver	1.4	16	↑

Obverse 1 Head 1, right; EDWARDVS VII D G BRITT OMN REX F D IND IMP

Reverse 1 Crowned '3' and divided date, all within wreath

Edge plain

Obv. 1   Rev. 1

No.	Date	Features	Obv.	Rev.	F	VF	EF	UNC
E73D-005	1902	1	1	1	3	5	8	12
E73D-010	1903		1	1	4	7	14	20
E73D-015	1904		1	1	5	10	25	40
E73D-020	1905		1	1	5	10	25	40

No.	Date	Features	Obv.	Rev.	F	VF	EF	UNC
E73D-025	1906		1	1	4	8	20	32
E73D-030	1907		1	1	4	7	14	20
E73D-035	1908		1	1	4	7	14	20
E73D-040	1909		1	1	4	7	14	20
E73D-045	1910		1	1	4	6	12	18

1. Matt proofs included in Maundy set listings.

George V 1910–1936

Denomination	Metal	Weight (grams)	Diameter (mm)	Rev. alignment
Maundy Threepence 1911-1920	0.925 Silver	1.4	16	↑
Maundy Threepence 1921-1936	0.5 Silver	1.4	16	↑

Obverse 1 Head 1, left; GEORGIVS V D G BRITT OMN REX F D IND IMP

Obverse 2 Head 2, so-called 'modified effigy', left; same legend

Obverse 3 Head 2, re-engraved, left; same legend

Reverse 1 Crowned '3' and divided date, all within wreath

Edge plain

No.	Date	Features	Obv.	Rev.	EF	FDC
G53M-005	1911-1927 [1]		1	1	14	20
G53M-010	1928-1929		2	1	14	20
G53M-015	1930-1936		3	1	14	20

1. See note on 1911 issue under Maundy sets.

The currency threepence again used the same design as the Maundy threepence at the beginning of the reign, but underwent a radical change in 1927. The proof set of that year introduced the new acorn reverse, a smaller version of the new sixpence reverse. In 1927 the only threepences bearing the new acorn design were the ones struck for the proof set, and the currency coin bearing the new design entered circulation in 1928. Occasionally one comes across worn coins of 1927-1936 bearing the earlier '3' reverse, but these are invariably refugees from a Maundy set which were spent at the time.

Anyone buying or selling currency threepences by weight should note that these coins wear considerably in circulation. A fine condition coin weighs about 1.34 grams, about 5% less than when it was struck. The writer has weighed a counted quantity of 1300 average circulated (F-VF) threepences dated 1919/1920 at 1783 grams.

Denomination	Metal	Weight (grams)	Diameter (mm)	Rev. alignment
Non-Maundy Threepence 1911-20	0.925 Silver	1.4	16	↑
Non-Maundy Threepence 1920-22	Silver 50%; Copper 40%; Nickel 10%	1.4	16	↑
Non-Maundy Threepence 1922-27	Silver 50%; Copper 50%	1.4	16	↑
Non-Maundy Threepence 1927-36	Silver 50%; Copper 40%; Nickel 5%; Zinc 5%	1.4	16	↑

Obverse 1 Head 1, left; GEORGIVS V D G BRITT OMN REX F D IND IMP

Obverse 2 Head 2, so-called 'modified effigy', left; same legend

Reverse 1 Crowned '3' and divided date, all within wreath

Reverse 2 Three oak-sprigs with three acorns; G in centre; THREE PENCE (date)

Edge plain

Obv. 1

Obv. 2

Rev. 1

Rev. 2

No.	Date	Features	Obv.	Rev.	VF	EF	UNC
G53D-005	1911	[1]	1	1	2	5	8
G53D-010	1912		1	1	2	5	8
G53D-015	1913		1	1	2	5	8
G53D-020	1914		1	1	2	5	8
G53D-025	1915		1	1	2	5	8
G53D-030	1916		1	1	2	5	8
G53D-035	1917		1	1	2	5	8
G53D-040	1918		1	1	2	5	8
G53D-045	1919		1	1	2	5	8
G53D-050	1920	[2]	1	1	2	5	8
G53D-055	1921		1	1	2	5	8
G53D-060	1922		1	1	2	6	10
G53D-065	1925		1	1	2	12	25
G53D-070	1926		1	1	2	12	25
G53D-075	1926		2	1	2	6	10
G53D-080	1927	PROOF [3]	2	2	40	45	55
G53D-085	1927	PROOF from sandblasted dies [4]	2	2			200
G53D-090	1928		2	2	4	16	35
G53D-095	1928	PROOF	2	2			300
G53D-100	1930		2	2	2	8	18
G53D-105	1930	PROOF	2	2			250
G53D-110	1931		2	2	2	4	6
G53D-115	1931	PROOF	2	2			250
G53D-120	1932		2	2	2	4	6
G53D-125	1932	PROOF	2	2			250
G53D-130	1933		2	2	2	4	6
G53D-135	1933	PROOF	2	2			250
G53D-140	1934		2	2	2	4	6
G53D-145	1934	PROOF	2	2			250
G53D-150	1935		2	2	2	4	6
G53D-155	1935	PROOF	2	2			250
G53D-160	1936		2	2	2	4	5
G53D-165	1936	PROOF	2	2			250

1. Minor obverse variations occur.
2. Struck in both 0.500 and 0.925 silver.
3. Issued in cased proof sets.
4. Struck to facilitate photography of coin.

Edward VIII 1936

The Edward VIII silver threepence is strictly speaking a pattern, as probable Royal approval was about to be granted at the time of the abdication. However, because its official status rests only on this technicality, and to provide continuity, it is included in this catalogue.

The portrait of Edward VIII is by Thomas Humphrey Paget, and faces left at the insistence of the king, who considered this placement more flattering and wished to discontinue the tradition of opposite facings for successive monarchs. The reverse is by George Kruger Gray (1880-1943)

Denomination	Metal	Weight (grams)	Diameter (mm)	Rev. alignment
Non-Maundy Threepence	Silver	1.4	16	↑

Obverse 1 Head 1, left; EDWARDVS VIII D G BR OMN REX

Reverse 1 Three interlinked rings of St Edmund; FID DEF IND IMP 1937 THREE PENCE

Edge plain

Obv. 1

Rev. 1

No.	Date	Obv.	Rev.	Unc
E83D-005	1937	1	1	10000

George VI 1937–1952

Denomination	Metal	Weight (grams)	Diameter (mm)	Rev. alignment
Maundy Threepence 1937-46	0.5 Silver (see below)	1.4	16	↑
Maundy Threepence 1947-52	0.925 Silver	1.4	16	↑

There is a very slight difference in the base metal constituency of the 1937 Maundy set given at the Maundy ceremony compared with that of the set included in the 1937 proof set.

Obverse 1 Head 1, left; GEORGIVS VI D G BR OMN REX F D IND IMP

Obverse 2 Head 1, left; GEORGIVS VI D G BR OMN REX FIDEI DEF

Reverse 1 Crowned '3' and divided date, all within wreath

Edge plain

No.	Date	Features	Obv.	Rev.	EF	FDC
G63M-005	1937-1948 [1]		1	1	12	18
G63M-010	1949-1952		2	1	14	20

1. See note on 1937 issue under Maundy sets.

On the currency coin, the acorn reverse was abandoned in 1937 in favour of an elegant and simple shield and rose design by George Kruger Gray (1880-1943). This tiny coin was to last only a few more years. It did not survive long enough to suffer the indignity of the changeover to cupronickel, and in 1944/45 was superseded by its larger brother, the twelve-sided nickel-brass threepence; the two had coexisted since 1937.

Denomination	Metal	Weight (grams)	Diameter (mm)	Rev. alignment
Non-Maundy Threepence	0.5 Silver	1.4	16	↑

Obverse 1 Head 1, left; GEORGIVS VI D G BR OMN REX

Reverse 1 Shield of St George lying on Tudor rose with divided date; FID DEF IND IMP THREE PENCE

Edge plain

Obv. 1   Rev. 1

No.	Date	Features	Obv.	Rev.	VF	EF	UNC
G63D-005	1937		1	1	1	2	3
G63D-010	1937	PROOF [1]	1	1			10
G63D-015	1937	PROOF from sandblasted dies [2]	1	1			150
G63D-020	1938		1	1	1	3	4
G63D-025	1938	PROOF	1	1			150
G63D-030	1939		1	1	1	4	7
G63D-035	1939	PROOF	1	1			150
G63D-040	1940		1	1	1	3	4
G63D-045	1940	PROOF	1	1			150
G63D-050	1941		1	1	1	3	4
G63D-055	1941	PROOF	1	1			150
G63D-060	1942	[3]	1	1	2	10	20
G63D-065	1943	[3]	1	1	2	12	25
G63D-070	1944	[3]	1	1	3	20	35
G63D-075	1945	[4]	1	1	4000		

1. Issued in cased proof sets.
2. Struck to facilitate photography of coin.
3. Issued for circulation in the West Indies.
4. Almost all melted down.

Elizabeth II 1952 -

Denomination	Metal	Weight (grams)	Diameter (mm)	Rev. alignment
Maundy Threepence	Silver	1.4	16	↑

Obverse 1 Head 1, right; ELIZABETH II DEI GRA BRITT OMN REGINA F D

Obverse 2 Head 2, recut, right; ELIZABETH II DEI GRATIA REGINA F D

Reverse 1 Crowned '3' and divided date, all within wreath

Edge plain

No.	Date	Features	Obv.	Rev.	VF	EF	FDC
EL23M-005	1953	[1]	1	1	55	65	70
EL23M-010	1954-1995		2	1	14	17	20

1. Varieties: see under Maundy sets.

Brass Threepence

Edward VIII 1936

The Edward VIII threepence is strictly speaking a pattern, as probable royal approval was about to be granted at the time of the abdication. However, because its official status rests only on this technicality, and also to provide continuity, it is included in this catalogue.

The portrait of Edward VIII is by Thomas Humphrey Paget, and faces left at the insistence of the king, who considered this placement more flattering. He saw no reason to continue the tradition of opposite facings for successive monarchs. The reverse is by Percy Metcalfe, and was a modification of a proposed design by Frances Madge Kitchener.

Denomination	Metal	Weight (grams)	Diameter (mm)	Rev. alignment
Threepence	'Nickel-brass' (Copper 79%, Zinc 20%, Nickel 1%)	6.8	12-sided figure: across sides: 21mm across corners: 22mm	↑

Obverse 1 Head 1, left; EDWARDVS VIII D G BR OMN REX F D IND IMP

Reverse 1 Thrift plant; THREE PENCE 1937

Edge plain, 12 sides

Obv. 1   Rev. 1

No.	Date	Obv.	Rev.	UNC
E83DB-005	1937	1	1	20000

George VI 1937–1952

At the end of the reign of George V, the silver threepence had become somewhat unpopular in England, and especially in London, mainly on account of its small size. Inexplicably, the coin was popular in Scotland. The alternative, bronze pennies and halfpennies, were heavy and cumbersome in quantities of more than two or three. Because of this, it was decided to introduce a somewhat more substantial threepenny piece which had a more convenient weight/value ratio than the bronze coins. The silver threepence continued to be minted, however; it is possible that there was some doubt as to whether the new coin would prove successful. It is worthy of note that between 1937 and 1944 no fewer than three different types of threepence (including the Maundy coin) were being struck, and this excludes the Edward VIII coins dated 1937.

The new threepence was coined in a brass alloy (copper 80%, zinc 20%) to which 1% of nickel was substituted in lieu of an equal weight of copper, possibly to make the alloy more wear resistant. Initially, the coin was to have been thinner than the piece eventually produced, but during experimentation for production of the Edward VIII coinage it was found that some sixpence and shilling slot machines could be worked using the trial pieces coined for testing purposes. Of special concern were the many electricity meters which at the time were fed using shillings and sixpences. The adopted coins were too thick to be inserted into the slots.

The resulting coin was distinctive in thickness and colour, and furthermore was given a unique shape for a coin of a regular 12-sided figure (a dodecagon). The obverse used the portrait of George VI by Thomas Humphrey Paget (1893-1974). The reverse design, a thrift plant, was a departure from the classical designs hitherto used on almost all base metal coinage in Britain, and continued the plant motif of the later sixpences and threepences of George V. It was a modification by Percy Metcalfe of the proposed design by Frances Madge Kitchener for the Edward VIII threepence. This had originally had the word 'THRIFT' under the plant, and Miss Kitchener possibly considered this appropriate for a coin extensively used for saving in money boxes.

Initially, the twelve-sided collar used in the striking had sharp corners, but it was found that metal fatigue occurred frequently because of the high stresses obtaining at these points. During 1941 the corners were rounded slightly, and the collars subsequently lasted longer at a time when the steel used in their manufacture was in short supply. After the war, when steel was more plentiful, some of the collars were again made with sharp corners.

Collecting Hints

The series should be collected in extremely fine or mint state with original lustre. The sharpness of the reverse is lost when the coin becomes worn below very fine condition.

Denomination	Metal	Weight (grams)	Diameter (mm)	Rev. alignment
Threepence	'Nickel-brass' (Copper 79%, Zinc 20%, Nickel 1%)	6.8	12-sided figure: across sides: 21mm across corners: 22mm	↑

Obverse 1 Head 1, left; GEORGIVS VI D G BR OMN REX F D IND IMP

Obverse 2 Head 1, left; GEORGIVS D G BR OMN REX FIDEI DEF

Reverse 1 Thrift plant; THREE PENCE (date)

Edge plain, 12 sides; corners sharp unless stated

Obv. 1   Obv. 2   Rev. 1

No.	Date	Features	Obv.	Rev.	VF	EF	UNC
G63DB-005	1937		1	1	1	3	5
G63DB-010	1937	PROOF [1]	1	1		4	8
G63DB-015	1937	PROOF from sandblasted dies [2]	1	1			150
G63DB-020	1937	struck on round nickel blank for Hong Kong 10 cents [3]	1	1			300
G63DB-025	1938		1	1	1	4	9
G63DB-030	1938	PROOF	1	1			200

No.	Date	Features	Obv.	Rev.	VF	EF	UNC
G63DB-035	1939		1	1	1	5	14
G63DB-040	1939	PROOF	1	1			200
G63DB-045	1940		1	1	1	3	6
G63DB-050	1940	PROOF	1	1			200
G63DB-055	1941		1	1	1	3	5
G63DB-060	1941	rounded corners	1	1	1	3	5
G63DB-065	1941	PROOF	1	1			200
G63DB-070	1942	rounded corners	1	1	1	3	5
G63DB-075	1942	PROOF; rounded corners	1	1			200
G63DB-080	1943	rounded corners	1	1	1	3	5
G63DB-085	1943	PROOF; rounded corners	1	1			200
G63DB-090	1944	rounded corners	1	1	1	3	6
G63DB-095	1944	PROOF; rounded corners	1	1			200
G63DB-100	1945	rounded corners	1	1	1	4	8
G63DB-105	1945	PROOF; rounded corners	1	1			200
G63DB-110	1946	rounded corners	1	1	8	60	220
G63DB-115	1946	PROOF; rounded corners	1	1			400
G63DB-120	1948	rounded corners	1	1	1	5	14
G63DB-125	1948		1	1	1	5	14
G63DB-130	1948	PROOF	1	1			200
G63DB-135	1949	rounded corners	2	1	10	60	200
G63DB-140	1949	PROOF; rounded corners	2	1			500
G63DB-145	1950		2	1	4	15	50
G63DB-150	1950	PROOF [1]	2	1			20
G63DB-155	1950	PROOF from sandblasted dies [2]	2	1			200
G63DB-160	1951		2	1	4	16	55
G63DB-165	1951	PROOF [1]	2	1			22
G63DB-170	1951	PROOF from sandblasted dies [2]	2	1			200
G63DB-175	1952		2	1	1	4	8
G63DB-180	1952	PROOF	2	1			200

1. Issued in cased proof sets.
2. Struck to facilitate photography of coin.
3. Weight 4.5 grams; diameter 20mm.

Elizabeth II 1952 —

The brass threepence for this reign used the obverse portrait of Elizabeth II by Mary Gillick and a Tudor portcullis design on the reverse by William Gardner.

The first threepences of this reign were issued in 1953 in the so-called 'plastic sets' of nine coins in a plastic envelope. These sets were sold at seven shillings and sixpence, not much more than the total face value of the coins. The threepence was not issued for general circulation until some months later, and the design was different in a few minute details. The proof set of that year contained a proof example of the second type.

In 1954, in common with other denominations, the low relief portrait was retouched because of striking difficulties with the 1953 coin. In addition, the legend was altered nd the stops were made slightly more rounded in shape.

Denomination	Metal	Weight (grams)	Diameter (mm)	Rev. alignment
Threepence	'Nickel-brass' (Copper 79%, Zinc 20%, Nickel 1%)	6.8	12-sided figure: across sides: 21mm across corners: 22mm	↑

Obverse 1 Head 1, right; ELIZABETH II DEI GRA BRITT OMN REGINA F D. Stops are oval

Obverse 2 Head 2, recut, right; ELIZABETH II DEI GRATIA REGINA F D. Stops are rounder

Reverse 1 Tudor portcullis with chains; crown or coronet above. THREE PENCE (date)

Edge plain, 12 sides

Obv. 1   Obv. 2   Rev. 1

No.	Date	Features	Obv.	Rev.	EF	UNC
EL23DB-005	1953	[1]	1	1	1	3
EL23DB-010	1953	PROOF	1	1	4	8
EL23DB-015	1953	PROOF from sandblasted dies [2]	1	1		150
EL23DB-020	1954		2	1	2	8
EL23DB-025	1954	PROOF	2	1		150
EL23DB-030	1955		2	1	2	8
EL23DB-035	1955	PROOF	2	1		150
EL23DB-040	1956		2	1	2	8
EL23DB-045	1956	PROOF	2	1		150
EL23DB-050	1957		2	1	2	6
EL23DB-055	1957	PROOF	2	1		150
EL23DB-060	1958		2	1	2	8
EL23DB-065	1958	struck in cupronickel	2	1	300	400
EL23DB-070	1958	PROOF	2	1		150
EL23DB-075	1959		2	1	2	6
EL23DB-080	1959	PROOF	2	1		150
EL23DB-085	1960		2	1	2	6
EL23DB-090	1960	PROOF	2	1		150
EL23DB-095	1961		2	1	1	2
EL23DB-100	1961	PROOF	2	1		150
EL23DB-105	1962		2	1	1	2
EL23DB-110	1962	PROOF	2	1		150
EL23DB-115	1963		2	1	1	2
EL23DB-120	1963	PROOF	2	1		150
EL23DB-125	1964		2	1	1	2
EL23DB-130	1964	PROOF	2	1		150
EL23DB-135	1965		2	1	1	2
EL23DB-140	1965	PROOF	2	1		150
EL23DB-145	1966		2	1	1	2
EL23DB-150	1966	struck in cupronickel [3]	2	1	300	400
EL23DB-155	1966	PROOF	2	1		150
EL23DB-160	1967		2	1	1	2
EL23DB-165	1967	PROOF	2	1	1	150
EL23DB-170	1970	PROOF [4]	2	1	1	3
EL23DB-175		'double headed' error	2	obv 2		350

1. Two almost identical types.
2. Struck to facilitate photography of coin.
3. Weight 5.9 grams.
4. Issued in sealed proof sets.

Silver Twopence

Charles II 1660–1685

The first machine-struck twopence belonged to the series of four coins usually referred to as the 'Undated Maundy'. The dies for these coins were probably the work of Thomas Simon. The first of the dated twopences was, exceptionally, struck in 1668, two years before the first dated fourpence, threepence and penny. Catalogues do not usually record die axes, and it is not generally realised that this one date is the only one struck 'en medaille', i.e. with obverse/reverse axis alignment top to top. All other silver coinage for the next century or so, apart from a few proofs, was struck 'top to bottom'. It has been conjectured that this single piece was a pattern by Roettier for his small silver coinage introduced in 1670. The fact that this coin is struck in this manner would lend some credence to this theory, as it has been the practice down the years of striking many pattern pieces 'en medaille'. It will be seen from this catalogue, however, that Charles II crowns, halfcrowns and shillings were all to a limited extent struck 'en medaille' in the first year of issue. Whether these are all worn patterns or proofs cannot be determined. Only the twopence appears to be exclusively struck thus during the first year.

The small silver coinage introduced a few years prior to the dated issue had been hoarded to an extent, and this fact was responsible for the issue of low denomination coinage in copper in 1672. The royal Proclamation of 16 August 1672 legalising this copper currency stated that 'we have found by experience...by having our small silver money bought in and hoarded up, so that there might be a scarcity thereof in common payments...'

Denomination	Metal	Weight (grams)	Diameter (mm)	Rev. alignment
Twopence undated	Silver	1.0	14	varies
Twopence 1668	Silver	1.0	14	↑
Twopence 1670-1684	Silver	1.0	14	↓

Obverse 1 Head 1, left; II behind head; CAROLVS II D G M B F & H REX

Obverse 2 Head 2, right; CAROLVS II DEI GRATIA

Reverse 1 Shield enclosing arms of England, Scotland, Ireland, France; CHRISTO AVSPICE REGNO

Reverse 2 Two crowned interlinked 'C's; MAG BR FRA ET HIB REX (date)

Edge plain

| Obv. 1 | Obv. 2 | Rev. 1 | Rev. 2 |

No.	Date	Features	Obv.	Rev.	F	VF	EF
C22MM-005	none		1	1	16	30	60
C22MM-010	1668	unusual rev. ↑ as stated [1]	2	2	20	35	100
C22MM-015	1670		2	2	16	25	50
C22MM-020	1671		2	2	16	25	50
C22MM-025	1672	2 over 1 [2]	2	2	16	25	50
C22MM-030	1673		2	2	16	25	50
C22MM-035	1674		2	2	16	25	50
C22MM-040	1675		2	2	18	30	55
C22MM-045	1676		2	2	16	25	50
C22MM-050	1677		2	2	18	30	55
C22MM-055	1678		2	2	16	25	50
C22MM-060	1678	8 over 6	2	2	16	25	50
C22MM-065	1679		2	2	16	25	50
C22MM-070	1679	struck on large flan [3]	2	2	16	25	50
C22MM-075	1679	HIB over FRA (rev.)	2	2	20	30	70
C22MM-080	1680		2	2	16	25	50
C22MM-085	1680	80 over 79	2	2	18	28	60
C22MM-090	1681		2	2	16	25	50
C22MM-095	1682		2	2	16	25	50
C22MM-100	1682	2 over 1	2	2	16	25	50
C22MM-105	1682	2 over 1 ERA instead of FRA (rev.)	2	2	16	25	50
C22MM-110	1683		2	2	16	25	50
C22MM-115	1683	3 over 2	2	2	16	25	50
C22MM-120	1684	[4]	2	2	18	30	55

1. Possibly a pattern; see text above.
2. Coin without overdate may exist.
3. Diameter 15-16 mm; weight 1.2 grams.
4. Stop varieties exist.

James II 1685–1688

The short series for James II was, as with the other small coinage, designed and engraved by John Roettier.

Denomination	Metal	Weight (grams)	Diameter (mm)	Rev. alignment
Twopence	Silver	1.0	14	↓

Obverse 1 Head 1, left; IACOBVS II DEI GRATIA

Reverse 1 Large II, crowned; MAG BR FRA ET HIB REX (date)

Edge plain

| Obv. 1 | Rev. 1 |

No.	Date	Features	Obv.	Rev.	F	VF	EF
J22M-005	1686	[1]	1	1	16	25	50
J22M-010	1686	IΛCOBVS instead of IACOBVS (obv.) [1]	1	1	16	25	50
J22M-015	1687		1	1	18	30	60
J22M-020	1687	ERA instead of FRA (rev.)	1	1	30	45	100
J22M-025	1688		1	1	16	25	50
J22M-030	1688	latter 8 over 7	1	1	16	25	50

1. O in IACOBVS sometimes smaller (obv.).

William and Mary 1688–1694

Unlike the threepence and fourpence, the twopence has only a single obverse type. Like the other pieces, it bears a rather caricatured portrayal of the two monarchs by an unknown designer, possibly George Bower (see fourpences). The reverse introduces the crowned Arabic numeral which still exists on the modern Maundy coinage.

This issue is rare in extremely fine or better condition.

Denomination	Metal	Weight (grams)	Diameter (mm)	Rev. alignment
Twopence	Silver	1.0	14	↓

Obverse 1 Heads 1, right; GVLIELMVS ET MARIA D G

Reverse 1 Crowned '2'; MAG BR FR ET HIB REX ET REGINA (date)

Edge plain

Obv. 1

Rev. 1

No.	Date	Features	Obv.	Rev.	F	VF	EF
WM2M-005	1689		1	1	14	22	50
WM2M-010	1691		1	1	16	25	55
WM2M-015	1692		1	1	14	22	50
WM2M-020	1693	[1]	1	1	14	22	50
WM2M-025	1693	3 over 2	1	1	14	22	50
WM2M-030	1694	[2]	1	1	16	25	55
WM2M-035	1694	4 over 3	1	1	18	30	60
WM2M-040	1694	MARLA instead of MARIA (obv.)	1	1	16	25	55
WM2M-045	1694	HI instead of HIB (rev.)	1	1	16	25	55

1. Positioning of obv. lettering varies.
2. Positioning of obv. lettering and spacing varies.

William III 1695–1701

The William III twopence continues the general design concept of the previous reign, but unlike the other small silver the reverse appears to have undergone some modification. In particular the numeral is thinner and shorter. It is generally held that the obverses were by Johann Crocker (John Croker) and the reverses probably by him and/or an assistant.

There are no mintmarks on these coins as they were produced after the closure of the provincial mints.

Denomination	Metal	Weight (grams)	Diameter (mm)	Rev. alignment
Twopence	Silver	1.0	14	↓

Obverse 1 Head 1, right; GVLIELMVS III DEI GRA

Reverse 1 Crowned '2'; MAG BR FRA ET HIB REX (date)

Edge plain

Obv. 1

Rev. 1

No.	Date	Obv.	Rev.	F	VF	EF
W32M-005	1698	1	1	20	32	55
W32M-010	1699	1	1	18	30	50
W32M-015	1700	1	1	18	30	50
W32M-020	1701	1	1	18	30	50

The denomination numeral '2' varies in style and thickness.

Anne 1702–1714

John Croker and/or Samuel Bull may have been responsible for the obverse of this series, but there is some doubt about the identity of the designers and engravers of the reverse. The '2' on the reverse reverted to a design much nearer that used during the reign of William and Mary. On some of the William III twopences the numeral had varied in style somewhat.

Denomination	Metal	Weight (grams)	Diameter (mm)	Rev. alignment
Twopence	Silver	1.0	14	↓

Obverse 1 Head 1, left; ANNA DEI GRATIA

Reverse 1 Crowned '2'; MAG BR FRA ET HIB REG (date)

Reverse 2 Similar but MAG BRI FR ET HIB REG; crown is larger

Edge plain

Obv. 1

Rev. 1

No.	Date	Features	Obv.	Rev.	F	VF	EF
A2M-005	1703		1	1	18	35	65
A2M-010	1704	[1]	1	1	15	30	55
A2M-015	1704	no obverse stops	1	1	15	30	55
A2M-020	1705		1	1	15	30	55
A2M-025	1706		1	1	15	30	55
A2M-030	1707		1	1	15	30	55
A2M-035	1708		1	2	16	32	60
A2M-040	1709		1	2	16	32	60
A2M-045	1710		1	2	15	30	55
A2M-050	1713		1	2	15	30	55

1. Date position varies.

George I 1714–1727

The series continued with little alteration to the basic format. John Croker and Samuel Bull were responsible for the designs. The German titles of the king were omitted as they would not fit conveniently on such a small coin.

Denomination	Metal	Weight (grams)	Diameter (mm)	Rev. alignment
Twopence	Silver	1.0	14	↓

Obverse 1 Head 1, right; GEORGIVS DEI GRA

Reverse 1 Crowned '2'; MAG BRI FR ET HIB REX (date)

Edge plain

Obv. 1

Rev. 1

No.	Date	Features	Obv.	Rev.	F	VF	EF
G12M-005	1717		1	1	15	25	50
G12M-010	1721		1	1	15	25	50
G12M-015	1723		1	1	20	32	65
G12M-020	1726		1	1	15	25	50
G12M-025	1727	[1]	1	1	16	28	55

1. 0 in GEORGIVS varies in size (obv.).

George II 1727–1760

As on the other small silver, the John Croker young portrait of the monarch was used throughout the series. It will be remembered that on the larger silver the young portrait was replaced in 1743. The reverse of the twopence was possibly executed by Johann Tanner.

Denomination	Metal	Weight (grams)	Diameter (mm)	Rev. alignment
Twopence	Silver	1.0	14	↓

Obverse 1 Head 1, left; GEORGIVS II DEI GRATIA

Reverse 1 Crowned '2'; MAG BRI FR ET HIB REX (date)

Edge plain

Obv. 1

Rev. 1

No.	Date	Features	Obv.	Rev.	F	VF	EF
G22M-005	1729		1	1	14	22	35
G22M-010	1731		1	1	14	22	35
G22M-015	1732		1	1	14	22	35
G22M-020	1735		1	1	14	22	35
G22M-025	1737		1	1	14	22	35
G22M-030	1739	1	1	1	14	22	35
G22M-035	1740		1	1	18	30	55
G22M-040	1743		1	1	14	22	35
G22M-045	1743	3 over 0	1	1	14	22	35
G22M-050	1746		1	1	14	22	35
G22M-055	1756		1	1	14	22	35
G22M-060	1756	large date	1	1	14	22	35
G22M-065	1759		1	1	14	22	35
G22M-070	1760		1	1	14	22	35

1. Some struck from cracked die.

George III 1760–1820

The first date of George III twopence, 1763, is not as common as sometimes thought. The error arises because of the large numbers of fourpences and threepences that were minted. In fact, apart from the very rare 1765 and the 1792, it is probably the scarcest date. As with the other small silver, the young head type was minted in isolated years until 1786, when after a gap the 'Wire Money' issue of 1792 was followed by the five different date issues up to 1820, the same years as the minting of the other three small silver coins. This period marks the beginning of the true Maundy 'set' of four coins, as opposed to a somewhat artificial assembling of the four small silver pieces in earlier years.

Denomination	Metal	Weight (grams)	Diameter (mm)	Rev. alignment
Twopence 1762-1786	Silver	1.0	14	↓
Twopence 1792-1800	Silver	1.0	14	↑
Twopence 1817-1820	Silver	0.9	13	↑

Obverse 1 Head 1, right; GEORGIVS III DEI GRATIA

Obverse 2 Head 2, right; same legend

Obverse 3 Head 3, laureate, right; GEORGIUS III DEI GRATIA (date)

Reverse 1 Crowned '2' in high relief; MAG BRI FR ET HIB REX (date, across crown)

Reverse 2 Completely redesigned; stylised '2' under small crown; date below '2'; same legend

Reverse 3 Redesigned; more similar to Reverse 1 but crown very different; same legend; date is below '2'

Reverse 4: Crowned '2'; BRITANNIARUM REX FID DEF (no date)

Edge plain

Obv. 1   Obv. 2   Obv. 3

Rev. 1   Rev. 2   Rev. 3   Rev. 4

No.	Date	Features	Obv.	Rev.	F	VF	EF
G32M-005	1763		1	1	16	25	40
G32M-010	1763	PROOF; rev. ↑	1	1			600
G32M-015	1765		1	1	120	280	700
G32M-020	1766		1	1	12	18	26
G32M-025	1772		1	1	12	18	26
G32M-030	1772	second 7 over 6	1	1	12	18	26
G32M-035	1776		1	1	12	18	26
G32M-040	1780		1	1	12	18	26
G32M-045	1784		1	1	12	18	26
G32M-050	1786		1	1	12	18	26
G32M-055	1792	1	2	2	20	35	70
G32M-060	1795		2	3	10	15	22
G32M-065	1800		2	3	8	14	20
G32M-070	1817		3	4	8	12	18
G32M-075	1818		3	4	8	12	18
G32M-080	1820		3	4	8	12	18

1. 'Wire Money' issue.

George IV 1820–1830

The twopence was by now primarily a Maundy coin. From 1822 onwards the coin was struck each year until the present day for Maundy purposes. Some may have been struck for circulation in the Colonies. Because of the change in use of this coin from about this time, the tables below from 1822 until the present day are abbreviated, but the detailed and expanded tables will be found under the heading of Maundy sets.

Denomination	Metal	Weight (grams)	Diameter (mm)	Rev. alignment
Maundy Twopence	Silver	0.9	13	↓

Obverse 1 Head 1, left; GEORGIUS IIII BRITANNIARUM REX F D

Reverse 1 Crowned '2' and divided date, all within wreath

Edge plain

No.	Date	Features	Obv.	Rev.	VF	EF	FDC
G42M-005	1822-1830 1		1	1	8	12	20

1. Proofs were struck in 1822, 1828.

William IV 1830–1837

Denomination	Metal	Weight (grams)	Diameter (mm)	Rev. alignment
Maundy Twopence	Silver	0.9	13	↓

Obverse 1 Head 1, right; GULIELMUS IIII D G BRITANNIAR REX F D

Reverse 1 Crowned '2' and divided date, all within wreath

Edge plain

No.	Date	Features	Obv.	Rev.	VF	EF	FDC
W42M-005	1831-1837 1		1	1	8	14	20

1. Proofs in gold and silver were struck in 1831.

Victoria 1837–1901

Denomination	Metal	Weight (grams)	Diameter (mm)	Rev. alignment
Maundy Twopence 1838-1887	Silver	0.9	13	↓
Maundy Twopence 1888-1901	Silver	0.9	13	↑

Obverse 1 Head 1, left; VICTORIA D G BRITANNIAR REGINA F D (this obverse is identical to that on the quarter farthing)

Obverse 2 Head 2, left; same legend

Obverse 3 Head 3, left; VICTORIA DEI GRA BRITT REGINA FID DEF IND IMP

Reverse 1 Crowned '2' and divided date, all within wreath

Reverse 2 Similar but crown and '2' very different

Edge plain

No.	Date	Features	Obv.	Rev.	VF	EF	FDC
VY2M-005	1838-1887 [1]		1	1	7	10	14
VJ2M-010	1888-1892 [2]		2	2	8	12	16
VO2M-015	1893-1901		3	2	5	8	12

1. Proofs were struck in 1838 1839 1853 1867 1871 1878 1881.
2. Proofs were struck in 1888.

For details of proofs see Maundy listings.

Currency twopences of identical design but inferior strike were minted for colonial use (mainly for British Guiana) as below:

Denomination	Metal	Weight (grams)	Diameter (mm)	Rev. alignment
Twopence (currency issue)	Silver	0.9	13	↓

Obverse 1 Head 1, left; VICTORIA D G BRITANNIAR REGINA F D

Reverse 1 Crowned '2' and divided date, all within wreath

Edge plain

No.	Date	Features	Obv.	Rev.	F	VF	EF	UNC
VY2M-020	1838	[1]	1	1	5	7	10	16
VY2M-025	1843		1	1	5	7	12	18
VY2M-030	1848		1	1	5	7	12	18

1. Latter '8' occurs in two very different styles.

Edward VII 1902–1910

Denomination	Metal	Weight (grams)	Diameter (mm)	Rev. alignment
Maundy Twopence	Silver	0.9	13	↑

Obverse 1 Head 1, right; EDWARDVS VII D G BRITT OMN REX F D IND IMP

Reverse 1 Crowned '2' and divided date, all within wreath

Edge plain

No.	Date	Features	Obv.	Rev.	VF	EF	FDC
E72M-005	1902-1910 [1]		1	1	6	10	14

1. Matt proofs were struck in 1902.

George V 1910–1936

Denomination	Metal	Weight (grams)	Diameter (mm)	Rev. alignment
Maundy Twopence 1911-1920	0.925 Silver	0.9	13	↑
Maundy Twopence 1921-1936	0.5 Silver	0.9	13	↑

Obverse 1 Head 1, left; GEORGIVS V D G BRITT OMN REX F D IND IMP

Obverse 2 Head 2, so-called 'modified effigy', left; same legend

Obverse 3 Head 2, re-engraved, left; same legend

Reverse 1 Crowned '2' and divided date, all within wreath

Edge plain

No.	Date	Features	Obv.	Rev.	VF	EF	FDC
G52M-005	1911-1927 [1]		1	1	8	11	16
G52M-010	1928-1929		2	1	8	11	16
G52M-015	1930-1936		3	1	8	11	16

1. See note on 1911 issue under Maundy sets.

George VI 1937–1952

Denomination	Metal	Weight (grams)	Diameter (mm)	Rev. alignment
Maundy Twopence 1937-1946	0.5 Silver	0.9	13	↑
Maundy Twopence 1947-1952	0.925 Silver	0.9	13	↑

There is a very slight difference in the base metal constituency of the 1937 Maundy set given at the Maundy ceremony from that of the set included in the 1937 proof set.

Obverse 1 Head 1, left; GEORGIVS VI D G BR OMN REX F D IND IMP

Obverse 2 Head 1, left; GEORGIVS VI D G BR OMN REX FIDEI DEF

Reverse 1 Crowned '2' and divided date, all within wreath

Edge plain

No.	Date	Obv.	Rev.	VF	EF	FDC
G62M-005	1937-1948 [1]	1	1	8	10	14
G62M-010	1949-1952	2	1	8	11	15

1. See note on 1937 issue under Maundy sets.

Elizabeth II 1952 -

Denomination	Metal	Weight (grams)	Diameter (mm)	Rev. alignment
Maundy Twopence	0.925 Silver	0.9	13	↑

Obverse 1 Head 1, right; ELIZABETH II DEI GRA BRITT OMN REGINA F D

Obverse 2 Head 2, recut, right; ELIZABETH II DEI GRATIA REGINA F D

Reverse 1 Crowned '2' and divided date, all within wreath

Edge plain

No.	Date	Features	Obv.	Rev.	VF	EF	FDC
EL22M-005	1953	[1]	1	1	55	65	70
EL22M-010	1954-1995		2	1	14	17	20

1. Varieties, see under Maundy sets.

Copper Twopence

George III 1760–1820

By the end of the 18th century the amount of counterfeit coinage had grown enormously. Indeed, it is difficult in modern times to imagine the state of affairs that existed. Stephen Martin Leake, writing in *An Historical Account of English Money* in 1793, noted that 'very few indeed of the shillings and sixpences now in use appear ever to have been legally coined'. The copper coinage appears to have been the subject of a mass industry in counterfeiting. Genuine coins were melted down and the metal refashioned into lightweight thin specimens of roughly correct diameter. Traders were offering goods priced at double value in counterfeit coinage which was then taken to Scotland and resold, where the best price could be obtained.

Into this maelstrom came one Matthew Boulton, a man with high ideals. His dream was to produce a coinage which was difficult to counterfeit, and in which the value of the coin and that of the intrinsic metal content were closely matched. Boulton opened a mint at Soho, near Birmingham, containing coining presses operated by steam, with many refinements in the preparation of blanks and dies.

For some years Boulton urged the Government to allow him to strike coinage, and finally secured a contract with them in 1797. In a Proclamation dated 26 July 1797, it was declared that 'certain pieces of copper should be coined, which should go and pass for one Penny and two Pennies, and that each of such pieces of one Penny should weigh one ounce Avoirdupois and that each such two Penny pieces should weigh two Ounces Avoirdupois; the intrinsic value of such pieces of 1 Penny and 2 Pennies, workmanship included, corresponding as nearly as possible with the nominal value of the same respectively.'

The new coinage was designed by Heinrich Küchler. The twopence is remarkable in a number of respects. It is the only predecimal base metal coin of this denomination, and it was struck bearing only one date. The coin had a most innovative design. It was inordinately large and thick, in order to fit Boulton's requirements as to intrinsic value. It was one of the heaviest regular British coins ever struck, heavier even than the five guinea piece. It has subsequently become known as the 'Cartwheel Twopence'. Because of its weight, it became very susceptible to edge damage, the pressure on the sharp rim when dropped on the floor being several tons per square inch. The incuse lettering around the broad rim on both sides was intended to foil the counterfeiters as well as being a means to reducing wear on the legend.

The issue is much complicated by the existence of what are usually referred to as 'late Soho' strikings (possibly up to as late as 1830) and 'restrikes' (1848 and later). The former, in various metals, were struck at Soho for unofficial reasons and, under the Proclamation of 1797, might be considered coinage and are included in this catalogue. The restrikes are not included. These were unofficially struck by one W.J. Taylor, who bought the dies in 1848 and produced the restrikes for collectors. Although more or less identical, they cannot be considered to be coinage.

Further complication is caused by the use of what was probably an internal code for identifying coins struck from a specific die. Rather like the harp strings of the early milled coinage, the ship on the reverse was subjected to various minor alterations in design. In addition, other small alterations of punctuation and design occur throughout the series. These are considered too numerous to list, and any collector interested should refer to a specialist work on the subject.

Collectors wishing to embark on the task of collecting by variety will probably be content with any coin bearing sufficient detail to identify it. The collector by type only should aim for a specimen in extremely fine or uncirculated condition, with original lustre, paying special attention to the rim which should be free of nicks.

Unofficially gilded ordinary and proof specimens exist and are sometimes difficult to detect; comparison may need to be made with the specific dies of the official gilt proofs using a reference work such as Peck. 'Late Soho' strikings may be distinguished by similar reference to the dies used.

Denomination	Metal	Weight (grams)	Diameter (mm)	Thickness (mm)	Rev. alignment
Twopence	Copper	56.7	41	5	↓

Obverse 1 Head 1, right; GEORGIUS III D G REX

Reverse 1 Britannia, seated, with shield, facing left, holding olive branch and trident; BRITANNIA 1797

Edge plain

Collecting Hints

Although the twopence bears only the date 1797, the 'Cartwheel' coinage is numismatically a complex subject. There are numerous varieties struck over as long period; attribution requires painstaking checking of minor details of the design against specialist descriptions such as in Peck's *English Copper, Tin and Bronze Coins*, and even then in many cases it is impossible. Peck himself devoted about fifty pages to the coinage of 1797. Anyone intending to collect the varieties exhaustively must be prepared to work hard and have much patience.

Obv. 1

Rev. 1

No.	Date	Features	Obv.	Rev.	F	VF	EF	UNC
G32D-005	1797	[1]	1	1	20	40	150	350
G32D-010	1797	PROOF	1	1				500
G32D-015	1797	bronzed PROOF [2]	1	1				500
G32D-020	1797	gilt PROOF	1	1				700
G32D-025	1797	PROOF [3]	1	1				500
G32D-030	1797	PROOF on thin flan [3]	1	1				500
G32D-035	1797	bronzed PROOF [4]	1	1				500
G32D-040	1797	bronzed PROOF on thin flan [5]	1	1				450
G32D-045	1797	gilt PROOF [4]	1	1				500
G32D-050	1797	gilt PROOF on thin flan [3]	1	1				800
G32D-055	1797	PROOF in silver	1	1				8000
G32D-060	1797	PROOF in silver on thin flan [6]	1	1				6000
G32D-065	1797	PROOF in gold	1	1				15000

1. Many minor varieties; see below.
2. At least 2 different dies.
3. 'Late Soho' issue.
4. 'Late Soho' issue; at least 2 different dies.
5. 'Late Soho' issue; some or all have rev. ↑.
6. Thickness 3.5 mm.

The currency coin was struck from a number of different dies, and details on the ship on the reverse appear to have been frequently altered as a die identification mark. Dots on the drapery folds on the obverse may have been used similarly. Other minor variations can be found on the wreath berries, leaves and hair (obverse); waves, rock, drapery, sea position and stops (reverse).

Three Halfpence

William IV 1830–1837 & Victoria 1837–1901

The silver three-halfpence (1½ pence) was issued for circulation in the colonies, mainly Ceylon and the West Indies, and not in Britain. However, it resembles the British coinage to such an extent that it has come to be regarded as a British denomination, and as such it merits inclusion in this catalogue.

The history of the coin parallels to some extent that of the Britannia groat, but was much more limited. As with the groat, the issue straddles only the reigns of William IV and Victoria, and, like the groat, there are no proofs struck in metals other than silver. For the sake of expediency, the issues of the two reigns are catalogued together rather than broken into two halves. The two issues share the same reverse, and all other characteristics are identical except for the change in monarch.

The portraits of William IV and Victoria are both by William Wyon, while Johann Baptiste Merlen designed the reverses.

Collecting Hints

While no doubt many of these coins became so worn that they were unusable, and others no doubt were lost through holes in pockets, it is surprising how many turn up in very fine or better condition. However, some of the dates are rare, and it is a considerable achievement to assemble a set in extremely fine or near mint state. The 1843 over 1834 overdate is possibly not as rare as some catalogues indicate.

Denomination	Metal	Weight (grams)	Diameter (mm)	Rev. alignment
1½ pence	Silver	0.7	12	↓

Obverse 1 Head 1 (William IV), right; GULIELMUS IIII D G BRITANNIAR REX F D

Obverse 2 Head 2 (Victoria), left; VICTORIA D G BRITANNIAR REGINA F D

Reverse 1 '1½', date below, crown above, all within wreath
Edge plain

Obv. 1   Obv. 2   Rev. 1

William IV

No.	Date	Features	Obv.	Rev.	F	VF	EF	UNC
W43HD-005	1834		1	1	5	8	20	30
W43HD-010	1835		1	1	6	10	26	38
W43HD-015	1835	5 over 4	1	1	5	8	22	32
W43HD-020	1836		1	1	6	9	24	35
W43HD-025	1837		1	1	12	20	70	110

Victoria

No.	Date	Features	Obv.	Rev.	F	VF	EF	UNC
VY3HD-005	1838		2	1	4	7	20	28
VY3HD-010	1839		2	1	4	7	20	28
VY3HD-015	1840		2	1	8	15	50	80
VY3HD-020	1841		2	1	6	10	26	38
VY3HD-025	1842		2	1	6	11	30	42
VY3HD-030	1843		2	1	4	7	18	25
VY3HD-035	1843	PROOF	2	1				400
VY3HD-040	1843	43 over 34	2	1	8	16	50	80
VY3HD-045	1843	43 over 34; PROOF	2	1				700
VY3HD-050	1860		2	1	8	15	50	80
VY3HD-055	1862		2	1	8	15	50	80
VY3HD-060	1862	PROOF	2	1				700
VY3HD-065	1870	PROOF or PATTERN	2	1				1200

Silver Penny

Charles II 1660–1685

The silver penny is the only one of the small silver coins to have been regularly used for the Maundy ceremony in the 17th century. Although the 2-, 3-and 4-pence silver are often referred to as Maundy coinage, there is no doubt that their primary (or even their only) use was as currency coins. It was only during the reign of George III that the Maundy 'set' became an established feature. The silver penny was, of course, also used as currency, otherwise the recipients at the Maundy ceremony would have had no benefit from receiving it. All of the four small silver coins usually turn up in about fine condition; however, there is a tendency for the pennies to be found in the higher grades more often than the other three coins. This would be expected if one assumes that some of the Maundy coinage would have been kept as keepsakes. In addition, the currency small silver coinage was also hoarded, and it was this that was to some extent responsible for the issue of copper coinage in 1672. The hoarding of the silver coinage was mentioned in the royal Proclamation of 16 August 1672 declaring the copper coinage to be current (see under SILVER TWOPENCES).

Apart from some of the later coinage in the hammered series, the first regular machine struck pennies, probably by Thomas Simon (c.1623-1665) appeared around 1664 or 1665, and are undated. The issue of pennies by John Roettier, which began in 1670, established the basic design which was to continue for many years. The portrait of the monarch on the obverse was augmented by a crowned 'C' (for Charles) on the reverse.

Denomination	Metal	Weight (grams)	Diameter (mm)	Rev. alignment
Penny undated	Silver	0.5	12	varies
Penny 1670-1684	Silver	0.5	12	↓

Obverse 1 Head 1, left; 'I' behind head; CAROLVS II D G M B F & H REX

Obverse 2 Head 2, right; CAROLVS II DEI GRATIA

Reverse 1 Shield enclosing Arms of England, Scotland, Ireland, France; CHRISTO AVSPICE REGNO

Reverse 2 Crowned 'C'; MAG BR FRA ET HIB REX (date)

Edge plain

| Obv. 1 | Obv. 2 | Rev. 1 | Rev. 2 |

No.	Date	Features	Obv.	Rev.	F	VF	EF
C21MM-005	none	¹	1	1	20	40	80
C21MM-010	1670	²	2	2	18	35	75
C21MM-015	1671		2	2	18	35	75
C21MM-020	1672	2 over 1	2	2	18	35	75
C21MM-025	1673		2	2	18	35	75
C21MM-030	1674		2	2	18	35	75
C21MM-035	1674	G of GRATIA inverted (obv.)	2	2	18	35	75
C21MM-040	1674	as last but GRACIA instead of GRATIA	2	2	18	35	75
C21MM-045	1675		2	2	20	40	85
C21MM-050	1676		2	2	22	45	90
C21MM-055	1676	G of GRATIA inverted (obv.)	2	2	22	45	90
C21MM-060	1677		2	2	18	35	75
C21MM-065	1677	G of GRATIA inverted (obv.)	2	2	18	35	75
C21MM-070	1678		2	2	22	45	90

No.	Date	Features	Obv.	Rev.	F	VF	EF
C21MM-075	1678	G of GRATIA inverted (obv.)	2	2	22	45	90
C21MM-080	1679		2	2	20	40	85
C21MM-085	1680		2	2	18	35	75
C21MM-090	1680	struck on larger thin flan ³	2	2	100		
C21MM-095	1681		2	2	22	45	90
C21MM-100	1682		2	2	20	40	85
C21MM-105	1682	2 over 1	2	2	20	40	85
C21MM-110	1682	ERA instead of FRA (rev.)	2	2	22	45	90
C21MM-115	1683		2	2	18	35	75
C21MM-120	1684		2	2	20	40	85
C21MM-125	1684	4 over 3	2	2	20	40	85

1. Scarcer than 2, 3 or 4-pence.
2. Date sometimes resembles 1679.
3. Lettering anomalies exist — coins genuine?

James II 1685–1688

John Roettier continued the basic design, replacing the 'C' on the reverse with 'I', which served not only as the initial of the monarch (IACOBVS), but also as a mark of denomination (1 penny).

Denomination	Metal	Weight (grams)	Diameter (mm)	Rev. alignment
Penny	Silver	0.5	12	↓

Obverse 1 Head 1, left; IACOBVS II DEI GRATIA

Reverse 1 Large I, crowned; MAG BR FRA ET HIB REX (date)

Edge plain

| Obv. 1 | Rev. 1 |

No.	Date	Features	Obv.	Rev.	F	VF	EF
J21M-005	1685		1	1	20	35	80
J21M-010	1686		1	1	22	40	90
J21M-015	1687		1	1	20	35	80
J21M-020	1687	7 over 6	1	1	20	35	80
J21M-025	1688		1	1	20	35	80
J21M-030	1688	latter 8 over 7	1	1	20	35	80

William and Mary 1688–1694

The first issue of silver penny in this reign is a strange beast indeed. Not only does it have a different obverse from those of the remaining years, it is also very rare, and the date is unreadable! The writer has seen examples which appear to read 1681 and 1691, and on others the tiny distorted numerals are illegible. Luckily, the date can be identified by the fact that all silver pennies with the first obverse (continuous legend over the heads) are of 1689.

The identity of the designer of the small silver of William and Mary is uncertain. The heads of the monarchs are more stylized than on the other denominations, and are in relatively high relief. The portraits were possibly the work of George Bower (see under FOURPENCES).

Although on the 2-, 3-and 4-pence coins the denomination on the reverse is changed to an Arabic numeral on the William and Mary series, on the penny the '1' was still engraved as a Roman 'I'. The general form of the reverse thus appears very similar to that of the James II penny.

As with the other small silver denominations, the penny is rare in Extremely Fine or better condition.

Denomination	Metal	Weight (grams)	Diameter (mm)	Rev. alignment
Penny	Silver	0.5	12	↓

Obverse 1 Heads 1, right; legend GVLIELMVS ET MARIA D G continuous over heads

Obverse 2 Similar but legend divided by heads

Reverse 1 Crowned 'I'; MAG BR FR ET HIB REX ET REGINA (date)

Edge plain

| Obv. 1 | Obv. 2 | Rev. 1 |

No.	Date	Features	Obv.	Rev.	F	VF	EF
WM1M-005	1689	[1]	1	1	120	300	500
WM1M-010	1689	GVIELMVS instead of GVLIELMVS (obv.) [2]	1	1	150	400	700
WM1M-015	1690		2	1	20	35	80
WM1M-020	1691	latter 1 over 0	2	1	20	35	80
WM1M-025	1692		2	1	40	60	120
WM1M-030	1692	2 over 1	2	1	40	60	120
WM1M-035	1693		2	1	25	40	90
WM1M-040	1694	stops on obv	2	1	20	35	80
WM1M-045	1694	no stops on obv	2	1	20	35	80
WM1M-050	1694	HI instead of HIB (rev.) [3]	2	1	20	35	80
WM1M-055	1694	9 over 6 or inverted 9; HI instead of HIB (rev.) [3]	2	1	20	35	80

1. Date can appear to read 1681, 1691 or be illegible. Minor stop and lettering varieties exist.
2. Date can be illegible. Minor stop and lettering varieties exist.
3. Occur with and without stops on obv.

William III 1695–1701

Johann Crocker, aka John Croker (1670-1741) designed the new portrait for the silver penny after the death of Mary in 1694. This was a more conventional representation of William following the somewhat cartoon-style effigies on the William and Mary small coinage. The reverse, continuing the Roman I denomination, were designed by Croker and/or an assistant.

The small silver coinage was struck after the closure of the provincial mints and thus no mintmarks were placed on them.

Denomination	Metal	Weight (grams)	Diameter (mm)	Rev. alignment
Penny	Silver	0.5	12	↓

Obverse 1 Head 1, right; GVLIELMVS (Head) III DEI GRA

Reverse 1 Crowned 'I'; MAG BR FRA ET HIB REX (date)

Edge plain

| Obv. 1 | Rev. 1 |

No.	Date	Features	Obv.	Rev.	F	VF	EF
W31M-005	1698	[1]	1	1	20	32	55
W31M-010	1698	IRA instead of FRA (rev.)	1	1	20	32	55
W31M-015	1698	HI.BREX instead of HIB.REX (rev.)	1	1	20	32	55
W31M-020	1699		1	1	25	40	75
W31M-025	1700		1	1	25	40	75
W31M-030	1701		1	1	20	32	55

1. Position of date varies.

Anne 1702–1714

The Anne penny was probably designed by John Croker and/or Samuel Bull, although the attribution of the reverse is in some doubt. The coin continues the general design of previous reigns.

Denomination	Metal	Weight (grams)	Diameter (mm)	Rev. alignment
Penny	Silver	0.5	12	↓

Obverse 1 Head 1, left; ANNA DEI GRATIA

Reverse 1 Crowned 'I'; MAG BR FRA ET HIB REG (date)

Reverse 2 Similar but MAG BR FR ET HIB REG

Reverse 3 Similar but MAG BRI FR ET HIB REG

Edge plain

| Obv. 1 | Rev. 3 |

No.	Date	Features	Obv.	Rev.	F	VF	EF
A1M-005	1703		1	1	20	40	70
A1M-010	1705		1	2	22	45	80
A1M-015	1706	[1]	1	2	20	40	70
A1M-020	1708		1	3	35	70	120
A1M-025	1709		1	3	20	40	70
A1M-030	1710		1	3	30	60	110
A1M-035	1713	3 over 0	1	3	20	40	70

1. Position of date varies.

George I 1714–1727

John Croker and Samuel Bull continued as designers and engravers of the small silver coinage. The design of this series is very similar to that of earlier reigns.

In the first year of minting of the silver penny, 1716, no other small silver coinage was struck. In 1717, the other three were struck without the penny; in 1718 and 1720, pennies only were struck, and in 1721 again the penny was the only piece not minted! One had to wait until 1723 before a full so-called 'Maundy set' was issued. Another anomaly which sets the penny apart in the period 1716-23 was that the reverse legend reads MAG BR, etc. whereas on the other three small silver coins the legend reads MAG BRI, etc.

Denomination	Metal	Weight (grams)	Diameter (mm)	Rev. alignment
Penny	Silver	0.5	12	↓

Obverse 1 Head 1, right; GEORGIVS DEI GRA

Reverse 1 Crowned 'I'; MAG BR FR ET HIB REX (date)

Reverse 2 Similar but BRI instead of BR

Edge plain

| Obv. 1 | Rev. 2 |

No.	Date	Features	Obv.	Rev.	F	VF	EF
G11M-005	1716		1	1	15	25	45
G11M-010	1718		1	1	15	25	45
G11M-015	1720		1	1	15	25	45
G11M-020	1720	HIPEX or HIPREX instead of HIB REX (rev.)	1	1	15	25	45
G11M-025	1723		1	1	15	25	45
G11M-030	1725	[1]	1	2	15	25	45
G11M-035	1726		1	2	18	30	55
G11M-040	1727	[2]	1	2	20	35	60

1. Lettering size varies.
2. Lettering smaller than on previous dates.

George II 1727–1760

While the sixpence and larger silver coins used an older portrait of the king by Tanner from 1743 onwards, the small silver coins used the young portrait by John Croker throughout until the king's death in 1760. Tanner, however, may have been responsible for the reverses of the small silver.

For seven of the years between 1750 and 1758 the silver penny was the only coin of the small silver series issued. This fact, coupled with the proliferation of these years in the higher grades, indicate that they were primarily issued for the Maundy ceremony.

Denomination	Metal	Weight (grams)	Diameter (mm)	Rev. alignment
Penny	Silver	0.5	12	↓

Obverse 1 Head 1, left; GEORGIVS II DEI GRATIA

Reverse 1 Crowned 'I'; MAG BRI FR ET HIB REX (date)

Edge plain

Obv. 1   Rev. 1

No.	Date	Features	Obv.	Rev.	F	VF	EF
G21M-005	1729		1	1	14	20	30
G21M-010	1731		1	1	14	20	30
G21M-015	1732	¹	1	1	14	20	30
G21M-020	1735		1	1	15	22	35
G21M-025	1737		1	1	15	22	35
G21M-030	1739		1	1	14	20	30
G21M-035	1740		1	1	14	20	30
G21M-040	1743		1	1	14	20	30
G21M-045	1746		1	1	14	20	30
G21M-050	1746	6 over 3 (?)	1	1	15	22	35
G21M-055	1750		1	1	14	20	30
G21M-060	1752		1	1	14	20	30
G21M-065	1752	2 over 0	1	1	14	20	30
G21M-070	1753		1	1	14	20	30
G21M-075	1753	3 over 2	1	1	15	22	35
G21M-080	1754		1	1	14	20	30
G21M-085	1755		1	1	14	20	30
G21M-090	1756	²	1	1	14	20	30
G21M-095	1757	no colon after GRATIA (obv.) ²	1	1	14	20	30
G21M-100	1757	colon after GRATIA (obv.) ²	1	1	14	20	30
G21M-105	1758		1	1	14	20	30
G21M-110	1759		1	1	14	20	30
G21M-115	1760	³	1	1	14	20	30

1. Head design varies slightly.
2. Date size varies.
3. Obv. lettering size varies.

George III 1760–1820

The silver penny underwent a number of changes during the long reign of George III. Unlike the threepence and fourpence, the first date, 1763, is scarce, but not noticeably more so in the higher grades, since it was primarily used as a Maundy coin. By the end of the reign all of the four small silver coins were used mainly as Maundy pieces.

In 1781 the silver penny was redesigned with a much flatter '1' on the reverse; other minor changes were also made. The next issues, in 1784 and 1786, also featured this new design, and the fourpence was similarly redesigned in lower relief. However, the twopence and threepence retained the high relief reverse. The 1784 and 1786 small silver coinage was the last struck before an even more radical redesign in 1792.

It is possible that the redesign of the '1' in 1781 was because of trouble with metal flowing from the obverse to fill the reverse die during striking. Some of the pennies prior to 1781 have a deep groove across the head of George III resembling a cut. If one examines the alignment of the axes carefully, however, it will be

seen that this flaw follows exactly the line of the '1' on the reverse. The lower relief numeral used from 1781 onwards caused no trouble in this respect. Similar problems occurred with the early George V bronze pennies.

Denomination	Metal	Weight (grams)	Diameter (mm)	Rev. alignment
Penny 1763-1786	Silver	0.5	12	↓
Penny 1792-1800	Silver	0.5	12	↑
Penny 1817-1820	Silver	0.5	11	↑

Obverse 1 Head 1, right; GEORGIVS III DEI GRATIA

Obverse 2 Head 2, right; same legend

Obverse 3 Head 3, laureate, right; GEORGIUS III DEI GRATIA (date)

Reverse 1 Crowned '1' in high relief; MAG BRI FR ET HIB REX (date, across crown)

Reverse 2 Similar but in lower relief; the '1' is much flatter

Reverse 3 Completely redesigned; stylized '1' under small crown; date below '1'; same legend

Reverse 4 Redesigned; more similar to Reverse 1 but crown very different; same legend; date is below '1'

Reverse 5 Crowned '1'; BRITANNIARUM REX FID DEF (no date)

Edge plain

Obv. 1   Obv. 2   Obv. 3

Rev. 1   Rev. 2

Rev. 3   Rev. 4   Rev. 5

No.	Date	Features	Obv.	Rev.	F	VF	EF
G31M-005	1763		1	1	16	22	32
G31M-010	1763	PROOF; rev. ↑	1	1			500
G31M-015	1766		1	1	12	18	24
G31M-020	1770		1	1	12	18	24
G31M-025	1772		1	1	12	18	24
G31M-030	1776		1	1	12	18	24
G31M-035	1779		1	1	12	18	24
G31M-040	1780		1	1	12	18	24
G31M-045	1781		1	2	12	18	24
G31M-050	1784		1	2	12	18	24
G31M-055	1786		1	2	12	18	24
G31M-060	1792	¹	2	3	15	22	28
G31M-065	1795		2	4	10	15	20
G31M-070	1800		2	4	7	11	15
G31M-075	1817		3	5	8	12	18
G31M-080	1818		3	5	8	12	18
G31M-085	1820		3	5	8	12	18

1. 'Wire Money' issue.

George IV 1820–1830

By the reign of George IV, the role of the silver penny was simply that of the smallest of the four silver Maundy coins. From 1822, the four coins have been minted yearly up to the present day, and full details are listed under the heading of Maundy sets. For the sake of continuity, however, the listing of silver pence also continues below in an abbreviated form.

Denomination	Metal	Weight (grams)	Diameter (mm)	Rev. alignment
Maundy Penny	Silver	0.5	11	↓

Obverse 1 Head 1, left; GEORGIUS IIII BRITANNIAR REX F D

Reverse 1 Crowned '1' and divided date, all within wreath

Edge plain

No.	Date	Features	Obv.	Rev.	VF	EF	FDC
G41M-005	1822-1830 [1]		1	1	7	10	18

1. Proofs were struck in 1822, 1828.

William IV 1830–1837

Denomination	Metal	Weight (grams)	Diameter (mm)	Rev. alignment
Maundy Penny	Silver	0.5	11	↓

Obverse 1 Head 1, right; GULIELMUS IIII D G BRITANNIAR REX F D

Reverse 1 Crowned '1' and divided date, all within wreath

Edge plain

No.	Date	Features	Obv.	Rev.	VF	EF	FDC
W41M-005	1831-1837 [1]		1	1	8	14	20

1. Proofs in gold and silver were struck in 1831.

Victoria 1837–1901

Denomination	Metal	Weight (grams)	Diameter (mm)	Rev. alignment
Maundy Penny 1838-1887	Silver	0.5	11	↓
Maundy Penny 1888-1901	Silver	0.5	11	↑

Obverse 1 Head 1, left; VICTORIA D G BRITANNIAR REGINA F D

Obverse 2 Head 2, left; same legend

Obverse 3 Head 3, left; VICTORIA DEI GRA BRITT REGINA FID DEF IND IMP

Reverse 1 Crowned '1' and divided date, all within wreath

Reverse 2 Similar but crown very different

Edge plain

No.	Date	Features	Obv.	Rev.	VF	EF	FDC
VY1M-005	1838-1887 [1]		1	1	6	9	12
VJ1M-010	1888-1892 [2]		2	2	8	12	16
VO1M-015	1893-1901		3	2	5	8	12

1. Proofs were struck in 1838 1839 1853 1867 1871 1878 1881.
2. Proofs were struck in 1888.

For details of proofs see Maundy listings.

Edward VII 1902–1910

Denomination	Metal	Weight (grams)	Diameter (mm)	Rev. alignment
Maundy Penny	Silver	0.5	11	↑

Obverse 1 Head 1, right; EDWARDVS VII D G BRITT OMN REX F D IND IMP

Reverse 1 Crowned '1' and divided date, all within wreath

Edge plain

No.	Date	Features	Obv.	Rev.	VF	EF	FDC
E71M-005	1902-1910 [1]		1	1	6	10	14

No.	Date	Features	Obv.	Rev.	VF	EF	FDC

1. Matt proofs were struck in 1902.

George V 1910–1936

Denomination	Metal	Weight (grams)	Diameter (mm)	Rev. alignment
Maundy Penny 1911-1920	0.925 Silver	0.5	11	↑
Maundy Penny 1921-1936	0.5 Silver	0.5	11	↑

Obverse 1 Head 1, left; GEORGIVS V D G BRITT OMN REX F D IND IMP

Obverse 2 Head 2, so-called 'modified effigy', left; same legend

Obverse 3 Head 2, re-engraved, left; same legend

Reverse 1 Crowned '1' and divided date, all within wreath

Edge plain

No.	Date	Features	Obv.	Rev.	VF	EF	FDC
G51M-005	1911-1927 [1]		1	1	9	12	18
G51M-010	1928-1929		2	1	9	12	18
G51M-015	1930-1936		3	1	9	12	18

1. See note on 1911 issue under Maundy sets.

George VI 1937–1952

Denomination	Metal	Weight (grams)	Diameter (mm)	Rev. alignment
Maundy Penny 1937-1946	0.5 Silver	0.5	11	↑
Maundy Penny 1947-1952	0.925 Silver	0.5	11	↑

There is a very slight difference in the base metal constituency of the 1937 Maundy set given at the Maundy ceremony from that of the set included in the 1937 proof set

Obverse 1 Head 1, left; GEORGIVS VI D G BR OMN REX F D IND IMP

Obverse 2 Head 1, left; GEORGIVS VI D G BR OMN REX FIDEI DEF

Reverse 1 Crowned '1' and divided date, all within wreath

Edge plain

No.	Date	Features	Obv.	Rev.	VF	EF	FDC
G61M-005	1937-1948 [1]		1	1	10	12	16
G61M-010	1949-1952		2	1	10	14	18

1. See note on 1937 issue under Maundy sets.

Elizabeth II 1952 -

Denomination	Metal	Weight (grams)	Diameter (mm)	Rev. alignment
Maundy Penny	0.925 Silver	0.5	11	↑

Obverse 1 Head 1, right; ELIZABETH II DEI GRA BRITT OMN REGINA F D

Obverse 2 Head 2, recut, right; ELIZABETH II DEI GRATIA REGINA F D

Reverse 1 Crowned '1' and divided date, all within wreath

Edge plain

No.	Date	Features	Obv.	Rev.	VF	EF	FDC
EL21M-005	1953 [1]		1	1	60	70	80
EL21M-010	1954-1995		2	1	16	20	24

1. Varieties: see under Maundy sets.

Copper/Bronze Penny

George III 1760 -1820

Although Newton had considered minting a copper penny in 1702, the first were struck in 1797, coincidentally with the copper twopence, and the notes on the twopence apply generally also to the penny. Following Matthew Boulton's ideals about intrinsic value, the weight of the penny is exactly half that of the twopence.

As on the twopence, the details on the ship may have been used as an identification mark for a particular die. However, the penny has many more varieties of ship. Ernest Bramah, in *English Regal Copper Coins* (London, 1929) suggested that there may be as many as a hundred ship varieties on the penny against about eighteen for the twopence. This is probably because, unlike the twopence, the penny remained in circulation for some years. It appears to have been issued for a few years with the date unchanged from 1797.

The pennies of 1806 and 1807 were again struck at the Soho mint and designed by Küchler. The innovative format of the 1797 series was abandoned, and the coinage presents a more conventional appearance.

Edge (1797): plain; (1806-08): grooved down the centre and milled with diagonal lines across the groove

Obv. 1   Obv. 2

Rev. 1   Rev. 2

Collecting Hints

Because the 1797 penny remained in circulation longer than the twopence, the average condition as found is lower than that of the larger coin. However, it appears to be somewhat easier to locate in the top grades. In addition, the penny is less prone to have suffered edge knocks than the twopence. Unless one is intending to assemble a specialised collection of the minor varieties, a single specimen in extremely fine or mint state with original lustre should be the minimum standard to aim for.

The 1806 and 1807 coins are not difficult to find in the higher grades and these should be sought. These pieces exist in large quantities in fine condition.

No.	Date	Features	Obv.	Rev.	F	VF	EF	UNC
G31D-005	1797	[1]	1	1	15	28	100	200
G31D-010	1797	PROOF [2]	1	1				500
G31D-015	1797	bronzed PROOF [2]	1	1				250
G31D-020	1797	gilt PROOF [2]	1	1				200
G31D-025	1797	silvered PROOF [3]	1	1				800
G31D-030	1797	PROOF in tin [3]	1	1				800
G31D-035	1797	PROOF in silver [3]	1	1				1200
G31D-040	1797	PROOF in silver on thin flan [3]	1	1				1000
G31D-045	1797	PROOF in gold [4]	1	1				18000
G31D-050	1806		2	2	6	15	75	140
G31D-055	1806	gilt PROOF	2	2				400
G31D-060	1806	PROOF [5]	2	2				350
G31D-065	1806	PROOF on thin flan; edge plain [3]	2	2				500
G31D-070	1806	bronzed PROOF [5]	2	2				300
G31D-075	1806	bronzed PROOF; edge plain [3]	2	2				400
G31D-080	1806	bronzed PROOF on thin flan; edge plain [3]	2	2				450
G31D-085	1806	gilt PROOF [6]	2	2				400
G31D-090	1806	gilt PROOF; edge plain [3]	2	2				500
G31D-095	1806	gilt PROOF on thin flan; edge plain [3]	2	2				500
G31D-100	1806	PROOF in silver; edge plain [3]	2	2				1500
G31D-105	1807		2	2	6	15	80	150
G31D-110	1807	bronzed PROOF	2	2				700
G31D-115	1807	gilt PROOF	2	2				1000

Denomination	Metal	Weight (grams)	Diameter (mm)	Rev. alignment
Penny 1797	Copper	28.3	36	↓
Penny 1806-1808	Copper	18.9	34	↓

Obverse 1 Head 1, right; GEORGIUS III D G REX

Obverse 2 Head 2, right; GEORGIUS III D G REX (date)

Reverse 1 Britannia, seated, with shield, facing left, holding olive branch and trident; BRITANNIA 1797

Reverse 2 Britannia facing left, holding olive branch and trident; BRITANNIA

No.	Date	Features	Obv.	Rev.	F	VF	EF	UNC
G31D-120	1808	7	2	2				35000

1. Many minor varieties; see below.
2. 'Late Soho' issue; several varieties.
3. 'Late Soho' issue.
4. 'Late Soho' issue; thickness varies; weight 27 to 39 grams.
5. 'Late Soho' issue; several varieties; some may have reverse ↑.
6. 'Late Soho' issue; at least 2 varieties.
7. Unique. Probably a proof.

The currency coin of 1797 was struck from a number of different dies, and details on the ship on the reverse appear to have been frequently altered as a die identification mark. Dots on the drapery folds on the obverse may have been used similarly. Other minor variations can be found on the wreath berries, leaves and hair (obverse); waves, rock, drapery, sea position and stops (reverse).

George IV 1820–1830

At the beginning of the 'Great Recoinage' in 1816, only silver coins were produced. The first copper coins were farthings of 1821-26 bearing the Pistrucci head of the king. By the time the first pennies were minted in 1825, Pistrucci had come into some disgrace at the Mint, not least because of his refusal to engrave a portrait of the monarch based on that of another artist, Chantrey. Pistrucci, an Italian with an inflated ego, considered that by doing so his position as an artist would be compromised. The king did not like Pistrucci's representation of himself, especially as depicted on the crown piece. He presumably had no wish to see another coin of similar size issued with such an unflattering portrait. William Wyon was therefore commissioned to engrave the portrait for the penny, and comparison with the obverse of the first issue of farthings will show that the decision was a wise one.

The penny was issued for only three years, including 1826, when a proof example was included in the proof set of that year. The penny of 1827, the last year of issue, is particularly rare.

Collecting Hints

Although the series spans only three years, a collection containing all of the varieties is difficult to achieve, as many of them are elusive. In particular, brilliant uncirculated specimens are very rare.

Denomination	Metal	Weight (grams)	Diameter (mm)	Rev. alignment
Penny	Copper	18.8	34	↑

Obverse 1 Head 1, left; GEORGIUS IV DEI GRATIA (date)

Reverse 1 Britannia, seated, with shield, facing right, holding trident; the arms of the saltire on the Union Flag on the shield has no central line; BRITANNIAR REX FID DEF

Reverse 2 Similar but thin line down arms of saltire

Reverse 3 Similar but thick line down arms of saltire

Edge plain

Obv. 1

Rev. 1   Rev. 3

No.	Date	Features	Obv.	Rev.	F	VF	EF	UNC
G41D-005	1825		1	1	12	24	75	150
G41D-010	1825	PROOF	1	1				500
G41D-015	1826		1	1	10	20	60	120
G41D-020	1826	PROOF	1	1				350
G41D-025	1826	bronzed PROOF 1	1	1				250
G41D-030	1826		1	2	12	24	75	150
G41D-035	1826	bronzed PROOF	1	2				250
G41D-040	1826		1	3	15	30	100	250
G41D-045	1826	PROOF	1	3				600
G41D-050	1826	bronzed PROOF	1	3				350
G41D-055	1827	2	1	1	50	150	1500	3000

1. Issued in cased proof sets.
2. Struck for circulation in Australia.

William IV 1830–1837

The obverse of the penny was engraved by William Wyon from a model by Sir Francis Chantrey. The layout of the obverse is similar to that of the George IV coin, while the reverse is identical.

Ernest Bramah (*English Regal Copper Coins*, 1929) reported that 'on very good authority' a penny of 1836 existed in Australia and that it had been sent to Britain for inspection. Montagu (*Copper, Tin and Bronze Coinage of England*, 1893) believed that its existence was doubtful. It is included in the tables below, therefore, with these provisos.

Collecting Hints

Specimens in extremely fine condition should be sought. Brilliant uncirculated specimens are very rare.

Denomination	Metal	Weight (grams)	Diameter (mm)	Rev. alignment
Penny	Copper	18.8	34	↑

Obverse 1 Head 1, right; .W.W incuse on truncation; GULIELMUS IIII DEI GRATIA (date)

Obverse 2 Similar but no initials on truncation

Reverse 1 Britannia, seated, with shield, facing right, holding trident; BRITANNIAR REX FID DEF (as Reverse 1 of George IV issue)

Edge plain

Obv. 2   Rev. 1

No.	Date	Features	Obv.	Rev.	F	VF	EF	UNC
W41D-005	1831	¹	1	1	14	60	180	350
W41D-010	1831		2	1	12	50	150	300
W41D-015	1831	bronzed PROOF	2	1				400
W41D-020	1831	bronzed PROOF; rev. ↓	2	1				300
W41D-025	1834		2	1	14	60	160	320
W41D-030	1836	²	2	1				
W41D-035	1837		2	1	16	80	250	450

1. Some exist without stop before first W on truncation.
2. Existence doubtful; see above.

Victoria 1837–1901

The Victorian penny is one of the most intricate and involved denominations of the British coinage. It comprises two broad divisions, the copper and the bronze series. Although the copper series possesses many varieties, mainly in colon position and type of trident, it is the bronze series from 1860 onwards which exhibits a remarkably wide range of varieties of all kinds. This is especially true up to the year 1883.

The Victorian penny has been the subject of much study, and a number of specialised books exist on the subject. Many of the varieties will be of interest only to a specialist collector of the series, and in a catalogue such as this some abbreviation is obviously necessary. For this reason, many of the minor varieties will be given in annotated form rather than allocating each variety a separate entry, and some may be omitted.

The copper penny was designed by William Wyon. He died in 1851, and the task of designing and engraving the bronze coinage fell to his elder son, Leonard Charles Wyon (1826-91). Unlike the silver coinage, there was no jubilee issue of bronze coins, and the veiled head design was not introduced on the bronze coinage until 1895. This was designed by Thomas Brock and engraved by G. W. de Saulles.

Some dates of Victoria young head pennies bear a small 'H' beneath the date. This signifies coins struck by Messrs. Ralph Heaton of Birmingham. This firm also assisted in the production during other years in which the mintmark was not used.

Collecting Hints

The minimum grade of this series acceptable to a serious collector would be about very fine. Fine specimens, especially in the bronze series, do not show enough of the delicate workmanship of the design. In addition, if one is collecting the minor varieties, a fine condition specimen may not be detailed enough to provide identification.

The bronze penny provides an excellent subject for study by the serious numismatist, and is likely to appeal more to the intellectually inclined collector. However, because the collecting of bronze is not perhaps as popular as, say, the larger silver coins, there are excellent chances for the discovery of rarities. Many go unnoticed through ignorance. Indeed, one of the leading writers in this field once bought an unnoticed coronetted head pattern penny of Victoria from the tray of one of the top London dealers!

'Ghosting', caused by clashed dies, is prevalent throughout the Victorian series, and should not be a deterrent to the purchase of a specimen. What happens is that, prior to striking, the dies clash together when a blank is not in position and traces of design transfer between the dies on impact. The 1860 copper penny appears always to have ghosting markings under the chin of Victoria. These originate from the drapery of Britannia on the reverse, and provide a useful identification mark, as some forgeries exist where the date has been altered. A further check is that the genuine 1860 copper penny will not have W.W. on the truncation, although of course this does not preclude any forgeries made from pennies dated 1858 and 1859. Note also that the genuine 1860 penny itself has the date altered from 1859 on the die.

Proofs were never prepared from dies bearing clashing marks, and any prooflike specimen with ghosting may be assumed not to be a proof.

Original mint lustre is more important with copper and bronze than it is with silver. Not only does the retention of original lustre make the coin more pleasing, but it is also difficult or impossible to restore it artificially. One should become aware of the characteristics of various types of artificial lustre, and pay special attention to the amount of structural wear that the coin possesses. It is all too easy to see a lustrous coin, and fail to notice that much detail has worn off. Collectors are often convinced they possess an 1860 (bronze) beaded border specimen, or even a mule beaded/toothed specimen, when they do not. This is because the border on some of the toothed issue is very prominent and the teeth are almost round. On a genuine beaded border specimen, the dots are circular and stand apart from the border in a way that leaves no room for doubt.

Denomination	Metal	Weight (grams)	Diameter (mm)	Rev. alignment
Penny 1839-1860	Copper	18.8	34	↑
Penny 1860-1901	Bronze (copper 95%; tin 4%; zinc 1%)	9.4	31	↑

Obverse 1 Head 1, left, W.W. on truncation; VICTORIA DEI GRATIA (date)

Obverse 2 Similar but no W.W. on truncation

Obverse 3 Head 2, left; VICTORIA D G BRITT REG F D; 'L.C. Wyon' on bust near rim; beaded border

Obverse 4 Similar but toothed border

Obverse 5 Similar but 'L.C. Wyon' between bust and rim

Obverse 6 Similar but no 'L.C. Wyon'

Obverse 7 Head 3, left; slightly older features; same legend

Obverse 8 Head 4, left; VICTORIA DEI GRA BRITT REGINA FID DEF IND IMP

Reverse 1 Britannia, seated, with shield, holding trident, facing right; BRITANNIAR REG FID DEF (as reverse of William IV issue but trident head is ornamented except where stated, and REX becomes REG)

Reverse 2 Redesigned Britannia, seated with shield, holding trident, facing right; ONE PENNY; date in exergue below Britannia; 'L.C.W' on base line near shield; beaded border

Reverse 3 Similar but toothed border

Reverse 4 Similar but 'L.C.W.' below Britannia's foot at right

Reverse 5 Similar to Reverse 3 but 'L.C.W.' replaced by rock formation

Reverse 6 Similar but Britannia completely redesigned; 'P' of 'PENNY' is 2mm from trident head

Reverse 7 Similar but 'P' of 'PENNY' is 1mm from trident head. Sea level is higher

Reverse 8 Similar but sea level is even higher

Edge plain

It must be emphasised that on the young head bronze coinage (obverses 3 to 6; reverses 2 to 5) there exist a great many varieties. It would be impossible to cover these in detail or allocate different obverse/reverse numbers in a work of this nature. The major varieties are allocated different die types as above but the minor ones are referred to in annotated form in the tables, with details such as where on the die the varieties occur. Collectors requiring detailed information should refer to a specialised work such as by Peck, Gouby or Freeman.

Rev. 2

Rev. 3

Rev. 6

Rev. 7

Obv. 1

Obv. 3

Obv. 5

Obv. 7

Obv. 8

Rev. 1

Rev. 1: plain trident

Rev. 1: ornamental trident

No.	Date	Features	Obv.	Rev.	F	VF	EF	UNC
VY1D-005	1839	bronzed PROOF [1]	1	1		180	300	400
VY1D-010	1841	no colon after REG	1	1	5	10	45	80
VY1D-015	1841	colon after REG	1	1	10	25	100	200
VY1D-020	1841	colon after REG PROOF	1	1				700
VY1D-025	1841	colon after REG bronzed PROOF	1	1				600
VY1D-030	1841	colon after REG PROOF in silver [2]	1	1				4000
VY1D-035	1843	no colon after REG	1	1	50	160	600	900
VY1D-040	1843	colon after REG	1	1	35	120	400	600
VY1D-045	1844		1	1	5	12	55	100
VY1D-050	1845		1	1	10	24	100	200
VY1D-055	1846		1	1	5	14	65	130
VY1D-060	1846	near colon (see below)	1	1	7	18	80	170
VY1D-065	1847		1	1	5	14	65	130
VY1D-070	1847	near colon	1	1	5	14	65	130
VY1D-075	1848		1	1	5	14	65	130
VY1D-080	1848	8 over 6	1	1	10	22	120	220
VY1D-085	1848	8 over 7	1	1	5	14	70	140
VY1D-090	1849		1	1	80	200	800	1400
VY1D-095	1851	[3]	1	1	5	14	65	130
VY1D-100	1851	near colon	1	1	5	15	75	150
VY1D-105	1853		1	1	4	9	32	55
VY1D-110	1853	PROOF	1	1			350	700
VY1D-115	1853	bronzed PROOF rev.↓[4]	1	1			200	400
VY1D-120	1853	near colon; trident head not ornamented	1	1	5	11	40	70
VY1D-125	1854		1	1	5	10	35	65
VY1D-130	1854	near colon; trident head not ornamented	1	1	5	10	35	65
VY1D-135	1854	PROOF; near colon; trident head not ornamented	1	1				250
VY1D-140	1854	near colon; trident head not ornamented 4 over 3	1	1	20	50	150	250
VY1D-145	1855		1	1	5	10	40	70
VY1D-150	1855	near colon; trident head not ornamented	1	1	5	10	40	70
VY1D-155	1856		1	1	10	30	150	280

No.	Date	Features	Obv.	Rev.	F	VF	EF	UNC
VY1D-160	1856	near colon; trident head not ornamented	1	1	18	50	250	400
VY1D-165	1856	near colon; trident head not ornamented PROOF	1	1				700
VY1D-170	1857		1	1	6	12	48	90
VY1D-175	1857	near colon; trident head not ornamented	1	1	5	10	40	70
VY1D-180	1857	near colon; trident head not ornamented small date	1	1	5	10	40	70
VY1D-185	1858	small date	1	1	4	8	30	65
VY1D-190	1858	small date	1	1	4	8	30	65
VY1D-195	1858	latter 8 over 7	1	1	4	8	30	65
VY1D-200	1858		2	1	4	8	30	65
VY1D-205	1859		2	1	5	10	40	70
VY1D-210	1859	small date	2	1	5	11	45	75
VY1D-215	1859	PROOF	2	1				500
VY1D-220	1860	60 altered from 59 [5]	2	1		350	700	1400
VY1D-225	1860	60 altered from 59 rev. ↓[6]	2	1		450	850	1700
VY1D-230	1860	[7]	3	2	7	15	70	120
VY1D-235	1860	rev. ↓	3	2	12	25	120	200
VY1D-240	1860	PROOF [8]	3	2				500
VY1D-245	1860	bronzed PROOF in copper	3	2				600
VY1D-250	1860	bronzed PROOF in copper on thick flan [9]	3	2			500	800
VY1D-255	1860	PROOF in silver on thick flan [10]	3	2				2500
VY1D-260	1860	PROOF in gold [11]	3	2				15000
VY1D-265	1860	[12]	3	3	100	150	350	600
VY1D-270	1860	[13]	4	2	200	300	700	1200
VY1D-275	1860	[14]	4	3	5	12	50	90
VY1D-280	1860	on thick flan [15]	4	3	300	600		
VY1D-285	1860	on very thick flan [16]	4	3	300	600		
VY1D-290	1860	PROOF	4	3				500
VY1D-295	1860		4	4	90	150	400	900
VY1D-300	1860	[17]	5	3	8	20	100	160
VY1D-305	1860	[18]	6	3	10	30	150	220
VY1D-310	1861	[19]	4	3	5	15	60	110
VY1D-315	1861	[20]	4	5	5	15	60	110
VY1D-320	1861	on thick flan [21]	5	3	200	500		
VY1D-330	1861	[20]	5	5	5	15	60	110
VY1D-335	1861	[22]	6	3	5	15	60	110
VY1D-340	1861	6 over 8	6	3	120	300		
VY1D-345	1861	PROOF	6	3				400
VY1D-350	1861	[23]	6	5	5	15	60	110
VY1D-355	1861	8 over 6	6	5	200	500		
VY1D-360	1861	PROOF	6	5				400
VY1D-365	1861	PROOF in gold; rev. ↓[24]	6	5				8000
VY1D-370	1861	PROOF in silver on thin flan	6	5				1500
VY1D-375	1861	PROOF in silver on thick flan [25]	6	5				2000
VY1D-380	1861	PROOF in copper [26]	6	5				500
VY1D-385	1862		4	5	150			
VY1D-390	1862		6	5	4	10	40	70
VY1D-395	1862	8 over 6	6	5	100	200		
VY1D-400	1862	date numerals from halfpenny die	6	5	250	500		
VY1D-405	1862	PROOF	6	5				400
VY1D-410	1863	[27]	6	5	4	10	40	70
VY1D-415	1863	die number 2 below date	6	5	300	600		
VY1D-420	1863	die number 3 below date	6	5	250	500		
VY1D-425	1863	die number 4 below date	6	5	300	600		
VY1D-430	1863	PROOF	6	5				400
VY1D-435	1864	[28]	6	5	8	25	140	220
VY1D-440	1865		6	5	6	15	65	110
VY1D-445	1865	5 over 3	6	5	40	100	400	1000
VY1D-450	1866		6	5	6	15	55	95
VY1D-455	1867		6	5	6	15	65	170
VY1D-460	1867	PROOF	6	5				500
VY1D-465	1867	bronzed PROOF in copper	6	5				500
VY1D-470	1868		6	5	10	24	110	180
VY1D-475	1868	PROOF	6	5				500
VY1D-480	1868	PROOF in copper [29]	6	5				600
VY1D-485	1868	PROOF in cupronickel [30]	6	5			350	500
VY1D-490	1869		6	5	45	120	500	750
VY1D-495	1870		6	5	10	30	150	250
VY1D-500	1871		6	5	25	80	280	420
VY1D-505	1872		6	5	6	15	55	95
VY1D-510	1872	PROOF; rev. ↓	6	5				1000
VY1D-515	1873		6	5	6	15	55	95
VY1D-520	1874		6	5	7	18	65	110
VY1D-525	1874	narrow date [31]	6	5	7	20	70	130
VY1D-530	1874	H below date [32]	6	5	8	22	75	140
VY1D-535	1874	H below date narrow date	6	5	8	22	75	140
VY1D-540	1874	[33]	7	5	7	18	65	110
VY1D-545	1874	narrow date [34]	7	5	7	20	70	130
VY1D-550	1874	H below date [33]	7	5	8	22	75	140
VY1D-555	1874	H below date narrow date	7	5	8	22	75	140
VY1D-560	1874	H below date narrow date PROOF	7	5				400
VY1D-565	1875	[32]	7	5	4	10	35	65
VY1D-570	1875	narrow date [31]	7	5	4	10	35	65
VY1D-575	1875	narrow date PROOF	7	5				800
VY1D-580	1875	PROOF in cupronickel	7	5				1200
VY1D-585	1875	PROOF on thick flan [35]	7	5				1200
VY1D-590	1875	H below date	7	5	20	80	400	650
VY1D-595	1875	H below date PROOF	7	5				800
VY1D-600	1876	H below date	7	5	6	14	45	80
VY1D-605	1876	H below date narrow date	7	5	4	10	35	65
VY1D-610	1876	H below date narrow date PROOF	7	5				600
VY1D-615	1877	narrow date	7	5	250			
VY1D-620	1877	[31]	7	5	4	10	35	65
VY1D-625	1877	PROOF	7	5				500
VY1D-630	1877	PROOF in cupronickel [36]	7	5				1200
VY1D-635	1878		7	5	5	12	45	75
VY1D-640	1878	PROOF	7	5				400
VY1D-645	1879	[37]	7	5	3	8	30	50
VY1D-650	1879	PROOF	7	5				800
VY1D-655	1879	narrow date [31]	7	5	15	35	85	150
VY1D-660	1880	[38]	7	5	5	11	40	70
VY1D-665	1880	PROOF	7	5				600
VY1D-670	1881	[37]	7	5	5	11	40	70
VY1D-675	1881	PROOF [38]	7	5				600
VY1D-680	1881	H below date	7	5	4	10	35	65
VY1D-685	1881	H below date PROOF	7	5				600
VY1D-690	1882	[39]	7	5	200	400	700	1000
VY1D-695	1882	H below date [40]	7	5	3	8	28	55
VY1D-700	1882	H below date 2 over 1 [41]	7	5	5	12	40	75
VY1D-705	1882	H below date PROOF [42]	7	5				800
VY1D-710	1883	[43]	7	5	4	9	35	60
VY1D-715	1883	PROOF	7	5				400
VY1D-720	1884		7	5	3	7	25	50
VY1D-725	1884	PROOF	7	5				400
VY1D-730	1885		7	5	3	7	25	50
VY1D-735	1885	PROOF	7	5				400
VY1D-740	1886		7	5	3	7	25	50
VY1D-745	1886	PROOF	7	5				400
VY1D-750	1887		7	5	3	7	25	50
VY1D-755	1887	PROOF	7	5				400
VY1D-760	1888	[44]	7	5	3	7	25	50

No.	Date	Features	Obv.	Rev.	F	VF	EF	UNC
VY1D-765	1888	both 'I's in VICTORIA have no top left serif [45]	7	5	5	11	40	80
VY1D-770	1889	[46]	7	5	3	6	22	40
VY1D-775	1889	PROOF [46]	7	5				400
VY1D-780	1890		7	5	3	6	22	40
VY1D-785	1890	PROOF	7	5				400
VY1D-790	1891		7	5	3	6	20	35
VY1D-795	1891	PROOF	7	5				400
VY1D-800	1892		7	5	3	6	20	35
VY1D-805	1892	PROOF	7	5				400
VY1D-810	1893		7	5	3	6	20	35
VY1D-815	1893	PROOF	7	5				400
VY1D-820	1894		7	5	4	8	30	50
VY1D-825	1894	PROOF	7	5				500
VO1D-830	1895		8	6	7	30	110	180
VO1D-835	1895	PROOF	8	6				1000
VO1D-840	1895		8	7	2	5	12	18
VO1D-845	1895	PROOF	8	7				400
VO1D-850	1896		8	7	2	5	10	16
VO1D-855	1896	PROOF	8	7				400
VO1D-860	1897		8	7	2	5	10	16
VO1D-865	1897		8	8	10	40	120	250
VO1D-870	1898		8	7	2	6	15	25
VO1D-875	1899		8	7	2	5	10	16
VO1D-880	1900		8	7	2	5	10	16
VO1D-885	1900	PROOF	8	7				350
VO1D-890	1901		8	7	2	4	6	10
VO1D-895	1901	PROOF	8	7				350

1. Issued in cased proof sets; specimens with reverse ↓ not recorded (cf. halfpenny and farthing).
2. Slightly thicker than ordinary issue.
3. Issued also during 1852.
4. Issued in cased proof sets.
5. See COLLECTING HINTS above.
6. Unrecorded in Peck but a specimen (uncatalogued) sold at Glendining's March 1992.
7. Slight variations in: portrait; shield; drapery; sea, etc.
8. Two slightly different obv. dies.
9. Weight 12.5–13.5 grams; thickness c. 2.3mm.
10. Weight c. 14.5 grams; thickness c. 2.3mm.
11. Weight c. 13.7 grams.
12. A 'mule' with beaded obverse and toothed reverse.
13. A 'mule' with toothed obverse and beaded reverse.
14. Slight variations (obv.) in: legend; portrait; position of 'L.C. Wyon'.
15. Possibly a proof; weight c. 11.3 grams.
16. Weight 16.0–16.5 grams.
17. Some have the N in 'ONE' over a sideways N (rev.).
18. Some read 'ONF' instead of 'ONE' (rev.) (die flaw) slight variations (obv.) in: portrait; legend and portrait position.
19. Slight variations (obv.) in: position of 'L.C. Wyon'; legend size and alignment.
20. Slight variations (rev.) in: shield; legend size; sea; lighthouse; ship; trident, etc.
21. Weight c. 11 grams.
22. Slight variations (obv.) in: portrait; legend and portrait position.
23. Many slight variations on obv. and rev.
24. Weight c. 16 grams.
25. Weight c. 18 grams.
26. Exists with or without bronzed finish.
27. Possibly occurs with narrow '3' in date.
28. Two different types of 4 in date; slight axis misalignments occur.
29. Rim is slightly wider.
30. See also halfpenny and farthing.
31. Minor rev. differences from coin above.
32. Minor rev. differences occur.
33. Minor portrait differences occur.
34. Minor portrait differences occur minor rev. differences from coin above.
35. Weight c. 11.6 grams.
36. Weight c. 9.0 grams.
37. Minor obv. differences occur.
38. Minor obv./rev. differences occur.
39. No H below date; a major omission by Peck but noted by Freeman.
40. Minor rev. differences occur. Horizontal bar of H mintmark may be missing.
41. Overdate faint and fragmented.
42. Rev. is slightly modified and exists only on this coin. May be considered a pattern or proof.
43. Minor obv. differences occur, esp: hair; lettering.
44. Presumably proofs may have been struck.
45. Compare double florin of 1888/89.
46. Minor obv. differences occur, esp. wreath.

The term 'near colon' refers to copper pennies on which the colon after DEF (reverse) is decidedly nearer to DEF than midway between the F and Britannia's foot.

Edward VII 1901–1910

The obverse of the penny uses the portrait of Edward VII by George William de Saulles (1862-1903) as on the silver coinage. The reverse is very similar to that on the veiled head penny of Victoria. Both obverse and reverse exhibit minor alterations in design during this reign, of which by far the best known is the so-called 'Low Tide' penny of 1902. Other slight die variations

exist in the series, and the 1908 penny actually exhibits at least four distinct varieties, not including the proof.

There is some variation in metal colour with the pennies of this reign, and specimens are sometimes found with a somewhat unpleasant yellow streaky appearance.

Collecting Hints

Unless one is collecting the die varieties, one specimen of each date in mint state with original lustre should be acquired. Most collectors will want to obtain a 1902 'Low Tide' specimen, and it is not too difficult to find this coin in extremely fine or better. This is because, being the first year of issue, many were put away as keepsakes.

Denomination	Metal	Weight (grams)	Diameter (mm)	Rev. alignment
Penny	Bronze (copper 95%; tin 4%; zinc 1%)	9.4	31	↑

Unofficial variations in metal composition occurred, resulting in some coins being lighter in colour than others

Obverse 1 Head 1, right; EDWARDVS VII DEI GRA BRITT OMN REX FID DEF IND IMP

Reverse 1 Britannia, seated, with shield, facing right; ONE PENNY; date in exergue below Britannia

Reverse 2 Similar but sea is higher

Edge plain

Obv. 1

Rev. 1

Rev. 1 (enl.)

Rev. 2 (enl.)

No.	Date	Features	Obv.	Rev.	VF	EF	UNC
E71D-005	1902	[1]	1	1	8	20	50
E71D-010	1902		1	2	4	7	12
E71D-015	1903	[2]	1	2	6	12	25
E71D-020	1904		1	2	7	15	30
E71D-025	1905	[3]	1	2	6	12	25
E71D-030	1906		1	2	6	11	22
E71D-035	1907		1	2	6	11	22
E71D-040	1908	[4]	1	2	6	12	24
E71D-045	1908	matt PROOF on thick flan [5]	1	2			1000
E71D-050	1909	[6]	1	2	6	12	24
E71D-055	1910		1	2	5	10	20

1. Known as 'Low Tide' variety.
2. 3 in date varies in shape.
3. Orientation of 'E' in PENNY (rev.) varies.
4. Minor obverse/reverse differences occur.

No.	Date	Features	Obv.	Rev.	VF	EF	UNC

5. Weight c. 12.5 grams.
6. Minor reverse differences occur; colour of metal varies widely with composition variation.

George V 1910–1936

The portrait of George V used on the penny was by Sir Bertram MacKennal (1863-1931), while the reverse continued the same Britannia design used for the Edward VII series.

In the first years of production of the penny, problems were encountered with 'ghosting' (see penny of Victoria). The nature of this was different from that experienced on the Victorian coinage. While many Victorian coins had suffered faint but sharply defined 'ghost' images caused by clashed dies, the ghosting on the George V pennies was vague in outline and yet more widespread. It was caused by the dies, especially the obverse, being in too high relief. When the coin was struck, the amount of metal needed to fill the hollow of the portrait die was so much that it drew metal from the corresponding area on the reverse. This phenomenon can be seen on many specimens of penny, especially before 1920, where the field either side of Britannia exhibits a characteristic striation. The pennies of this period are also somewhat weakly struck, and this is particularly noticeable on the 'KN' specimens of 1918 and 1919 (see below).

A reduction in ghosting was achieved with the introduction of striking in lower relief in 1921 and 1926; finally the small head introduced in 1928 produced a sharply struck coin with little or no ghosting.

Metal colouration of toned coins is a subject not normally touched on in catalogues, but which is worthy of some research. It is noticeable, for example, that while 'H' pennies normally tone to black, the 'KN' pieces and the 1928-36 series almost always achieve a yellow-ochre finish, except for those of 1934 and some of 1935, which were issued artificially darkened.

Some pennies of 1912, 1918 and 1919 were struck with a small 'H' to the left of the date, while some of 1918 and 1919 have the letters 'KN' in this position; these coins were struck at the Heaton works (later The Mint, Birmingham, Ltd.) and by the Kings Norton Metal Co. Ltd. (also at Birmingham) respectively.

Collecting Hints

Collect this series in extremely fine or mint state, with as much original lustre as possible. The 'H' and 'KN' varieties are difficult to find in this condition, but in considering specimens it must be remembered that these are invariably weakly struck.

The 1926 'modified effigy' penny is not at all easy to find in the higher grades, and some collectors have difficulty in distinguishing between the two heads of the 1926 coin. One distinguishing feature is that on the first obverse the lower dot of the colon between GRA and BRITT lies almost centrally between the A and the B. On the modified head obverse the dot is much nearer the A.

Only about seven specimens of the legendary 1933 penny exist, and it is unlikely that others will be found after this time. One should not therefore waste time and effort in checking dates of the 1928-36 type, the remainder of which are all fairly common. One is more likely to encounter one of the many forgeries with an altered date.

It must be remembered that pennies of 1934 and some of 1935 were issued artificially darkened with sodium thiosulphate, and particular attention must be paid to the structural wear when grading. As with all of this series, wear becomes apparent first on the hand gripping the trident, and on the arm which extends to the shield.

The 1922 penny with reverse 2 is not a well known coin but is very rare and worth looking for. An experienced collector will be able to distinguish reverse 2 at a glance, not by comparing characteristics but simply by the way this reverse is struck and the way it wears, quite differently from reverse 1. The reverse in fine condition resembles a halfpenny reverse of the later George V period on account of the larger border teeth.

Denomination	Metal	Weight (grams)	Diameter (mm)	Rev. alignment
Penny 1911-22	Bronze (copper 95%; tin 4%; zinc 1%)	9.4	31	↑
Penny 1926-36	Bronze (copper 95.5%; tin 3%; zinc 1.5%)	9.4	31	↑

Obverse 1 Head 1, left, B.M. on truncation; GEORGIVS V DEI GRA BRITT OMN REX FID DEF IND IMP

Obverse 2 Head 2, known as 'modified effigy', left; initials BM are without stops and further to right; same legend

Obverse 3 Head 3, smaller, more sharply struck, left; same legend

Reverse 1 Britannia, seated, with shield, facing right; ONE PENNY; date in exergue below Britannia

Reverse 2 Similar but redesigned and more sharply struck

Edge plain

Obv. 1   Obv. 2

Obv. 3   Rev. 1: 'ghosting'

Rev. 2 early   Rev. 2 late

No.	Date	Features	Obv.	Rev.	VF	EF	UNC
G51D-005	1911	[1]	1	1	6	10	20
G51D-010	1912		1	1	6	10	20
G51D-015	1912	H to left of date	1	1	10	40	100
G51D-020	1913	[2]	1	1	6	11	22
G51D-025	1914		1	1	6	12	25
G51D-030	1915		1	1	6	12	28
G51D-035	1916		1	1	6	12	25
G51D-040	1917		1	1	6	10	18
G51D-045	1918		1	1	6	10	20
G51D-050	1918	H to left of date	1	1	15	80	180
G51D-055	1918	KN to left of date	1	1	20	120	240
G51D-060	1919		1	1	6	10	20
G51D-065	1919	H to left of date	1	1	15	80	180
G51D-070	1919	KN to left of date	1	1	22	140	280
G51D-075	1920	[3]	1	1	6	10	20
G51D-080	1921	[3]	1	1	6	10	20
G51D-085	1922		1	1	10	30	70
G51D-090	1922	[4]	1	2	1500	4000	
G51D-095	1926		1	1	12	45	100
G51D-100	1926	PROOF	1	1			500
G51D-105	1926		2	1	24	200	600
G51D-110	1926	PROOF	2	1			1000
G51D-115	1927		2	2	4	7	10
G51D-120	1927	PROOF	2	2			250
G51D-125	1928		3	2	4	7	10
G51D-130	1928	PROOF	3	2			250
G51D-135	1929		3	2	4	8	11
G51D-140	1929	PROOF	3	2			250
G51D-145	1930		3	2	4	8	12
G51D-150	1930	PROOF	3	2			250
G51D-155	1931		3	2	4	9	14
G51D-160	1931	PROOF	3	2			300
G51D-165	1932		3	2	4	15	30
G51D-170	1932	PROOF	3	2			400
G51D-175	1933	artificially darkened at mint (?) [5]	3	2			30000
G51D-180	1934	artificially darkened at mint	3	2	4	14	28
G51D-185	1934	PROOF	3	2			400
G51D-190	1935	artificially darkened at mint	3	2	2	5	8
G51D-195	1935		3	2	2	5	8
G51D-200	1935	PROOF	3	2			250
G51D-205	1936		3	2	3	5	7
G51D-210	1936	PROOF	3	2			220

1. Minor obverse varieties exist.
2. Slightly different obverse/reverse dies introduced during this year.
3. Slightly different obverse dies introduced during 1920/21.
4. Minor differences from the later Reverse 2; border teeth are longer.
5. Not issued for circulation.

Edward VIII 1936

The Edward VIII penny is strictly speaking a pattern, as probable Royal approval was about to be granted at the time of the abdication. However, because its official status rests only on this technicality, and to provide continuity, it is included in this catalogue.

The portrait of Edward VIII is by Thomas Humphrey Paget, and faces left at the insistence of the king, who considered this placement more flattering and wished to discontinue the tradition of opposite facings for successive monarchs. The reverse was a revamped version of that used on previous reigns.

Denomination	Metal	Weight (grams)	Diameter (mm)	Rev. alignment
Penny	Bronze (copper 95.5%; tin 3%; zinc 1.5%)	9.4	31	↑

Obverse 1 Head 1, left; EDWARDVS VIII D G BR OMN REX F D IND IMP

Reverse 1 Britannia, seated, with shield, facing right; ONE PENNY; date 1937 in exergue below Britannia

Edge plain

Obv. 1   Rev. 1

No.	Date	Obv.	Rev.	Unc
E81D-005	1937	1	1	20000

George VI 1937–1952

The pennies of George VI use a portrait of the king by Thomas Humphrey Paget, with a redesigned Britannia reverse. While pennies of the latter years of George V had been struck in proof in small quantities, a relatively large number of proofs of the 1937 penny needed to be struck to satisfy the issue of cased proof sets for the Coronation year. These proofs were struck to a higher standard than the George V proofs. Thereafter, proofs were again struck in small quantities for each year of the regular issue, but again in 1950 and 1951 the mintage was augmented by the issue of proof sets.

Although there were a number of minor changes to both obverse and reverse during this series, basically there were two main obverses and one reverse, the legend on the obverse being amended in 1949 when the title IND IMP (Emperor of India) was removed.

In 1940 it became apparent that a large amount of pennies were in circulation. Consequently, no pennies bearing the dates 1941 to 1943 were struck, and the few required for colonial issue were struck from dies with the 1940 date. When the issue was resumed in 1944, the world scarcity of tin had necessitated a reduction of the content of this metal in the bronze from 3% to 0.5%. It had been found that this reduced-tin bronze tarnished unattractively, and consequently the penny issue of 1944 to 1946 was treated with sodium thiosulphate, which gave it a darkened appearance. Subsequent coinage had the tin content increased to its original amount.

In 1950 and 1951 the issues of pennies in Great Britain was again discontinued, but unlike in 1941 those sent for colonial use bore the actual date of issue. In the early sixties, collecting by date became fashionable, and initially no denomination was more fashionable to collect than the bronze penny. The 1951 penny, in particular, acquired something of a cult status. At that time, someone in the coin business discovered that almost the entire issue had been sent to Bermuda. Considerable effort was made to buy as many of the 120,000 specimens as possible, and many wild claims were made about the investment potential of the coin.

Collecting Hints

This series should be collected in mint state with original lustre, or, in the case of the 1944-46 issue, with original patina. The 1951 penny overall is scarcer than the 1950, but in mint state the 1950 is considerably scarcer. The proofs of 1950 and 1951 are somewhat difficult to find with full lustre because the cases of the proof sets had a tendency to induce toning on the coins.

Denomination	Metal	Weight (grams)	Diameter (mm)	Rev. alignment
Penny 1937-1940	Bronze (copper 95.5%; tin 3%; zinc 1.5%)	9.4	31	↑
Penny 1944-1945	Bronze (copper 97%; tin 0.5%; zinc 2.5%)	9.4	31	↑
Penny 1945-1951	Bronze (copper 95.5%; tin 3%; zinc 1.5%)	9.4	31	↑

Obverse 1 Head 1, left; GEORGIVS VI D G BR OMN REX F D IND IMP

Obverse 2 Head 1, left; GEORGIVS VI D G BR OMN REX FIDEI DEF

Reverse 1 Britannia, seated, with shield, facing right; ONE PENNY; date in exergue below Britannia

Edge plain

Obv. 1

Obv. 2

Rev. 1

No.	Date	Features	Obv.	Rev.	VF	EF	UNC
G61D-005	1937	[1]	1	1	1	3	5
G61D-010	1937	PROOF [2]	1	1		4	10
G61D-015	1937	PROOF from sandblasted dies [3]	1	1			200
G61D-020	1938		1	1	1	3	5
G61D-025	1938	PROOF	1	1			250
G61D-030	1939		1	1	1	4	7
G61D-035	1939	PROOF	1	1			250
G61D-040	1940	[4]	1	1	1	4	7
G61D-045	1940	PROOF	1	1			250
G61D-050	1944	artificially darkened at mint	1	1	1	4	7
G61D-055	1944	PROOF; artificially darkened at mint	1	1			300
G61D-060	1945	artificially darkened at mint	1	1	1	3	6
G61D-065	1945	PROOF; artificially darkened at mint	1	1			300
G61D-070	1946	artificially darkened at mint	1	1	1	3	5

No.	Date	Features	Obv.	Rev.	VF	EF	UNC
G61D-075	1946	PROOF; artificially darkened at mint	1	1			300
G61D-080	1947		1	1	1	3	5
G61D-085	1947	PROOF	1	1			200
G61D-090	1948		1	1	1	3	5
G61D-095	1948	PROOF	1	1			200
G61D-100	1949		2	1	1	3	5
G61D-105	1949	PROOF	2	1			200
G61D-110	1950	[5]	2	1	5	10	30
G61D-115	1950	PROOF [2]	2	1			15
G61D-120	1950	PROOF from sandblasted dies [3]	2	1			220
G61D-125	1951	[6]	2	1	10	15	25
G61D-130	1951	PROOF [2]	2	1			18
G61D-135	1951	PROOF from sandblasted dies [3]	2	1			250

1. Slight border teeth differences occur.
2. Issued in cased proof sets.
3. Struck to facilitate photography of coin.
4. Exergual line becomes double during this year.
5. Issued for colonial use.
6. Issued mainly for Bermuda.

Elizabeth II 1952 -

The series continues the general overall design of the George VI penny, using a portrait of Elizabeth II by Mary Gillick. The toothed border of the George VI coinage was replaced by a border of fine circular dots, although at least one specimen of the 1953 penny exists with a toothed border on both sides. The reverse is a slightly redesigned Britannia.

Because of a surplus of pennies in circulation, no pennies dated 1953 were struck for circulation, but a large number of specimen sets of 1953 was issued, in which the coins were sealed in a plastic holder. Colloquially known as 'plastic sets', many of these were split open and the coinage spent, as they were issued for only a small premium over their face value. Later, in the mid-sixties, when date collecting of pennies became popular, many more were split open to obtain the penny.

The 1953 penny was also issued in proof condition in the cased proof sets marking the coronation of the queen. The penny of this date, as well as being scarce because it was not issued for circulation, is a popular piece also because it is a one-year type. On later coins the words 'BRITT OMN' were omitted from the obverse.

At least one specimen exists of a penny dated 1954, apparently struck for private internal purposes at the mint, but it was not until 1961 that demand again required the penny to be struck for circulation. The series was to last only another six years, during which a very large quantity of this coin was issued.

The amount of coinage struck between 1961 and 1967 necessitated a considerable amount of retouching to the waves and sealine on the reverse dies to maintain their sharpness, so much so that an expert in this field could no doubt date a coin from a close examination of the details on the sea.

Collecting Hints

The series should be collected in mint state. Apart from the 1953, the proofs are very difficult to find.

Denomination	Metal	Weight (grams)	Diameter (mm)	Rev. alignment
Penny 1953-1954	Bronze (copper 95.5%; tin 3%; zinc 1.5%)	9.4	31	↑
Penny 1961-1967	Bronze (copper 97%; tin 0.5%; zinc 2.5%)	9.4	31	↑

Obverse 1 Head 1, right; ELIZABETH II DEI GRA BRITT OMN REGINA F D. Border is toothed

Obverse 2 Similar but border is of fine circular or near-circular dots

Obverse 3 Similar but ELIZABETH II DEI GRATIA REGINA F D

Obverse J Obverse intended for Jersey Elizabeth II penny:

Head 2, crowned, right: QUEEN ELIZABETH THE SECOND

Reverse 1 Britannia, seated, with shield, facing right; ONE PENNY; date in exergue below Britannia. Border is toothed

Reverse 2 Similar but border is of fine circular or near-circular dots

Edge plain

Obv. 1

Obv. 3

Rev. 2

No.	Date	Features	Obv.	Rev.	EF	UNC
EL21D-005	1953	[1]	1	1		300
EL21D-010	1953	PROOF [1]	2	1		300
EL21D-015	1953	[2]	2	2	4	6
EL21D-020	1953	PROOF [3]	2	2	5	8
EL21D-025	1953	PROOF from sandblasted dies [4]	2	2		200
EL21D-030	1954	[5]	3	2		25000
EL21D-035	1961	[6]	3	2		1
EL21D-040	1961	PROOF	3	2		250
EL21D-045	1962	[7]	3	2		1
EL21D-050	1962	struck on heavy flan [8]	3	2		400
EL21D-055	1962	PROOF	3	2		250
EL21D-060	1963	[9]	3	2		1
EL21D-065	1963	PROOF	3	2		250
EL21D-070	1964	[10]	3	2		1
EL21D-075	1964	struck without collar in cupronickel [11]	3	2		150
EL21D-080	1964	PROOF	3	2		250
EL21D-085	1965	[12]	3	2		1
EL21D-090	1965	struck in gold [13]	3	2		2500
EL21D-095	1965	struck in cupronickel [14]	3	2		300
EL21D-100	1966	[12]	3	2		1
EL21D-105	1966	struck in cupronickel [15]	3	2		300
EL21D-110	1966	[16]	J	2		1200
EL21D-115	1967	[17]	3	2		1
EL21D-120	1967	struck on thin flan [18]	3	2		200
EL21D-125	1967	struck on heavy flan [19]	3	2		400
EL21D-130	1967	struck in nickel-brass [20]	3	2	250	350
EL21D-135	1970	PROOF [21]	3	2	2	3

1. Struck in 1952.
2. Issued in 'plastic sets'.
3. Issued in cased proof sets.
4. Struck to facilitate photography of coin.
5. Only 1 known but several struck; both sides slightly redesigned.
6. Both sides slightly redesigned.
7. Rev. slightly retouched.
8. Weight c. 13 grams.
9. Reverse slightly redesigned.
10. Reverse slightly retouched (waves).
11. Weight 11.3 grams.
12. Reverse again retouched (waves).
13. Weight c. 18.3 grams.
14. Weight c. 11.5 grams.
15. Weight c. 11 grams.
16. Obverse is of Jersey Elizabeth II penny; weight 9.3 grams.
17. Reverse again retouched (waves and sealine); minor lighthouse varieties exist (rev.).
18. Weight c. 7 grams.
19. Weight c. 13 grams.
20. Weight 9.6 grams.
21. Issued in sealed cased proof sets.

Halfpenny

Charles II 1660–1685

In the early part of the reign of Charles II there was a clear need for coins of low denomination to fund the day-to-day purchases of the common man. The silver penny and twopence issued in the first few years of the reign had been extensively hoarded, and it was the practice of tradesmen in many parts of the country to issue private tokens in base metal. Although, strictly speaking, the issue of such tokens was an offence, in practice any penalties exacted were minimal. This was no doubt because the authorities appreciated the need for such coinage which was not available legally.

A problem with the issuance of coinage is that if the face value is less than the cost of manufacture (including the metal), the exercise is conducted at a loss, and the coins may be subsequently clipped or melted down; if the face value is higher, counterfeit coins begin to appear.

It was not until 1672 that the mint was ready to produce coins in copper. By that time, the issue of 'Maundy-type' small silver was underway, and these were circulating widely. No copper pennies were therefore struck, but the Royal Proclamation in August decreed that halfpennies and farthings would be issued, and that these would have a face value equal to the value of the metal less the cost of producing them.

It was soon found that the mint was incapable of producing the copper blanks necessary, and these eventually had to be imported from Sweden. Further delays ensued, not least because of transportation problems. The first halfpennies did not appear until after Christmas (remembering that in those days the year ended on March 24, there were still three months until 1673 began).

The ideals of striking coinage with a value equal to its production costs were not maintained, and the coins were given a face value slightly higher. Inevitably, counterfeit coins began to appear within a few years.

The dies for the Charles II halfpenny were prepared by John Roettier, and the reverse has been compared by some to a sestertius of Antoninus Pius. The reverse legend 'BRITANNIA' was presumably considered a wiser choice than 'QVATTVOR MARIA VINDICO' (I claim the four seas) seen on the pattern halfpenny of about 1665, especially following the naval defeat by the Dutch off Kent in 1667.

It is worthy of note that on the copper coinage the head of Charles II faces left, i.e. the opposite attitude to that on the silver and gold coins.

Denomination	Metal	Weight (grams)	Diameter (mm)	Rev. alignment
Halfpenny	Copper	10.0–12.0	28–31	↓

Obverse 1 Head 1, left; CAROLVS A CAROLO

Reverse 1 Britannia, seated, with shield, facing left, holding spray and spear; BRITANNIA; (date) in exergue

Edge plain

Obv. 1   Rev. 1

No.	Date	Features	Obv.	Rev.	VG	F	VF	EF
C2HDM-005	1672		1	1	50	100	400	1500
C2HDM-010	1672	CRAOLVS instead of CAROLVS (obv.)	1	1	150	250	1800	
C2HDM-015	1672	PROOF	1	1				1500
C2HDM-020	1672	PROOF in silver	1	1				2500
C2HDM-025	1673		1	1	20	40	150	650
C2HDM-030	1673	No stops on obverse	1	1	30	80	450	1400
C2HDM-035	1673	No stop on reverse	1	1	25	60	250	1000
C2HDM-040	1673	CRAOLVS instead of CAROLVS (obv.)	1	1	45	110	800	
C2HDM-045	1673	PROOF [1]	1	1				1500
C2HDM-050	1673	PROOF in silver [1]	1	1				1500
C2HDM-055	1675		1	1	25	50	200	800
C2HDM-060	1675	5 over 3	1	1	75	150	800	
C2HDM-065	1675	No stops on obverse	1	1	25	50	200	800

1. No stop on reverse.

Minor variations exist in: position of ribbon and lettering (obv.); position of B, N, N in legend (reverse).

James II 1685–1688

The halfpennies of this reign were struck in tin with a square plug of copper through the centre. A small quantity of farthings in copper-plugged tin had been struck at the end of the previous reign. By using tin, it was hoped that coinage could be produced at a profit while at the same time producing a coin which would be difficult to counterfeit. A further object was to assist the ailing tin industry.

The obverse for the halfpenny was by John Roettier, and the reverse used a Britannia from the same punch as for the Charles II coin. The date, however, appeared not in the exergue but on the edge of the coin, a notable departure from common practice. In addition, as on the Charles II coins, the king's head faced the opposite way to the depiction on the silver and gold coins.

It is possible that the reason for the extensive corrosion of plugged coinage lies with the electrochemical difference in potential between copper and tin when in contact. Copper itself resists corrosion reasonably well, and tin is so resistant that it is used to plate steel to protect it from corrosion. This is a field requiring further research.

Collecting Hints

These coins are scarce in any condition, but especially so in the higher grades. Most specimens have corroded so badly that what is left is virtually unreadable. Unlike copper, where the oxidation of the metal forms a layer which is largely protective, the corrosion of tin is progressive and can continue until little is left. The coins should be collected in the best grade possible, and good condition specimens highly prized. Do not underestimate the value of such pieces.

Denomination	Metal	Weight (grams)	Diameter (mm)	Rev. alignment
Halfpenny	Tin with a central copper plug	10.5–11.6	28–30	↓

Obverse 1 Head 1, right; IACOBVS SECVNDVS

Reverse 1 Britannia, seated, with shield, facing left, holding spray and spear; BRITANNIA. The exergue is blank

Edge NVMMORVM FAMVLVS (date)

Obv. 1	Rev. 1

No.	Date	Features	Edge date	Obv.	Rev.	VG	F	VF	EF
J2HD-005	1685	[1]	1685	1	1	40	80	300	900
J2HD-010	1685	no star between NVMMORVM and FAMVLVS	1685	1	1	60	120	500	1500
J2HD-015	1686		1686	1	1	40	80	300	900
J2HD-020	1687		1687	1	1	40	80	300	900

1. Star varieties exist (edge).

William and Mary 1688–1694

The production of tin halfpennies with a copper plug continued, with dies prepared by George Bower and James Roettier. However, the new tin coinage was becoming increasingly unpopular. By now, the corrosive tendencies of the coins were very apparent, and in addition the public did not feel that the coinage had any intrinsic value. Even worse, counterfeits in lead had begun to appear. The prevention of counterfeiting had been one of the principal reasons for introducing the tin coinage. The tin halfpenny survived until 1692, and in 1694, just before the queen's death from smallpox, a copper halfpenny was reintroduced. The obverse of this issue was designed by James or Norbert Roettier. The contract stipulated that the copper should be English and that the blanks should be struck at the Mint. Previously, blanks had been imported from Sweden for the Charles II copper coinage. It is noticeable that the Charles II issue tones to a dark red, while the William and Mary coins tone to black. This is presumably because of different trace elements in the copper. The English copper was difficult to strike, so in order to render it more malleable the blanks were made by casting the molten metal into moulds.

Collecting Hints

All of the tin series is as scarce as that of the previous reign, while the 1689 coin is considerably rarer. This should be acquired in any condition, almost irrespective of price. All of the other dates are desirable if in fine condition and attractive. The 1694 halfpenny is less scarce but is a useful one-year type. All of the dates, including 1694, are rare in extremely fine condition.

Denomination	Metal	Weight (grams)	Diameter (mm)	Rev. alignment
Halfpenny 1689-1692	Tin with a central copper plug	10.5–11.7	28–30	↓
Halfpenny 1694	Copper	9.1–11.7	28–31	↓

The weight range is narrower on the 1689 coin, averaging 10.8 grams.

Obverse 1 Heads 1, right; GVLIELMVS ET MARIA (heads divide GVLIELMVS... ET)

Obverse 2 Heads 2, more drapery, right; same legend (heads divide ET...MARIA)

Obverse 3 Heads 3, larger, with king wearing breastplate, right; same legend with lettering larger (heads divide GVLIELMVS...ET)

Obverse 4 Heads 4, right, the king with shorter hair; same legend (heads divide GVLIELMVS... ET)

Reverse 1 Britannia, seated, with shield, facing left, holding spray and spear; BRITANNIA. The exergue is blank

Reverse 2 Similar but the exergue contains the date

Edge (1689-1692): NVMMORVM FAMVLVS (date)

Edge (1694): plain

Obv. 1	Obv. 3

Obv. 4

Rev. 1	Rev. 2

No.	Date	Features	Edge date	Obv.	Rev.	VG	F	VF	EF
WMHD-005	1689		1689	1	1	350	700	1600	
WMHD-010	(1689)	PROOF, plain edge [1]		1	1				10000
WMHD-015	1689	[2]	1689	1	2				
WMHD-020	1689		1689	2	1	1500			
WMHD-025	1690	[3]	1690	3	1	40	75	200	800
WMHD-030	1691	[3]	1691	3	2	40	75	200	800
WMHD-035	1691	[4]	1692	3	2	40	75	200	800
WMHD-040	1692		1692	3	2	40	75	200	800
WMHD-045	1694			4	2	15	30	70	500
WMHD-050	1694	GVLEELMVS instead of GVLIELMVS (obv.)		4	2	25	60	150	1000
WMHD-055	1694	GVLIEMVS instead of GVLIELMVS (obv.)		4	2	25	60	150	1000
WMHD-060	1694	MVRIA instead of MARIA (obv.)		4	2	25	60	150	1000
WMHD-065	1694	MΛRIΛ instead of MARIA (obv.)		4	2	20	40	90	700
WMHD-070	1694	BRITΛNNIΛ (last I over Λ) instead of BRITANNIA (rev.)		4	2	20	40	90	700
WMHD-075	1694	no stop on rev.		4	2	20	40	90	700
WMHD-080	1694	PROOF [5]		4	2				600
WMHD-085	1694	PROOF, edge striated		4	2				600
WMHD-090	1694	PROOF on thin flan		4	2				600
WMHD-095	1694	PROOF in silver		4	2				1500
WMHD-100	1694	PROOF in silver on thin flan		4	2				1200
WMHD-105	1694	PROOF in gold on thin flan [6]		4	2				8000

1. Coin bears no date at all; possibly unique.
2. Reported by Snelling but unconfirmed.
3. Edge punctuation varies.
4. '1691' is the date on the reverse.
5. Minor varieties exist.
6. Possibly unique.

William III 1694–1701

The production of halfpennies continued under the contract granted during the previous reign, but it was soon apparent that the terms of the contract were not always being kept. To save costs, not only were many of the blanks being cast rather than struck, but some of the coins themselves were being cast as a single operation. Claims were made about the convenience of casting and the quality of the product, but despite this there was no doubt that the manufacturers were in breach of contract.

There were other ways in which the contractors were saving on expenses. Cheap labour was used, including foreigners, and some could not spell the words they engraved on the dies, nor punctuate correctly. A somewhat similar situation existed in the provincial mints at around this time, when large quantities of silver coinage were being produced using an inefficient work-force.

Towards the end of the reign, both the workmanship and the design and production of dies for the copper coins had sunk to their lowest depths. It is curious that, at this time, the mint were producing the highest quality five-and two-guinea pieces made, the 'fine work' 1701 pieces.

By 1698 there was a glut of inferior copper coinage, and following representation from the public, an act was passed to stop the coining for one year. Stephen Martin Leake, writing in 1726, stated that the act 'seems to have had no effect', and that the proliferation continued. Further parliamentary efforts were later made to try to stop the glut of coinage.

James Roettier engraved the obverse dies for the halfpenny, including, according to Peck, those for the last type, which dated from 1699, after Roettier's death. The reverse initially continued the John Roettier Britannia from previous reigns until the last

issue in 1699. Then a new and poorly executed Britannia reverse was introduced, possibly by Samuel Bull.

Because of the poor quality of many of the coins of this reign, it is not always possible to determine whether minor punctuation varieties are caused by such vagaries as die wear or poor striking. In addition, many of the variations are so minor and so widespread that they are of little interest except to a dedicated collector of varieties. Included in these are the substitution of an inverted 'V' for 'A' and vice versa, and the omission of one or more stops. Because of this, the tables below allocate a separate number only to major varieties, e.g. when a word is completely misspelt, although minor varieties are still included in the Remarks column. Because minor varieties are so commonplace in the William III series, they may be referred to only in annotated form where they would have received separate treatment if they had occurred, say, in the reign of William IV.

Collecting Hints

The whole of this series is rare in the highest grades, and the coins should be acquired in very fine condition or better, with the rarer varieties in fine condition or better. Ernest Bramah (English Regal Copper Coins, 1929) estimated the scarcity of the first issue as this distribution from 100 randomly acquired examples: 1695, 12; 1696, 38; 1697, 47; 1698, 3. He estimated the last issue as: 1699, 44; 1700, 38; 1701, 18.

Denomination	Metal	Weight (grams)	Diameter (mm)	Rev. alignment
Halfpenny	Copper	8.9–11.5	28–29	↓

Obverse 1 Head 1, right; GVLIELMVS TERTIVS

Obverse 2 Head 2, right; same legend

Reverse 1 Britannia, seated, with shield, facing left, holding spray and spear; BRITANNIA; date in exergue below

Reverse 2 Similar but legend reads BRITANNIA (date); exergue is blank

Reverse 3 Redesigned Britannia, seated, with shield, facing left, crude style; BRITANNIA; date in exergue below

Edge plain

Obv. 1   Obv. 2

Rev. 1   Rev. 2   Rev. 3

No.	Date	Features	Obv.	Rev.	F	VF	EF
W3HD-005	1695	[1]	1	1	18	75	350
W3HD-010	1695	struck on thick flan [2]	1	1	100		
W3HD-015	1696		1	1	15	65	300
W3HD-020	1696	GVLIEMVS instead of GVLIELMVS (obv.) [3]	1	1	100		
W3HD-025	1696	TERTVS instead of TERTIVS (obv.)	1	1	100		
W3HD-030	1696	PROOF in silver	1	1			1200
W3HD-035	1696	PROOF in silver on thin flan [4]	1	1			1200
W3HD-040	1697	[5]	1	1	15	65	300
W3HD-045	1697	I of TERTIVS over E (obv.)	1	1	50	180	
W3HD-050	1697	GVLILMVS instead of GVLIELMVS (obv.) [3]	1	1	150		
W3HD-055	1697	gap instead of first N in BRITANNIA [6]	1	1	50	180	
W3HD-060	1698		1	1	20	90	450
W3HD-065	no date	[7]	1	obv 1	150		
W3HD-070	1698	[8]	1	2	18	75	350
W3HD-075	1699	[9]	1	2	18	75	350
W3HD-080	1699	GVLIEMVS instead of GVLIELMVS (obv.)	1	2	100		
W3HD-085	1699	[1]	2	3	15	65	300
W3HD-090	1699	GVILELMVS instead of GVLIELMVS (obv.)	2	3	100		
W3HD-095	1699	TERTVS instead of TERTIVS (obv.) [5]	2	3	100		
W3HD-100	1699	PROOF in silver	2	3			1500
W3HD-105	1700	[1]	2	3	15	65	300
W3HD-110	1700	GVLIELMS instead of GVLIELMVS (obv.)	2	3	70		
W3HD-115	1700	GVLIEEMVS instead of GVLIELMVS (obv.)	2	3	70		
W3HD-120	1700	I of TERTIVS over V (obv.)	2	3	50		
W3HD-125	1700	TER TIVS instead of TERTIVS (obv.)	2	3	40		
W3HD-130	1700	BRIVANNIA instead of BRITANNIA (obv.)	2	3	100		
W3HD-135	1701	[10]	2	3	18	75	350
W3HD-140	1701	PROOF in silver [11]	2	3			1800
W3HD-145	no date	[7]	2	obv 2	150		

1. Inverted 'V' and stop varieties exist.
2. Weight c. 14.4 grams.
3. No stop on reverse.
4. Diameter 31mm.
5. Stop varieties exist.
6. Gap is possibly die wear.
7. 'Double headed' coin.
8. Stop after date.
9. No stop after date; inverted 'V' varieties exist.
10. Inverted 'V', 'A' and stop varieties exist.
11. Edge striated.

Anne 1701–1714

When Anne came to the throne, a very large quantity of copper coinage was in circulation. It was therefore decided to suspend striking until more was required. Consequently, no halfpennies of Anne were produced except for patterns.

George I 1714–1727

No currency halfpennies had been struck during the reign of Anne, and by 1717 there was again a shortage of copper coinage. A new contract was signed and a Royal Warrant in 1717 proclaimed the issuance of a new halfpenny.

The first halfpennies struck had a somewhat unusual appearance. They were smaller, thicker, and somewhat lighter than those previously issued. Both obverse and reverse were boldly struck and in high relief, a marked difference from the poor strikings and cast specimens of William III. This first issue of George I has become known as the 'dump' issue. The dies were probably produced by Croker and/or Johann Rudolph Ochs, senior.

In 1719, a new issue of halfpennies began. These were nearer in proportions to those of earlier reigns. The diameter was greater than that of the 'dump' halfpenny, but the coin was thinner, thus retaining the same weight.

Unlike on most of the silver coinage, the Hanoverian titles of the king did not form part of the legend. The result was an uncluttered and simple design which resulted on one of the more attractive issues of copper halfpenny, despite the shortcomings of the king's appearance. Whether they were appreciated at the time is more doubtful; Leake, writing in 1726, described them as 'very clumsy pieces'.

Collecting Hints

The 'dump' issue halfpenny is a popular coin on account of its chunky appearance and scarcity in the higher grades. The George I halfpenny should be collected in very fine condition or better.

Despite the high relief of this series, blemishes on the coins are common. It seems that faulty blanks were often used, and the high pressure needed to strike the high relief impression was not always sufficient. This resulted in parts of the design not being properly struck up. Care should thus be taken in grading, as what appears to be wear may be weak striking. It is a matter of personal preference as to whether a weak strike is preferable to wear or not.

Denomination	Metal	Weight (grams)	Diameter (mm)	Rev. alignment
Halfpenny 1717-18	Copper	9.4–10.3	25–27	↓
Halfpenny 1719-24	Copper	9.4–10.3	25–27	↓

Proofs are usually of diameter 27mm.

Obverse 1 Head 1, right; GEORGIVS REX

Obverse 2 Head 2, slightly different (tie, shoulder-strap) and rather larger, right; same legend

Obverse 3 Head 3, slightly different (shoulder-strap, hair, leaves), right; same legend

Reverse 1 Britannia, seated, with shield, facing left, holding spray and spear; BRITANNIA; date in exergue below

Edge plain

Obv. 1

Obv. 2

Obv. 3

Rev. 1

No	Date	Features	Obv.	Rev.	F	VF	EF
G1HD-005	1717		1	1	15	60	300
G1HD-010	1717	no stops on obv.	1	1	30	110	500
G1HD-015	1717	PROOF	1	1			500
G1HD-020	1717	PROOF in silver	1	1		250	400
G1HD-025	1718		1	1	15	60	300
G1HD-030	1718	no stops on obv	1	1	30	110	500
G1HD-035	1718	in silver [1]	1	1		300	500
G1HD-040	1719	[2]	1	1	500		
G1HD-045	1719	diagonally grained edge	1	1	500		
G1HD-050	1719		2	1	10	60	300
G1HD-055	1719	diagonally grained edge	2	1	100		
G1HD-060	1719		3	1	15	90	450
G1HD-065	1719	diagonally grained edge	3	1	150		
G1HD-070	1720		3	1	10	60	300
G1HD-075	1721		3	1	10	60	300
G1HD-080	1721	latter 1 over 0	3	1	14	80	400
G1HD-085	1721	stop after date	3	1	12	70	350
G1HD-090	1721	struck on thick flan [3]	3	1	150		
G1HD-095	1722		3	1	10	60	300
G1HD-100	1722	GEORGIⱯS instead of GEORGIVS	3	1	20	100	500
G1HD-105	1722	PROOF in brass; rev. ↑ [4]	3	1			500
G1HD-110	1723		3	1	10	60	300
G1HD-115	1723	no stop on rev.	3	1	15	85	500
G1HD-120	1723	struck on thin flan	3	1	40	200	
G1HD-125	1724		3	1	10	60	300

1. Possibly a proof.
2. On larger flan from now on.
3. Thickness 3mm.
4. Weight c. 10.8 grams.

George II 1727–1760

The halfpennies of George II were the most prolific issue yet produced, spanning a quarter of a century. To them was added a large number of counterfeits and curious pieces similar in appearance. Many of these sported legends markedly different from those on the genuine coin, in order to circumvent any accusation that the pieces were coined as imitations of coinage. Many genuine coins were melted down and underweight fabrications made from the molten metal. It is difficult in modern times to appreciate the extent to which counterfeiting had debased the currency, and for long periods forgeries outnumbered the genuine pieces.

The early head of George II used on the halfpennies of 1729 to 1739 was by Croker. The later head of the king from 1740 to 1754 was by Tanner. The reverses were possibly by Tanner and/ or Johann Ochs, junior, although Peck considered that the early Britannia reverse was of such good workmanship that it was probably by Croker.

Denomination	Metal	Weight (grams)	Diameter (mm)	Rev. alignment
Halfpenny	Copper	9.7-10.3	28–30	↓

Obverse 1 Head 1, left; GEORGIVS II REX

Obverse 2 Head 2, older, left; GEORGIUS II REX

Obverse 3 Head 2, left; GEORGIVS II REX

Reverse 1 Britannia, seated, with shield, facing left, holding spray and spear; BRITANNIA; date in exergue below

Reverse 2 Redesigned Britannia, cruder style; other details similar

Edge plain

Obv. 1

Obv. 2

Rev. 1

Rev. 2

No.	Date	Features	Obv.	Rev.	F	VF	EF
G2HD-005	1729	stop after legend (rev.)	1	1	8	35	140
G2HD-010	1729	no stop after legend (rev.)	1	1	12	50	200
G2HD-015	1729	PROOF [1]	1	1			400
G2HD-020	1729	PROOF in silver [2]	1	1			1200
G2HD-025	1729	PROOF in silver on thick flan [3]	1	1			1800
G2HD-030	1730	[4]	1	1	10	40	160
G2HD-035	1730	GEOGIVS instead of GEORGIVS (obv.) [5]	1	1	30	100	600
G2HD-040	1731	stop after legend (rev.)	1	1	8	35	140
G2HD-045	1731	no stop after legend (rev.)	1	1	10	45	180
G2HD-050	1732		1	1	10	40	160
G2HD-055	1732	no stop after legend (rev.)	1	1	14	55	220

No.	Date	Features	Obv.	Rev.	F	VF	EF
G2HD-060	1732	on thick wide flan [6]	1	1	50	150	600
G2HD-065	1733	[4]		1	1	8	35	140
G2HD-070	1734			1	1	8	35	140
G2HD-075	1734	4 over 3	1	1	15	60	220
G2HD-080	1734	no stops on obv.	1	1	12	45	170
G2HD-085	1735			1	1	8	35	140
G2HD-090	1736			1	1	10	40	160
G2HD-095	1737			1	1	10	40	160
G2HD-100	1738			1	1	8	35	140
G2HD-105	1738	V in GEORGIVS over S (obv.)	1	1	11	55	200
G2HD-110	1739		1	1	8	35	140
G2HD-115	1740		2	2	8	30	120
G2HD-120	1742		2	2	8	30	120
G2HD-125	1742	2 over 0	2	2	10	40	160
G2HD-130	1743		2	2	8	30	120
G2HD-135	1744		2	2	8	30	120
G2HD-140	1745		2	2	8	30	120
G2HD-145	1746		3	2	8	30	120
G2HD-150	1747		3	2	8	30	120
G2HD-155	1748		3	2	8	30	120
G2HD-160	1749		3	2	8	30	120
G2HD-165	1750		3	2	8	30	120
G2HD-170	1751		3	2	8	30	120
G2HD-175	1752		3	2	8	30	120
G2HD-180	1753		3	2	8	30	120
G2HD-185	1754		3	2	8	30	120

1. Occurs with and without stop after GEORGIVS.
2. No stop after GEORGIVS; weight c. 10 grams.
3. No stop after GEORGIVS; thickness 2mm.
4. Stop varieties exist.
5. No stop on reverse.
6. Weight c. 13.8 grams; diam. 33mm.

George III 1760–1820

The first issue of halfpennies was in 1770, ten years after the accession of George III. Counterfeiting was now rampant, and in 1771 the utterance of counterfeit copper coin became a felony. This, however, had little effect, and for the next twenty or so years most of the so-called coins in circulation were forgeries.

Boulton's contract in 1797 to produce the 'cartwheel' coinage thwarting the counterfeiters did not extend to the production of halfpennies, although Boulton clearly expected that it would, and had indeed prepared patterns of proportionate weight and size in accordance with his theories on intrinsic value. The reason given by the government for the omission of the halfpenny from the contract was that the large number of de facto halfpennies (including tokens and fakes!) would be driven out of circulation, and that Boulton would be unable to cope with the demand for his coinage that would ensue. Many tradesmen had at this time issued privately struck halfpenny tokens.

Public demand for legally struck halfpennies soon forced the Government to reconsider its position, and in 1798 a contract was effected with Boulton to strike at the Soho mint a quantity of halfpennies and farthings dated 1799. However, in the meantime the price of copper had risen, and in accordance with Boulton's theories the weight had to be reduced slightly. Moreover, the original cartwheel design had been discontinued in favour of a more conventional design, and the net result was that the new halfpennies were not popular at first. Perhaps if the weight reduction had been more, it might have been accepted, but it was less than 5%, and it was probably seen as some sort of deception.

In 1806, a further issue of halfpennies was struck by Boulton, but the price of copper had again risen, and the weight of these was even less than that of the 1799 issue. This time, there was no adverse reaction from the public. Perhaps the national obsession with 'intrinsic value' was over.

The first series of 1770-75 was probably designed by Richard Yeo. The coins of 1799 and 1806-07 produced by Boulton were designed by Conrad Heinrich Küchler (c.1740-c.1810).

Denomination	Metal	Weight (grams)	Diameter (mm)	Rev. alignment
Halfpenny 1770-75	Copper	9.2–10.8	29–30	↓
Halfpenny 1799	Copper	12.0–13.1	30–31	↓
Halfpenny 1806-07	Copper	9.2–9.8	29	↓

Obverse 1 Head 1, right; GEORGIVS III REX

Obverse 2 Head 2, with fuller face, right; same legend

Obverse 3 Head 3, right; GEORGIUS III DEI GRATIA REX

Obverse 4 Head 4, right; GEORGIUS III D G REX (date)

Reverse 1 Britannia, seated, with shield, facing left, holding spray and spear; BRITANNIA; date in exergue below

Reverse 2 Redesigned Britannia, smaller; BRITANNIA 1799

Reverse 3 Slightly different Britannia; BRITANNIA (no date)

Edge 1770-1775: plain (1770 proofs slightly striated);

1799-1807: diagonally grained in groove

Obv. 1   Obv. 2

Obv. 3   Obv. 4

Rev. 1   Rev. 2

Rev. 3

No.	Date	Features	Obv.	Rev.	F	VF	EF
G3HD-005	1770		1	1	8	24	100
G3HD-010	1770	no stop on rev.	1	1	12	35	140
G3HD-015	1770	PROOF	1	1			600
G3HD-020	1770	PROOF in silver [1]	1	1			1200
G3HD-025	1771	[1]	1	1	7	20	90
G3HD-030	1771	no stop on rev.	1	1	10	30	120
G3HD-035	1772	[2]	1	1	7	20	90
G3HD-040	1772	GEORIVS instead of GEORGIVS (obv.)	1	1	20	60	240
G3HD-045	1772	no stop on rev.	1	1	10	30	120
G3HD-050	1773		1	1	7	20	90
G3HD-055	1773	no stop after REX (obv.)	1	1	9	25	110
G3HD-060	1773	no stop on rev.	1	1	10	30	120
G3HD-065	1774		2	1	8	22	95
G3HD-070	1775	[3]	2	1	8	22	95
G3HD-075	1799	[3]	3	2	5	8	30
G3HD-080	1799	PROOF [4]	3	2			500
G3HD-085	1806	[5]	4	3	4	7	25
G3HD-090	1806	PROOF edge grained [5]	4	3			150
G3HD-095	1806	gilt PROOF edge grained [5]	4	3			150
G3HD-100	1807	[5]	4	3	5	8	30

1. Slight reverse differences exist.
2. Slight obverse and reverse differences exist.
3. Minor varieties exist.
4. Prooflike currency coins exist.
5. Varieties exist.

George IV 1820–1830

After the mint moved to Tower Hill, coinage in gold and silver took precedence. The production of copper coins did not resume until 1821, when farthings were produced, and the first halfpennies were not issued until 1825. This was after the disagreements between the egocentric Pistrucci and the authorities, and the designing of the halfpenny fell to William Wyon. If one examines the farthing of 1821, one may be forgiven for considering that the halfpenny of George IV had a lucky escape. The designs of William Wyon are generally considered to be amongst the most elegant of the British coinage.

In 1826, a proof set of British coins in a leather case was issued, and the proof halfpenny of that year was included in this set.

Wyon followed Pistrucci's practice on the George III silver of placing the date on the obverse under the head. Under the exergue on the reverse he depicted a rose, thistle and shamrock.

Collecting Hints

Counterfeits were no longer a problem during the minting of this series. The coins should be sought in extremely fine condition or better.

Denomination	Metal	Weight (grams)	Diameter (mm)	Rev. alignment
Halfpenny	Copper	9.1–9.5	28	↑

Obverse 1 Head 1, left; GEORGIUS IV DEI GRATIA (date)

Reverse 1 Britannia, seated, with shield, facing right, holding trident; two incuse lines down arms of saltire; BRITANNIAR REX FID DEF

Reverse 2 Similar but one raised line down arms of saltire; same legend

Edge plain

Obv. 1   Rev. 1

No.	Date	Features	Obv.	Rev.	F	VF	EF	UNC
G4HD-005	1825		1	1	15	45	120	180
G4HD-010	1825	PROOF	1	1				400
G4HD-015	1826		1	1	6	12	40	65
G4HD-020	1826	PROOF	1	1				250
G4HD-025	1826	bronzed PROOF	1	1				180
G4HD-030	1826		1	2	12	35	100	150
G4HD-035	1826	PROOF	1	2				300
G4HD-040	1826	bronzed PROOF	1	2				180
G4HD-045	1827		1	1	7	16	60	90

William IV 1830–1837

The halfpenny series of William IV was a continuation of that of George IV, using a William Wyon obverse from a model by Sir Francis Chantrey. The reverse was virtually identical to that of the issue for the previous reign.

Collecting Hints

The series should be collected in extremely fine or mint state, with original lustre.

Denomination	Metal	Weight (grams)	Diameter (mm)	Rev. alignment
Halfpenny	Copper	9.2–9.5	28	↑

Obverse 1 Head 1, right; W.W. incuse on truncation; GULIELMUS IIII DEI GRATIA (date)

Reverse 1 Britannia, seated, with shield, facing right, holding trident; BRITANNIAR REX FID DEF (almost identical to Reverse 1 of George IV issue)

Edge plain

Obv. 1   Rev. 1

No.	Date	Features	Obv.	Rev.	F	VF	EF	UNC
W4HD-005	1831		1	1	7	15	60	90
W4HD-010	1831	Bronzed PROOF	1	1				300
W4HD-015	1831	Bronzed PROOF; rev. ↓[1]	1	1				200
W4HD-020	1834		1	1	7	15	60	90
W4HD-025	1837		1	1	6	12	50	75

1. Issued in cased proof sets.

Victoria 1837–1901

The halfpenny of Victoria has, as a series, many of the characteristics of the Victorian penny, but on inspection many differences are revealed. Although the designers, William Wyon and his son Leonard Charles Wyon, later followed by Thomas Brock, are the same, the halfpenny series is not simply a scaled down version of the penny. Indeed, in some ways it is more interesting. It is probably also more challenging, as specimens in top condition are more difficult to find.

The copper halfpenny, struck from 1838 to 1860, is, like the penny, notable for a number of overdate varieties. 'Ghosting' caused by clashed dies is probably even more prevalent than on the penny. However, the copper series has fewer design variations than the penny. The trident on the reverse, for example, is always ornamented, and this reverse appears to be identical to that of the William IV halfpenny (apart from REX becoming REG). The head on the obverse has William Wyon's initials on the truncation on all dates, unlike the penny.

The bronze halfpenny, like the penny, has a large number of minor varieties and has been the subject of almost as much specialised study as the penny. In this work, many of these varieties will be referred to only in annotated form and not as a separate entry. A few may be omitted on the grounds that they are so minor as to be of little interest except to a specialised student.

Collecting Hints

The halfpenny suffered more wear generally than the penny. This is almost always the case with smaller coins, as the percentage of surface area making contact during circulation is greater with small coins. A minimum acceptable grade, unless the coin is very rare, is probably fine to very fine. Many of the minor varieties will not be identifiable on a fine condition coin. If possible, higher grade coins with original lustre should be sought.

Most dealers do not concern themselves with very minor varieties, and the serious collector or student with sufficient knowledge has an excellent chance of picking up rarities cheaply.

As mentioned, ghosting is prevalent on the halfpenny series. For collectors who do not object to the products of clashed dies, or even welcome them, superb crystal-sharp examples of this phenomenon can frequently be found.

Denomination	Metal	Weight (grams)	Diameter (mm)	Rev. alignment
Halfpenny 1838-1860 Obv. 1, Rev. 1	Copper	9.1–9.5	28	↑
Halfpenny 1860-1901 Obvs 2-6, Revs 2-5	Bronze	5.5–5.8	25	↑

Obverse 1 Head 1, left; VICTORIA DEI GRATIA (date)

Obverse 2 Head 2, left; VICTORIA D G BRITT REG F D; beaded border

Obverse 3 Similar but toothed border

Obverse 4 Head 3, left; slightly older features; same legend

Obverse 5 Head 3, left; drapery includes seven-pearled brooch (rose on previous obverses)

Obverse 6 Head 4, veiled, left; VICTORIA DEI GRA BRITT REGINA FID DEF IND IMP

Reverse 1 Britannia, seated, with shield, facing right; BRITANNIA REG FID DEF (as reverse of William IV issue but REX becomes REG)

Reverse 2 Redesigned Britannia, seated, with shield, facing right; HALF PENNY; date in exergue below Britannia; beaded border.

Reverse 3 Similar but toothed border

Reverse 4 Similar but Britannia completely redesigned.

Reverse 5 Similar but waterline slightly higher

Edge plain

Obv. 1   Obv. 2

Obv. 3   Obv. 4

Obv. 5   Obv. 6

Rev. 1

Rev. 2

Rev. 3

Rev. 4

No.	Date	Features	Obv.	Rev.	F	VF	EF	UNC
VYHD-005	1838		1	1	5	9	35	60
VYHD-010	1839	PROOF	1	1				220
VYHD-015	1839	PROOF rev. ↓[1]	1	1				180
VYHD-020	1841		1	1	5	9	35	60
VYHD-025	1841	rev. ↓	1	1	25	50	150	250
VYHD-030	1841	Bronzed PROOF	1	1				350
VYHD-035	1841	PROOF in silver on thick flan [2]	1	1				2000
VYHD-040	1843		1	1	8	15	60	100
VYHD-045	1844		1	1	6	11	40	70
VYHD-050	1845		1	1	25	70	250	450
VYHD-055	1846		1	1	7	14	55	85
VYHD-060	1847		1	1	7	15	60	90
VYHD-065	1848	8 not over 7	1	1	20	50	150	300
VYHD-070	1848	8 over 7	1	1	6	11	40	70
VYHD-075	1851	[3]	1	1	6	11	40	70
VYHD-080	1852	[3]	1	1	6	12	45	75
VYHD-085	1853	[3]	1	1	5	8	25	45
VYHD-090	1853	3 over 2 [3]	1	1	15	25	75	140
VYHD-095	1853	PROOF [3]	1	1				250
VYHD-100	1853	Bronzed PROOF; rev. ↓[3]	1	1				300
VYHD-105	1854	[3]	1	1	5	8	25	45
VYHD-110	1855	[3]	1	1	5	10	35	60
VYHD-115	1856	[3]	1	1	8	14	60	90
VYHD-120	1857	[3]	1	1	6	11	40	70
VYHD-125	1858	[4]	1	1	5	8	30	55
VYHD-130	1858	latter 8 over 6	1	1	7	10	40	70
VYHD-135	1858	latter 8 over 7	1	1	5	8	30	55
VYHD-140	1859		1	1	15	25	80	150
VYHD-145	1859	9 over 8	1	1	10	16	55	95
VYHD-150	1860	[5]	1	1	1000	2000	3000	3800
VYHD-155	1860	[6]	2	2	5	9	24	40
VYHD-160	1860	PROOF	2	2				600
VYHD-165	1860	Bronzed PROOF [6]	2	2				500
VYHD-170	1860	[7]	3	2	200	1000		
VYHD-175	1860	[8]	3	3	8	16	50	100
VYHD-180	1860	PROOF	3	3				800
VYHD-185	1860	Bronzed PROOF	3	3				800
VYHD-190	1861	[8]	3	3	5	9	24	40
VYHD-195	1861	HALP instead of HALF (rev.)	3	3	50	100		
VYHD-200	1861	6 over 8 [9]	3	3	50	100		
VYHD-205	1861	PROOF [10]	3	3				500
VYHD-210	1861	Bronzed PROOF	3	3				500
VYHD-215	1861	PROOF in brass	3	3				500
VYHD-220	1861	PROOF in cupronickel	3	3				800
VYHD-225	1861	PROOF in silver [10]	3	3				2000
VYHD-230	1861	PROOF in gold; rev. ↓[11]	3	3				5000
VYHD-235	1862		3	3	5	9	22	36
VYHD-240	1862	'A' to left of lighthouse (rev.) [12]	3	3	100	400		

No.	Date	Features	Obv.	Rev.	F	VF	EF	UNC
VYHD-245	1862	'B' to left of lighthouse (rev.) [13]	3	3	150	600		
VYHD-250	1862	'C' to left of lighthouse (rev.) [13]	3	3	150	600		
VYHD-255	1862	PROOF [14]	3	3				500
VYHD-260	1863	[15]	3	3	5	11	30	55
VYHD-265	1863	PROOF	3	3				500
VYHD-270	1864	[16]	3	3	6	14	45	80
VYHD-275	1864	PROOF	3	3				700
VYHD-280	1865		3	3	7	18	60	110
VYHD-285	1865	5 over 3	3	3	18	80	250	400
VYHD-290	1866		3	3	7	16	55	95
VYHD-295	1866	PROOF	3	3				600
VYHD-300	1867		3	3	8	18	65	120
VYHD-305	1867	PROOF; rev. ↓	3	3				800
VYHD-310	1867	PROOF in copper	3	3				700
VYHD-315	1868		3	3	7	16	55	95
VYHD-320	1868	PROOF	3	3				400
VYHD-325	1868	PROOF in copper	3	3				500
VYHD-330	1868	PROOF in cupronickel [17]	3	3			140	200
VYHD-335	1869		3	3	12	35	130	200
VYHD-340	1870		3	3	7	16	55	90
VYHD-345	1871		3	3	20	60	200	350
VYHD-350	1872		3	3	7	15	50	85
VYHD-355	1872	PROOF in brass	3	3				600
VYHD-360	1873	[18]	3	3	7	16	55	90
VYHD-365	1874		3	3	8	18	65	110
VYHD-370	1874	narrow date [19]	3	3	8	18	65	110
VYHD-375	1874	[18]	4	3	8	18	65	110
VYHD-380	1874	narrow date	4	3	8	18	65	110
VYHD-385	1874	narrow date 'H' below date	4	3	5	9	25	45
VYHD-390	1874	narrow date 'H' below date struck on thick flan [20]	4	3	120	450		
VYHD-395	1874	narrow date 'H' below date PROOF	4	3				500
VYHD-400	1875	[21]	4	3	5	9	25	45
VYHD-405	1875	'H' below date	4	3	10	18	50	95
VYHD-410	1875	'H' below date struck on thick flan	4	3	200	800		
VYHD-415	1875	'H' below date PROOF [22]	4	3				900
VYHD-420	1876	'H' below date [21]	4	3	4	8	25	45
VYHD-425	1876	'H' below date struck on thick flan	4	3	120	450		
VYHD-430	1876	'H' below date PROOF	4	3				500
VYHD-435	1877	[21]	4	3	4	8	25	45
VYHD-440	1877	PROOF	4	3				500
VYHD-445	1878	[21]	4	3	6	12	45	90
VYHD-450	1878	PROOF	4	3				500
VYHD-455	1879	[19]	4	3	4	8	25	45
VYHD-460	1880	[19]	4	3	5	10	30	50
VYHD-465	1880	PROOF	4	3				500
VYHD-470	1881	[21]	4	3	5	10	30	50
VYHD-475	1881	PROOF	4	3				500
VYHD-480	1881	'H' below date	4	3	4	8	25	40
VYHD-485	1881	PROOF	5	3				500
VYHD-490	1882	'H' below date	4	3	4	8	25	40
VYHD-495	1882	'H' below date PROOF [23]	4	3				600
VYHD-500	1883	[21]	4	3	10	20	55	95
VYHD-505	1883	PROOF	4	3				500
VYHD-510	1883		5	3	5	10	30	50
VYHD-515	1884		5	3	3	7	20	35
VYHD-520	1884	PROOF	5	3				400
VYHD-525	1885		5	3	3	7	20	35
VYHD-530	1885	PROOF	5	3				400
VYHD-535	1886		5	3	3	7	20	35
VYHD-540	1886	PROOF	5	3				400
VYHD-545	1887		5	3	3	6	18	30
VYHD-550	1887	PROOF	5	3				400
VYHD-555	1888		5	3	3	7	20	35
VYHD-560	1889		5	3	3	7	20	35
VYHD-565	1889	9 over 8	5	3	15	40	120	250
VYHD-570	1889	9 over 8 PROOF [24]	5	3				1500

No.	Date	Features	Obv.	Rev.	F	VF	EF	UNC
VYHD-575	1890		5	3	3	6	18	28
VYHD-580	1890	PROOF	5	3				400
VYHD-585	1891		5	3	3	6	18	28
VYHD-590	1891	PROOF	5	3				350
VYHD-595	1892		5	3	4	8	24	36
VYHD-600	1892	PROOF	5	3				450
VYHD-605	1893		5	3	3	6	18	28
VYHD-610	1893	PROOF	5	3				400
VYHD-615	1894		5	3	4	8	24	36
VYHD-620	1894	PROOF	5	3				400
VOHD-625	1895		6	4	2	6	12	18
VOHD-630	1895	PROOF	6	4				350
VOHD-635	1896	[18]	6	4	2	5	8	12
VOHD-640	1896	PROOF	6	4				350
VOHD-645	1897		6	4	4	10	18	28
VOHD-650	1897		6	5	2	5	9	14
VOHD-655	1898		6	4	2	5	9	14
VOHD-660	1899		6	4	2	5	9	14
VOHD-665	1900		6	4	2	4	6	10
VOHD-670	1900	PROOF	6	4				300
VOHD-675	1901		6	4	2	4	5	8
VOHD-680	1901	PROOF	6	4				300

1. Some (all?) issued in cased proof sets.
2. Thickness 2.8 mm.
3. Some examples of 1851, 1852, 1857, and all examples of 1853 to 1856, have seven incuse dots on and above the shield on the reverse.
4. Date size varies.
5. Some struck in bronze; some struck between 1860 and 1872; some or all proofs.
6. Minor portrait varieties exist.
7. Toothed/beaded 'mule'.
8. Many minor obverse/reverse varieties exist.
9. Some minor varieties exist.
10. At least two slightly different types.
11. One known; weight 8.3 grams.
12. Die identification letter; the 'A' is unbarred.
13. Die identification letter.
14. Minor differences from usual reverse.
15. '3' in date varies.
16. '4' has only one serif.
17. Weight c. 5.5 grams.
18. Minor reverse varieties exist.
19. Minor obverse varieties exist.
20. Weight c. 8.0 grams.
21. Minor obverse/reverse varieties exist.
22. Possibly early striking currency pieces; price if genuine proofs.
23. Possibly a pattern; reverse slightly different from any used on currency.
24. All overdate proofs are extremely rare.

Edward VII 1901–1910

The halfpenny is at first sight a scaled-down version of the penny, but on closer inspection it appears to be more straightforward. Although the 'low tide' variety of 1902 exists as on the penny, some of the minor varieties seen on the penny do not appear. Apart from the low tide variety, the only change in the series is the alteration of the date numerals.

The portrait of Edward is by George William de Saulles (1862-1903), with the reducing machine being used to effect the alteration of the portrait to the correct size. The reverse is virtually identical to that used for the veiled head halfpennies of Victoria.

The colour variation of toned pieces ranges from light to very dark brown, according to the composition of the alloy used.

Collecting Hints

The series should be collected in mint state or near. These coins usually occur sharply struck, and are very attractive when none or little of their original lustre has been lost. It should be noted that the 'low tide' halfpenny is rarer than this variety on the penny and commands a higher price.

Denomination	Metal	Weight (grams)	Diameter (mm)	Rev. alignment
Halfpenny	Bronze	5.7	25	↑

Obverse 1 Head 1, right; EDWARDVS VII DEI GRA BRITT OMN REX FID DEF IND IMP

Reverse 1 Britannia, seated, with shield, facing right; HALF PENNY; date in exergue below Britannia

Reverse 2 Similar but sea is higher

Edge plain

Obv. 1   Rev. 2

No.	Date	Features	Obv.	Rev.	VF	EF	UNC
E7HD-005	1902	[1]	1	1	12	35	80
E7HD-010	1902		1	2	3	6	10
E7HD-015	1903		1	2	5	12	22
E7HD-020	1904		1	2	5	15	30
E7HD-025	1905		1	2	5	15	30
E7HD-030	1906		1	2	5	14	26
E7HD-035	1907		1	2	4	10	20
E7HD-040	1908		1	2	4	10	20
E7HD-045	1909		1	2	5	15	30
E7HD-050	1910		1	2	4	12	18

1. Known as 'Low Tide' variety.

George V 1910–1936

The design for the halfpenny is again very similar to that of the penny, and uses a portrait of George V by Sir Bertram Mac-Kennal (1863-1931). The reverse is more or less identical to that of the previous reign.

Ghosting (see George V penny) was a problem in the earlier years. Attempts were made to reduce it in 1925, when a new obverse and reverse were introduced, but it was not until the introduction of the later obverse in 1928 that the problem was eradicated.

Unlike the pennies, no halfpennies were struck with provincial mintmarks.

Collecting Hints

The earlier dates of halfpenny were very prone to circulation wear on the reverse, owing to the fact that there was no significant raised rim on the obverse. Consequently, fine or very fine specimens before 1925 are somewhat scarcer than those after that date.
The series should be collected in mint state with original lustre. Some of the dates are significantly more difficult to find than is indicated in some catalogues. Unlike with the penny, it is possible to collect an unbroken series of dates throughout the reign, and no dates were issued artificially darkened at the mint.

Denomination	Metal	Weight (grams)	Diameter (mm)	Rev. alignment
Halfpenny	Bronze	5.7	25	↑

Obverse 1 Head 1, left; B.M. on truncation; GEORGIVS V DEI GRA BRITT OMN REX FID DEF IND IMP

Obverse 2 Head 2, left; known as 'modified effigy'; initials BM are without stops and further to right; same legend

Obverse 3 Head 3, smaller, more sharply struck, left; same legend

Reverse 1 Britannia, seated, with shield, facing right; HALF PENNY; date in exergue below Britannia

Reverse 2 Similar but redesigned and more sharply struck

Edge plain

| Obv. 1 | Obv. 2 | Obv. 3 |

| Rev. 1 | Rev. 2 |

No.	Date	Features	Obv.	Rev.	VF	EF	UNC
G5HD-005	1911	1	1	1	3	7	12
G5HD-010	1912		1	1	3	7	12
G5HD-015	1913		1	1	3	8	14
G5HD-020	1914		1	1	3	7	12
G5HD-025	1915		1	1	3	7	12
G5HD-030	1916		1	1	3	7	12
G5HD-035	1917		1	1	3	7	12
G5HD-040	1918		1	1	3	7	12
G5HD-045	1919		1	1	3	7	12
G5HD-050	1920		1	1	3	7	12
G5HD-055	1921		1	1	3	7	12
G5HD-060	1922		1	1	4	9	16
G5HD-065	1923		1	1	3	8	14
G5HD-070	1924		1	1	3	8	14
G5HD-075	1925		1	1	3	8	14
G5HD-080	1925		2	2	4	9	16
G5HD-085	1926		2	2	4	9	16
G5HD-090	1926	PROOF	2	2			180
G5HD-095	1927		2	2	2	5	10
G5HD-100	1927	PROOF	2	2			150
G5HD-105	1928		3	2	2	4	8
G5HD-110	1928	PROOF	3	2			150
G5HD-115	1929		3	2	2	4	8
G5HD-120	1929	PROOF	3	2			150
G5HD-125	1930		3	2	2	4	8
G5HD-130	1930	PROOF	3	2			150
G5HD-135	1931		3	2	2	4	8
G5HD-140	1931	PROOF	3	2			150
G5HD-145	1932		3	2	2	4	8
G5HD-150	1932	PROOF	3	2			150
G5HD-155	1933		3	2	2	4	8
G5HD-160	1933	PROOF	3	2			150
G5HD-165	1934		3	2	2	5	10
G5HD-170	1934	PROOF	3	2			170
G5HD-175	1935		3	2	2	4	8
G5HD-180	1935	PROOF	3	2			150
G5HD-185	1936		3	2	2	3	4
G5HD-190	1936	PROOF	3	2			140

1. Minor obverse varieties exist.

Edward VIII 1936

The Edward VIII halfpenny is strictly speaking a pattern, as probable Royal approval was about to be granted at the time of the abdication. However, because its official status rests only on this technicality, and to provide continuity, it is included in this catalogue.

The portrait of Edward VIII is by Thomas Humphrey Paget, and faces left at the insistence of the king, who considered this placement more flattering and wished to discontinue the tradition of opposite facings for successive monarchs. The reverse is by Thomas Humphrey Paget.

Denomination	Metal	Weight (grams)	Diameter (mm)	Rev. alignment
Halfpenny	Bronze	5.7	25	↑

Obverse 1 Head 1, left; EDWARDVS VIII D G BR OMN REX F D IND IMP

Reverse 1 Sailing ship; HALF PENNY 1937

Edge plain

| Obv. 1 | Rev. 1 |

No.	Date	Obv.	Rev.	Unc
E8HD-005	1937	1	1	15000

George VI 1937–1952

The omission of Britannia from the reverse of the George VI halfpenny was a bold innovation. Britannia had graced the coin from its inception in 1672, and continued to be depicted on the penny in a somewhat modernistic style.

The choice of symbol to replace Britannia was a three-masted sailing ship. This was not entirely the revolutionary idea it seemed at first glance; ships had occurred from time to time on British coinage, and the ship was to some extent as symbolic of Britain 'ruling the waves' as was Britannia. The vessel was said to represent the 'Golden Hind' of Sir Francis Drake. Both obverse and reverse were designed by Thomas Humphrey Paget.

As with the George V series, the halfpenny was struck for every year of the reign. It was not found necessary to curtail production in some years, as was done with the penny.

The size and orientation of the ship and the reverse legend vary very slightly from year to year and also, during 1940, within the year itself. Although Peck commented on these variations, he allocated only one reverse to the series, whereas Freeman allocated 16. These minute intricacies are not considered here to be of interest except to a specialist student of this series, and we therefore follow the Peck example.

Proofs were struck for the cased sets of 1937, 1950 and 1951, and in small quantities in all of the other years.

Collecting Hints

Mint state with full lustre is the order of the day for this series. There are no real rarities except for those proofs not issued for cased sets. Collecting a set of these presents a real challenge.

Denomination	Metal	Weight (grams)	Diameter (mm)	Rev. alignment
Halfpenny	Bronze	5.7	25	↑

Obverse 1 Head 1, left; HP on truncation; GEORGIVS VI D G BR OMN REX F D IND IMP

Obverse 2 Head 1, left; GEORGIVS VI D G BR OMN REX FIDEI DEF

Reverse 1 Sailing ship; HALF PENNY (date)

Edge plain

Obv. 1   Obv. 2   Rev. 1

No.	Date	Features	Obv.	Rev.	EF	UNC
G6HD-005	1937		1	1	2	4
G6HD-010	1937	PROOF [1]	1	1		8
G6HD-015	1937	PROOF from sandblasted dies [2]	1	1		150
G6HD-020	1938		1	1	2	5
G6HD-025	1938	PROOF	1	1		180
G6HD-030	1939		1	1	2	5
G6HD-035	1939	PROOF	1	1		180
G6HD-040	1940		1	1	2	6
G6HD-045	1940	PROOF	1	1		180
G6HD-050	1941		1	1	2	5
G6HD-055	1941	PROOF	1	1		180
G6HD-060	1942		1	1	2	4
G6HD-065	1942	PROOF	1	1		180
G6HD-070	1943		1	1	2	4
G6HD-075	1943	PROOF	1	1		180
G6HD-080	1944		1	1	2	4
G6HD-085	1944	PROOF	1	1		180
G6HD-090	1945		1	1	2	4
G6HD-095	1945	PROOF	1	1		180
G6HD-100	1946		1	1	2	5
G6HD-105	1946	PROOF	1	1		180
G6HD-110	1947		1	1	2	4
G6HD-115	1947	PROOF	1	1		180
G6HD-120	1948		1	1	2	4
G6HD-125	1948	PROOF	1	1		180
G6HD-130	1949		2	1	2	5
G6HD-135	1949	PROOF	2	1		180
G6HD-140	1950		2	1	2	4
G6HD-145	1950	PROOF [1]	2	1		8
G6HD-150	1950	PROOF from sandblasted dies [2]	2	1		150
G6HD-155	1951		2	1	2	5
G6HD-160	1951	PROOF [1]	2	1		9
G6HD-165	1951	PROOF from sandblasted dies [2]	2	1		150
G6HD-170	1952		2	1	2	4
G6HD-175	1952	PROOF	2	1		180

1. Issued in cased proof sets.
2. Struck to facilitate photography of coin.

Size of ship, orientation of legend against border teeth vary minutely within this series.

Elizabeth II 1952 -

The series uses the portrait of Elizabeth II by Mary Gillick. The halfpenny was struck for every year from 1953 to 1967 except 1961, unlike the penny. Small quantities of proofs were struck each year, and larger quantities for insertion in the proof sets of 1953 and 1970.

Collecting Hints

The series should be collected in mint state. Apart from the 1953 and 1970, the proofs are very difficult to find.

Denomination	Metal	Weight (grams)	Diameter (mm)	Rev. alignment
Halfpenny	Bronze	5.7	25	↑

Obverse 1 Head 1, right; ELIZABETH II DEI GRA BRITT OMN REGINA F D.

Obverse 2 Similar but ELIZABETH II DEI GRATIA REGINA F D

Reverse 1 Ship; HALF PENNY (date)

Reverse NZ Reverse of regular issue New Zealand halfpenny dated 1965

Edge plain

Obv. 1   Obv. 2   Rev. 1

No.	Date	Features	Obv.	Rev.	UNC
EL2HD-005	1953	[1]	1	1	5
EL2HD-010	1953	PROOF [2]	1	1	7
EL2HD-015	1953	PROOF from sandblasted dies [3]	1	1	150
EL2HD-020	1954	[1]	2	1	6
EL2HD-025	1954	PROOF	2	1	140
EL2HD-030	1955		2	1	5
EL2HD-035	1955	PROOF	2	1	140
EL2HD-040	1956	[1]	2	1	6
EL2HD-045	1956	PROOF	2	1	140
EL2HD-050	1957	[1]	2	1	2
EL2HD-055	1957	PROOF	2	1	140
EL2HD-060	1958	[1]	2	1	2
EL2HD-065	1958	PROOF	2	1	140
EL2HD-070	1959		2	1	2
EL2HD-075	1959	PROOF	2	1	140
EL2HD-080	1960		2	1	2
EL2HD-085	1960	PROOF	2	1	140
EL2HD-090	1962		2	1	2
EL2HD-095	1962	PROOF	2	1	140
EL2HD-100	1963		2	1	2
EL2HD-105	1963	PROOF	2	1	140
EL2HD-110	1964		2	1	2
EL2HD-115	1964	PROOF	2	1	140
EL2HD-120	1965		2	1	2
EL2HD-125	1965	PROOF	2	1	140
EL2HD-130	1965	struck in gold [4]	2	1	1500
EL2HD-135	1965	[5]	2	NZ	500
EL2HD-140	1966		2	1	2
EL2HD-145	1966	PROOF	2	1	140
EL2HD-150	1966	struck in aluminium [6]	2	1	300
EL2HD-155	1966	struck in brass or nickel-brass [7]	2	1	400
EL2HD-160	1967	[1]	2	1	2
EL2HD-165	1967	PROOF	2	1	140
EL2HD-170	1967	struck in cupronickel [8]	2	1	400
EL2HD-175	1970	PROOF [9]	2	1	3

1. Minor design and orientation differences exist.
2. Issued in cased proof sets.
3. Struck to facilitate photography of coin.
4. Weight c. 12.5 grams.
5. Error coin with New Zealand reverse; weight 5.8 grams; possibly unique.
6. Weight 2.3 grams.
7. Weight 6.8 grams.
8. Weight 5.6 grams.
9. Issued in sealed cased proof sets; not legal tender.

Farthing

Charles II 1660–1685

In the first few years of this reign, there was a considerable shortage of coins of low denomination. It is always a sign that coins of a certain denomination are needed when tradesmen issue private tokens bearing that denomination, and the well-known farthing tokens of the 1660s are a clear indication of the need for this coin. An extensive series of pattern farthings was struck from the beginning of the reign, but it was not until 1672 that farthings were struck for circulation.

The royal Proclamation of 1672 authorised strikings of farthings and halfpennies, but the issue of halfpennies was delayed. The farthing thus became the first of the long series of base metal 'Britannia' coinage which was to last almost exactly 300 years.

The Proclamation decreed that there was to be a close correlation between the face value of the coins and their intrinsic metal content. Almost immediately, however, problems arose. The mint proved incapable of manufacturing the necessary blanks, and they had to be imported from Sweden. Eventually, the coins were struck with a face value slightly higher than the metal and production costs, and this resulted in counterfeits appearing shortly afterwards.

In 1684, five years after the last copper coinage of the reign had been struck, a quantity of tin farthings was issued, each coin having a plug of copper through its centre. It was hoped thus to produce coinage at a profit over production costs, while at the same time foiling the counterfeiters. An added bonus was that the ailing tin industry was bolstered by the new demand.

John Roettier prepared the dies for this series.

No.	Date	Features	Edge date	Obv.	Rev.	VG	F	VF	EF
C2FAM-005	1672	[1]		1	1	6	16	50	300
C2FAM-010	1672	no stops on obv		1	1	8	22	65	400
C2FAM-015	1673			1	1	6	16	50	300
C2FAM-020	1673	CAROLA instead of CAROLO (obv.)		1	1	15	50	150	900
C2FAM-025	1673	BRITINNIA instead of BRITANNIA (rev.)		1	1	20	65	220	1200
C2FAM-030	1673	no stops on obv		1	1	12	40	120	700
C2FAM-035	1673	no stop on rev.		1	1	8	22	65	400
C2FAM-040	1674			1	1	7	20	60	320
C2FAM-045	1675			1	1	7	20	60	300
C2FAM-050	1675	no stop after CAROLVS (obv.)		1	1	10	30	75	420
C2FAM-055	1679			1	1	10	30	80	450
C2FAM-060	1679	no stop on rev.		1	1	8	22	65	400
C2FAM-065	1684	[2]	1684	1	2	35	80	300	1200
C2FAM-070	1685	[3]	1685	1	2	800	1200		

1. Slight differences in drapery exist (reverse).
2. Edge punctuation varies.
3. Very few exist.

James II 1685–1688

The issue of farthings in copper plugged tin augmented the similar halfpenny of this reign, both attempting to foil counterfeiters and assist the ailing tin industry. The halfpenny was a new issue, but the farthing continued the general design of the previous reign, using a figure of Britannia from a punch used on the earlier coins.

The obverse portrait was by John Roettier. A later issue of farthing in 1687 used a somewhat different and draped bust, more like that on the halfpenny.

Collecting Hints

This series is collectable in any condition above fine. Specimens in extremely fine and better are rare. The Charles II farthing is of much interest historically and numismatically. It also includes a number of significant varieties.

Denomination	Metal	Weight (grams)	Diameter (mm)	Rev. alignment
Farthing 1672-1679	Copper	5.2–6.4	22–23	↓
Farthing 1684-1685	Tin with a central copper plug	5.4–6.0	23–24	↓

Obverse 1 Head 1, left; CAROLVS A CAROLO

Reverse 1 Britannia, seated, with shield, facing left, holding spray and spear; BRITANNIA; date in exergue below

Reverse 2 Similar but no date

Edge (1672-1679) plain; (1684-1685) NVMMORVM FAMVLVS (date)

Collecting Hints

Because the series is highly prone to corrosion, specimens in the higher grades are very difficult to obtain. The corrosion tends to be progressive, and does not form a protective oxide coating such as is obtained with, for example, copper. Attractive specimens should be pursued without paying too much heed to catalogue prices.

Denomination	Metal	Weight (grams)	Diameter (mm)	Rev. alignment
Farthing	Tin with a central copper plug	5.2–5.7	23–24	↓

Obverse 1 Head 1, right, with breastplate; IACOBVS SECVNDVS

Obverse 2 Head 2, right, draped; same legend

Reverse 1 Britannia, seated, with shield, facing left, holding spray and spear; BRITANNIA. The exergue is blank

Edge NVMMORVM FAMVLVS (date)

Obv. 1

Rev. 1

Rev. 2

The coin has a square plug of copper through the centre.

Obv. 1 Obv. 2 Rev. 1

No.	Date	Features	Edge date	Obv.	Rev.	VG	F	VF	EF
J2FA-05	1684		1684	1	1	800			
J2FA-10	1685 [1]		1685	1	1	30	60	250	900
J2FA-15	1685	no copper plug	1685	1	1	300	800		
J2FA-20	1686 [1]		1686	1	1	30	60	250	900
J2FA-25	1687		1687	1	1				
J2FA-30	1687 [1]		1687	2	1	50	90	450	1400

1. Punctuation varieties exist (edge).

William and Mary 1688–1694

The farthing issue again followed that of the halfpenny, but there were some significant differences. The first issue, in tin, bears a caricatured portrait of William and Mary by George Bower somewhat similar to that on the halfpenny (and, incidentally, very like that on the small silver pieces which are by an unknown designer). However, the reverse of the farthing is also by Bower, whereas the halfpenny reverse is a continuation of the John Roettier Britannia.

The first issue of farthing was discontinued in 1690 in favour of a tin issue with a more conventional portrait of the monarchs by James Roettier. This resembles more closely the sixpence rather than the small silver. The reverse uses the figure of Britannia by James Roettier as on the coins of Charles II.

By 1692 it had become clear that the use of tin as a coinage metal left a great deal to be desired. The tendency to corrosion was now much in evidence; moreover, the coins were, after all, easy to counterfeit. The copper coinage was missed, and in 1694 a new copper farthing was struck, together with a new halfpenny. Unlike the Charles II issue, the blanks were struck at the Mint rather than imported, and indeed this was one of the main conditions of the contract. The portrait of the monarchs was by James or Norbert Roettier.

In addition to the above, a very few farthings dated 1693 exist as a result of a (subsequently revoked) contract granted to one Andrew Corbet. These bear a portrait similar to that on the last issue.

Collecting Hints

All farthings of this reign are very difficult to find in top condition. The first issue of tin farthings by Bower is very elusive in any grade, and should be acquired whenever the chance arises.

Denomination	Metal	Weight (grams)	Diameter (mm)	Rev. alignment
Farthing 1689-1692	Tin with a central copper plug	5.2–5.8	22–24	↓
Farthing 1693-1694	Copper	4.7–6.2	22–25	↓

Obverse 1 Heads 1, right; GVLIELMVS ET MARIA (heads divide GVLIELMVS...ET)

Obverse 2 Heads 2, right, more drapery; same legend, which starts below busts. (heads divide ET...MARIA)

Obverse 3 Heads 3, right, with king wearing breastplate; same legend

Obverse 4 Heads 4, right; king's hair short; same legend

Reverse 1 Britannia, seated, with shield, facing left, crude style; date in exergue; BRITANNIA.

Reverse 2 Britannia, slightly different, same crude style; date in exergue; BRITANNIA

Reverse 3 Britannia, as on Charles II farthings; date in exergue; BRITANNIA

Edge (1689-1692): NVMMORVM FAMVLVS (date); (1693-1694): plain

Obv. 1 Obv. 2

Obv. 3 Obv. 4

Rev. 1 Rev. 2 Rev. 3

No.	Date	Features	Edge date	Obv.	Rev.	VG	F	VF	EF
WMFA-005	1689		1689	1	1	140	300	900	
WMFA-010	1689	PROOF in copper; edge plain		1	1				2000
WMFA-015	1689		1690	2	2	600			
WMFA-020	1690		1689	3	3	600			
WMFA-025	1690 [1]		1690	3	3	40	90	250	900
WMFA-030	1690	PROOF in copper; edge plain [2]		3	3				5000
WMFA-035	1691 [1]		1691	3	3	40	90	250	900
WMFA-040	1692		1692	3	3	40	90	250	900
WMFA-045	1693			3	3	800	1200		
WMFA-050	1694 [3]			4	3	12	40	80	600
WMFA-055	1694	struck on thick wide flan [4]		4	3	150	350	800	
WMFA-060	1694	GVLIELMS instead of GVLIELMVS (obv.)		4	3	120	250	600	
WMFA-065	1694	PROOF		4	3				2000
WMFA-070	1694	PROOF in silver [5]		4	3		120	240	500

1. Edge punctuation varies.
2. Possibly unique.
3. Exergue line single or double; some 'A's may be unbarred; punctuation varies.
4. Diameter 25–26 mm.
5. Some 'A's may be unbarred; punctuation varies.

William III 1694–1701

The farthings of William III suffered from the same lack of control of production techniques as did the halfpenny. The production of the tin farthing (or 'white farthing' as it was sometimes known) did not resume, but the coin itself was still in circulation, corroding rapidly. These unpopular pieces were, theoretically at least, exchangeable for the new copper coinage. After the death of the queen, the farthings bearing the head of William ruling as king continued to be produced under the contract granted during the reign of William and Mary. However, sloppiness was the order of the day at the mint. Blanks, and indeed entire coins, were sometimes cast instead of being struck, and some of those bene-fiting financially from the savings thus produced were vociferous in exhorting the benefits of cast coinage.

Savings were made in addition by hiring cheap labour, often for-eigners who were unable to spell even the king's name. Some of these craftsmen appear to have been selected to punch in the let-tering on the dies.

In 1698, production of copper coinage was supposed to have been stopped following an Act of Parliament, but Stephen Martin Leake noted in 1726 that this had little effect. Nevertheless, the 1698 farthing of the first type is particularly rare, and some doubts have been raised about the authenticity of the known specimens.

The last farthings of the reign were struck in 1700. The coin did not follow the halfpenny into the degradation of the final 1699-1701 issue of much inferior workmanship and the new crude de-sign of the reverse of the halfpenny.

The obverses of this series were engraved by James Roettier. The reverses continued to use the John Roettier punches of Britannia from the Charles II coins.

Collecting Hints

The series is rare in the top grades, and the serious collector will require specimens in very fine or better. As with the halfpenny, the scarcest date is 1698. As mentioned above, the 1698 first type farthing is parti-cularly rare.

Denomination	Metal	Weight (grams)	Diameter (mm)	Rev. alignment
Farthing	Copper	4.5–6.2	22–23	↓

Obverse 1 Head 1, right; GVLIELMVS TERTIVS

Reverse 1 Britannia, seated, with shield, facing left, holding spray and spear; date in exergue below; BRITANNIA

Reverse 2 Similar but legend reads BRITANNIA (date); exergue is blank

Edge plain

Obv. 1	Rev. 1	Rev. 2

No.	Date	Features	Obv.	Rev.	F	VF	EF
W3FA-005	1695		1	1	20	70	350
W3FA-010	1695	struck on thick flan [1]	1	1	100	400	
W3FA-015	1695	GVLIELMV instead of GVLIELMVS (obv.)	1	1	80	300	
W3FA-020	1695	M in GVLIELMVS over V (obv.)	1	1	40	150	
W3FA-025	1695	PROOF in silver	1	1		700	1200
W3FA-030	1696		1	1	16	55	280
W3FA-035	1696	PROOF in silver	1	1		700	1200
W3FA-040	1697		1	1	16	55	280
W3FA-045	1697	GVLIELMS instead of GVLIELMVS (obv.)	1	1	80	300	

No.	Date	Features	Obv.	Rev.	F	VF	EF
W3FA-050	1697	TERTIV instead of TERTIVS (obv.)	1	1	100	400	
W3FA-055	1697	PROOF in silver	1	1		700	1200
W3FA-060	1698		1	1	100	400	
W3FA-065	1698	B of BRITANNIA over G (rev.)	1	1	150	600	
W3FA-070	1698	[2]	1	2	40	130	550
W3FA-075	1698	PROOF in silver [2]	1	2	130	200	300
W3FA-080	1699		1	1	16	55	400
W3FA-085	1699	GVLILEMVS instead of GVLIELMVS (obv.)	1	1	80	300	
W3FA-090	1699	[3]	1	2	25	80	420
W3FA-095	1699	PROOF in silver [4]	1	2		700	1200
W3FA-100	1699	PROOF in silver on thick flan [5]	1	2		1000	1800
W3FA-105	1700	[6]	1	1	16	55	280
W3FA-110	1700	GVLILMVS instead of GVLIELMVS (obv.)	1	1	80	300	
W3FA-115	1700	RRITANNIA instead of BRITANNIA (rev.)	1	1	80	300	
W3FA-120	1700	R of BRITANNIA over B [7]	1	1	30	90	500
W3FA-125	1700	rev. ↑	1	1	30	90	500
W3FA-130	1700	PROOF in silver	1	1		450	750
W3FA-135	none	struck on wide flan [8]	1	obv 1	200		

1. Weight c. 7.2 grams.
2. Stop after date.
3. Stop varieties exist; one or both 'A's in BRITANNIA may be unbarred; obverse lettering spacing varies.
4. No stop after date.
5. No stop after date; weight c. 7.2 grams.
6. Stop varieties exist; 'A's in BRITANNIA may be unbarred; date size may vary.
7. First A of BRITANNIA may be unbarred.
8. 'Double headed' coin.

Anne 1701–1714

The 1714 farthing of Anne is the only copper coin which is generally thought of as a regular coin. In fact, its status is in some doubt. The reign was characterised by a large number of patterns of varying designs and metals. If Anne had not died in 1714, no doubt the farthing would have entered circulation in quantity, but its actual legal status may well be that of a pattern. However, it is so widely accepted and catalogued as a coin that it is included here.

Copper coinage of Anne was not considered necessary because a very large quantity of copper had been struck during the previous reign, much of it of poor quality. Isaac Newton was the Master of the Mint at this time, and he had high ideals about the quality of the coinage. The Anne farthing is certainly greatly superior to the pieces of William III, not only in striking but also in design. The old Britannia figure used since the days of Charles II was discarded in favour of a sharper high relief design by John Croker, who also designed the obverse portrait of Anne. The bare leg on the figure of Britannia as on earlier coins is thought to have been covered on the 1714 coin on the orders of the queen.

The Anne farthing is somewhat smaller than its predecessors, and the total effect is that of a coin of quality and value. Unfor-tunately, circumstances dictated that the coin was never to enter circulation widely.

Around 1802, a curious rumour swept the country that the Anne farthing was worth a fortune, around £500, no less, and many advertisements appeared in newspapers offering specimens for sale.

Collecting Hints

As the Anne farthing did not enter circulation to any great extent, the coin is probably scarcer in fine condition than in extremely fine, although many low grade specimens do turn up. An extremely fine or better specimen is the obvious candidate for any collection.

Many cast and other forgeries exist, and one must be on guard. Electrotypes are deceptive, and the edge should be examined; these pieces are made in two halves and the seam is usually evident.

Denomination	Metal	Weight (grams)	Diameter (mm)	Rev. alignment
Farthing	Copper	4.8–5.8	21–22	↓

Obverse 1 Head 1, left; ANNA DEI GRATIA

Reverse 1 Britannia, seated, with shield, facing left, holding spray and spear; 1714 in exergue below; BRITANNIA

Edge plain

Obv. 1   Rev. 1

No.	Date	Obv.	Rev.	F	VF	EF
AFA-005	1714	1	1	140	220	600

George I 1714–1727

The issue of the Anne farthing had been thwarted by the death of the queen, and when George I came to the throne there was again a need for copper coinage. However, the price of copper had risen. It was therefore decided to produce a somewhat lighter coin than previously. The first issue, known as the 'dump' issue, achieved this economy by means of a reduction in flan size, while the latter issue of 1719-1724 has a more conventional flan size but is thinner. Unfortunately, both issues suffer from metal and striking flaws. The dies, unlike those of the 17th century, were in bold relief, and difficulties were encountered in achieving the high pressure necessary to transfer all of the detail to the blanks.

Wisely, it was decided not to include the long abbreviated Hanoverian titles of the king, as had been done on most of the silver coinage. The result was a simple and elegant coin, despite the unattractiveness of the monarch. The dies were the work of John Croker, possibly assisted by Johann Rudolph Ochs, senior. The Britannia reverse is from the same punch as used on the Anne farthing.

Collecting Hints

As mentioned above, the series suffers from metal flaws and weak striking. However, the George I farthing is attractive and popular with collectors. The dump issue in particular has a chunky appearance and is much sought after in the higher grades. Collect in very fine condition or better. Remember that what appears as wear may in fact be weakness of strike.

Denomination	Metal	Weight (grams)	Diameter (mm)	Rev. alignment
Farthing 1717-18	Copper	4.5–5.3	20–21	↓
Farthing 1719-24	Copper	4.5–5.3	22–23	↓

Obverse 1 Head 1, right; GEORGIVS REX

Reverse 1 Britannia, seated, with shield, facing left, holding spray and spear; date in exergue below; BRITANNIA

Edge plain

Obv. 1   Rev. 1

No.	Date	Features	Obv.	Rev.	F	VF	EF
G1FA-005	1717		1	1	100	250	600
G1FA-010	1717	PROOF	1	1			1000
G1FA-015	1717	PROOF on thick flan [1]	1	1			2000
G1FA-020	1717	PROOF in silver; rev. ↑	1	1		200	500
G1FA-025	1717	PROOF in silver on thin flan [2]	1	1		200	500
G1FA-030	1718	PROOF in silver on thin flan	1	1		300	800
G1FA-035	1719	[3]	1	1	8	50	200
G1FA-040	1719	struck on 25mm diameter flan	1	1	20	100	400
G1FA-045	1719	obv. legend continues over head [4]	1	1	25	130	500
G1FA-050	1719	in silver [5]	1	1		300	800
G1FA-055	1720	[6]	1	1	8	50	200
G1FA-060	1720	edge vertically milled	1	1	20	120	600
G1FA-065	1720	edge vertically milled; struck on thin flan	1	1	20	120	600
G1FA-070	1721	[7]	1	1	8	50	200
G1FA-075	1721	latter 1 over 0	1	1	14	80	350
G1FA-080	1722	[6]	1	1	8	50	200
G1FA-085	1723		1	1	8	50	200
G1FA-090	1723	R of REX over horizontal R	1	1	16	100	400
G1FA-095	1724		1	1	8	50	200
G1FA-100	none	struck on 5 mm thick flan [8]	1	obv 1	500		

1. Thickness 2.5 mm.
2. Weight 3.9 grams.
3. Obverse lettering size varies; stop varieties exist.
4. Small obverse lettering.
5. Possibly a proof.
6. Obverse lettering size varies.
7. Exists with and without stop after date.
8. 'Double headed'; possibly only one exists.

George II 1727–1760

A large quantity of farthings was struck during this reign. Furthermore, counterfeits began to appear in very large numbers. The low denomination copper coinage did not have quite the same public image as it has in modern times, and was looked on separately from the silver coinage, rather like tokens which could be exchanged on demand. This public view of coins such as the farthing may have gone some way to explain the large proliferation of counterfeits, although greed was always the primary motive. Many of the counterfeits were produced from genuine coins which were melted down to produce lightweight copies.

The young head of George II used until 1739 was by John Croker, while the old head used from 1741 was by John Sigismund Tanner. The reverse continued to use the Britannia from the Anne farthing punch by John Croker.

According to Snelling, the 1754 farthing was minted at least as late as 1763, i.e. well into the reign of George III.

Collecting Hints

This series is more easily found in the high grades than are the farthings of earlier reigns. The minimum acceptable grade should be very fine.

Denomination	Metal	Weight (grams)	Diameter (mm)	Rev. alignment
Farthing	Copper	4.5–5.3	22–23	↓

Obverse 1 Head 1, left; GEORGIVS II REX

Obverse 2 Head 2, older, left; GEORGIUS II REX

Obverse 3 Head 2, left; GEORGIVS II REX

Reverse 1 Britannia, seated, with shield, facing left, holding spray and spear; BRITANNIA; date in exergue below

Edge plain

Obv. 1	Obv. 3	Rev. 1

No.	Date	Features	Obv.	Rev.	F	VF	EF
G2FA-005	1730		1	1	8	45	150
G2FA-010	1730	PROOF	1	1			350
G2FA-015	1730	PROOF in silver	1	1			500
G2FA-020	1730	PROOF in silver on thick flan; rev. ↑ [1]	1	1			700
G2FA-025	1731		1	1	8	45	150
G2FA-030	1732		1	1	8	45	150
G2FA-035	1733		1	1	8	45	150
G2FA-040	1734		1	1	8	45	150
G2FA-045	1734	no stops on obv.	1	1	15	80	250
G2FA-050	1735		1	1	7	40	130
G2FA-055	1735	3 over 5	1	1	15	80	250
G2FA-060	1735	3 over 5; struck on thick flan [2]	1	1	100		
G2FA-065	1736		1	1	7	40	130
G2FA-070	1737		1	1	7	40	130
G2FA-075	1737	large date	1	1	7	40	130
G2FA-080	1739		1	1	7	40	130
G2FA-085	1739	9 over 5	1	1	18	100	300
G2FA-090	1741		2	1	8	50	170
G2FA-095	1744		2	1	8	50	170
G2FA-100	1746		3	1	7	40	130
G2FA-105	1746	V of GEORGIVS over U (obv.)	3	1	16	90	250
G2FA-110	1749		3	1	7	40	130
G2FA-115	1750		3	1	7	40	130
G2FA-120	1754	[3]	3	1	5	24	70
G2FA-125	1754	4 over 0	3	1	15	80	220

1. 2mm thick; weight c. 7.8 grams.
2. Weight c. 7.1 grams.
3. Struck for several years.

George III 1760–1820

Apart from the 'posthumous' George II farthings dated 1754 mentioned earlier, the first farthings struck during this reign were those of 1771. In the same year, the production of counterfeit copper became a felony, but the new law did little to stop what had by now become an epidemic. For many years a situation existed in which the majority of copper pieces circulating were forgeries.

The Boulton anti-counterfeiting measures carried out at the Soho Mint to produce the 1797 'Cartwheel' coinage did not extend to the farthing, although several types of pattern cartwheel farthing were struck. Boulton was, however, granted a licence to produce farthings in 1799, but the weight of these was somewhat below those of the cartwheel patterns, owing to a rise in the price of copper. The wide-rimmed cartwheel design had by this time been abandoned, and the farthing of 1799 had a more conventional design, although one aspect of it was far from conventional. The reverse bore the legend '1 FARTHING', the first time that the name of a denomination had appeared on any English coin. The issue of 1806-07 was even lighter in weight than the 1799 issue, owing to a further rise in the price of copper.

The portrait of George III used on the issue of 1771-75 was possibly by Richard Yeo. The later coins were designed by Conrad Heinrich Küchler.

Collecting Hints

The series should be collected in extremely fine or better condition with original lustre. Counterfeits are easily detectable but are themselves an interesting field of study. The farthings of 1799-1807 did not wear as fast as those of the earlier series as the field on both sides was somewhat concave. The central design thus did not rub against other coins so readily when in circulation.

Denomination	Metal	Weight (grams)	Diameter (mm)	Rev. alignment
Farthing 1771-75	Copper	4.3–5.3	23–24	↓
Farthing 1799	Copper	5.8–6.6	23–24	↓
Farthing 1806-07	Copper	4.7–4.8	21–22	↓

Obverse 1 Head 1, right; GEORGIVS III REX

Obverse 2 Head 2, right; GEORGIUS III DEI GRATIA REX 1799

Obverse 3 Head 3, right; GEORGIUS III D G REX (date)

Reverse 1 Britannia, seated, with shield, facing left, holding spray and spear; BRITANNIA; date in exergue below

Reverse 2 Redesigned Britannia, smaller; BRITANNIA 1 FARTHING

Reverse 3 Slightly different Britannia; BRITANNIA

Edge 1771-1775: plain

1799-1807: diagonally grained

Obv. 1	Obv. 2	Obv. 3
Rev. 1	**Rev. 2**	**Rev. 3**

No.	Date	Features	Obv.	Rev.	F	VF	EF
G3FA-005	1771		1	1	25	60	180
G3FA-010	1771	PROOF [1]	1	1			800
G3FA-015	1773	[2]	1	1	6	18	80
G3FA-020	1773	no stop on rev. [2]	1	1	8	22	110
G3FA-025	1773	no stop after REX (obv.)	1	1	10	25	140
G3FA-030	1774	[2]	1	1	8	24	130
G3FA-035	1775		1	1	10	26	150
G3FA-040	1799	[3]	2	2	4	10	40
G3FA-045	1799	PROOF [4]	2	2			200
G3FA-050	1799	PROOF; edge plain [5]	2	2			200
G3FA-055	1799	Bronzed PROOF [6]	2	2			150
G3FA-060	1799	Bronzed PROOF; edge plain [5]	2	2			150
G3FA-065	1799	gilt PROOF [6]	2	2			200
G3FA-070	1799	gilt PROOF; edge plain [5]	2	2			200
G3FA-075	1799	PROOF in silver; edge plain [5]	2	2			800
G3FA-080	1799	PROOF in gold; edge plain [5]	2	2			3000
G3FA-085	1806	[7]	3	3	4	9	35
G3FA-090	1806	PROOF [4]	3	3			150
G3FA-095	1806	Bronzed PROOF [4]	3	3			150
G3FA-100	1806	Bronzed PROOF; edge plain [6]	3	3			150
G3FA-105	1806	gilt PROOF	3	3			150
G3FA-110	1806	gilt PROOF; edge plain [5]	3	3			150
G3FA-115	1806	PROOF in silver; edge plain [5]	3	3			500
G3FA-120	1806	PROOF in gold; edge plain [5]	3	3			3000
G3FA-125	1807		3	3	5	10	40

1. No stop on reverse.
2. Breastplate varieties exist (obv.).
3. Wreath may have 3 or 4 berries.
4. Several varieties; some are Late Soho issue.
5. Late Soho issue.
6. Several varieties; 'Late Soho' issue.
7. Several minor varieties.

George IV 1820–1830

The 'Great Recoinage' of 1816 ensured that the new mint at Tower Hill was working at full capacity. However, the production of gold and silver coinage was given priority, and the quantity of copper in circulation was sufficient for day-to-day needs. The first copper coins to be struck at the new mint were in 1821, when an issue of farthings was authorised. These were to be struck from copper at the mint which had already been obtained from melting down old coinage.

Pistrucci was still employed as a designer and engraver, and unfortunately for the farthing it fell to him to engrave the designs for the new coinage. He produced another of his ugly portraits of the king, with a bulging face and neck, and wiry hair. It was not difficult to see why his portraits caused the king so much displeasure. His treatment of Britannia was little better, cumbersome and pretentious, and facing the opposite way to the traditional position. This reversal of Britannia demonstrated Pistrucci's contempt for traditional design; on the silver coinage of George III he had already raised some eyebrows by placing the date on the obverse under the head.

Following Pistrucci's downgrading following his refusal to copy another artist's work, William Wyon was given the task of redesigning the coinage. This produced the so-called 'bare head' type farthing of 1826. The portrait of the king was more flattering, and the reverse Britannia was more elegant and uncluttered. It is interesting to note, however, that William Wyon continued Pis-

trucci's innovatory idea of placing the date under the head. The proof farthing of 1826 was included in the proof set issued in that year to inaugurate the new Wyon coinage.

Collecting Hints

The series should be collected in extremely fine condition or better. Counterfeits are no longer a problem.

Denomination	Metal	Weight (grams)	Diameter (mm)	Rev. alignment
Farthing 1821-26 Obv. 1; Rev. 1	Copper	4.5–4.8	22	↓
Farthing 1826-30 Obv. 2; Rev. 2	Copper	4.6–4.9	22	↑

Obverse 1 Head 1, left; GEORGIUS IIII DEI GRATIA

Obverse 2 Head 2, left; GEORGIUS IV DEI GRATIA (date)

Reverse 1 Britannia, seated, with shield, facing right, holding trident and spray; date in exergue below; BRITANNIAR REX FID DEF

Reverse 2 Redesigned Britannia, facing right, holding trident; same legend (no date)

Edge plain

Obv. 1   Obv. 2

Rev. 1   Rev. 2

No.	Date	Features	Obv.	Rev.	F	VF	EF	UNC
G4FA-005	1821	[1]	1	1	4	8	25	40
G4FA-010	1821	PROOF [1]	1	1				500
G4FA-015	1822	[2]	1	1	4	8	25	40
G4FA-020	1822	PROOF; rev. ↑	1	1				500
G4FA-025	1823	1 in date is I [3]	1	1	10	20	60	95
G4FA-030	1823	1 in date is 1	1	1	4	8	25	40
G4FA-035	1825	[2]	1	1	4	8	25	40
G4FA-040	1825	D of DEI over U (obv.)	1	1	8	16	50	80
G4FA-045	1825	PROOF in gold	1	1				4000
G4FA-050	1826		1	1	6	11	35	55
G4FA-055	1826		2	2	4	7	24	35
G4FA-060	1826	PROOF	2	2				150
G4FA-065	1826	Bronzed PROOF [4]	2	2				100
G4FA-070	1827		2	2	6	10	32	50
G4FA-075	1828		2	2	4	8	25	40
G4FA-080	1829		2	2	6	10	32	50
G4FA-085	1830		2	2	4	8	25	40

1. Stop after date (only on 1821).
2. Leaves vary (obverse).
3. Date 'I' is possibly '1' over inverted '1'.
4. Issued in cased proof sets.

William IV 1830–1837

The farthing continued the William Wyon design of the previous reign, the head of the king being based by Wyon on a model by

Sir Francis Chantrey. The reverse is identical to the George IV issue except that some of the dates have minor variations to the lines on the oval shield.

Collecting Hints

Collect in extremely fine or mint state with original lustre

Denomination	Metal	Weight (grams)	Diameter (mm)	Rev. alignment
Farthing	Copper	4.6–4.8	22	↑

Obverse 1 Head 1, right; W.W. incuse on truncation; GULIELMUS IIII DEI GRATIA (date)

Reverse 1 Britannia, seated, with shield, facing right, holding trident; BRITANNIAR REX FID DEF (almost identical to Reverse 2 of George IV issue)

Edge plain

Obv. 1

Rev. 1

No.	Date	Features	Obv.	Rev.	F	VF	EF	UNC
W4FA-005	1831		1	1	4	8	25	40
W4FA-010	1831	PROOF	1	1				250
W4FA-015	1831	Bronzed PROOF	1	1				180
W4FA-020	1831	Bronzed PROOF rev. ↓[1]	1	1				180
W4FA-025	1834	[2]	1	1	4	8	25	40
W4FA-030	1835	[2]	1	1	4	8	25	40
W4FA-035	1835	rev. ↓	1	1	8	16	60	100
W4FA-040	1836		1	1	5	10	35	55
W4FA-045	1837		1	1	8	16	60	100
W4FA-050	1837	7 over indeterminate digit	1	1	10	22	75	130

1. Issued in cased proof sets.
2. Minor shield variations (2 types).

Victoria 1837–1901

The long reign of Victoria produced in the farthing one of the longest series of copper and bronze coinage. The date sequence was broken only in 1870, 1871 and 1889. The curious 1877 proof was struck at a later date, but maintains the run of dates. It is possible that one reason contributing to the fact that the copper series has an unbroken run is that it appears that the same dies were used for the obverses of the sovereign and the farthing. Sovereigns were minted throughout the period, except for 1840. The use of the same dies may also explain the high prevalence of defects in the series. Presumably, it would have been considered that the gold coin was more important, and it is logical to assume that the new die was used to strike the sovereign first. By the time the die was used for the farthing, defects had appeared. It should be mentioned, however, that defects are also common on the reverses of farthings to a considerable degree. Bramah listed many of these as separate varieties, but it is not considered here that minor varieties which are the result of die wear or die defect should merit special treatment. Some, however, have been included in annotated form.

In 1860, the farthing was redesigned for the introduction of the bronze coinage. The weight was also considerably reduced. This series produced a number of interesting varieties but these are not as extensive as on the penny and halfpenny. In 1895, the coin was again completely redesigned to incorporate the veiled head of Victoria. This design lasted until the death of the Queen in 1901.

The copper farthing was designed and engraved by William Wyon, using the same reverse as on the previous reign (except for the alteration of REX to REG); the bronze issue was the work of Leonard Charles Wyon, while the veiled head farthing was engraved by George William de Saulles (1862-1903), the obverse being designed by Thomas Brock, and the reverse owing much to the Wyon reverse.

Collecting Hints

Very fine is probably the minimum acceptable grade for this extensive series. Anyone seeking to acquire the minor varieties will probably look for them in fine condition or better. Ghosting is not quite as prevalent as on the larger copper and bronze coins.

Some of the rare varieties (such as the 1875-H narrow bust) are not at all well known, and can be picked up cheaply if they can be found. Others, such as the 1874 G over rotated G, are well known but are not always checked by dealers, sometimes because the coin is so small, and the variety may not be spotted. This latter variety is, however, very seldom found.

The farthing is a fascinating series. It is perhaps more likely to appeal to the intellectual than, say, the five pound piece, and it is a coin worthy of considerable study.

Denomination	Metal	Weight (grams)	Diameter (mm)	Rev. alignment
Farthing 1838-1860, 1864 Obvs 1-2, Rev. 1	Copper	4.5–4.9	22	↑
Farthing 1860-1901 Obvs 3-6, Revs 2-5	Bronze	2.8–3.0	20	↑

Obverse 1 Head 1, left, WW raised on truncation; VICTORIA DEI GRATIA (date)

Obverse 2 Head 1, left, WW incuse on truncation; same legend

Obverse 3 Head 2, left; VICTORIA D G BRITT REG F D; beaded border

Obverse 4 Similar but toothed border

Obverse 5 Head 3, left; slightly older features; same legend

Obverse 6 Head 4, veiled, left; VICTORIA DEI GRA BRITT REGINA FID DEF IND IMP

Reverse 1 Britannia, seated, with shield, facing right; BRITANNIAR REG FID DEF (as reverse of William IV issue but REX becomes REG)

Reverse 2 Redesigned Britannia, seated, with shield, facing right; FARTHING; date in exergue below Britannia; beaded border.

Reverse 3 Similar but toothed border

Reverse 4 Similar but Britannia completely redesigned.

Reverse 5 Similar but waterline slightly higher

Obv. 2 | Obv. 3 | Obv. 4

Obv. 5 | Obv. 6 | Rev. 1

Rev. 2 | Rev. 3 | Rev. 4

No.	Date	Features	Obv.	Rev.	F	VF	EF	UNC
VYFA-005	1838	[1]	1	1	4	8	25	40
VYFA-010	1839	[1]	1	1	4	7	22	35
VYFA-015	1839	trident has only 2 prongs (rev.)	1	1	4	7	22	35
VYFA-020	1839	PROOF	1	1				180
VYFA-025	1839	Bronzed PROOF	1	1				150
VYFA-030	1839	Bronzed PROOF; rev. ↓[2]	1	1				150
VYFA-035	1839	PROOF in silver	1	1				1000
VYFA-040	1840	[1]	1	1	4	7	22	35
VYFA-045	1841	[1]	1	1	4	7	22	35
VYFA-050	1841	PROOF [3]	1	1				1000
VYFA-055	1842		1	1	5	10	45	75
VYFA-060	1843	1 in date is I	1	1	20	50	200	
VYFA-065	1843	1 in date is 1	1	1	4	7	22	35
VYFA-070	1844	[1]	1	1	50	150	800	
VYFA-075	1845		1	1	4	8	24	40
VYFA-080	1846	[1]	1	1	5	10	40	70
VYFA-085	1847	[1]	1	1	4	8	24	40
VYFA-090	1848	[1]	1	1	4	8	24	40
VYFA-095	1849	[1]	1	1	12	50	150	250
VYFA-100	1850	[4]	1	1	4	8	24	40
VYFA-105	1851		1	1	6	20	70	110
VYFA-110	1851	D of DEI over horizontal D (obv.)	1	1	20	70	200	300
VYFA-115	1852		1	1	6	20	70	110
VYFA-120	1853	[1]	1	1	4	7	22	35
VYFA-125	1853	PROOF	1	1				250
VYFA-130	1853	Bronzed PROOF rev. ↓[2]	1	1				250
VYFA-135	1853	[1]	2	1	6	15	45	70
VYFA-140	1853	PROOF	2	1				300
VYFA-145	1854		2	1	4	7	22	35
VYFA-150	1855		1	1	4	8	24	40
VYFA-155	1855		2	1	5	10	28	50
VYFA-160	1856	[1]	2	1	5	11	35	65
VYFA-165	1856	R of VICTORIA over E (obv.) [1]	2	1	7	14	50	85
VYFA-170	1857		2	1	4	8	24	40
VYFA-175	1858	[5]	2	1	4	8	24	40
VYFA-180	1859		2	1	8	16	50	90
VYFA-185	1860	[6]	2	1	1200	1800	3000	5000
VYFA-190	1860		3	2	5	9	20	35
VYFA-195	1860	PROOF	3	2				350
VYFA-200	1860	[7]	4	2	150	250	500	1500
VYFA-205	1860	[8]	4	3	3	5	12	20
VYFA-210	1860	PROOF	4	3				350
VYFA-215	1861	[8]	4	3	3	5	12	20
VYFA-220	1861	PROOF	4	3				300

No.	Date	Features	Obv.	Rev.	F	VF	EF	UNC
VYFA-225	1861	PROOF in 0.97 silver	4	3				1200
VYFA-230	1861	PROOF in gold; rev. ↓[9]	4	3				5000
VYFA-235	1862	[10]	4	3	3	5	12	20
VYFA-240	1862	PROOF	4	3				300
VYFA-245	1863	[11]	4	3	15	50	120	240
VYFA-250	1863	PROOF	4	3				1200
VYFA-255	1864	in copper; as copper issue [12]	2	1	6000	10000		
VYFA-260	1864	[10]	4	3	3	6	18	28
VYFA-265	1865	[10]	4	3	3	6	15	25
VYFA-270	1865	5 over 2	4	3	5	9	20	40
VYFA-275	1866		4	3	3	6	15	25
VYFA-280	1866	PROOF	4	3				400
VYFA-285	1867		4	3	4	7	16	28
VYFA-290	1867	PROOF	4	3				300
VYFA-295	1868		4	3	4	7	16	28
VYFA-300	1868	PROOF	4	3				250
VYFA-305	1868	PROOF in copper	4	3				400
VYFA-310	1868	PROOF in cupronickel	4	3				200
VYFA-315	1869		4	3	5	9	24	40
VYFA-320	1872		4	3	3	6	15	25
VYFA-325	1873		4	3	3	5	12	20
VYFA-330	1874	H below date [13]	5	3	3	5	12	20
VYFA-335	1874	H below date; 'G's on obv. both over horizontal 'G's [13]	5	3	100	200	800	
VYFA-340	1874	H below date; PROOF [13]	5	3				350
VYFA-345	1875	[14]	4	3	8	20	60	100
VYFA-350	1875	[13]	4	3	20	60	150	250
VYFA-355	1875	[13]	5	3	11	30	85	150
VYFA-360	1875	H below date [13]	4	3	20	50	150	250
VYFA-365	1875	H below date [13]	5	3	3	5	10	16
VYFA-370	1875	H below date; PROOF [13]	5	3				300
VYFA-375	1876	H below date [15]	5	3	10	24	60	120
VYFA-380	1877	PROOF	5	3				1500
VYFA-385	1878		5	3	3	5	10	15
VYFA-390	1878	PROOF	5	3				250
VYFA-395	1879	[16]	5	3	3	5	10	15
VYFA-400	1879	PROOF [16]	5	3				400
VYFA-405	1880	[17]	5	3	4	7	14	26
VYFA-410	1880	PROOF	5	3				300
VYFA-415	1881	[18]	5	3	3	5	12	18
VYFA-420	1881	PROOF	5	3				300
VYFA-425	1881	H below date	5	3	4	7	14	24
VYFA-430	1882	H below date	5	3	4	7	14	24
VYFA-435	1882	H below date; PROOF	5	3				300
VYFA-440	1883		5	3	6	10	20	35
VYFA-445	1883	PROOF	5	3				350
VYFA-450	1884		5	3	3	5	8	14
VYFA-455	1884	PROOF	5	3				300
VYFA-460	1885		5	3	3	5	8	12
VYFA-465	1885	PROOF	5	3				300
VYFA-470	1886		5	3	3	5	8	12
VYFA-475	1886	PROOF	5	3				300
VYFA-480	1887		5	3	3	6	10	15
VYFA-485	1888		5	3	3	6	10	15
VYFA-490	1890		5	3	3	6	10	15
VYFA-495	1890	PROOF	5	3				300
VYFA-500	1891		5	3	3	6	10	15
VYFA-505	1891	PROOF	5	3				300
VYFA-510	1892		5	3	7	14	35	60
VYFA-515	1892	PROOF	5	3				400
VYFA-520	1893		5	3	3	6	10	15
VYFA-525	1894		5	3	3	6	11	17
VYFA-530	1894	PROOF	5	3				300
VYFA-535	1895		5	3	10	24	50	80
VOFA-540	1895		6	4	2	4	8	12
VOFA-545	1895	PROOF	6	4				400
VOFA-550	1896		6	4	2	4	8	12
VOFA-555	1896	PROOF	6	4				400
VOFA-560	1897		6	4	4	8	14	20
VOFA-565	1897	issued artificially darkened	6	5	2	4	10	20
VOFA-570	1898	issued artificially darkened	6	4	2	4	10	20
VOFA-575	1899	issued artificially darkened	6	4	2	4	10	20

No.	Date	Features	Obv.	Rev.	F	VF	EF	UNC
VOFA-580	1900	issued artificially darkened	6	4	2	4	10	20
VOFA-585	1901	issued artificially darkened	6	4	2	4	10	20
VOFA-590	1901	issued with conventional bright finish	6	4				25

1. Punctuation may vary.
2. Issued in cased proof sets.
3. Possibly struck after 1841.
4. Head slightly redesigned; punctuation may vary.
5. 5 of date may resemble 3.
6. Possibly struck after 1860; proofs may exist.
7. Toothed/beaded 'mule'.
8. Minor obv differences occur.
9. One known; weight 3.9 grams.
10. Date variations occur.
11. Date variations occur; all have square-top '3' (occurs only on this date).
12. Has I in relief on truncation before WW.
13. Date in small figures.
14. Date in large figures.
15. 6 in date varies; date is in small figures from now on.
16. 9 in date varies.
17. 2 slightly different obverses.
18. 3 slightly different obverses.

Edward VII 1901–1910

The farthing continued to be issued in an artificially toned state to avoid confusion with the half sovereign. The only minor difference occurring to the design was in 1903, when the whole issue of that year had a 'low tide' reverse. This coin is not very well known amongst collectors. Presumably it would have achieved a greater fame if, like the halfpenny and penny, it had been a scarce variety of that year. The 'low tide' reverse is identical to that used on the Victorian veiled head farthing.

The portrait of Edward VII was by George William de Saulles (1862-1903), with the reducing machine being used to effect the correct size.

Collecting Hints

This issue is unusual and attractive in mint state, when the lustre of the original dark patina is untouched. A little care should be taken, however. Some years ago, the writer was told by a well-known dealer from the North of England that he always treated extremely fine or better farthings of this period with motor oil before selling them!

Denomination	Metal	Weight (grams)	Diameter (mm)	Rev. alignment
Farthing	Bronze	2.7–2.9	20	↑

Obverse 1 Head 1, right; EDWARDVS VII DEI GRA BRITT OMN REX FID DEF IND IMP

Reverse 1 Britannia, seated, with shield, holding trident, facing right; FARTHING; date in exergue below Britannia

Reverse 2 Similar but sea is lower

Edge plain

Obv. 1

Rev. 1

No.	Date			Obv.	Rev.	VF	EF	UNC
E7FA-005	1902			1	1	3	6	12
E7FA-010	1903			1	2	4	8	16
E7FA-015	1904			1	1	4	9	20
E7FA-020	1905			1	1	4	8	16
E7FA-025	1906			1	1	4	8	16
E7FA-030	1907			1	1	4	8	16
E7FA-035	1908			1	1	4	8	16
E7FA-040	1909			1	1	4	8	16
E7FA-045	1910			1	1	4	9	20

George V 1910–1936

The head of George V used on the farthings was the Sir Bertram MacKennal design used on the larger coins. The reverse carried through from the Edward VII farthing. The principal difference from the halfpenny and penny was that the 'modified effigy' introduced in 1926 continued through to 1936 instead of being replaced by a smaller version in 1928. The new reverse, also introduced in 1926, was a reduced version of that used on the penny and halfpenny from 1927 and 1925 respectively.

Ghosting does not occur as frequently on the farthing as it does on the two larger bronze coins, and disappears with the new 1926 issue.

Artificial darkening continued from the inception of the series until 1917. Half sovereigns were by that time no longer being struck at the mint.

Collecting Hints

The first seven years of the series were issued artificially darkened, and the remarks made for the Edward VII farthing apply. The series as a whole should be collected in extremely fine or mint state.

Denomination	Metal	Weight (grams)	Diameter (mm)	Rev. alignment
Farthing	Bronze	2.8–2.9	20	↑

Obverse 1 Head 1, left, B.M. on truncation; GEORGIVS V DEI GRA BRITT OMN REX FID DEF IND IMP

Obverse 2 Head 2, known as 'modified effigy', left; initials BM are without stops and further to right; same legend

Reverse 1 Britannia, seated, with shield, facing right; FARTHING; date in exergue below Britannia

Reverse 2 Similar but redesigned and more sharply struck

| Obv. 1 | Obv. 2 | Rev. 1 | Rev. 2 |

No.	Date	Features	Obv.	Rev.		EF	UNC
G5FA-005	1911	issued artificially darkened	1	1		4	8
G5FA-010	1912	issued artificially darkened	1	1		4	8
G5FA-015	1913	issued artificially darkened	1	1		4	8
G5FA-020	1914	issued artificially darkened [1]	1	1		4	8
G5FA-025	1915	issued artificially darkened [1]	1	1		5	10

No.	Date	Features	Obv.	Rev.	EF	UNC
G5FA-030	1916	issued artificially darkened	1	1	4	8
G5FA-035	1917	issued artificially darkened	1	1	4	8
G5FA-040	1918	Some issued artificially darkened	1	1	4	8
G5FA-045	1919		1	1	3	7
G5FA-050	1920		1	1	3	7
G5FA-055	1921		1	1	3	7
G5FA-060	1922		1	1	3	7
G5FA-065	1923		1	1	3	7
G5FA-070	1924		1	1	3	7
G5FA-075	1925		1	1	3	7
G5FA-080	1926		2	2	3	7
G5FA-085	1926	PROOF	2	2		200
G5FA-090	1927		2	2	3	6
G5FA-095	1927	PROOF	2	2		200
G5FA-100	1928		2	2	3	6
G5FA-105	1928	PROOF	2	2		200
G5FA-110	1929		2	2	3	6
G5FA-115	1929	PROOF	2	2		200
G5FA-120	1930		2	2	3	6
G5FA-125	1930	PROOF	2	2		200
G5FA-130	1931		2	2	3	6
G5FA-135	1931	PROOF	2	2		200
G5FA-140	1932		2	2	2	5
G5FA-145	1932	PROOF	2	2		200
G5FA-150	1933		2	2	2	5
G5FA-155	1933	PROOF	2	2		200
G5FA-160	1934		2	2	3	6
G5FA-165	1934	PROOF	2	2		200
G5FA-170	1935		2	2	4	8
G5FA-175	1935	PROOF	2	2		200
G5FA-180	1936		2	2	2	4
G5FA-185	1936	PROOF	2	2		200

1. Minor obverse lettering differences occur.

Edward VIII 1936

The Edward VIII farthing is strictly speaking a pattern, as probable Royal approval was about to be granted at the time of the abdication. However, because its official status rests only on this technicality, and to provide continuity, it is included in this catalogue.

The use of the reducing machine to fit a design of considerable detail on to a farthing flan was now seen as unsatisfactory from an aesthetic viewpoint. Although the later pennies and halfpennies of George V were visually pleasing, it needed a magnifying glass to appreciate the farthing reverse. A simpler design was proposed for the reverse of the Edward VIII issue. The adopted wren design by H. Wilson Parker was a bold departure from previous reverses depicting Britannia. Moreover, other denominations had not previously departed from traditional British heraldic and similar representations.

The portrait of Edward VIII is by Thomas Humphrey Paget, and faces left at the insistence of the king, who considered this position more flattering and wished to discontinue the tradition of opposite facings for successive monarchs.

Denomination	Metal	Weight (grams)	Diameter (mm)	Rev. alignment
Farthing	Bronze	2.8	20	↑

Obverse 1 Head 1, left; EDWARDVS VIII D G BR OMN REX F D IND IMP

Reverse 1 Wren; 1937 FARTHING

Edge plain

Obv. 1

Rev. 1

No.	Date	Features	Obv.	Rev.	UNC
E8FA-005	1937		1	1	12000

George VI 1937–1952

The wren design proposed for the reverse of the Edward VIII farthing was adopted for this series. The farthing was struck for every year of the reign but, unlike the halfpenny, it did not undergo minute differences of design from year to year.

Proofs were struck for the cased sets of 1937, 1950 and 1951, and in small quantities in all of the other years.

Collecting Hints

This series is easy to locate in mint state. However, the proofs of the years not issued for cased proof sets are very difficult to find. The edges of proofs of 1950 and 1951 should be examined for corrosion.

Denomination	Metal	Weight (grams)	Diameter (mm)	Rev. alignment
Farthing	Bronze	2.7–2.9	20	↑

Obverse 1 Head 1, left; HP on truncation; GEORGIVS VI D G BR OMN REX F D IND IMP

Obverse 2 Head 1, left; GEORGIVS VI D G BR OMN REX FIDEI DEF

Reverse 1 Wren; FARTHING (date)

Obv. 1	Obv. 2	Rev. 1

No.	Date	Features	Obv.	Rev.	UNC
G6FA-005	1937		1	1	3
G6FA-010	1937	PROOF [1]	1	1	7
G6FA-015	1937	PROOF from sandblasted dies [2]	1	1	150
G6FA-020	1937	uniface rev. in silver [3]		1	500
G6FA-025	1938		1	1	5
G6FA-030	1938	PROOF	1	1	200
G6FA-035	1939		1	1	3
G6FA-040	1939	PROOF	1	1	200
G6FA-045	1940		1	1	3
G6FA-050	1940	PROOF	1	1	200
G6FA-055	1941		1	1	3
G6FA-060	1941	PROOF	1	1	200
G6FA-065	1942		1	1	2
G6FA-070	1942	PROOF	1	1	200
G6FA-075	1943		1	1	2
G6FA-080	1943	PROOF	1	1	200
G6FA-085	1944		1	1	2
G6FA-090	1944	PROOF	1	1	200
G6FA-095	1945		1	1	2
G6FA-100	1945	PROOF	1	1	200
G6FA-105	1946		1	1	2
G6FA-110	1946	PROOF	1	1	200
G6FA-115	1947		1	1	2
G6FA-120	1947	PROOF	1	1	200
G6FA-125	1948		1	1	2
G6FA-130	1948	PROOF	1	1	200
G6FA-135	1949		2	1	2
G6FA-140	1949	PROOF	2	1	200
G6FA-145	1950		2	1	2
G6FA-150	1950	PROOF [1]	2	1	7
G6FA-155	1950	PROOF from sandblasted dies [2]	2	1	150
G6FA-160	1951		2	1	2

No.	Date	Features	Obv.	Rev.	UNC
G6FA-165	1951	PROOF [1]	2	1	8
G6FA-170	1951	PROOF from sandblasted dies [2]	2	1	150
G6FA-175	1951	in cupronickel [4]	2	1	200
G6FA-180	1952		2	1	2
G6FA-185	1952	PROOF	2	1	200

1. Issued in cased proof sets.
2. Struck to facilitate photography of coin.
3. Weight 3.4 grams.
4. Weight c. 2.8 grams.

Elizabeth II 1952 -

The farthing series of Elizabeth II consists of only four dates. The first date, 1953, is a one-year type, owing to the change to the legend in 1954. However, minor changes occurred to both obverse and reverse during 1953. In particular, the first coins did not strike up the portrait at all well, and it was recut in slightly higher relief. Later, when the 1954 obverse was introduced, the portrait was recut even more sharply.

The obverse head of Elizabeth II was by Mary Gillick. The series retained the wren design by H. Wilson Parker.

Proofs were again struck for the 1953 cased proof sets, and in small quantities in the other years. Some of the 1953 ordinary coins were issued in the 'plastic sets' of that year. The farthing of 1953 issued in that set is from a die pairing very slightly different from that used on the circulation issue.

The ravages of inflation meant that by 1956 the farthing had outlived its usefulness as a circulation coin, and no farthings were minted after that date.

Denomination	Metal	Weight (grams)	Diameter (mm)	Rev. alignment
Farthing	Bronze	2.8–2.9	20	↑

Obverse 1 Head 1, right; ELIZABETH II DEI GRA BRITT OMN REGINA F D

Obverse 2 Head 1, recut, right; ELIZABETH II DEI GRATIA REGINA F D

Reverse 1 Wren; FARTHING (date)

Edge plain

Obv. 1   Obv. 2   Rev. 1

No.	Date	Features	Obv.	Rev.	UNC
EL2FA-005	1953	[1]	1	1	2
EL2FA-010	1953	PROOF [2]	1	1	5
EL2FA-015	1953	PROOF from sandblasted dies [3]	1	1	150
EL2FA-020	1954		2	1	2
EL2FA-025	1954	PROOF	2	1	150
EL2FA-030	1955		2	1	2
EL2FA-035	1955	PROOF	2	1	150
EL2FA-040	1956		2	1	4
EL2FA-045	1956	PROOF	2	1	200

1. Minor obverse/reverse differences exist.
2. Minor reverse differences exist; issued in cased proof sets.
3. Struck to facilitate photography of coin.

Half Farthing

George IV 1820–1830

The first issue of the half farthing was in 1828. Initially, it was issued for use only in Ceylon, and did not become a legal tender coin in Britain until 1842. The coin, however, bore no indication of the country of origin and, along with the third-and quarter farthing, is commonly regarded as a British coin.

The half farthing was the last denomination to be issued in this reign. Consequently, the controversies surrounding Pistrucci did not touch it, and by the time the coin was introduced William Wyon was safely established as the principal designer and engraver at the mint. Wyon's dies for obverse and reverse were similar to those used on the larger copper coins, but the obverse head does appear inordinately large compared with the size of the flan.

The coin was minted again during this reign only in 1830. The death of the king in June of that year may explain why the 1830 coin is markedly scarcer than the 1828.

Denomination	Metal	Weight (grams)	Diameter (mm)	Rev. alignment
Half farthing	Copper	2.4	18	↑

Obverse 1 Head 1, left; GEORGIUS IV DEI GRATIA (date)

Reverse 1 Britannia, seated, with shield, facing right, holding trident; BRITANNIAR REX FID DEF

Edge plain

Obv. 1   Rev. 1

No.	Date	Features	Obv.	Rev.	F	VF	EF	UNC
G4HF-005	1828	1	1	1	12	30	120	180
G4HF-010	1828	PROOF	1	1				240
G4HF-015	1828	Bronzed PROOF rev. ↓	1	1				700
G4HF-020	1830	2	1	1	15	35	140	200
G4HF-025	1830	PROOF	1	1				300

1. Reverse legend/design orientation varies.
2. Reverse legend/design orientation varies; date numerals vary in size.

William IV 1830–1837

The half farthing was again minted in 1837 for circulation in Ceylon. The coin uses the William Wyon head of William IV as used on the larger coins. The reverse is virtually identical to that used on the George IV half farthing.

As with the half farthing of George IV, the minting and issue of the coin was interrupted by the death of the monarch, again in June. Consequently, the William IV half farthing became one of the most elusive of this denomination.

Denomination	Metal	Weight (grams)	Diameter (mm)	Rev. alignment
Half farthing	Copper	2.3	18	↑

Obverse 1 Head 1, right; GULIELMUS IIII DEI GRATIA 1837

Reverse 1 Britannia, seated, with shield, facing right, holding trident; BRITANNIAR REX FID DEF

Edge plain

Obv. 1   Rev. 1

No.	Date	Obv.	Rev.	F	VF	EF	UNC
W4HF-005	1837	1	1	25	75	300	500

Victoria 1837–1901

With the accession of Victoria to the throne, the half farthing was approaching its prime. Moreover, in 1842 it acquired legal tender status in Britain. Much cynicism was, however, displayed over this decision. It was widely commented that very little could be bought for a farthing, let alone half a farthing, and the inevitable letters to *The Times* appeared on the subject. Nevertheless, the coin did circulate widely both in Britain and in Ceylon.

The preparation of the dies again fell to William Wyon. The obverse portrayed the head of Victoria, and for the first time the obverse legend differed from that on the larger copper coins; this obverse is identical to that on the Maundy fourpence, both in design and size. The reverse was radically redesigned. At the beginning of the reign, silver groats were circulating in Ceylon, and these bore a Britannia reverse somewhat similar to that on the half farthings of the previous reign. In order to prevent the half farthings being silvered and passed off as groats, the new Victoria half farthing was given a reverse bearing the words HALF FARTHING, together with the date, sandwiched between a crown and a rose. It is often not realised, however, that the series bears two different reverses. When the coin acquired legal tender status on 13 June, 1842, the rose was replaced by a rose, thistle and shamrock. This was to make the design compatible with those of the farthing, halfpenny and penny. There is some doubt as to whether the coin entered circulation; Peter Seaby (*The Story of the English Coinage*) notes that street traders used to sell them at three-farthings each!

The 1868 proofs are curious anomalies to this series. Other coins in the bronze series were struck in cupronickel in 1868, possibly as trial strikings in connection with the forthcoming Jamaican issue in this metal. Although the legislation introducing the Jamaican coinage refers to this issue as being struck in nickel, both it and the 1868 British proofs are non-magnetic and must therefore be in cupronickel. It seems to have been decided to strike bronze proofs at the same time as these cupronickel proofs, but no circulation coins were struck dated 1868. The entire denomination was demonetised the following year.

Collecting Hints

The half farthing is a challenging series to collect. Several of the dates are so rare in top condition as to be almost unobtainable, and their rarity is probably underestimated in most catalogues. Rarely does one come across a series with such a profusion of coins concentrated on one date, in this case 1844. Bramah estimated that the 1844 coin is between 10 and 20 times more common than almost all of the other dates.

There are a considerable number of minor varieties in this series caused by die wear and flaws. Batty (*Copper Coinage of Great Britain*), a master of attention to detail, listed 142 different die flaws for the 1844 half farthing alone! It is not intended that this catalogue will provide this sort of service to its readers.

The series should be collected generally in extremely fine condition, but it will probably be difficult to find some of the dates in this grade. The 1844 should always be checked for the E over N variety as this is a popular coin. The 1856 coin appears to occur frequently with a rough surface, possibly because of die damage, although it has been speculated that some may have been cast.

Denomination	Metal	Weight (grams)	Diameter (mm)	Rev. alignment
Half farthing 1839-1856	Copper	2.4	18	↑
Half farthing 1868 (proof)	Bronze	2.4	18	↑

Obverse 1 Head 1, left; VICTORIA D G BRITANNIAR REGINA F D

Reverse 1 Crown above; rose with three leaves below; HALF FARTHING (date)

Reverse 2 Similar but rose replaced by rose, thistle and shamrock

Edge plain

Obv. 1   Rev. 1   Rev. 2

No.	Date	Features	Obv.	Rev.	F	VF	EF	UNC
VYHF-005	1839	[1]	1	1	5	10	35	60
VYHF-010	1839	Bronzed PROOF [1]	1	1				200
VYHF-015	1842	[2]	1	2	5	10	35	60
VYHF-020	1843	[3]	1	2	4	7	15	22
VYHF-025	1844	[3]	1	2	3	5	12	20
VYHF-030	1844	E of REGINA over N (obv.)	1	2	20	35	75	150
VYHF-035	1847		1	2	5	10	30	50
VYHF-040	1851		1	2	5	12	40	70
VYHF-045	1851	first 1 over 5	1	2	10	20	80	140
VYHF-050	1852		1	2	5	10	40	70
VYHF-055	1853		1	2	8	20	80	150
VYHF-060	1853	PROOF	1	2				200
VYHF-065	1853	Bronzed PROOF rev. ↓ [4]	1	2				200
VYHF-070	1854		1	2	10	25	95	170
VYHF-075	1856	[5]	1	2	10	25	95	170
VYHF-080	1868	PROOF [6]	1	2				250
VYHF-085	1868	PROOF in cupronickel [7]	1	2				350

1. Date numerals larger than on most years.
2. Becomes legal tender in Britain.
3. Many minor varieties exist.
4. Issued in cased proof sets.
5. Date numerals vary in size; many have rough surface.
6. Struck in bronze as stated above.
7. Weight 2.3 grams.

Third Farthing

George IV 1820–1830

The third farthing was minted in 1827 exclusively for circulation in Malta. However, it is widely thought of as being included within the ambit of British coinage, and for this reason it is included in this catalogue. The coin bears no indication of the country of origin, and closely resembles a British coin. Furthermore, Malta, having become a British Possession in 1814, was considered more as a part of Britain at that time than during the twentieth century. The farthing was already in circulation there as a '3 grani' coin, and the third farthing was introduced as '1 grano'. A proclamation issued in Malta on 3 November 1827 legalised the new coins, referring to them as 'British Grains'. The cost of living in Malta was lower than in Britain, and the new coin was thought inappropriate for circulation in the home country.

As with the half farthing, minted for Ceylon in the following year, the dies were prepared by William Wyon. Pistrucci had already fallen into disfavour. The obverse was of smaller proportion relative to the flan than on the half farthing, and the striking was somewhat sharper.

Collecting Hints

The third farthing is easier to find in top condition than the half farthing, and should be collected in Extremely Fine or mint state. Beware of coins which have been bronzed to resemble proofs.

Denomination	Metal	Weight (grams)	Diameter (mm)	Rev. alignment
Third farthing	Copper	1.5–1.6	16	↑

Obverse 1 Head 1, left; GEORGIUS IV DEI GRATIA 1827

Reverse 1 Britannia, seated, with shield, facing right, holding trident; BRITANNIAR REX FID DEF

Edge plain

Obv. 1

Rev. 1

No.	Date	Features	Obv.	Rev.	F	VF	EF	UNC
G4TF-005	1827		1	1	5	10	24	40
G4TF-010	1827	PROOF	1	1				180

William IV 1830–1837

The third farthing was again issued for Malta for only one of the years of this reign, in 1835. The obverse was by William Wyon as on the larger coinage, and once again the proportion of the head in relation to the flan was smaller than on the half farthing. The reverse was virtually identical to that of the third farthing of George IV.

Collecting Hints

The third farthing is far easier to locate than the half farthing, and should be sought in mint state.

Denomination	Metal	Weight (grams)	Diameter (mm)	Rev. alignment
Third farthing	Copper	1.5–1.6	16	↑

Obverse 1 Head 1, right; GULIELMUS IIII DEI GRATIA 1835

Reverse 1 Britannia, seated, with shield, right, holding trident; BRITANNIAR REX FID DEF

Edge plain

Obv. 1

Rev. 1

No.	Date	Features	Obv.	Rev.	F	VF	EF	UNC
W4TF-005	1835		1	1	5	10	26	45
W4TF-010	1835	PROOF	1	1				150

Victoria 1837–1901

The relatively few coins required for circulation in Malta resulted in the minting of the copper issue of third farthings for one year only, in 1844. This issue used the young head of Victoria by William Wyon, with a Britannia reverse. This resembled to some extent a small version of the farthing, unlike the half farthing which had a different obverse legend and a redesigned reverse, to prevent its being silvered and passed off as a groat.

The bronze issue, again for circulation in Malta, was more prolific, being minted from 1866 to 1885. The head of Victoria, engraved by Leonard Charles Wyon, was very different. The Britannia reverse was discontinued in favour of a 'value in wreath' design.

Collecting Hints

The young head copper issue is difficult to find in the high grades. The reverse should be checked for the 'missing G' variety, but this is particularly rare. The bronze series is easier to find and should be collected in mint state.

Denomination	Metal	Weight (grams)	Diameter (mm)	Rev. alignment
Third farthing 1844	Copper	1.5–1.6	16	↑
Third farthing 1866-1885	Bronze	0.9–1.0	15	↑

Obverse 1 Head 1, left; VICTORIA DEI GRATIA 1844

Obverse 2 Head 2, left; VICTORIA D G BRITT REG F D

Reverse 1 Britannia, seated, with shield, facing right, holding trident; BRITANNIAR REG FID DEF

Reverse 2 ONE THIRD FARTHING (date) within wreath, crown above

Edge plain

| Obv. 1 | Obv. 2 | Rev. 1 | Rev. 2 |

No.	Date	Features	Obv.	Rev.	F	VF	EF	UNC
VYTF-005	1844		1	1	12	30	100	160
VYTF-010	1844	large G in REG (obv.)	1	1	18	45	140	220
VYTF-015	1844	RE instead of REG (obv.) [1]	1	1	120	250	800	1200
VYTF-020	1866		2	2	4	8	16	24
VYTF-025	1866	PROOF	2	2				200
VYTF-030	1868	[2]	2	2	4	8	16	24
VYTF-035	1868	PROOF	2	2				180
VYTF-040	1868	PROOF in cupronickel	2	2				250
VYTF-045	1868	PROOF in aluminium	2	2				500
VYTF-050	1876		2	2	4	8	16	24
VYTF-055	1878		2	2	4	8	16	24
VYTF-060	1881		2	2	4	8	16	24
VYTF-065	1881	PROOF	2	2				200
VYTF-070	1884	[2]	2	2	4	8	16	24
VYTF-075	1885		2	2	4	8	16	24

1. Flan thickness varies.
2. Minor obverse differences exist.

On reverse 2, minor variations occur on the wreath, and the number of leaves and acorns may vary.

Edward VII 1902–1910

The third farthing continued to be struck for Malta. The face value of the mintage was £100 sterling, i.e. 288,000 pieces, and all were dated 1902. The general design was based on that for the last Victoria issue, using the head of Edward VII by George William de Saulles (1862-1903). The reverse was of identical layout, but the crown was the Imperial crown instead of the Royal crown used on the Victorian series.

As it was a coin minted for Malta, the third farthing was not included in the cased proof set for 1902.

Collecting Hints

The coin can be found in mint state without much difficulty.

Denomination	Metal	Weight (grams)	Diameter (mm)	Rev. alignment
Third farthing	Bronze	0.9–1.0	15	↑

Obverse 1 Head 1, right; EDWARDVS VII D G BRITT OMN REX F D IND IMP

Reverse 1 ONE THIRD FARTHING 1902 within wreath, crown above

Edge plain

| Obv. 1 Enlarged | Rev. 1 Enlarged |

No.	Date	Obv.	Rev.	F	VF	EF	UNC
E7TF-005	1902	1	1	3	5	8	12

George V 1910–1936

A final issue of the third farthing for Malta was made in 1913, again to the total face value of £100 sterling. The head of the monarch was by Sir Bertram MacKennal (1863-1931), as used on the larger coinage. The reverse was identical to the 1902 issue, apart from the date change.

Collecting Hints

The coin can be found in mint state without much difficulty.

Denomination	Metal	Weight (grams)	Diameter (mm)	Rev. alignment
Third farthing	Bronze	0.9–1.0	15	↑

Obverse 1 Head 1, left; GEORGIVS V D G BRITT OMN REX F D IND IMP

Reverse 1 ONE THIRD FARTHING 1913 within wreath, crown above

Edge plain

| Obv. 1 Enlarged | Rev. 1 Enlarged |

No.	Date	Obv.	Rev.	F	VF	EF	UNC
G5TF-005	1913	1	1	3	5	8	12

Quarter Farthing

Victoria 1837–1901

Like the half farthing, the quarter farthing was introduced for use in Ceylon, but it did not subsequently become legal tender in Britain as the half farthing did. The denomination was simply too small to have any purchasing power in the home country. In Ceylon, where the cost of living was lower, it was more useful.

Although the quarter farthing was never a British legal tender coin, it has become accepted as a British coin, as has the third farthing. It is consequently included in this catalogue.

The series is relatively short, consisting of only five dates, including the curious 1868 proofs. It is interesting to note that the British 1853 proof set (but not the 1839) included the quarter farthing, even though the coin had no legal tender status in Britain. This is possibly an indication of how much more closely the British colonies were regarded in the 19th century, almost as a part of the British Isles. The 1868 proofs may have been struck in connection with the proposed cupronickel issue of Jamaican coinage.

The obverse bears a head of Victoria by William Wyon, and is in fact taken from a die for the Maundy twopence. The reverse is very similar in design to the Victorian half farthing of 1839, i.e. before the rose was replaced by a larger emblem.

Before the coins were brought back to Britain for collectors, the series was regarded in numismatic circles as very rare. Batty (*Copper Coinage of Great Britain*, 1886) stated that he had only seen one specimen dated 1853.

Collecting Hints

This is a popular coin, and its limited mintage renders it scarcer than usual for a complete series. In addition, only a relatively small proportion of minted coins have survived in collectable condition. Some years ago a London dealer took space in newspapers in Ceylon to buy this coin in quantity, and received large numbers of tiny green corroded discs! The salty air of Ceylon had taken its toll on the coins in much the same way as the polluted air of London had destroyed the tin coinage two centuries earlier. Even otherwise fine or very fine coins are frequently encountered with pitting marks and edge corrosion. Consequently, mint state coins without damage are much sought after and are a worthy addition to any serious collection.

Denomination	Metal	Weight (grams)	Diameter (mm)	Rev. alignment
Quarter farthing 1839–1853	Copper	1.2	13.5	↑
Quarter farthing 1868	Bronze	1.2	13.5	↑

A wide weight range exists for this denomination

Obverse 1 Head 1, left; VICTORIA D G BRITANNIAR REGINA F D

Reverse 1 Crown above; rose with three leaves below; QUARTER FARTHING (date)

Edge plain

Obv. 1   Rev. 1

No.	Date	Features	Obv.	Rev.	F	VF	EF	UNC
VYQF-005	1839		1	1	14	22	45	80
VYQF-010	1851		1	1	15	24	50	90
VYQF-015	1852		1	1	14	22	45	80
VYQF-020	1852	Bronzed PROOF [1]	1	1				1000
VYQF-025	1853	[2]	1	1	15	24	50	90
VYQF-030	1853	PROOF	1	1				300
VYQF-035	1853	Bronzed PROOF [3]	1	1				350
VYQF-040	1868	PROOF	1	1				250
VYQF-045	1868	PROOF in cupronickel [4]	1	1				300

1. Possibly unique.
2. Many minor varieties exist, esp. pearls on crown (rev.).
3. Issued in cased proof sets.
4. Weight c.1.1 grams.

Maundy Sets

Charles II — George III 1660–1820

The origin of the Maundy ceremony is unclear. However, some form of ceremony in which the sovereign performed an act of benevolence towards the poor existed long before the reign of Charles II. Queen Elizabeth I introduced redemption money to be paid at a ceremony instead of the gifts which had been given hitherto.

Although the Maundy 'set' of the four minor silver coins is usually thought of as the coinage of the Maundy ceremony, in the early years probably only the silver penny was used for this purpose. It was not until some time during the reign of George III that the set of four coins was distributed as Maundy.

During the period up to 1820, the small silver coinage was primarily used as circulation coinage. For this reason, the coins are listed in this catalogue as separate denominations, and their individual varieties will be found in these listings. From 1822 onwards, when the coins were minted mainly for the provision of sets of Maundy, the detailed listings are under the heading of Maundy sets. 1822 also marks the year from which sets were issued without a break up to the present day.

The Maundy ceremony currently takes place on Maundy Thursday (the day before Good Friday). The coins are given in a leather bag, the total number of pence equalling the age of the monarch. As one set totals 10 pence, the amount is made up by a number of complete sets plus, when appropriate, a part set.

George IV 1820–1830

As mentioned elsewhere, by the time George IV ascended the throne, the Maundy set of four coins was primarily used for the Maundy ceremony rather than for circulation. This is evident from the fact that these coins usually turn up in very fine or better condition.

The series used the laureate head of the king designed by Benedetto Pistrucci throughout the series. The William Wyon bare head used on the larger silver did not appear on the Maundy coinage, even though the king greatly disapproved of the Pistrucci portrayal of his image.

A curious incident produced an unusual obverse on the 1822 threepence. Before the coins were struck, the punch broke, and a die was hurriedly made with a punch of the twopence head. The portrait on this coin therefore appears unusually small.

Denomination	Metal	Weight (grams)	Diameter (mm)	Rev. alignment
Maundy Set	Silver	0.5; 0.9; 1.4; 1.9	11; 13; 16; 18	↓

Obverse 1 Head 1, left; GEORGIUS IIII D G BRITANNIAR REX F D
Reverse 1 Crowned numeral and divided date, all within wreath.
Edge plain

No.	Date	Features	Obv.	Rev.	EF	FDC
G4MS-005	1822	[1]	1	1	100	220
G4MS-010	1822	PROOFS [1]	1	1		800
G4MS-015	1823		1	1	90	200
G4MS-020	1824		1	1	90	200
G4MS-025	1825		1	1	90	200
G4MS-030	1826		1	1	90	200

No.	Date	Features	Obv.	Rev.	EF	FDC
G4MS-035	1827		1	1	90	200
G4MS-040	1828		1	1	90	200
G4MS-045	1828	PROOFS	1	1		1000
G4MS-050	1829		1	1	90	200
G4MS-055	1830		1	1	90	200

1. Threepence has small king's head (obv.) from twopence punch.

William IV 1830–1837

The William Wyon portrait of the king was adopted for the Maundy coinage, the reverse continuing as on the previous series. The first date, 1831, boasts not only a proof Maundy set included in the proof set of that year, but also a small number of sets of the four pieces struck in gold.

Denomination	Metal	Weight (grams)	Diameter (mm)	Rev. alignment
Maundy Set	Silver	0.5; 0.9; 1.4; 1.9	11; 13; 16; 18	↓

Obverse 1 Head 1, right; GULIELMUS IIII D G BRITANNIAR REX F D
Reverse 1 Crowned numeral and divided date, all within wreath.
Edge plain

No.	Date	Features	Obv.	Rev.	EF	FDC
W4MS-005	1831		1	1	100	180
W4MS-010	1831	PROOFS	1	1		500
W4MS-015	1831	PROOFS in gold	1	1		18000
W4MS-020	1832		1	1	100	180
W4MS-025	1833		1	1	100	180
W4MS-030	1834		1	1	100	180
W4MS-035	1835		1	1	100	180
W4MS-040	1836		1	1	120	200
W4MS-045	1837		1	1	120	200

Victoria 1837–1901

The Maundy sets of Victoria are amongst the most popular with collectors of this series. When one considers the longevity of the reign, and the fact that the denominations were minted for every year, one appreciates the uniqueness of this series. To assemble a complete set in perfect condition or near is a mammoth task.

The early Maundy sets bear the young head portrait of Victoria by William Wyon, and this was unchanged for fifty years! Unlike on the larger silver coins and the gold, the jubilee head portrait did not appear until 1888, as the Maundy ceremony in 1887 occurred before the jubilee.

Confusion sometimes occurs with Victorian young head Maundy sets over the status of the threepence. Many sets are encountered with fields which are not prooflike, and this sometimes leads to the description of sets bearing 'currency threepences' when in fact they do not. Experience is the only way to determine whether a threepence is a currency or Maundy strike. The distinguishing marks are often more to do with the quality of the strike rather than whether the field has a mirror finish. Particular attention should be paid to the fineness of the wreath on the reverse, and comparison with the other Maundy pieces of the set, if available, is helpful.

Maundy coins continued to be presented to recipients at the Maundy service in leather purses, but at some stage towards the end of the Victorian era those given to other recipients were in official presentation cases. Initially, these were rectangular and covered in black or dark red leather, and usually bore the date on the lid.

From 1888 to 1901 the obverses are similar to those of the larger coinage, with the jubilee head by Sir Joseph Edgar Boehm (engraved by L.C. Wyon) and the old head by Sir Thomas Brock (engraved by de Saulles).

Denomination	Metal	Weight (grams)	Diameter (mm)	Rev. alignment
Maundy set 1838-1887	Silver	0.5; 0.9; 1.4; 1.9	11; 13; 16; 18	↓
Maundy set 1888-1901	Silver	0.5; 0.9; 1.4; 1.9	11; 13; 16; 18	↑

Obverse 1 Head 1, left; VICTORIA D G BRITANNIAR REGINA F D

Obverse 2 Head 2, left; same legend

Obverse 3 Head 3, left; VICTORIA DEI GRA BRITT REGINA FID DEF IND IMP

Reverse 1 Crowned numeral and divided date, all within wreath.

Reverse 2 Similar but crown very different; on the twopence the '2' is different

Edge plain

Obv. 1 Obv. 2 Obv. 3

Rev. 1

Rev. 2

No.	Date	Features	Obv.	Rev.	EF	FDC
VYMS-005	1838		1	1	85	130
VYMS-010	1838	PROOFS	1	1		600
VYMS-015	1838	PROOFS in gold; revs ↑	1	1		18000
VYMS-020	1839		1	1	80	120
VYMS-025	1839	PROOFS; revs ↑ ¹	1	1		450
VYMS-030	1840		1	1	85	130
VYMS-035	1841		1	1	90	140
VYMS-040	1842		1	1	90	140
VYMS-045	1843		1	1	80	120
VYMS-050	1844		1	1	85	130
VYMS-055	1845		1	1	80	120
VYMS-060	1846		1	1	90	140
VYMS-065	1847		1	1	80	120
VYMS-070	1848		1	1	80	120
VYMS-075	1849		1	1	90	140
VYMS-080	1850		1	1	60	100
VYMS-085	1851		1	1	60	100
VYMS-090	1852		1	1	60	100
VYMS-095	1853		1	1	80	120
VYMS-100	1853	PROOFS	1	1		400
VYMS-105	1854		1	1	60	100
VYMS-110	1855		1	1	60	100
VYMS-115	1856		1	1	60	100
VYMS-120	1857		1	1	60	100
VYMS-125	1857	2 pence reads BRITANNIAE EEGINA (obv.)	1	1	120	200
VYMS-130	1858		1	1	55	90
VYMS-135	1859		1	1	55	90

No.	Date	Features	Obv.	Rev.	EF	FDC
VYMS-140	1859	2 pence reads BEITANNIAR (rev.)	1	1	80	120
VYMS-145	1860		1	1	55	90
VYMS-150	1861	2 pence has 6 not over 1	1	1	100	130
VYMS-155	1861	2 pence has 6 over 1	1	1	55	90
VYMS-160	1862		1	1	55	90
VYMS-165	1863		1	1	55	90
VYMS-170	1864		1	1	55	90
VYMS-175	1865		1	1	55	90
VYMS-180	1866		1	1	55	90
VYMS-185	1867		1	1	55	90
VYMS-190	1867	PROOFS	1	1		500
VYMS-195	1868		1	1	55	90
VYMS-200	1869		1	1	55	90
VYMS-205	1870		1	1	55	90
VYMS-210	1871		1	1	55	90
VYMS-215	1871	PROOFS; revs ↑	1	1		800
VYMS-220	1872		1	1	55	90
VYMS-225	1873		1	1	55	90
VYMS-230	1874		1	1	55	90
VYMS-235	1875		1	1	55	90
VYMS-240	1876		1	1	55	90
VYMS-245	1877		1	1	55	90
VYMS-250	1878		1	1	55	90
VYMS-255	1878	PROOFS	1	1		500
VYMS-260	1879		1	1	55	90
VYMS-265	1879	PROOFS; revs ↑	1	1		1200
VYMS-270	1880		1	1	55	90
VYMS-275	1881		1	1	55	90
VYMS-280	1881	PROOFS	1	1		500
VYMS-285	1882		1	1	55	90
VYMS-290	1883		1	1	55	90
VYMS-295	1884		1	1	55	90
VYMS-300	1885		1	1	55	90
VYMS-305	1886		1	1	55	90
VYMS-310	1887		1	1	55	90
VJMS-315	1888		2	2	55	90
VJMS-320	1888	PROOFS	2	2		400
VJMS-325	1889		2	2	55	90
VJMS-330	1890		2	2	55	90
VJMS-335	1891		2	2	55	90
VJMS-340	1892		2	2	55	90
VOMS-345	1893	²	3	2	40	60
VOMS-350	1894		3	2	40	60
VOMS-355	1895		3	2	40	60
VOMS-360	1896		3	2	40	60
VOMS-365	1897		3	2	40	60
VOMS-370	1898		3	2	40	60
VOMS-375	1899		3	2	40	60
VOMS-380	1900		3	2	40	60
VOMS-385	1901		3	2	40	60

1. Issued in cased proof sets.
2. Only the 4 pence has flat-top '3' in date.

Edward VII 1902–1910

The Maundy set used the portrait of Edward VII by de Saulles which was adjusted to the size required using a mechanical reduction machine. The first year mintage included the matt proof set for the cased Royal Mint proof sets of that year. This set has a very distinctive appearance with wider rims. The unattractive streaky tarnish which is often found on the matt proof sets can be removed with chemical silver tarnish remover, as this does not affect the matt finish.

Until 1908 it was possible to obtain sets of Maundy money through banks and other outlets, but from 1909 the issue was restricted to Maundy ceremony recipients and a number of other specified persons. This is why the 1909 and 1910 sets are considerably scarcer than those of other years, and also why sets of later reigns are more difficult to find than those of Victoria and Edward VII.

Maundy cases continued to be similar to those issued in the late Victorian era.

Denomination	Metal	Weight (grams)	Diameter (mm)	Rev alignment
Maundy set	Silver	0.5; 0.9; 1.4; 1.9	11; 13; 16; 18	↑

The Phoenix is our monthly catalogue of British and world coins, as well as British and world banknotes, ancient coins and antiquities. Each month there are different offers to excite and entice collectors. Just fill in one of the cards below and post it to us and we will be happy to send you a complimentary copy. If the cards are missing just drop us a note and mention that you saw it in the Standard Catalogue and send it to Department 'SC', The Phoenix, c/o Coincraft, 45 Great Russell Street, London WC1B 3LU, England. Or you can fax it to either of our numbers – 0171-323 2860 or 0171-637 7635.

Obverse 1 Head 1, right; EDWARDVS VII D G BRITT OMN REX F D IND IMP

Reverse 1 Crowned numeral and divided date, all within wreath.

Edge plain

Rev. 1

No.	Date	Features	Obv	Rev	EF	FDC
E7MS-005	1902		1	1	40	55
E7MS-010	1902	PROOFS [1]	1	1	40	60
E7MS-015	1903	[2]	1	1	40	60
E7MS-020	1904	[3]	1	1	40	60
E7MS-025	1905		1	1	40	60
E7MS-030	1906		1	1	40	60
E7MS-035	1907		1	1	40	60
E7MS-040	1908		1	1	40	60
E7MS-045	1909	[4]	1	1	55	80
E7MS-050	1910	[4]	1	1	55	80

1. Matt surface; issued in cased proof sets.
2. Only the 4 pence has flat-top '3' in date.
3. Some issued in unusual oval case.
4. See notes above re distribution.

No.	Date	Features	Obv	Rev	EF	FDC
G5MS-005	1911	[1]	1	1	40	55
G5MS-010	1912		1	1	40	60
G5MS-015	1913		1	1	40	60
G5MS-020	1914		1	1	50	75
G5MS-025	1915		1	1	40	60
G5MS-030	1916		1	1	40	60
G5MS-035	1917		1	1	40	60
G5MS-040	1918		1	1	40	60
G5MS-045	1919		1	1	40	60
G5MS-050	1920		1	1	40	60
G5MS-055	1921		1	1	40	60
G5MS-060	1922		1	1	40	60
G5MS-065	1923		1	1	40	60
G5MS-070	1924		1	1	40	60
G5MS-075	1925		1	1	40	60
G5MS-080	1926		1	1	40	60
G5MS-085	1927		1	1	40	60
G5MS-090	1928		2	1	40	60
G5MS-095	1929		2	1	40	60
G5MS-100	1930		3	1	40	60
G5MS-105	1931		3	1	40	60
G5MS-110	1932	[2]	3	1	40	60
G5MS-115	1933		3	1	40	60
G5MS-120	1934		3	1	40	60
G5MS-125	1935		3	1	40	60
G5MS-130	1936	[3]	3	1	45	70

1. So-called 'proof' sets exist with a minor variation to the shape of the 4 pence rim.
2. Distributed by George V; first distribution by reigning monarch since 17th century.
3. Distributed by Edward VIII.

George V 1910–1936

Sir Bertram MacKennal (1863-1931) executed the portrait of George V which replaced that of Edward VII on the new Maundy series. The reverse remained unchanged. Along with the other coinage, but a year later, a change was made to the metal content in 1921, the silver constituent of the alloy falling to 50%. In 1928, and again in 1930, minor alterations were made to the portrait.

One of the more common myths of British numismatics, repeated in most catalogues, is that of the 1911 proof Maundy set. Examination of a Royal Mint proof set of that year will reveal that, whilst all of the other coins have a prooflike field, the Maundy set is identical to the other Maundy sets of that year. Indeed, the field is less prooflike than many of the sets of previous or subsequent years! Nevertheless, there is a slight difference between the shape of the rim of the fourpence in the proof sets and that on the presentation Maundy set.

The set of 1932 was personally distributed by George V. Distribution of Maundy by the monarch had generally been discontinued in the 17th century. The set of 1936, although bearing the portrait of George V, was distributed by Edward VIII.

Maundy cases of this reign were usually rectangular, although some square and octagonal cases were issued. They were usually covered in red leather with embossed gold lettering, with or without a date.

Denomination	Metal	Weight (grams)	Diameter (mm)	Rev alignment
Maundy Set 1911-1920	0.925 Silver	0.5; 0.9; 1.4; 1.9	11; 13; 16; 18	↑
Maundy Set 1921-1936	0.5 Silver	0.5; 0.9; 1.4; 1.9	11; 13; 16; 18	↑

Obverse 1 Head 1, left; GEORGIVS V D G BRITT OMN REX F D IND IMP

Obverse 2 Head 2, so-called 'modified effigy', left; same legend

Obverse 3 Head 2, re-engraved, left; same legend

Reverse 1 Crowned numeral and divided date, all within wreath

Edge plain

Obv. 1   Obv. 2

George VI 1937–1952

The obverse portrait of George VI was designed by Thomas Humphrey Paget, the reverse continuing a slightly modified version of the previous reign. The Maundy set of the first year, 1937, was included in the Royal Mint proof set of that year, but there is no difference in the quality of the strike between the regular Maundy set and that included in the proof set. However, unlike the 1911 set, the 1937 set exhibit highly prooflike fields, as indeed do all of the George VI sets.

A somewhat curious decision was made when the changeover to cupronickel was made for silver coinage in 1947. It was considered inappropriate to strike Maundy money, to be distributed by the monarch, in such a debased material as cupronickel. However, rather than continuing to strike it in 0.500 silver, the silver content was once again upgraded to 0.925. This is one of the few times in which a regular denomination has had its precious metal content increased.

Maundy cases were usually square, undated, and covered in red leather.

Denomination	Metal	Weight (grams)	Diameter (mm)	Rev alignment
Maundy set 1937-1946	0.5 Silver	0.5; 0.9; 1.4; 1.9	11; 13; 16; 18	↑
Maundy set 1947-1952	0.925 Silver	0.5; 0.9; 1.4; 1.9	11; 13; 16; 18	↑

Obverse 1 Head 1, left; GEORGIVS VI D G BR OMN REX F D IND IMP

Obverse 2 Head 1, left; GEORGIVS VI D G BR OMN REX FIDEI DEF

Reverse 1 Crowned numeral and divided date, all within wreath.

Edge plain

Obv. 1

Obv. 2

Rev. 1

No.	Date	Features	Obv	Rev	EF	FDC
G6MS-005	1937		1	1	40	60
G6MS-010	1937	PROOF from sandblasted dies [1]	1	1		250
G6MS-015	1938		1	1	40	65
G6MS-020	1939		1	1	40	65
G6MS-025	1940		1	1	40	65
G6MS-030	1941		1	1	40	65
G6MS-035	1942		1	1	40	65
G6MS-040	1943		1	1	40	65
G6MS-045	1944		1	1	40	65
G6MS-050	1945		1	1	40	65
G6MS-055	1946		1	1	40	65
G6MS-060	1947		1	1	45	70
G6MS-065	1948		1	1	45	70
G6MS-070	1949		2	1	45	70
G6MS-075	1950		2	1	45	70
G6MS-080	1951		2	1	45	70
G6MS-085	1951	PROOF from sandblasted dies [1]	2	1		250
G6MS-090	1952		2	1	45	70
G6MS-095	1952	struck in copper[2]	2	1		1200

1. Struck to facilitate photography of coin.
2. Weights 0.6; 0.9; 1.4; 1.6 grams.

Elizabeth II 1952 -

The Maundy coinage continued to be struck in sterling (0.925) silver, using the portrait of Elizabeth II by Mary Gillick. As with the other coinage, there were problems with weak striking, and the obverse dies were recut in time to strike the 1954 coinage. In addition, the obverse legend was revised in 1954, making the 1953 set a unique type which is much in demand by collectors. The fact that, unlike in 1911 and 1937, the Maundy set was not included in the Royal Mint proof set only served to increase its scarcity.

By 1953 the monarch or representative was distributing the Maundy personally each year, usually in London. Later, distributions were made at cathedrals in the Home Counties (e.g. St. Albans, Canterbury, Rochester). It was not until 1967 that the ceremony was held some considerable distance from London, at Durham. Thereafter, ceremonies were held in many parts of the country.

When the changeover to decimal currency occurred in 1971, there was no apparent change to the Maundy coinage. Certainly, no alterations were made to the design. However, Maundy coinage has always been legal tender, otherwise strictly speaking the recipients are receiving only trinkets (although they are usually exhorted to sell their sets by dealers!). Because the post-1971 sets could clearly not continue to be denominated in old pence, the entire series (including the older sets) was upgraded to legal tender status in New Pence. This is yet another unique aspect of this remarkable coinage — an overnight revaluation by a factor of 2.4. Very few people nowadays spend Maundy sets as currency, but perhaps it is something to fall back on if ever coin collecting goes out of fashion!

Maundy cases were square and covered in red leather, with the Royal Mint crest on the inside of the lid. From 1989, the coins were placed in a hard plastic insert inside the cases. Some 1953 sets were issued in blue and maroon cases.

Denomination	Metal	Weight (grams)	Diameter (mm)	Rev alignment
Maundy set	0.925 Silver	0.5; 0.9; 1.4; 1.9	11; 13; 16; 18	↑

Obverse 1 Head 1, right; ELIZABETH II DEI GRA BRITT OMN REGINA F D

Obverse 2 Head 2, recut, right; ELIZABETH II DEI GRATIA REGINA F D

Reverse 1 Crowned numeral and divided date, all within wreath.

Edge plain

Obv. 1   Obv. 2

Rev. 1

No.	Date	Features	Obv	Rev	EF	FDC
EL2MS-005	1953		1	1	240	300
EL2MS-010	1953	PROOF from sandblasted dies [1]	1	1		800
EL2MS-015	1953	struck in gold [2]	1	1		7000
EL2MS-020	1954		2	1	60	80
EL2MS-025	1955		2	1	60	80
EL2MS-030	1956		2	1	60	80
EL2MS-035	1957		2	1	60	80
EL2MS-040	1958		2	1	60	80
EL2MS-045	1959		2	1	60	80
EL2MS-050	1960		2	1	60	80
EL2MS-055	1961		2	1	60	80
EL2MS-060	1962		2	1	60	80
EL2MS-065	1963		2	1	60	80
EL2MS-070	1964		2	1	60	80
EL2MS-075	1965		2	1	60	80
EL2MS-080	1966		2	1	60	80
EL2MS-085	1967		2	1	60	80
EL2MS-090	1968		2	1	60	80
EL2MS-095	1969		2	1	60	80
EL2MS-100	1970		2	1	60	80
EL2MS-105	1971		2	1	60	80
EL2MS-110	1972		2	1	60	80
EL2MS-115	1973		2	1	60	80
EL2MS-120	1974		2	1	60	80
EL2MS-125	1975		2	1	60	80
EL2MS-130	1976		2	1	60	80
EL2MS-135	1977		2	1	60	80
EL2MS-140	1978		2	1	60	80
EL2MS-145	1979		2	1	60	80
EL2MS-150	1980		2	1	60	80
EL2MS-155	1981		2	1	60	80
EL2MS-160	1982		2	1	60	80
EL2MS-165	1983		2	1	60	80
EL2MS-170	1984		2	1	60	80
EL2MS-175	1985		2	1	60	80
EL2MS-180	1986		2	1	60	80
EL2MS-185	1987		2	1	70	90
EL2MS-190	1988		2	1	70	90
EL2MS-195	1989		2	1	70	90
EL2MS-200	1990		2	1	75	95
EL2MS-205	1991		2	1	80	100
EL2MS-210	1992		2	1	85	110
EL2MS-215	1993		2	1	85	110
EL2MS-220	1994		2	1	90	120
EL2MS-225	1995		2	1	90	120

1. Struck to facilitate photography of coins.
2. Weights 1.2 ; 1.8; 2.6; 2.9 grams.

Decimal Coinage Primarily Struck In Base Metals

A Committee of Enquiry appointed in 1961 to consider the adoption of decimal currency reported its findings in 1968. Despite the success of changeovers in Australia and New Zealand adopting a two-dollar pound, the Committee recommended that the pound be retained as the basic unit. The florin would become ten new pence (10p), the shilling five new pence (5p), and the sixpence a rather awkward 2½ new pence. New coinage of values 2, 1 and ½ pence would be introduced for use at the inception of decimal currency, together with a 50 pence coin which would replace the ten shilling note prior to the changeover date. The old halfcrown, threepence, penny and halfpenny would have no place in the new system.

Decimal day was fixed as 15th February 1971. The 50 pence coin was introduced in 1969, and the new bronze coinage was made available in 1968 as part of a specimen set in a wallet. The bronze coins in this set were dated 1971 and were not legal tender until decimal day in 1971. Despite some protests, the old sixpence was withdrawn in 1980 after it became obvious that a 2½ pence denomination was something of an anomaly. In 1982, a 20 pence coin was introduced, followed in 1983 by a nickel-brass pound coin. The new halfpenny was discontinued after 1984, and a few years later the 10 and 5 pence coins were reduced in size.

Base metal five pounds, two pounds and twenty-five pence coins were also issued from time to time but, although legal tender, they were not primarily intended for circulation. Some commemorative versions of the 50 pence coin were also struck.

Base Metal Five Pounds

Commemorative crowns of five shillings (later 25 new pence) in cupronickel were first issued in 1951 for the Festival of Britain. Subsequently they were struck on a number of occasions until the final issue in 1981 for the wedding of the Prince of Wales and Lady Diana. When in 1990 it was decided to strike a similar coin for the 90th Birthday of the Queen Mother, it was obvious that the cost of issuing the piece would be a substantial portion of the face value if the 25 pence value was retained. Moreover, a large coin weighing almost one ounce would sit distinctly oddly alongside the tiny 20 pence and the 50 pence coins. It was decided, therefore, that the denomination of the crown-size piece should be five pounds, no doubt also with one eye on the lucrative issue income which would ensue! The description of the coin as a 'crown' is unfortunate, as it debases a term used for well over 400 years to denote a coin of five shillings.

The striking of versions of these cupronickel commemoratives in gold is a source of some confusion alongside gold five pounds of the same years with a different design. In which listings should they be included? In this catalogue, these pieces are considered to be varieties of the base metal five pounds and are therefore listed in that section.

Denomination	Metal	Weight (grams)	Diameter (mm)	Rev. alignment
Five Pounds	Cupronickel	28.3	39	↑

Obverse 1 Head 1, right; ELIZABETH II DEI GRATIA REGINA F D FIVE POUNDS

Obverse 2 Head 2, right, within mounted trumpeters separated by swords and sceptres; ELIZABETH II DEI GRATIA REGINA FID DEF FIVE POUNDS *(for the 40th anniversary of the Coronation)*

Reverse 1 Two intertwined 'E's, crown above, flanked by rose and thistle; QUEEN ELIZABETH THE QUEEN MOTHER 1900 1990

Reverse 2 Crown within 40 radiating trumpets; FAITH AND TRUTH I WILL BEAR UNTO YOU *(for the 40th anniversary of the Coronation)*

Edge milled

Obv. 1 Obv. 2

Rev. 1 Rev. 2

No.	Date	Features	Obv.	Rev.	UNC
D5P/90-1	1990		1	1	8
D5P/90-2	1990	SPECIMEN [1]	1	1	12
D5P/90-4	1990	PROOF in silver [2]	1	1	35
D5P/90-6	1990	PROOF in gold [2]	1	1	800
D5P/93-1	1993		2	2	8
D5P/93-2	1993	SPECIMEN [1]	2	2	12
D5P/93-3	1993	PROOF [3]	2	2	12
D5P/93-4	1993	PROOF in silver [2]	2	2	35
D5P/93-6	1993	PROOF in gold [2]	2	2	900

1. Issued in card holder.
2. Issued cased.
3. Issued in cased proof sets.

Base Metal Two Pounds

Two pound coins were struck in nickel-brass to commemorate the Commonwealth Games in 1986; in 1989 for the 300th Anniversary of the Bill of Rights and (in Scotland) the Claim of Right; in 1994 for the 300th anniversary of the Bank of England, and in 1995 both for the 50th anniversary of the end of World War II and for the 50th anniversary of the United Nations.

The two pounds of 1986, 1994 and 1995 have designs identical to those of the gold two pounds issued in the proof sets. This gives rise to something of a dilemma for cataloguers, as confusion arises as to which section the gold piece properly belongs. Normally, an identical gold version of a base metal coin would properly be incorporated in the base metal listings, but because of the inclusion of the gold coin in the proof sets it is considered here more appropriate to place the main listing in the gold section but to include a secondary listing in the base metal section but with the gold section reference number.

Denomination	Metal	Weight (grams)	Diameter (mm)	Rev. alignment
Two Pounds	Nickel-brass	16.0	28	↑

Obverse 1 Head 1, right; ELIZABETH II DEI GRATIA REGINA F D TWO POUNDS

Obverse 2 Similar but ELIZABETH II DEI GRA REG F D

Reverse 1 Thistle on St Andrew's Cross; 1986 *(for the Commonwealth Games)*

Reverse 2 Cypher of William and Mary (intertwined W and M) threaded by mace, with crown above; TERCENTENARY OF THE BILL OF RIGHTS 1689 1989

Reverse 3 As above but with crown of Scotland; legend reads TERCENTENARY OF THE CLAIM OF RIGHT 1689 1989

Reverse 4 Bank of England's Corporate Seal with Crown and Cyphers of William and Mary; BANK OF ENGLAND 1694 1994

Reverse 5 Dove carrying olive branch *(for 50th anniversary of end of World War II)*

Reverse 6 Array of flags rising from UN 50 logo; NATIONS UNITED FOR PEACE 1945-1995 *(for 50th anniversary of United Nations)*

Edge 1 XIII COMMONWEALTH GAMES SCOTLAND 1986 incuse on milling

Edge 2 milled

Edge 3 SIC VOC NON VOBIS incuse on milling

Edge 4 1945 IN PEACE GOODWILL 1995 incuse on milling

Rev. 6

Obv. 1

Obv. 2

Rev. 1

Rev. 2

Rev. 3

Rev. 4

Rev. 5

No.	Date	Features	Obv.	Rev.	Edge	UNC
D2P/86-1	1986		1	1	1	4
D2P/86-2	1986	SPECIMEN [1]	1	1	1	8
D2P/86-3	1986	PROOF [2]	1	1	1	7
D2P/86SP-4	1986	SPECIMEN in 0.500 silver [3]	1	1	1	20
D2P/86-4	1986	PROOF in silver [3]	1	1	1	30
EL22P-030	1986	PROOF in gold [4]	1	1	2	220
D2P/89CB-1	1989		1	2	2	4
D2P/89CB-2	1989	SPECIMEN [1]	1	2	2	8
D2P/89CB-3	1989	PROOF [2]	1	2	2	7
D2P/89CB-4	1989	PROOF in silver [3]	1	2	2	25
D2P/89CB-5	1989	PIEDFORT PROOF in silver [3]	1	2	2	50
D2P/89CC-1	1989		1	3	2	4
D2P/89CC-2	1989	SPECIMEN [1]	1	3	2	8
D2P/89CC-3	1989	PROOF [2]	1	3	2	7
D2P/89CC-4	1989	PROOF in silver [3]	1	3	2	25
D2P/89CC-5	1989	PIEDFORT PROOF in silver [3]	1	3	2	50
D2P/94-1	1994		1	4	3	4
D2P/94-2	1994	SPECIMEN [1]	1	4	3	7
D2P/94-3	1994	PROOF [2]	1	4	3	6
D2P/94-4	1994	PROOF in silver [3]	1	4	3	25
D2P/94-5	1994	PIEDFORT PROOF in silver [3]	1	4	3	50
EL22P-070	1994	PROOF in gold [4]	1	4	2	350
EL22P-075	1994	PROOF in gold [5]	2	4	2	450
D2P/95C1-1	1995		1	5	4	4
D2P/95C1-2	1995	SPECIMEN [1]	1	5	4	7
D2P/95C1-3	1995	PROOF [2]	1	5	4	6
D2P/95C1-4	1995	PROOF in silver [3]	1	5	4	25
EL22P-080	1995	PROOF in gold [4]	1	5	2	350
D2P/95C2-1	1995		1	6	2	4
D2P/95C2-2	1995	SPECIMEN [1]	1	6	2	7
D2P/95C2-3	1995	PROOF [2]	1	6	2	6
D2P/95C2-4	1995	PROOF in silver [3]	1	6	2	25
EL22P-085	1995	PROOF in gold [4]	1	6	2	350

1. Issued in card holder.
2. Issued in cased proof sets.
3. Issued cased.
4. Gold section reference number; issued cased and in cased proof sets.
5. Error obverse; gold section reference number; see gold section for details; issued cased.

Base Metal One Pound

Inflationary pressures dictated that by 1983 it was considered more appropriate that the pound should be represented by a coin rather than a banknote. Although at first unpopular, the coin has now become widely accepted.

An unusual feature of the coin has been the annual change of reverse rotating through six different designs. These feature aspects of different nations within the United Kingdom. The obverse at first used the Machin portrait of the queen, but from 1985 the Maklouf design was used. A number of collectors' versions were also struck each year, including cased silver proofs and, for some years, cased piedforts.

Denomination	Metal	Weight (grams)	Diameter (mm)	Rev. alignment
Pound	Nickel-brass	9.5	22.5	↑

Piedfort pounds weigh 19.0 grams.

Obverse 1 Head 1, right; ELIZABETH II D G REG F D (date)

Obverse 2 Head 2, right; same legend

Reverse 1 Royal Arms; ONE POUND

Reverse 2 Thistle sprig inside coronet (Scottish design); ONE POUND

Reverse 3 Leek inside coronet (Welsh design); ONE POUND

Reverse 4 Flax inside coronet (Northern Ireland design); ONE POUND

Reverse 5 Oak Tree inside coronet (English design); ONE POUND

Reverse 6 Arms within shield, crown above; ONE POUND

Reverse 7 Lion rampant within ornate border (Scottish design); ONE POUND

Reverse 8 Dragon of Wales; ONE POUND

All of the edge letterings below are superimposed on a milled edge:

Edge 1 DECUS ET TUTAMEN

Edge 2 NEMO ME IMPUNE LACESSIT

Edge 3 PLEIDOIL WYF I'M GWLAD

Obv. 1 Obv. 2

Rev. 1 Rev. 2

Rev. 3 Rev. 4

Rev. 5 Rev. 6

Rev. 7 Rev. 8

No.	Date	Features	Obv.	Rev.	Edge	UNC
D1P/83-1	1983		1	1	1	4
D1P/83-2	1983	SPECIMEN [1]	1	1	1	10
D1P/83-3	1983	PROOF [2]	1	1	1	6
D1P/83-4	1983	PROOF in silver [3]	1	1	1	40
D1P/83-5	1983	PIEDFORT PROOF in silver [3]	1	1	1	220
D1P/84-1	1984		1	2	2	5
D1P/84-2	1984	SPECIMEN [1]	1	2	2	12
D1P/84-3	1984	PROOF [2]	1	2	2	6
D1P/84-4	1984	PROOF in silver [3]	1	2	2	30
D1P/84-5	1984	PIEDFORT PROOF in silver [3]	1	2	2	75
D1P/85-1	1985		2	3	3	5
D1P/85-2	1985	SPECIMEN [1]	2	3	3	10
D1P/85-3	1985	PROOF [2]	2	3	3	6
D1P/85-4	1985	PROOF in silver [3]	2	3	3	35
D1P/85-5	1985	PIEDFORT PROOF in silver [3]	2	3	3	80
D1P/86-1	1986		2	4	1	5
D1P/86-2	1986	SPECIMEN [1]	2	4	1	10
D1P/86-3	1986	PROOF [2]	2	4	1	6
D1P/86-4	1986	PROOF in silver [3]	2	4	1	35
D1P/86-5	1986	PIEDFORT PROOF in silver [3]	2	4	1	75
D1P/87-1	1987		2	5	1	5
D1P/87-2	1987	SPECIMEN [1]	2	5	1	10
D1P/87-3	1987	PROOF [2]	2	5	1	6
D1P/87-4	1987	PROOF in silver [3]	2	5	1	35
D1P/87-5	1987	PIEDFORT PROOF in silver [3]	2	5	1	75
D1P/88-1	1988		2	6	1	4
D1P/88-2	1988	SPECIMEN [1]	2	6	1	9
D1P/88-3	1988	PROOF [2]	2	6	1	5
D1P/88-4	1988	PROOF in silver [3]	2	6	1	40
D1P/88-5	1988	PIEDFORT PROOF in silver [3]	2	6	1	75
D1P/89-1	1989		2	2	2	4
D1P/89-2	1989	SPECIMEN [1]	2	2	2	9
D1P/89-3	1989	PROOF [2]	2	2	2	5
D1P/89-4	1989	PROOF in silver [3]	2	2	2	35
D1P/89-5	1989	PIEDFORT PROOF in silver [3]	2	2	2	80
D1P/90-1	1990		2	3	3	4
D1P/90-3	1990	PROOF [2]	2	3	3	5
D1P/90-4	1990	PROOF in silver [3]	2	3	3	35
D1P/91-1	1991		2	4	1	4
D1P/91-3	1991	PROOF [2]	2	4	1	6
D1P/91-4	1991	PROOF in silver [3]	2	4	1	35
D1P/92-1	1992		2	5	1	4
D1P/92-3	1992	PROOF [2]	2	5	1	6
D1P/92-4	1992	PROOF in silver [3]	2	5	1	35
D1P/93-1	1993		2	1	1	4
D1P/93-3	1993	PROOF [2]	2	1	1	6
D1P/93-4	1993	PROOF in silver [3]	2	1	1	35
D1P/93-5	1993	PIEDFORT PROOF in silver [3]	2	1	1	75
D1P/94-1	1994		2	7	2	3
D1P/94-3	1994	PROOF [2]	2	7	2	5

No.	Date	Features	Obv.	Rev.	Edge	UNC
D1P/94-4	1994	PROOF in silver [3]	2	7	2	35
D1P/94-5	1994	PIEDFORT PROOF in silver [3]	2	7	2	75
D1P/95-1	1995		2	8	3	3
D1P/95-3	1995	PROOF [2]	2	8	3	5
D1P/95-4	1995	PROOF in silver [3]	2	8	3	35
D1P/95-5	1995	PIEDFORT PROOF in silver [3]	2	8	3	75

1. Issued in card holder.
2. Issued in cased proof sets.
3. Issued cased.

50 Pence

The 50 pence was first issued in 1969, before the decimal change-over in 1971, and it circulated alongside the ten shilling note of equal value. The coin was of an unusual shape, with seven sides which were each slightly curved, so that the 'diameter' from one side to the other through the centre of the coin was always the same length (30mm) wherever it was measured. This enabled the coin to activate slot machines without any problem.

Although widely encountered in circulation, several of the dates were struck only either as proofs or for incorporation in the yearly specimen sets in card wallets.

Denomination	Metal	Weight (grams)	Diameter (mm)	Rev. alignment (see footnote)
50 pence	Cupronickel (copper 75%; nickel 25%)	13.5	30	↑

The coin is seven-sided but the diameter from any point on the edge across the centre of the face is constant.

Obverse 1 Head 1, right; ELIZABETH II D G REG F D (date)

Obverse 2 Head 1, right; ELIZABETH II D G REG F D

Obverse 3 Head 2, right; ELIZABETH II D G REG F D (date)

Obverse 4 Head 2, right; ELIZABETH II DEI GRA REG F D

Reverse 1 Britannia, seated, with shield, facing right; 50 in exergue; NEW PENCE

Reverse 2 Nine clasped hands forming circle; 1973 50 PENCE *(for Britain's entry into the EC)*

Reverse 3 As Reverse 1 but legend reads FIFTY PENCE

Reverse 4 Plan of Conference table top and seats, with 12 stars; 1992 1993 50 PENCE *(for completion of the EC Single Market and Britain's Presidency)*

Reverse 5 Invasion Force of planes and ships; 50 PENCE *(for 50th anniversary of D-Day)*

Edge plain

Obv. 1

Obv. 2

Obv. 3   Obv. 4

Rev. 1   Rev. 2

Rev. 3   Rev. 4

Rev. 5

No.	Date	Features	Obv.	Rev.	UNC
D50/69-1	1969		1	1	4
D50/69-1E	1969	[1]	1	obv 1	200
D50/70-1	1970		1	1	5
D50/71-3	1971	PROOF [2]	1	1	8
D50/72-3	1972	PROOF [2]	1	1	7
D50/73-1	1973		2	2	4
D50/73-3	1973	PROOF [3]	2	2	4
D50/74-3	1974	PROOF [2]	1	1	8
D50/75-3	1975	PROOF [2]	1	1	8
D50/76-1	1976		1	1	5
D50/76-3	1976	PROOF [2]	1	1	7
D50/77-1	1977		1	1	4
D50/77-3	1977	PROOF [2]	1	1	8
D50/78-1	1978		1	1	4
D50/78-3	1978	PROOF [2]	1	1	7
D50/79-1	1979		1	1	4
D50/79-3	1979	PROOF [2]	1	1	7
D50/80-1	1980		1	1	4
D50/80-3	1980	PROOF [2]	1	1	6
D50/81-1	1981		1	1	4
D50/81-3	1981	PROOF [2]	1	1	6
D50/RR-1E		[4]	rev. 1	1	250
D50/82-1	1982		1	3	4
D50/82-3	1982	PROOF [2]	1	3	6
D50/83-1	1983		1	3	4
D50/83-3	1983	PROOF [2]	1	3	6
D50/84-1	1984	[5]	1	3	6
D50/84-3	1984	PROOF [2]	1	3	7
D50/85-1	1985		3	3	4
D50/85-3	1985	PROOF [2]	3	3	6
D50/86-1	1986	[5]	3	3	6
D50/86-3	1986	PROOF [2]	3	3	7

No.	Date	Features	Obv.	Rev.	UNC
D50/87-1	1987	5	3	3	6
D50/87-3	1987	PROOF [2]	3	3	7
D50/88-1	1988	5	3	3	6
D50/88-3	1988	PROOF [2]	3	3	7
D50/89-1	1989	5	3	3	6
D50/89-3	1989	PROOF [2]	3	3	7
D50/90-1	1990	5	3	3	6
D50/90-3	1990	PROOF [2]	3	3	7
D50/91-1	1991	5	3	3	6
D50/91-3	1991	PROOF [2]	3	3	7
D50/92-1	1992	5	3	3	6
D50/92-3	1992	PROOF [2]	3	3	7
D50/93-1	1993	5	3	3	6
D50/93-3	1993	PROOF [2]	3	3	7
D50/92C-1	1992/93		4	4	4
D50/92C-3	1992/93	PROOF [2]	4	4	7
D50/92C-4	1992/93	PROOF in silver [6]	4	4	50
D50/92C-5	1992/93	PIEDFORT PROOF in silver [7]	4	4	95
D50/92C-6	1992/93	PROOF in gold [8]	4	4	600
D50/94C-1	1994		3	5	4
D50/94C-2	1994	SPECIMEN [9]	3	5	8
D50/94C-3	1994	PROOF [2]	3	5	8
D50/94C-4	1994	PROOF in silver [6]	3	5	50
D50/94C-5	1994	PIEDFORT PROOF in silver [7]	3	5	95
D50/94C-6	1994	PROOF in gold [8]	3	5	600

1. 'double headed' coin.
2. Issued in cased proof sets.
3. Issued cased and in cased proof sets.
4. 'Double tailed' coin; bears no date.
5. All issued in uncirculated sets in holders.
6. Issued cased.
7. Weight 27.0 grams; issued cased.
8. Weight 26.3 grams; issued cased.
9. Issued in card holder.

25 Pence

During the reign of Elizabeth II, crowns of five shillings had been issued on three occasions, but these were not intended as circulation pieces. The year after decimalization, a crown denominated at 25 pence was struck for the Royal Silver Wedding, although no mark of denomination appears on this, or on any subsequent 25 pence coin. Three further commemorative crowns were struck as listed, and proof versions in silver were also issued. The 1977 coin is unusual in having no legend or digits whatsoever on the reverse.

In 1990 a cupronickel crown-size coin of five pounds was issued, and it appears unlikely that any future crowns of 25 pence will be issued.

Denomination	Metal	Weight (grams)	Diameter (mm)	Rev. alignment
25 Pence	Cupronickel (copper 75%; nickel 25%)	28.3	38	↑

Obverse 1 Head 1, right; ELIZABETH II D G REG F D

Obverse 2 Queen on horseback; ELIZABETH II D G REG F D 1977 *(for the 25th anniversary of the Queen's accession)*

Reverse 1 EP on floral motif, crown above; ELIZABETH AND PHILIP 20 NOVEMBER 1947-1972

Reverse 2 Coronation regalia with floral border, crown above

Reverse 3 Head of Queen Mother, left, within decoration; QUEEN ELIZABETH THE QUEEN MOTHER AUGUST 4TH 1980 *(for the Queen Mother's 80th Birthday)*

Reverse 4 Conjoined heads of Charles and Diana, left; HRH THE PRINCE OF WALES AND LADY DIANA SPENCER 1981 *(for the Wedding of Prince of Wales and Lady Diana)*

Edge milled

Obv. 1   Obv. 2

Rev. 1   Rev. 2

Rev. 3   Rev. 4

No.	Date	Features	Obv.	Rev.	UNC
D25/72-1	1972		1	1	3
D25/72-3	1972	PROOF [1]	1	1	12
D25/72-4	1972	PROOF in 0.500 silver [2]	1	1	25
D25/77-1	1977	[3]	2	2	3
D25/77-2	1977	SPECIMEN [4]	2	2	8
D25/77-3	1977	PROOF [1]	2	2	12
D25/77-4	1977	PROOF in silver [2]	2	2	25
D25/80-1	1980		1	3	3
D25/80-2	1980	SPECIMEN [4]	1	3	8
D25/80-4	1980	PROOF in silver [2]	1	3	30
D25/81-1	1981		1	4	3
D25/81-2	1981	SPECIMEN [4]	1	4	10
D25/81-4	1981	PROOF in silver [2]	1	4	35

1. Issued in cased proof sets.
2. Issued cased.
3. Has no words or figures on reverse.
4. Issued in card holder.

20 Pence

Although crowns denominated at 25 pence had been issued from time to time, these were not primarily intended for circulation, and in any event were too large for practical use. After decimal currency had been circulating for some time it became obvious that it would be convenient to have a new coin to bridge the gap between the 50 pence and 10 pence coins. The 20 pence was first issued in 1982, and soon became a popular addition to the decimal range, with its distinctive seven-sided shape, a smaller version of the 50 pence coin. It is interesting to contrast the success of the 20 pence with the unpopularity of the double florin (equivalent face value) in 1887. The latter coin failed to survive beyond 1890 in competition with the crown piece. Ironically, the proclamation of 1971 included the double florin in the list of coins which continued to have legal tender status after decimal day.

The first 20 pence was issued in the same year that the term 'new pence' was abandoned in favour of 'pence', and so no specimens with the old wording were struck. The coin were issued also in proof each year for the proof set, and in 1986 no ordinary coins were struck except for those issued in official card wallets.

The cupronickel used for the 20 pence has a copper content of 84%, compared with the 75% in the cupronickel used for the 50, 10 and 5 pence coins.

Denomination	Metal	Weight (grams)	Diameter (mm)	[1]Rev. alignment
20 Pence	Cupronickel (copper 84%; nickel 16%)	5.0	21	↑

The coin is seven-sided but the diameter from any point on the edge across the centre of the face is constant.

Obverse 1 Head 1, right; ELIZABETH II D G REG F D

Obverse 2 Head 2, right; same legend

Reverse 1 Crowned double rose; TWENTY PENCE (date), '20' below

Edge plain

| Obv. 1 | Obv. 2 | Rev. 1 |

No.	Date	Features	Obv.	Rev.	UNC
D20/82-1	1982		1	1	2
D20/82-3	1982	PROOF [1]	1	1	5
D20/82-5	1982	PIEDFORT PROOF in silver [2]	1	1	60
D20/83-1	1983		1	1	2
D20/83-3	1983	PROOF [1]	1	1	5
D20/84-1	1984		1	1	2
D20/84-3	1984	PROOF [1]	1	1	5
D20/85-1	1985		2	1	2
D20/85-3	1985	PROOF [1]	2	1	5
D20/86-1	1986	[3]	2	1	3
D20/86-3	1986	PROOF [1]	2	1	6
D20/87-1	1987		2	1	2
D20/87-3	1987	PROOF [1]	2	1	5
D20/88-1	1988		2	1	2
D20/88-3	1988	PROOF [1]	2	1	5
D20/89-1	1989		2	1	2
D20/89-3	1989	PROOF [1]	2	1	5
D20/90-1	1990		2	1	2
D20/90-3	1990	PROOF [1]	2	1	5
D20/91-1	1991		2	1	2
D20/91-3	1991	PROOF [1]	2	1	5
D20/92-1	1992		2	1	2
D20/92-3	1992	PROOF [1]	2	1	5
D20/93-1	1993		2	1	2
D20/93-3	1993	PROOF [1]	2	1	5
D20/94-1	1994		2	1	2
D20/94-3	1994	PROOF [1]	2	1	5

1. Issued in cased proof sets.
2. Weight 10.0 grams; issued cased.
3. All issued in uncirculated sets in holders.

10 Pence

The 10 new pence coin was one of the two denominations intended to circulate alongside a pre-decimal coin of the same size, weight and value (the florin). There was therefore no bar to its being introduced prior to decimalization in order to familiarise the public, and consequently in 1968, 1969 and 1970 a large quantity was struck and issued. In 1968 the 10 pence was also issued

as part of an official decimal set in a blue wallet. This set also contained three bronze coins dated 1971.

In 1992, a smaller size 10 pence was issued, and the larger coins were progressively withdrawn.

Denomination	Metal	Weight (grams)	Diameter (mm)	Rev. alignment
10 Pence 1968-1992	Cupronickel (copper 75%; nickel 25%)	11.3	28.5	↑
10 Pence 1992-1994	Cupronickel (copper 75%; nickel 25%)	6.5	24.5	↑

Obverse 1 Head 1, right; ELIZABETH II D G REG F D (date)

Obverse 2 Head 2, right; same legend

Obverse 3 As Obverse 2 on smaller flan

Reverse 1 Lion Passant, '10' below; NEW PENCE

Reverse 2 Similar but legend reads TEN PENCE

Reverse 3 As Reverse 2 on smaller flan

Edge milled

| Obv. 1 | Obv. 2 | Obv. 3 |

| Rev. 1 | Rev. 2 | Rev. 3 |

No.	Date	Features	Obv.	Rev.	UNC
D10/68-1	1968	[1]	1	1	2
D10/69-1	1969		1	1	3
D10/70-1	1970		1	1	4
D10/71-1	1971		1	1	4
D10/71-3	1971	PROOF [2]	1	1	5
D10/72-3	1972	PROOF [2]	1	1	6
D10/73-1	1973		1	1	3
D10/73-3	1973	PROOF [2]	1	1	5
D10/74-1	1974		1	1	3
D10/74-1E	1974	struck on thin flan [3]	1	1	
D10/74-3	1974	PROOF [2]	1	1	5
D10/75-1	1975		1	1	4
D10/75-3	1975	PROOF [2]	1	1	5
D10/76-1	1976		1	1	4
D10/76-3	1976	PROOF [2]	1	1	5
D10/77-1	1977		1	1	3
D10/77-3	1977	PROOF [2]	1	1	4
D10/78-3	1978	PROOF [2]	1	1	8
D10/79-1	1979		1	1	4
D10/79-3	1979	PROOF [2]	1	1	5
D10/80-1	1980		1	1	3
D10/80-3	1980	PROOF [2]	1	1	5
D10/81-1	1981		1	1	4
D10/81-3	1981	PROOF [2]	1	1	7
D10/82-1	1982	[4]	1	2	7
D10/82-3	1982	PROOF [2]	1	2	8
D10/83-1	1983	[4]	1	2	8
D10/83-3	1983	PROOF [2]	1	2	9
D10/84-1	1984	[4]	1	2	4
D10/84-3	1984	PROOF [2]	1	2	4
D10/85-1	1985	[4]	2	2	4
D10/85-3	1985	PROOF [2]	2	2	4

No.	Date	Features	Obv.	Rev.	UNC
D10/86-1	1986	[4]	2	2	3
D10/86-3	1986	PROOF [2]	2	2	4
D10/87-1	1987	[4]	2	2	4
D10/87-3	1987	PROOF [2]	2	2	5
D10/88-1	1988	[4]	2	2	4
D10/88-3	1988	PROOF [2]	2	2	5
D10/89-1	1989	[4]	2	2	4
D10/89-3	1989	PROOF [2]	2	2	5
D10/90-1	1990	[4]	2	2	5
D10/90-3	1990	PROOF [2]	2	2	6
D10/91-1	1991	[4]	2	2	5
D10/91-3	1991	PROOF [2]	2	2	6
D10/92-1L	1992	[4]	2	2	6
D10/92-3L	1992	PROOF [2]	2	2	7
D10/92-4L	1992	PROOF in silver [5]	2	2	20
D10/92-1S	1992		3	3	2
D10/92-3S	1992	PROOF [2]	3	3	4
D10/92-4S	1992	PROOF in silver [5]	3	3	10
D10/92-5S	1992	PIEDFORT PROOF in silver [6]	3	3	50
D10/93-1	1993		3	3	4
D10/93-3	1993	PROOF [2]	3	3	4
D10/94-1	1994		3	3	3
D10/94-3	1994	PROOF [2]	3	3	4

1. Some issued in 1968 in decimal set wallets.
2. Issued in cased proof sets.
3. Weight 8.1 grams.
4. All issued in uncirculated sets in holders.
5. Issued cased.
6. Weight 13.0 grams; issued cased.

5 Pence

As with the 10 pence, the 5 pence coin was first issued in 1968, and took its place alongside the old shilling, having the same size and value. So many were issued prior to decimalization that no more were needed to be struck between 1972 and 1974 apart from proofs.

In 1990, the coin was succeeded by a 5 pence of similar design but reduced size, resulting in arguably the most unpopular coin since the double florin. Indeed, it is very difficult to find anyone who approves of the coin.

Denomination	Metal	Weight (grams)	Diameter (mm)	Rev. alignment
5 Pence 1968-1990	Cupronickel (copper 75%; nickel 25%)	5.65	24	↑
5 Pence 1990-1994	Cupronickel (copper 75%; nickel 25%)	3.25	18	↑

Obverse 1 Head 1, right; ELIZABETH II D G REG F D (date)

Obverse 2 Head 2, right; same legend

Obverse 3 As Obverse 2 on smaller flan

Reverse 1 Crowned thistle, '5' below; NEW PENCE

Reverse 2 Similar but legend reads FIVE PENCE

Reverse 3 As Reverse 2 on smaller flan

Edge milled

Obv. 1   Obv. 2   Obv. 3

Rev. 1   Rev. 2   Rev. 3

No.	Date	Features	Obv.	Rev.	UNC
D05/68-1	1968	[1]	1	1	
D05/69-1	1969		1	1	2
D05/70-1	1970		1	1	2
D05/71-1	1971		1	1	2
D05/71-3	1971	PROOF [2]	1	1	5
D05/72-3	1972	PROOF [2]	1	1	7
D05/73-3	1973	PROOF [2]	1	1	7
D05/74-3	1974	PROOF [2]	1	1	8
D05/75-1	1975		1	1	
D05/75-3	1975	PROOF [2]	1	1	4
D05/76-3	1976	PROOF [2]	1	1	8
D05/77-1	1977		1	1	
D05/77-3	1977	PROOF [2]	1	1	4
D05/78-1	1978		1	1	
D05/78-3	1978	PROOF [2]	1	1	5
D05/79-1	1979		1	1	2
D05/79-3	1979	PROOF [2]	1	1	4
D05/80-1	1980		1	1	2
D05/80-3	1980	PROOF [2]	1	1	4
D05/81-3	1981	PROOF [2]	1	1	7
D05/82-1	1982	[3]	1	2	7
D05/82-3	1982	PROOF [2]	1	2	7
D05/83-1	1983	[3]	1	2	7
D05/83-3	1983	PROOF [2]	1	2	7
D05/84-1	1984	[3]	1	2	5
D05/84-3	1984	PROOF [2]	1	2	6
D05/85-1	1985	[3]	2	2	4
D05/85-3	1985	PROOF [2]	2	2	5
D05/86-1	1986	[3]	2	2	3
D05/86-3	1986	PROOF [2]	2	2	4
D05/87-1	1987		2	2	2
D05/87-3	1987	PROOF [2]	2	2	4
D05/88-1	1988		2	2	2
D05/88-3	1988	PROOF [2]	2	2	4
D05/89-1	1989		2	2	2
D05/89-3	1989	PROOF [2]	2	2	4
D05/90-1L	1990	[3]	2	2	8
D05/90-3L	1990	PROOF [2]	2	2	8
D05/90-4L	1990	PROOF in silver [4]	2	2	20
D05/90-1S	1990		3	3	
D05/90-3S	1990	PROOF [2]	3	3	5
D05/90-4S	1990	PROOF in silver [4]	3	3	10
D05/90-5S	1990	PIEDFORT PROOF in silver [5]	3	3	40
D05/91-1	1991		3	3	
D05/91-3	1991	PROOF [2]	3	3	5
D05/92-1	1992		3	3	
D05/92-3	1992	PROOF [2]	3	3	6
D05/93-1	1993		3	3	3
D05/93-3	1993	PROOF [2]	3	3	7
D05/94-1	1994		3	3	3
D05/94-3	1994	PROOF [2]	3	3	4

1. Some issued in 1968 in decimal set wallets.
2. Issued in cased proof sets.
3. All issued in uncirculated sets in holders.
4. Issued cased.
5. Weight 6.5 grams; issued cased.

2 Pence

Although the bronze 2 pence coin had no legal tender status until decimal day in 1971, it was first issued to the public in 1968 in the official decimal sets in blue wallets. All of the bronze coins in this set were dated 1971.

In 1982, the words NEW PENCE on the reverse were replaced by TWO PENCE, but a few coins dated 1983 have been found with the earlier NEW PENCE legend; all were from specimen sets.

From 1992 the 2 pence was struck in steel which was subsequently plated with copper. These coins have a bright pink hue, and are slightly magnetic.

Denomination	Metal	Weight (grams)	Diameter (mm)	Rev. alignment
2 Pence 1971-1992	Bronze	7.1	26	↑
2 Pence 1992-1994	Copper-plated steel	7.1	26	↑

Obverse 1 Head 1, right; ELIZABETH II D G REG F D (date)

Obverse 2 Head 2, right; same legend

Reverse 1 Plumes within coronet (Badge of the Prince of Wales), '2' below; ICH DIEN (on ribbon); NEW PENCE

Reverse 2 Similar but TWO PENCE instead of NEW PENCE

Edge plain

Obv. 1

Obv. 2

Rev. 1

Rev. 2

No.	Date	Features	Obv.	Rev.	UNC
D02/71-1	1971	[1]	1	1	
D02/71-3	1971	PROOF [2]	1	1	4
D02/72-3	1972	PROOF [2]	1	1	6
D02/73-3	1973	PROOF [2]	1	1	7
D02/74-3	1974	PROOF [2]	1	1	7
D02/75-1	1975		1	1	2
D02/75-3	1975	PROOF [2]	1	1	4
D02/76-1	1976		1	1	2
D02/76-3	1976	PROOF [2]	1	1	4
D02/77-1	1977		1	1	
D02/77-3	1977	PROOF [2]	1	1	3
D02/78-1	1978		1	1	2
D02/78-3	1978	PROOF [2]	1	1	5
D02/79-1	1979		1	1	
D02/79-3	1979	PROOF [2]	1	1	3
D02/80-1	1980		1	1	
D02/80-3	1980	PROOF [2]	1	1	3
D02/81-1	1981		1	1	
D02/81-3	1981	PROOF [2]	1	1	3
D02/RR-1		[3]	rev. 1	1	150
D02/82-1	1982	[4]	1	2	7
D02/82-3	1982	PROOF [2]	1	2	4
D02/83-1E	1983	[5]	1	1	1500
D02/83-1	1983	[4]	1	2	7
D02/83-3	1983	PROOF [2]	1	2	4
D02/84-1	1984	[4]	1	2	3
D02/84-3	1984	PROOF [2]	1	2	5
D02/85-1	1985		2	2	
D02/85-3	1985	PROOF [2]	2	2	4
D02/86-1	1986		2	2	
D02/86-3	1986	PROOF [2]	2	2	4

No.	Date	Features	Obv.	Rev.	UNC
D02/87-1	1987		2	2	
D02/87-3	1987	PROOF [2]	2	2	4
D02/88-1	1988		2	2	
D02/88-3	1988	PROOF [2]	2	2	4
D02/89-1	1989		2	2	
D02/89-3	1989	PROOF [2]	2	2	4
D02/90-1	1990		2	2	
D02/90-3	1990	PROOF [2]	2	2	4
D02/91-1	1991		2	2	
D02/91-3	1991	PROOF [2]	2	2	4
D02/92-1BR	1992	bronze issue [4]	2	2	6
D02/92-3	1992	bronze issue PROOF [2]	2	2	6
D02/92-1ST	1992	copper plated steel issue	2	2	
D02/93-1	1993		2	2	
D02/93-3	1993	PROOF [2]	2	2	6
D02/94-1	1994		2	2	
D02/94-3	1994	PROOF [2]	2	2	6

1. Some issued in 1968 in decimal set wallets.
2. Issued in cased proof sets.
3. 'Double tailed' coin.
4. All issued in uncirculated sets in holders.
5. Error rev; probably all issued in uncirculated sets in holders.

1 Penny

As with the 2 pence and half penny coins, the decimal penny was issued in 1968 in decimal set wallets, but at that time had no legal tender status and the issue was all dated 1971.

From 1992 the penny was struck in steel which was subsequently plated with copper. These coins have a bright pink hue, and are slightly magnetic.

Denomination	Metal	Weight (grams)	Diameter (mm)	Rev. alignment
Penny 1971-1992	Bronze	3.6	20	↑
Penny 1992-1994	Copper-plated steel	3.6	20	↑

Obverse 1 Head 1, right; ELIZABETH II D G REG F D (date)

Obverse 2 Head 2, right; same legend

Reverse 1 Crowned portcullis, '1' below; NEW PENNY

Reverse 2 Similar but ONE PENNY instead of NEW PENNY

Edge plain

Obv. 1

Obv. 2

Rev. 1

Rev. 2

No.	Date	Features	Obv.	Rev.	UNC
D01/71-1	1971	[1]	1	1	
D01/71-3	1971	PROOF [2]	1	1	4
D01/72-3	1972	PROOF [2]	1	1	7
D01/73-1	1973		1	1	2
D01/73-3	1973	PROOF [2]	1	1	4
D01/74-1	1974		1	1	2
D01/74-3	1974	PROOF [2]	1	1	4
D01/75-1	1975		1	1	2
D01/75-3	1975	PROOF [2]	1	1	4
D01/76-1	1976		1	1	2
D01/76-3	1976	PROOF [2]	1	1	4
D01/77-1	1977		1	1	
D01/77-3	1977	PROOF [2]	1	1	3
D01/78-1	1978		1	1	5
D01/78-3	1978	PROOF [2]	1	1	4
D01/79-1	1979		1	1	
D01/79-3	1979	PROOF [2]	1	1	4
D01/80-1	1980		1	1	
D01/80-3	1980	PROOF [2]	1	1	4
D01/81-1	1981		1	1	3
D01/81-3	1981	PROOF [2]	1	1	4
D01/82-1	1982		1	2	
D01/82-3	1982	PROOF [2]	1	2	4
D01/83-1	1983		1	2	3
D01/83-3	1983	PROOF [2]	1	2	4
D01/84-1	1984	[3]	1	2	4

No.	Date	Features	Obv.	Rev.	UNC
D01/84-3	1984	PROOF [2]	1	2	5
D01/85-1	1985		2	2	
D01/85-3	1985	PROOF [2]	2	2	4
D01/86-1	1986		2	2	
D01/86-3	1986	PROOF [2]	2	2	4
D01/87-1	1987		2	2	
D01/87-3	1987	PROOF [2]	2	2	4
D01/88-1	1988		2	2	
D01/88-3	1988	PROOF [2]	2	2	4
D01/89-1	1989		2	2	
D01/89-3	1989	PROOF [2]	2	2	4
D01/90-1	1990		2	2	
D01/90-3	1990	PROOF [2]	2	2	4
D01/91-1	1991		2	2	
D01/91-3	1991	PROOF [2]	2	2	4
D01/92-1BR	1992	bronze issue [3]	2	2	6
D01/92-3	1992	bronze issue PROOF [2]	2	2	6
D01/92-1ST	1992	copper plated steel issue	2	2	
D01/93-1	1993		2	2	
D01/93-3	1993	PROOF [2]	2	2	4
D01/94-1	1994		2	2	
D01/94-3	1994	PROOF [2]	2	2	4

1. Some issued in 1968 in decimal set wallets.
2. Issued in cased proof sets.
3. All issued in uncirculated sets in holders.

Half Penny

As with the 2 pence and penny coins, the decimal halfpenny was issued in 1968 in decimal set wallets, but at that time had no legal tender status and the issue was all dated 1971.

The coin was not popular, being very small and also causing problems with electronic accounting systems, which began in the early 1970s. High inflation of the period soon made the halfpenny too trivial a coin to serve any useful function, and it was demonetised in 1984. No circulation pieces were issued that year, but some were struck for inclusion in official decimal sets.

Denomination	Metal	Weight (grams)	Diameter (mm)	Rev. alignment
Half Penny	Bronze	1.8	17	↑

Obverse 1 Head 1, right; ELIZABETH II D G REG F D (date)

Reverse 1 Crown, '1/2' below; NEW PENNY

Reverse 2 Similar but HALF PENNY instead of NEW PENNY

Edge plain

Obv. 1	Rev. 1	Rev. 2

No.	Date	Features	Obv.	Rev.	UNC
DHP/71-1	1971	[1]	1	1	
DHP/71-1E	1971	[2]	1	obv 1	200
DHP/71-3	1971	PROOF [3]	1	1	4
DHP/72-3	1972	PROOF [3]	1	1	7
DHP/73-1	1973		1	1	
DHP/73-3	.1973	PROOF [3]	1	1	5
DHP/74-1	1974		1	1	
DHP/74-3	1974	PROOF [3]	1	1	4
DHP/75-1	1975		1	1	
DHP/75-3	1975	PROOF [3]	1	1	4
DHP/76-1	1976		1	1	
DHP/76-3	1976	PROOF [3]	1	1	4
DHP/77-1	1977		1	1	
DHP/77-3	1977	PROOF [3]	1	1	3
DHP/78-1	1978		1	1	
DHP/78-3	1978	PROOF [3]	1	1	5
DHP/79-1	1979		1	1	
DHP/79-3	1979	PROOF [3]	1	1	4
DHP/80-1	1980		1	1	
DHP/80-3	1980	PROOF [3]	1	1	4
DHP/81-1	1981		1	1	2
DHP/81-3	1981	PROOF [3]	1	1	4
DHP/82-1	1982		1	2	
DHP/82-3	1982	PROOF [3]	1	2	4
DHP/83-1	1983		1	2	2
DHP/83-3	1983	PROOF [3]	1	2	4
DHP/84-1	1984	[4]	1	2	3
DHP/84-3	1984	PROOF	1	2	6

1. Some issued in 1968 in decimal set wallets.
2. 'Double headed' coin.
3. Issued in cased proof sets.
4. All issued in uncirculated sets in holders.

Britannia Gold Coinage

From 1987 a series of bullion gold issues was struck annually. The coins were denominated at 100, 50, 25 and 10 pounds, and contained respectively fine gold contents of 1, 1/2, 1/4 and 1/10th ounces. This closely followed the South African Krugerrand and fractional Krugerrand gold specifications, and, like the South African issues, the coins were struck in 22 carat gold, the actual weight of the coins being about 9.1% above the stated fine gold content.

The reverse of the Britannia series depicted an elegant portrayal of a standing Britannia, strongly reminiscent of the de Saulles engraving for the reverse of the Edward VII florin. Proofs of the coins were also struck annually, these generally being issued cased.

100 Pounds

Denomination	Metal	Weight (grams)	Diameter (mm)	Rev. alignment
100 Pounds	Gold	33.9	32	↑

Obverse 1 Head 1, right; ELIZABETH II DEI GRATIA REGINA F D 100 POUNDS

Reverse 1 Britannia, standing, with trident and shield; ONE OUNCE FINE GOLD BRITANNIA (date)

Edge milled

Obv. 1   Rev. 1

No.	Date	Features	Obv.	Rev.	Unc
BR100-005	1987		1	1	BV
BR100-010	1987	PROOF	1	1	350
BR100-015	1988		1	1	BV
BR100-020	1988	PROOF	1	1	350
BR100-025	1989		1	1	BV
BR100-030	1989	PROOF	1	1	350
BR100-035	1990		1	1	BV
BR100-040	1990	PROOF	1	1	350
BR100-045	1991		1	1	BV
BR100-050	1991	PROOF	1	1	380
BR100-055	1992		1	1	BV
BR100-060	1992	PROOF	1	1	400
BR100-065	1993		1	1	BV
BR100-070	1993	PROOF	1	1	420
BR100-075	1994		1	1	BV
BR100-080	1994	PROOF	1	1	440
BR100-085	1995		1	1	BV
BR100-090	1995	PROOF	1	1	440

50 Pounds

Denomination	Metal	Weight (grams)	Diameter (mm)	Rev. alignment
50 Pounds	Gold	17.0	26	↑

Obverse 1 Head 1, right; ELIZABETH II DEI GRATIA REGINA F D 50 POUNDS

Reverse 1 Britannia, standing, with trident and shield; 1/2 OUNCE FINE GOLD BRITANNIA (date)

Edge milled

Obv. 1   Rev. 1

No.	Date	Features	Obv.	Rev.	Unc
BR50-005	1987		1	1	BV
BR50-010	1987	PROOF	1	1	180
BR50-015	1988		1	1	BV
BR50-020	1988	PROOF	1	1	180
BR50-025	1989		1	1	BV
BR50-030	1989	PROOF	1	1	190
BR50-035	1990		1	1	BV
BR50-040	1990	PROOF	1	1	200
BR50-045	1991		1	1	BV
BR50-050	1991	PROOF	1	1	200
BR50-055	1992		1	1	BV
BR50-060	1992	PROOF	1	1	220
BR50-065	1993		1	1	BV
BR50-070	1993	PROOF	1	1	240
BR50-075	1994		1	1	BV
BR50-080	1994	PROOF	1	1	240
BR50-085	1995		1	1	BV
BR50-090	1995	PROOF	1	1	250

25 Pounds

Denomination	Metal	Weight (grams)	Diameter (mm)	Rev. alignment
25 Pounds	Gold	8.5	21	↑

Obverse 1 Head 1, right; ELIZABETH II DEI GRATIA REGINA F D 25 POUNDS

Reverse 1 Britannia, standing, with trident and shield; 1/4 OUNCE FINE GOLD BRITANNIA (date)

Edge milled

Obv. 1   Rev. 1

No.	Date	Features	Obv.	Rev.	Unc
BR25-005	1987		1	1	BV
BR25-010	1987	PROOF	1	1	100
BR25-015	1988		1	1	BV
BR25-020	1988	PROOF	1	1	100
BR25-025	1989		1	1	BV
BR25-030	1989	PROOF	1	1	110
BR25-035	1990		1	1	BV
BR25-040	1990	PROOF	1	1	120
BR25-045	1991		1	1	BV
BR25-050	1991	PROOF	1	1	120
BR25-055	1992		1	1	BV
BR25-060	1992	PROOF	1	1	130
BR25-065	1993		1	1	BV
BR25-070	1993	PROOF	1	1	130
BR25-075	1994		1	1	BV
BR25-080	1994	PROOF	1	1	130
BR25-085	1995		1	1	BV
BR25-090	1995	PROOF	1	1	130

10 Pounds

Denomination	Metal	Weight (grams)	Diameter (mm)	Rev. alignment
10 Pounds	Gold	3.4	16	↑

Obverse 1 Head 1, right; ELIZABETH II DEI GRATIA REGINA F D 10 POUNDS

Reverse 1 Britannia, standing, with trident and shield; 1/10 OUNCE FINE GOLD BRITANNIA (date)

Edge milled

Obv. 1

Rev. 1

No.	Date	Features	Obv.	Rev.	Unc
BR10-005	1987		1	1	BV
BR10-010	1987	PROOF	1	1	55
BR10-015	1988		1	1	BV
BR10-020	1988	PROOF	1	1	55
BR10-025	1989		1	1	BV
BR10-030	1989	PROOF	1	1	60
BR10-035	1990		1	1	BV
BR10-040	1990	PROOF	1	1	60
BR10-045	1991		1	1	BV
BR10-050	1991	PROOF	1	1	65
BR10-055	1992		1	1	BV
BR10-060	1992	PROOF	1	1	65
BR10-065	1993		1	1	BV
BR10-070	1993	PROOF	1	1	65
BR10-075	1994		1	1	BV
BR10-080	1994	PROOF	1	1	70
BR10-085	1995		1	1	BV
BR10-090	1995	PROOF	1	1	70

Proof and Specimen Sets

From time to time over the last 200 years or so coins have been issued as sets in cases rather than individually for circulation. In recent times several such sets have been issued by the Royal Mint each year as a commercial exercise, but in the early years the sets were issued by the Mint or by the engravers, usually at the time of a change of monarch or when the design of the coinage underwent a radical revision. These earlier sets were invariably specially struck proofs, but in recent times the issues have been supplemented by sets of specimen or ordinary coinage, usually in card holders.

The listings below include the conventional issues but omit some of the isolated rare proofs such as the 1877 three-coin bronze set or the 1879 silver set.

George II 1727–1760

No.	Date	Striking Standard	No. of Coins	Price
PS-1746	1746	Proof [1]	4	10000

1. Issued in wedge shaped case.

Denomination	Metal
Crown	Silver
Halfcrown	Silver
Shilling	Silver
Sixpence	Silver

George IV 1820–1830

No.	Date	Striking Standard	No. of Coins	Price
PS-1826	1826	Proof [1]	11	22000

1. Issued in oval case; probably about 150 struck.

Denomination	Metal
Five Pounds	Gold
Two Pounds	Gold
Sovereign	Gold
Half Sovereign	Gold
Crown	Silver
Halfcrown	Silver
Shilling	Silver
Sixpence	Silver
Penny	Copper
Halfpenny	Copper
Farthing	Copper

William IV 1830–1837

No.	Date	Striking Standard	No. of Coins	Price
PS-1831	1831	Proof [1]	14	20000

1. Issued in round case.

Denomination	Metal
Two Pounds	Gold
Sovereign	Gold
Half Sovereign	Gold
Crown	Silver
Halfcrown	Silver
Shilling	Silver
Sixpence	Silver
Maundy set	Silver

Denomination	Metal
Penny	Copper
Halfpenny	Copper
Farthing	Copper

Victoria 1837–1901

No.	Date	Striking Standard	No. of Coins	Price
PS-1839	1839	Proof [1]	15	30000

1. Issued in spade-shaped case.

Denomination	Metal
Five Pounds	Gold
Sovereign	Gold
Half Sovereign	Gold
Crown	Silver
Halfcrown	Silver
Shilling	Silver
Sixpence	Silver
Groat	Silver
Maundy set	Silver
Penny	Copper
Halfpenny	Copper
Farthing	Copper

No.	Date	Striking Standard	No. of Coins	Price
PS-1853	1853	Proof [1]	16	25000

1. A small number of sets exist with additional proof penny, halfpenny and farthing of 1862 (total 19 coins).

Denomination	Metal
Sovereign	Gold
Half Sovereign	Gold
Crown	Silver
Halfcrown	Silver
Florin	Silver
Shilling	Silver
Sixpence	Silver
Groat	Silver
Maundy set	Silver
Penny	Copper
Halfpenny	Copper
Farthing	Copper
Half Farthing	Copper

No.	Date	Striking Standard	No. of Coins	Price
PS-1887L	1887	Proof	11	6500

Denomination	Metal
Five Pounds	Gold
Two Pounds	Gold
Sovereign	Gold
Half Sovereign	Gold
Crown	Silver
Double Florin	Silver
Halfcrown	Silver
Florin	Silver
Shilling	Silver
Sixpence	Silver
Threepence	Silver

No.	Date	Striking Standard	No. of Coins	Price
PS-1887S	1887	Proof	7	1300

Denomination	Metal
Crown	Silver
Double Florin	Silver
Halfcrown	Silver
Florin	Silver
Shilling	Silver
Sixpence	Silver
Threepence	Silver

No.	Date	Striking Standard	No. of Coins	Price
PS-1893L	1893	Proof	10	7000

Denomination	Metal
Five Pounds	Gold
Two Pounds	Gold
Sovereign	Gold
Half Sovereign	Gold
Crown	Silver
Halfcrown	Silver
Florin	Silver
Shilling	Silver
Sixpence	Silver

No.	Date	Striking Standard	No. of Coins	Price
PS-1893S	1893	Proof	6	1400

Denomination	Metal
Crown	Silver
Halfcrown	Silver
Florin	Silver
Shilling	Silver
Sixpence	Silver
Threepence	Silver

Edward VII 1902–1910

No.	Date	Striking Standard	No. of Coins	Price
PS-02L	1902	Matt Proof [1]	13	1800

1. 8066 issued in red leatherette case.

Denomination	Metal
Five Pounds	Gold
Two Pounds	Gold
Sovereign	Gold
Half Sovereign	Gold
Crown	Silver
Halfcrown	Silver
Florin	Silver
Shilling	Silver
Sixpence	Silver
Maundy set	Silver

No.	Date	Striking Standard	No. of Coins	Price
PS-02S	1902	Matt Proof [1]	11	600

1. 7057 issued in red leatherette case.

Denomination	Metal
Sovereign	Gold
Half Sovereign	Gold
Crown	Silver
Halfcrown	Silver
Florin	Silver
Shilling	Silver
Sixpence	Silver
Maundy set	Silver

George V 1910–1936

No.	Date	Striking Standard	No. of Coins	Price
PS-11L	1911	Proof but see [1]	12	3000

1. Maundy set does not have proof surface but rim of 4d slightly different from that on standard Maundy set; 2812 issued in red leatherette case.

Denomination	Metal
Five Pounds	Gold
Two Pounds	Gold
Sovereign	Gold
Half Sovereign	Gold
Halfcrown	Silver
Florin	Silver
Shilling	Silver
Sixpence	Silver
Maundy set	Silver

No.	Date	Striking Standard	No. of Coins	Price
PS-11SH	1911	Proof but see [1]	10	900

1. Maundy set does not have proof surface but rim of 4d slightly different from that on standard Maundy set; 952 issued in red leatherette case.

Denomination	Metal
Sovereign	Gold
Half Sovereign	Gold
Halfcrown	Silver
Florin	Silver
Shilling	Silver
Sixpence	Silver
Maundy set	Silver

No.	Date	Striking Standard	No. of Coins	Price
PS-11SV	1911	Proof but see [1]	8	450

1. Maundy set does not have proof surface but rim of 4d slightly different from that on standard Maundy set; 2241 issued in red leatherette case (a few in a card box).

Denomination	Metal
Halfcrown	Silver
Florin	Silver
Shilling	Silver
Sixpence	Silver
Maundy set	Silver

No.	Date	Striking Standard	No. of Coins	Price
PS-27	1927	Proof or Prooflike [1]	6	300
PS-27SB	1927	as above; struck from sandblasted dies [2]	6	1500

1. 5 of the 6 coins are proof only issues; 15030 issued in red leatherette case or card box.
2. As above; struck to facilitate photography of coin.

Denomination	Metal
Crown	0.5 Silver
Halfcrown	0.5 Silver
Florin	0.5 Silver
Shilling	0.5 Silver
Sixpence	0.5 Silver
Threepence	0.5 Silver

Help Us Correct Our Errors and Omissions

If you have spotted a mistake or know of something that we have missed, please fill in one of the cards below. Your help will be greatly appreciated and we will take the appropriate action.

Thank you for your help –

Richard

I have found the following errors or feel that you have left something out!

....
....
....
....
....
....

NAME .... ADDRESS ....

....

COUNTRY........................ POST CODE ....

I have found the following errors or feel that you have left something out!

....
....
....
....
....
....

NAME .... ADDRESS ....

....

COUNTRY........................ POST CODE ....

I have found the following errors or feel that you have left something out!

....
....
....
....
....
....

NAME .... ADDRESS ....

....

COUNTRY........................ POST CODE ....

I have found the following errors or feel that you have left something out!

....
....
....
....
....
....

NAME .... ADDRESS ....

....

COUNTRY........................ POST CODE ....

I have found the following errors or feel that you have left something out!

....
....
....
....
....
....

NAME .... ADDRESS ....

....

COUNTRY........................ POST CODE ....

I have found the following errors or feel that you have left something out!

....
....
....
....
....
....

NAME .... ADDRESS ....

....

COUNTRY........................ POST CODE ....

Help Us Correct Our Errors and Omissions

you have spotted a mistake or know of something that we have
missed, please fill in one of the cards below. Your help will be greatly
appreciated and we will take the appropriate action.

Thank you for your help –

Richard

By Air Mail
Par Avion

PLEASE
PLACE
STAMP
HERE

Standard Catalogue

c/o Coincraft

45 Great Russell Street

London WC1B 3LU

ENGLAND

By Air Mail
Par Avion

PLEASE
PLACE
STAMP
HERE

Standard Catalogue

c/o Coincraft

45 Great Russell Street

London WC1B 3LU

ENGLAND

By Air Mail
Par Avion

PLEASE
PLACE
STAMP
HERE

Standard Catalogue

c/o Coincraft

45 Great Russell Street

London WC1B 3LU

ENGLAND

By Air Mail
Par Avion

PLEASE
PLACE
STAMP
HERE

Standard Catalogue

c/o Coincraft

45 Great Russell Street

London WC1B 3LU

ENGLAND

By Air Mail
Par Avion

PLEASE
PLACE
STAMP
HERE

Standard Catalogue

c/o Coincraft

45 Great Russell Street

London WC1B 3LU

ENGLAND

By Air Mail
Par Avion

PLEASE
PLACE
STAMP
HERE

Standard Catalogue

c/o Coincraft

45 Great Russell Street

London WC1B 3LU

ENGLAND

George VI 1937–1952

No.	Date	Striking Standard	No. of Coins	Price
PS-37G	1937	Proof [1]	4	2200

1. 5501 issued in red leatherette case.

Denomination	Metal
Five Pounds	Gold
Two Pounds	Gold
Sovereign	Gold
Half Sovereign	Gold

No.	Date	Striking Standard	No. of Coins	Price
PS-37S	1937	Proof [1]	15	180
PS-37SSB	1937	Proof struck from sandblasted dies [2]	15	1500

1. 26402 issued in red leatherette case or card box.
2. As above; struck to facilitate photography of coin.

Denomination	Metal
Crown	0.5 Silver
Halfcrown	0.5 Silver
Florin	0.5 Silver
Scottish Shilling	0.5 Silver
English Shilling	0.5 Silver
Sixpence	0.5 Silver
Maundy set	0.5 Silver
Threepence	0.5 Silver
Threepence	Nickel-brass
Penny	Bronze
Halfpenny	Bronze
Farthing	Bronze

No.	Date	Striking Standard	No. of Coins	Price
PS-50	1950	Proof [1]	9	75
PS-50SB	1950	Proof struck from sandblasted dies [2]	9	1500

1. 17513 issued in red box.
2. As above; struck to facilitate photography of coin.

Denomination	Metal
Halfcrown	Cupronickel
Florin	Cupronickel
Scottish Shilling	Cupronickel
English Shilling	Cupronickel
Sixpence	Cupronickel
Threepence	Nickel-brass
Penny	Bronze
Halfpenny	Bronze
Farthing	Bronze

No.	Date	Striking Standard	No. of Coins	Price
PS-51	1951	Proof [1]	10	100
PS-51SB	1951	Proof struck from sandblasted dies [2]	10	1500

1. 20000 issued in maroon, green or blue card box
2. As above; struck to facilitate photography of coin.

Denomination	Metal
Crown	Cupronickel
Halfcrown	Cupronickel
Florin	Cupronickel
Scottish Shilling	Cupronickel
English Shilling	Cupronickel
Sixpence	Cupronickel
Threepence	Nickel-brass
Penny	Bronze
Halfpenny	Bronze
Farthing	Bronze

Elizabeth II 1952 -

No.	Date	Striking Standard	No. of Coins	Price
PS-53	1953	Proof [1]	10	70
PS-53SB	1953	Proof struck from sandblasted dies [2]	10	1500

1. 40000 issued in maroon leatherette case. A very small number are in a dark blue case.
2. As above; struck to facilitate photography of coin.

Denomination	Metal
Crown	Cupronickel
Halfcrown	Cupronickel
Florin	Cupronickel
Scottish Shilling	Cupronickel
English Shilling	Cupronickel
Sixpence	Cupronickel
Threepence	Nickel-brass
Penny	Bronze
Halfpenny	Bronze
Farthing	Bronze

No.	Date	Striking Standard	No. of Coins	Price
MS-53	1953	Currency [1]	9	15

1. Issued in clear plastic holder.

Denomination	Metal
Halfcrown	Cupronickel
Florin	Cupronickel
Scottish Shilling	Cupronickel
English Shilling	Cupronickel
Sixpence	Cupronickel
Threepence	Nickel-brass
Penny	Bronze
Halfpenny	Bronze
Farthing	Bronze

No.	Date	Striking Standard	No. of Coins	Price
DMS-68	1968/1971	Currency [1]	5	5

1. Issued in 1968 in blue wallet.

Denomination	Metal
10 pence 1968	Cupronickel
5 pence 1968	Cupronickel
2 pence 1971	Bronze
1 penny 1971	Bronze
half penny 1971	Bronze

No.	Date	Striking Standard	No. of Coins	Price
PS-70	1970	Proof [1]	8	25

1. Issued in hard plastic holder with outer maroon card cover.

Denomination	Metal
Halfcrown	Cupronickel
Florin	Cupronickel
Scottish Shilling	Cupronickel
English Shilling	Cupronickel
Sixpence	Cupronickel
Threepence	Nickel-brass
Penny	Bronze
Halfpenny	Bronze

No.	Date	Striking Standard	No. of Coins	Price
DPS-71	1971	Proof [1]	6	18

1. Issued in hard plastic holder with outer black card cover.

Denomination	Metal
50 pence	Cupronickel
10 pence	Cupronickel
5 pence	Cupronickel
2 pence	Bronze
1 penny	Bronze
half penny	Bronze

No.	Date	Striking Standard	No. of Coins	Price
DPS-72	1972	Proof [1]	7	22

1. Issued in hard plastic holder with outer dark blue card cover.

Denomination	Metal
50 pence	Cupronickel
25 pence	Cupronickel
10 pence	Cupronickel
5 pence	Cupronickel
2 pence	Bronze
1 penny	Bronze
half penny	Bronze

No.	Date	Striking Standard	No. of Coins	Price
DPS-73	1973	Proof [1]	6	18

1. Issued in hard plastic holder with outer red card cover.

Denomination	Metal
50 pence	Cupronickel
10 pence	Cupronickel
5 pence	Cupronickel
2 pence	Bronze
1 penny	Bronze
half penny	Bronze

No.	Date	Striking Standard	No. of Coins	Price
DPS-74	1974	Proof [1]	6	18

1. Issued in hard plastic holder with outer brown card cover.

Denomination	Metal
50 pence	Cupronickel
10 pence	Cupronickel
5 pence	Cupronickel
2 pence	Bronze
1 penny	Bronze
half penny	Bronze

No.	Date	Striking Standard	No. of Coins	Price
DPS-75	1975	Proof [1]	6	18

1. Issued in hard plastic holder with outer green card cover.

Denomination	Metal
50 pence	Cupronickel
10 pence	Cupronickel
5 pence	Cupronickel
2 pence	Bronze
1 penny	Bronze
half penny	Bronze

No.	Date	Striking Standard	No. of Coins	Price
DPS-76	1976	Proof [1]	6	18

1. Issued in hard plastic holder with outer grey card cover.

Denomination	Metal
50 pence	Cupronickel
10 pence	Cupronickel
5 pence	Cupronickel
2 pence	Bronze
1 penny	Bronze
half penny	Bronze

No.	Date	Striking Standard	No. of Coins	Price
DPS-77	1977	Proof [1]	7	22

1. Issued in hard plastic holder with outer blue card cover.

Denomination	Metal
50 pence	Cupronickel
25 pence	Cupronickel
10 pence	Cupronickel
5 pence	Cupronickel
2 pence	Bronze
1 penny	Bronze
half penny	Bronze

No.	Date	Striking Standard	No. of Coins	Price
DPS-78	1978	Proof [1]	6	30

1. Issued in hard plastic holder with outer brown card cover.

Denomination	Metal
50 pence	Cupronickel
10 pence	Cupronickel
5 pence	Cupronickel
2 pence	Bronze
1 penny	Bronze
half penny	Bronze

No.	Date	Striking Standard	No. of Coins	Price
DPS-79	1979	Proof [1]	6	18

1. Issued in hard plastic holder with outer slate blue card cover.

Denomination	Metal
50 pence	Cupronickel
10 pence	Cupronickel
5 pence	Cupronickel
2 pence	Bronze
1 penny	Bronze
half penny	Bronze

No.	Date	Striking Standard	No. of Coins	Price
DPS-80GL	1980	Proof [1]	4	1000

1. Issued in green leatherette case.

Denomination	Metal
Five Pounds	Gold
Two Pounds	Gold
Sovereign	Gold
Half Sovereign	Gold

No.	Date	Striking Standard	No. of Coins	Price
DPS-80	1980	Proof [1]	6	20

1. Issued in hard plastic holder with outer purple card cover.

Denomination	Metal
50 pence	Cupronickel
10 pence	Cupronickel
5 pence	Cupronickel
2 pence	Bronze
1 penny	Bronze
half penny	Bronze

No.	Date	Striking Standard	No. of Coins	Price
DPS-81G	1981	Proof [1]	9	700

1. Issued in red leatherette case.

Denomination	Metal
Five Pounds	Gold
Sovereign	Gold
50 pence	Cupronickel
25 pence	Cupronickel
10 pence	Cupronickel
5 pence	Cupronickel
2 pence	Bronze
1 penny	Bronze
half penny	Bronze

No.	Date	Striking Standard	No. of Coins	Price
DPS-81	1981	Proof [1]	6	20

1. Issued in hard plastic holder with outer black card cover.

Denomination	Metal
50 pence	Cupronickel
10 pence	Cupronickel
5 pence	Cupronickel
2 pence	Bronze
1 penny	Bronze
half penny	Bronze

No.	Date	Striking Standard	No. of Coins	Price
DPS-82G	1982	Proof [1]	4	1000

1. Issued in dark blue leatherette case.

Denomination	Metal
Five Pounds	Gold
Two Pounds	Gold
Sovereign	Gold
Half Sovereign	Gold

No.	Date	Striking Standard	No. of Coins	Price
DPS-82	1982	Proof [1]	7	20
DMS-82	1982	Specimen [2]	7	10

1. Issued in hard plastic holder with outer blue card cover.
2. Issued in card holder.

Denomination	Metal
50 pence	Cupronickel
20 pence	Cupronickel
10 pence	Cupronickel
5 pence	Cupronickel
2 pence	Bronze
1 penny	Bronze
half penny	Bronze

No.	Date	Striking Standard	No. of Coins	Price
DPS-83G	1983	Proof [1]	3	450

1. Issued in brown leatherette case.

Denomination	Metal
Two Pounds	Gold
Sovereign	Gold
Half Sovereign	Gold

No.	Date	Striking Standard	No. of Coins	Price
DPS-83	1983	Proof [1]	8	30
DMS-83	1983	Specimen [2]	8	20

1. Issued in hard plastic and dark blue leatherette case.
2. Issued in card holder.

Denomination	Metal
1 pound	Nickel-brass
50 pence	Cupronickel
20 pence	Cupronickel
10 pence	Cupronickel
5 pence	Cupronickel
2 pence	Bronze
1 penny	Bronze
half penny	Bronze

No.	Date	Striking Standard	No. of Coins	Price
DPS-84G	1984	Proof [1]	3	750

1. Issued in leatherette case.

Denomination	Metal
Five Pounds	Gold
Sovereign	Gold
Half Sovereign	Gold

No.	Date	Striking Standard	No. of Coins	Price
DPS-84	1984	Proof [1]	8	30
DMS-84	1984	Specimen [2]	8	15

1. Issued in hard plastic and dark blue leatherette case.
2. Issued in card holder.

Denomination	Metal
1 pound	Nickel-brass
50 pence	Cupronickel
20 pence	Cupronickel
10 pence	Cupronickel
5 pence	Cupronickel
2 pence	Bronze
1 penny	Bronze
half penny	Bronze

No.	Date	Striking Standard	No. of Coins	Price
DPS-85G	1985	Proof [1]	4	1000

1. Issued in leatherette case.

Denomination	Metal
Five Pounds	Gold
Two Pounds	Gold
Sovereign	Gold
Half Sovereign	Gold

No.	Date	Striking Standard	No. of Coins	Price
DPS-85DL	1985	Proof [1]	7	28
DPS-85	1985	Proof [2]	7	24
DMS-85	1985	Specimen [3]	7	10

1. Issued in hard plastic and red leatherette case.
2. Issued in hard plastic and dark blue leatherette case.
3. Issued in card holder.

Denomination	Metal
1 pound	Nickel-brass
50 pence	Cupronickel
20 pence	Cupronickel
10 pence	Cupronickel
5 pence	Cupronickel
2 pence	Bronze
1 penny	Bronze

No.	Date	Striking Standard	No. of Coins	Price
DPS-86G	1986	Proof [1]	3	450

1. Issued in red leatherette case.

Denomination	Metal
Two Pounds	Gold
Sovereign	Gold
Half Sovereign	Gold

No.	Date	Striking Standard	No. of Coins	Price
DPS-86DL	1986	Proof [1]	8	30
DPS-86	1986	Proof [2]	8	26
DMS-86	1986	Specimen [3]	8	18

1. Issued in hard plastic and red leatherette case.
2. Issued in hard plastic and dark blue leatherette case.
3. Issued in card holder.

Denomination	Metal
2 pounds	Nickel-brass
1 pound	Nickel-brass
50 pence	Cupronickel
20 pence	Cupronickel
10 pence	Cupronickel
5 pence	Cupronickel
2 pence	Bronze
1 penny	Bronze

No.	Date	Striking Standard	No. of Coins	Price
DPS-87BRL	1987	Proof [1]	4	800

1. Issued in black leatherette case.

Denomination	Metal
100 Pounds	Gold
50 Pounds	Gold
25 Pounds	Gold
10 Pounds	Gold

No.	Date	Striking Standard	No. of Coins	Price
DPS-87BRS	1987	Proof [1]	2	200

1. Issued in brown leatherette case.

Denomination	Metal
25 Pounds	Gold
10 Pounds	Gold

No.	Date	Striking Standard	No. of Coins	Price
DPS-87G	1987	Proof [1]	3	450

1. Issued in red leatherette case.

Denomination	Metal
Two Pounds	Gold
Sovereign	Gold
Half Sovereign	Gold

No.	Date	Striking Standard	No. of Coins	Price
DPS-87DL	1987	Proof [1]	7	32
DPS-87	1987	Proof [2]	7	28
DMS-87	1987	Specimen [3]	7	10

1. Issued in hard plastic and red leatherette case.
2. Issued in hard plastic and dark blue leatherette case.
3. Issued in card holder.

Denomination	Metal
1 pound	Nickel-brass
50 pence	Cupronickel
20 pence	Cupronickel
10 pence	Cupronickel
5 pence	Cupronickel
2 pence	Bronze
1 penny	Bronze

No.	Date	Striking Standard	No. of Coins	Price
DPS-84PFP	1984-1987	Piedfort Proof [1]	4	240

1. Issued in black leatherette case.

Denomination	Metal
Pound 1984	Silver
Pound 1985	Silver
Pound 1986	Silver
Pound 1987	Silver

No.	Date	Striking Standard	No. of Coins	Price
DPS-84PP	1984-1987	Proof [1]	4	120

1. Issued in red leatherette case.

Denomination	Metal
Pound 1984	Silver
Pound 1985	Silver
Pound 1986	Silver
Pound 1987	Silver

No.	Date	Striking Standard	No. of Coins	Price
DPS-88BRL	1988	Proof [1]	4	800

1. Issued in leatherette case.

Denomination	Metal
100 Pounds	Gold
50 Pounds	Gold
25 Pounds	Gold
10 Pounds	Gold

No.	Date	Striking Standard	No. of Coins	Price
DPS-88BRS	1988	Proof [1]	2	200

1. Issued in leatherette case.

Denomination	Metal
25 Pounds	Gold
10 Pounds	Gold

No.	Date	Striking Standard	No. of Coins	Price
DPS-88G	1988	Proof [1]	3	450

1. Issued in blue leatherette case.

Denomination	Metal
Two Pounds	Gold
Sovereign	Gold
Half Sovereign	Gold

No.	Date	Striking Standard	No. of Coins	Price
DPS-88DL	1988	Proof [1]	7	32
DPS-88	1988	Proof [2]	7	28
DMS-88	1988	Specimen [3]	7	12

1. Issued in hard plastic and red leatherette case.
2. Issued in hard plastic and dark blue leatherette case.
3. Issued in card holder.

Denomination	Metal
1 pound	Nickel-brass
50 pence	Cupronickel
20 pence	Cupronickel
10 pence	Cupronickel
5 pence	Cupronickel
2 pence	Bronze
1 penny	Bronze

No.	Date	Striking Standard	No. of Coins	Price
DPS-89BRL	1989	Proof [1]	4	900

1. Issued in leatherette case.

Denomination	Metal
100 Pounds	Gold
50 Pounds	Gold
25 Pounds	Gold
10 Pounds	Gold

No.	Date	Striking Standard	No. of Coins	Price
DPS-89BRS	1989	Proof [1]	2	240

1. Issued in leatherette case.

Denomination	Metal
25 Pounds	Gold
10 Pounds	Gold

No.	Date	Striking Standard	No. of Coins	Price
DPS-89GL	1989	Proof [1]	4	1100

1. For the 500th anniversary of the gold sovereign; issued in black leatherette case.

Denomination	Metal
Five Pounds	Gold
Two Pounds	Gold
Sovereign	Gold
Half Sovereign	Gold

No.	Date	Striking Standard	No. of Coins	Price
DPS-89GS	1989	Proof [1]	3	550

1. For the 500th anniversary of the gold sovereign; issued in leatherette case.

Denomination	Metal
Two Pounds	Gold
Sovereign	Gold
Half Sovereign	Gold

No.	Date	Striking Standard	No. of Coins	Price
DPS-89DL	1989	Proof [1]	9	40
DPS-89	1989	Proof [2]	9	35

1. Issued in hard plastic and red leatherette case.
2. Issued in hard plastic and dark blue leatherette case.

Denomination	Metal
2 pounds (Bill of Rights)	Nickel-brass
2 pounds (Claim of Right)	Nickel-brass
1 pound	Nickel-brass
50 pence	Cupronickel
20 pence	Cupronickel
10 pence	Cupronickel
5 pence	Cupronickel
2 pence	Bronze
1 penny	Bronze

No.	Date	Striking Standard	No. of Coins	Price
DPS-89PF2P	1989	Piedfort Proof [1]	2	100
DPS-89P2P	1989	Proof [2]	2	50

1. 10000 issued in brown leatherette case.
2. 25000 issued in blue leatherette case.

Denomination	Metal
2 pound	Silver
2 pound	Silver

No.	Date	Striking Standard	No. of Coins	Price
DMS-89	1989	Specimen [1]	7	20

1. Issued in card holder.

Denomination	Metal
1 pound	Nickel-brass
50 pence	Cupronickel
20 pence	Cupronickel
10 pence	Cupronickel
5 pence	Cupronickel
2 pence	Bronze

No.	Date	Striking Standard	No. of Coins	Price
DMS-89-2P	1989	Specimen [1]	2	20

1. Issued in card holder. Also issued in two separate card holders.

Denomination	Metal
2 pounds (Bill of Rights)	Nickel-brass
2 pounds (Claim of Right)	Nickel-brass

No.	Date	Striking Standard	No. of Coins	Price
DPS-83PFP	1983-1989	Piedfort Proof [1]	7	600

1. 500 sets issued in black leatherette case.

Denomination	Metal
Pound 1983	Silver
Pound 1984	Silver
Pound 1985	Silver
Pound 1986	Silver
Pound 1987	Silver
Pound 1988	Silver
Pound 1989	Silver

No.	Date	Striking Standard	No. of Coins	Price
DPS-90BR	1990	Proof [1]	4	900

1. Issued in leatherette case.

Denomination	Metal
100 Pounds	Gold
50 Pounds	Gold
25 Pounds	Gold
10 Pounds	Gold

No.	Date	Striking Standard	No. of Coins	Price
DPS-90GL	1990	Proof [1]	4	1000

1. Issued in red leatherette case.

Denomination	Metal
Five Pounds	Gold
Two Pounds	Gold
Sovereign	Gold
Half Sovereign	Gold

No.	Date	Striking Standard	No. of Coins	Price
DPS-90GS	1990	Proof [1]	3	520

1. Issued in red leatherette case.

Denomination	Metal
Two Pounds	Gold
Sovereign	Gold
Half Sovereign	Gold

No.	Date	Striking Standard	No. of Coins	Price
DPS-90DL	1990	Proof [1]	8	40
DPS-90	1990	Proof [2]	8	35
DMS-90	1990	Specimen [3]	8	20

1. Issued in hard plastic and red leatherette case.
2. Issued in hard plastic and dark blue leatherette case.
3. Issued in card holder.

Denomination	Metal
1 pound	Nickel-brass
50 pence	Cupronickel
20 pence	Cupronickel
10 pence	Cupronickel
5 pence (on 24mm flan)	Cupronickel
5 pence (on 18mm flan)	Cupronickel
2 pence	Bronze
1 penny	Bronze

No.	Date	Striking Standard	No. of Coins	Price
DPS-90-05	1990	Proof [1]	2	30

1. 35000 issued in red case.

Denomination	Metal
5 pence	Silver
5 pence	Silver

No.	Date	Striking Standard	No. of Coins	Price
DPS-91BR	1991	Proof [1]	4	900

1. issued in leatherette case.

Denomination	Metal
100 Pounds	Gold
50 Pounds	Gold
25 Pounds	Gold
10 Pounds	Gold

No.	Date	Striking Standard	No. of Coins	Price
DPS-91GL	1991	Proof [1]	4	1100

1. Issued in red leatherette case.

Denomination	Metal
Five Pounds	Gold
Two Pounds	Gold
Sovereign	Gold
Half Sovereign	Gold

No.	Date	Striking Standard	No. of Coins	Price
DPS-91GS	1991	Proof [1]	3	550

1. Issued in leatherette case.

Denomination	Metal
Two Pounds	Gold
Sovereign	Gold
Half Sovereign	Gold

No.	Date	Striking Standard	No. of Coins	Price
DPS-91DL	1991	Proof [1]	7	40
DPS-91	1991	Proof [2]	7	35
DMS-91	1991	Specimen [3]	7	18

1. Issued in hard plastic and red leatherette case.
2. Issued in hard plastic and dark blue leatherette case.
3. Issued in card holder.

Denomination	Metal
1 pound	Nickel-brass
50 pence	Cupronickel
20 pence	Cupronickel
10 pence	Cupronickel
5 pence	Cupronickel
2 pence	Bronze
1 penny	Bronze

No.	Date	Striking Standard	No. of Coins	Price
DPS-92BR	1992	Proof [1]	4	1000

1. Issued in leatherette case.

Denomination	Metal
100 Pounds	Gold
50 Pounds	Gold
25 Pounds	Gold
10 Pounds	Gold

No.	Date	Striking Standard	No. of Coins	Price
DPS-92GL	1992	Proof [1]	4	1150

1. Issued in red leatherette case.

Denomination	Metal
Five Pounds	Gold
Two Pounds	Gold
Sovereign	Gold
Half Sovereign	Gold

No.	Date	Striking Standard	No. of Coins	Price
DPS-92BRS	1992	Proof [1]	3	580

1. Issued in leatherette case.

Denomination	Metal
Two Pounds	Gold
Sovereign	Gold
Half Sovereign	Gold

No.	Date	Striking Standard	No. of Coins	Price
DPS-92DL	1992	Proof [1]	9	38
DPS-92	1992	Proof [2]	9	32
DMS-92	1992	Specimen [3]	9	15

1. Issued in hard plastic and red leatherette case.
2. Issued in hard plastic and dark blue leatherette case; at least one set contains two regular issue (non-EEC) Proof 50 pence coins in error.
3. Issued in card holder.

Denomination	Metal
1 pound	Nickel-brass
50 pence (regular issue)	Cupronickel
50 pence (EEC issue)	Cupronickel
20 pence	Cupronickel
10 pence (on 28.5 mm flan)	Cupronickel
10 pence (on 24.5mm flan)	Cupronickel
5 pence	Cupronickel
2 pence	Bronze
1 penny	Bronze

No.	Date	Striking Standard	No. of Coins	Price
DPS-92-10	1992	Proof [1]	2	30

1. 35000 issued in blue case.

Denomination	Metal
10 pence	Silver
10 pence	Silver

No.	Date	Striking Standard	No. of Coins	Price
DPS-92-50	1992 1993 double dated coin	Proof & Piedfort Proof [1]	2	200

1. Issued in red case.

Denomination	Metal
Piedfort proof 50 pence (Single Market issue)	Silver
proof 50 pence (Single Market issue)	Silver

No.	Date	Striking Standard	No. of Coins	Price
DPS-93BR	1993	Proof [1]	4	1000

1. Issued in leatherette case.

Denomination	Metal
100 Pounds	Gold
50 Pounds	Gold
25 Pounds	Gold
10 Pounds	Gold

No.	Date	Striking Standard	No. of Coins	Price
DPS-93GL	1993	Proof [1]	4	1150

1. 1250 issued in purple leatherette case.

Denomination	Metal
Five Pounds	Gold
Two Pounds	Gold
Sovereign	Gold
Half Sovereign	Gold

No.	Date	Striking Standard	No. of Coins	Price
DPS-93GS	1993	Proof [1]	3	550

1. 1250 issued in red leatherette case.

Denomination	Metal
Two Pounds	Gold
Sovereign	Gold
Half Sovereign	Gold

No.	Date	Striking Standard	No. of Coins	Price
DPS-93DL	1993	Proof [1]	8	60
DPS-93	1993	Proof [2]	8	50

1. Issued in hard plastic and red leatherette case.
2. Issued in hard plastic and dark blue leatherette case.

Denomination	Metal
5 pounds	Cupronickel
1 pound	Nickel-brass
50 pence	Cupronickel
20 pence	Cupronickel
10 pence	Cupronickel
5 pence	Cupronickel
2 pence	Copper-plated steel
1 penny	Copper-plated steel

No.	Date	Striking Standard	No. of Coins	Price
DMS-93	1993	Specimen [1]	8	12

1. Issued in card holder.

Denomination	Metal
1 pound	Nickel-brass
50 pence (regular issue)	Cupronickel
50 pence (Single Market issue)	Cupronickel
20 pence	Cupronickel
10 pence	Cupronickel
5 pence	Cupronickel
2 pence	Copper-plated steel
1 penny	Copper-plated steel

No.	Date	Striking Standard	No. of Coins	Price
DPS-94BR	1994	Proof [1]	4	1150

1. Issued in leatherette case.

Denomination	Metal
100 Pounds	Gold
50 Pounds	Gold
25 Pounds	Gold
10 Pounds	Gold

No.	Date	Striking Standard	No. of Coins	Price
DPS-94GL	1994	Proof [1]	4	1300

1. Issued in leatherette case.

Denomination	Metal
Five Pounds	Gold
Two Pounds	Gold
Sovereign	Gold
Half Sovereign	Gold

No.	Date	Striking Standard	No. of Coins	Price
DPS-94GS	1994	Proof [1]	3	620

1. Issued in leatherette case.

Denomination	Metal
Two Pounds	Gold
Sovereign	Gold
Half Sovereign	Gold

No.	Date	Striking Standard	No. of Coins	Price
DPS-94DL	1994	Proof [1]	8	35
DPS-94	1994	Proof [2]	8	30
DMS-94	1994	Specimen [3]	8	12

1. Issued in hard plastic and red leatherette case.
2. Issued in hard plastic and dark blue leatherette case.
3. Issued in card holder.

Denomination	Metal
2 pounds	Nickel-brass
1 pound	Nickel-brass
50 pence	Cupronickel
20 pence	Cupronickel
10 pence	Cupronickel
5 pence	Cupronickel
2 pence	Copper-plated steel
1 penny	Copper-plated steel

No.	Date	Striking Standard	No. of Coins	Price
DPS-95BR	1995	Proof [1]	4	1200

1. Issued in leatherette case.

Denomination	Metal
100 Pounds	Gold
50 Pounds	Gold
25 Pounds	Gold
10 Pounds	Gold

No.	Date	Striking Standard	No. of Coins	Price
DPS-95GL	1995	Proof [1]	4	1300

1. Issued in leatherette case.

Denomination	Metal
Five Pounds	Gold
Two Pounds	Gold
Sovereign	Gold
Half Sovereign	Gold

No.	Date	Striking Standard	No. of Coins	Price
DPS-95GS	1995	Proof [1]	3	650

1. Issued in leatherette case.

Denomination	Metal
Two Pounds	Gold
Sovereign	Gold
Half Sovereign	Gold

No.	Date	Striking Standard	No. of Coins	Price
DPS-95DL	1995	Proof [1]	8	35
DPS-95	1995	Proof [2]	8	28
DMS-95	1995	Specimen [3]	8	10

1. Issued in hard plastic and red leatherette case.
2. Issued in hard plastic and dark blue leatherette case.
3. Issued in card holder.

Denomination	Metal
2 pounds (Peace issue)	Nickel-brass
1 pound	Nickel-brass
50 pence	Cupronickel
20 pence	Cupronickel
10 pence	Cupronickel
5 pence	Cupronickel
2 pence	Copper-plated steel
1 penny	Copper-plated steel

Appendix

The Maundy Ceremony

The ceremony of distribution of coins on Maundy Thursday can be traced back through several centuries. Nowadays, the changes in how we communicate with one another necessarily make the manner in which recipients are chosen very different from that of centuries ago.

The documentation which follows imparts something of the flavour of the modern Maundy ceremony, and provides a fascinating insight into the mechanics of choosing one particular recipient.

Royal Almonry Office
Buckingham Palace
London SW1A 1AA
01–930 4832 ext 142
25 January 1979

The Secretary of the Royal Almonry
write to acknowledge the receipt of the
Royal Maundy application form from
Mrs M.L. Woolford

All applications will receive careful and sympathetic consideration and a letter will be sent to you towards the end of March stating whether or not the application has been successful. Any information stated on your form will, of course, be treated as confidential to the this Office, and it is suggested that for the time being the fact that you have been nominated for the Royal Maundy gift be regarded as private.

Royal Almonry Office
Buckingham Palace
London SW1A 1AA
01–930 4832 ext 142
March 1979

Dear Mrs. Woolford,

I am very pleased to be able to tell you that you have been selected to receive Her Majesty's Royal Maundy gifts at the distribution to be made in Winchester Cathedral on Thursday, April 12th.

A letter giving further details will be sent to you later in the month. You will be allowed to bring two members of your family or friends with you to the Ceremony, and the appropriate tickets will be sent with the next letter. Due to limited accommodation however, it is regretted that in no circumstances can this ticket allocation be exceeded.

Will you please complete and return the enclosed form without delay. Car parking facilities are also very limited, and it is therefore hoped that you will only ask for a windscreen label if it is absolutely necessary.

We shall look forward to seeing you on Maundy Thursday.

Yours sincerely,

[signed Peter A. Wright]

Secretary.

The Royal Almonry Office
Buckingham Palace, S.W.1.

THE ROYAL FULL MAUNDY

First Distribution

Allowance in lieu of clothing, contained in a
Green Purse for women, and in a
White Purse for men £3

Second Distribution

Allowance in lieu of provisions £1.50
For the redemption of the Sovereign's gown
worn on the day of distribution £1

  (These amounts are contained in a Red Purse.)

Also given in this distribution is a White Purse containing
in Maundy Money as many Pence as the Sovereign is years of
age.

OFFICE

FOR

THE ROYAL MAUNDY

WINCHESTER CATHEDRAL

Maundy Thursday

12 APRIL 1979

The Distribution of Alms and the washing of feet on the Thursday of Holy Week are of great antiquity. The Maundy can be traced back in England with certainty to the 12th century, and there are continuous records of the Distribution having been made on Maundy Thursday from the reign of King Edward I.

The Service derives its name from the Latin word *mandatum,* meaning a commandment, and its opening words are "I give you a new commandment".

From the 15th century the number of recipients has been related to the years of the Sovereign's life. At one time recipients were required to be of the same sex as the Sovereign, but since the 18th century they have numbered as many men and women as the Sovereign has years of age. Recipients are now selected because of the Christian service thy have rendered to the Church and the community. The gifts distributed are symbolic and highly prized. During the first Distribution green purses are handed to the women and white purses to the men. The money contain in these purses is in lieu of items of clothing which were given in earlier times. The recipients are handed two purses in the second Distribution; the red purse contains an allowance for provisions formerly given in kind and a payment for the redemption of the royal gown; the white purse contains in Maundy coin silver pennies, twopences, threepences and fourpences, as many pence as the Sovereign is years of age. Maundy coins are, of course, legal tender, and when the United Kingdom changed to decimal currency in 1971, the face value of a set of four coins became 10 new pence instead of 10d in the £sd system.

The Maundy Dish used in the first Distribution is part of the Regalia, and though it bears the cypher of William and Mary, it does in fact date back to the reign of King Charles II.

Two of the alms dishes used in the second Distribution also date from the reign of Charles II and were once part of the Chapel Plate. They are commonly referred to as the Fish Dishes, and on the rims are four oval panels representing on one dish Love, Death, Industry and Strength, and on the other dish Faith, Hope, Justice and Fortitude. These dishes were first used in a Maundy Service at Tewkesbury in 1971. The other dish dates from the reign of Edward VII and has been kindly loaned by the Marquess of Exeter who is the Hereditary Grand Almoner.

Though the act of washing the feet seems to have been discontinued about 1730, the Lord High Almoner and his assistants are still girded with linen towels in remembrance, and carry the traditional nosegays of sweet herbs. The pieces of linen at present in use bear the date 1883 and have been worn annually since that year.

The Chapel Royal Choir which takes part in this Service has a notable musical history and remains a distinctive part of the Royal establishment. That it sang at Agincourt and that it was present at "The Field of the Cloth of Gold" indicate the place it took in the royal entourage.

The Queen's Bodyguard of the Yeomen of the Guard (the "Indoor Guard") also plays an important part in the Service. It is the oldest Military Corps now existing, having been created in 1485 by King Henry VII.

In earlier times the Ceremony was observed wherever the Sovereign was in residence. For many years the Maundy gifts were distributed in the old Chapel Royal (now the Banqueting Hall) in Whitehall, but from 1890 to 1952 the Service was usually held at Westminster Abbey. During the present Reign the Service has been held at Westminster Abbey on twelve occasions. In other years it has been held at the following places: -

1953 St Paul's	1963 Chelmsford	1972 York
1955 Southwark	1965 Canterbury	1974 Salisbury
1957 St. Albans	1967 Durham	1975 Peterborough
1959 Windsor	1969 Selby	1976 Hereford
1961 Rochester	1971 Tewkesbury	1978 Carlisle

Winchester was the capital of the Kings of England from the days of Alfred the Great to the Norman Conquest. The present Cathedral, celebrating its 900th anniversary this year, was built immediately adjacent to a church founded by the King of the West Saxons in about 648 A.D. and which Bishop Hedda made his Cathedral some forty years later. Five Bishops of Winchester have held the office of Lord High Almoner including Lancelot Andrewes and Samuel Wilberforce

Royal Almonry Office,
Buckingham Palace

Royal Almonry Office
Buckingham Palace
London SW1A 1AA
01-930 4832 ext 142
1 May 1979

Dear Mrs Woolford,

I am writing to tell you that your recent letter about the Maundy Service has now been seen by The Queen.

Her Majesty was pleased to read the many messages of gratitude and to know that this occasion brought so much happiness to those who had been selected to receive the Maundy gifts. Your thoughtfulness in writing was much appreciated.

Yours truly,

[signed Peter A. Wright]
Secretary.

Bibliography

Bibliography

Besley, E., *Coins and Medals of the Civil War*, Batsfords, 1950.

Boon, George C., *Cardiganshire Silver and the Aberystwyth Mint in Peace and War*, National Museum of Wales, 1981.

Bramah, E., *Varieties of English Regal Copper Coins,* Methuen, 1929.

Bressett, K., *Guide Book of English Coins*, Western Publishing, USA, 1982.

Brooke, G., *English Coins*, Methuen, 1942.

Challis, C. E., *A New History of the Royal Mint*, Cambridge University Press, 1992.

Cleveland Museum, *English Gold Coins*, Cleveland, 1968.

Cope, G. and A. Rayner, *English Milled Coinage 1662–1972*, Spink, 1972.

Craig, J., *The Mint*, Cambridge University Press, 1953.

Crowther, Rev. G.F., *A Guide to English Pattern Coins in Gold, Silver, Copper and Pewter*, L. Upcolt Gill, 1887.

Cullimore Allen, J., *Sovereigns of the British Empire*, Spink, 1965.

Dickinson, M., *Victorian Godless and Gothic Florins*, SCMB, 1978/80.

Doty, Richard C., *Encyclopaedic Dictionary of Numismatics*, Robert Hale, 1972.

Dyer, G., ed., *Royal Sovereign, 1489–1989*, Royal Mint, 1989.

Dyer, G., *The proposed Coinage of King Edward VIII*, HMSO, 1973.

Farquhar, H., *Portraiture of our Stuart Monarchs on their Coins and Medals*, Harrison, 1914.

Farquhar, H., *Royal Charities*, Harrison, 1929.

Freeman, M., *Bronze Coinage of Great Britain*, Barrie and Jenkins, 1985.

Garside, H., *British Imperial Copper and Bronze Coinage 1838–1920*, Spink,1920, suppl. 1925.

Gouby, M., *The British Bronze Penny,* Michael Coins, 1986.

Hawkins, E., *The Silver Coins of England*, Quaritch, 1887.

Henfrey, H. W., *A Guide to the Study of English Coins*, Bell, 1885.

Jackson Kent, E., *The Silver Coinage of William III*, Spink, 1961.

Junge, E. Ward, *The Seaby Coin Encyclopaedia*, Seaby, 1992.

Kenyon, R., *Gold Coins of England*, Quaritch, 1884.

Krause, Mishler and Bruce II, *Standard Catalogue of World Coins and Talers, 1601 to Date*, Krause, 1994.

Krause, Mishler and Bruce II, *Standard Catalogue of World Coins, 1701–1801*, Krause, 1993.

Lawrence, L.A., *The Coinage of Edward III from 1351*.

Leake, S. Martin, *Historical account of English Money*, London, 1793.

Li, Ming-Hsun, *The Great Recoinage of 1696–9*, Weidenfeld and Nicolson, 1963.

Linecar, H. and Stone, A., *English Proof and Pattern Crown-size Pieces 1658–1960*, Spink, 1968.

Linecar, H., *British Coin Designs and Designers*, Bell, 1977.

Linecar, H., *Crown Pieces of Great Britain*, Benn, 1969.

Linecar, H., ed., *The Milled Coinage of England 1662–1946*, Spink, 1950.

Marles, J., *Collectors' Coins*, Rotographic Publications.

Marsh, M., *The Gold Half Sovereign*, Cambridge Coins.

Marsh, M., *The Gold Sovereign*, Cambridge Coins.

Mayhew, N.J., *Sterling Imitations of Edwardian type (Pennies)*, Royal Numismatic Society, 1983.

Mays, James O'Donald, *The Splendid Shilling*, New Forest Leaves, 1982.

McDonald, G., *Australian Coin and Banknote Guide*, Rigby, Australia, 1983.

Montagu, H., *The Copper, Tin, and Bronze Coinage of England*, Rollin and Feuardent, 1885.

Nicholson, Alan J., *Thomas Simon, his life and works, 1618–1665*, Seaby, 1975.

North, J.J. and P.J. Preston, *The John Brooker Collection, Coins of Charles I*, Spink, 1984.

North, J.J., *Edwardian English Silver Coins, 1279–1351*, Spink.

North, J.J., *English Hammered Coinage*, Spink, Vol. 1: 1994, Vol. 2: 1992 (revised editions).

Oman, C., *The Coinage of England*, Clarendon, 1931.

Peck, C.W., *English Copper, Tin and Bronze Coins in the British Museum 1558–1958*, British Museum, 1964.

Purvey, Frank, *Collecting Coins*, Seaby, 1985.

Rayner, P. Alan, *English Silver Coinage since 1649*, Seaby, 1992.

Robinson, B., *Silver Pennies & Linen Towels, The Story of the Royal Maundy*, Spink, 1992.

Robinson, B., *The Royal Maundy*, Kaye and Ward, 1977.

Royal Almonry, *The Royal Maundy*, Royal Almonry, 1952.

Royal Mint, *Statutes relating to Coinage*, HMSO, 1915.

Ruding, R., *Annals of the Coinage of Great Britain*, 1840.

Salzman, M., *Modern British Coins and their varieties 1797–1970*, Salzman, 1982.

Seaby, Mitchell and Reeds, *Standard Catalogue, Coins of England and the United Kingdom*, 30th edition, Seaby, 1995.

Seaby, P., *The Story of the English Coinage*, Seaby, 1952.

Stainer, C.L., *Oxford Silver Pennies*, 1904.

Sutherland, C.H.V., *English Coins*, Oxford, 1973.

Thorburn, S., *Guide to the Coins of Great Britain and Ireland*, Upcott Gill, 1884.

Wren, C.R., *The English Long Cross Pennies, 1279–1489*, Plantagenet Books, 1995.

Wren, C.R., *The Short Cross Coinage, 1180–1247*, Plantagenet Books, 1992.

Wren, C.R., *The Voided Cross Coinage, 1247–1279*, Plantagenet Books, 1993.

Index

Index

Page numbers in **bold** type refer to the Hammered section, those in *italic* type refer to the Milled section.